About Pearson

Pearson is the world's learning company, with presence across 70 countries worldwide. Our unique insights and world-class expertise comes from a long history of working closely with renowned teachers, authors and thought leaders, as a result of which, we have emerged as the preferred choice for millions of teachers and learners across the world.

We believe learning opens up opportunities, creates fulfilling careers and hence better lives. We hence collaborate with the best of minds to deliver you class-leading products, spread across the Higher Education and K12 spectrum.

Superior learning experience and improved outcomes are at the heart of everything we do. This product is the result of one such effort.

Your feedback plays a critical role in the evolution of our products and you can contact us - reachus@pearson.com. We look forward to it.

SECOND EDITION

BIOSTATISTICS

FOR THE BIOLOGICAL AND HEALTH SCIENCES

MARC M. TRIOLA, MD, FACP
New York University School of Medicine

MARIO F. TRIOLA
Dutchess Community College

JASON ROY, PHD
University of Pennsylvania
Perelman School of Medicine

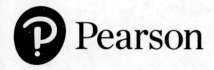

Original edition, entitled *Biostatistics for The Biological and Health Sciences,* 2nd Edition, by Triola, Marc M.; Triola, Mario F.; Roy, Jason., published by Pearson Education, Limited. Copyright © 2011 by Pearson Education, Inc.

Indian Subcontinent Reprint

ISBN 978-93-534-3653-7

First Impression

This edition is manufactured in India and is authorized for sale only in India, Bangladesh, Bhutan, Pakistan, Nepal, Sri Lanka and the Maldives. Circulation of this edition outside of these territories is UNAUTHORIZED.

Published by Pearson India Education Services Pvt. Ltd, CIN: U72200TN2005PTC057128.

Head Office: 15th Floor, Tower-B, World Trade Tower, Plot No. 1, Block-C, Sector-16, Noida 201 301, Uttar Pradesh, India.

Registered Office: The HIVE, 3rd Floor, Metro zone, No 44, Pilliayar Koil Street, Jawaharlal Nehru Road, Anna Nagar, Chennai, Tamil Nadu 600040.
Phone: 044-66540100, Website: in.pearson.com, Email: companysecretary.india@pearson.com

Printed in India at Sai Printo Pack Pvt Ltd

ABOUT THE AUTHORS

Marc Triola, MD, FACP is the Associate Dean for Educational Informatics at NYU School of Medicine, the founding director of the NYU Langone Medical Center Institute for Innovations in Medical Education (IIME), and an Associate Professor of Medicine. Dr. Triola's research experience and expertise focus on the disruptive effects of the present revolution in education, driven by technological advances, big data, and learning analytics. Dr. Triola has worked to create a "learning ecosystem" that includes interconnected computer-based e-learning tools and new ways to effectively integrate growing amounts of electronic data in educational research. Dr. Triola and IIME have been funded by the National Institutes of Health, the Integrated Advanced Information Management Systems program, the National Science Foundation Advanced Learning Technologies program, the Josiah Macy, Jr. Foundation, the U.S. Department of Education, and the American Medical Association Accelerating Change in Medical Education program. He chairs numerous committees at the state and national levels focused on the future of health professions educational technology development and research.

Mario F. Triola is a Professor Emeritus of Mathematics at Dutchess Community College, where he has taught statistics for over 30 years. Marty is the author of *Elementary Statistics,* 13th edition, *Essentials of Statistics,* 5th edition, *Elementary Statistics Using Excel,* 6th edition, and *Elementary Statistics Using the TI-83/84 Plus Calculator,* 4th edition, and he is a co-author of *Statistical Reasoning for Everyday Life,* 5th edition. *Elementary Statistics* is currently available as an International Edition, and it has been translated into several foreign languages. Marty designed the original Statdisk statistical software, and he has written several manuals and workbooks for technology supporting statistics education.

He has been a speaker at many conferences and colleges. Marty's consulting work includes the design of casino slot machines and the design of fishing rods. He has worked with attorneys in determining probabilities in paternity lawsuits, analyzing data in medical malpractice lawsuits, identifying salary inequities based on gender, and analyzing disputed election results. He has also used statistical methods in analyzing medical school surveys and in analyzing survey results for the New York City Transit Authority. Marty has testified as an expert witness in the New York State Supreme Court.

Jason Roy, PhD, is Associate Professor of Biostatistics in the Department of Biostatistics and Epidemiology, Perelman School of Medicine, University of Pennsylvania. He received his PhD in Biostatistics in 2000 from the University of Michigan. He was recipient of the 2002 David P. Byar Young Investigator Award from the American Statistical Association Biometrics Section. His statistical research interests are in the areas of causal inference, missing data, and prediction modeling. He is especially interested in the statistical challenges with analyzing data from large health care databases. He collaborates in many different disease areas, including chronic kidney disease, cardiovascular disease, and liver diseases. Dr Roy is Associate Editor of *Biometrics, Journal of the American Statistical Association,* and *Pharmacoepidemiology & Drug Safety,* and has over 90 peer-reviewed publications.

CONTENTS

PREFACE

Statistics permeates nearly every aspect of our lives, and its role has become particularly important in the biological, life, medical, and health sciences. From opinion polls to clinical trials in medicine and analysis of big data from health applications, statistics influences and shapes the world around us. *Biostatistics for the Health and Biological Sciences* forges the relationship between statistics and our world through extensive use of a wide variety of real applications that bring life to theory and methods.

Goals of This Second Edition

- Incorporate the latest and best methods used by professional statisticians.

- Include features that address all of the recommendations included in the *Guidelines for Assessment and Instruction in Statistics Education* (GAISE) as recommended by the American Statistical Association.

- Provide an abundance of new and interesting data sets, examples, and exercises.

- Foster personal growth of students through critical thinking, use of technology, collaborative work, and development of communication skills.

- Enhance teaching and learning with the most extensive and best set of supplements and digital resources.

Audience/Prerequisites

Biostatistics for the Health and Biological Sciences is written for students majoring in the biological and health sciences, and it is designed for a wide variety of students taking their first statistics course. Algebra is used minimally, and calculus is not required. It is recommended that students have completed at least an elementary algebra course or that students should learn the relevant algebra components through an integrated or co-requisite course. In many cases, underlying theory is included, but this book does not require the mathematical rigor more appropriate for mathematics majors.

Hallmark Features

Great care has been taken to ensure that each chapter of *Biostatistics for the Health and Biological Sciences* will help students understand the concepts presented. The following features are designed to help meet that objective.

Real Data

Hundreds of hours have been devoted to finding data that are real, meaningful, and interesting to students. Fully 87% of the examples are based on real data, and 89% of the exercises are based on real data. Some exercises refer to the 18 data sets listed in Appendix B, and 12 of those data sets are new to this edition. Exercises requiring use of the Appendix B data sets are located toward the end of each exercise set and are marked with a special data set icon .

Real data sets are included throughout the book to provide relevant and interesting real-world statistical applications, including biometric security, body measurements, brain sizes and IQ scores, and data from births. Appendix B includes descriptions of the 18 data sets that can be downloaded from the companion website www.pearsoned.co.in/triola.

Readability

Great care, enthusiasm, and passion have been devoted to creating a book that is readable, understandable, interesting, and relevant. Students pursuing any major in the biological, life, medical, or health fields are sure to find applications related to their future work.

Chapter Features

Chapter Opening Features

- Chapters begin with a *Chapter Problem* that uses real data and motivates the chapter material.
- *Chapter Objectives* provide a summary of key learning goals for each section in the chapter.

Exercises

Many exercises require the *interpretation* of results. Great care has been taken to ensure their usefulness, relevance, and accuracy. Exercises are arranged in order of increasing difficulty, and they begin with *Basic Skills and Concepts*. Most sections include additional *Beyond the Basics* exercises that address more difficult concepts or require a stronger mathematical background. In a few cases, these exercises introduce a new concept.

End-of-Chapter Features

- *Chapter Quick Quiz* provides review questions that require brief answers.
- *Review Exercises* offer practice on the chapter concepts and procedures.
- *Cumulative Review Exercises* reinforce earlier material.
- *Technology Project* provides an activity that can be used with a variety of technologies.
- *From Data to Decision* is a capstone problem that requires critical thinking and writing.
- *Cooperative Group Activities* encourage active learning in groups.

Other Features

Margin Essays There are 57 margin essays designed to highlight real-world topics and foster student interest.

Flowcharts The text includes flowcharts that simplify and clarify more complex concepts and procedures.

Quick-Reference Table A-3 (*t* distribution) is reproduced at the end of the book.

Formula and Table Supplement This supplement, organized by chapter, gives students a quick reference for studying, or for use when taking tests (if allowed by the instructor). It also includes the most commonly used tables. This is also available for download at www.pearsoned.co.in/triola.

Technology Integration

As in the preceding edition, there are many displays of screens from technology throughout the book, and some exercises are based on displayed results from technology. Where appropriate, sections include a reference to an online *Tech Center* subsection that includes detailed instructions for Statdisk, Minitab®, Excel®, StatCrunch, or a TI-83/84 Plus® calculator. (Throughout this text, "TI-83/84 Plus" is used to identify a TI-83 Plus or TI-84 Plus calculator). The end-of-chapter features include a *Technology Project*.

The Statdisk statistical software package is designed specifically for this textbook and contains all Appendix B data sets. Statdisk is free to users of this book, and it can be downloaded at www.statdisk.org.

Changes in This Edition

New Features

Chapter Objectives provide a summary of key learning goals for each section in the chapter.

Larger Data Sets: Some of the data sets in Appendix B are much larger than in the previous edition. It is no longer practical to print all of the Appendix B data sets in this book, so the data sets are *described* in Appendix B, and they can be downloaded at www.pearsoned.co.in/triola.

New Content: New examples, new exercises, and Chapter Problems provide relevant and interesting real-world statistical applications, including biometric security, drug testing, gender selection, and analyzing ultrasound images.

	Number	New to This Edition	Use Real Data
Exercises	1600	85%	89%
Examples	200	84%	87%

Major Organization Changes

All Chapters

- *New Chapter Objectives*: All chapters now begin with a list of key learning goals for that chapter. *Chapter Objectives* replaces the former *Overview* numbered sections. The first numbered section of each chapter now covers a major topic.

Chapter 1

- *New Section 1-1: Statistical and Critical Thinking*
- *New Subsection 1-3, Part 2: Big Data and Missing Data: Too Much and Not Enough*

Chapters 2 and 3

- *Chapter Partitioned:* Chapter 2 (Describing, Exploring, and Comparing Data) from the first edition has been partitioned into Chapter 2 (Summarizing and Graphing) and Chapter 3 (Statistics for Describing, Exploring, and Comparing Data).

- *New Section 2-4: Scatterplots, Correlation, and Regression* This new section includes scatterplots in Part 1, the linear correlation coefficient r in Part 2, and linear regression in Part 3. These additions are intended to greatly facilitate coverage for those professors who prefer some early coverage of correlation and regression concepts. Chapter 10 includes these topics discussed with much greater detail.

Chapter 4

- *Combined Sections:* Section 3-3 (Addition Rule) and Section 3-4 (Multiplication Rule) from the first edition are now combined into one section: 4-2 (Addition Rule and Multiplication Rule).

- *New Subsection 4-3, Part 3: Bayes' Theorem*

Chapter 5

- *Combined Sections:* Section 4-3 (Binomial Probability Distributions) and Section 4-4 (Mean, Variance, and Standard Deviation for the Binomial Distribution) from the first edition are now combined into one section: 5-2 (Binomial Probability Distributions).

Chapter 6

- *Switched Sections:* Section 6-5 (Assessing Normality) now precedes Section 6-6 (Normal as Approximation to Binomial).

Chapter 7

- *Combined Sections:* Sections 6-4 (Estimating a Population Mean: σ Known) and 6-5 (Estimating a Population Mean: σ Not Known) from the first edition have been combined into one section: 7-2 (Estimating a Population Mean). The coverage of the σ known case has been substantially reduced and it is now limited to Part 2 of Section 7-2.

- *New Section 7-4: Bootstrapping: Using Technology for Estimates*

Chapter 8

- *Combined Sections:* Sections 7-4 (Testing a Claim About a Population Mean: σ Known) and 7-5 (Testing a Claim About a Population Mean: σ Not Known) from the first edition have been combined into one section: 8-3 (Testing a Claim About a Mean). Coverage of the σ known case has been substantially reduced and it is now limited to Part 2 of Section 8-3.

Chapter 10

- *New Section: 10-5 Dummy Variables and Logistic Regression*

Chapter 11

- *New Subsection: Section 11-2, Part 2 Test of Homogeneity, Fisher's Exact Test, and McNemar's Test for Matched Pairs*

Chapter 14

- *Combined Sections:* Section 13-2 (Elements of a Life Table) and Section 13-3 (Applications of Life Tables) from the first edition have been combined into Section 14-1 (Life Tables).

- *New Section: 14-2 Kaplan-Meier Survival Analysis*

Flexible Syllabus

This book's organization reflects the preferences of most statistics instructors, but there are two common variations:

- *Early Coverage of Correlation and Regression:* Some instructors prefer to cover the basics of correlation and regression early in the course. Section 2-4 now includes basic concepts of scatterplots, correlation, and regression without the use of formulas and greater depth found in Sections 10-1 (*Correlation*) and 10-2 (*Regression*).

- *Minimum Probability:* Some instructors prefer extensive coverage of probability, while others prefer to include only basic concepts. Instructors preferring minimum coverage can include Section 4-1 while skipping the remaining sections of Chapter 4, as they are not essential for the chapters that follow. Many instructors prefer to cover the fundamentals of probability along with the basics of the addition rule and multiplication rule (Section 4-2).

GAISE

This book reflects recommendations from the American Statistical Association and its *Guidelines for Assessment and Instruction in Statistics Education* (GAISE). Those guidelines suggest the following objectives and strategies.

1. *Emphasize statistical literacy and develop statistical thinking:* Each section exercise set begins with *Statistical Literacy and Critical Thinking* exercises. Many of the book's exercises are designed to encourage statistical thinking rather than the blind use of mechanical procedures.

2. *Use real data:* 87% of the examples and 89% of the exercises use real data.

3. *Stress conceptual understanding rather than mere knowledge of procedures:* Instead of seeking simple numerical answers, most exercises and examples involve conceptual understanding through questions that encourage practical interpretations of results. Also, each chapter includes a *From Data to Decision* project.

4. *Foster active learning in the classroom:* Each chapter ends with several *Cooperative Group Activities.*

5. *Use technology for developing conceptual understanding and analyzing data:* Computer software displays are included throughout the book. Special *Tech Center* subsections are available online, and they include instruction for using the software. Each chapter includes a *Technology Project.* When there are discrepancies between answers based on tables and answers based on technology, Appendix D provides *both* answers. The website www.pearsoned.co.in/triola includes free text-specific software (Statdisk), data sets formatted for several different technologies, and instructional videos for technologies.

6. *Use assessments to improve and evaluate student learning:* Assessment tools include an abundance of section exercises, *Chapter Quick Quizzes, Review Exercises, Cumulative Review Exercises, Technology Projects, From Data to Decision* projects, and *Cooperative Group Activities.*

Acknowledgments

We would like to thank the many statistics professors and students who have contributed to the success of this book. We thank the reviewers for their suggestions for this second edition:

James Baldone, Virginia College
Naomi Brownstein, Florida State University
Christina Caruso, University of Guelph
Erica A. Corbett, Southeastern Oklahoma State University
Xiangming Fang, East Carolina University
Phil Gona, UMASS Boston
Sharon Homan, University of North Texas
Jackie Milton, Boston University
Joe Pick, Palm Beach State College
Steve Rigdon, St. Louis University
Brian Smith, Black Hills State University
Mahbobeh Vezvaei, Kent State University
David Zeitler, Grand Valley State University

We also thank Paul Lorczak, Joseph Pick and Erica Corbett for their help in checking the accuracy of the text and answers.

Marc Triola
Mario Triola
Jason Roy
September 2016

Supplements

For the Student

The following resources are available for download from the website, www.pearsoned.co.in/triola.

The below listed technology manuals, include instructions, examples from the main text, and interpretations to complement those given in the text.

Excel Student Laboratory Manual and Workbook (Download Only), by Laurel Chiappetta (University of Pittsburgh).
(ISBN-13: 978-0-13-446427-5; ISBN-10: 0-13-446427-3)

MINITAB Student Laboratory Manual and Workbook (Download Only), by Mario F. Triola.
(ISBN-13: 978-0-13-446418-3; ISBN-10: 0-13-446418-4)

Graphing Calculator Manual for the TI-83 Plus, TI-84 Plus, TI-84 Plus C and TI-84 Plus CE (Download Only), by Kathleen McLaughlin (University of Connecticut) & Dorothy Wakefield (University of Connecticut Health Center).
(ISBN-13: 978-0-13-446414-5; ISBN 10: 0-13-446414-1)

Statdisk Student Laboratory Manual and Workbook (Download Only), by Mario F. Triola. These files are available to instructors and students.

SPSS Student Laboratory Manual and Workbook (Download Only), by James J. Ball (Indiana State University). These files are available to instructors and students.

For the Instructor

Instructor's Solutions Manual (Download Only), by James Lapp (Colorado Mesa University) contains solutions to all the exercises. These files are available to qualified instructors through Pearson Education's online catalog at www.pearsoned.co.in/triola.

Insider's Guide to Teaching with the Triola Statistics Series, by Mario F. Triola, contains sample syllabi and tips for incorporating projects, as well as lesson overviews, extra examples, minimum outcome objectives, and recommended assignments for each chapter.
(ISBN-13: 978-0-13-446425-1; ISBN-10: 0-13-446425-7)

TestGen® Computerized Test Bank (www.pearsoned.com/testgen) enables instructors to build, edit, print, and administer tests using a computerized bank of questions developed to cover all the objectives of the text. TestGen is algorithmically based, allowing instructors to create multiple but equivalent versions of the same question or test with the click of a button. Instructors can also modify test bank questions or add new questions. The software and testbank are available for download from Pearson Education's online catalog at www.pearsoned.co.in/triola. A test bank (Download Only) is also available from the online catalog.

Technology Resources

The following resources can be found on the website www.pearsoned.co.in/triola.

- Appendix B data sets formatted for Minitab, SPSS, SAS, Excel, JMP, and as text files. Additionally, these data sets are available as an APP for the TI-83/84 Plus calculators, and supplemental programs for the TI-83/84 Plus calculator are also available.

- Statdisk statistical software instructions for download. New features include the ability to directly use lists of data instead of requiring the use of their summary statistics.

Video resources have been expanded, updated and now supplement most sections of the book, with many topics presented by the author. The videos aim to support both instructors and students through lecture, reinforcing statistical basics through technology, and applying concepts:

- **Section Lecture Videos**
- **New! Technology Video Tutorials** - These short, topical videos address how to use Excel, Statdisk, and the TI graphing calculator to complete exercises.
- **StatTalk Videos: 24 Conceptual Videos to Help You Actually Understand Statistics.** Fun-loving statistician Andrew Vickers takes to the streets of Brooklyn, NY, to demonstrate important statistical concepts through interesting stories and real-life events. These fun and engaging videos will help students actually understand statistical concepts. Available with an instructors user guide and assessment questions.

1

Introduction to Statistics

CHAPTER PROBLEM — **Survey Question: Do You Need Caffeine to Start Up Your Brain for the Day?**

Surveys provide data that enable us to improve products or services. Surveys guide political candidates, shape business practices, identify effective medical treatments, and affect many aspects of our lives. Surveys give us insight into the opinions and behaviors of others. As an example, the National Health and Nutrition Examination Survey (NHANES) is part of a research program that studies the health and nutrition of thousands of adults and children in the United States.

Let's consider one *USA Today* survey in which respondents were asked if they need caffeine to start up their brain for the day. Among 2,006 respondents, 74% said that they did need the caffeine. Figure 1-1 includes graphs that depict these results.

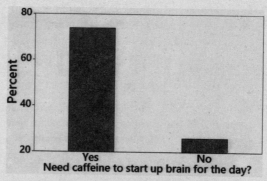

FIGURE 1-1(a)   Survey Results

People Needing Caffeine to Start
Up Brain for the Day

People *Not* Needing Caffeine to Start
Up Brain for the Day

FIGURE 1-1(b)   Survey Results

The survey results suggest that people overwhelmingly need caffeine to start up their brains for the day. The graphs in Figure 1-1 visually depict the survey results. One of the most important objectives of this book is to encourage the use of critical thinking so that such results are not blindly accepted. We might question whether the survey results are valid. Who conducted the survey? How were respondents selected? Do the graphs in Figure 1-1 depict the results well, or are those graphs somehow misleading?

The survey results presented here have major flaws that are among the most common, so they are especially important to recognize. Here are brief descriptions of each of the major flaws:

Flaw 1: Misleading Graphs   The bar chart in Figure 1-1(a) is very deceptive. By using a vertical scale that does not start at zero, the difference between the two percentages is grossly exaggerated. Figure 1-1(a) makes it appear that approximately eight times as many people need the caffeine. However, with 74% needing caffeine and 26% not needing caffeine, the ratio is actually about 3:1, rather than the 8:1 ratio that is suggested by the graph.

The illustration in Figure 1-1(b) is also deceptive. Again, the difference between the actual response rates of 74% (needing caffeine) and 26% (not needing caffeine) is a difference that is grossly distorted. The picture graph (or "pictograph") in Figure 1-1(b) makes it appear that the ratio of people needing caffeine to people not needing caffeine is roughly 9:1 instead of the correct ratio of about 3:1. (Objects with area or volume can distort perceptions because they can be drawn to be disproportionately larger or smaller than the data indicate.) Deceptive graphs are discussed in more detail in Section 2-3, but we see here that the illustrations in Figure 1-1 grossly exaggerate the number of people needing caffeine.

Flaw 2: Bad Sampling Method The aforementioned survey responses are from a *USA Today* survey of Internet users. The survey question was posted on a website and Internet users decided whether to respond. This is an example of a *voluntary response sample*—a sample in which respondents themselves decide whether to participate. With a voluntary response sample, it often happens that those with a strong interest in the topic are more likely to participate, so the results are very questionable. For example, people who strongly feel that they cannot function without their morning cup(s) of coffee might be more likely to respond to the caffeine survey than people who are more ambivalent about caffeine or coffee. When using sample data to learn something about a population, it is *extremely* important to obtain sample data that are representative of the population from which the data are drawn. As we proceed through this chapter and discuss types of data and sampling methods, we should focus on these key concepts:

- **Sample data must be collected in an appropriate way, such as through a process of *random* selection.**

- **If sample data are not collected in an appropriate way, the data may be so completely useless that no amount of statistical torturing can salvage them.**

It would be easy to accept the preceding survey results and blindly proceed with calculations and statistical analyses, but we would miss the critical two flaws described above. We could then develop conclusions that are fundamentally wrong and misleading. Instead, we should develop skills in statistical thinking and critical thinking so that we are better prepared to analyze such data.

CHAPTER OBJECTIVES

The single most important concept presented in this chapter is this: When using methods of statistics with sample data to form conclusions about a population, it is absolutely essential to collect sample data in a way that is appropriate. Here are the main chapter objectives:

1-1 Statistical and Critical Thinking
- Analyze sample data relative to context, source, and sampling method.
- Understand the difference between statistical significance and practical significance.
- Define and identify a *voluntary response sample* and know that statistical conclusions based on data from such a sample are generally not valid.

Types of Data

- Distinguish between a *parameter* and a *statistic.*

- Distinguish between *quantitative data* and *categorical* (or *qualitative* or *attribute*) *data.*

- Distinguish between *discrete* data and *continuous* data.

- Determine whether basic statistical calculations are appropriate for a particular data set.

 Collecting Sample Data

- Define and identify a *simple random sample.*

- Understand the importance of sound sampling methods and the importance of good design of experiments.

 Statistical and Critical Thinking

Key Concept In this section we begin with a few very basic definitions, and then we consider an *overview* of the process involved in conducting a statistical study. This process consists of "prepare, analyze, and conclude." "Preparation" involves consideration of the *context,* the *source* of data, and *sampling method.* In future chapters we construct suitable graphs, explore the data, and execute computations required for the statistical method being used. In future chapters we also form conclusions by determining whether results have statistical significance and practical significance.

Statistical thinking involves critical thinking and the ability to make sense of results. Statistical thinking demands so much more than the ability to execute complicated calculations. Through numerous examples, exercises, and discussions, this text will help you develop the statistical thinking skills that are so important in today's world.

We begin with some very basic definitions.

DEFINITIONS

Data are collections of observations, such as measurements, or survey responses. (A single data value is called a *datum,* a term rarely used. The term "data" is plural, so it is correct to say "data *are…*" not "data *is…*")

Statistics is the science of planning studies and experiments; obtaining data; and organizing, summarizing, presenting, analyzing, and interpreting those data and then drawing conclusions based on them.

A **population** is the complete collection of *all* measurements or data that are being considered. Typically, the population is the complete collection of data that we would like to make inferences about.

A **census** is the collection of data from *every* member of the population.

A **sample** is a *subcollection* of members selected from a population.

Because populations are often very large, a common objective of the use of statistics is to obtain data from a sample and then use those data to form a conclusion about the population.

EXAMPLE 1 **Residential Carbon Monoxide Detectors**

In the journal article "Residential Carbon Monoxide Detector Failure Rates in the United States" (by Ryan and Arnold, *American Journal of Public Health,* Vol. 101, No. 10), it was stated that there are 38 million carbon monoxide detectors installed in the United States. When 30 of them were randomly selected and tested, it was found that 12 of them failed to provide an alarm in hazardous carbon monoxide conditions. In this case, the population and sample are as follows:

Population: All 38 million carbon monoxide detectors in the United States

Sample: The 30 carbon monoxide detectors that were selected and tested

The objective is to use the sample data as a basis for drawing a conclusion about the population of all carbon monoxide detectors, and methods of statistics are helpful in drawing such conclusions.

We now proceed to consider the process involved in a statistical study. See Figure 1-2 for a summary of this process and note that the focus is on critical thinking, not mathematical calculations. Thanks to wonderful developments in technology, we have powerful tools that effectively do the number crunching so that we can focus on understanding and interpreting results.

Prepare

1. **Context**
   - What do the data represent?
   - What is the goal of study?
2. **Source of the Data**
   - Are the data from a source with a special interest so that there is pressure to obtain results that are favorable to the source?
3. **Sampling Method**
   - Were the data collected in a way that is unbiased, or were the data collected in a way that is biased (such as a procedure in which respondents volunteer to participate)?

↓

Analyze

1. **Graph the Data**
2. **Explore the Data**
   - Are there any outliers (numbers very far away from almost all of the other data)?
   - What important statistics summarize the data (such as the mean and standard deviation described in Chapter 3)?
   - How are the data distributed?
   - Are there missing data?
   - Did many selected subjects refuse to respond?
3. **Apply Statistical Methods**
   - Use technology to obtain results.

↓

Conclude

1. **Significance**
   - Do the results have statistical significance?
   - Do the results have practical significance?

FIGURE 1-2   Statistical Thinking

Survivorship Bias

In World War II, statistician Abraham Wald saved many lives with his work on the Applied Mathematics Panel. Military leaders asked the panel how they could improve the chances of aircraft bombers returning after missions. They wanted to add some armor for protection, and they recorded locations on the bombers where damaging holes were found. They reasoned that armor should be placed in locations with the most holes, but Wald said that strategy would be a big mistake. He said that armor should be placed where returning bombers were *not* damaged. His reasoning was this: The bombers that made it back with damage were survivors, so the damage they suffered could be survived. Locations on the aircraft that were not damaged were the most vulnerable, and aircraft suffering damage in those vulnerable areas were the ones that did not make it back. The military leaders would have made a big mistake with survivorship bias by studying the planes that survived instead of thinking about the planes that did not survive.

TABLE 1-1 IQ Scores and Brain Volumes (cm^3)

IQ	96	87	101	103	127	96	88	85	97	124
Brain Volume (cm^3)	1005	1035	1281	1051	1034	1079	1104	1439	1029	1160

Prepare

Context   Figure 1-2 suggests that we begin our preparation by considering the *context* of the data, so let's start with context by considering the data in Table 1-1. (The data are from Data Set 9 "IQ and Brain Size" in Appendix B.) The data in Table 1-1 consist of measured IQ scores and measured brain volumes from 10 different subjects. The data are matched in the sense that each individual "IQ/brain volume" pair of values is from the same person. The first subject had a measured IQ score of 96 and a brain volume of 1005 cm^3. The format of Table 1-1 suggests the following goal: Determine whether there is a *relationship* between IQ score and brain volume. This goal suggests a possible hypothesis: People with larger brains tend to have higher IQ scores.

Source of the Data   The data in Table 1-1 were provided by M. J. Tramo, W. C. Loftus, T. A. Stukel, J. B. Weaver, and M. S. Gazzaniga, who discuss the data in the article "Brain Size, Head Size, and IQ in Monozygotic Twins," *Neurology,* Vol. 50. The researchers are from reputable medical schools and hospitals, and they would not gain by presenting the results in way that is misleading. In contrast, Kiwi Brands, a maker of shoe polish, commissioned a study that resulted in this statement, which was printed in some newspapers: "According to a nationwide survey of 250 hiring professionals, scuffed shoes was the most common reason for a male job seeker's failure to make a good first impression."

When physicians who conduct clinical experiments on the efficacy of drugs receive funding from drug companies, they have an incentive to obtain favorable results. Some professional journals, such as the *Journal of the American Medical Association,* now require that physicians report sources of funding in journal articles. We should be skeptical of studies from sources that may be biased.

Sampling Method   Figure 1-2 suggests that we conclude our preparation by considering the sampling method. The data in Table 1-1 were obtained from subjects whose medical histories were reviewed in an effort to ensure that no subjects had neurologic or psychiatric disease. In this case, the sampling method appears to be sound, but we cannot be sure of that without knowing how the subjects were recruited and whether any payments may have affected participation in the study.

Sampling methods and the use of randomization will be discussed in Section 1-3, but for now, we stress that a sound sampling method is absolutely essential for good results in a statistical study. It is generally a bad practice to use voluntary response (or self-selected) samples, even though their use is common.

> **DEFINITION**
>
> A **voluntary response sample** (or **self-selected sample**) is one in which the respondents themselves decide whether to be included.

The following types of polls are common examples of voluntary response samples. By their very nature, all are seriously flawed because we should not make conclusions about a population on the basis of samples with a strong possibility of bias:

- Internet polls, in which people online can decide whether to respond
- Mail-in polls, in which people decide whether to reply

- Telephone call-in polls, in which newspaper, radio, or television announcements ask that you voluntarily call a special number to register your opinion

The Chapter Problem involves a *USA Today* survey with a voluntary response sample. See also the following Example 2.

EXAMPLE 2   Voluntary Response Sample

USA Today posted this question on the electronic edition of their newspaper: "Have you ever been bitten by an animal?" Internet users who saw that question then decided themselves whether to respond. Among the 2361 responses, 65% said "yes" and 35% said "no." Because the 2361 subjects themselves chose to respond, they are a voluntary response sample and the results of the survey are highly questionable. It would be much better to get results through a poll in which the pollster randomly selects the subjects, instead of allowing the subjects to volunteer themselves.

Analyze

Figure 1-2 indicates that after completing our preparation by considering the context, source, and sampling method, we begin to *analyze* the data.

Graph and Explore An analysis should begin with appropriate graphs and explorations of the data. Graphs are discussed in Chapter 2, and important statistics are discussed in Chapter 3.

Apply Statistical Methods Later chapters describe important statistical methods, but application of these methods is often made easy with technology (calculators and/or statistical software packages). A good statistical analysis does not require strong computational skills. A good statistical analysis does require using common sense and paying careful attention to sound statistical methods.

Conclude

Figure 1-2 shows that the final step in our statistical process involves conclusions, and we should develop an ability to distinguish between statistical significance and practical significance.

Statistical Significance *Statistical significance* is achieved in a study when we get a result that is very unlikely to occur by chance. A common criterion is that we have statistical significance if the likelihood of an event occurring by chance is 5% or less.

- Getting 98 girls in 100 random births is statistically significant because such an extreme outcome is not likely to result from random chance.
- Getting 52 girls in 100 births is not statistically significant because that event could easily occur with random chance.

Practical Significance It is possible that some treatment or finding is effective, but common sense might suggest that the treatment or finding does not make enough of a difference to justify its use or to be practical, as illustrated in Example 3 which follows.

EXAMPLE 3 **Statistical Significance Versus Practical Significance**

ProCare Industries once supplied a product named Gender Choice that supposedly increased the chance of a couple having a baby with the gender that they desired. In the absence of any evidence of its effectiveness, the product was banned by the Food and Drug Administration (FDA) as a "gross deception of the consumer." But suppose that the product was tested with 10,000 couples who wanted to have baby girls, and the results consist of 5200 baby girls born in the 10,000 births. This result is statistically significant because the likelihood of it happening due to chance is only 0.003%, so chance doesn't seem like a feasible explanation. That 52% rate of girls is statistically significant, but it lacks practical significance because 52% is only slightly above 50%. Couples would not want to spend the time and money to increase the likelihood of a girl from 50% to 52%. (*Note*: In reality, the likelihood of a baby being a girl is about 48.8%, not 50%.)

Analyzing Data: Potential Pitfalls

Here are a few more items that could cause problems when analyzing data.

Misleading Conclusions When forming a conclusion based on a statistical analysis, we should make statements that are clear even to those who have no understanding of statistics and its terminology. We should carefully avoid making statements not justified by the statistical analysis. For example, later in this book we introduce the concept of a correlation, or association between two variables, such as smoking and pulse rate. A statistical analysis might justify the statement that there is a correlation between the number of cigarettes smoked and pulse rate, but it would not justify a statement that the number of cigarettes smoked *causes* a person's pulse rate to change. Such a statement about causality can be justified by physical evidence, not by statistical analysis.

Correlation does not imply causation.

Sample Data Reported Instead of Measured When collecting data from people, it is better to take measurements yourself instead of asking subjects to *report* results. Ask people what they weigh and you are likely to get their *desired* weights, not their actual weights. People tend to round, usually down, sometimes *way* down. When asked, someone with a weight of 187 lb might respond that he or she weighs 160 lb. Accurate weights are collected by using a scale to measure weights, not by asking people what they weigh.

Loaded Questions If survey questions are not worded carefully, the results of a study can be misleading. Survey questions can be "loaded" or intentionally worded to elicit a desired response. Here are the actual rates of "yes" responses for the two different wordings of a question:

> 97% yes: "Should the President have the line item veto to eliminate waste?"

> 57% yes: "Should the President have the line item veto, or not?"

Order of Questions Sometimes survey questions are unintentionally loaded by such factors as the order of the items being considered. See the following two questions from a poll conducted in Germany, along with the very different response rates:

> "Would you say that traffic contributes more or less to air pollution than industry?" (45% blamed traffic; 27% blamed industry.)

> "Would you say that industry contributes more or less to air pollution than traffic?" (24% blamed traffic; 57% blamed industry.)

In addition to the order of items within a question, as illustrated above, the order of separate questions could also affect responses.

Nonresponse A *nonresponse* occurs when someone either refuses to respond to a survey question or is unavailable. When people are asked survey questions, some firmly refuse to answer. The refusal rate has been growing in recent years, partly because many persistent telemarketers try to sell goods or services by beginning with a sales pitch that initially sounds as though it is part of an opinion poll. (This "selling under the guise" of a poll is called *sugging*.) In *Lies, Damn Lies, and Statistics,* author Michael Wheeler makes this very important observation:

> **People who refuse to talk to pollsters are likely to be different from those who do not. Some may be fearful of strangers and others jealous of their privacy, but their refusal to talk demonstrates that their view of the world around them is markedly different from that of those people who will let poll-takers into their homes.**

Percentages Some studies cite misleading or unclear percentages. Note that 100% of some quantity is *all* of it, but if there are references made to percentages that exceed 100%, such references are often not justified. If a medical researcher claims that she has developed a treatment for migraine headaches and the treatment results in a 150% reduction in those headaches, that researcher cannot be correct, because totally eliminating *all* migraine headaches would be a 100% reduction. It is impossible to reduce the number of migraine headaches by more than 100%.

When working with percentages, we should know that % or "percent" really means "divided by 100." Here is a principle used often in this book.

> **Percentage of:** To find a percentage of an amount, replace the % symbol with division by 100, and then interpret "of" to be multiplication. The following calculation shows that 6% of 1200 is 72:

$$6\% \text{ of } 1200 \text{ responses} = \frac{6}{100} \times 1200 = 72$$

1-1 Basic Skills and Concepts

Statistical Literacy and Critical Thinking

1. Online Medical Info *USA Today* posted this question on its website: "How often do you seek medical information online?" Of 1072 Internet users who chose to respond, 38% of them responded with "frequently." What term is used to describe this type of survey in which the people surveyed consist of those who decided to respond? What is wrong with this type of sampling method?

2. Reported Versus Measured In a survey of 10,000 adults conducted by GlaxoSmithKline, subjects were asked if they brushed or flossed their teeth at night, and 45% of the respondents said "no."

a. Identify the sample and the population.

b. Why would better results be obtained by observing the activity instead of asking about it?

3. Statistical Significance Versus Practical Significance When testing a new treatment, what is the difference between statistical significance and practical significance? Can a treatment have statistical significance, but not practical significance?

4. Correlation One study showed that for a recent period of 11 years, there was a strong correlation (or association) between the numbers of people who drowned in swimming pools and the amounts of power generated by nuclear power plants (based on data from the Centers for Disease Control and Prevention and the Department of Energy). Does this imply that increasing power from nuclear power plants is the cause of more deaths in swimming pools? Why or why not?

Consider the Source.   *In Exercises 5–8, determine whether the given source has the potential to create a bias in a statistical study.*

5. BioMed Central Public Health The BioMed Central tends to support the use of sunscreen, especially by adolescents. The organization and data analysts involved in this survey have no competing interests.

6. Nicotine in Cigarettes Amounts of nicotine in samples of Camel cigarettes produced by R.J. Reynolds Tobacco Company were measured by William Esty Co., an advertising agency working for the tobacco company.

7. Brain Size A data set in Appendix B includes brain volumes from 10 pairs of monozygotic (identical) twins. The data were collected by researchers at Harvard University, Massachusetts General Hospital, Dartmouth College, and the University of California at Davis.

8. Chocolate An article in *Journal of Nutrition* (Vol. 130, No. 8) noted that chocolate is rich in flavonoids. The article notes "regular consumption of foods rich in flavonoids may reduce the risk of coronary heart disease." The study received funding from Mars, Inc., the candy company, and the Chocolate Manufacturers Association.

Sampling Method.   *In Exercises 9–12, determine whether the sampling method appears to be sound or is flawed.*

9. Nuclear Power Plants In a survey of 1368 subjects, the following question was posted on the *USA Today* website: "In your view, are nuclear plants safe?" The survey subjects were Internet users who chose to respond to the question posted on the electronic edition of *USA Today*.

10. Clinical Trials Researchers at Yale University conduct a wide variety of clinical trials by using subjects who volunteer after reading advertisements soliciting paid volunteers.

11. NHANES Examinations In a recent year, the National Health and Nutrition Examination Survey (NHANES), sponsored by the National Center for Health Statistics, selected more than 9000 subjects who were given physical exams. Subjects were selected through a somewhat complicated procedure designed to obtain results that are representative of the population.

12. Health In a survey of 3014 randomly selected U.S. adults, 45% reported that they have at least one chronic health condition, such as diabetes or high blood pressure. The survey was conducted by Princeton Survey Research Associates International.

Statistical Significance and Practical Significance.   *In Exercises 13–16, determine whether the results appear to have statistical significance, and also determine whether the results appear to have practical significance.*

13. Diet and Exercise Program In a study of the Kingman diet and exercise program, 40 subjects lost an average of 22 pounds. There is about a 1% chance of getting such results with a program that has no effect.

14. MCAT The Medical College Admissions Test (MCAT) is commonly used as part of the decision-making process for determining which students to accept into medical schools. To test the effectiveness of the Siena MCAT preparation course, 16 students take the MCAT test, then they complete the preparatory course, and then they retake the MCAT test, with the result that the average (mean) score for this group rises from 25 to 30. There is a 0.3% chance of getting those results by chance. Does the course appear to be effective?

15. Gender Selection In a study of the Gender Aide method of gender selection used to increase the likelihood of a baby being born a girl, 2000 users of the method gave birth to 980 boys and 1020 girls. There is about a 19% chance of getting that many girls if the method had no effect.

16. Systolic Blood Pressure High systolic blood pressure is 140 mm Hg or higher. (Normal values are less than 120 mm Hg, and prehypertension levels are between 120 mm Hg and 139 mm Hg.) Subjects with high blood pressure are encouraged to take action to lower it. A pharmaceutical company develops a new medication designed to lower blood pressure, and tests on 25 subjects result in an average (mean) decrease of 2 mm Hg. Analysis of the results shows that there is a 15% chance of getting such results if the medication has no effect.

In Exercises 17–20, refer to the sample of body temperatures (degrees Fahrenheit) in the table below. (The body temperatures are recorded on the same day from a sample of five randomly selected males listed in a data set in Appendix B.)

	Subject				
	1	2	3	4	5
8 AM	97.0	98.5	97.6	97.7	98.7
12 AM	97.6	97.8	98.0	98.4	98.4

17. Context of the Data Refer to the table of body temperatures. Is there some meaningful way in which each body temperature recorded at 8 AM is *matched* with the 12 AM temperature?

18. Source The listed body temperatures were obtained from Dr. Steven Wasserman, Dr. Philip Mackowiak, and Dr. Myron Levine, who were researchers at the University of Maryland. Is the source of the data likely to be biased?

19. Conclusion Given the body temperatures in the table, what issue can be addressed by conducting a statistical analysis of the data?

20. Conclusion If we analyze the listed body temperatures with suitable methods of statistics, we conclude that when the differences are found between the 8 AM body temperatures and the 12 AM body temperatures, there is a 64% chance that the differences can be explained by random results obtained from populations that have the same 8 AM and 12 AM body temperatures. What should we conclude about the statistical significance of those differences?

In Exercises 21–24, refer to the data in the table below. The entries are white blood cell counts (1000 cells / μL) and red blood cell counts (million cells / μL) from male subjects examined as part of a large health study conducted by the National Center for Health Statistics. The data are matched, so that the first subject has a white blood cell count of 8.7 and a red blood cell count of 4.91, and so on.

	Subject				
	1	2	3	4	5
White	8.7	5.9	7.3	6.2	5.9
Red	4.91	5.59	4.44	4.80	5.17

continued

21. Context Given that the data (on the bottom of the preceding page) are matched and considering the units of the data, does it make sense to use the difference between each white blood cell count and the corresponding red blood cell count? Why or why not?

22. Analysis Given the context of the data in the table (on the bottom of the preceding page), what issue can be addressed by conducting a statistical analysis of the measurements?

23. Source of the Data Considering the source of the data (on the bottom of the preceding page), does that source appear to be biased in some way?

24. Conclusion If we analyze the sample data (on the bottom of the preceding page) and conclude that there is a correlation between white and red blood cell counts, does it follow that higher white are the cause of higher red blood cell counts?

What's Wrong?   *In Exercises 25–28, identify what is wrong.*

25. Potatoes In a poll sponsored by the Idaho Potato Commission, 1000 adults were asked to select their favorite vegetables, and the favorite choice was potatoes, which were selected by 26% of the respondents.

26. Healthy Water In a *USA Today* online poll, 951 Internet users chose to respond, and 57% of them said that they prefer drinking bottled water instead of tap water.

27. Cheese and Bedsheet Deaths In recent years, there has been a strong correlation between per capita consumption of cheese in the United States and the numbers of people who died from being tangled in their bedsheets. Really. Therefore, consumption of cheese causes bedsheet entanglement fatalities.

28. Smokers The electronic cigarette maker V2 Cigs sponsored a poll showing that 55% of smokers surveyed say that they feel ostracized "sometimes," "often," or "always."

Percentages.   *In Exercises 29 and 30, answer the given questions, which are related to percentages.*

29. Health It was noted in Exercise 12 "Health" that in a survey of 3014 randomly selected U.S. adults, 45% reported that they have at least one chronic health condition, such as diabetes or high blood pressure.

a. What is 45% of 3014 adults?

b. Could the result from part (a) be the actual number of survey subjects who have at least one chronic condition?

c. What is the actual number of survey subjects who have at least one chronic condition?

d. Among those surveyed, 1808 were called by landline and 1206 were called by cell phone. What percentage of the survey subjects were called by cell phone?

30. Chillax *USA Today* reported results from a Research Now for Keurig survey in which 1458 men and 1543 women were asked this: "In a typical week, how often can you kick back and relax?"

a. Among the women, 19% responded with "rarely, if ever." What is the exact value that is 19% of the number of women surveyed?

b. Could the result from part (a) be the actual number of women who responded with "rarely, if ever"? Why or why not?

c. What is the actual number of women who responded with "rarely, if ever"?

d. Among the men who responded, 219 responded with "rarely, if ever." What is the percentage of men who responded with "rarely, if ever"?

e. Consider the question that the subjects were asked. Is that question clear and unambiguous so that all respondents will interpret the question the same way? How might the survey be improved?

1-1   Beyond the Basics

31. What's Wrong with This Picture? The *Newport Chronicle* ran a survey by asking readers to call in their response to this question: "Do you support a ban on electronic cigarettes, which foster smoking among our children?" It was reported that 20 readers responded and that 87% said "no," while 13% said "yes." Identify four major flaws in this survey.

32. Falsifying Data A researcher at the Sloan-Kettering Cancer Research Center was once criticized for falsifying data. Among his data were figures obtained from 6 groups of mice, with 20 individual mice in each group. The following values were given for the percentage of successes in each group: 53%, 58%, 63%, 46%, 48%, 67%. What's wrong with those values?

Types of Data

Key Concept A major use of statistics is to collect and use sample data to make conclusions about populations. We should know and understand the meanings of the terms *statistic* and *parameter,* as defined below. In this section we describe a few different types of data. The type of data is one of the key factors that determine the statistical methods we use in our analysis.

In Part 1 of this section we describe the basics of different types of data, and then in Part 2 we consider "big data" and missing data.

PART 1   Basic Types of Data

Parameter / Statistic

> **DEFINITIONS**
>
> A **parameter** is a numerical measurement describing some characteristic of a *population*.
>
> A **statistic** is a numerical measurement describing some characteristic of a *sample*.

> **HINT** The alliteration in "population parameter" and "sample statistic" helps us remember the meanings of these terms.

If we have more than one statistic, we have "statistics." Another meaning of "statistics" was given in Section 1-1, where we defined *statistics* to be the science of planning studies and experiments; obtaining data; organizing, summarizing, presenting, analyzing, and interpreting those data; and then drawing conclusions based on them. We now have two different definitions of statistics, but we can determine which of these two definitions applies by considering the context in which the term *statistics* is used, as in the following example.

    EXAMPLE 1   Parameter / Statistic

There are 17,246,372 high school students in the United States. In a study of 8505 U.S. high school students 16 years of age or older, 44.5% of them said that they texted while driving at least once during the previous 30 days (based on data in

continued

"Texting While Driving and Other Risky Motor Vehicle Behaviors Among U.S. High School Students," by Olsen, Shults, Eaton, *Pediatrics*, Vol. 131, No. 6).

1. **Parameter:** The population size of all 17,246,372 high school students is a parameter, because it is the size of the entire population of all high school students in the United States. If we somehow knew the percentage of all 17,246,372 high school students who reported they had texted while driving, that percentage would also be a parameter.

2. **Statistic:** The value of 44.5% is a statistic, because it is based on the sample, not on the entire population.

Quantitative/Categorical

Some data are numbers representing counts or measurements (such as a systolic blood pressure of 118 mm Hg), whereas others are attributes (such as eye color of green or brown) that are not counts or measurements. The terms *quantitative data* and *categorical data* distinguish between these types.

DEFINITIONS

Quantitative (or numerical) data consist of *numbers* representing counts or measurements.

Categorical (or qualitative or attribute) data consist of names or labels (not numbers that represent counts or measurements).

CAUTION Categorical data are sometimes coded with numbers, with those numbers replacing names. Although such numbers might appear to be quantitative, they are actually categorical data. See the third part of Example 2.

Include Units of Measurement With quantitative data, it is important to use the appropriate units of measurement, such as dollars, hours, feet, or meters. We should carefully observe information given about the units of measurement, such as "all amounts are in *thousands of dollars*," or "all units are in *kilograms*." Ignoring such units of measurement can be very costly. The National Aeronautics and Space Administration (NASA) lost its $125 million Mars Climate Orbiter when the orbiter crashed because the controlling software had acceleration data in *English* units, but they were incorrectly assumed to be in *metric* units.

EXAMPLE 2 **Quantitative/Categorical**

1. **Quantitative Data:** The ages (in years) of subjects enrolled in a clinical trial

2. **Categorical Data as Labels:** The genders (male/female) of subjects enrolled in a clinical trial

3. **Categorical Data as Numbers:** The identification numbers 1, 2, 3, . . . , 25 are assigned randomly to the 25 subjects in a clinical trial. Those numbers are substitutes for names. They don't measure or count anything, so they are categorical data, not quantitative data.

Discrete / Continuous

Quantitative data can be further described by distinguishing between *discrete* and *continuous* types.

DEFINITIONS

Discrete data result when the data values are quantitative and the number of values is finite or "countable." (If there are infinitely many values, the collection of values is countable if it is possible to count them individually, such as the number of tosses of a coin before getting tails or the number of births in Houston before getting a male.)

Continuous (numerical) data result from infinitely many possible quantitative values, where the collection of values is not countable. (That is, it is impossible to count the individual items because at least some of them are on a continuous scale, such as the lengths of distances from 0 cm to 12 cm.)

CAUTION The concept of *countable* data plays a key role in the preceding definitions, but it is not a particularly easy concept to understand. Continuous data can be measured, but not counted. If you select a particular data value from continuous data, there is no "next" data value. See Example 3.

Continuous Data

Discrete Data

EXAMPLE 3 Discrete / Continuous

1. **Discrete Data of the Finite Type:** Each of several physicians plans to count the number of physical examinations given during the next full week. The data are *discrete* data because they are finite numbers, such as 27 and 46 that result from a counting process.

2. **Discrete Data of the Infinite Type:** Researchers plan to test the accuracy of a blood typing test by repeating the process of submitting a sample of the same blood (Type O+) until the test yields an error. It is possible that each researcher could repeat this test forever without ever getting an error, but they can still count the number of tests as they proceed. The collection of the numbers of tests is countable, because you can count them, even though the counting could go on forever.

3. **Continuous Data:** When the typical patient has blood drawn as part of a routine examination, the volume of blood drawn is between 0 mL and 50 mL. There are infinitely many values between 0 mL and 50 mL. Because it is impossible to count the number of different possible values on such a continuous scale, these amounts are continuous data.

GRAMMAR: FEWER VERSUS LESS When describing smaller amounts, it is correct grammar to use "fewer" for discrete amounts and "less" for continuous amounts. It is correct to say that we drank *fewer* cans of cola and that, in the process, we drank *less* cola. The numbers of cans of cola are discrete data, whereas the volume amounts of cola are continuous data.

Levels of Measurement

Another common way of classifying data is to use four levels of measurement: nominal, ordinal, interval, and ratio, all defined below. (Also see Table 1-2 for brief descriptions of the four levels of measurements.) When we are applying statistics to real problems, the level of measurement of the data helps us decide which procedure to use. There will be references to these levels of measurement in this book, but the important point here is based on common sense: *Don't do computations and don't use statistical methods that are not appropriate for the data.* For example, it would not make sense to compute an average (mean) of Social Security numbers, because those numbers are data used for identification, and they don't represent measurements or counts of anything.

DEFINITION

The **nominal level of measurement** is characterized by data that consist of names, labels, or categories only. It is not possible to arrange the data in some order (such as low to high).

 EXAMPLE 4   **Nominal Level**

Here are examples of sample data at the nominal level of measurement.

1. **Yes/No/Undecided:** Survey responses of *yes, no,* and *undecided*

2. **Coded Survey Responses:** For an item on a survey, respondents are given a choice of possible answers, and they are coded as follows: "I agree" is coded as 1; "I disagree" is coded as 2; "I don't care" is coded as 3; "I refuse to answer" is coded as 4; "Go away and stop bothering me" is coded as 5. The numbers 1, 2, 3, 4, 5 don't measure or count anything.

Because nominal data lack any ordering or numerical significance, they should not be used for calculations. Numbers such as 1, 2, 3, and 4 are sometimes assigned to the different categories (especially when data are coded for computers), but these numbers have no real computational significance and any average (mean) calculated from them is meaningless and possibly misleading.

DEFINITION

Data are at the **ordinal level of measurement** if they can be arranged in some order, but differences (obtained by subtraction) between data values either cannot be determined or are meaningless.

EXAMPLE 5 Ordinal Level

Here is an example of sample data at the ordinal level of measurement.

Course Grades: A biostatistics professor assigns grades of A, B, C, D, or F. These grades can be arranged in order, but we can't determine differences between the grades. For example, we know that A is higher than B (so there is an ordering), but we cannot subtract B from A (so the difference cannot be found).

Ordinal data provide information about relative comparisons, but not the *magnitudes* of the differences. Usually, ordinal data should not be used for calculations such as an average (mean), but this guideline is sometimes disregarded (such as when we use letter grades to calculate a grade-point average).

DEFINITION

Data are at the **interval level of measurement** if they can be arranged in order, and differences between data values can be found and are meaningful; but data at this level do not have a natural zero starting point at which none of the quantity is present.

 EXAMPLE 6 Interval Level

These examples illustrate the interval level of measurement.

1. **Temperatures:** Body temperatures of 98.2°F and 98.8°F are examples of data at this interval level of measurement. Those values are ordered, and we can determine their difference of 0.6°F. However, there is no natural starting point. The value of 0°F might seem like a starting point, but it is arbitrary and does not represent the total absence of heat.

2. **Years:** The years 1492 and 1776 can be arranged in order, and the difference of 284 years can be found and is meaningful. However, time did not begin in the year 0, so the year 0 is arbitrary instead of being a natural zero starting point representing "no time."

DEFINITION

Data are at the **ratio level of measurement** if they can be arranged in order, differences can be found and are meaningful, and there is a natural zero starting point (where zero indicates that *none* of the quantity is present). For data at this level, differences and ratios are both meaningful.

 EXAMPLE 7 Ratio Level

The following are examples of data at the ratio level of measurement. Note the presence of the natural zero value, and also note the use of meaningful ratios of "twice" and "three times."

1. **Heights of Students:** Heights of 180 cm and 90 cm for a high school student and a preschool student (0 cm represents no height, and 180 cm is twice as tall as 90 cm.)

2. **Class Times:** The times of 50 min and 100 min for a statistics class (0 min represents no class time, and 100 min is twice as long as 50 min.)

See Table 1-2 for brief descriptions of the four levels of measurements.

TABLE 1-2 Levels of Measurement

Level of Measurement	Brief Description	Example
Ratio	There is a natural zero starting point and ratios make sense.	Heights, lengths, distances, volumes
Interval	Differences are meaningful, but there is no natural zero starting point and ratios are meaningless.	Body temperatures in degrees Fahrenheit or Celsius
Ordinal	Data can be arranged in order, but differences either can't be found or are meaningless.	Ranks of colleges in *U.S. News & World Report*
Nominal	Categories only. Data cannot be arranged in order.	Eye colors

HINT The distinction between the interval and ratio levels of measurement can be a bit tricky. Here are two tools for help with that distinction:

1. **Ratio Test** Focus on the term "ratio" and know that the term "twice" describes the ratio of one value to be double the other value. To distinguish between the interval and ratio levels of measurement, use a "ratio test" by asking this question: Does use of the term "twice" make sense? "Twice" makes sense for data at the ratio level of measurement, but it does not make sense for data at the interval level of measurement.

2. **True Zero** For ratios to make sense, there must be a value of "true zero," where the value of zero indicates that none of the quantity is present, and zero is not simply an arbitrary value on a scale. The temperature of 0°F is arbitrary and does not indicate that there is no heat, so temperatures on the Fahrenheit scale are at the interval level of measurement, not the ratio level.

EXAMPLE 8 **Distinguishing Between the Ratio Level and Interval Level**

For each of the following, determine whether the data are at the ratio level of measurement or the interval level of measurement:

    a. Times (minutes) it takes to complete a statistics test.

    b. Body temperatures (Celsius) of statistics students.

SOLUTION

    a. Apply the "ratio test" described in the preceding hint. If one student completes the test in 40 minutes and another student completes the test in 20 min, does it make sense to say that the first student used *twice* as much time? Yes! *So the times are at the ratio level of measurement.* Also, a time of 0 minutes does represent "no time," so the value of 0 is a true zero indicating that no time was used.

    b. Apply the "ratio test" described in the preceding hint. If one student has a body temperature of 40°C and another student has a body temperature of 20°C, does it make sense to say that the first student is *twice* as hot as the second student? (Ignore subjective amounts of attractiveness and consider only science.) No! *So the body temperatures are not at the ratio level of measurement.* Because the difference between 40°C and 20°C is the same as the difference between 90°C and 70°C, the differences are meaningful, but because ratios do not make sense, the body temperatures are at the interval level of measurement. Also, the temperature of 0°C does not represent "no heat" so the value of 0 is not a true zero indicating that no heat is present.

PART 2 Big Data and Missing Data: Too Much and Not Enough

When working with data, we might encounter some data sets that are excessively large, and we might also encounter some data sets with individual elements missing. Here in Part 2 we briefly discuss both cases.

Big Data

Edward Snowden used his employment at the NSA (National Security Agency) to reveal substantial top secret documents that led to the realization that the NSA was conducting telephone and Internet surveillance of U.S. citizens as well as world leaders. The NSA was collecting massive amounts of data that were analyzed in an attempt to prevent terrorism. Monitoring telephone calls and Internet communications is made possible with modern technology. The NSA can compile *big data,* and such ginormous data sets have led to the birth of *data science.* There is not universal agreement on the following definitions, and various other definitions can be easily found elsewhere.

> **DEFINITIONS**
>
> **Big data** refers to data sets so large and so complex that their analysis is beyond the capabilities of traditional software tools. Analysis of big data may require software simultaneously running in parallel on many different computers.
>
> **Data science** involves applications of statistics, computer science, and software engineering, along with some other relevant fields (such as biology and epidemiology).

Examples of Data Set Magnitudes We can see from the above definition of big data that there isn't a fixed number that serves as an exact boundary for determining whether a data set qualifies as being big data, but big data typically involves amounts of data such as the following.

- Terabytes (10^{12} or 1,000,000,000,000 bytes) of data
- Petabytes (10^{15} bytes) of data
- Exabytes (10^{18} bytes) of data
- Zettabytes (10^{21} bytes) of data
- Yottabytes (10^{24} bytes) of data

Examples of Applications of Big Data The following are a few examples involving big data:

- Attempt to forecast flu epidemics by analyzing Internet searches of flu symptoms.
- The Spatio Temporal Epidemiological Modeler developed by IBM is providing a means for using a variety of data that are correlated with disease data.

continued

Big Data Instead of a Clinical Trial

Nicholas Tatonetti of Columbia University searched Food and Drug Administration databases for adverse reactions in patients that resulted from different pairings of drugs. He discovered that the paroxetine drug for depression and the pravastatin drug for high cholesterol interacted to create increases in glucose (blood sugar) levels. When taken separately by patients, neither drug raised glucose levels, but the increase in glucose levels occurred when the two drugs were taken together. This finding resulted from a general database search of interactions from many pairings of drugs, not from a clinical trial involving patients using Paxil and pravastatin.

- A National Electronic Disease Surveillance System is used to monitor disease trends and identify outbreaks of infectious disease.

- Google provides live traffic maps by recording and analyzing GPS (global positioning system) data collected from the smartphones of people traveling in their vehicles.

- Amazon monitors and tracks 1.4 billion items in its store that are distributed across hundreds of fulfillment centers around the world.

Examples of Jobs According to Analytic Talent, there are 6000 companies hiring data scientists, and here are some job posting examples:

- Facebook: Data Scientist
- IBM: Data Scientist
- PayPal: Data Scientist
- The College Board: SAS Programmer/Data Scientist
- Netflix: Senior Data Engineer/Scientist

Statistics in Data Science The modern data scientist has a solid background in statistics and computer systems as well as expertise in fields that extend beyond statistics. The modern data scientist might be skilled with Hadoop software, which uses parallel processing on many computers for the analysis of big data. The modern data scientist might also have a strong background in some other field, such as psychology, biology, medicine, chemistry, or economics. Because of the wide range of disciplines required, a data science project might typically involve a team of collaborating individuals with expertise in different fields. An introductory statistics course is a great first step in becoming a data scientist.

Missing Data

When collecting sample data, it is quite common to find that some values are missing. Ignoring missing data can sometimes create misleading results. If you make the mistake of skipping over a few different sample values when you are manually typing them into a statistics software program, the missing values are not likely to have a serious effect on the results. However, if a survey includes many missing salary entries because those with very low incomes are reluctant to reveal their salaries, those missing low values will have the serious effect of making salaries appear higher than they really are.

For an example of missing data, see the following table. The body temperature for Subject 2 at 12 AM on day 2 is missing. (The table below includes the first three rows of data from Data Set 2 "Body Temperatures" in Appendix B.)

Body Temperatures (in degrees Fahrenheit) of Healthy Adults

Subject	Age	Sex	Smoke	Temperature Day 1		Temperature Day 2	
				8 AM	12 AM	8 AM	12 AM
1	22	M	Y	98.0	98.0	98.0	98.6
2	23	M	Y	97.0	97.6	97.4	----
3	22	M	Y	98.6	98.8	97.8	98.6

There are different categories of missing data. See the following definitions.

> **DEFINITION**
>
> A data value is **missing completely at random** if the likelihood of its being missing is independent of its value or any of the other values in the data set. That is, any data value is just as likely to be missing as any other data value.

(*Note*: More complete discussions of missing data will distinguish between *missing completely at random* and *missing at random,* which means that the likelihood of a value being missing is independent of its value after controlling for another variable. There is no need to know this distinction in this book.)

Example of Missing Data—Random When using a keyboard to manually enter ages of survey respondents, the operator is distracted by a colleague singing "Daydream Believer" and makes the mistake of failing to enter the age of 37 years. This data value is missing completely at random.

> **DEFINITION**
>
> A data value is **missing not at random** if the missing value is related to the reason that it is missing.

Example of Missing Data—Not at Random A survey question asks each respondent to enter his or her annual income, but respondents with very low incomes skip this question because they find it embarrassing.

Biased Results? Based on the above two definitions and examples, it makes sense to conclude that if we ignore data missing completely at random, the remaining values are not likely to be biased and good results should be obtained. However, if we ignore data that are missing not at random, it is very possible that the remaining values are biased and results will be misleading.

Correcting for Missing Data There are different methods for dealing with missing data.

1. **Delete Cases:** One very common method for dealing with missing data is to delete all subjects having any missing values.

   - If the data are missing completely at random, the remaining values are not likely to be biased and good results can be obtained, but with a smaller sample size.

   - If the data are missing not at random, deleting subjects having any missing values can easily result in a bias among the remaining values, so results can be misleading.

2. **Impute Missing Values:** We *impute* missing data values when we substitute values for them. There are different methods of determining the replacement values, such as using the mean of the other values, or using a randomly selected value from other similar cases, or using a method based on regression analysis (which will make more sense after studying Chapter 10).

In this book we do not work much with missing data, but it is important to understand this:

When analyzing sample data with missing values, try to determine *why* they are missing, and then decide whether it makes sense to treat the remaining values as being representative of the population. If it appears that there are missing values that are missing not at random (that is, their values are related to the reasons why they are missing), know that the remaining data may well be biased and any conclusions based on those remaining values may well be misleading.

1-2 Basic Skills and Concepts

Statistical Literacy and Critical Thinking

1. Health Survey In a survey of 1020 adults in the United States, 44% said that they wash their hands after riding public transportation (based on data from KRC Research).

a. Identify the sample and the population.

b. Is the value of 44% a statistic or a parameter?

2. Health Survey For the same survey from Exercise 1, answer the following.

a. What is the level of measurement of the value of 44%? (nominal, ordinal, interval, ratio)

b. Are the numbers of subjects in such surveys discrete or continuous?

c. The responses are "yes," "no," "not sure," or "refused to answer." Are these responses quantitative data or categorical data?

3. Quantitative/Categorical Data Identify each of the following as quantitative data or categorical data.

a. The packaging date of an intravenous drip

b. The length of the IV infusion set of an intravenous drip

c. The birth weight of exam subjects in Data Set 3 "Births" in Appendix B

d. The names of the insurance companies that offer medical insurance

4. Discrete/Continuous Data Which of the following describe discrete data?

a. The numbers of people surveyed in each of the next several National Health and Nutrition Examination Surveys

b. The exact foot lengths (cm) of a random sample of statistics students

c. The exact times that randomly selected drivers spend texting while driving during the past 7 days

In Exercises 5–12, identify whether the given value is a statistic or a parameter.

5. JAL Flight 123 A study was conducted of all 520 people aboard the Japanese Airlines Flight 123 when it crashed.

6. CHIS A recent California Health Interview Survey (CHIS) included 2799 adolescent residents of California.

7. Element Density The average (mean) density of all elements in the periodic table is 9.86 grams per cm^3.

8. Triangle Fire Fatalities A deadly disaster in the United States was the Triangle Shirtwaist Factory Fire in New York City. A population of 146 garment workers died in that fire.

9. Birth Weight In a study of 400 babies born at four different hospitals in New York State, it was found that the average (mean) weight at birth was 3152.0 grams.

10. Birth Genders In the same study cited in the preceding exercise, 51% of the babies were girls.

11. Cuckoo Egg Length The average (mean) length of the hedge sparrow eggs included in Data Set 17 "Cuckoo Egg Lengths" in Appendix B is 23.12 cm.

12. Heights A data set in Appendix B includes height measurements of 134 fathers, and their average mean height is 69.3 inches.

In Exercises 13–20, determine whether the data are from a discrete or continuous data set.

13. Height Data Set 1 "Body Data" in Appendix B includes the heights (cm) for each person in a sample of 300 adults. The first few values are 172, 186, 154.4, 160.5 and 179.

14. Body Temperature In a study documenting the changes in body temperature from 8 AM to 12 PM, researchers record the values of temperatures as observed in randomly selected adults (as in Data Set 2 "Body Temperatures" in Appendix B).

15. CHIS Among the subjects surveyed as part of the California Health Interview Survey (CHIS), several subjects are randomly selected and their heights are recorded.

16. Head Circumference A sample of graduation students is randomly selected and the head circumference of each such student is recorded.

17. BMI From Data Set 1 "Body Data" in Appendix B, we see that the average BMI of males is 28.16.

18. Criminal Forensics When studying the relationship between lengths of feet and heights so that footprint evidence at a crime scene can be used to estimate the height of the suspect, a researcher records the exact lengths of feet from a large sample of random subjects.

19. Stitch In Time The Emergency Room of the Albany Medical Center records the numbers of stitches used for patients in a week.

20. Texting Fatalities The Insurance Institute for Highway Safety collects data consisting of the numbers of motor vehicle fatalities caused by driving while texting.

In Exercises 21–28, determine which of the four levels of measurement (nominal, ordinal, interval, ratio) is most appropriate.

21. Manatee Deaths Deaths listed in Data Set 12 "Manatee Deaths" in Appendix B

22. Egg Lengths Lengths (in mm) of eggs of Tree Pippit listed in Data Set 17 "Cuckoo Egg Lengths" in Appendix B

23. Student Registration The students enrolling in a statistics course are allotted consecutive registration numbers.

24. Gender Codes Instead of using actual gender, children born in the Albany Medical Center Hospital are coded with gender codes for males and females.

25. Hospitals A research project on the effectiveness of heart transplants begins with a compilation of the U.S. hospitals that provide heart transplants.

26. Colleges A research project on the IQ of statistics graduates begins with a compilation of the colleges that provide statistics graduation courses.

27. College Fees A research project on the IQ of statistics graduates begins with a compilation of the fees (dollars) for the undergraduate courses that were conducted within the past year.

28. Pharmaceuticals Pfizer records the years in which new products were launched, beginning with 1849.

In Exercises 29–32, identify the level of measurement of the data as nominal, ordinal, interval, or ratio. Also, explain what is wrong with the given calculation.

29. Hospital ID The four hospitals included in Data Set 3 "Births" in Appendix B are coded as follows: Albany Medical Center (1); Bellevue Hospital Center (1438); Olean General Hospital (66); Strong Memorial Hospital (413). The average (mean) of those numbers is 479.5.

30. Social Security Numbers As part of a clinical study, the Social Security number of each subject is recorded and the average (mean) of the individual digits is computed to be 4.7.

31. Temperatures A person has a body temperature of 98.0°F during the time when the outside air temperature is 49.0°F, so the person is twice as warm as the outside air.

32. Medical School Ranks As of this writing, *U.S. News & World Report* ranked medical schools, including these results: Harvard (1), Stanford (2), Johns Hopkins (3), University of California at San Francisco (4), and University of Pennsylvania (5). The difference between Harvard and Stanford is the same as the difference between Johns Hopkins and University of California at San Francisco.

1-2   Beyond the Basics

33. Countable For each of the following, categorize the nature of the data using one of these three descriptions: (1) discrete because the number of possible values is finite; (2) discrete because the number of possible values is infinite but countable; (3) continuous because the number of possible values is infinite and not countable.

a. Exact lengths of the feet of members of the band the Monkees

b. Shoe sizes of members of the band the Monkees (such as 9, 9½, and so on)

c. The number of albums sold by the Monkees band

d. The numbers of monkeys sitting at keyboards before one of them randomly types the lyrics for the song "Daydream Believer"

1-3   Collecting Sample Data

Key Concept When using statistics in a study, planning is very important, and it is essential to use an appropriate method for collecting the sample data. This section includes comments about various methods and sampling procedures. Of particular importance is the method of using a *simple random sample*. We will make frequent use of this sampling method throughout the remainder of this book.

As you read this section, remember this:

If sample data are not collected in an appropriate way, the data may be so utterly useless that no amount of statistical torturing can salvage them.

PART 1   Basics of Design of Experiments and Collecting Sample Data

The Gold Standard Randomization with placebo/treatment groups is sometimes called the "gold standard" because it is so effective. (A placebo such as a sugar pill has no medicinal effect.) The following example describes how the gold standard was used in the largest health experiment ever conducted.

EXAMPLE 1 **The Salk Vaccine Experiment**

In 1954, an experiment was designed to test the effectiveness of the Salk vaccine in preventing polio, which had killed or paralyzed thousands of children. By random selection, 401,974 children were randomly assigned to two groups: (1) 200,745 children were given a *treatment* consisting of Salk vaccine injections; (2) 201,229 children were injected with a *placebo* that contained no drug. Children were assigned to the treatment or placebo group through a process of random selection, equivalent to flipping a coin. Among the children given the Salk vaccine, 33 later developed paralytic polio, and among the children given a placebo, 115 later developed paralytic polio.

Example 1 describes an *experiment* because subjects were given a treatment, but ethical, cost, time, and other considerations sometimes prohibit the use of an experiment. We would never want to conduct a driving/texting experiment in which we ask subjects to text while driving—some of them could die. It would be far better to observe past crash results to understand the effects of driving while texting. See the following definitions.

> **DEFINITIONS**
>
> In an **experiment,** we apply some *treatment* and then proceed to observe its effects on the individuals. (The individuals in experiments are called **experimental units,** and they are often called **subjects** when they are people.)
>
> In an **observational study,** we observe and measure specific characteristics, but we don't attempt to *modify* the individuals being studied.

Experiments are often better than observational studies because well-planned experiments typically reduce the chance of having the results affected by some variable that is not part of a study. A *lurking variable* is one that affects the variables included in the study, but it is not included in the study.

EXAMPLE 2 **Ice Cream and Drownings**

Observational Study: Observe past data to conclude that ice cream causes drownings (based on data showing that increases in ice cream sales are associated with increases in drownings). The mistake is to miss the lurking variable of temperature and the failure to see that as the temperature increases, ice cream sales increase and drownings increase because more people swim.

Experiment: Conduct an *experiment* with one group treated with ice cream while another group gets no ice cream. We would see that the rate of drowning victims is about the same in both groups, so ice cream consumption has no effect on drownings.

Here, the experiment is clearly better than the observational study.

Design of Experiments

Good design of experiments includes replication, blinding, and randomization.

- **Replication** is the repetition of an experiment on more than one individual. Good use of replication requires sample sizes that are large enough so that we can see

Clinical Trials vs. Observational Studies

In a *New York Times* article about hormone therapy for women, reporter Denise Grady wrote about randomized clinical trials that involve subjects who were randomly assigned to a treatment group and another group not given the treatment. Such randomized clinical trials are often referred to as the "gold standard" for medical research. In contrast, observational studies can involve patients who decide themselves to undergo some treatment. Subjects who decide themselves to undergo treatments are often healthier than other subjects, so the treatment group might appear to be more successful simply because it involves healthier subjects, not necessarily because the treatment is effective. Researchers criticized observational studies of hormone therapy for women by saying that results might appear to make the treatment more effective than it really is.

Hawthorne and Experimenter Effects

The well-known placebo effect occurs when an untreated subject incorrectly believes that he or she is receiving a real treatment and reports an improvement in symptoms. The Hawthorne effect occurs when treated subjects somehow respond differently, simply because they are part of an experiment. (This phenomenon was called the "Hawthorne effect" because it was first observed in a study of factory workers at Western Electric's Hawthorne plant.) An experimenter effect (sometimes called a Rosenthal effect) occurs when the researcher or experimenter unintentionally influences subjects through such factors as facial expression, tone of voice, or attitude.

effects of treatments. In the Salk experiment in Example 1, the experiment used sufficiently large sample sizes, so the researchers could see that the Salk vaccine was effective.

- **Blinding** is used when the subject doesn't know whether he or she is receiving a treatment or a placebo. Blinding is a way to get around the **placebo effect,** which occurs when an untreated subject reports an improvement in symptoms. (The reported improvement in the placebo group may be real or imagined.) The Salk experiment in Example 1 was **double-blind,** which means that blinding occurred at two levels: (1) The children being injected didn't know whether they were getting the Salk vaccine or a placebo, and (2) the doctors who gave the injections and evaluated the results did not know either. Codes were used so that the researchers could objectively evaluate the effectiveness of the Salk vaccine.

- **Randomization** is used when individuals are assigned to different groups through a process of random selection, as in the Salk vaccine experiment in Example 1. The logic behind randomization is to use chance as a way to create two groups that are similar. The following definition refers to one common and effective way to collect sample data in a way that uses randomization.

DEFINITION

A **simple random sample** of n subjects is selected in such a way that every possible *sample of the same size n* has the same chance of being chosen. (A simple random sample is often called a random sample, but strictly speaking, a *random sample* has the weaker requirement that all members of the population have the same chance of being selected. That distinction is not so important in this text. (See Exercise 38 "Simple Random Sample vs. Random Sample.")

Throughout, we will use various statistical procedures, and we often have a requirement that we have collected a *simple random sample,* as defined above.

Unlike careless or haphazard sampling, random sampling usually requires very careful planning and execution.

Other Sampling Methods In addition to simple random sampling, here are some other sampling methods commonly used for surveys. Figure 1-3 illustrates these different sampling methods.

DEFINITIONS

In **systematic sampling,** we select some starting point and then select every kth (such as every 50th) element in the population.

With **convenience sampling,** we simply use data that are very easy to get.

In **stratified sampling,** we subdivide the population into at least two different subgroups (or strata) so that subjects within the same subgroup share the same characteristics (such as gender). Then we draw a sample from each subgroup (or stratum).

In **cluster sampling,** we first divide the population area into sections (or clusters). Then we randomly select some of those clusters and choose *all* the members from those selected clusters.

Simple Random Sample
A sample of *n* subjects is selected so that every sample of the same size *n* has the same chance of being selected.

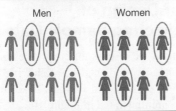

Systematic Sample
Select every *k*th subject.

3rd   *6th*

Convenience Sample
Use data that are very easy to get.

Men   Women

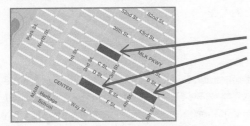

Stratified Sample
Subdivide population into strata (groups) with the same characteristics, then randomly sample within those strata.

Cluster Sample
Partition the population in clusters (groups), then randomly select some clusters, then select all members of the selected clusters.

FIGURE 1-3   Common Sampling Methods

Multistage Sampling Professional pollsters and government researchers often collect data by using some combination of the preceding sampling methods. In a **multistage sample design,** pollsters select a sample in different stages, and each stage might use different methods of sampling, as in the following example.

EXAMPLE 3 Multistage Sample Design

The U.S. government's unemployment statistics are based on surveys of households. It is impractical to personally survey each household in a simple random sample, because they would be scattered all over the country. Instead, the U.S. Census Bureau and the Bureau of Labor Statistics collaborate to conduct a survey called the Current Population Survey. A recent survey incorporates a multistage sample design, roughly following these steps:

1. The entire United States is partitioned into 2,007 different regions called *primary sampling units* (PSUs). The primary sampling units are metropolitan areas, large counties, or combinations of smaller counties. The 2,007 primary sampling units are then grouped into 824 different strata.

continued

Value of a Statistical Life

The *value of a statistical life* (VSL) is a measure routinely calculated and used for making decisions in fields such as medicine, insurance, environmental health, and transportation safety. As of this writing, the value of a statistical life is $6.9 million.

Many people oppose the concept of putting a value on a human life, but the word *statistical* in the "value of a statistical life" is used to ensure that we don't equate it with the true worth of a human life. Some people legitimately argue that every life is priceless, but others argue that there are conditions in which it is impossible or impractical to save every life, so a value must be somehow assigned to a human life in order that sound and rational decisions can be made. Not far from the author's home, a parkway was modified at a cost of about $3 million to improve safety at a location where car occupants had previously died in traffic crashes. In the cost-benefit analysis that led to this improvement in safety, the value of a statistical life was surely considered.

2. In each of the 824 different strata, one of the primary sampling units is selected so that the probability of selection is proportional to the size of the population in each primary sampling unit.

3. In each of the 824 selected primary sampling units, census data are used to identify a census *enumeration district,* with each containing about 300 households. Enumeration districts are then randomly selected.

4. In each of the selected enumeration districts, clusters of about four addresses (contiguous whenever possible) are randomly selected.

5. A responsible person in each of the 60,000 selected households is interviewed about the employment status of each household member of age 16 or older.

This multistage sample design includes a combination of random, stratified, and cluster sampling at different stages. The end result is a very complicated sampling design, but it is much more practical, less expensive, and faster than using a simpler design, such as a simple random sample.

PART 2 Beyond the Basics of Design of Experiments and Collecting Sample Data

Observational Studies In Part 2 of this section, we discuss different types of observational studies and different ways of designing experiments. The following definitions identify the standard terminology used in professional journals for different types of observational studies. These definitions are illustrated in Figure 1-4.

DEFINITIONS

In a **cross-sectional study,** data are observed, measured, and collected at one point in time, not over a period of time.

In a **retrospective (or case-control) study,** data are collected from a past time period by going back in time (through examination of records, interviews, and so on).

In a **prospective (or longitudinal or cohort) study,** data are collected in the future from groups that share common factors (such groups are called *cohorts*).

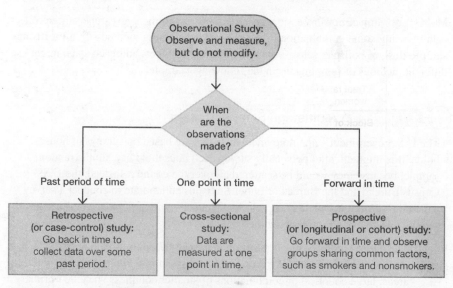

FIGURE 1-4   **Types of Observational Studies**

Experiments In a study, **confounding** occurs when we can see some effect, but we can't identify the specific factor that caused it, as in the ice cream and drowning observational study in Example 2. See also the bad experimental design illustrated in Figure 1-5(a), where confounding can occur when the treatment group of women shows strong positive results. Because the treatment group consists of women and the placebo group consists of men, confounding has occurred because we cannot determine whether the treatment or the gender of the subjects caused the positive results. The Salk vaccine experiment in Example 1 illustrates one method for controlling the effect of the treatment variable: Use a *completely randomized experimental design,* whereby randomness is used to assign subjects to the treatment group and the placebo group. A completely randomized experimental design is one of the following methods that are used to control effects of variables.

Completely Randomized Experimental Design: Assign subjects to different treatment groups through a process of *random selection,* as illustrated in Figure 1-5(b).

(a)
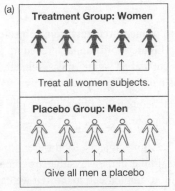

Bad experimental design:
Treat all women subjects
and give the men a placebo.
(Problem: We don't know if
effects are due to sex or
to treatment.)

(b)
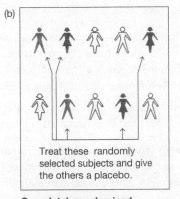

**Completely randomized
experimental design:**
Use randomness to
determine who gets the
treatment and who gets
the placebo.

(c)
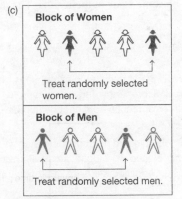

Randomized block design:
1. Form a block of women
   and a block of men.
2. Within each block,
   randomly select subjects
   to be treated.

(d)
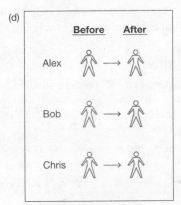

Matched pairs design:
Get measurements from the
same subjects before and after
some treatment.

FIGURE 1-5 Designs of Experiments

Randomized Block Design: See Figure 1-5c. A **block** is a group of subjects that are similar, but blocks differ in ways that might affect the outcome of the experiment. Use the following procedure, as illustrated in Figure 1-5(c):

1. Form blocks (or groups) of subjects with similar characteristics.
2. Randomly assign treatments to the subjects within each block.

For example, in designing an experiment to test the effectiveness of aspirin treatments on heart disease, we might form a block of men and a block of women, because it is known that the hearts of men and women can behave differently. By controlling for gender, this randomized block design eliminates gender as a possible source of confounding.

A randomized block design uses the same basic idea as stratified sampling, but randomized block designs are used when designing experiments, whereas stratified sampling is used for surveys.

Matched Pairs Design: Compare two treatment groups (such as treatment and placebo) by using subjects matched in pairs that are somehow related or have similar characteristics, as in the following cases.

- Before/After: Matched pairs might consist of measurements from subjects before and after some treatment, as illustrated in Figure 1-5(d) on the preceding page. Each subject yields a "before" measurement and an "after" measurement, and each before/after pair of measurements is a matched pair.

- Twins: A test of Crest toothpaste used matched pairs of twins, where one twin used Crest and the other used another toothpaste.

Rigorously Controlled Design: Carefully assign subjects to different treatment groups, so that those given each treatment are similar in the ways that are important to the experiment. This can be extremely difficult to implement, and often we can never be sure that we have accounted for all of the relevant factors.

Sampling Errors

In statistics, you could use a good sampling method and do everything correctly, and yet it is possible to get wrong results. No matter how well you plan and execute the sample collection process, there is likely to be some error in the results. The different types of sampling errors are described here.

DEFINITIONS

A **sampling error** (or **random sampling error**) occurs when the sample has been selected with a random method, but there is a discrepancy between a sample result and the true population result; such an error results from chance sample fluctuations.

A **nonsampling error** is the result of human error, including such factors as wrong data entries, computing errors, questions with biased wording, false data provided by respondents, forming biased conclusions, or applying statistical methods that are not appropriate for the circumstances.

A **nonrandom sampling error** is the result of using a sampling method that is not random, such as using a convenience sample or a voluntary response sample.

Experimental design requires much more thought and care than we can describe in this relatively brief section. Taking a complete course in the design of experiments is a good start in learning so much more about this important topic.

1-3 Basic Skills and Concepts

Statistical Literacy and Critical Thinking

1. Back Pain Treatment In a study designed to test the effectiveness of paracetamol (also known as acetaminophen) as a treatment for lower back pain, 1643 patients were randomly assigned to one of three groups: (1) the 547 subjects in the placebo group were given pills containing no medication; (2) 550 subjects were in a group given pills with paracetamol taken at regular intervals; (3) 546 subjects were in a group given pills with paracetamol to be taken when needed for pain relief. (See "Efficacy of Paracetamol for Acute Low-Back Pain," by Williams et al., *Lancet*.) Is this study an experiment or an observational study? Explain.

2. Blinding What does it mean when we say that the study cited in Exercise 1 was "double-blind"?

3. Replication In what specific way was replication applied in the study cited in Exercise 1?

4. Sampling Method The patients included in the study cited in Exercise 1 were those "who sought care for low-back pain directly or in response to a community advertisement." What type of sampling best describes the way in which the 1634 subjects were chosen: simple random sample, systematic sample, convenience sample, stratified sample, cluster sample? Does the method of sampling appear to adversely affect the quality of the results?

Exercises 5–8 refer to the study of an association between which ear is used for cell phone calls and whether the subject is left-handed or right-handed. The study is reported in "Hemispheric Dominance and Cell Phone Use," by Seidman et al., **JAMA Otolaryngology—Head & Neck Surgery,** *Vol. 139, No. 5. The study began with a survey e-mailed to 5000 people belonging to an otology online group, and 717 surveys were returned.* **(Otology** *relates to the ear and hearing.)*

5. Sampling Method What type of sampling best describes the way in which the 717 subjects were chosen: simple random sample, systematic sample, convenience sample, stratified sample, cluster sample? Does the method of sampling appear to adversely affect the quality of the results?

6. Experiment or Observational Study Is the study an experiment or an observational study? Explain.

7. Response Rate What percent of the 5000 surveys were returned? Does that response rate appear to be low? In general, what is a problem with a very low response rate?

8. Sampling Method Assume that the population consists of all students currently in your statistics class. Describe how to obtain a sample of six students so that the result is a sample of the given type.

a. Simple random sample

b. Systematic sample

c. Stratified sample

d. Cluster sample

In Exercises 9–20, identify which of these types of sampling is used: random, systematic, convenience, stratified, or cluster.

9. Cormorant Density Cormorant bird population densities were studied by using the "line transect method" with aircraft observers flying along the shoreline of Lake Huron and collecting sample data at intervals of every 20 km (based on data from *Journal of Great Lakes Research*).

10. Sexuality of Women The sexuality of women was discussed in Shere Hite's book *Women and Love: A Cultural Revolution.* Her conclusions were based on sample data that consisted of 4500 mailed responses from 100,000 questionnaires that were sent to women.

11. Acupuncture Study In a study of treatments for back pain, 641 subjects were randomly assigned to the four different treatment groups of individualized acupuncture, standardized acupuncture, simulated acupuncture, and usual care (based on data from "A Randomized Trial Comparing Acupuncture, Simulated Acupuncture, and Usual Care for Chronic Low Back Pain," by Cherkin et al., *Archives of Internal Medicine,* Vol. 169, No. 9).

12. Homeopathic Survey A homeopathic medicine manufacturer conducts a survey by randomly selecting two categories of medicines and surveying all the medicines in those two categories.

13. Homeopathic Survey A homeopathic medicine manufacturer surveys medicines obtained from three groups—plants, animals, and minerals—then randomly selects a few medicines from each of those three groups.

14. Health Survey A researcher collects sample data by randomly selecting 15 individuals from each of the categories of suitably insured, insufficiently insured, and uninsured.

15. Black Plum In a study designed to test the effectiveness of black plum in lowering blood glucose level, 641 subjects were randomly assigned to these two different groups: (1) group given regular diet consisting of black plum; (2) group given no black plums.

16. Deforestation Rates Satellites are used to collect sample data for estimating deforestation rates. The Forest Resources Assessment of the United Nations (UN) Food and Agriculture Organization uses a method of selecting a sample of a 10-km-wide square at every 1° intersection of latitude and longitude.

17. Testing Lipitor In a clinical trial of the cholesterol drug Lipitor (atorvastatin), subjects were partitioned into groups given a placebo or Lipitor doses of 10 mg, 20 mg, 40 mg, or 80 mg. The subjects were randomly assigned to the different treatment groups (based on data from Pfizer, Inc.).

18. Blood Drives A researcher for the American Red Cross randomly selected five different blood donor sites and then interviewed all blood donors as they left the sites.

19. Smoking Prevalence A medical student collects sample data on the prevalence of smoking among adults by surveying all of the patients she encounters in the clinic where she is doing her residency.

20. Health Survey The Texas Health and Human Services Commission obtains an alphabetical listing of all 20,126,759 adults and constructs a sample by selecting every 10,000th name on that list.

Critical Thinking: What's Wrong? *In Exercises 21–28, determine whether the study is an experiment or an observational study, and then identify a major problem with the study.*

21. Online Medical Information In a survey conducted by *USA Today,* 1072 Internet users chose to respond to this question posted on the *USA Today* electronic edition: "How often do you seek medical information online?" 38% of the respondents said "frequently."

22. Physicians' Health Study The Physicians' Health Study involved 22,071 male physicians. Based on random selections, 11,037 of them were treated with aspirin and the other 11,034 were given placebos. The study was stopped early because it became clear that aspirin reduced the risk of myocardial infarctions by a substantial amount.

23. Drinking and Driving A researcher for a consortium of insurance companies plans to test for the effects of drinking on driving ability by randomly selecting 1000 drivers and then randomly assigning them to two groups: One group of 500 will drive in New York City after no alcohol consumption, and the second group will drive in New York City after consuming three shots of Jim Beam bourbon whiskey.

24. Blood Pressure A medical researcher tested for a difference in systolic blood pressure levels between male and female students who are 20 years of age. She randomly selected four males and four females for her study.

25. Salt Deprivation In a program designed to investigate the effects of salt deprivation in diets, the original plan was to use a sample of 500 adults randomly selected throughout the country. The program managers know that they would get a biased sample if they limit their study to adults in New York City, so they planned to compensate for that bias by using a larger sample of 2000 adults in New York City.

26. Atkins Weight Loss Program An independent researcher tested the effectiveness of the Atkins weight loss program by randomly selecting 1000 subjects using that program. Each of the subjects was called to report his or her weight before the diet and after the diet.

27. Crime Research A researcher has created a brief survey to be given to 2000 adults randomly selected from the U.S. population. Here are her first two questions: (1) Have you ever been the victim of a felony crime? (2) Have you ever been convicted of a felony?

28. Medications The Pharmaceutical Research and Manufacturers of America wants information about the consumption of various medications. An independent researcher conducts a survey by mailing 10,000 questionnaires to randomly selected adults in the United States, and she receives 152 responses.

1-3 Beyond the Basics

In Exercises 29–32, indicate whether the observational study used is cross-sectional, retrospective, or prospective.

29. Nurses' Health Study II Phase II of the Nurses' Health Study was started in 1989 with 116,000 female registered nurses. The study is ongoing.

30. Heart Health Study Samples of subjects with and without heart disease were selected, then researchers looked back in time to determine whether they took aspirin on a regular basis.

31. Marijuana Study Researchers from the National Institutes of Health want to determine the current rates of marijuana consumption among adults living in states that have legalized the use of marijuana. They conduct a survey of 500 adults in those states.

32. Framingham Heart Study The Framingham Heart Study was started in 1948 and is ongoing. Its focus is on heart disease.

In Exercises 33–36, identify which of these designs is most appropriate for the given experiment: completely randomized design, randomized block design, or matched pairs design.

33. Lunesta Lunesta (eszopiclone) is a drug designed to treat insomnia. In a clinical trial of Lunesta, amounts of sleep each night are measured before and after subjects have been treated with the drug.

34. Lipitor A clinical trial of Lipitor treatments is being planned to determine whether its effects on diastolic blood pressure are different for men and women.

35. West Nile Vaccine Currently, there is no approved vaccine for the prevention of West Nile virus infection. A clinical trial of a possible vaccine is being planned to include subjects treated with the vaccine while other subjects are given a placebo.

36. HIV Vaccine The HIV Trials Network is conducting a study to test the effectiveness of two different experimental HIV vaccines. Subjects will consist of 80 pairs of twins. For each pair of twins, one of the subjects will be treated with the DNA vaccine and the other twin will be treated with the adenoviral vector vaccine.

37. Sample Design Literacy In "Cardiovascular Effects of Intravenous Triiodothyronine in Patients Undergoing Coronary Artery Bypass Graft Surgery" (*Journal of the American Medical Association,* Vol. 275, No. 9), the authors explain that patients were assigned to one of three groups: (1) a group treated with triiodothyronine, (2) a group treated with normal saline bolus and dopamine, and (3) a placebo group given normal saline. The authors summarize the sample design as a "prospective, randomized, double-blind, placebo-controlled trial." Describe the meaning of each of those terms in the context of this study.

38. Simple Random Sample vs. Random Sample Refer to the definition of *simple random sample* in this section and the accompanying definition of *random sample* enclosed within parentheses. Determine whether each of the following is a simple random sample and a random sample.

a. A statistics class with 36 students is arranged so that there are 6 rows with 6 students in each row, and the rows are numbered from 1 through 6. A die is rolled and a sample consists of all students in the row corresponding to the outcome of the die.

b. For the same class described in part (a), the 36 student names are written on 36 individual index cards. The cards are shuffled and six names are drawn from the top.

c. For the same class described in part (a), the six youngest students are selected.

Chapter Quick Quiz

1. Clinical Study When conducting a clinical study, it is common to maintain the privacy of subjects by assigning them number codes that will be used instead of their actual names. Several subjects are assigned these codes: 1, 2, 3, 5, 6, 9, 11, 13, 16, 20, 22, 26, 32, and 40. Does it make sense to calculate the average (mean) of these numbers?

2. Clinical Study Which of the following best describes the level of measurement of the data listed in Exercise 1: nominal, ordinal, interval, ratio?

3. Waist Data Set 1 "Body Data" includes measurements of waist circumferences. Are waist circumferences values that are discrete or continuous?

4. Waist Are the waist circumferences described in Exercise 3 quantitative data or categorical data?

5. Waist Which of the following best describes the level of measurement of the waist circumferences described in Exercise 3: nominal, ordinal, interval, ratio?

6. Waist If you construct a sample by selecting every sixth waist circumference from those listed in Data Set 1 "Body Data," is the result a simple random sample of the listed waist circumferences?

7. Gallup Poll In a recent Gallup poll, pollsters randomly selected adults and asked them whether they smoke. Because the subjects agreed to respond, is the sample a voluntary response sample?

8. Parameter and Statistic In a recent Gallup poll, pollsters randomly selected adults and asked them whether they smoke. Among the adults who responded to the survey question, 21% said that they did smoke. Is that value of 21% an example of a statistic or a parameter?

9. Observational Study or Experiment Are the data described in Exercise 8 the result of an observational study or an experiment?

10. Statistical Significance and Practical Significance True or false: If data lead to a conclusion with statistical significance, then the results also have practical significance.

Review Exercises

1. Hospitals Currently, there are 5723 registered hospitals in the United States.

a. Are the numbers of hospitals in different states discrete or continuous?

b. What is the level of measurement for the numbers of hospitals in different years? (nominal, ordinal, interval, ratio)

c. If a survey is conducted by randomly selecting 10 patients in every hospital, what type of sampling is used? (random, systematic, convenience, stratified, cluster)

d. If a survey is conducted by randomly selecting 20 hospitals and interviewing all of the members of each board of directors, what type of sampling is used? (random, systematic, convenience, stratified, cluster)

e. What is wrong with surveying patient satisfaction by mailing questionnaires to 10,000 randomly selected patients?

2. What's Wrong? A survey sponsored by the American Laser Centers included responses from 575 adults, and 24% of the respondents said that the face is their favorite body part (based on data from *USA Today*). What is wrong with this survey?

3. What's Wrong? A survey included 2028 responses from Internet users who decided to respond to a question posted by AOL. Here is the question: "How often do you drink soda?" Among the respondents, 33% said that they drink soda almost every day. What is wrong with this survey?

4. Sampling Seventy-two percent of Americans squeeze their toothpaste tube from the top. This and other not-so-serious findings are included in *The First Really Important Survey of American Habits*. Those results are based on 7000 responses from the 25,000 questionnaires that were mailed.

a. What is wrong with this survey?

b. As stated, the value of 72% refers to all Americans, so is that 72% a statistic or a parameter? Explain.

c. Does the survey constitute an observational study or an experiment?

5. Percentages

a. The labels on U-Turn protein energy bars include the statement that these bars contain "125% less fat than the leading chocolate candy brands" (based on data from *Consumer Reports* magazine). What is wrong with that claim?

b. In a Pew Research Center poll on driving, 58% of the 1182 respondents said that they like to drive. What is the actual number of respondents who said that they like to drive?

c. In a Pew Research Center poll on driving, 331 of the 1182 respondents said that driving is a chore. What percentage of respondents said that driving is a chore?

6. Simple Random Sample Which of the following is/are simple random samples?

a. As Lipitor pills are being manufactured, a quality control plan is to select every 500th pill and test it to confirm that it contains 80 mg of atorvastatin.

b. To test for a gender difference in the way that men and women make online purchases, Gallup surveys 500 randomly selected men and 500 randomly selected women.

c. A list of all 10,877 adults in Trinity County, California, is obtained; the list is numbered from 1 to 10,877; and then a computer is used to randomly generate 250 different numbers between 1 and 10,877. The sample consists of the adults corresponding to the selected numbers.

7. Statistical Significance and Practical Significance The Gengene Research Group has developed a procedure designed to increase the likelihood that a baby will be born a girl. In a clinical trial of their procedure, 112 girls were born to 200 different couples. If the method has no effect, there is about a 4% chance that such extreme results would occur. Does the procedure appear to have statistical significance? Does the procedure appear to have practical significance?

8. Marijuana Survey In a recent Pew poll of 1500 adults, 52% of the respondents said that the use of marijuana should not be made legal. In the same poll, 23% of the respondents said that the use of marijuana for medical purposes should not be legal.

a. The sample of 1500 adults was selected from the population of all adults in the United States. The method used to select the sample was equivalent to placing the names of all adults in a giant bowl, mixing the names, and then drawing 1500 names. What type of sampling is this? (random, systematic, convenience, stratified, cluster)

b. If the sampling method consisted of a random selection of 30 adults from each of the 50 states, what type of sampling would this be? (random, systematic, convenience, stratified, cluster)

c. What is the level of measurement of the responses of yes, no, don't know, and refused to respond?

d. Is the given value of 52% a statistic or a parameter? Why?

e. What would be wrong with conducting the survey by mailing a questionnaire that respondents could complete and mail back?

9. Marijuana Survey Identify the type of sampling (random, systematic, convenience, stratified, cluster) used when a sample of the 1500 survey responses is obtained as described. Then determine whether the sampling scheme is likely to result in a sample that is representative of the population of all adults.

a. A complete list of all 241,472,385 adults in the United States is compiled, and every 150,000th name is selected until the sample size of 1500 is reached.

b. A complete list of all 241,472,385 adults in the United States is compiled, and 1500 adults are randomly selected from that list.

c. The United States is partitioned into regions with 100 adults in each region. Then 15 of those regions are randomly selected, and all 100 people in each of those regions are surveyed.

d. The United States is partitioned into 150 regions with approximately the same number of adults in each region; then 10 people are randomly selected from each of the 150 regions.

e. A survey is mailed to 10,000 randomly selected adults, and the 1500 responses are used.

10. Marijuana Survey Exercise 8 referred to a Pew poll of 1500 adults, and 52% of the respondents said that the use of marijuana should not be made legal.

a. Among the 1500 adults who responded, what is the number of respondents who said that the use of marijuana should not be made legal?

b. In the same poll of 1500 adults, 345 of the respondents said that the use of marijuana for medical purposes should not be legal. What is the percentage of respondents who said that the use of marijuana for medical purposes should not be legal?

c. In this survey of 1500 adults, 727 are men and 773 are women. Find the percentage of respondents who are men, and then find the percentage of respondents who are women.

d. Does the difference between the two percentages from part (c) appear to have statistical significance?

e. Does the difference between the two percentages from part (c) appear to have practical significance?

Cumulative Review Exercises

For Chapter 2 through Chapter 14, the Cumulative Review Exercises include topics from preceding chapters. For this chapter, we present a few calculator warm-up exercises, with expressions similar to those found throughout this book. Use your calculator to find the indicated values.

1. Cigarette Contents Listed below are the tar contents (mg) in 100-mm cigarettes of some popular brands. What value is obtained when those tar contents are added and the total is divided by the number of brands? (This result, called the *mean*, is discussed in Chapter 3.) What is notable about these values, and what does it tell us about how the tar contents were measured?

$$5 \quad 16 \quad 17 \quad 13 \quad 13 \quad 14 \quad 15 \quad 15$$

2. Six Children Jule Cole is a founder of Mabel's Labels, and she is the mother of six children. The probability that six randomly selected children are all girls is found by evaluating 0.5^6. Find that value.

3. Tallest Person Robert Wadlow (1918–1940) is the tallest known person to have lived. The expression below converts his height of 272 cm to a standardized score. Find this value and round the result to two decimal places. Such standardized scores are considered to be significantly high if they are greater than 2 or 3. Is the result significantly high?

$$\frac{272 - 176}{6}$$

4. Body Temperature The given expression is used for determining the likelihood that the average (mean) human body temperature is different from the value of 98.6°F that is commonly used. Find the given value and round the result to two decimal places.

$$\frac{98.2 - 98.6}{\frac{0.62}{\sqrt{106}}}$$

5. Determining Sample Size The given expression is used to determine the size of the sample necessary to estimate the proportion of college students who have the profound wisdom to take a statistics course. Find the value and round the result to the nearest whole number.

$$\frac{1.96^2 \cdot 0.25}{0.03^2}$$

6. Standard Deviation One way to get a very rough approximation of the value of a standard deviation of sample data is to find the range, then divide it by 4. The range is the difference between the highest sample value and the lowest sample value. In using this approach, what value is obtained from the sample data listed in Exercise 1 "Cigarette Contents"?

7. Standard Deviation The standard deviation is an extremely important concept introduced in Chapter 3. Using the sample data from Exercise 1 "Cigarette Contents," part of the calculation of standard deviation is shown in the expression below. Evaluate this expression. (Fortunately, calculators and software are designed to automatically execute such expressions, so our future work with standard deviation will not be burdened with cumbersome calculations.)

$$\frac{(5 - 13.5)^2}{7}$$

8. Standard Deviation The given expression is used to compute the standard deviation of three randomly selected body temperatures. Perform the calculation and round the result to two decimal places.

$$\sqrt{\frac{(98.4 - 98.6)^2 + (98.6 - 98.6)^2 + (98.8 - 98.6)^2}{3 - 1}}$$

Scientific Notation. *In Exercises 9–12, the given expressions are designed to yield results expressed in a form of scientific notation. For example, the calculator-displayed result of 1.23E5 can be expressed as 123,000, and the result of 1.23E-4 can be expressed as 0.000123. Perform the indicated operation and express the result as an ordinary number that is not in scientific notation.*

9. 0.6^7 **10.** 12^{14} **11.** 7^{12} **12.** 0.4^{15}

Technology Project

Missing Data The focus of this project is to download a data set and manipulate it to work around missing data.

a. First, download Data Set 2 "Body Temperatures" in Appendix B from www.TriolaStats.com. Choose the download format that matches your technology. (If you have no preferred technology, you can download a free copy of Statdisk (from www.statdisk.org), which is designed for this book and contains all Appendix B data sets.)

b. Some statistical procedures, such as those involved with correlation and regression (discussed in later chapters) require data that consist of matched pairs of values, and those procedures ignore pairs in which at least one of the data values in a matched pair is missing. Assume that we want to conduct analyses for correlation and regression on the last two columns of data in Data Set 2: body temperatures measured at 8 AM on day 2 and again at 12 AM on day 2. For those last two columns, identify the rows with at least one missing value. Note that in some technologies, such as TI-83/84 Plus calculators, missing data must be represented by a constant such as −9 or 999.

c. Here are two different strategies for reconfiguring the data set to work around the missing data in the last two columns (assuming that we need matched pairs of data with no missing values):

i. Manual Deletion Highlight rows with at least one missing value in the last two columns, then delete those rows. This can be tedious if there are many rows with missing data and those rows are interspersed throughout instead of being adjacent rows.

ii. Sort Most technologies have a Sort feature that allows you to rearrange all rows using one particular column as the basis for sorting (TI-83/84 Plus calculators *do not* have this type of sort feature). The result is that all rows remain the same but they are in a different order. First use the technology's Sort feature to rearrange all rows using the "8 AM day 2" column as the basis for sorting (so that all missing values in the "8 AM day 2" column are at the beginning); then highlight and delete all of those rows with missing values in the "8 AM day 2" column. Next, use the technology's Sort feature to rearrange all rows using the "12 AM day 2" column as the basis for sorting (so that all missing values in the "12 AM day 2" column are at the beginning); then highlight and delete all of those rows with missing values in the "12 AM day 2" column. The remaining rows will include matched pairs of body temperatures, and those rows will be suitable for analyses such as correlation and regression. Print the resulting reconfigured data set.

FROM DATA TO DECISION

Critical Thinking:
Do Male Symphony Conductors Really Live Longer?

Several media reports made the interesting observation that male symphony conductors live longer than other males. John Amaral wrote in *Awaken* that orchestra conductors "live longer than almost any other group of people by three to seven years." Robert Levine wrote in Polyphonic.org that

Analysis

1. Consider the statement that "male symphony conductors live longer." Identify the specific group that they supposedly live longer than. Does that other group consist of males randomly selected from the general population?

2. It is reasonable to assume that males do not become symphony conductors until they have reached at least the age of 40 years. When comparing life spans of male conductors, should we compare them to other males in the general population, or should we compare them to other males who lived until at least 40 years of age? Explain.

they live longer "because they stand up while working." Some provided other explanations for this phenomenon, often referring to cardiovascular activity. But do male symphony conductors really live longer than other groups of males? The Internet can be researched for possible answers. Let's also consider the following.

3. Without any disabilities, males qualify for Medicare if they are 65 or older and meet a few other requirements. If we compare life spans of males on Medicare to life spans of males randomly selected from the general population, why would we find that males on Medicare have longer life spans?

4. Explain in detail how to design a study for collecting data to determine whether it is misleading to state that male symphony conductors live longer. Should the study be an experiment or an observational study?

Cooperative Group Activities

1. In-class activity Working in groups of three or four, design an experiment to determine whether pulse rates of college students are the same while the students are standing and sitting. Conduct the experiment and collect the data. Save the data so that they can be analyzed with methods presented in the following chapters.

2. In-class activity Working in groups of three or four, construct a brief survey that includes only a few questions that can be quickly asked. Include some objective questions along with some that are biased, such as the first question below.

- Should your college force all students to pay a $100 activity fee?

- Should your college fund activities by collecting a $100 fee?

Conduct the survey and try to detect the effect that the biased wording has on the responses.

3. In-class activity Identify problems with a mailing from *Consumer Reports* magazine that included an annual questionnaire about cars and other consumer products. Also included were a request for a voluntary contribution of money and a voting ballot for the board of directors. Responses were to be mailed back in envelopes that required postage stamps.

4. Out-of-class activity Find a report of a survey that used a voluntary response sample. Describe how it is quite possible that the results do not accurately reflect the population.

5. Out-of-class activity Find a professional journal with an article that includes a statistical analysis of an experiment. Describe and comment on the design of the experiment. Identify one particular issue addressed by the study, and determine whether the results were found to be statistically significant. Determine whether those same results have practical significance.

2 Exploring Data with Tables and Graphs

 CHAPTER PROBLEM   **Does Exposure to Lead Affect IQ Scores?**

Data Set 8 "IQ and Lead" in Appendix B includes full IQ scores from three groups of children who lived near a lead smelter. The children in Group 1 had *low* levels of measured lead in their blood (with blood levels less than 40 micrograms/100 mL in each of two years). Group 2 had *medium* levels of measured lead in their blood (with blood levels of at least 40 micrograms/100 mL in exactly one of two years). Group 3

had *high* levels of measured lead in their blood (with blood levels of at least 40 micrograms/100 mL in each of two years).

Let's consider the measured full IQ scores from Group 1 (low lead level) and Group 3 (high lead level), as listed in Table 2-1. It is an exceptionally rare person who can look at both lists of IQ scores and form meaningful conclusions. Almost all of us must work at describing, exploring, and comparing the two sets of data. In this chapter we present methods that focus on summarizing the data and using graphs that enable us to understand important characteristics of the data, especially the *distribution* of the data. These methods will help us compare the two sets of data so that we can determine whether the IQ scores of the *low* lead group are somehow different from the IQ scores of the *high* lead group. Such comparisons will be helpful as we try to address this important and key issue: Does exposure to lead have an effect on IQ score?

TABLE 2-1 Full IQ Scores of the Low Lead Group and the High Lead Group

Low Lead Level (Group 1)

70	85	86	76	84	96	94	56	115	97	77	128	99	80	118	86
141	88	96	96	107	86	80	107	101	91	125	96	99	99	115	106
105	96	50	99	85	88	120	93	87	98	78	100	105	87	94	89
80	111	104	85	94	75	73	76	107	88	89	96	72	97	76	107
104	85	76	95	86	89	76	96	101	108	102	77	74	92		

High Lead Level (Group 3)

82	93	85	75	85	80	101	89	80	94	88	104	88	88	83	104
96	76	80	79	75											

CHAPTER OBJECTIVES

This chapter and the following chapter focus on important characteristics of data, including the following:

Characteristics of Data

1. **Center:** A representative value that shows us where the middle of the data set is located.

2. **Variation:** A measure of the amount that the data values vary.

3. **Distribution:** The nature or shape of the spread of the data over the range of values (such as bell-shaped).

4. **Outliers:** Sample values that lie very far away from the vast majority of the other sample values. (Later, a more objective definition of "outlier" will be given.)

5. **Time:** Any change in the characteristics of the data over time.

This chapter provides tools that enable us to gain insight into data by organizing, summarizing, and representing them in ways that enable us to see important characteristics of the data. Here are the chapter objectives:

 Frequency Distributions for Organizing and Summarizing Data

- Develop an ability to summarize data in the format of a frequency distribution and a relative frequency distribution.

- For a frequency distribution, identify values of class width, class midpoint, class limits, and class boundaries.

Histograms

- Develop the ability to picture the distribution of data in the format of a histogram or relative frequency histogram.

- Examine a histogram and identify common distributions, including a uniform distribution and a normal distribution.

 Graphs That Enlighten and Graphs That Deceive

- Develop an ability to graph data using a dotplot, stemplot, time-series graph, Pareto chart, pie chart, and frequency polygon.

- Determine when a graph is deceptive through the use of a nonzero axis or a pictograph that uses an object of area or volume for one-dimensional data.

 Scatterplots, Correlation, and Regression

- Develop an ability to construct a scatterplot of paired data.

- Analyze a scatterplot to determine whether there appears to be a correlation between two variables.

Frequency Distributions for Organizing and Summarizing Data

Key Concept When working with large data sets, a *frequency distribution* (or *frequency table*) is often helpful in organizing and summarizing data. A frequency distribution helps us to understand the nature of the *distribution* of a data set.

> **DEFINITION**
>
> A **frequency distribution** (or **frequency table**) shows how data are partitioned among several categories (or *classes*) by listing the categories along with the number (frequency) of data values in each of them.

TABLE 2-2 IQ Scores of the Low Lead Group

IQ Score	Frequency
50–69	2
70–89	33
90–109	35
110–129	7
130–149	1

Consider the IQ scores of the low lead group listed in Table 2-1. Table 2-2 is a frequency distribution summarizing those IQ scores. The **frequency** for a particular class is the number of original values that fall into that class. For example, the first class in Table 2-2 has a frequency of 2, so 2 of the IQ scores are between 50 and 69 inclusive.

The following standard terms are often used in constructing frequency distributions and graphs.

> **DEFINITIONS**
>
> **Lower class limits** are the smallest numbers that can belong to each of the different classes. (Table 2-2 has lower class limits of 50, 70, 90, 110, and 130.)
>
> **Upper class limits** are the largest numbers that can belong to each of the different classes. (Table 2-2 has upper class limits of 69, 89, 109, 129, and 149.)
>
> **Class boundaries** are the numbers used to separate the classes, but without the gaps created by class limits. In Figure 2-1 we see that the values of 69.5, 89.5, 109.5, and 129.5 are in the centers of those gaps, and following the pattern of those class boundaries, we see that the lowest class boundary is 49.5 and the

highest class boundary is 149.5. Thus the complete list of class boundaries is 49.5, 69.5, 89.5, 109.5, 129.5, and 149.5.

Class midpoints are the values in the middle of the classes. Table 2-2 has class midpoints of 59.5, 79.5, 99.5, 119.5, and 139.5. Each class midpoint is computed by adding the lower class limit to the upper class limit and dividing the sum by 2.

Class width is the difference between two consecutive lower class limits (or two consecutive lower class boundaries) in a frequency distribution. Table 2-2 uses a class width of 20. (The first two lower class boundaries are 50 and 70, and their difference is 20.)

CAUTION Finding the correct class width can be tricky. For class width, don't make the most common mistake of using the difference between a lower class limit and an upper class limit. See Table 2-2 and note that the class width is 20, not 19.

CAUTION For class boundaries, remember that they split the difference between the end of one class and the beginning of the next class, as shown in Figure 2-1.

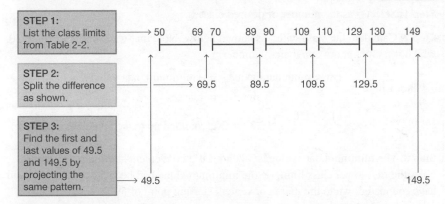

FIGURE 2-1   Finding Class Boundaries from Class Limits in Table 2-2

Procedure for Constructing a Frequency Distribution

We construct frequency distributions to (1) summarize large data sets, (2) see the distribution and identify outliers, and (3) have a basis for constructing graphs (such as *histograms,* introduced in Section 2-2). Technology can generate frequency distributions, but here are the steps for manually constructing them:

1. Select the number of classes, usually between 5 and 20. The number of classes might be affected by the convenience of using round numbers.

2. Calculate the class width.

$$\text{Class width} \approx \frac{(\text{maximum data value}) - (\text{minimum data value})}{\text{number of classes}}$$

Round this result to get a convenient number. (It's usually best to round *up*.) Using a specific number of classes is not too important, and it's usually wise to change the number of classes so that they use convenient values for the class limits.

3. Choose the value for the first lower class limit by using either the minimum value or a convenient value below the minimum.

continued

4. Using the first lower class limit and the class width, list the other lower class limits. (Do this by adding the class width to the first lower class limit to get the second lower class limit. Add the class width to the second lower class limit to get the third lower class limit, and so on.)

5. List the lower class limits in a vertical column and then determine and enter the upper class limits.

6. Take each individual data value and put a tally mark in the appropriate class. Add the tally marks to find the total frequency for each class.

When constructing a frequency distribution, be sure the classes do not overlap. Each of the original values must belong to exactly one class. Include all classes, even those with a frequency of zero. Try to use the same width for all classes, although it is sometimes impossible to avoid open-ended intervals, such as "65 years or older."

 EXAMPLE 1   **IQ Scores of Low Lead Group**

Using the IQ scores of the low lead group in Table 2-1, follow the above procedure to construct the frequency distribution shown in Table 2-2. Use five classes.

SOLUTION

Step 1: Select 5 as the number of desired classes.

Step 2: Calculate the class width as shown below. Note that we round 18.2 up to 20, which is a much more convenient number.

$$\text{Class width} \approx \frac{(\text{maximum data value}) - (\text{minimum data value})}{\text{number of classes}}$$

$$= \frac{141 - 50}{5} = 18.2 \approx 20 \text{ (rounded up to a convenient number)}$$

Step 3: The minimum data value is 50 and it is a convenient starting point, so use 50 as the first lower class limit. (If the minimum value had been 52 or 53, we would have rounded down to the more convenient starting point of 50.)

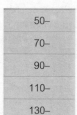

Step 4: Add the class width of 20 to 50 to get the second lower class limit of 70. Continue to add the class width of 20 until we have five lower class limits. The lower class limits are therefore 50, 70, 90, 110, and 130.

Step 5: List the lower class limits vertically, as shown in the margin. From this list, we identify the corresponding upper class limits as 69, 89, 109, 129, and 149.

Step 6: Enter a tally mark for each data value in the appropriate class. Then add the tally marks to find the frequencies shown in Table 2-2.

Categorical Data So far we have discussed frequency distributions using only quantitative data sets, but frequency distributions can also be used to summarize categorical (or qualitative or attribute) data, as illustrated in Example 2.

EXAMPLE 2   **Emergency Room Visits for Injuries from Sports and Recreation**

Table 2-3 lists data for the highest seven sources of injuries resulting in a visit to a hospital emergency room (ER) in a recent year (based on data from the Centers for Disease Control and Prevention). The activity names are categorical data at the nominal level of measurement, but we can create the frequency distribution as shown. It might be surprising to see that bicycling is at the top of this list, but this doesn't mean that bicycling is the most dangerous of these activities; many more people bicycle than play football or ride an all-terrain vehicle or do any of the other listed activities.

TABLE 2-3 Annual ER Visits for Injuries from Sports and Recreation

Activity	Frequency
Bicycling	26,212
Football	25,376
Playground	16,706
Basketball	13,987
Soccer	10,436
Baseball	9,634
All-terrain vehicle	6,337

Relative Frequency Distribution

A variation of the basic frequency distribution is a **relative frequency distribution** or **percentage frequency distribution,** in which each class frequency is replaced by a relative frequency (or proportion) or a percentage. In this text we use the term "relative frequency distribution" whether we use relative frequencies or percentages. Relative frequencies and percentages are calculated as follows.

$$\text{Relative frequency for a class} = \frac{\text{frequency for a class}}{\text{sum of all frequencies}}$$

$$\text{Percentage for a class} = \frac{\text{frequency for a class}}{\text{sum of all frequencies}} \times 100\%$$

Table 2-4 is an example of a relative frequency distribution. It is a variation of Table 2-2 in which each class frequency is replaced by the corresponding percentage value. Because there are 78 data values, divide each class frequency by 78, and then multiply by 100%. The first class of Table 2-2 has a frequency of 2, so divide 2 by 78 to get 0.0256, and then multiply by 100% to get 2.56%, which we rounded to 2.6%. The sum of the percentages should be 100%, with a small discrepancy allowed for rounding errors, so a sum such as 99% or 101% is acceptable. The sum of the percentages in Table 2-4 is 100.1%.

The sum of the percentages in a relative frequency distribution must be very close to 100%.

Cumulative Frequency Distribution

Another variation of a frequency distribution is a **cumulative frequency distribution** in which the frequency for each class is the sum of the frequencies for that class and all previous classes. Table 2-5 is a cumulative frequency distribution based on Table 2-2. Using the original frequencies of 2, 33, 35, 7, and 1, we add 2 + 33 to get the second cumulative frequency of 35; then we add 2 + 33 + 35 to get the third; and so on. See Table 2-5, and note that in addition to the use of cumulative frequencies, the class limits are replaced by "less than" expressions that describe the new ranges of values.

TABLE 2-4 Relative Frequency Distribution of IQ Scores of Low Lead Group

IQ Score	Frequency
50–69	2.6%
70–89	42.3%
90–109	44.9%
110–129	9.0%
130–149	1.3%

TABLE 2-5 Cumulative Frequency Distribution of IQ Scores of Low Lead Group

IQ Score	Cumulative Frequency
Less than 70	2
Less than 90	35
Less than 110	70
Less than 130	77
Less than 150	78

Critical Thinking: Using Frequency Distributions to Understand Data

At the beginning of this section we noted that a frequency distribution can help us understand the *distribution* of a data set, which is the nature or shape of the spread of the data over the range of values (such as bell-shaped). In statistics we are often interested in determining whether the data have a *normal distribution*. (Normal distributions are discussed extensively in Chapter 6.) Data that have an approximately normal distribution are characterized by a frequency distribution with the following features:

Normal Distribution

1. The frequencies start low, then increase to one or two high frequencies, and then decrease to a low frequency.

2. The distribution is approximately symmetric: Frequencies preceding the maximum frequency should be roughly a mirror image of those that follow the maximum frequency.

Table 2-6 satisfies these two conditions. The frequencies start low, increase to the maximum of 56, and then decrease to a low frequency. Also, the frequencies of 1 and 10 that precede the maximum are a mirror image of the frequencies 10 and 1 that follow the maximum. Real data sets are usually not so perfect as Table 2-6, and judgment must be used to determine whether the distribution comes "close enough" to satisfying the above two conditions. (There are more objective procedures included later.)

TABLE 2-6 Frequency Distribution Showing a Normal Distribution

Score	Frequency	Normal Distribution
50–69	1	← Frequencies start low, . . .
70–89	10	
90–109	56	← Increase to a maximum, . . .
110–129	10	
130–149	1	← Decrease to become low again.

Analysis of Last Digits   Example 3 illustrates this principle:

Frequencies of last digits sometimes reveal how the data were collected or measured.

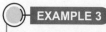 **EXAMPLE 3** **Exploring Data: How Were the Weights Obtained in California?**

When collecting weights of people, it's better to actually weigh people than to ask them what they weigh. People often tend to round *way* down, so that a weight of 196 lb might be reported as 170 lb. Table 2-7 summarizes the *last digits* of the weights of 100 people used in the California Health Interview Survey. If people are actually weighed on a scale, the last digits of weights tend to have frequencies that are approximately the same, but Table 2-6 shows that the vast majority of weights have last digits of 0 or 5, and this is strong evidence that people reported their weights and were not physically weighed. (Also, the word "interview" in the title of the California Health Interview Survey reveals that people were interviewed and were not physically measured.)

TABLE 2-7 Last Digits of Weights from the California Health Interview Survey

Last Digit of Weight	Frequency
0	46
1	1
2	2
3	3
4	3
5	30
6	4
7	0
8	8
9	3

Gaps Example 4 illustrates this principle:

The presence of gaps can suggest that the data are from two or more different populations.

The converse of this principle is not true, because data from different populations do not necessarily result in gaps.

EXAMPLE 4 Exploring Data: What Does a Gap Tell Us?

Table 2-8 is a frequency distribution of the heights (in.) of males. Examination of the frequencies reveals a large *gap* between the shortest males and the tallest males. This can be explained by the fact that half of the males are 7 years old and the other half are adults, so we really have samples from two different populations.

TABLE 2-8 Heights of Males

Height (in.)	Frequency
40–44	3
45–49	17
50–54	29
55–59	1
60–64	0
65–69	24
70–74	23
75–79	3

Comparisons Example 5 illustrates this principle:

Combining two or more relative frequency distributions in one table makes comparisons of data much easier.

EXAMPLE 5 **Comparing IQ Scores of the Low Lead Group and the High Lead Group**

Table 2-1, which is given with the Chapter Problem at the beginning of this chapter, lists IQ scores from the low lead group and the high lead group. Because the sample sizes of 78 and 21 are so different, a comparison of frequency distributions is not easy, but Table 2-9 shows the relative frequency distributions for those two groups. By comparing those relative frequencies, we see that the majority of children in the low lead group had IQ scores of 90 or higher, but the majority of children in the high lead group had IQ scores below 90. This suggests that perhaps high lead exposure has a detrimental effect on IQ scores.

TABLE 2-9 IQ Scores from the Low Lead Group and the High Lead Group

IQ Score	Low Lead Group	High Lead Group
50–69	2.6%	
70–89	42.3%	71.4%
90–109	44.9%	28.6%
110–129	9.0%	
130–149	1.3%	

TECH CENTER

Frequency Distributions

Access tech instructions, videos, and data sets at www.TriolaStats.com

2-1 Basic Skills and Concepts

Statistical Literacy and Critical Thinking

Cotinine (ng/mL)	Frequency
0–99	11
100–199	12
200–299	14
300–399	1
400–499	2

1. Cotinine in Smokers Refer to the accompanying table summarizing measured amounts of serum cotinine (ng/mL) from a sample of smokers (from Data Set 14 "Passive and Active Smoke" in Appendix B). When nicotine is absorbed by the body, cotinine is produced. How many subjects are included in the summary? Is it possible to identify the exact values of all of the original cotinine measurements?

2. Cotinine in Smokers Refer to the accompanying frequency distribution. What problem is created by using classes of 0–100, 100–200, . . . ?

3. Relative Frequency Distribution Use percentages to construct the relative frequency distribution corresponding to the accompanying frequency distribution for cotinine amounts.

Height (cm)	Relative Frequency
130–144	23%
145–159	25%
160–174	22%
175–189	27%
190–204	28%

4. What's Wrong? Heights of adult males are known to have a normal distribution, as described in this section. A researcher claims to have randomly selected adult males and measured their heights with the resulting relative frequency distribution as shown here. Identify two major flaws with theses results.

In Exercises 5–8, identify the class width, class midpoints, and class boundaries for the given frequency distribution. The frequency distributions are based on real data from Appendix B.

5.

Cotinine (NonSmokers Exposed to Smoke in ng/mL)	Frequency
0–99	34
100–199	2
200–299	1
300–399	1
400–499	0
500–599	2

6.

Brain Volume (cm^3)	Frequency
960–1049	6
1050–1139	7
1140–1229	3
1230–1319	2
1320–1409	1
1410–1499	1

7.

Weight (in kg) of Females	Frequency
30–49	8
50–69	53
70–89	49
90–109	28
110–129	5
130–149	3
150–169	1

8.

Weight (in kg) of Males	Frequency
50–69	30
70–89	66
90–109	43
110–129	12
130–149	2

Normal Distributions.   *In Exercises 9–12, answer the given questions, which are related to normal distributions.*

9. Cotinine Determine whether the frequency distribution given in Exercise 5 is approximately a normal distribution. Explain.

10. Brain Volume Refer to the frequency distribution given in Exercise 6 and ignore the given frequencies. Assume that the first three frequencies are 1, 3, and 6, respectively. Assuming that the distribution of the 20 sample values is a normal distribution, identify the remaining three frequencies.

11. Normal distribution Refer to the frequency distribution given in Exercise 7 and ignore the given frequencies. Assume that the first three frequencies are 7, 9, and 20, respectively. Assuming that the distribution of the 147 sample values is a normal distribution, identify the remaining four frequencies.

12. Normal Distribution Refer to the frequency distribution given in Exercise 8 and determine whether it appears to be a normal distribution. Explain.

Constructing Frequency Distributions.   *In Exercises 13–22, use the indicated data and construct the frequency distribution. (The data for Exercises 13–22 can be downloaded at TriolaStats.com.)*

13. Pulse Rates of Males Refer to Data Set 1 "Body Data" in Appendix B and use the pulse rates (beats per minute) of males. Begin with a lower class limit of 40 and use a class width of 10. Do the pulse rates of males appear to have a normal distribution?

14. Pulse Rates of Females Refer to Data Set 1 "Body Data" in Appendix B and use the pulse rates (beats per minute) of females. Begin with a lower class limit of 30 and use a class width of 10. Do the pulse rates of females appear to have a normal distribution?

15. Lead and IQ Refer to Data Set 8 "IQ and Lead" in Appendix B and use the *verbal* IQ scores of the low lead group. Begin with a lower class limit of 50 and use a class width of 10. Do these IQ scores appear to be normally distributed?

16. Lead and IQ Refer to Data Set 8 "IQ and Lead" in Appendix B and use the verbal IQ scores of the high lead group. Begin with a lower class limit of 60 and use a class width of 10. Do these IQ scores appear to be normally distributed?

17. Male Red Blood Cell Counts Refer to Data Set 1 "Body Data" in Appendix B and use the red blood cell counts (million cells/μL) for males. Begin with a lower class limit of 3.00 and use a class width of 0.50. Using a very loose interpretation of the requirements for a normal distribution, do the red blood cell counts appear to be normally distributed?

18. Female Red Blood Cell Counts Repeat the preceding exercise using the red blood cell counts for females.

19. Freshman 15 Refer to Data Set 10 "Freshman 15" in Appendix B and use the weights (kg) of males in September of their freshman year. Begin with a lower class limit of 50 kg and use a class width of 10 kg.

20. Freshman 15 Repeat the preceding exercise using the weights (kg) of males in April. Compare the result to the frequency distribution from the preceding exercise. Does it appear that males gain 15 lb (or 6.8 kg) during their freshman year?

21. Analysis of Last Digits Weights of statistics students were obtained as part of an experiment conducted for the class. The last digits of those weights are listed below. Construct a frequency distribution with 10 classes. Based on the distribution, do the weights appear to be reported or actually measured? What do you know about the accuracy of the results?

0 0 0 0 0 1 1 1 1 1 1 2 2 2 2 3 3 3 3 4 4 4 4 5 5 5 5 5 6 6 6 6 7 7 7 7 8 8 8 8 8 8 9 9 9 9 9

22. Analysis of Last Digits Listed below are the last digits of heights of subjects. After constructing the frequency distribution, does it appear that the heights were reported or physically measured? Explain.

5 5 0 1 8 6 5 4 0 2 9 0 5 0 8 4 3 2 0 0 5 5 5 0 5 0

1 5 0 4 5 8 0 7 0 0 5 5 1 0 4 0 5 5 8 0 6 5 4 5 5

Relative Frequencies for Comparisons. *In Exercises 23 and 24, find the relative frequencies and answer the given questions.*

23. Cotinine Construct one table (similar to Table 2-9 on page 64) that includes relative frequencies based on the frequency distributions from Exercise 1 (smokers) and Exercise 5 (nonsmokers exposed to smoke), and then compare them. Are there notable differences?

24. Weights Construct one table (similar to Table 2-9 on page 64) that includes relative frequencies based on the frequency distributions from Exercises 7 and 8, and then compare them. Are there notable differences?

Cumulative Frequency Distributions. *In Exercises 25 and 26, construct the cumulative frequency distribution that corresponds to the frequency distribution in the exercise indicated.*

25. Exercise 5

26. Exercise 6

2-1   Beyond the Basics

27. Interpreting Effects of Outliers Exercise 5 in this section involved cotinine levels of nonsmokers who were exposed to tobacco smoke. (See the middle column in Data Set 14 "Passive and Active Smoke" in Appendix B.)

a. Identify any outliers.

b. After adding another value of 999 to the cotinine levels of nonsmokers exposed to smoke, construct the frequency distribution as in Exercise 5. How is the frequency distribution affected by the addition of the outlier 999? State a generalization about the effect of an outlier on a frequency distribution.

2-2   Histograms

PART 1   Basic Concepts of Histograms

Key Concept While a frequency distribution is a useful tool for summarizing data and investigating the distribution of data, an even better tool is a *histogram,* which is a graph that is easier to interpret than a table of numbers.

> **DEFINITION**
>
> A **histogram** is a graph consisting of bars of equal width drawn adjacent to each other (unless there are gaps in the data). The horizontal scale represents classes of quantitative data values, and the vertical scale represents frequencies. The heights of the bars correspond to frequency values.

Important Uses of a Histogram

- Visually displays the shape of the *distribution* of the data
- Shows the location of the *center* of the data
- Shows the *spread* of the data
- Identifies *outliers*

A histogram is basically a graph of a frequency distribution. For example, Figure 2-2 shows the histogram corresponding to the frequency distribution given in Table 2-2 on page 58.

Class frequencies should be used for the vertical scale and that scale should be labeled as in Figure 2-2. There is no universal agreement on the procedure for selecting which values are used for the bar locations along the horizontal scale, but it is common to use class boundaries (as shown in Figure 2-2) or class midpoints or class limits or something else. It is often easier for us mere mortals to use class midpoints for the horizontal scale. Histograms can usually be generated using technology.

Relative Frequency Histogram

A **relative frequency histogram** has the same shape and horizontal scale as a histogram, but the vertical scale uses relative frequencies (as percentages or proportions) instead of actual frequencies. Figure 2-3 is the relative frequency histogram corresponding to Figure 2-2.

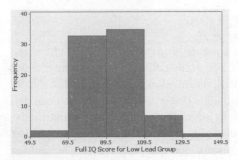

FIGURE 2-2   Histogram

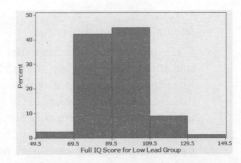

FIGURE 2-3   Relative Frequency Histogram

Critical Thinking: Interpreting Histograms

The ultimate objective of a histogram is to *understand* characteristics of the data. Explore the data by analyzing the histogram to see what can be learned about "CVDOT": the center of the data, the variation (which will be discussed at length in Section 3-2), the shape of the distribution, whether there are any outliers (values far away from the other values), and time (whether there is any change in the characteristics of the data over time). Examining Figure 2-2, we see that the histogram is centered close to 90, the values vary from around 50 to 150, and the distribution is roughly bell-shaped. There aren't any outliers and any changes in time are irrelevant for these data.

Common Distribution Shapes

The histograms shown in Figure 2-4 depict four common distribution shapes.

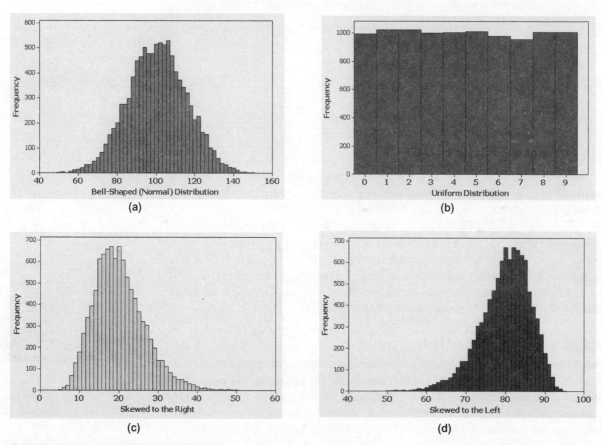

FIGURE 2-4   **Common Distributions**

Normal Distribution

When graphed as a histogram, data with a normal distribution have a "bell" shape similar to the one superimposed in Figure 2-5. *Many* collections of data have a distribution that is approximately normal. Many statistical methods require that sample data come from a population having a distribution that is approximately a normal distribution, and we can often use a histogram to judge whether this requirement is satisfied. There are more advanced and less subjective methods for determining whether the distribution is a normal distribution. Normal quantile plots are very helpful for assessing normality: see Part 2 of this section.

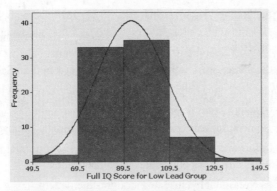

FIGURE 2-5   **Bell-Shaped Distribution**
Because this histogram is roughly bell-shaped, we say that the
data have a normal distribution. (A more rigorous definition will be
given in Chapter 6.)

Uniform Distribution

The different possible values occur with approximately the same frequency, so the
heights of the bars in the histogram are approximately uniform, as in Figure 2-4(b).
Figure 2-4(b) depicts outcomes of last digits of weights from a large sample of randomly selected subjects, and such a graph is helpful in determining whether the subjects were actually weighed or whether they reported their weights.

   Population sizes of an organism are often uniformly distributed when they are
found in equally sized areas of a region where they must compete for a limited resource. For example, redwood trees must compete for light, and numbers of redwood
trees in equally sized areas of a region tend to be uniformly distributed.

Skewness

A distribution of data is **skewed** if it is not symmetric and extends more to one side
than to the other. Data **skewed to the right** (also called *positively skewed*) have a
longer right tail, as in Figure 2-4(c). Annual incomes of adult Americans are skewed
to the right; death rates of nations are skewed to the right. Data **skewed to the left**
(also called *negatively skewed*) have a longer left tail, as in Figure 2-4(d). Life span
data in humans are skewed to the left. (Here's a mnemonic for remembering skewness: A distribution skewed to the right resembles the toes on your right foot, and
one skewed to the left resembles the toes on your left foot.) Distributions skewed to
the right are more common than those skewed to the left because it's often easier to
get exceptionally large values than values that are exceptionally small. With annual
incomes, for example, it's impossible to get values below zero, but there are a few
people who earn millions or billions of dollars in a year. Annual incomes therefore
tend to be skewed to the right.

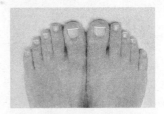

Remembering Skewness:
Skewed Left: Resembles
                   toes on left
                   foot
Skewed Right: Resembles
                   toes on right
                   foot

PART 2   Assessing Normality with Normal Quantile Plots

Some methods presented in later chapters have a requirement that sample data must
be from a population having a normal distribution. Histograms can be helpful in determining whether the normality requirement is satisfied, but they are not very helpful with small data sets. Section 6-5 discusses methods for *assessing normality*—that
is, determining whether the sample data are from a normally distributed population.
Section 6-5 includes a procedure for constructing *normal quantile plots,* which are

easy to generate using technology such as Statdisk, SPSS, JMP, Minitab, XLSTAT, StatCrunch, or a TI-83/84 Plus calculator. Interpretation of a normal quantile plot is based on the following criteria:

Criteria for Assessing Normality with a Normal Quantile Plot

Normal Distribution: The population distribution is normal if the pattern of the points in the normal quantile plot is reasonably close to a straight line, and the points do not show some systematic pattern that is not a straight-line pattern.

Not a Normal Distribution: The population distribution is *not* normal if the normal quantile plot has either or both of these two conditions:

- The points do not lie reasonably close to a straight-line pattern.
- The points show some *systematic pattern* that is not a straight-line pattern.

The following are examples of normal quantile plots. Procedures for creating such plots are described in Section 6-5.

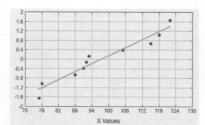

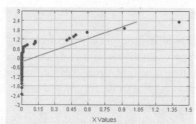

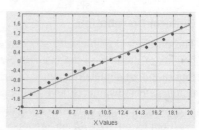

Normal Distribution: The points are reasonably close to a straight-line pattern, and there is no other systematic pattern that is not a straight-line pattern.

Not a Normal Distribution: The points do not lie reasonably close to a straight line.

Not a Normal Distribution: The points show a systematic pattern that is not a straight-line pattern.

TECH CENTER

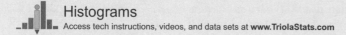

Histograms
Access tech instructions, videos, and data sets at **www.TriolaStats.com**

2-2   Basic Skills and Concepts

Statistical Literacy and Critical Thinking

1. Histogram Table 2-2 is a frequency distribution summarizing the IQ scores of the low lead group listed in Table 2-1 on page 57, and Figure 2-2 on page 67 is a histogram depicting that same data set. When trying to better understand the IQ data, what is the advantage of examining the histogram instead of the frequency distribution?

2. Voluntary Response Sample The histogram in Figure 2-2 on page 67 is constructed from a *simple random sample* of children. If you construct a histogram with data collected from a *voluntary response sample,* will the distribution depicted in the histogram reflect the true distribution of the population? Why or why not?

3. HDL Counts Listed below are HDL counts (mg/dL) randomly selected from adults in India. Why does it *not* make sense to construct a histogram for this data set?

42   56   75   41   53   89   33   51   67   29

4. Normal Distribution When it refers to a normal distribution, does the term "normal" have the same meaning as in ordinary language? What criterion can be used to determine whether the data depicted in a histogram have a distribution that is approximately a normal distribution? Is this criterion totally objective, or does it involve subjective judgment?

Interpreting a Histogram. *In Exercises 5–8, answer the questions by referring to the following histogram, which represents the sepal widths (mm) of a sample of irises. (See Data Set 16 "Iris Measurements" in Appendix B.)*

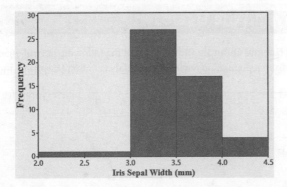

5. Sample Size Based on the histogram, what is the approximate number of irises in the sample?

6. Class Width and Class Limits What is the class width? What are the approximate lower and upper class limits of the first class?

7. Outlier? What is the largest possible value? Would that value be an outlier?

8. Normal Distribution Does it appear that the sample is from a population having a normal distribution?

Constructing Histograms. *In Exercises 9–18, construct the histograms and answer the given questions. Use class midpoint values for the horizontal scale.*

9. Pulse Rates of Males Use the frequency distribution from Exercise 13 in Section 2-1 on page 65 to construct a histogram. Do the pulse rates of males appear to have a normal distribution?

10. Pulse Rates of Females Use the frequency distribution from Exercise 14 in Section 2-1 on page 65 to construct a histogram. Do the pulse rates of females appear to have a normal distribution?

11. Lead and IQ Use the frequency distribution from Exercise 15 in Section 2-1 on page 65 to construct a histogram. Do the IQ scores appear to have a normal distribution?

12. Lead and IQ Use the frequency distribution from Exercise 16 in Section 2-1 on page 66 to construct a histogram. Do the IQ scores appear to have a normal distribution?

13. Male Red Blood Cell Counts Use the frequency distribution from Exercise 17 in Section 2-1 on page 66 to construct a histogram. Do the red blood cell counts appear to have a normal distribution?

14. Female Red Blood Cell Counts Use the frequency distribution from Exercise 18 in Section 2-1 on page 66 to construct a histogram. Do the red blood cell counts appear to have a normal distribution?

15. Freshman 15 Use the frequency distribution from Exercise 19 in Section 2-1 on page 66 to construct a histogram.

16. Freshman 15 Use the frequency distribution from Exercise 20 in Section 2-1 on page 66 to construct a histogram.

17. Last Digit Analysis Use the frequency distribution from Exercise 21 in Section 2-1 on page 66 to construct a histogram. What does the histogram suggest about the method used to collect the weights?

18. Last Digit Analysis Use the frequency distribution from Exercise 22 in Section 2-1 on page 66 to construct a histogram. What does the histogram suggest about the method used to collect the heights?

2-2 Beyond the Basics

19. Interpreting Normal Quantile Plots Which of the following normal quantile plots appear to represent data from a population having a normal distribution? Explain.

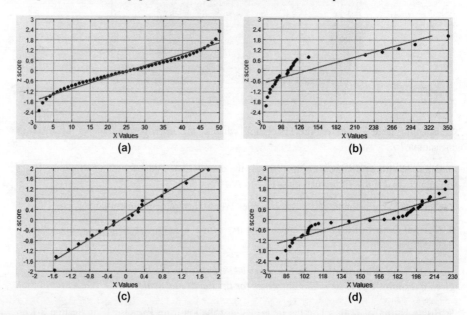

2-3 Graphs That Enlighten and Graphs That Deceive

Key Concept Section 2-2 introduced the histogram, and this section introduces other common graphs that foster understanding of data. We also discuss some graphs that are deceptive because they create impressions about data that are somehow misleading or wrong.

The era of charming and primitive hand-drawn graphs has passed, and technology now provides us with powerful tools for generating a wide variety of graphs. Here we go.

Graphs That Enlighten

Dotplots

A **dotplot** consists of a graph of quantitative data in which each data value is plotted as a point (or dot) above a horizontal scale of values. Dots representing equal values are stacked.

Features of a Dotplot

- Displays the shape of the distribution of data.
- It is usually possible to recreate the original list of data values.

EXAMPLE 1   Dotplot of Pulse Rates of Males

Figure 2-6 shows a dotplot of the pulse rates (beats per minute) of males from Data Set 1 "Body Data" in Appendix B. The two stacked dots above the position at 50 indicate that two of the pulse rates are 66. (In this dotplot, the horizontal scale allows even numbers only, but the original pulse rates are all even numbers.)

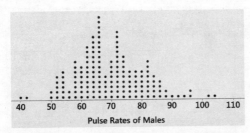

FIGURE 2-6   Dotplot of Pulse Rates of Males

Stemplots

A **stemplot** (or **stem-and-leaf plot**) represents *quantitative* data by separating each value into two parts: the stem (such as the leftmost digit) and the leaf (such as the rightmost digit). Better stemplots are often obtained by first rounding the original data values. Also, stemplots can be *expanded* to include more rows and can be *condensed* to include fewer rows.

Features of a Stemplot

- Shows the shape of the distribution of the data.
- Retains the original data values.
- The sample data are sorted (arranged in order).

EXAMPLE 2   Stemplot of Male Pulse Rates

The following stemplot displays the pulse rates of the males in Data Set 1 "Body Data" in Appendix B. The lowest pulse rate of 40 is separated into the stem of 4 and the leaf of 0. The stems and leaves are arranged in increasing order, not the order in which they occur in the original list. If you turn the stemplot on its side, you can see the distribution of the IQ scores in the same way you would see it in a histogram or dotplot.

```
 4 | 02  ←───────────── Pulse rates are 40 and 42
 5 | 00222224444446688888888
 6 | 000000022222222222444444444444446666666666666666688888
 7 | 00000000222222222222224444444444666668888888
 8 | 000000222222224444446666688
 9 | 02466  ←───────────── Pulse rates are 90, 92, 94, 96, 96
10 | 24
```

Time-Series Graph

A **time-series graph** is a graph of *time-series data,* which are quantitative data that have been collected at different points in time, such as monthly or yearly. An advantage of a time-series graph is that it reveals information about trends over time.

Features of a Time-series Graph

- Reveals information about trends over time

The Power of a Graph

With annual sales around $13 billion and with roughly 50 million people using it, Pfizer's prescription drug Lipitor (atorvastatin) has become the most profitable and most widely used prescription drug ever marketed. In the early stages of its development, Lipitor was compared to other drugs (Zocor [simvastatin], Mevacor [lovastatin], Lescol [fluvastatin], and Pravachol pravastatin) in a process that involved controlled trials. The summary report included a graph showing a Lipitor curve that had a steeper rise than the curves for the other drugs, visually showing that Lipitor was more effective in reducing cholesterol than the other drugs. Pat Kelly, who was then a senior marketing executive for Pfizer, said, "I will never forget seeing that chart.... It was like 'Aha!' Now I know what this is about. We can communicate this!" The Food and Drug Administration approved Lipitor and allowed Pfizer to include the graph with each prescription. Pfizer sales personnel also distributed the graph to physicians.

EXAMPLE 3 Time-Series Graph of Fatalities of Law Enforcement Officers

The time-series graph shown in Figure 2-7 depicts the yearly number of fatalities of law enforcement officers in the United States. See that a spike occurred in 2001, the year of the September 11, 2001 terrorist attacks. Except for the data from 2001, there appears to be a slight downward trend.

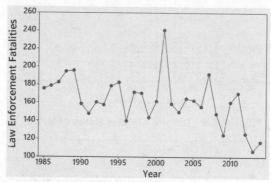

FIGURE 2-7   **Time-Series Graph of Law Enforcement Fatalities**

Bar Graphs

A **bar graph** uses bars of equal width to show frequencies of categories of *categorical* (or qualitative) data. The bars may or may not be separated by small gaps.

Feature of a Bar Graph

- Shows the relative distribution of categorical data so that it is easier to compare the different categories

Pareto Charts

A **Pareto chart** is a bar graph for categorical data, with the added stipulation that the *bars are arranged in descending order* according to frequencies, so the bars decrease in height from left to right.

Features of a Pareto Chart

- Shows the relative distribution of categorical data so that it is easier to compare the different categories
- Draws attention to the more important categories

EXAMPLE 4 Pareto Chart of Causes of Accidental Deaths

For the accidental deaths in a recent year, Figure 2-8 shows the most common causes. We can see that deaths from poison represent the most serious problem. (Deaths from poison include deaths from drug overdoses.)

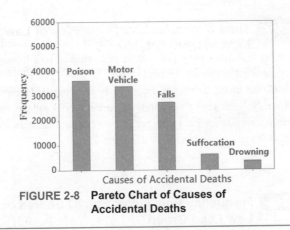

FIGURE 2-8   **Pareto Chart of Causes of Accidental Deaths**

Pie Charts

A **pie chart** is a very common graph that depicts categorical data as slices of a circle, in which the size of each slice is proportional to the frequency count for the category. Although pie charts are very common, they are not as effective as Pareto charts.

Feature of a Pie Chart

- Shows the distribution of categorical data in a commonly used format

EXAMPLE 5   **Pie Chart of Causes of Accidental Deaths**

Figure 2-9 is a pie chart of the same cause of death data from Example 4. Construction of a pie chart involves slicing up the circle into the proper proportions that represent relative frequencies. For example, the category poison accounts for 34% of the total, so the slice representing poison should be 34% of the total (with a central angle of $0.34 \times 360° = 122°$).

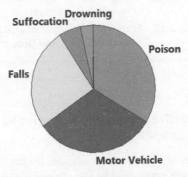

FIGURE 2-9   **Pie Chart of Causes of Accidental Deaths**

The Pareto chart in Figure 2-8 and the pie chart in Figure 2-9 depict the same data in different ways, but the Pareto chart does a better job of showing the relative sizes of the different components. Graphics expert Edwin Tufte makes the following suggestion:

Never use pie charts because they waste ink on components that are not data, and they lack an appropriate scale.

Frequency Polygon

A **frequency polygon** uses line segments connected to points located directly above class midpoint values. A frequency polygon is very similar to a histogram, but a frequency polygon uses line segments instead of bars.

A variation of the basic frequency polygon is the **relative frequency polygon,** which uses relative frequencies (proportions or percentages) for the vertical scale. An advantage of relative frequency polygons is that two or more of them can be combined on a single graph for easy comparison, as in Figure 2-11.

EXAMPLE 6 Frequency Polygon of Full IQ Scores of Low Lead Group

See Figure 2-10 for the frequency polygon corresponding to the full IQ scores of the low lead group summarized in the frequency distribution of Table 2-2 on page 58 (from Data Set 8 in Appendix B). The heights of the points correspond to the class frequencies, and the line segments are extended to the right and left so that the graph begins and ends on the horizontal axis. The points are plotted directly above class midpoint values.

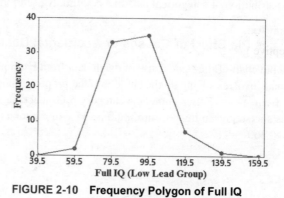

FIGURE 2-10 Frequency Polygon of Full IQ Scores of Low Lead Group

EXAMPLE 7 Relative Frequency Polygon: IQ Scores of Lead Groups

Figure 2-11 shows the relative frequency polygons for the full IQ scores of two groups: (1) group with low blood lead levels; (2) group with high blood lead levels. Here, relative frequency polygons are much better than frequency polygons because the different sample sizes of 21 and 78 would have made a comparison difficult, but that difficulty is removed by using relative percentages.

Figure 2-11 shows that the group with high blood lead levels has full IQ scores that are somewhat lower than those in the low blood level group. This suggests that exposure to lead has an effect on IQ scores. Later chapters will provide us with more tools that allow us to examine this issue beyond the subjective interpretation of a graph.

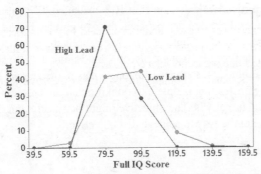

FIGURE 2-11 **Relative Frequency Polygons for Full IQ Scores of High and Low Lead Groups**

Graphs That Deceive

Deceptive graphs are commonly used to mislead people, and we really don't want statistics students to be among those susceptible to such deceptions. Graphs should be constructed in a way that is fair and objective. The readers should be allowed to make their own judgments, instead of being manipulated by misleading graphs. We present two of the ways in which graphs are commonly used to misrepresent data.

Nonzero Vertical Axis

A common deceptive graph involves using a vertical scale that starts at some value greater than zero to exaggerate differences between groups.

> **NONZERO AXIS:** Always examine a graph carefully to see whether a vertical axis begins at some point other than zero so that differences are exaggerated.

EXAMPLE 8 **Nonzero Axis**

Figure 2-12(a) and Figure 2-12(b) are based on the same data from a clinical trial of OxyContin (oxycodone), a drug used to treat moderate to severe pain. The results of that clinical trial included the percentage of subjects who experienced nausea in an OxyContin treatment group and the percentage in a group given a placebo.

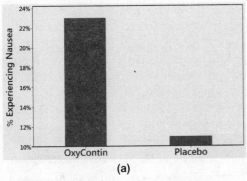
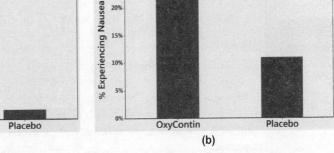

(a)   (b)

FIGURE 2-12 **Nausea in a Clinical Trial**

continued

By using a vertical scale that starts at 10% instead of 0%, Figure 2-12(a) grossly exaggerates the difference between the two groups. Figure 2-12(a) makes it appear that those using OxyContin experience nausea at a rate that is about 12 times higher than the rate for those using a placebo, but Figure 2-12(b) shows that the true ratio is about 2:1, not 12:1. Perhaps someone wants to discourage recreational use of OxyContin by misleading people into thinking that the problem with nausea is much greater than it really is. The objective might be sincere, but the use of a misleading graph is not the way to achieve that objective.

Pictographs

Drawings of objects, called *pictographs,* are often misleading. Data that are one-dimensional in nature (such as budget amounts) are often depicted with two-dimensional objects (such as dollar bills) or three-dimensional objects (such as stacks of coins, homes, or barrels). With pictographs, artists can create false impressions that grossly distort differences by using these simple principles of basic geometry: (1) When you double each side of a square, its area doesn't merely double; it increases by a factor of *four*. (2) When you double each side of a cube, its volume doesn't merely double; it increases by a factor of *eight*.

> **PICTOGRAPHS:** When examining data depicted with a pictograph, determine whether the graph is misleading because objects of area or volume are used to depict amounts that are actually one-dimensional. (Histograms and bar charts represent one-dimensional data with two-dimensional bars, but they use bars with the same width so that the graph is not misleading.)

EXAMPLE 9 Pictograph of Cigarette Smokers

Refer to Figure 2-13 and see that the larger cigarette is about twice as long, twice as tall, and twice as deep as the smaller cigarette, so the volume of the larger cigarette is about *eight times* the volume of the smaller cigarette. (The data are from the Centers for Disease Control and Prevention.) The larger cigarette *appears* to be eight times as large as the smaller cigarette, but the actual percentages show that the 37% smoking rate in 1970 is about *twice* that of the 18% rate in 2013.

1970: 37% of U.S. adults smoked.   **2013: 18% of U.S. adults smoked.**

FIGURE 2-13   Smoking by U.S. Adults

Concluding Thoughts

In addition to the graphs we have discussed in this section, there are many other useful graphs—some of which have not yet been created. The world desperately needs more people who can create original graphs that enlighten us about the nature of data. In *The Visual Display of Quantitative Information,* Edward Tufte offers these principles:

- For small data sets of 20 values or fewer, use a table instead of a graph.
- A graph of data should make us focus on the true nature of the data, not on other elements, such as eye-catching but distracting design features.
- Do not distort data; construct a graph to reveal the true nature of the data.
- Almost all of the ink in a graph should be used for the data, not for other design elements.

TECH CENTER

Graphing Capabilities
Access tech instructions, videos, and data sets at **www.TriolaStats.com**

2-3 Basic Skills and Concepts

Statistical Literacy and Critical Thinking

1. Body Temperatures Listed below are body temperatures (°F) of healthy adults. Why is it that a graph of these data would not be very effective in helping us understand the data?

   98.6   98.6   98.0   98.0   99.0   98.4   98.4   98.4   98.4   98.6

2. Voluntary Response Data If we have a large voluntary response sample consisting of weights of subjects who chose to respond to a survey posted on the Internet, can a graph help to overcome the deficiency of having a voluntary response sample?

3. Ethics There are data showing that smoking is detrimental to good health. Given that people could be helped and lives could be saved by reducing smoking, is it ethical to graph the data in a way that is misleading by exaggerating the health risks of smoking?

4. CVDOT Section 2-1 introduced important characteristics of data summarized by the acronym CVDOT. What characteristics do those letters represent, and which graph does the best job of giving us insight into the last of those characteristics?

Dotplots.   *In Exercises 5 and 6, construct the dotplot.*

5. Systolic Blood Pressure Listed below are systolic blood pressure measurements (mm Hg) of males selected from Data Set 1 "Body Data" in Appendix B. All of these values are even numbers. Is there a systolic blood pressure measurement that appears to be an outlier? What is its value?

   112   126   114   134   118   124   138   116   134   124   158   132   116
   132   128

6. Pulse Rates Listed below are pulse rates (beats per minute) of males selected from Data Set 1 "Body Data" in Appendix B. All of the values are even numbers. Are there any outliers? If so, identify their values.

   58   66   58   58   68   70   84   58   78   66   86   70   54
   84   72   74   64   66   62   62   82   54   62   54   104

Stemplots.   *In Exercises 7 and 8, construct the stemplot.*

7. Systolic Blood Pressure Refer to the data listed in Exercise 5. How are the data sorted in the stemplot?

8. Pulse Rates Refer to the data listed in Exercise 6. Identify the value in the middle when the data are sorted in order from lowest to highest. (This value is the *median,* which is defined in Section 3-1.)

Time-Series Graphs.   *In Exercises 9 and 10, construct the time-series graph.*

9. Accidental Deaths Listed below are the numbers of accidental deaths in Scotland each year beginning with 1999. Is there a trend?

| 1359 | 1341 | 1350 | 1315 | 1326 | 1390 | 1284 | 1264 | 1289 |
| 1261 | 1332 | 1295 | 1657 | 1629 | 1664 | 1750 | 1892 | 2216 |

10. Drunk Driving Fatalities Listed below are annual fatality rates (per 100,000 population) from drunk driving. The first entry represents the year 1991. Is there a trend? Any explanation?

| 6.3 | 5.5 | 5.3 | 5.1 | 5.1 | 5.1 | 4.8 | 4.6 | 4.6 | 4.7 | 4.7 |
| 4.7 | 4.5 | 4.5 | 4.6 | 4.5 | 4.3 | 3.9 | 3.5 | 3.3 | 3.2 | 3.3 |

Pareto Charts.   *In Exercises 11 and 12 construct the Pareto chart.*

11. Journal Retractions In a study of retractions in biomedical journals, 436 were due to error, 201 were due to plagiarism, 888 were due to fraud, 291 were duplications of publications, and 287 had other causes (based on data from "Misconduct Accounts for the Majority of Retracted Scientific Publications," by Fang, Steen, Casadevall, *Proceedings of the National Academy of Sciences of the United States of America,* Vol. 110, No. 3). Among such retractions, does misconduct (fraud, duplication, plagiarism) appear to be a major factor?

12. Getting a Job In a survey, subjects seeking a job were asked to whom they send a thank-you note after having a job interview. Results were as follows: 40 said only the person they spent the most time with, 40 said only the most senior-level person, 396 said everyone that they met, 15 said the person that they had the best conversation with, and 10 said that they don't send thank-you notes (based on data from TheLadders.com). Comment on the results.

Pie Charts.   *In Exercises 13 and 14, construct the pie chart.*

13. Journal Retractions Use the data from Exercise 11 "Journal Retractions."

14. Getting a Job Use the data from Exercise 12 "Getting a Job."

Frequency Polygon.   *In Exercises 15 and 16, construct the frequency polygons.*

15. Pulse Rates of Males Use the frequency distribution for the pulse rates of males from Exercise 13 in Section 2-1 on page 65 to construct a frequency polygon. Comment on the shape of the distribution.

16. Pulse Rates of Females Use the frequency distribution for the pulse rates of females from Exercise 14 in Section 2-1 on page 65 to construct a frequency polygon. Comment on the shape of the distribution.

Deceptive Graphs.   *In Exercises 17–18, identify how the graph is deceptive.*

17. Self-Driving Vehicles In a survey of adults, subjects were asked if they felt comfortable being in a self-driving vehicle. The accompanying graph depicts the results (based on data from TE Connectivity).

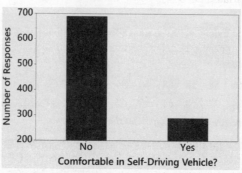

18. Cost of Giving Birth According to the Agency for Healthcare Research and Quality Healthcare Cost and Utilization Project, the typical cost of a C-section baby delivery is $4500, and the typical cost of a vaginal delivery is $2600. See the accompanying illustration.

Cost of C-Section Delivery: $4500   **Cost of Vaginal Delivery: $2600**

2-4 Scatterplots, Correlation, and Regression

Key Concept This section introduces the analysis of *paired* (or "bivariate") sample data, which are data from two different variables that are paired in some way, such as the variables of heights and weights from subjects. In Part 1 of this section we discuss *correlation* and the role of a graph called a *scatterplot*. In Part 2 we provide an introduction to the use of the *linear correlation coefficient*. In Part 3 we provide a very brief discussion of *linear regression,* which involves the equation and graph of the straight line that best fits the sample paired data.

All of the principles discussed in this section are discussed more fully in Chapter 10, but this section serves as a quick introduction to some important concepts of correlation and regression. This section does not include details for executing manual calculations, and those calculations are rarely done. Instructions for using technology to obtain results can be found at www.TriolaStats.com; refer to the instructions for Chapter 10.

PART 1 Scatterplot and Correlation

Our objective in this section is to explore whether there is a *correlation*, or association, between two variables. We begin with basic definitions.

DEFINITIONS

A **correlation** exists between two variables when the values of one variable are somehow associated with the values of the other variable.

A **linear correlation** exists between two variables when there is a correlation and the plotted points of paired data result in a pattern that can be approximated by a straight line.

A **scatterplot** or **scatter diagram** is a plot of paired (x, y) quantitative data with a horizontal x-axis and a vertical y-axis. The horizontal axis is used for the first variable (x), and the vertical axis is used for the second variable (y).

CAUTION: The presence of a correlation between two variables is not evidence that one of the variables *causes* the other. We might find a correlation between beer consumption and weight, but we cannot conclude from the statistical evidence that drinking beer has a direct effect on weight.

Correlation does not imply causality!

A scatterplot can be used as a visual aid in determining whether there is a correlation (or relationship) between the two variables. (This issue is discussed at length when the topic of correlation is considered in Section 10-1.)

EXAMPLE 1   **Correlation: Waist and Arm Circumference**

Data Set 1 "Body Data" in Appendix B includes waist circumferences (cm) and arm circumferences (cm) of randomly selected adult subjects. Figure 2-14 is a scatterplot of the paired waist/arm measurements. The points show a pattern of increasing values from left to right. This pattern suggests that there is a correlation or relationship between waist circumferences and arm circumferences.

EXAMPLE 2   **No Correlation: Weight and Pulse Rate**

Data Set 1 "Body Data" in Appendix B includes weights (kg) and pulse rates (beats per minute) of randomly selected adult subjects. Figure 2-15 is a scatterplot of the paired weight/pulse rate measurements. The points in Figure 2-15 do not show any obvious pattern, and this lack of a pattern suggests that there is no correlation or relationship between weights and pulse rates.

The preceding two examples involve making decisions about a correlation based on subjective judgments of scatterplots, but Part 2 introduces the *linear correlation coefficient* as a numerical measure that can help us make such decisions more objectively. Using paired data, we can calculate the value of the *linear correlation coefficient r*.

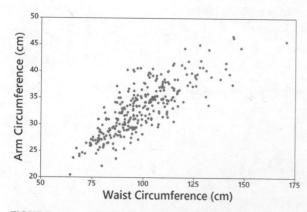

FIGURE 2-14   Waist and Arm Circumferences
Correlation: The distinct straight-line pattern of the plotted points suggests that there is a correlation between waist circumferences and arm circumference.

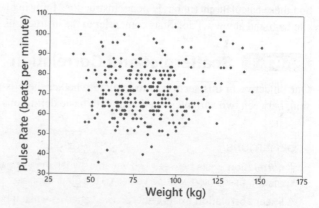

FIGURE 2-15   Weights and Pulse Rates
No Correlation: The plotted points do not show a distinct pattern, so it appears that there is no correlation between weights and pulse rates.

PART 2 Linear Correlation Coefficient *r*

Using paired data, we can calculate the value of the *linear correlation coefficient r.*

> **DEFINITION**
>
> The **linear correlation coefficient** is denoted by ***r,*** and it measures the strength of the linear association between two variables.

The value of a linear correlation coefficient *r* can be manually computed by applying Formula 10-1 or Formula 10-2 found in Section 10-1 on page 463, but in practice, *r* is almost always found by using technology.

Using *r* for Determining Correlation

The computed value of the linear correlation coefficient is always between -1 and 1. A value of exactly -1 or 1 implies that all of the data fall exactly on a line, which reflects a perfect correlation. If *r* is close to -1 or close to 1, there appears to be a strong correlation, but if *r* is close to 0, there appears to be a weak or no linear correlation. For the data depicted in the scatterplot of Figure 2-14, $r = 0.802$ (somewhat close to 1), and the data in the scatterplot of Figure 2-15 result in $r = 0.082$ (pretty close to 0). These descriptions of "close to" -1 or 1 or 0 are vague, but there are other objective criteria discussed in Chapter 10. See the following example illustrating the interpretation of the linear correlation coefficient *r.*

 EXAMPLE 3   Correlation Between Shoe Print Lengths and Heights?

Consider the data in Table 2-10 (using data from Data Set 7 "Foot and Height" in Appendix B). From the accompanying scatterplot of the paired data in Table 2-10, it isn't very clear whether there is a linear correlation. The Statdisk display of the results shows that the linear correlation coefficient has the value of $r = 0.591$ (rounded).

TABLE 2-10 Shoe Print Lengths and Heights of Males

Shoe Print Length (cm)	29.7	29.7	31.4	31.8	27.6
Height (cm)	175.3	177.8	185.4	175.3	172.7

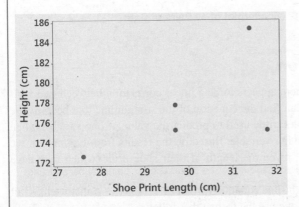

Statdisk

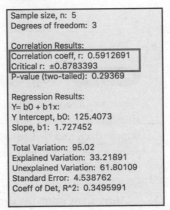

Sample size, n: 5
Degrees of freedom: 3

Correlation Results:
Correlation coeff, r: 0.5912691
Critical r: ±0.8783393
P-value (two-tailed): 0.29369

Regression Results:
Y= b0 + b1x:
Y Intercept, b0: 125.4073
Slope, b1: 1.727452

Total Variation: 95.02
Explained Variation: 33.21891
Unexplained Variation: 61.80109
Standard Error: 4.538762
Coeff of Det, R^2: 0.3495991

In Example 3, we know from the Statdisk display that using the five pairs of data from Table 2-10, the linear correlation coefficient is computed to be $r = 0.591$. The value of $r = 0.591$ is not very close to 0 or 1, so based on that value and the displayed scatterplot, it does not appear that there is a strong correlation between shoeprint lengths and heights of males.

 EXAMPLE 4 Correlation Between Shoe Print Lengths and Heights?

Example 3 used only five pairs of data from Data Set 7 "Foot and Height" in Appendix B. If we use the shoe print lengths and heights from all of the 40 subjects listed in Data Set 7 in Appendix B, we get the scatterplot shown in Figure 2-16 and we get the Minitab results shown in the accompanying display. The scatterplot does show a distinct pattern instead of having points scattered about willy-nilly. Also, we see that the value of the linear correlation coefficient is $r = 0.813$. Because $r = 0.813$ is reasonably close to 1 and because of the pattern of points in the scatterplot, it appears that there is a linear correlation between shoe print lengths and heights.

In Example 3 with only five pairs of data, we did not have enough evidence to conclude that there is a linear correlation, but in this example with 40 pairs of data, it does appear that there is a linear correlation between shoe print lengths and heights.

Minitab

Correlation: Shoe Print, Height
Pearson correlation of Shoe Print and Height = 0.813

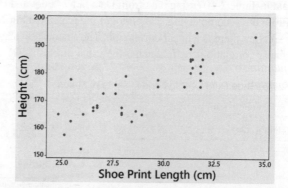

FIGURE 2-16   Scatterplot of 40 Pairs of Data

PART 3 Regression

When we do conclude that there appears to be a linear correlation between two variables (as in Example 4), we can find the equation of the straight line that best fits the sample data, and that equation can be used to predict the value of one variable when given a specific value of the other variable. Based on the results from Example 4, we can predict someone's height given the length of their shoe print (which may have been found at a crime scene).

Instead of using the straight-line equation format of $y = mx + b$ that we have all learned in prior math courses, we use the format that follows.

DEFINITION

Given a collection of paired sample data, the **regression line** (or *line of best fit* or *least-squares line*) is the straight line that "best" fits the scatterplot of the data. (The specific criterion for the "best"-fitting straight line is the "least squares" property described in Section 10-2.)

The **regression equation**

$$\hat{y} = b_0 + b_1 x$$

algebraically describes the regression line.

Section 10-2 gives a good reason for using the format of $\hat{y} = b_0 + b_1 x$ instead of the format of $y = mx + b$. Section 10-2 also provides formulas that could be used to identify the values of the y-intercept b_0 and the slope b_1, but those values are usually found by using technology.

EXAMPLE 5 Regression Line

Example 4 included a scatterplot of the 40 pairs of shoe print lengths and heights from Data Set 7 "Foot and Height" in Appendix B. Figure 2-17 shown here is that same scatterplot with the graph of the regression line included. Also shown is the Statdisk display from the 40 pairs of data.

From the Statdisk display, we see that the general form of the regression equation has a y-intercept of $b_0 = 80.9$ (rounded) and slope $b_1 = 3.22$ (rounded), so the equation of the regression line shown in Figure 2-17 is $\hat{y} = 80.9 + 3.22x$. It might be helpful to express that equation more clearly by using the names of the variables:

$$\text{Height} = 80.9 + 3.22\,(\text{Shoe Print Length})$$

Note that the *equation* shows the y-intercept of 80.9 that does not appear on the vertical scale in the *graph*. The leftmost vertical scale in Figure 2-19 is not the actual y-axis that passes through 0 on the x-axis. If the graph were extended to the left, the regression line would intercept the actual y-axis at the height of $y = 80.9$ cm.

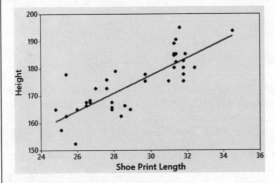

Statdisk

Correlation Results:
Correlation coeff, r: 0.812948
Critical r: ±0.3120061
P-value (two-tailed): 0.000

Regression Results:
Y= b0 + b1x:
Y Intercept, b0: 80.93041
Slope, b1: 3.218561

FIGURE 2-17   Regression Line

2-4   Basic Skills and Concepts

Statistical Literacy and Critical Thinking

1. Linear Correlation In this section we use r to denote the value of the linear correlation coefficient. Why do we refer to this correlation coefficient as being *linear*?

2. Causation A study has shown that there is a correlation between body weight and blood pressure. Higher body weights are associated with higher blood pressure levels. Can we conclude that gaining weight is a cause of increased blood pressure?

3. Scatterplot What is a scatterplot and how does it help us?

4. Estimating r For each of the following, estimate the value of the linear correlation coefficient r for the given paired data obtained from 50 randomly selected adults.

a. Their visions (x) are measured and their pulse rates (y) are measured in beats per minute.

b. Their weights (x) are measured in kilograms and those same weights are listed again, but with negative signs (y) preceding each of these second listings.

c. Their weights are measured in kilograms (x) and those same weights are recorded in grams (y).

d. Their systolic blood pressure (x) are measured and their platelet counts are measured (y).

Scatterplot.   *In Exercises 5–8, use the sample data to construct a scatterplot. Use the first variable for the x-axis. Based on the scatterplot, what do you conclude about a linear correlation?*

5. Systolic and Diastolic Blood Pressure The table lists systolic and diastolic blood pressure (in mm Hg) of five males (from Data Set 1 "Body Data" in Appendix B).

Diastolic BP	82	74	54	76	52
Systolic BP	158	132	116	132	128

6. Heights of mothers and daughters The Table lists heights (in.) of mothers and the heights (in.) of their first daughters (from Francis Galton).

Heights of mother (in)	66.0	65.5	62.0	64.5	63.0	63.0	65.0	65.0	63.5	63.5
Height of daughter (in)	66.5	63.0	68.0	66.5	63.7	63.0	65.0	65.0	67.0	69.0

7. Shoe Size Measurements The Table lists shoe sizes and heights (cm) of females that were measured (from Data Set 7 in Appendix B).

Shoe Size (in)	8	9	8.5	8	11	8	9.5
Height (cm)	167.6	168.3	165.7	165.1	165.1	165.1	152.4

8. Body Temperatures The Table lists body temperatures (°F) of 10 healthy adults at 12 AM on one day and at 12 AM on the following day (from Data Set 2 "Body Temperatures" in Appendix B).

Day 1	98.0	98.8	98.8	98.0	97.0	97.2	98.4	97.8	97.6	98.6
Day 2	98.0	98.0	98.4	98.8	97.0	97.0	98.0	98.7	98.2	98.6

Linear Correlation Coefficient.   *In Exercises 9–12, the linear correlation coefficient r is provided. What do you conclude about a linear correlation?*

9. Using the data from Exercise 5 "Systolic and Diastolic Blood Pressure," the linear correlation coefficient is $r = 0.781$.

10. Using the data from Exercise 6 "Heights of mothers and daughters," the linear correlation coefficient is $r = -0.177$.

11. Using the data from Exercise 7 "Shoe Size Measurements," the linear correlation coefficient is $r = -0.283$.

12. Using the data from Exercise 8 "Body Temperatures," the linear correlation coefficient is $r = 0.374$.

Chapter Quick Quiz

1. BAC When constructing a table representing the frequency distribution of blood alcohol content (g/dL) of drunk drivers involved in fatal car crashes, the first two classes of a frequency distribution are $0.08 - 0.11$ and $0.12 - 0.15$. What is the class width?

2. BAC Using the same first two classes from Exercise 1, identify the class boundaries of the first class.

3. BAC The first class described in Exercise 1 has a frequency of 36. If you know only the class limits given in Exercise 1 and the frequency of 36, can you identify the original 36 data values?

4. BAC A stemplot is created from the ages of drunk drivers involved in fatal car crashes and the first row is 1 | 67889. Identify the values represented by that row.

5. Reaction Times A large sample is randomly selected from a normally distributed population of reaction times, and a histogram is constructed from a frequency distribution. What is the shape of the histogram?

6. Tylenol In testing samples of regular Tylenol pills to verify that they have close to the desired amount of 325 mg of acetaminophen, which important characteristic of data is missing from this list: center, distribution, outliers, changes over time?

7. Tylenol A quality control manager wants to monitor the production of regular Tylenol pills to be sure that the mean amount of acetaminophen does not change over time. Which of the following graphs is most helpful for that purpose: histogram, Pareto chart, pie chart, scatterplot, time-series graph, dotplot?

8. Blood Pressure In an investigation of the relationship between systolic blood pressure and diastolic blood pressure, which of the following graphs is most helpful: histogram; pie chart; scatterplot; stemplot; dotplot?

9. Blood Pressure Thing The W. A. Baum Company manufactures sphygmomanometers used to measure blood pressure. Quality control managers at such companies monitor defects and identify various causes, including worn machinery, human error, bad supplies, and packaging mistreatment. Which of the following graphs would be best for describing the causes of defects: histogram, scatterplot, Pareto chart, dotplot, stemplot?

10. Frequency Distribution and Histogram What is the basic difference between a frequency distribution and a histogram?

Review Exercises

1. Frequency Distribution of Birth Weights Construct a frequency distribution of the 20 birth weights (grams) listed below. (These data are from Data Set 3 "Births" in Appendix B). Use a class width of 500 grams and a starting value of 2000 grams.

| 3500 | 3800 | 2100 | 3400 | 2600 | 3000 | 4100 | 4100 | 4300 | 3400 | 2700 | 3300 |
| | 2900 | 3300 | 3500 | 2800 | 3500 | 3700 | 3000 | 3600 | | | |

2. Histogram of Birth Weights Construct the histogram that corresponds to the frequency distribution from Exercise 1. Use class midpoint values for the horizontal scale. Does the histogram suggest that the data are from a population having a normal distribution? Why or why not?

3. Dotplot of Birth Weights Construct a dotplot of the birth weights listed in Exercise 1. Which does a better job of illustrating the distribution of the data: the histogram from Exercise 2 or the dotplot?

4. Stemplot of Birth Weights Construct a stemplot of the birth weights listed in Exercise 1. Are there any outliers?

5. Bears Listed below are the neck sizes (in.) and weights (lb) of bears (from Data Set 11 "Bear Measurements" in Appendix B). Construct a scatterplot. Based on the graph, does there appear to be a relationship between neck sizes and weights of bears?

Neck Size (in.)	16	28	31	31.5	22	21	26.5	27	20	18
Weight (lb)	80	344	416	348.0	166	220	262.0	360	204	144

6. Monitoring Weight

a. After collecting the average (mean) weight of adult males in the United States for each of the most recent 100 years, we want to construct the graph that is most appropriate for these data. Which graph is best?

b. After collecting the average (mean) weight and height of males for the most recent 100 years, we want to construct a graph to investigate the association between those two variables. Which graph is best?

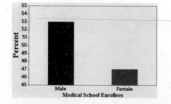

c. An investigation of health problems associated with overweight males includes heart disease, stroke, high blood pressure, diabetes, and breathing problems. If we want to construct a graph that illustrates the relative importance of these adverse effects, which graph is best?

7. Medical School Enrollees The accompanying graph illustrates male and female enrollees in U.S. medical schools in a recent year. What is wrong with the graph?

Cumulative Review Exercises

1. Hygiene Listed below are times (minutes) spent on hygiene and grooming in the morning by randomly selected subjects (based on data from a Svenska Cellulosa Aktiebolaget survey). Construct a table representing the frequency distribution. Use the classes 0–9, 10–19, and so on.

0   5   12   15   15   20   22   24   25   25   25   27   27   28   30   30   35   35   40   45

2. Hygiene Histogram Use the frequency distribution from Exercise 1 to construct a histogram. Use class midpoint values for the horizontal scale. Based on the result, do the data appear to be from a population with a normal distribution? Explain.

3. Hygiene Stemplot Use the data from Exercise 1 to construct a stemplot.

4. Analysis of Last Digits Use the data from Exercise 1 and construct a frequency distribution of the last digits of the grooming times. What does the result suggest about the grooming times?

5. Hygiene Refer to the grooming times given in Exercise 1.

a. What is the level of measurement of those times? (nominal, ordinal, interval, ratio)

b. Are the exact unrounded grooming times discrete data or continuous data?

c. Are the grooming times categorical data?

d. The average (mean) of the grooming times is 24.3 minutes. Is that value a statistic or a parameter?

6. Mother / Daughter Heights Refer to the following list of heights of mothers and the heights of their first daughters (from Data Set 6 "Family Heights" in Appendix B). What issue would be investigated with these data? Construct the best graph for investigating that issue. What does that graph suggest?

Mother's Height (in.)	67.0	66.5	64	64	58.5	68.0	62	66.5	65.0	64.5
Daughter's Height (in.)	69.2	65.5	68	67	66.5	70.5	68	66.7	68.7	66.5

Technology Project

It was stated in this chapter that the days of charming and primitive hand-drawn graphs are well behind us, and technology now provides us with powerful tools for generating a wide variety of different graphs. This project therefore serves as a good preparation for professional presentations that will be inevitably made in the future.

The complete data sets in Appendix B can be downloaded from www.TriolaStats.com. They can be opened by statistical software packages, such as Minitab, Excel, SPSS, and JMP. Statdisk already includes the data sets. Use a statistical software package to open Data Set 1 "Body Data." Use this statistical software with the methods of this chapter to describe, explore, and compare the ages of males and females. Does there appear to be a difference? Reports of randomized clinical trials typically include "baseline characteristics" of the subjects in the different groups so that we can see whether the groups are similar in ways that are important. Based on ages, do the males and females in Data Set 1 appear to be similar? (Later chapters will present more formal methods for making such comparisons.)

FROM DATA TO DECISION

Car crash fatalities are tragic losses of lives and they are devastating to the families involved. Listed below are the ages of 100 randomly selected drivers who were killed in car crashes. Also given is a frequency distribution of licensed drivers by age (based on recent data from the Insurance Institute for Highway Safety).

Ages (in years) of Drivers Killed in Car Crashes

41 43 38 31 57 29 65 18 42 47
69 50 22 60 30 30 34 18 18 42
18 16 74 25 41 43 50 34 54 45
32 20 50 36 27 59 19 23 57 74
27 38 29 24 56 72 21 22 74 20
43 34 38 62 39 45 56 70 68 75
37 49 25 24 21 25 31 21 76 69
28 62 69 26 22 62 64 24 56 70
21 52 32 30 38 73 35 52 38 29
23 17 44 25 24 70 16 49 45 34

Age	Licensed Drivers (millions)
16–19	9.7
20–29	33.6
30–39	40.2
40–49	40.3
50–59	29.6
60–69	18.3
70–79	13.4
80–89	5.4

Analysis

Convert the given frequency distribution to a relative frequency distribution, then create a relative frequency distribution using the 100 ages of drivers killed in car crashes. Compare the two relative frequency distributions. Which age categories appear to have substantially greater proportions of fatalities than the proportions of licensed drivers? If you were responsible for establishing the rates for auto insurance, which age categories would you select for higher rates? Construct a graph that is effective in identifying age categories that are more prone to fatal car crashes.

Cooperative Group Activities

1. In-class activity In class, each student should record two pulse rates by counting the number of heartbeats in 1 minute. The first pulse rate should be measured while the student is seated, and the second pulse rate should be measured while the student is standing. Using the pulse rates measured while seated, construct a frequency distribution and histogram for the pulse rates of males, and then construct another frequency distribution and histogram for the pulse rates of females. Using the pulse rates measured while standing, construct a frequency distribution and histogram for the pulse rates of males, and then construct another frequency distribution and histogram for the pulse rates of females. Compare the results. Do males and females appear to have different pulse rates? Do pulse rates measured while seated appear to be different from pulse rates measured while standing? Use an appropriate graph to determine whether there is a relationship between sitting pulse rate and standing pulse rate.

2. In-class activity Given below are the ages of motorcyclists at the time they were fatally injured in traffic accidents (based on data from the U.S. Department of Transportation). If your objective is to dramatize the dangers of motorcycles for young people, which graph would be most effective: histogram, Pareto chart, pie chart, dotplot, stemplot, frequency polygon, time-series graph? Construct the graph that best meets that objective. Is it okay to deliberately distort data if the objective is one such as saving lives of motorcyclists?

17 38 27 14 18 34 16 42 28 24 40 20 23 31
37 21 30 25 17 28 33 25 23 19 51 18 29

3. Out-of-class activity In each group of three or four students, select one of the following items and construct a graph that is effective in addressing the question:

a. Is there a difference between the body mass index (BMI) values for men and for women? (See Data Set 1 "Body Data" in Appendix B.)

b. Is there a relationship between the heights of sons (or daughters) and the heights of their fathers (or mothers)? (See Data Set 6 "Family Heights" in Appendix B.)

4. Out-of-class activity Search the Internet to find an example of a graph that is misleading. Describe how the graph is misleading. Redraw the graph so that it depicts the information correctly. If possible, please submit your graph to www.TriolaStats.com.

5. Out-of-class activity Find Charles Joseph Minard's graph describing Napoleon's march to Moscow and back, and explain why Edward Tufte says that "it may well be the best graphic ever drawn." (See *The Visual Display of Quantitative Information* by Edward Tufte, Graphics Press). Minard's graph can be seen at www.TriolaStats.com under "Textbook Supplements."

6. Out-of-class activity In *The Visual Display of Quantitative Information* by Edward Tufte (Graphics Press), find the graph that appeared in *American Education,* and explain why Tufte says that "this may well be the worst graphic ever to find its way into print." The graph can be seen at www.TriolaStats.com under "Textbook Supplements." Construct a graph that is effective in depicting the same data.

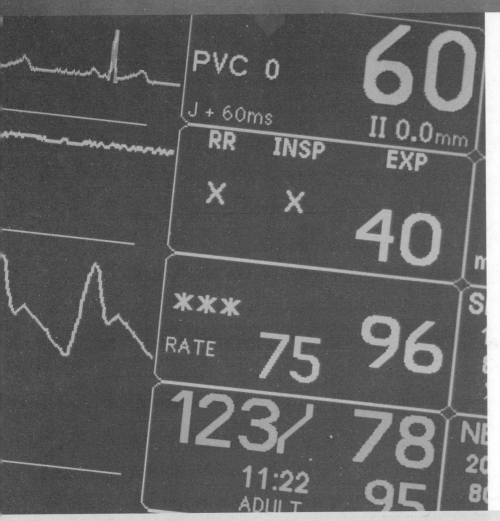

3 Describing, Exploring, and Comparing Data

3-1 Measures of Center

3-2 Measures of Variation

3-3 Measures of Relative Standing and Boxplots

CHAPTER PROBLEM — **Do men and women have the same pulse rates?**

Data Set 1 "Body Data" in Appendix B includes pulse rates of men and women. The full data set contains measurements from 300 adults, and the first 5 cases are printed in Appendix B. Figure 3-1 shows dotplots of the pulse rates categorized according to gender. Close examination of Figure 3-1 reveals that the pulse rates consist of even numbers only. This suggests that the pulse rates were measured for 30 seconds, and the result was doubled to provide a pulse rate in beats per minute. Examine Figure 3-1 closely to see that the pulse rates of males tend to be generally a little lower (farther to the left) than the pulse rates of females. This observation suggests a hypothesis: Males have lower pulse rates than females. A conclusion about such a hypothesis should not be made on the basis of a graph alone. We should consider whether the sample data were collected with an appropriate method. We should also consider whether the apparent difference between male pulse rates and female pulse rates is actually a *significant* difference and not just a random chance anomaly.

Instead of relying solely on subjective interpretations of a graph like Figure 3-1, this chapter introduces *measures* that are essential to any study of statistics. This chapter introduces the mean, median, standard deviation, and variance, which are among the most important statistics presented in this book, and they are among the most important statistics in the study of statistics. We will use these statistics for describing, exploring, and comparing the measured pulse rates for males and females in Data Set 1 "Body Data."

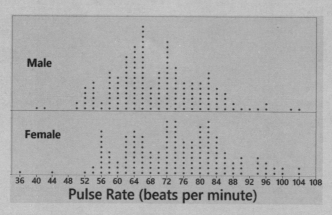

FIGURE 3-1   Dotplot of Pulse Rates of Males and Females

CHAPTER OBJECTIVES

Critical Thinking and Interpretation: Going Beyond Formulas and Arithmetic
In this modern biostatistics course, it isn't so important to memorize formulas or manually do messy arithmetic. We can get results with a calculator or software so that we can focus on making practical sense of results through critical thinking. Although this chapter includes detailed steps for important procedures, it isn't always necessary to master those steps. It is, however, generally helpful to perform a few manual calculations before using technology, so that understanding is enhanced.

The methods and tools presented in this chapter are often called methods of **descriptive statistics,** because they summarize or *describe* relevant characteristics of data. In later chapters we use **inferential statistics** to make *inferences*, or generalizations, about populations. Here are the chapter objectives:

 Measures of Center

- Develop the ability to measure the center of data by finding the mean, median, mode, and midrange.

- Determine whether an outlier has a substantial effect on the mean and median.

 Measures of Variation

- Develop the ability to measure variation in a set of sample data by finding values of the range, variance, and standard deviation.

- Develop the ability to interpret values of the standard deviation by applying the *range rule of thumb* to determine whether a particular value is *significantly low* or *significantly high*.

 Measures of Relative Standing and Boxplots

- Develop the ability to compute a z score and use the result to determine whether a given value x is *significantly low* or *significantly high*.

- Identify *percentile* values and *quartile* values from a set of data.

- Develop the ability to construct a boxplot from a set of data.

 Measures of Center

Key Concept The focus of this section is to obtain a value that measures the *center* of a data set. We present measures of center, including *mean* and *median*. Our objective here is not only to find the value of each measure of center, but also to interpret and make sense of those values. Part 1 of this section includes core concepts that should be understood before considering Part 2.

PART 1   Basic Concepts of Measures of Center

In Part 1 of this section, we introduce the mean, median, mode, and midrange as different measures of center. Measures of center are widely used to provide representative values that "summarize" data sets.

> **DEFINITION**
>
> A **measure of center** is a value at the center or middle of a data set.

There are different approaches for measuring the center, so we have different definitions for those different approaches. We begin with the mean.

Mean

The mean (or arithmetic mean) is generally the most important of all numerical measurements used to describe data, and it is what many people call an *average*.

> **DEFINITION**
>
> The **mean** (or **arithmetic mean**) of a set of data is the measure of center found by adding all of the data values and dividing the total by the number of data values.

Important Properties of the Mean

- Sample means drawn from the same population tend to vary less than other measures of center.

- The mean of a data set uses every data value.

continued

- A disadvantage of the mean is that just one extreme value (outlier) can change the value of the mean substantially. (Using the following definition, we say that the mean is not *resistant*.)

DEFINITION

A statistic is **resistant** if the presence of extreme values (outliers) does not cause it to change very much.

Calculation and Notation of the Mean

The definition of the mean can be expressed as Formula 3-1, in which the Greek letter Σ (uppercase sigma) indicates that the data values should be added, so Σx represents the sum of all data values. The symbol n denotes the **sample size,** which is the number of data values.

FORMULA 3-1

$$\text{Mean} = \frac{\Sigma x \quad \leftarrow \text{sum of all data values}}{n \quad \leftarrow \text{number of data values}}$$

If the data are a *sample* from a population, the mean is denoted by $\bar{x}$ (pronounced "x-bar"); if the data are the entire population, the mean is denoted by μ (lowercase Greek mu).

NOTATION *Hint:* Sample statistics are usually represented by English letters, such as $\bar{x}$, and population parameters are usually represented by Greek letters, such as μ.

Σ	denotes the *sum* of a set of data values.
x	is the *variable* usually used to represent the individual data values.
n	represents the number of data values in a *sample*.
N	represents the number of data values in a *population*.
$\bar{x} = \dfrac{\Sigma x}{n}$	is the mean of a set of *sample* values.
$\mu = \dfrac{\Sigma x}{N}$	is the mean of all values in a *population*.

⊙ **EXAMPLE 1** **Mean**

Data Set 1 "Body Data" in Appendix B includes measures of pulse rates. Find the mean of the first five pulse rates for males: 84, 74, 50, 60, 52 (all in beats per minute, or BPM).

SOLUTION

The mean is computed by using Formula 3-1. First add the data values, then divide by the number of data values:

$$\bar{x} = \frac{\Sigma x}{n} = \frac{84 + 74 + 50 + 60 + 52}{5} = \frac{320}{5}$$
$$= 64.0\,\text{BPM}$$

The mean of the first five male pulse rates is 64.0 BPM.

CAUTION Never use the term *average* when referring to a measure of center. The word *average* is often used for the mean, but it is sometimes used for other measures of center. The term *average* is not used by statisticians, it is not used in professional journals, and it will not be used throughout the remainder of this book when referring to a specific measure of center.

Median

The median can be thought of loosely as a "middle value" in the sense that about half of the values in a data set are less than the median and half are greater than the median. The following definition is more precise.

DEFINITION

The **median** of a data set is the measure of center that is the *middle value* when the original data values are arranged in order of increasing (or decreasing) magnitude.

Important Properties of the Median

- The median does not change by large amounts when we include just a few extreme values, so the median is a *resistant* measure of center.

- The median does not directly use every data value. (For example, if the largest value is changed to a much larger value, the median does not change.)

Calculation and Notation of the Median

The median of a sample is sometimes denoted by $\tilde{x}$ (pronounced "*x*-tilde") or M or Med; there isn't a commonly accepted notation and there isn't a special symbol for the median of a population. To find the median, first *sort* the values (arrange them in order), and then follow one of these two procedures:

1. If the number of data values is *odd,* the median is the number located in the exact middle of the sorted list.

2. If the number of data values is *even,* the median is found by computing the mean of the two middle numbers in the sorted list.

 EXAMPLE 2 Median with an *Odd* Number of Data Values

Find the median of the first five pulse rates for males: 84, 74, 50, 60, 52 (all in BPM).

SOLUTION

First sort the data values by arranging them in ascending order, as shown below:

$$50 \quad 52 \quad 60 \quad 74 \quad 84$$

Because there are 5 data values, the number of data values is an odd number (5), so the median is the number located in the exact middle of the sorted list, which is 60.0 BPM. The median is therefore 60.0 BPM. Note that the *median* of 60.0 BPM is different from the *mean* of 64.0 BPM found in Example 1.

What the Median Is Not

Harvard biologist Stephen Jay Gould wrote, "The Median Isn't the Message." In it, he describes how he learned that he had abdominal mesothelioma, a form of cancer. He went to the library to learn more, and he was shocked to find that mesothelioma was incurable, with a median survival time of only *eight months* after it was discovered. Gould wrote this: "I suspect that most people, without training in statistics, would read such a statement as 'I will probably be dead in eight months' the very conclusion that must be avoided, since it isn't so, and since attitude (in fighting the cancer) matters so much." Gould went on to carefully interpret the value of the median. He knew that his chance of living longer than the median was good because he was young, his cancer was diagnosed early, and he would get the best medical treatment. He also reasoned that some could live much longer than eight months, and he saw no reason why he could not be in that group. Armed with this thoughtful interpretation of the median and a strong positive attitude, Gould lived for *20 years* after his diagnosis. He died of another cancer not related to the mesothelioma.

EXAMPLE 3 **Median with an *Even* Number of Data Values**

Repeat Example 2 after including the sixth pulse rate of 62 BPM. That is, find the median of these pulse rates: 84, 74, 50, 60, 52, 62 (all in BPM).

SOLUTION

First arrange the values in ascending order: 50, 52, 60, 62, 74, 84.

Because the number of data values is an even number (6), the median is found by computing the mean of the two middle numbers, which are 60 and 62.

$$\text{Median} = \frac{60 + 62}{2} = \frac{122}{2} = 61.0 \text{ BPM}$$

The median is 61.0 BPM.

Mode

The mode isn't used much with quantitative data, but it's the only measure of center that can be used with qualitative data (consisting of names, labels, or categories only).

DEFINITION

The **mode** of a data set is the value(s) that occurs with the greatest frequency.

Important Properties of the Mode

- The mode can be found with qualitative data.
- A data set can have no mode or one mode or multiple modes.

Finding the Mode: A data set can have one mode, more than one mode, or no mode.

- When two data values occur with the same greatest frequency, each one is a mode and the data set is said to be **bimodal.**
- When more than two data values occur with the same greatest frequency, each is a mode and the data set is said to be **multimodal.**
- When no data value is repeated, we say that there is **no mode.**

 EXAMPLE 4 **Mode**

Find the mode of these pulse rates (in BPM):

58   58   58   58   60   60   62   64

SOLUTION

The mode is 58 BPM, because it is the pulse rate occurring most often (four times).

In Example 4, the mode is a single value. Here are other possible circumstances:

Two modes: The pulse rates (BPM) of 58, 58, 58, 60, 60, 60, 62, 64 have two modes: 58 BPM and 60 BPM.

No mode: The pulse rates of 58, 60, 64, 68, 72 have no mode because no value is repeated.

Midrange

Another measure of center is the midrange.

> **DEFINITION**
>
> The **midrange** of a data set is the measure of center that is the value midway between the maximum and minimum values in the original data set. It is found by adding the maximum data value to the minimum data value and then dividing the sum by 2, as in the following formula:
>
> $$\text{Midrange} = \frac{\text{maximum data value} + \text{minimum data value}}{2}$$

Important Properties of the Midrange

- Because the midrange uses only the maximum and minimum values, it is very sensitive to those extremes so the midrange is not *resistant*.

- In practice, the midrange is rarely used, but it has three redeeming features:

  1. The midrange is very easy to compute.

  2. The midrange helps reinforce the very important point that there are several different ways to define the center of a data set.

  3. The value of the midrange is sometimes used incorrectly for the median, so confusion can be reduced by clearly defining the midrange along with the median.

 EXAMPLE 5 Midrange

Find the midrange of these five pulse rates for males used in Example 1: 84, 74, 50, 60, 52 (BPM).

SOLUTION

The midrange is found as follows:

$$\text{Midrange} = \frac{\text{maximum data value} + \text{minimum data value}}{2}$$

$$= \frac{84 + 50}{2} = 67.0 \text{ BPM}$$

The midrange is 67.0 BPM.

Rounding Measures of Center

When calculating measures of center, we often need to round the result. We use the following rule.

> **ROUND-OFF RULES FOR MEASURES OF CENTER:**
>
> - **For the mean, median, and midrange, carry one more decimal place than is present in the original set of values.**
>
> - **For the mode, leave the value as is without rounding** (because values of the mode are the same as some of the original data values).

When applying any rounding rules, round only the final answer, *not intermediate values that occur during calculations*. For example, the mean of 2, 3, and 5 is 3.333333..., which is rounded to 3.3, which has one more decimal place than the original values of 2, 3, and 5. As another example, the mean of 80.4 and 80.6 is 80.50 (one more decimal place than was used for the original values). Because the mode is one or more of the original data values, we do not round values of the mode; we simply use the same original values that are modes.

Critical Thinking

We can always calculate measures of center from a sample of numbers, but we should always think about whether it makes sense to do that. In Section 1-2 we noted that it makes no sense to do numerical calculations with data at the nominal level of measurement, because those data consist of names, labels, or categories only, so statistics such as the mean and median are meaningless for such data. We should also think about the sampling method used to collect the data. If the sampling method is not sound, the statistics we obtain may be very misleading.

EXAMPLE 6   Critical Thinking and Measures of Center

Each of the following illustrates data for which the mean and median are *not* meaningful statistics.

    a. Zip codes of the hospitals in the United States. (The zip codes don't measure or count anything. The numbers are just labels for geographic locations.)

    b. Ranks of selected medical schools: 2, 3, 7, 10, 14. (The ranks reflect an ordering, but they don't measure or count anything.)

    c. Numbers on the jerseys of the starting defense for the Seattle Seahawks when they won Super Bowl XLVIII: 31, 28, 41, 56, 25, 54, 69, 50, 91, 72, 29. (The numbers on the football jerseys don't measure or count anything; they are just substitutes for names.)

    d. Top 5 incomes of hospital chief executive officers. (Such "top 5" or "top 10" lists include data that are not at all representative of the larger population.)

    e. The 50 mean ages computed from the means in each of the 50 states. (If you calculate the mean of those 50 values, the result is not the mean age of people in the entire United States. The population sizes of the 50 different states must be taken into account, as described in the *weighted mean* introduced in Part 2 of this section.)

In the spirit of describing, exploring, and comparing data, we provide Table 3-1, which summarizes the different measures of center for the 300 pulse rates referenced in the Chapter Problem. Figure 3-1 on page 92 suggests that males have lower pulse rates, and comparison of the means and medians in Table 3-1 also suggests that males have lower pulse rates. The following chapters will describe other tools that can be used for an effective comparison.

TABLE 3-1 Male and Female Pulse Rates

	Male	Female
Mean	69.6	74.0
Median	68.0	74.0
Mode	66	72, 74, 82
Midrange	72.0	70.0

PART 2   Beyond the Basics of Measures of Center

Calculating the Mean from a Frequency Distribution

Formula 3-2 is the same calculation for the mean that was presented in Part 1, but it incorporates this approach: When working with data summarized in a frequency distribution, we make calculations possible by pretending that all sample values in each class are equal to the class midpoint. Formula 3-2 is not really a new concept; it is simply a variation of Formula 3-1 for the mean.

FORMULA 3-2   MEAN FROM A FREQUENCY DISTRIBUTION

First multiply each frequency and
class midpoint; then add the products.
↓

$$\bar{x} = \frac{\Sigma\,(f \cdot x)}{\Sigma f} \quad \text{(Result is an approximation)}$$

↑
Sum of frequencies
(equal to n)

Example 7 illustrates the procedure for finding the mean from a frequency distribution.

EXAMPLE 7   Computing the Mean from a Frequency Distribution

The first two columns of Table 3-2 on the next page constitute a frequency distribution summarizing the pulse rates from males in Data Set 1 "Body Data" from Appendix B. Use the frequency distribution in the first two columns to find the mean.

SOLUTION

Remember, when working with data summarized in a frequency distribution, we make calculations possible by pretending that all sample values in each class are equal to the class midpoint. For example, see Table 3-2 and consider the first class interval of 40–54 with a frequency of 15. We pretend that each of the 15 pulse rates is 47 (the class midpoint). With the pulse rate of 47 repeated 15 times, we have a total of $47 \cdot 15 = 705$, as shown in the last column of Table 3-2. We can then add those results to find the sum of all sample values.

The bottom row of Table 3-2 shows the two components we need for the calculation of the mean (as in Formula 3-2): $\Sigma f = 153$ and $\Sigma\,(f \cdot x) = 10{,}611$. We calculate the mean using Formula 3-2 as follows:

$$\bar{x} = \frac{\Sigma\,(f \cdot x)}{\Sigma f} = \frac{10{,}611}{153} = 69.4 \text{ BPM}$$

continued

The result of $\bar{x} = 69.4$ BPM is an *approximation* because it is based on the use of class midpoint values instead of the original list of pulse rates. The mean of 69.6 BPM found by using all of the original pulse rates for males is a more accurate result.

TABLE 3-2 Pulse Rates (BPM) of Males

Pulse Rate	Frequency f	Class Midpoint x	$f \cdot x$
40–54	15	47	705
55–69	63	62	3906
70–84	62	77	4774
85–99	11	92	1012
100–114	2	107	214
Totals:	$\Sigma f = 153$		$\Sigma (f \cdot x) = 10{,}611$

Calculating a Weighted Mean

When different x data values are assigned different weights w, we can compute a **weighted mean.** Formula 3-3 can be used to compute the weighted mean.

FORMULA 3-3

$$\text{Weighted mean: } \bar{x} = \frac{\Sigma (w \cdot x)}{\Sigma w}$$

Formula 3-3 tells us to first multiply each weight w by the corresponding value x, then to add the products, and then finally to divide that total by the sum of the weights, Σw.

EXAMPLE 8 **Computing Grade-Point Average**

In her first semester of college, a student of one of the authors took five courses. Her final grades along with the number of credits for each course were A (3 credits), A (4 credits), B (3 credits), C (3 credits), and F (1 credit). The grading system assigns quality points to letter grades as follows: A = 4; B = 3; C = 2; D = 1; F = 0. Compute her grade-point average.

SOLUTION

Use the numbers of credits as weights: $w = 3, 4, 3, 3, 1$. Replace the letter grades of A, A, B, C, and F with the corresponding quality points: $x = 4, 4, 3, 2$, and 0. We now use Formula 3-3 as shown below. The result is a first-semester grade-point average of 3.07. (In using the preceding round-off rule, the result should be rounded to 3.1, but it is common to round grade-point averages to two decimal places.)

$$\bar{x} = \frac{\Sigma (w \cdot x)}{\Sigma w}$$

$$= \frac{(3 \times 4) + (4 \times 4) + (3 \times 3) + (3 \times 2) + (1 \times 0)}{3 + 4 + 3 + 3 + 1}$$

$$= \frac{43}{14} = 3.07$$

TECH CENTER

Descriptive Statistics
Access tech instructions, videos, and data sets at www.TriolaStats.com

3-1 Basic Skills and Concepts

Statistical Literacy and Critical Thinking

1. Average A report includes a statement that the "average" Medical College Admission Test (MCAT) score of applicants to medical schools is 28.4. What is the role of the term *average* in statistics? Should another term be used in place of *average*?

2. What's Wrong? The Centers for Disease Control and Prevention (CDC) publishes a list of smoking rates in each state. If we add the 50 percentages and then divide by 50, we get 19.67%. Is the value of 19.67% the mean smoking rate for all of the United States? Why or why not?

3. Measures of Center In what sense are the mean, median, mode, and midrange measures of "center"?

4. Resistant Measures Here are five systolic blood pressures (mm Hg) of females: 120, 110, 115, 125, 135. Find the mean and median of these five values. Then find the mean and median after including a sixth value of 1000, which is an outlier. (One of the female systolic blood pressure is 100, but 1000 is used here as an error resulting from an incorrect data entry.) Compare the two sets of results. How much was the mean affected by the inclusion of the outlier? How much is the median affected by the inclusion of the outlier?

Critical Thinking. *Each of Exercises 5–16 involves some feature that is somewhat tricky. Find the (a) mean, (b) median, (c) mode, and (d) midrange, and then answer the given question.*

5. Charges for Births Data Set 3 "Births" in Appendix B includes total charges for births at four Hospitals in New York State, and the bottom 10 least amounts (in dollars) are listed below. What do the results tell us about the population of all such charges?

322.00	619.50	663.50	689.00	755.00
800.45	844.00	945.50	1060.00	1060.00

6. MCAT Score Listed below are mean MCAT scores listed in order by year, starting with the year 2002. What important feature of the data is not revealed by any of the measures of center?

27.0 26.8 27.1 27.3 27.4 27.7 28.1 27.9 28.3 28.2 28.3 28.4

7. Football Player Numbers Listed below are the jersey numbers of 11 players randomly selected from the roster of the Seattle Seahawks when they won Super Bowl XLVIII. What do the results tell us?

89 91 55 7 20 99 25 81 19 82 60

8. Football Player Weights Listed below are the weights in pounds of 11 players randomly selected from the roster of the Seattle Seahawks when they won Super Bowl XLVIII (the same players from the preceding exercise). Are the results likely to be representative of all National Football League (NFL) players?

189 254 235 225 190 305 195 202 190 252 305

9. Peas in a Pod Biologists conducted experiments to determine whether a deficiency of carbon dioxide in the soil affects the phenotypes of peas. Listed below are the phenotype codes, where 1 = smooth-yellow, 2 = smooth-green, 3 = wrinkled-yellow, and

continued

$4 =$ wrinkled-green. Can the measures of center be obtained for these values? Do the results make sense?

$$2 \quad 1 \quad 1 \quad 1 \quad 1 \quad 1 \quad 1 \quad 4 \quad 1 \quad 2 \quad 2 \quad 1 \quad 2 \quad 3 \quad 3 \quad 2 \quad 3 \quad 1 \quad 3 \quad 1 \quad 3 \quad 1 \quad 3 \quad 2 \quad 2$$

10. TV Prices A physician plans to buy a television for her large waiting room. Listed below are selling prices in dollars of TVs that are 60 inches or larger and rated as a "best buy" by *Consumer Reports* magazine. Are the resulting statistics representative of the population of all TVs that are 60 inches and larger? If you decide to buy one of these TVs, what statistic is most relevant, other than the measures of central tendency?

$$1800 \quad 1500 \quad 1200 \quad 1500 \quad 1400 \quad 1600 \quad 1500 \quad 950 \quad 1600 \quad 1150 \quad 1500 \quad 1750$$

11. Cell Phone Radiation Listed below are the measured radiation absorption rates (in W/kg) corresponding to these cell phones: iPhone 5S, BlackBerry Z30, Sanyo Vero, Optimus V, Droid Razr, Nokia N97, Samsung Vibrant, Sony Z750a, Kyocera Kona, LG G2, and Virgin Mobile Supreme. The data are from the Federal Communications Commission (FCC). The media often report about the dangers of cell phone radiation as a cause of cancer. The FCC has a standard that a cell phone absorption rate must be 1.6 W/kg or less. If you are planning to purchase a cell phone, are any of the measures of center the most important statistic? Is there another statistic that is most relevant? If so, which one?

$$1.18 \quad 1.41 \quad 1.49 \quad 1.04 \quad 1.45 \quad 0.74 \quad 0.89 \quad 1.42 \quad 1.45 \quad 0.51 \quad 1.38$$

12. Caffeine in Soft Drinks Listed below are measured amounts of caffeine (mg per 12 oz of drink) obtained in one can from each of 20 brands (7-UP, A&W Root Beer, Cherry Coke, . . . , Tab). Are the statistics representative of the population of all cans of the same 20 brands consumed by Americans?

$$0 \quad 0 \quad 34 \quad 34 \quad 34 \quad 45 \quad 41 \quad 51 \quad 55 \quad 36 \quad 47 \quad 41 \quad 0 \quad 0 \quad 53 \quad 54 \quad 38 \quad 0 \quad 41 \quad 47$$

13. Firefighter Fatalities Listed below are the number of heroic firefighters who suffered major injuries in the United Kingdom each year while fighting fires. The numbers are listed in order by year, starting with the year 2004. What important feature of the data is not revealed by any of the measures of center?

$$129 \quad 111 \quad 133 \quad 127 \quad 108 \quad 106 \quad 112 \quad 75 \quad 171$$

14. Foot Lengths Listed below are foot lengths in inches of randomly selected Army women measured in the 1988 Anthropometric Survey (ANSUR). Are the statistics representative of the current population of all Army women?

$$10.4 \quad 9.3 \quad 9.1 \quad 9.3 \quad 10.0 \quad 9.4 \quad 8.6 \quad 9.8 \quad 9.9 \quad 9.1 \quad 9.1$$

15. Medical School Tuition Listed below in dollars are the annual costs of tuition at the 10 most expensive private medical schools in the United States for a recent year (based on data from *U.S. News & World Report*). What does this "top 10" list tell us about those costs for the population of all U.S. private medical school tuitions?

$$57{,}261 \quad 56{,}784 \quad 55{,}196 \quad 54{,}976 \quad 54{,}653 \quad 54{,}528 \quad 54{,}268 \quad 54{,}050 \quad 53{,}581 \quad 53{,}323$$

16. California Smokers In the California Health Interview Survey, randomly selected adults are interviewed. One of the questions asks how many cigarettes are smoked per day, and results are listed below for 50 randomly selected respondents. How well do the results reflect the smoking behavior of California adults?

$$9 \quad 10 \quad 10 \quad 20 \quad 40 \quad 50 \quad 0 \quad 0 \quad 0 \quad 0 \quad 0 \quad 0 \quad 0 \quad 0$$
$$0 \quad 0 \quad 0 \quad 0 \quad 0 \quad 0 \quad 0 \quad 0 \quad 0 \quad 0 \quad 0 \quad 0 \quad 0 \quad 0$$
$$0 \quad 0 \quad 0 \quad 0 \quad 0 \quad 0 \quad 0 \quad 0 \quad 0 \quad 0 \quad 0 \quad 0 \quad 0 \quad 0$$
$$0 \quad 0 \quad 0 \quad 0 \quad 0$$

In Exercises 17–20, find the **mean** *and* **median** *for each of the two samples, then compare the two sets of results.*

17. Blood Pressure A sample of blood pressure measurements is taken from Data Set 1 "Body Data" in Appendix B, and those values (mm Hg) are listed below. The values are matched so that 10 subjects each have systolic and diastolic measurements. (Systolic is a measure of the force of blood being pushed through arteries, but diastolic is a measure of blood pressure when the heart is at rest between beats.) Are the measures of center the best statistic to use with these data? What else might be better?

Systolic:	136	94	118	146	106	106	120	106	118	144
Diastolic:	82	58	80	68	64	64	66	72	64	98

18. Weight/Height Measurement Listed below are weights (in kg) and heights (in cm) from different subjects (from Data Set 1 "Body data" in Appendix B). The values are matched so that each of the 12 subjects has a weight measurement and a height measurement. Are the measures of center the best statistics to use with these data? What else might be better?

Weight:	98.6	96.9	108.2	73.1	83.1	86.5	64.1	79.2	64.2	118.8	71.3	98.2
Height:	172.0	186.0	154.4	160.5	179	166.7	178.5	155.7	157.6	180.4	166.3	168.6

19. Weight Measurement Listed below are weights (kg) of males and females (from Data Set 1 "Body Data" in Appendix B). Do they appear to be different?

Female:	54.4	55.6	57.8	57.8	60.5	64.0	64.2	66.5	67.1	69.8	70.9	71.5
Male:	59.5	64.1	71.3	71.7	72.3	73.1	75.3	75.9	76.5	78.5	81.3	83.1

20. Queues A Providence Hospital experiment involves two different waiting line configurations for patients arriving for admission. The waiting times (in seconds) are recorded with a single line configuration that feeds four stations and another configuration with individual lines at the four stations. Determine whether there is a difference between the two data sets that is not apparent from a comparison of the measures of center. If so, what is it?

Single Line	390	396	402	408	426	438	444	462	462	462
Individual Lines	252	324	348	372	402	462	462	510	558	600

Large Data Sets from Appendix B. *In Exercises 21–24, refer to the indicated data set in Appendix B. Use software or a calculator to find the* **means** *and* **medians.**

21. HDL Use the high-density lipoprotein (HDL) cholesterol measurements (mg/dL) from the 300 subjects included in Data Set 1 "Body Data" in Appendix B. Identify the highest value. Does it appear to be an outlier? Do the mean and median change much when that highest value is deleted?

22. LDL Repeat the preceding exercise using the low-density lipoprotein (LDL) measurements (mg/dL).

23. Body Temperatures Refer to Data Set 2 "Body Temperatures" in Appendix B and use the body temperatures for 12:00 AM on day 2. Do the results support or contradict the common belief that the mean body temperature is 98.6°F?

24. Births Use the birth weights (grams) of the 400 babies listed in Data Set 3 "Births" in Appendix B. Examine the list of birth weights to make an observation about those numbers. How does that observation affect the way that the results should be rounded?

In Exercises 25 and 26, find the **mean** *of the data summarized in the frequency distribution. Also, compare the* **computed means** *to the* **actual means** *obtained by using the original list of data values, which are as follows: (Exercise 25) 224.3; (Exercise 26) 255.1.*

25.

Blood Platelet Count of Males	Frequency
0–99	1
100–199	51
200–299	90
300–399	10
400–499	0
500–599	0
600–699	1

26.

Blood Platelet Count of Females	Frequency
100–199	25
200–299	92
300–399	28
400–499	0
500–599	2

27. Weighted Mean A student of one of the authors earned grades of A, C, B, A, and D. Those courses had these corresponding numbers of credit hours: 3, 3, 3, 4, and 1. The grading system assigns quality points to letter grades as follows: A = 4; B = 3; C = 2; D = 1; F = 0. Compute the grade-point average (GPA) and round the result with two decimal places. If the dean's list requires a GPA of 3.00 or greater, did this student make the dean's list?

28. Weighted Mean A student of one of the authors earned grades of 63, 91, 88, 84, and 79 on her five regular statistics tests. She earned a grade of 86 on the final exam and 90 on her class projects. Her combined homework grade was 70. The five regular tests count for 60% of the final grade, the final exam counts for 10%, the project counts for 15%, and homework counts for 15%. What is her weighted mean grade? What letter grade did she earn (A, B, C, D, or F)? Assume that a mean of 90 or above is an A, a mean of 80 to 89 is a B, and so on.

3-1   Beyond the Basics

29. Degrees of Freedom Five pulse rates randomly selected from Data Set 1 "Body Data" in Appendix B have a mean of 78.0 beats per minute. Four of the pulse rates are 82, 78, 56, and 84.

a. Find the missing value.

b. We need to create a list of *n* values that have a specific known mean. We are free to select any values we desire for some of the *n* values. How many of the *n* values can be freely assigned before the remaining values are determined? (The result is referred to as the *number of degrees of freedom*.)

30. Censored Data Recently, five U.S. presidents were still alive and after their first inauguration, they have lived 37 years, 25 years, 21 years, 13 years, and 5 years so far. We might use the values of 37+, 25+, 21+, 13+, and 5+, where the positive signs indicate that the actual value is equal to or greater than the current value. (These values are said to be *censored* at the current time that this list was compiled.) If we ignore the presidents who took office because of an assassination or resignation and if we ignore the five presidents who are still alive, the mean of the 33 remaining presidents is 15.0 years. What do we know about the mean if we include the censored values of 37+, 25+, 21+, 13+, and 5+? Do the two results differ by much?

31. Trimmed Mean Because the mean is very sensitive to extreme values, we say that it is not a *resistant* measure of center. By deleting some low values and high values, the **trimmed mean** (or truncated mean) is more resistant. To find the 10% trimmed mean for a data set, first arrange the data in order, next delete the bottom 10% of the values and delete the top 10% of the values, and then calculate the mean of the remaining values. Use the LDL measurements of the 300 subjects from Data Set 1 "Body Data" in Appendix B. Compare the mean, the 10% trimmed mean, and the 20% trimmed mean.

3-2 Measures of Variation

Key Concept Variation is the single most important topic in statistics, so this is the single most important section in this book. This section presents three important measures of variation: *range, standard deviation,* and *variance.* These statistics are numbers, but our focus is not just computing those numbers but developing the ability to *interpret* and *understand* them. This section is not a study of arithmetic; it is about understanding and interpreting measures of variation, especially the standard deviation.

> **STUDY HINT:** Part 1 of this section presents basic concepts of variation, and Part 2 presents additional concepts related to the standard deviation. Part 1 and Part 2 both include formulas for computation, but do not spend too much time memorizing formulas or doing arithmetic calculations. Instead, focus on *understanding* and *interpreting* values of standard deviation.

PART 1 Basic Concepts of Variation

To visualize the property of variation, see Figure 3-2, which illustrates pulse rates (beats per minute or BPM) for subjects given a treatment and subjects given a placebo. (A high priority is placed on using real data, but these pulse rates are fabricated for the purposes of making an important point here.) Verify this important observation: The pulse rates in the treatment group (top dotplot) have more *variation* than those in the placebo group (bottom dotplot). Both sets of pulse rates have the *same mean* of 70.2 BPM, they have the *same median* of 70.0 BPM, and they have the *same mode* of 70 BPM. Those measures of center do not "see" the difference in variation.

To keep our round-off rules as consistent and as simple as possible, we will round the measures of variation using this rule:

> **ROUND-OFF RULE FOR MEASURES OF VARIATION** When rounding the value of a measure of variation, carry one more decimal place than is present in the original set of data.

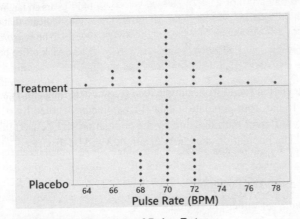

FIGURE 3-2 Dotplots of Pulse Rates

Range

Let's begin with the range because it is quick and easy to compute, but it is not as important as other measures of variation.

DEFINITION

The **range** of a set of data values is the difference between the maximum data value and the minimum data value.

$$\text{Range} = (\text{maximum data value}) - (\text{minimum data value})$$

Important Properties of the Range

- The range uses only the maximum and the minimum data values, so it is very sensitive to extreme values. The range is not *resistant*.

- Because the range uses only the maximum and minimum values, it does not take every value into account and therefore does not truly reflect the variation among all of the data values.

EXAMPLE 1   **Range**

Find the range of the first five pulse rates for males from Data Set 1 "Body Data" in Appendix B: 84, 74, 50, 60, 52 (all in BPM).

SOLUTION

The range is found by subtracting the lowest value from the largest value, so we get

$$\text{Range} = (\text{maximum value}) - (\text{minimum value}) = 84 - 50 = 34.0 \text{ BPM}$$

The range of 34.0 BPM is shown with one more decimal place than is present in the original data values.

Standard Deviation of a Sample

The *standard deviation* is the measure of variation most commonly used in statistics.

DEFINITION

The **standard deviation** of a set of sample values, denoted by s, is a measure of how much data values deviate away from the mean. It is calculated by using Formula 3-4 or 3-5. Formula 3-5 is just a different version of Formula 3-4; both formulas are algebraically the same.

The standard deviation found from sample data is a statistic denoted by s, but the standard deviation found from population data is a parameter denoted by σ. The formula for σ is slightly different with division by the population size N used instead of division by $n - 1$. The population standard deviation σ will be discussed later.

Notation

$s = sample$ standard deviation

$\sigma = population$ standard deviation

FORMULA 3-4

$$s = \sqrt{\frac{\Sigma(x - \bar{x})^2}{n-1}} \quad \text{sample standard deviation}$$

FORMULA 3-5

$$s = \sqrt{\frac{n(\Sigma x^2) - (\Sigma x)^2}{n(n-1)}} \quad \begin{array}{l}\text{shortcut formula for sample standard} \\ \text{deviation (used by calculators and software)}\end{array}$$

Later we give the reasoning behind these formulas, but for now we recommend that you use Formula 3-4 for an example or two, and then learn how to find standard deviation values using a calculator or software.

Important Properties of Standard Deviation

- The standard deviation is a measure of how much data values deviate away from the *mean*.
- The value of the standard deviation s is never negative. It is zero only when all of the data values are exactly the same.
- Larger values of s indicate greater amounts of variation.
- The standard deviation s can increase dramatically with one or more outliers.
- The units of the standard deviation s (such as minutes, feet, pounds) are the same as the units of the original data values.
- The sample standard deviation s is a **biased estimator** of the population standard deviation σ, which means that values of the sample standard deviation s do not center around the value of σ. (This is explained in Part 2.)

Example 2 illustrates a calculation using Formula 3-4 because that formula better illustrates that the standard deviation is based on deviations of sample values away from the mean.

EXAMPLE 2 **Calculating Standard Deviation with Formula 3-4**

Use Formula 3-4 to find the standard deviation of the first five pulse rates for males from Data Set 1 "Body Data" in Appendix B: 84, 74, 50, 60, 52 (all in BPM).

SOLUTION

The left column of Table 3-3 on the next page summarizes the general procedure for finding the standard deviation using Formula 3-4, and the right column illustrates that procedure using the sample values 84, 74, 50, 60, 52. The result shown in Table 3-3 is 14.6 BPM, which is rounded to one more decimal place than is present in the original list of sample values. Also, the units for the standard deviation are the same as the units of the original data. Because the original data values are all in units of BPM, the standard deviation is 14.6 BPM.

Variation in Faces

Researchers commented that "if everyone looked more or less the same, there would be total chaos." They studied human body measurements and found that facial traits *varied* more than other body traits, and the greatest variation occurred within the triangle formed by the eyes and mouth. They learned that facial traits vary independently of each other. For example, there is no relationship between the distance between your eyes and how big your mouth is. The researchers stated that our facial variation played an important role in human evolution. (See "Morphological and Population Genomic Evidence That Human Faces Have Evolved to Signal Individual Identity," by Sheehan and Nachman, *Nature Communications,* Vol. 5, No. 4800.)

TABLE 3-3

General Procedure for Finding Standard Deviation with Formula 3-4	Specific Example Using These Sample Values: 84, 74, 50, 60, 52
Step 1: Compute the mean $\bar{x}$.	The sum of 84, 74, 50, 60, 52 is 320; therefore: $$\bar{x} = \frac{\Sigma x}{n} = \frac{84 + 74 + 50 + 60 + 52}{5}$$ $$= \frac{320}{5} = 64.0$$
Step 2: Subtract the mean from each individual sample value. [The result is a list of deviations of the form $(x - \bar{x})$.]	Subtract the mean of 64.0 from each sample value to get these deviations away from the mean: 20, 10, −14, −4, −12.
Step 3: Square each of the deviations obtained from Step 2. [This produces numbers of the form $(x - \bar{x})^2$.]	The squares of the deviations from Step 2 are: 400, 100, 196, 16, 144.
Step 4: Add all of the squares obtained from Step 3. The result is $\Sigma(x - \bar{x})^2$.	The sum of the squares from Step 3 is 856.
Step 5: Divide the total from Step 4 by the number $n - 1$, which is 1 less than the total number of sample values present.	With $n = 5$ data values, $n - 1 = 4$, so we divide 856 by 4 to get this result: $$\frac{856}{4} = 214$$
Step 6: Find the square root of the result of Step 5. The result is the standard deviation, denoted by s.	The standard deviation is $\sqrt{214} = 14.6287$. Rounding the result, we get $s = 14.6$ BPM.

 EXAMPLE 3 Calculating Standard Deviation with Formula 3-5

Use Formula 3-5 to find the standard deviation of the first five pulse rates of males from Data Set 1 "Body Data": 84, 74, 50, 60, 52.

SOLUTION

Here are the components needed in Formula 3-5.

$n = 5$ (because there are 5 values in the sample)
$\Sigma x = 320$ (found by adding the original sample values)
$\Sigma x^2 = 21{,}336$ (found by adding the squares of the sample values, as in
    $84^2 + 74^2 + 50^2 + 60^2 + 52^2 = 21{,}336$)

Using Formula 3-5, we get

$$s = \sqrt{\frac{n(\Sigma x^2) - (\Sigma x)^2}{n(n - 1)}} = \sqrt{\frac{5(21{,}336) - (320)^2}{5(5 - 1)}} = \sqrt{\frac{4280}{20}} = 14.6 \text{ BPM}$$

The result of $s = 14.6$ BPM is the same as the result in Example 2.

Range Rule of Thumb for Understanding Standard Deviation

The *range rule of thumb* is a crude but simple tool for understanding and interpreting standard deviation. It is based on the principle that for many data sets, the vast majority (such as 95%) of sample values lie within 2 standard deviations of the mean. We could improve the accuracy of this rule by taking into account such factors as the size of the sample and the distribution, but here we sacrifice accuracy for the sake of simplicity. The concept of *significance* as given below will be enhanced in later chapters, especially those that include the topic of hypothesis tests, which are also called tests of significance. The following range rule of thumb is based on the population mean μ and the population standard deviation σ, but for large and representative samples, we could use $\bar{x}$ and s instead.

Range Rule of Thumb for Identifying Significant Values

Significantly low values are $\mu - 2\sigma$ or lower.

Significantly high values are $\mu + 2\sigma$ or higher.

Values not significant: Between $(\mu - 2\sigma)$ and $(\mu + 2\sigma)$

See Figure 3-3, which illustrates the above criteria.

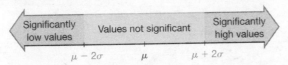

FIGURE 3-3 Range Rule of Thumb for Identifying Significant Values

Range Rule of Thumb for Estimating a Value of the Standard Deviation s

To roughly estimate the standard deviation from a collection of known sample data, use

$$ s \approx \frac{\text{range}}{4} $$

 EXAMPLE 4 Range Rule of Thumb for Interpreting s

Using the 153 pulse rates of males listed in Data Set 1 "Body Data" in Appendix B, the mean is $\bar{x} = 69.6$ BPM and the standard deviation is $s = 11.3$ BPM. Use $\bar{x}$ and s as estimates of μ and σ, and use the range rule of thumb to find the limits separating values that are significantly low or significantly high. Then determine whether a male pulse rate of 100 BPM is significantly high.

SOLUTION

With a mean of 69.6 and a standard deviation of 11.3, we use the range rule of thumb to find values that are significantly low or significantly high as follows:

Significantly low values are $(69.6 - 2 \times 11.3)$ or lower,

    so significantly low values are 47.0 BPM or lower.

Significantly high values are $(69.6 + 2 \times 11.3)$ or higher,

    so significantly high values are 92.2 BPM or higher.

Values not significant: Between 47.0 and 92.2 BPM

INTERPRETATION

Based on these results, we expect that typical pulse rates of males are between 47.0 BPM and 92.2 BPM. Because the given value of 100 BPM falls above 92.2 BPM, we consider it to be a significantly high pulse rate for a male.

EXAMPLE 5   Range Rule of Thumb for Estimating *s*

Use the range rule of thumb to estimate the standard deviation of the sample of 153 pulse rates of males listed in Data Set 1 "Body Data" in Appendix B. Those 153 values have a minimum of 40 BPM and a maximum of 104 BPM.

SOLUTION

The range rule of thumb indicates that we can estimate the standard deviation by finding the range and dividing it by 4. With a minimum of 40 BPM and a maximum of 104 BPM, the range rule of thumb can be used to estimate the standard deviation *s* as follows:

$$s \approx \frac{\text{range}}{4} = \frac{104 - 40}{4} = 16.0 \text{ BPM}$$

INTERPRETATION

The actual value of the standard deviation is $s = 11.3$ BPM, so the estimate of 16.0 BPM is very roughly in the general neighborhood of the exact result. Because this estimate is based on only the minimum and maximum values, it might be off by a considerable amount.

Standard Deviation of a Population

The definition of standard deviation and Formulas 3-4 and 3-5 apply to the standard deviation of *sample* data. A slightly different formula is used to calculate the standard deviation σ (lowercase sigma) of a *population:* Instead of dividing by $n - 1$, we divide by the population size *N,* as shown here:

$$\text{Population standard deviation } \sigma = \sqrt{\frac{\Sigma (x - \mu)^2}{N}}$$

Because we generally deal with sample data, we will usually use Formula 3-4, in which we divide by $n - 1$. Many calculators give both the sample standard deviation and the population standard deviation, but they use a variety of different notations.

> **CAUTION** When using a calculator to find standard deviation, identify the notation used by your particular calculator so that you get the *sample* standard deviation, not the population standard deviation.

Variance of a Sample and a Population

So far, we have used the term *variation* as a general description of the amount that values vary among themselves. (The terms *dispersion* and *spread* are sometimes used instead of *variation.*) Unlike the term variation, the term *variance* has a specific meaning.

> **DEFINITION**
>
> The **variance** of a set of values is a measure of variation equal to the square of the standard deviation.
>
> • Sample variance: $s^2 =$ square of the standard deviation *s.*
> • Population variance: $\sigma^2 =$ square of the population standard deviation σ.

Notation Here is a summary of notation for the standard deviation and variance:

s = *sample* standard deviation

s^2 = *sample* variance

σ = *population* standard deviation

σ^2 = *population* variance

Note: Articles in professional journals and reports often use SD for standard deviation and VAR for variance.

Important Properties of Variance

- The units of the variance are the *squares* of the units of the original data values. (If the original data values are in feet, the variance will have units of ft^2; if the original data values are in seconds, the variance will have units of $\sec^2$.)

- The value of the variance can increase dramatically with the inclusion of outliers. (The variance is not *resistant*.)

- The value of the variance is never negative. It is zero only when all of the data values are the same number.

- The sample variance s^2 is an **unbiased estimator** of the population variance σ^2, as described in Part 2 of this section. (The sample standard deviation s is a *biased* estimator of the population standard deviation σ.)

The variance is a statistic used in some statistical methods, but for our present purposes, the variance has the serious disadvantage of using units that are *different than the units of the original data set.* This makes it difficult to understand variance as it relates to the original data set. Because of this property, it is better to first focus on the standard deviation when trying to develop an understanding of variation.

PART 2 Beyond the Basics of Variation

In Part 2, we focus on making sense of the standard deviation so that it is not some mysterious number devoid of any practical significance. We begin by addressing common questions that relate to the standard deviation.

Why Is Standard Deviation Defined as in Formula 3-4?

In measuring variation in a set of sample data, it makes sense to begin with the individual amounts by which values deviate from the mean. For a particular data value x, the amount of **deviation** is $x - \bar{x}$. It makes sense to somehow combine those deviations into one number that can serve as a measure of the variation. Adding the deviations isn't good, because the sum will always be zero. To get a statistic that measures variation, it's necessary to avoid the canceling out of negative and positive numbers. One approach is to add absolute values, as in $\Sigma|x - \bar{x}|$. If we find the mean of that sum, we get the **mean absolute deviation** (or **MAD**), which is the mean distance of the data from the mean:

$$\text{Mean absolute deviation} = \frac{\Sigma|x - \bar{x}|}{n}$$

Why Not Use the Mean Absolute Deviation Instead of the Standard Deviation? Computation of the mean absolute deviation uses absolute values, so it uses an operation that is not "algebraic." (The algebraic operations include addition, multiplication, extracting roots, and raising to powers that are integers or fractions.) The use of absolute values would be simple, but it would create algebraic difficulties in inferential methods of statistics discussed in later chapters. The standard deviation has the advantage of using only algebraic operations. Because it is based on the square root of a sum of squares, the standard deviation closely parallels distance formulas found in algebra. There are many instances where a statistical procedure is based on a similar sum of squares. Consequently, instead of using absolute values, we *square* all deviations $(x - \bar{x})$ so that they are nonnegative, and those squares are used to calculate the standard deviation.

Why Divide by $n - 1$? After finding all of the individual values of $(x - \bar{x})^2$ we combine them by finding their sum. We then divide by $n - 1$ because there are only $n - 1$ values that can assigned without constraint. With a given mean, we can use any numbers for the first $n - 1$ values, but the last value will then be automatically determined. With division by $n - 1$, sample variances s^2 tend to center around the value of the population variance σ^2; with division by n, sample variances s^2 tend to *underestimate* the value of the population variance σ^2.

Comparing Variation in Different Samples or Populations

It's a good practice to compare two sample standard deviations only when the sample means are approximately the same. When comparing variation in samples or populations with very different means, it is better to use the *coefficient of variation*. Also use the coefficient of variation to compare variation from two samples or populations with different scales or units of values, such as the comparison of variation of pulse rates of men and heights of men. (See Example 6.)

DEFINITION

The **coefficient of variation** (or **CV**) for a set of nonnegative sample or population data, expressed as a percent, describes the standard deviation relative to the mean, and is given by the following:

Sample	Population
$CV = \dfrac{s}{\bar{x}} \cdot 100\%$	$CV = \dfrac{\sigma}{\mu} \cdot 100\%$

ROUND-OFF RULE FOR THE COEFFICIENT OF VARIATION Round the coefficient of variation to one decimal place (such as 25.3%).

EXAMPLE 6   Pulse Rates and Heights

Compare the variation of the 153 male pulse rates listed in Data Set 1 "Body Data" in Appendix B and the heights of the same males. For the male pulse rates, $\bar{x} = 69.6$ BPM and $s = 11.3$ BPM; for their heights, $\bar{x} = 174.12$ cm and $s = 7.10$ cm. Note that we want to compare variation among *pulse rates* to variation among *heights*.

SOLUTION

We can compare the standard deviations if the same scales and units are used and the two means are approximately equal, but here we have different scales and different units of measurement, so we use the coefficients of variation:

Male Pulse Rates: $CV = \dfrac{s}{\bar{x}} \cdot 100\% = \dfrac{11.3 \text{ BPM}}{69.6 \text{ BPM}} \cdot 100\% = 16.2\%$

Male Heights: $CV = \dfrac{s}{\bar{x}} \cdot 100\% = \dfrac{7.10 \text{ cm}}{174.12 \text{ cm}} \cdot 100\% = 4.1\%$

We can now see that the male pulse rates (with $CV = 16.2\%$) vary more than male heights (with $CV = 4.1\%$).

Biased and Unbiased Estimators

The sample standard deviation s is a **biased estimator** of the population standard deviation σ, which means that values of the sample standard deviation s do *not* tend to center around the value of the population standard deviation σ. While individual values of s could equal or exceed σ, values of s generally tend to *underestimate* the value of σ. For example, consider an IQ test designed so that the population standard deviation is 15. If you repeat the process of randomly selecting 100 subjects, giving them IQ tests, and calculating the sample standard deviation s in each case, the sample standard deviations that you get will tend to be less than 15, which is the population standard deviation. There is no correction that allows us to fix the bias for all distributions of data. There is a correction that allows us to fix the bias for normally distributed populations, but it is rarely used because it is too complex and makes relatively minor corrections.

The sample variance s^2 is an **unbiased estimator** of the population variance σ^2, which means that values of s^2 tend to center around the value of σ^2 instead of systematically tending to overestimate or underestimate σ^2. Consider an IQ test designed so that the population variance is 225. If you repeat the process of randomly selecting 100 subjects, giving them IQ tests, and calculating the sample variance s^2 in each case, the sample variances that you obtain will tend to center around 225, which is the population variance.

Biased estimators and unbiased estimators will be discussed more in Section 6-3.

TECH CENTER

Measures of Variation
Access tech instructions, videos, and data sets at **www.TriolaStats.com**

3-2 Basic Skills and Concepts

Statistical Literacy and Critical Thinking

1. Range Rule of Thumb for Estimating s The 20 brain areas (cm^2) from Data Set 9 "IQ and Brain Size" in Appendix B vary from a low of 1684.89 cm^2 to a high of 2264.25 cm^2. Use the range rule of thumb to estimate the standard deviation s and compare the result to the exact standard deviation of 174.8 cm^2.

2. Range Rule of Thumb for Interpreting s The 20 brain areas (cm^2) from Data Set 9 "IQ and Brain Size" in Appendix B have a mean of 1906.3 cm^2 and a standard deviation of 174.8 cm^2. Use the range rule of thumb to identify the limits separating values that are significantly low or significantly high. For such a data, would a brain area of 1500 cm^2 be significantly low?

3. Variance The 20 subjects used in Data Set 9 "IQ and Brain Size" in Appendix B have head circumference with a standard deviation of 56.125 cm. What is the variance of their head circumference? Include the appropriate units with the result.

4. Symbols Identify the symbols used for each of the following: (a) sample standard deviation; (b) population standard deviation; (c) sample variance; (d) population variance.

In Exercises 5–20, find the **range, variance,** *and* **standard deviation** *for the given sample data. Include appropriate units (such as "minutes") in your results. (The same data were used in Section 3-1 where we found measures of center. Here we find measures of variation.) Then answer the given questions.*

5. Charges for Births Data Set 3 "Births" in Appendix B includes total charges for births at four hospitals in New York State, and the bottom 10 least amounts, (in dollars) are listed below. What do the results tell us about the population of all such charges?

> 322.00 619.50 663.50   689.00   755.00
> 800.45 844.00 945.50 1060.00 1060.00

6. MCAT Score Listed below are mean MCAT scores listed in order by year, starting with the year 2002. What important feature of the data is not revealed by any of the measures of center?

> 27.0 26.8 27.1 27.3 27.4 27.7 28.1 27.9 28.3 28.2 28.3 28.4

7. Football Player Numbers Listed below are the jersey numbers of 11 players randomly selected from the roster of the Seattle Seahawks when they won Super Bowl XLVIII. What do the results tell us?

> 89 91 55 7 20 99 25 81 19 82 60

8. Football Player Weights Listed below are the weights (lb) of 11 players randomly selected from the roster of the Seattle Seahawks when they won Super Bowl XLVIII (the same players from the preceding exercise). Are the results likely to be representative of all NFL players?

> 189 254 235 225 190 305 195 202 190 252 305

9. Peas in a Pod Biologists conducted experiments to determine whether a deficiency of carbon dioxide in the soil affects the phenotypes of peas. Listed below are the phenotype codes, where 1 = smooth-yellow, 2 = smooth-green, 3 = wrinkled-yellow, and 4 = wrinkled-green. Do the results make sense?

> 2 1 1 1 1 1 1 4 1 2 2 1 2 3 3 2 3 1 3 1 3 1 3 2 2

10. TV Prices A physician plans to buy a television for her large waiting room. Listed below are selling prices (in dollars) of TVs that are 60 inches or larger and rated as a "best buy" by *Consumer Reports* magazine. Are the resulting statistics representative of the population of all TVs that are 60 inches and larger?

> 1800 1500 1200 1500 1400 1600 1500 950 1600 1150 1500 1750

11. Cell Phone Radiation Listed below are the measured radiation absorption rates (in W/kg) corresponding to these cell phones: iPhone 5S, BlackBerry Z30, Sanyo Vero, Optimus V, Droid Razr, Nokia N97, Samsung Vibrant, Sony Z750a, Kyocera Kona, LG G2, and Virgin Mobile Supreme. The data are from the Federal Communications Commission. If one of each model of cell phone is measured for radiation and the results are used to find the measures of variation, are the results typical of the population of cell phones that are in use?

> 1.18 1.41 1.49 1.04 1.45 0.74 0.89 1.42 1.45 0.51 1.38

12. Caffeine in Soft Drinks Listed below are measured amounts of caffeine (mg per 12 oz of drink) obtained in one can from each of 20 brands (7-UP, A&W Root Beer, Cherry Coke, . . . , Tab). Are the statistics representative of the population of all cans of the same 20 brands consumed by Americans?

       0 0 34 34 34 45 41 51 55 36 47 41 0 0 53 54 38 0 41 47

13. Firefighter Fatalities Listed below are the number of heroic firefighters who suffered major injuries in the United Kingdom each year while fighting fires. The numbers are listed in order by year, starting with the year 2004. What important feature of the data is not revealed by any of the measures of variation?

       129 111 133 127 108 106 112 75 171

14. Foot Lengths Listed below are foot lengths in inches of randomly selected Army women measured in the 1988 Anthropometric Survey (ANSUR). Are the statistics representative of the current population of all Army women?

       10.4 9.3 9.1 9.3 10.0 9.4 8.6 9.8 9.9 9.1 9.1

15. Medical School Tuition Listed below in dollars are the annual costs of tuition at the 10 most expensive private medical schools in the United States for a recent year (based on data from *U.S. News & World Report*). What does this "top 10" list tell us about those costs for the population of all U.S. private medical school tuitions?

  57,261 56,784 55,196 54,976 54,653 54,528 54,268 54,050 53,581 53,323

16. California Smokers In the California Health Interview Survey, randomly selected adults are interviewed. One of the questions asks how many cigarettes are smoked per day, and results are listed below for 50 randomly selected respondents. How well do the results reflect the smoking behavior of California adults?

      9 10 10 20 40 50   (Plus 44 other values that are all 0)

In Exercises 17–20, find the **coefficient of variation** *for each of the two samples; then compare the variation. (The same data were used in Section 3-1.)*

17. Blood Pressure A sample of blood pressure measurements is taken from Data Set 1 "Body Data" in Appendix B, and those values (mm Hg) are listed below. The values are matched so that 10 subjects each have systolic and diastolic measurements.

Systolic:	136	94	118	146	106	106	120	106	118	144
Diastolic:	82	58	80	68	64	64	66	72	64	98

18. Weight/Height Measurement Listed below are weights (in kg) and heights (in cm) from different subject (from Data Set 1 "Body data" in Appendix B). The values are matched so that each of the 12 subjects has a weight measurement and a height measurement. Are the measures of center the best statistics to use with these data? What else might be better?

Weight:	98.6	96.9	108.2	73.1	83.1	86.5	64.1	79.2	64.2	118.8	71.3	98.2
Height:	172.0	186.0	154.4	160.5	179	166.7	178.5	155.7	157.6	180.4	166.3	168.6

19. Weight measurement Listed below are weight measurements (kg) of males and females (from Data Set 1 "Body Data" in Appendix B). Do they appear to be different?

Female:	54.4	55.6	57.8	57.8	60.5	64.0	64.2	66.5	67.1	69.8	70.9	71.5
Male:	59.5	64.1	71.3	71.7	72.3	73.1	75.3	75.9	76.5	78.5	81.3	83.1

20. Queues A Providence Hospital experiment involves two different waiting line configurations for patients arriving for admission. The waiting times (in seconds) are recorded with a single line configuration that feeds four stations and another configuration with individual lines at the four stations.

Single Line	390	396	402	408	426	438	444	462	462	462
Individual Lines	252	324	348	372	402	462	462	510	558	600

Large Data Sets from Appendix B. *In Exercises 21–24, refer to the indicated data set in Appendix B. Use software or a calculator to find the range, variance, and standard deviation. Express answers using appropriate units, such as "minutes."*

21. HDL Use the HDL cholesterol measurements (mg/dL) from the 300 subjects included in Data Set 1 "Body Data" in Appendix B. Identify the highest value. Does it appear to be an outlier? Do the measures of variation change much when that highest value is deleted?

22. LDL Repeat the preceding exercise using the LDL measurements (mg/dL).

23. Body Temperatures Refer to Data Set 2 "Body Temperatures" in Appendix B and use the body temperatures for 12:00 AM on day 2.

24. Births Use the birth weights (grams) of the 400 babies listed in Data Set 3 "Births" in Appendix B. Examine the list of birth weights to make an observation about those numbers. How does that observation affect the way that the results should be rounded?

Estimating Standard Deviation with the Range Rule of Thumb. *In Exercises 25–28, refer to the data in the indicated exercise. After finding the range of the data, use the range rule of thumb to estimate the value of the standard deviation. Compare the result to the standard deviation computed with all of the data.*

25. HDL Exercise 21

26. LDL Exercise 22

27. Body Temperatures Exercise 23

28. Births Exercise 24

Identifying Significant Values with the Range Rule of Thumb. *In Exercises 29–32, use the range rule of thumb to identify the limits separating values that are significantly low or significantly high.*

29. Pulse Rates of Females Based on Data Set 1 "Body Data" in Appendix B, females have pulse rates with a mean of 74.0 beats per minute and a standard deviation of 12.5 beats per minute. Is a female pulse rate of 44 beats per minute significantly low or significantly high? (All of these pulse rates are measured at rest.)

30. Pulse Rates of Males Based on Data Set 1 "Body Data" in Appendix B, males have pulse rates with a mean of 69.6 beats per minute and a standard deviation of 11.3 beats per minute. Is a male pulse rate of 50 beats per minute significantly low or significantly high? (All of these pulse rates are measured at rest.) Explain.

31. Foot Lengths Based on Data Set 7 "Foot and Height" in Appendix B, adult males have foot lengths with a mean of 27.32 cm and a standard deviation of 1.29 cm. Is the adult male foot length of 30 cm significantly low or significantly high? Explain.

32. Body Temperatures Based on Data Set 2 "Body Temperatures" in Appendix B, body temperatures of adults have a mean of 98.20°F and a standard deviation of 0.62°F. Is an adult body temperature of 100°F significantly low or significantly high?

Finding Standard Deviation from a Frequency Distribution.   *In Exercises 33 and 34, refer to the frequency distribution in the given exercise and find the standard deviation by using the formula below, where x represents the class midpoint, f represents the class frequency, and n represents the total number of sample values. Also, compare the computed standard deviations to these standard deviations obtained by using Formula 3-4 with the original list of data values: (Exercise 33) 59.5; (Exercise 34) 65.4.*

$$s = \sqrt{\frac{n\left[\Sigma\left(f \cdot x^2\right)\right] - \left[\Sigma\left(f \cdot x\right)\right]^2}{n(n-1)}}$$

33.

Blood Platelet Count of Males	Frequency
0–99	1
100–199	51
200–299	90
300–399	10
400–499	0
500–599	0
600–699	1

34.

Blood Platelet Count of Females	Frequency
100–199	25
200–299	92
300–399	28
400–499	0
500–599	2

3-2   Beyond the Basics

35. Why Divide by n − 1? Let a *population* consist of these values: 9 cigarettes, 10 cigarettes, and 20 cigarettes smoked in a day (based on data from the California Health Interview Survey). Assume that samples of two values are randomly selected *with replacement* from this population. (That is, a selected value is replaced before the second selection is made.)

a. Find the variance σ^2 of the population {9 cigarettes, 10 cigarettes, 20 cigarettes}.

b. After listing the nine different possible samples of two values selected with replacement, find the sample variance s^2 (which includes division by $n - 1$) for each of them; then find the mean of the nine sample variances s^2.

c. For each of the nine different possible samples of two values selected with replacement, find the variance by treating each sample as if it is a population (using the formula for population variance, which includes division by n); then find the mean of those nine population variances.

d. Which approach results in values that are better estimates of σ^2: part (b) or part (c)? Why? When computing variances of samples, should you use division by n or $n - 1$?

e. The preceding parts show that s^2 is an unbiased estimator of σ^2. Is s an unbiased estimator of σ? Explain.

36. Mean Absolute Deviation Use the same population of {9 cigarettes, 10 cigarettes, 20 cigarettes} from Exercise 35. Show that when samples of size 2 are randomly selected with replacement, the samples have mean absolute deviations that do not center about the value of the mean absolute deviation of the population. What does this indicate about a sample mean absolute deviation being used as an estimator of the mean absolute deviation of a population?

3-3 Measures of Relative Standing and Boxplots

Key Concept This section introduces measures of relative standing, which are numbers showing the location of data values relative to the other values within the same data set. The most important concept in this section is the z score, which will be used often in following chapters. We also discuss percentiles and quartiles, which are common statistics, as well as another statistical graph called a boxplot.

PART 1   Basics of z Scores, Percentiles, Quartiles, and Boxplots

z Scores

A z score is found by converting a value to a standardized scale, as given in the following definition. This definition shows that a z score is the number of standard deviations that a data value is away from the mean. The z score is used often in Chapter 6 and later chapters.

DEFINITION

A **z score** (or **standard score** or **standardized value**) is the number of standard deviations that a given value x is above or below the mean. The z score is calculated by using one of the following:

Sample		Population
$z = \dfrac{x - \bar{x}}{s}$	or	$z = \dfrac{x - \mu}{\sigma}$

ROUND-OFF RULE FOR z SCORES Round z scores to two decimal places (such as 2.31).

This round-off rule is motivated by the format of standard tables in which z scores are expressed with two decimal places, as in Table A-2 in Appendix A. Example 1 illustrates how z scores can be used to compare values, even if they come from different populations.

Important Properties of z Scores

1. A z score is the number of standard deviations that a given value x is above or below the mean.

2. z Scores are expressed as numbers with no units of measurement.

3. A data value is *significantly low* if its z score is less than or equal to -2 or the value is *significantly high* if its z score is greater than or equal to $+2$.

4. If an individual data value is less than the mean, its corresponding z score is a negative number.

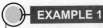 **EXAMPLE 1** **Comparing a Baby's Weight and Adult Body Temperature**

Which of the following two data values is more extreme relative to the data set from which it came?

- The 4000 g weight of a newborn baby (among 400 weights with sample mean $\bar{x} = 3152.0$ g and sample standard deviation $s = 693.4$ g)

- The 99°F temperature of an adult (among 106 adults with sample mean $\bar{x} = 98.20$°F and sample standard deviation $s = 0.62$°F)

SOLUTION

The 4000 g weight and the 99°F body temperature can be standardized by converting each of them to z scores as shown below.

4000 g birth weight:

$$z = \frac{x - \bar{x}}{s} = \frac{4000 \text{ g} - 3152.0 \text{ g}}{693.4 \text{ g}} = 1.22$$

99°F body temperature:

$$z = \frac{x - \bar{x}}{s} = \frac{99°\text{F} - 98.20°\text{F}}{0.62°\text{F}} = 1.29$$

INTERPRETATION

The z scores show that the 4000 g birth weight is 1.22 standard deviations above the mean, and the 99°F body temperature is 1.29 standard deviations above the mean. Because the body temperature is farther above the mean, it is the more extreme value, but not by much. A 99°F body temperature is slightly more extreme than a birth weight of 4000 g.

Using z Scores to Identify Significant Values In Section 3-2 we used the range rule of thumb to conclude that a value is significantly low or significantly high if it is at least 2 standard deviations away from the mean. It follows that significantly low values have z scores less than or equal to -2 and significantly high values have z scores greater than or equal to $+2$, as illustrated in Figure 3-4. Using this criterion with the two individual values used in Example 1 above, we see that neither value is significant because both z scores are between -2 and $+2$.

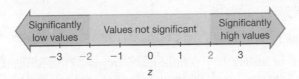

FIGURE 3-4 Interpreting z Scores
Significant values are those with z scores ≤ -2.00 or ≥ 2.00.

Detecting Phony Data

A class is given the homework assignment of recording the results when a coin is tossed 500 times. One dishonest student decides to save time by just making up the results instead of actually flipping a coin. Because people generally cannot make up results that are really random, we can often identify such phony data. With 500 tosses of an actual coin, it is extremely likely that you will get a run of six heads or six tails, but people almost never include such a run when they make up results.

Another way to detect fabricated data is to establish that the results violate Benford's law: For many collections of data, the leading digits are not uniformly distributed. Instead, the leading digits of 1, 2,..., 9 occur with rates of 30%, 18%, 12%, 10%, 8%, 7%, 6%, 5%, and 5%, respectively. (See "The Difficulty of Faking Data," by Theodore Hill, *Chance*, Vol. 12, No. 3.)

EXAMPLE 2 Is a Platelet Count of 75 Significantly Low?

The lowest platelet count in Data Set 1 "Body Data" in Appendix B is 75. (The platelet counts are measured in 1000 cells/μL). Is that value significantly low? Based on the platelet counts from Data Set 1 in Appendix B, assume that platelet counts have a mean of $\bar{x} = 239.4$ and a standard deviation of $s = 64.2$.

SOLUTION

The platelet count of 75 is converted to a z score as shown below:

$$z = \frac{x - \bar{x}}{s} = \frac{75 - 239.4}{64.2} = -2.56$$

INTERPRETATION

The platelet count of 75 converts to the z score of -2.56. Refer to Figure 3-4 to see that $z = -2.56$ is less than -2, so the platelet count of 75 is significantly low. (Low platelet counts are called thrombocytopenia. What a wonderful name.)

A z score is a measure of position, in the sense that it describes the location of a value (in terms of standard deviations) relative to the mean. Percentiles and quartiles are other measures of position useful for comparing values within the same data set or between different sets of data.

Percentiles

Percentiles are one type of *quantiles*—or *fractiles*—which partition data into groups with roughly the same number of values in each group.

DEFINITION

Percentiles are measures of location, denoted $P_1, P_2, \ldots, P_{99}$, which divide a set of data into 100 groups with about 1% of the values in each group.

The 50th percentile, denoted P_{50}, has about 50% of the data values below it and about 50% of the data values above it, so the 50th percentile is the same as the median. There is not universal agreement on a single procedure for calculating percentiles, but we will describe relatively simple procedures for (1) finding the percentile of a data value and (2) converting a percentile to its corresponding data value. We begin with the first procedure.

Finding the Percentile of a Data Value

The process of finding the percentile that corresponds to a particular data value x is given by the following (round the result to the nearest whole number):

$$\text{Percentile of value } x = \frac{\text{number of values less than } x}{\text{total number of values}} \cdot 100$$

EXAMPLE 3 **Finding a Percentile**

Table 3-4 lists the 40 cotinine measures (ng/mL) of smokers from Data Set 14 "Passive and Active Smoke" in Appendix B, and they are listed in order. Find the percentile for the cotinine level of 198 ng/mL.

TABLE 3-4 *Sorted* Cotinine Measures of Smokers

0	1	1	3	17	32	35	44	48	86
87	103	112	121	123	130	131	149	164	167
173	173	198	208	210	222	227	234	245	250
253	265	266	277	284	289	290	313	477	491

SOLUTION

From the sorted list of cotinine levels in Table 3-4, we see that there are 22 values less than 198 ng/mL, so

$$\text{Percentile of 198 ng/mL} = \frac{22}{40} \cdot 100 = 55$$

INTERPRETATION

A cotinine level of 198 ng/mL is in the 55th percentile. This can be interpreted loosely as this: A cotinine level of 198 ng/mL separates the lowest 55% of values from the highest 45% of values. We have $P_{55} = 198$ ng/mL.

Example 3 shows how to convert from a given sample value to the corresponding percentile. There are several different methods for the reverse procedure of converting a given percentile to the corresponding value in the data set. The procedure we will use is summarized in Figure 3-5 on the next page, which uses the following notation.

Notation

n total number of values in the data set

k percentile being used (Example: For the 25th percentile, $k = 25$.)

L locator that gives the *position* of a value (Example: For the 12th value in the sorted list, $L = 12$.)

P_k kth percentile (Example: P_{25} is the 25th percentile.)

EXAMPLE 4 **Converting a Percentile to a Data Value**

Refer to the sorted cotinine levels of smokers in Table 3-4 and use the procedure in Figure 3-5 to find the value of the 33rd percentile, P_{33}.

continued

SOLUTION

From Figure 3-5, we see that the sample data are already sorted, so we can proceed to find the value of the locator L. In this computation we use $k = 33$ because we are trying to find the value of the 33rd percentile. We use $n = 40$ because there are 40 data values.

$$L = \frac{k}{100} \cdot n = \frac{33}{100} \cdot 40 = 13.2$$

Since $L = 13.2$ is not a whole number, we proceed to the next lower box in Figure 3-5 where we change L by rounding it up from 13.2 to the next larger whole number: 14. (In this book we typically round off the usual way, but this is one of two cases where we round *up* instead of rounding *off*.) From the bottom box we see that the value of P_{33} is the 14th value, counting from the lowest. In Table 3-4, the 14th value is 121. That is, $P_{33} = 121$ ng/mL. Roughly speaking, about 33% of the cotinine levels in Table 3-4 are less than 121 ng/mL and 67% of them are more than 121 ng/mL.

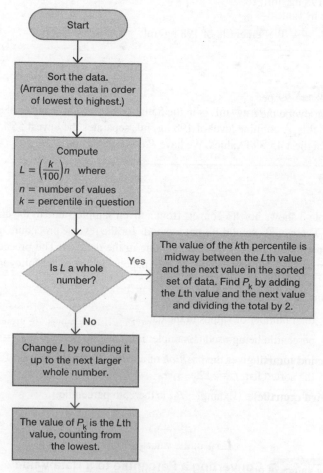

FIGURE 3-5   Converting from the *k*th percentile to the corresponding data value

EXAMPLE 5 Converting a Percentile to a Data Value

Refer to the sorted pulse rates in Table 3-4. Use Figure 3-5 to find the 25th percentile, denoted by P_{25}.

SOLUTION

Referring to Figure 3-5, we see that the sample data are already sorted, so we can proceed to compute the value of the locator L. In this case, we use $k = 25$ because we are attempting to find the value of the 25th percentile, and we use $n = 40$ because there are 40 data values.

$$L = \frac{k}{100} \cdot n = \frac{25}{100} \cdot 40 = 10$$

Since $L = 10$ is a whole number, we proceed to the box in Figure 3-5 located at the right. We now see that the value of the 25th percentile is midway between the Lth (10th) value and the next higher value in the original set of data. That is, the value of the 25th percentile is midway between the 10th value and the 11th value. The 10th value in Table 3-4 is 86 and the 11th value is 87, so the value midway between them is 86.5 ng/mL. We conclude that the 25th percentile is $P_{25} = 86.5$ ng/mL.

Quartiles

Just as there are 99 percentiles that divide the data into 100 groups, there are three quartiles that divide the data into four groups.

DEFINITION

Quartiles are measures of location, denoted Q_1, Q_2, and Q_3, which divide a set of data into four groups with about 25% of the values in each group.

Here are descriptions of quartiles that are more accurate than those given in the preceding definition:

Q_1 **(First quartile):**	Same value as P_{25}. It separates the bottom 25% of the sorted values from the top 75%. (To be more precise, at least 25% of the sorted values are less than or equal to Q_1, and at least 75% of the values are greater than or equal to Q_1.)	$Q_1 = P_{25}$
Q_2 **(Second quartile):**	Same as P_{50} and same as the median. It separates the bottom 50% of the sorted values from the top 50%.	$Q_2 = P_{50}$
Q_3 **(Third quartile):**	Same as P_{75}. It separates the bottom 75% of the sorted values from the top 25%. (To be more precise, at least 75% of the sorted values are less than or equal to Q_3, and at least 25% of the values are greater than or equal to Q_3.)	$Q_3 = P_{75}$

Finding values of quartiles can be accomplished with the same procedure used for finding percentiles. Simply use the relationships shown in the margin. In Example 4 we found that $P_{25} = 86.5$ ng/mL, so it follows that $Q_1 = 86.5$ ng/mL.

CAUTION Just as there is not universal agreement on a procedure for finding percentiles, there is not universal agreement on a single procedure for calculating quartiles, and different technologies often yield different results. If you use a calculator or software for exercises involving quartiles, you may get results that differ somewhat from the answers obtained by using the procedures described here.

In earlier sections of this chapter we described several statistics, including the mean, median, mode, range, and standard deviation. Some other statistics are defined using quartiles and percentiles, as in the following:

Interquartile range (or IQR) $= Q_3 - Q_1$

Semi-interquartile range $= \dfrac{Q_3 - Q_1}{2}$

Midquartile $= \dfrac{Q_3 + Q_1}{2}$

10–90 percentile range $= P_{90} - P_{10}$

5-Number Summary and Boxplot

The values of the minimum, maximum and three quartiles (Q_1, Q_2, Q_3) are used for the 5-number summary and the construction of boxplot graphs.

DEFINITION

For a set of data, the **5-number summary** consists of these five values:

1. Minimum
2. First quartile, Q_1
3. Second quartile, Q_2 (same as the median)
4. Third quartile, Q_3
5. Maximum

EXAMPLE 6 Finding a 5-Number Summary

Use the cotinine measurements in Table 3-4 to find the 5-number summary.

SOLUTION

Because the cotinine measurements in Table 3-4 are sorted, it is easy to see that the minimum is 0 ng/mL and the maximum is 491 ng/mL. The value of the first quartile is $Q_1 = 86.5$ ng/mL (from Example 5). The median is equal to Q_2, and it is 170.0 ng/mL. Also, we can find that $Q_3 = 251.5$ ng/mL by using the procedure for finding P_{75} (as summarized in Figure 3-5). The 5-number summary is therefore 0, 86.5, 170.0, 251.5, and 491 (all in units of ng/mL).

DEFINITION

A **boxplot** (or **box-and-whisker diagram**) is a graph of a data set that consists of a line extending from the minimum value to the maximum value, and a box with lines drawn at the first quartile Q_1, the median, and the third quartile Q_3. (See Figure 3-6.)

Procedure for Constructing a Boxplot

1. Find the 5-number summary (minimum value, Q_1, Q_2, Q_3, maximum value).

2. Construct a line segment extending from the minimum data value to the maximum data value.

3. Construct a box (rectangle) extending from Q_1 to Q_3, and draw a line in the box at the value of Q_2 (median).

> **CAUTION** Because there is not universal agreement on procedures for finding quartiles, and because boxplots are based on quartiles, different technologies may yield different boxplots.

EXAMPLE 7 Constructing a Boxplot

Use the cotinine measurements listed in Table 3-4 to construct a boxplot.

SOLUTION

The boxplot uses the 5-number summary found in Example 6: 0, 86.5, 170.0, 251.5, and 491 (all in units of ng/mL). Figure 3-6 is the boxplot representing the cotinine measurements listed in Table 3-4.

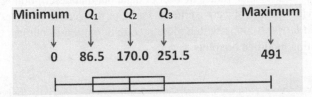

FIGURE 3-6   Boxplot of Cotinine Measurements (ng/mL)

Skewness A boxplot can often be used to identify skewness (discussed in Section 2-2). The boxplot in Figure 3-6 isn't exactly symmetric; it shows that the data are slightly skewed to the right.

Because the shape of a boxplot is determined by the five values from the 5-number summary, a boxplot is not a graph of the distribution of the data, and it doesn't show as much detailed information as a histogram or stemplot. However, boxplots are often great for comparing two or more data sets. When using two or more boxplots for comparing different data sets, graph the boxplots on the same scale so that comparisons can be easily made. Methods discussed later in this book allow us to analyze comparisons of data sets more formally than subjective conclusions based on a graph. It is always wise to construct suitable graphs, such as histograms, dotplots, and boxplots, but we should not rely solely on subjective judgments based on graphs.

EXAMPLE 8 Comparing the Pulse Rates of Men and Women

The Chapter Problem involves pulse rates of men and women, and the data are found in Data Set 1 "Body Data" in Appendix B. Construct boxplots of those two different sets of pulse rates.

continued

SOLUTION

The Statdisk-generated boxplots are shown in Figure 3-7. The three quartiles for males are all lower than the corresponding three quartiles for females, which suggests that males generally have lower pulse rates than females. The minimums and maximums are not very different in the two boxplots, and we shouldn't place too much importance on those differences because they are not very reliable measures.

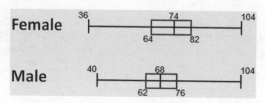

FIGURE 3-7   **Boxplots of Pulse Rates of Men and Women**

Outliers

When analyzing data, it is important to identify and consider outliers because they can strongly affect values of some important statistics (such as the mean and standard deviation), and they can also strongly affect important methods discussed later in this book. In Chapter 2 we described outliers as sample values that lie very far away from the vast majority of the other values in a set of data, but that description is vague and it does not provide specific objective criteria. Part 2 of this section includes a description of *modified boxplots* along with a more precise definition of outliers used in the context of creating modified boxplots.

CAUTION When analyzing data, always identify outliers and consider their effects, which can be substantial.

PART 2   Outliers and Modified Boxplots

We noted that the description of outliers is somewhat vague, but for the purposes of constructing *modified boxplots*, we can consider outliers to be data values meeting specific criteria based on quartiles and the interquartile range. (The interquartile range is often denoted by IQR, and IQR = $Q_3 - Q_1$.)

Identifying Outliers for Modified Boxplots

1. Find the quartiles Q_1, Q_2, and Q_3.
2. Find the interquartile range (IQR), where IQR = $Q_3 - Q_1$.
3. Evaluate $1.5 \times$ IQR.
4. **In a modified boxplot, a data value is an *outlier* if it is**

    above Q_3, by an amount greater than $1.5 \times$ IQR

    or   **below Q_1, by an amount greater than $1.5 \times$ IQR**

Modified Boxplots

The boxplots described earlier in Part 1 are called **skeletal** (or **regular**) **boxplots,** but some statistical software packages provide modified boxplots, which represent outliers as special points. A **modified boxplot** is a regular boxplot constructed with these modifications: (1) A special symbol (such as an asterisk or point) is used to identify outliers as defined above, and (2) the solid horizontal line extends only as far as the minimum data value that is not an outlier and the maximum data value that is not an outlier. (*Note:* Exercises involving modified boxplots are found in the "Beyond the Basics" exercises only.)

EXAMPLE 9 **Constructing Modified Boxplots**

Use the pulse rates of males in Data Set 1 "Body Data" from Appendix B to construct a modified boxplot. The five-number summary is 40, 62.0, 68.0, 76.0, 104 (all in BPM).

SOLUTION

Let's begin with the four steps for identifying outliers in a modified boxplot.

1. Using the pulse rates of males, the three quartiles are $Q_1 = 62.0$, the median is $Q_2 = 68.0$, and $Q_3 = 76.0$.
2. The interquartile range is IQR $= Q_3 - Q_1 = 76.0 - 62.0 = 14.0$.
3. $1.5 \times$ IQR $= 1.5 \times 14.0 = 21.0$.
4. Any outliers are

   - Greater than $Q_3 = 76.0$ by more than 21.0 or
   - Less than $Q_1 = 62.0$ by more than 21.0.

This means that any outliers are *greater than 97.0* or *less than 41.0*. We can now examine the original pulse rates of males to identify any that are greater than 97.0 or less than 41.0. We find that the pulse rates of 102 and 104 are greater than 97.0, and the pulse rate of 40 is less than 41.0. The outliers are 102, 104, and 40.

We can now construct the modified boxplot shown in Figure 3-8. In Figure 3-8, the three outliers (40, 102, 104) are identified as special points, the three quartiles (62.0, 68.0, 76.0) are shown as in a regular boxplot, and the horizontal line extends from the lowest data value that is not an outlier (42) to the highest data value that is not an outlier (96).

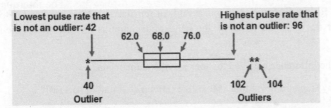

FIGURE 3-8 **Modified Boxplot of Male Pulse Rates (BPM)**

CAUTION Because there is not universal agreement on procedures for finding quartiles, and because modified boxplots are based on quartiles, different technologies may yield different modified boxplots.

3-3 Basic Skills and Concepts

Statistical Literacy and Critical Thinking

1. z Scores LeBron James, one of the most successful basketball players of all time, has a height of 6 feet 8 inches, or 203 cm. Based on statistics from Data Set 1 "Body Data" in Appendix B, his height converts to the z score of 4.07. How many standard deviations is his height above the mean?

2. Heights The boxplot shown below results from the heights (cm) of males listed in Data Set 1 "Body Data" in Appendix B. What do the numbers in that boxplot tell us?

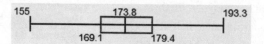

3. Boxplot Comparison Refer to the boxplots shown below that are drawn on the same scale. One boxplot represents weights of men and the other boxplot represents weights of women. Which boxplot represents weights of women? Explain.

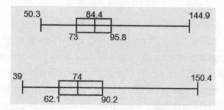

4. z Scores If your score on your next statistics test is converted to a z score, which of these z scores would you prefer: $-2.00, -1.00, 0, 1.00, 2.00$? Why?

z Scores. *In Exercises 5–8, express all z scores with two decimal places.*

5. Female Pulse Rates For the pulse rates of females listed in Data Set 1 "Body Data" in Appendix B, the mean is 74.0 BPM, the standard deviation is 12.5 BPM, and the maximum is 104 BPM.

a. What is the difference between the maximum and the mean?

b. How many standard deviations is that [the difference found in part (a)]?

c. Convert the maximum pulse rate to a z score.

d. If we consider pulse rates that convert to z scores between -2 and 2 to be neither significantly low nor significantly high, is the maximum pulse rate significant?

6. Female Pulse Rates For the pulse rates of females listed in Data Set 1 "Body Data" in Appendix B, the mean is 74.0 BPM, the standard deviation is 12.5 BPM, and the minimum is 36 BPM.

a. What is the difference between the minimum and the mean?

b. How many standard deviations is that [the difference found in part (a)]?

c. Convert the minimum pulse rate to a z score.

d. If we consider pulse rates that convert to z scores between -2 and 2 to be neither significantly low nor significantly high, is the minimum pulse rate significantly low or significantly high?

7. Body Temperatures For the body temperatures at 12 AM on day 2 (listed in Data Set 2 "Body Temperatures" in Appendix B), the mean is 98.20°F, the standard deviation is 0.62°F, and the minimum is 96.5°F.

a. What is the difference between the minimum and the mean?

b. How many standard deviations is that [the difference found in part (a)]?

c. Convert the minimum temperature to a z score.

d. If we consider body temperatures that convert to z scores between -2 and 2 to be neither significantly low nor significantly high, is the minimum body temperature significant?

8. Body Temperatures For the body temperatures at 12 AM on day 2 (listed in Data Set 2 "Body Temperatures" in Appendix B), the mean is 98.20°F, the standard deviation is 0.62°F, and $Q_3 = 98.60$°F.

a. What is the difference between Q_3 and the mean?

b. How many standard deviations is that [the difference found in part (a)]?

c. Convert Q_3 to a z score.

d. If we consider temperatures that convert to z scores between -2 and 2 to be neither significantly low nor significantly high, is Q_3 significant?

Significant Values.   *In Exercises 9–12, consider a value to be significantly low if its z score is less than or equal to -2 or consider the value to be significantly high if its z score is greater than or equal to 2.*

9. ACT The ACT test is used to assess readiness for college. In a recent year, the mean ACT score was 21.1 and the standard deviation was 5.1. Identify the ACT scores that are significantly low or significantly high.

10. MCAT In a recent year, scores on the MCAT had a mean of 25.2 and a standard deviation of 6.4. Identify the MCAT scores that are significantly low or significantly high.

11. Birth Weights Data Set 3 "Births" lists birth weights (g) of 400 babies. Those weights have a mean of 3152.0 g and a standard deviation of 693.4 g. Identify birth weights that are significantly low or significantly high.

12. Ergonomics in Aircraft Seats In the process of designing aircraft seats, it was found that men have hip breadths with a mean of 36.6 cm and a standard deviation of 2.5 cm (based on anthropometric survey data from Gordon, Clauser, et al.). Identify the hip breadths of men that are significantly low or significantly high.

Comparing Values.   *In Exercises 13–16, use z scores to compare the given values.*

13. Tallest and Shortest Men The tallest living man at the time of this writing is Sultan Kosen, who has a height of 251 cm. The shortest living man is Chandra Bahadur Dangi, who has a height of 54.6 cm. Heights of men have a mean of 174.12 cm and a standard deviation of 7.10 cm. Which of these two men has the height that is more extreme?

14. Red Blood Cell Counts Based on Data Set 1 "Body Data" in Appendix B, males have red blood cell counts with a mean of 4.719 and a standard deviation of 0.490, while females have red blood cell counts with a mean of 4.349 and a standard deviation of 0.402. Who has the higher count relative to the sample from which it came: a male with a count of 5.58 or a female with a count of 5.23? Explain.

15. Birth Weights Based on Data Set 3 "Births" in Appendix B, newborn males have weights with a mean of 3272.8 g and a standard deviation of 660.2 g. Newborn females have weights with a mean of 3037.1 g and a standard deviation of 706.3 g. Who has the weight that is more

continued

extreme relative to the group from which they came: a male who weighs 1500 g or a female who weighs 1500 g? Who has the larger weight relative to the group from which they came?

16. Oscars In the 87th Academy Awards, Eddie Redmayne won for best actor at the age of 33 and Julianne Moore won for best actress at the age of 54. For all best actors, the mean age is 44.1 years and the standard deviation is 8.9 years. For all best actresses, the mean age is 36.2 years and the standard deviation is 11.5 years. (All ages are determined at the time of the awards ceremony.) Relative to their genders, who had the more extreme age when winning the Oscar: Eddie Redmayne or Julianne Moore? Explain.

Percentiles.   *In Exercises 17–20, use the following weights (kg) of bears (from Data Set 11 "Bear Measurements" in Appendix B). Find the percentile corresponding to the given weight.*

26	29	34	40	46	48	60	62	64	65	76	79
80	86	90	94	105	114	116	120	125	132	140	140
144	148	150	150	154	166	166	180	182	202	202	204
204	212	220	220	236	262	270	316	332	334	348	356
360	365	416	436	446	514						

17. 114 kg   **18.** 236 kg   **19.** 166 kg   **20.** 365 kg

In Exercises 21–28, use the same list of bear weights (kg) given for Exercise 17–20. Find the indicated percentile or quartile.

21. P_{65} **22.** P_{50}

23. P_{20} **24.** P_{25}

25. Q_3 **26.** P_{70}

27. Q_1 **28.** P_{80}

Boxplots.   *In Exercises 29–32, use the given data to construct a boxplot and identify the 5-number summary.*

29. Foot Lengths The following are the foot lengths (cm) of 19 males (from Data Set 7 "Foot and Height" in Appendix B).

25.1   25.4   25.7   25.9   26.4   26.7   26.7   26.7   26.8   27.5

27.8   27.9   27.9   28.1   28.6   28.7   28.8   29.2   29.2

30. Cell Phone Radiation Listed below are the measured radiation absorption rates (in W/kg) corresponding to these cell phones: iPhone 5S, BlackBerry Z30, Sanyo Vero, Optimus V, Droid Razr, Nokia N97, Samsung Vibrant, Sony Z750a, Kyocera Kona, LG G2, and Virgin Mobile Supreme. The data are from the Federal Communications Commission.

1.18   1.41   1.49   1.04   1.45   0.74   0.89   1.42   1.45   0.51   1.38

31. Radiation in Baby Teeth Listed below are amounts of strontium-90 (in millibecquerels, or mBq) in a simple random sample of baby teeth obtained from Pennsylvania residents born after 1979 (based on data from "An Unexpected Rise in Strontium-90 in U.S. Deciduous Teeth in the 1990s," by Mangano et. al., *Science of the Total Environment*).

128   130   133   137   138   142   142   144   147   149   151   151   151   155

156   161   163   163   166   172

32. Blood Pressure Measurements Fourteen different second-year medical students at Bellevue Hospital measured the blood pressure of the same person. The systolic readings (mm Hg) are listed below.

138   130   135   140   120   125   120   130   130   144   143   140   130   150

Boxplots from Large Data Sets in Appendix B. *In Exercises 33 and 34, use the given data sets from Appendix B. Use the boxplots to compare the two data sets.*

33. BMI Use the body mass indexes (BMI) for males and use the BMI measures for females listed in Data Set 1 "Body Data."

34. Lead and IQ Use the same scale to construct boxplots for the full IQ scores (IQF) for the low lead level group and the high lead level group in Data Set 8 "IQ and Lead" in Appendix B.

3-3 Beyond the Basics

35. Outliers and Modified Boxplots Repeat Exercise 33 "BMI" using modified boxplots. Identify any outliers as defined in Part 2 of this section.

Chapter Quick Quiz

1. Sleep Mean As part of the National Health and Nutrition Examination Survey, subjects were asked how long they slept the preceding night and the following times (hours) were reported: 8, 7, 5, 7, 4, 7, 6, 7, 8, 8, 8, 6. Find the mean.

2. Sleep Median What is the median of the sample values listed in Exercise 1?

3. Sleep Mode What is the mode of the sample values listed in Exercise 1?

4. Sleep Variance The standard deviation of the sample values in Exercise 1 is 1.3 hours. What is the variance (including units)?

5. Sleep Outlier If the sleep time of 0 hours is included with the sample data given in Exercise 1, is it an outlier? Why or why not?

6. Sleep z Score A larger sample of 50 sleep times (hours) has a mean of 6.3 hours and a standard deviation of 1.4 hours. What is the z score for a sleep time of 5 hours?

7. Sleep Q_3 For a sample of 80 sleep times, approximately how many of those times are less than Q_3?

8. Sleep 5-Number Summary For a sample of 100 sleep times, give the *names* of the values that constitute the 5-number summary. (The actual values can't be identified; just give the *names* of those values.)

9. Estimating s A large sample of sleep times includes values ranging from a low of 4 hours to a high of 10 hours. Use the range rule of thumb to estimate the standard deviation.

10. Sleep Notation Consider a sample of sleep times taken from the population of all adults living in Alaska. Identify the symbols used for the sample mean, population mean, sample standard deviation, population standard deviation, sample variance, and the population variance.

Review Exercises

1. Ergonomics When designing an eye-recognition security device, engineers must consider the eye heights of standing women. (It's easy for men to bend lower, but it's more difficult for women to rise higher.) Listed below are the eye heights (in millimeters) obtained from a simple random sample of standing adult women (based on anthropometric survey data from Gordon, Churchill, et al.). Use the given eye heights to find the (a) mean; (b) median; (c) mode; (d) midrange; (e) range; (f) standard deviation; (g) variance.

1550   1642   1538   1497   1571

2. z Score Using the sample data from Exercise 1, find the z score corresponding to the eye height of 1642 mm. Is that eye height significantly low or significantly high? Why or why not?

3. ER Codes In an analysis of activities that resulted in brain injuries presenting at hospital emergency rooms (ERs), the following activities were identified by the code shown in parentheses: bicycling (12); football (14); playground (22); basketball (27); swimming (40). Find the mean of 12, 14, 22, 27, and 40. What is wrong with this result?

4. Comparing Birth Weights The birth weights of a sample of males have a mean of 3273 g and a standard deviation of 660 g. The birth weights of a sample of females have a mean of 3037 g and a standard deviation of 706 g (based on Data Set 3 "Births" in Appendix B). When considered among members of the same gender, which baby has the relatively larger birth weight: a boy with a birth weight of 3400 g or a girl with a birth weight of 3200 g? Why?

5. Effects of an Outlier Listed below are platelet counts (1000 cells/μL) from subjects included in Data Set 1 "Body Data." Identify the outlier and then comment on the effect it has on the mean and standard deviation by finding the values of those statistics with the outlier included and then with the outlier excluded.

263   206   185   246   188   191   308   262   198   253   646

6. Interpreting a Boxplot Shown below is a boxplot of a sample of 30 maximal skull breadths (mm) measured from Egyptian skulls from around 4000 B.C. What do the numbers in the boxplot represent?

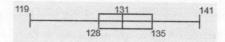

7. Interpreting Standard Deviation A physician routinely makes physical examinations of children. She is concerned that a three-year-old girl has a height of only 87.8 cm. Heights of three-year-old girls have a mean of 97.5 cm and a standard deviation of 6.9 cm (based on data from the National Health and Nutrition Examination Survey). Use the range rule of thumb to find the limits separating heights of three-year-old girls that are significantly low or significantly high. Based on the result, is the height of 87.8 cm significant? Should the physician be concerned?

8. Mean or Median? A biostatistics class consists of 30 students with no income, 10 students with small incomes from part-time jobs, plus a professor with a very large income that is well deserved. Which is better for describing the income of a typical person in this class: mean or median? Explain.

Cumulative Review Exercises

1. Arsenic in Rice Listed below are measured amounts (μg per serving) of arsenic in a sample of servings of brown rice [data from the Food and Drug Administration (FDA)]. Construct a frequency distribution. Use a class width of 2 μg, and use 0 μg as the lower class limit of the first class.

6.1   5.4   6.9   4.9   6.6   6.3   6.7   8.2   7.8   1.5   5.4   7.3

2. Histogram Use the frequency distribution from Exercise 1 to construct a histogram. Use class midpoint values for the horizontal scale.

3. Stemplot Use the amounts of arsenic from Exercise 1 to construct a stemplot.

4. Descriptive Statistics Use amounts of arsenic in Exercise 1 and find the following: (a) mean; (b) median; (c) standard deviation; (d) variance; (e) range. Include the appropriate units of measurement.

5. a. A medical researcher has a collection of data at the nominal level of measurement and she wants to obtain a representative data value. Which of the following is most appropriate: mean, median, mode, or midrange? Why?

b. A botanist wants to obtain data about the plants being grown in homes. If a sample is obtained by telephoning the first 250 people listed in the local telephone directory, what type of sampling is being used? (random, stratified, systematic, cluster, convenience)

c. A botanist is experimenting with fertilizer sticks used for growing plants. She finds that the amounts of fertilizer placed in the sticks are not very consistent, so that some fertilization lasts longer than claimed, but others don't last long enough. She wants to improve quality by making the amounts of fertilizer in the sticks more consistent. When analyzing the amounts of fertilizer for that purpose, which of the following statistics is most relevant: mean, median, mode, midrange, standard deviation, first quartile, third quartile? Should the value of that statistic be raised, lowered, or left unchanged?

Technology Project

Freshman 15 Refer to Data Set 10 "Freshman 15" in Appendix B, which includes results from a study of the legend that college freshmen tend to gain around 15 pounds (or 6.8 kilograms) during their freshman year. That data set includes 5 columns of data from 67 subjects. Use the methods of this chapter to make relevant comparisons, then form a subjective conclusion about the 15-pound (or 6.8-kilogram) weight gain. Write a brief report including your conclusions with supporting graphs and statistics.

FROM DATA TO DECISION

Second-Hand Smoke

Data Set 14 "Passive and Active Smoke" in Appendix B lists measures of cotinine from three groups of subjects: (1) smokers; (2) nonsmokers exposed to environmental tobacco smoke; and (3) nonsmokers not exposed to environmental tobacco smoke. Cotinine is an indicator of nicotine absorption.

Critical Thinking

Use the methods from this chapter to explore and compare the cotinine measures in the three groups. Are there any notable differences? Are there any outliers? What do you conclude about the effects that smokers have on nonsmokers? Write a brief report of your conclusions, and provide supporting statistical evidence.

Cooperative Group Activities

1. In-class activity In class, each student should record two pulse rates by counting the number of heartbeats in 1 minute. The first pulse rate should be measured while the student is seated, and the second pulse rate should be measured while the student is standing. Use the methods of this chapter to compare results. Do males and females appear to have different pulse rates? Do pulse rates measured while seated appear to be different from pulse rates measured while standing?

2. Out-of-class activity Appendix B includes many real and interesting data sets. In each group of three or four students, select a data set from Appendix B and analyze it using the methods discussed so far in this book. Write a brief report summarizing key conclusions.

3. Out-of-class activity In each group of three or four students, collect an original data set of values at the interval or ratio level of measurement. Provide the following: (1) a list of sample values; (2) printed software results of descriptive statistics and graphs; and (3) a written description of the nature of the data, the method of collection, and important characteristics.

4 Probability

4-1 **Basic Concepts of Probability**

4-2 **Addition Rule and Multiplication Rule**

4-3 **Complements, Conditional Probability, and Bayes' Theorem**

4-4 **Risks and Odds**

4-5 **Rates of Mortality, Fertility, and Morbidity**

4-6 **Counting**

CHAPTER PROBLEM

Drug Testing of Job Applicants

Approximately 85% of U. S. companies test employees and/or job applicants for drug use. A common and inexpensive (around $50) urine test is the EMIT (enzyme multiplied immunoassay technique) test, which tests for the presence of any of five drugs: marijuana, cocaine, amphetamines, opiates, or phencyclidine. Most companies require that positive test results be confirmed by a more reliable GC-MS (gas chromatography mass spectrometry) test.

Like nearly all medical tests, drug tests are sometimes wrong. Wrong results are of two different types: (1) false positive results and (2) false negative results. In today's society, these terms should be clearly understood. A job applicant or employee who gets a false positive result is someone who incorrectly appears to be using drugs when he or she is not actually using drugs. This type of mistake can unfairly result in job denial or termination of employment.

Analyzing the Results

Table 4-1 includes results from 555 adults in the United States. If one of the subjects from Table 4-1 is randomly selected from those who do *not* use drugs, what is the probability of a false positive result? If one of the subjects from Table 4-1 is randomly selected from those who do not use drugs, what is the probability of a true negative result? We will address such questions in this chapter.

- **Prevalence:** Proportion of the population having the condition (such as drug use or disease) being considered.

- **False positive:** *Wrong* test result that incorrectly indicates that the subject has a condition when the subject does not have that condition.

- **False negative:** *Wrong* test result that incorrectly indicates that the subject does not have a condition when the subject does have that condition.

- **True positive:** *Correct* test result that indicates that a subject has a condition when the subject does have the condition.

- **True negative:** *Correct* test result that indicates that a subject does not have a condition when the subject does not have the condition.

- **Test sensitivity:** The probability of a true positive test result, given that the subject actually has the condition being tested.

- **Test specificity:** The probability of a true negative test result, given that the subject does not have the condition being tested.

- **Positive predictive value:** Probability that a subject actually has the condition, given that the test yields a positive result (indicating that the condition is present).

- **Negative predictive value:** Probability that the subject does not actually have the condition, given that the test yields a negative result (indicating that the condition is not present).

TABLE 4-1 Results from Drug Tests of Job Applicants

	Positive Test Result (Test shows drug use.)	Negative Test Result (Test shows no drug use.)
Subject Uses Drugs	45 (True Positive)	5 (False Negative)
Subject Does Not Use Drugs	25 (False Positive)	480 (True Negative)

CHAPTER OBJECTIVES

The main objective of this chapter is to develop a sound understanding of probability values, because those values constitute the underlying foundation on which methods of inferential statistics are built. The important methods of hypothesis testing commonly use *P-values,* which are probability values expressed as numbers between 0 and 1, inclusive. Smaller probability values, such as 0.01, correspond to events that are very unlikely. Larger probability values, such as 0.99, correspond to events that are very likely. Here are the chapter objectives:

 4-1 **Basic Concepts of Probability**

- Identify probabilities as values between 0 and 1, and interpret those values as expressions of likelihood of events.

- Develop the ability to calculate probabilities of events.

- Define the *complement* of an event and calculate the probability of that complement.

Addition Rule and Multiplication Rule

- Develop the ability to calculate the probability that in a single trial, some event *A* occurs or some event *B* occurs or they both occur. Apply the addition rule by correctly adjusting for events that are not disjoint (or are overlapping).

- Develop the ability to calculate the probability of an event *A* occurring in a first trial and an event *B* occurring in a second trial. Apply the multiplication rule by adjusting for events that are not independent.

- Distinguish between independent events and dependent events.

 Complements, Conditional Probability, and Bayes' Theorem

- Compute the probability of "at least one" occurrence of an event *A*.

- Apply the multiplication rule by computing the probability of some event, given that some other event has already occurred.

 Risks and Odds

- Compare two probabilities using measures of absolute risk reduction and relative risk.

- Obtain a measure of risk by calculating the odds ratio.

- Measure the practical effectiveness of a treatment by determining the "number needed to treat," which is the number of subjects that must be treated in order to prevent one occurrence of some event.

 Rates of Mortality, Fertility, and Morbidity

- Use rates to describe the likelihood of an event.

- Determine mortality rates, fertility rates, and morbidity rates.

 Counting

- Develop the ability to apply the fundamental counting rule, factorial rule, permutations rule, and combinations rule.

- Distinguish between circumstances requiring the permutations rule and those requiring the combinations rule.

 Basic Concepts of Probability

Key Concept The single most important objective of this section is to learn how to *interpret* probability values, which are expressed as values between 0 and 1. A small probability, such as 0.001, corresponds to an event that rarely occurs.

Role of Probability in Statistics

Probability plays a central role in the important statistical method of *hypothesis testing* introduced later in Chapter 8. Statisticians make decisions using data by rejecting explanations (such as chance) based on very low *probabilities*. See the following example illustrating the role of probability and a fundamental way that statisticians think.

EXAMPLE 1 **Analyzing a Claim**

Researchers have made this claim (really, they have):

Claim: "We have developed a gender selection method that greatly increases the likelihood of a baby being a girl."

Hypothesis Used When Testing the Preceding Claim: The method of gender selection has *no effect,* so that for couples using this method, about 50% of the births result in girls.

(The probability of a girl in the United States is actually 0.488, but here we assume that boys and girls are equally likely.)

Figure 4-1 shows the sample data from two tests of 100 couples using the gender selection method and the conclusion reached for each test.

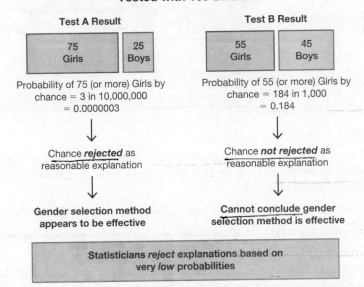

FIGURE 4-1   Gender Selection Method Test Data and Conclusions

INTERPRETATION

Among the 100 babies, 75 girls and 55 girls are both greater than the 50 girls that we typically expect, but only the event of 75 girls leads us to believe that the gender selection method is effective. Even though there is a chance of getting 75 girls (or more) in 100 births with no special treatment, the probability of that happening is so small (0.0000003) that we should reject chance as a reasonable explanation. Instead, it would be generally recognized that the results provide strong support for the claim that the gender selection method is effective. This is exactly how statisticians think: They reject explanations (such as chance) based on very low *probabilities.*

Basics of Probability

In probability, we deal with procedures (such as generating male/female births or manufacturing defective/nondefective pregnancy test kits) that produce outcomes.

Probabilities That Challenge Intuition

In certain cases, our subjective estimates of probability values are dramatically different from the actual probabilities. Here is a classical example: If you take a deep breath, there is better than a 99% chance that you will inhale a molecule that was exhaled in dying Caesar's last breath. In that same morbid and unintuitive spirit, if Socrates' fatal cup of hemlock was mostly water, then the next glass of water you drink will likely contain one of those same molecules. Here's another, less morbid example that can be verified: In classes of 25 students, there is better than a 50% chance that at least 2 students will share the same birthday (day and month).

> **DEFINITIONS**
>
> An **event** is any collection of results or outcomes of a procedure.
>
> A **simple event** is an outcome or an event that cannot be further broken down into simpler components.
>
> The **sample space** for a procedure consists of all possible *simple* events. That is, the sample space consists of all outcomes that cannot be broken down any further.

Example 2 illustrates the concepts defined above.

EXAMPLE 2   **Simple Event and Sample Spaces**

In the following display, we use "b" to denote a baby boy and "g" to denote a baby girl.

Procedure	Example of Event	Sample Space: Complete List of Simple Events
Single birth	1 girl (simple event)	{b, g}
3 births	2 boys and 1 girl (bbg, bgb, and gbb are all simple events resulting in 2 boys and 1 girl)	{bbb, bbg, bgb, bgg, gbb, gbg, ggb, ggg}

Simple Events:

- With one birth, the result of 1 girl is a *simple event* and the result of 1 boy is another simple event. They are individual simple events because they cannot be broken down any further.

- With three births, the result of 2 girls followed by a boy (ggb) is a simple event.

- When rolling a single die, the outcome of 5 is a simple event, but the outcome of an even number is not a simple event.

Not a Simple Event: With three births, the event of "2 girls and 1 boy" is *not a simple event* because it can occur with these different simple events: ggb, gbg, bgg.

Sample Space: With three births, the *sample space* consists of the eight different simple events listed in the above table.

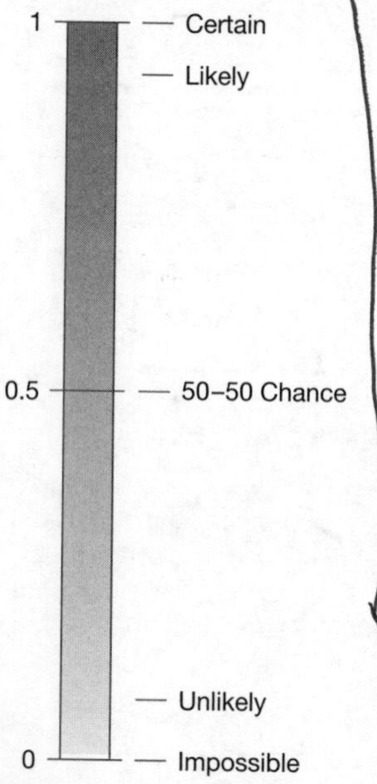

Three Common Approaches to Finding the Probability of an Event

We first list some basic notation, and then we present three common approaches to finding the probability of an event.

Notation for Probabilities

P denotes a probability.

A, B, and C denote specific events.

$P(A)$ denotes the "probability of event A occurring."

The following three approaches for finding probabilities result in values between 0 and 1: $0 \leq P(A) \leq 1$. Figure 4-2 shows the possible values of probabilities and the more familiar and common expressions of likelihood.

1 — Certain
— Likely

0.5 — 50–50 Chance

— Unlikely

0 — Impossible

FIGURE 4-2   Possible Values for Probabilities

1. **Relative Frequency Approximation of Probability** Conduct (or observe) a procedure and count the number of times that event *A* occurs. *P(A)* is then *approximated* as follows:

$$P(A) = \frac{\text{number of times } A \text{ occurred}}{\text{number of times the procedure was repeated}}$$

When referring to relative frequency approximations of probabilities, this text will not distinguish between results that are exact probabilities and those that are approximations, so an instruction to "find the probability" could actually mean "*estimate* the probability."

2. **Classical Approach to Probability (Requires Equally Likely Outcomes)** If a procedure has *n* different simple events that are *equally likely,* and if event *A* can occur in *s* different ways, then

$$P(A) = \frac{\text{number of ways } A \text{ occurs}}{\text{number of different simple events}} = \frac{s}{n}$$

CAUTION When using the classical approach, always confirm that the outcomes are *equally likely*.

3. **Subjective Probabilities** *P(A)*, the probability of event *A,* is *estimated* by using knowledge of the relevant circumstances.

Figure 4-3 illustrates the approaches of the preceding three definitions.

1. Relative Frequency Approach: When trying to determine the probability that an individual car crashes in a year, we must examine past results to determine the number of cars in use in a year and the number of them that crashed; then we find the ratio of the number of cars that crashed to the total number of cars. For a recent year, the result is a probability of 0.0480. (See Example 3.)

2. Classical Approach: When trying to determine the probability of randomly selecting three children who are of the same gender, there are two ways to get the same genders (boy/boy/boy and girl/girl/girl) among the eight equally likely outcomes, so the probability is 2/8 or 1/4. (See Example 4.)

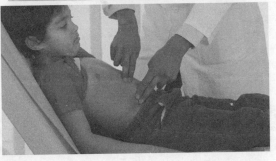

3. Subjective Probability: When trying to estimate the probability of someone with an appendix getting acute appendicitis in the next year, we know from personal experience that the probability is quite small. Let's estimate it to be, say, 0.001 (equivalent to 1 chance in 1000). (See Example 5.)

FIGURE 4-3   Three Approaches to Finding a Probability

Simulations Sometimes none of the preceding three approaches can be used. A *simulation* of a procedure is a process that behaves in the same ways as the procedure itself so that similar results are produced. Probabilities can sometimes be found by using a simulation. See the Technology Project near the end of this chapter.

Rounding Probabilities Although it is difficult to develop a universal rule for rounding off probabilities, the following guide will apply to most problems in this text.

ROUNDING PROBABILITIES

When expressing the value of a probability, either give the *exact* fraction or decimal or round off final decimal results to three significant digits. (*Suggestion:* When a probability is not a simple fraction such as 2/3 or 5/9, express it as a decimal so that the number can be better understood.) All digits in a number are significant except for the zeros that are included for proper placement of the decimal point. See the following examples.

- The probability of 0.4450323339 (from Example 6) has ten significant digits (4450323339), and it can be rounded to three significant digits as 0.445.

- The probability of 1/3 can be left as a fraction or rounded to 0.333. (Do *not* round to 0.3.)

- The probability of 2/8 can be expressed as 1/4 or 0.25. (Because 0.25 is exact, there's no need to express it with three significant digits as 0.250.)

Probabilities Expressed as Percentages? Mathematically, a probability of 0.25 is equivalent to 25%, but there are good reasons for sticking with fractions and decimals and not using percentages. Professional journals almost universally express probabilities as decimals, not as percentages. Later in this book, we will use probability values generated from statistical software, and they will always be in the form of decimals.

When finding probabilities with the relative frequency approach, we obtain an *approximation* instead of an exact value. As the total number of observations increases, the corresponding approximations tend to get closer to the actual probability. This property is commonly referred to as the *law of large numbers.*

LAW OF LARGE NUMBERS

As a procedure is repeated again and again, the relative frequency probability of an event tends to approach the actual probability.

The law of large numbers tells us that relative frequency approximations tend to get better with more observations. This law reflects a simple notion supported by common sense: A probability estimate based on only a few trials can be off by a substantial amount, but with a very large number of trials, the estimate tends to be much more accurate.

CAUTIONS

1. The law of large numbers applies to behavior over a large number of trials, and it does not apply to any one individual outcome. Gamblers sometimes foolishly lose large sums of money by incorrectly thinking that a string of losses increases the chances of a win on the next bet, or that a string of wins is likely to continue.

2. If we know nothing about the likelihood of different possible outcomes, we should not assume that they are equally likely. For example, we should not think that the probability of passing the next statistics test is 1/2, or 0.5 (because we either pass the test or do not). The actual probability depends on factors such as the amount of preparation and the difficulty of the test.

EXAMPLE 3 **Relative Frequency Probability: Skydiving**

Find the probability of dying when making a skydiving jump.

SOLUTION

In a recent year, there were about 3,000,000 skydiving jumps and 21 of them resulted in deaths. We use the relative frequency approach as follows:

$$P(\text{skydiving death}) = \frac{\text{number of skydiving deaths}}{\text{total number of skydiving jumps}} = \frac{21}{3,000,0000} = 0.000007$$

Here the classical approach cannot be used because the two outcomes (dying, surviving) are not equally likely. A subjective probability can be estimated in the absence of historical data.

 EXAMPLE 4 **Classical Probability: Three Children of the Same Gender**

When three children are born, the sample space of genders is as shown in Example 1: {bbb, bbg, bgb, bgg, gbb, gbg, ggb, ggg}. If boys and girls are equally likely, then those eight simple events are equally likely. Assuming that boys and girls are equally likely, find the probability of getting three children all of the same gender when three children are born. (In reality, the probability of a boy is 0.512 instead of 0.5.)

SOLUTION

The sample space {bbb, bbg, bgb, bgg, gbb, gbg, ggb, ggg} includes eight equally likely outcomes, and there are exactly two outcomes in which the three children are of the same gender: bbb and ggg. We can use the classical approach to get

$$P(\text{three children of the same gender}) = \frac{2}{8} = \frac{1}{4} \text{ or } 0.25$$

 EXAMPLE 5 **Subjective Probability: Acute Appendicitis**

What is the probability that you will get acute appendicitis next year?

SOLUTION

We could probably find past results and use the relative frequency approach, but for now, in the absence of historical data on acute appendicitis, we make a subjective estimate. Experience suggests that the probability is quite small. Let's estimate it to be, say, 0.001 (equivalent to 1 chance in 1000). Depending on our knowledge of the relevant circumstances, that subjective estimate might be reasonably accurate or it might be grossly wrong.

CAUTION Don't make the common mistake of finding a probability value by mindlessly dividing a smaller number by a larger number. Instead, *think* carefully about the numbers involved and what they represent. Carefully identify the total number of items being considered, as illustrated in Example 6.

EXAMPLE 6 **Texting and Driving**

In a study of U.S. high school drivers, it was found that 3785 texted while driving during the previous 30 days, and 4720 did not text while driving during that same time period (based on data from "Texting While Driving . . . . ," by Olsen, Shults, Eaton, *Pediatrics,* Vol. 131, No. 6). Based on these results, if a high school driver is randomly selected, find the probability that he or she texted while driving during the previous 30 days.

SOLUTION

> **CAUTION** A common *mistake* is to blindly plug in numbers to get the wrong probability of 3785/4720 = 0.802. We should *think* about what we are doing, as follows.

Instead of trying to determine an answer directly from the given statement, first summarize the information in a format that allows clear understanding, such as this format:

> 3785   texted while driving
>
> 4720   did not text while driving
> ———
> 8505   total number of drivers in the sample

We can now use the relative frequency approach as follows:

$$P(\text{texting while driving}) = \frac{\text{number of drivers who texted while driving}}{\text{total number of drivers in the sample}} = \frac{3785}{8505}$$

$$= 0.445$$

INTERPRETATION

There is a 0.445 probability that if a high school driver is randomly selected, he or she texted while driving during the previous 30 days.

 EXAMPLE 7 **Thanksgiving Day**

If a year is selected at random, find the probability that Thanksgiving Day in the United States will be (a) on a Wednesday or (b) on a Thursday.

SOLUTION

a. In the United States, Thanksgiving Day always falls on the fourth Thursday in November. It is therefore impossible for Thanksgiving to be on a Wednesday. When an event is impossible, its probability is 0.
$P(\text{Thanksgiving on Wednesday}) = 0$.

b. It is certain that a Thanksgiving Day in the United States will be on a Thursday. When an event is certain to occur, its probability is 1.
$P(\text{Thanksgiving on Thursday}) = 1$.

Because any event imaginable is impossible, certain, or somewhere in between, it follows that the mathematical probability of any event A is 0, 1, or a number between 0 and 1 (as shown in Figure 4-2). That is, $0 \le P(A) \le 1$.

Complementary Events

Sometimes we need to find the probability that an event A does *not* occur.

> **DEFINITION**
>
> The **complement** of event A, denoted by $\overline{A}$, consists of all outcomes in which event A does *not* occur.

 EXAMPLE 8 **Complement of Death from Skydiving**

Example 3 shows that in a recent year, there were 3,000,000 skydiving jumps and 21 of them resulted in death. Find the probability of *not* dying when making a skydiving jump.

SOLUTION

Among 3,000,000 jumps there were 21 deaths, so it follows that the other 2,999,979 jumps were survived. We get

$$P(\text{not dying when making a skydiving jump}) = \frac{2,999,979}{3,000,000} = 0.999993$$

INTERPRETATION

The probability of *not* dying when making a skydiving jump is 0.999993.

Relationship Between $P(A)$ and $P(\overline{A})$ If we denote the event of dying in a skydiving jump by D, Example 3 showed that $P(D) = 0.000007$ and Example 8 showed that $P(\overline{D}) = 0.999993$. The probability of $P(\overline{D})$ could be found by just subtracting $P(D)$ from 1.

Identifying Significant Results with Probabilities: The Rare Event Rule for Inferential Statistics

> If, under a given assumption, the probability of a particular observed event is very small and the observed event occurs *significantly less* than or *significantly greater* than what we typically expect with that assumption, we conclude that the assumption is probably not correct.

We can use probabilities to identify values that are *significantly low* or *significantly high* as follows.

Using Probabilities to Determine When Results Are Significantly High or Significantly Low

- **Significantly *high* number of successes:** x successes among n trials is a *significantly high* number of successes if the probability of x or more successes is unlikely with a probability of 0.05 or less. That is, x is a significantly high number of successes if $P(x \text{ or more}) \leq 0.05$.*

- **Significantly *low* number of successes:** x successes among n trials is a *significantly low* number of successes if the probability of x or fewer successes is unlikely with a probability of 0.05 or less. That is, x is a significantly low number of successes if $P(x \text{ or fewer}) \leq 0.05$.*

*The value 0.05 is not absolutely rigid. Other values, such as 0.01, could be used to distinguish between results that can easily occur by chance and events that are significant.

See Example 1 on page 137, which illustrates the following:

- Among 100 births, 75 girls is *significantly high* because the probability of 75 or more girls is 0.0000003, which is less than or equal to 0.05 (so the gender selection method appears to be effective).

- Among 100 births, 55 girls is *not significantly high* because the probability of 55 or more girls is 0.184, which is greater than 0.05 (so the gender selection does not appear to be effective).

Probability Review

Important Principles and Notation for Probability

- **The probability of an event is a fraction or decimal number between 0 and 1 inclusive.**

- **The probability of an impossible event is 0.**

- **The probability of an event that is certain to occur is 1.**

- **Notation: $P(A)$ = the probability of event A.**

- **Notation: $P(\overline{A})$ = the probability that event A does *not* occur.**

4-1   Basic Skills and Concepts

Statistical Literacy and Critical Thinking

1. Probability Given that the following statement is incorrect, rewrite it correctly: "The probability of a student passing the physical examination is 60-40."

2. Probability Rewrite the following statement with the probability expressed as a number with a decimal format: "The probability of selecting someone who is a postgraduate is 55%."

3. Births In Example 4 "Three Children of the Same Gender" it was noted that in reality, the probability of a boy is 0.512 instead of 0.5. Let A denote the event of getting a boy when a baby is born. What is the value of $P(\overline{A})$?

4. Subjective Probability Estimate the probability that the next time a physician walks into a patient's room and turns on a light switch, she discovers that the light bulb does work.

5. Identifying Probability Values Which of the following are probabilities?

$$1 \quad 7/4 \quad 4/7 \quad 360\% \quad -0.36 \quad 0 \quad 6:5 \quad 70\text{-}30 \quad 3.164 \quad 0.461 \quad 0.08$$

6. Anthrax "Who discovered vaccination for anthrax: Alexander Fleming, Louis Pasteur, Maurice Hilleman, or Edward Jenner?" If you make a random guess for the answer to that question, what is the probability that your answer is the correct answer of Louis Pasteur?

7. Avogadro Constant If you are asked on a quiz to give the first (leftmost) nonzero digit of the Avogadro constant and, not knowing the answer, you make a random guess, what is the probability that your answer is the correct answer of 6?

8. Births Example 2 in this section includes the sample space for genders from three births. Identify the sample space for the genders from two births.

In Exercises 9–12, assume that 50 births are randomly selected. Use subjective judgment to describe the given number of girls as (a) significantly low, (b) significantly high, or (c) neither significantly low nor significantly high.

9. 47 girls.   **10.** 26 girls.   **11.** 23 girls.   **12.** 5 girls.

In Exercises 13–20, express the indicated degree of likelihood as a probability value between 0 and 1.

13. Testing If you make a random guess for the answer to a true/false test question, there is a 50-50 chance of being correct.

14. MCAT Test When making a random guess for an answer to a multiple-choice question on an MCAT test, the possible answers are a, b, c, d, e, so there is 1 chance in 5 of being correct.

15. Genes One of the four DNA bases of A, G, C, and T is randomly selected, and the result is G. Assume that the four DNA bases are equally likely.

16. Sleepwalking Based on a report in *Neurology* magazine, 29.2% of survey respondents have sleepwalked.

17. Randomness When using a computer to randomly generate the last digit of a phone number to be called for a survey, there is 1 chance in 10 that the last digit is zero.

18. Job Applicant Mistakes Based on an Adecco survey of hiring managers who were asked to identify the biggest mistakes that job candidates make during an interview, there is a 50-50 chance that they will identify "inappropriate attire."

19. Square Peg Sydney Smith wrote in "On the Conduct of the Understanding" that it is impossible to fit a square peg in a round hole.

20. Death and Taxes Benjamin Franklin said that death is a certainty of life.

In Exercises 21–24, refer to the sample data in Table 4-1, which is included with the Chapter Problem. Assume that 1 of the 555 subjects included in Table 4-1 is randomly selected.

TABLE 4-1 Results from Drug Tests of Job Applicants

	Positive Test Result (Test shows drug use.)	Negative Test Result (Test shows no drug use.)
Subject Uses Drugs	45 (True Positive)	5 (False Negative)
Subject Does Not Use Drugs	25 (False Positive)	480 (True Negative)

21. Drug Testing Job Applicants Find the probability of selecting someone who got a result that is a false negative. Who would suffer from a false negative result? Why?

22. Drug Testing Job Applicants Find the probability of selecting someone who got a result that is a false positive. Who would suffer from a false positive result? Why?

23. Drug Testing Job Applicants Find the probability of selecting someone who uses drugs. Does the result appear to be reasonable as an estimate of the "prevalence rate" described in the Chapter Problem?

24. Drug Testing Job Applicants Find the probability of selecting someone who does not use drugs. Does the result appear to be reasonable as an estimate of the proportion of the adult population that does not use drugs?

In Exercises 25–32, find the probability and answer the questions.

25. XSORT Gender Selection MicroSort's XSORT gender selection technique was designed to increase the likelihood that a baby will be a girl. At one point before clinical trials of the XSORT gender selection technique were discontinued, 945 births consisted of 879 baby girls and 66 baby boys (based on data from the Genetics & IVF Institute). Based on these results, what is the probability of a girl born to a couple using MicroSort's XSORT method? Does it appear that the technique is effective in increasing the likelihood that a baby will be a girl?

26. YSORT Gender Selection MicroSort's YSORT gender-selection technique is designed to increase the likelihood that a baby will be a boy. At one point before clinical trials of the YSORT gender-selection technique were discontinued, 291 births consisted of 239 baby boys and 52 baby girls (based on data from the Genetics & IVF Institute). Based on these results, what is the probability of a boy born to a couple using MicroSort's YSORT method? Does it appear that the technique is effective in increasing the likelihood that a baby will be a boy?

27. Mendelian Genetics When Mendel conducted his famous genetics experiments with peas, one sample of offspring consisted of 428 green peas and 152 yellow peas. Based on those results, estimate the probability of getting an offspring pea that is green. Is the result reasonably close to the expected value of 3/4, as Mendel claimed?

28. Guessing Birthdays On their first date, Kelly asks Mike to guess the date of her birth, not including the year.

a. What is the probability that Mike will guess correctly? (Ignore leap years.)

b. Would it be unlikely for him to guess correctly on his first try?

c. If you were Kelly, and Mike did guess correctly on his first try, would you believe his claim that he made a lucky guess, or would you be convinced that he already knew when you were born?

d. If Kelly asks Mike to guess her age, and Mike's guess is too high by 15 years, what is the probability that Mike and Kelly will have a second date?

29. Online Medicine In a survey, 933 respondents say that they seek medical information online and 139 other respondents say that they *never* seek medical information online. What is the probability that a randomly selected person never seeks medical information online? Is it unlikely for someone to never seek medical information online? How are these results affected by the fact that the responses are from subjects who decided to respond to the survey posted on the Internet by AOL?

30. Car Rollovers In a recent year in the United States, 83,600 passenger cars rolled over when they crashed, and 5,127,400 passenger cars did not roll over when they crashed. Find the probability that a randomly selected passenger car crash results in a rollover. Is it unlikely for a car to roll over in a crash?

31. Genetics: Eye Color Each of two parents has the genotype brown/blue, which consists of the pair of alleles that determine eye color, and each parent contributes one of those alleles to a child. Assume that if the child has at least one brown allele, that color will dominate and the eyes will be brown. (The actual determination of eye color is more complicated than that.)

a. List the different possible outcomes. Assume that these outcomes are equally likely.

b. What is the probability that a child of these parents will have the blue/blue genotype?

c. What is the probability that the child will have brown eyes?

32. X-Linked Genetic Disease Men have XY (or YX) chromosomes and women have XX chromosomes. X-linked recessive genetic diseases (such as juvenile retinoschisis) occur when there is a defective X chromosome that occurs *without* a paired X chromosome that is *not* defective. In the following, represent a defective X chromosome with lowercase x, so a child with the xY or Yx pair of chromosomes will have the disease and a child with XX or XY or YX or xX or Xx will not have the disease. Each parent contributes one of the chromosomes to the child.

a. If a father has the defective x chromosome and the mother has good XX chromosomes, what is the probability that a son will inherit the disease?

b. If a father has the defective x chromosome and the mother has good XX chromosomes, what is the probability that a daughter will inherit the disease?

continued

c. If a mother has one defective x chromosome and one good X chromosome and the father has good XY chromosomes, what is the probability that a son will inherit the disease?

d. If a mother has one defective x chromosome and one good X chromosome and the father has good XY chromosomes, what is the probability that a daughter will inherit the disease?

Probability from a Sample Space. *In Exercises 33–36, use the given sample space or construct the required sample space to find the indicated probability.*

33. Three Children Use this sample space listing the eight simple events that are possible when a couple has three children (as in Example 2 on page 138): {bbb, bbg, bgb, bgg, gbb, gbg, ggb, ggg}. Assume that boys and girls are equally likely, so that the eight simple events are equally likely. Find the probability that when a couple has three children, there is exactly one girl.

34. Three Children Using the same sample space and assumption from Exercise 33, find the probability that when a couple has three children, there are exactly two girls.

35. Four Children Exercise 33 lists the sample space for a couple having three children. After identifying the sample space for a couple having four children, find the probability of getting three girls and one boy (in any order).

36. Four Children Using the same sample space and assumption from Exercise 35, find the probability that when a couple has four children, all four are of the same gender.

Using Probability to Form Conclusions. *In Exercises 37–40, use the given probability value to determine whether the sample results could easily occur by chance, then form a conclusion.*

37. Predicting Gender A study addressed the issue of whether pregnant women can correctly predict the gender of their baby. Among 104 pregnant women, 57 correctly predicted the gender of their baby (based on data from "Are Women Carrying 'Basketballs'...," by Perry, DiPietro, Constigan, *Birth*, Vol. 26, No. 3). If pregnant women have no such ability, there is a 0.327 probability of getting such sample results by chance. What do you conclude?

38. Clinical Trial of Tamiflu Clinical trials involved the use of Tamiflu (oseltamivir phosphate) for treating flu patients. Among 724 patients treated with Tamiflu, 72 (or about 10%) experienced nausea. (An untreated group experienced a 6% rate of nausea.) If Tamiflu really has no effect on nausea, there is a 0.00000246 probability of getting these sample results by chance. What do you conclude about the effect of Tamiflu on nausea?

39. Sleepiness In a clinical trial of OxyContin (oxycodone) used for pain relief, 227 subjects were treated with OxyContin and 52 of them experienced sleepiness (based on data from Purdue Pharma L.P.). If OxyContin has no effect on sleepiness, the probability of getting these sample results by chance is less than 0.001 (when comparing this sample group with another group not treated with OxyContin). What do you conclude?

40. Cell Phones and Cancer A study of 420,095 Danish cell phone users resulted in 135 who developed cancer of the brain or nervous system (based on data from the *Journal of the National Cancer Institute*). When comparing this sample group to another group of people who did not use cell phones, it was found that there is a probability of 0.512 of getting such sample results by chance. What do you conclude?

4-2 Addition Rule and Multiplication Rule

Key Concepts In this section we present the *addition rule* as a tool for finding $P(A \text{ or } B)$, which is the probability that either event A occurs or event B occurs (or they both occur) as the single outcome of a procedure. To find $P(A \text{ or } B)$, we begin by adding the number of ways that A can occur and the number of ways that B can occur, but add without double counting. The word "or" in the addition rule is associated with the addition of probabilities.

Proportions of Males / Females

It is well known that when a baby is born, boys and girls are not equally likely. It is currently believed that 105 boys are born for every 100 girls, so the probability of a boy is 0.512. Kristen Navara of the University of Georgia conducted a study showing that around the world, more boys are born than girls, but the difference becomes smaller as people are located closer to the equator. She used latitudes, temperatures, unemployment rates, and gross national products from 200 countries and conducted a statistical analysis showing that the proportions of boys appear to be affected only by latitude and its related weather. So far, no one has identified a reasonable explanation for this phenomenon.

This section also presents the basic *multiplication rule* used for finding $P(A \text{ and } B)$, which is the probability that event A occurs and event B occurs. If the outcome of event A somehow affects the probability of event B, it is important to adjust the probability of B to reflect the occurrence of event A. The rule for finding $P(A \text{ and } B)$ is called the *multiplication rule* because it involves the multiplication of the probability of event A and the probability of event B (where, if necessary, the probability of event B is adjusted because of the outcome of event A). The word "and" in the multiplication rule is associated with the multiplication of probabilities.

In Section 4-1 we considered only *simple* events, but in this section we consider *compound events.*

DEFINITION

A **compound event** is any event combining two or more simple events.

Addition Rule

Notation for Addition Rule

$P(A \text{ or } B) = P(\text{in a single trial, event } A \text{ occurs or event } B \text{ occurs or they both occur})$

The word "or" used in the preceding notation is the *inclusive or,* which means either one or the other or both. The formal addition rule is often presented as a formula, but blind use of formulas is not recommended. Instead, *understand* the spirit of the rule and use that understanding, as in the intuitive addition rule that follows.

INTUITIVE ADDITION RULE

To find $P(A \text{ or } B)$, add the number of ways event A can occur and the number of ways event B can occur, but *add in such a way that every outcome is counted only once.* $P(A \text{ or } B)$ is equal to that sum, divided by the total number of outcomes in the sample space.

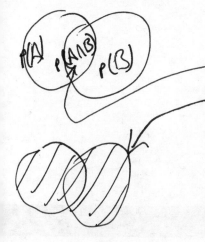

FORMAL ADDITION RULE

$$P(A \text{ or } B) = P(A) + P(B) - P(A \text{ and } B)$$

where $P(A \text{ and } B)$ denotes the probability that A and B both occur at the same time as an outcome in a trial of a procedure.

One way to apply the addition rule is to add the probability of event A and the probability of event B and, if there is any overlap that causes double-counting, compensate for it by subtracting the probability of outcomes that are included twice. This approach is reflected in the above formal addition rule.

EXAMPLE 1 Drug Testing of Job Applicants

Refer to Table 4-1, reproduced here for your convenience and viewing pleasure. If 1 subject is randomly selected from the 555 subjects given a drug test, find the probability of selecting a subject who had a positive test result *or* uses drugs.

TABLE 4-1 Results from Drug Tests of Job Applicants

	Positive Test Result (Test shows drug use.)	Negative Test Result (Test shows no drug use.)
Subject Uses Drugs	45 (True Positive)	5 (False Negative)
Subject Does Not Use Drugs	25 (False Positive)	480 (True Negative)

*Numbers in red correspond to positive test results or subjects who use drugs, and the total of those numbers is 75.

SOLUTION

Refer to Table 4-1 and carefully count the number of subjects who tested positive (first column) or use drugs (first row), but be careful to count subjects exactly once, not twice. *When adding the frequencies from the first column and the first row, include the frequency of 45 only once.* In Table 4-1, there are $45 + 25 + 5 = 75$ subjects who had positive test results or use drugs. We get this result:

$$P(\text{positive test result or subject uses drugs}) = 75/555 = 0.135$$

Disjoint Events and the Addition Rule

The addition rule is simplified when the events are *disjoint*.

DEFINITION

Events A and B are **disjoint** (or **mutually exclusive**) if they cannot occur at the same time. (That is, disjoint events do not overlap.)

EXAMPLE 2 **Disjoint Events**

Disjoint events:

Event A—Randomly selecting someone for a clinical trial who is a male

Event B—Randomly selecting someone for a clinical trial who is a female

(The selected person cannot be both.)

Events that are *not* disjoint:

Event A—Randomly selecting someone taking a statistics course

Event B—Randomly selecting someone who is a female

(The selected person *can* be both.)

Whenever A and B are disjoint, $P(A \text{ and } B)$ becomes zero in the formal addition rule, so for disjoint events A and B we have $P(A \text{ or } B) = P(A) + P(B)$. But again, instead of blind use of a formula, it is better to *understand* and use the intuitive addition rule.

Here is a summary of the key points of the addition rule:

1. **To find $P(A \text{ or } B)$, first associate the word *or* with addition.**

2. **To find the value of $P(A \text{ or } B)$, add the number of ways A can occur and the number of ways B can occur, but be careful to add without double counting.**

Complementary Events and the Addition Rule

In Section 4-1 we used $\overline{A}$ to indicate that event A does not occur. Common sense dictates this principle: We are certain (with probability 1) that either an event A occurs *or* it does not occur, so it follows that $P(A \text{ or } \overline{A}) = 1$. Because events A and $\overline{A}$ must be disjoint, we can use the addition rule to express this principle as follows:

$$P(A \text{ or } \overline{A}) = P(A) + P(\overline{A}) = 1$$

This result of the addition rule leads to the following three expressions that are "equivalent" in the sense that they are just different forms of the same principle.

RULE OF COMPLEMENTARY EVENTS

$$P(A) + P(\overline{A}) = 1 \qquad P(\overline{A}) = 1 - P(A) \qquad P(A) = 1 - P(\overline{A})$$

EXAMPLE 3 **Sleepwalking**

Based on a journal article, the probability of randomly selecting someone who has sleepwalked is 0.292, so $P(\text{sleepwalked}) = 0.292$ (based on data from "Prevalence and Comorbidity of Nocturnal Wandering in the U.S. General Population," by Ohayon et al., *Neurology,* Vol. 78, No. 20). If a person is randomly selected, find the probability of getting someone who has *not* sleepwalked.

SOLUTION

Using the rule of complementary events, we get

$$P(\text{has } not \text{ sleepwalked}) = 1 - P(\text{sleepwalked}) = 1 - 0.292 = 0.708$$

The probability of randomly selecting someone who has not sleepwalked is 0.708.

Multiplication Rule

Notation for Multiplication Rule

We begin with basic notation followed by the multiplication rule. We strongly suggest using the *intuitive* multiplication rule, because it is based on understanding instead of blind use of a formula.

Notation

$P(A \text{ and } B) = P(\text{event A occurs in one trial and event B occurs in a different trial})$

$P(B|A)$ represents the probability of event B occurring after it is assumed that event A has already occurred. (Interpret $B|A$ as "event B occurs after event A has already occurred.")

CAUTION The notation $P(A \text{ and } B)$ has two meanings, depending on its context. For the multiplication rule, $P(A \text{ and } B)$ denotes that event A occurs in one trial and event B occurs in another trial; for the addition rule we use $P(A \text{ and } B)$ to denote that events A and B both occur in the same trial.

INTUITIVE MULTIPLICATION RULE

To find the probability that event *A* occurs in one trial and event *B* occurs in another trial, multiply the probability of event *A* by the probability of event *B*, but *be sure that the probability of event B is found by assuming that event A has already occurred.*

FORMAL MULTIPLICATION RULE

$$P(A \text{ and } B) = P(A) \cdot P(B|A)$$

Independence and the Multiplication Rule

When applying the multiplication rule and considering whether the probability of event *B* must be adjusted to account for the previous occurrence of event *A,* we are focusing on whether events *A* and *B* are *independent.*

DEFINITIONS

Two events *A* and *B* are **independent** if the occurrence of one does not affect the *probability* of the occurrence of the other. (Several events are independent if the occurrence of any does not affect the probabilities of the occurrence of the others.) If *A* and *B* are not independent, they are said to be **dependent.**

CAUTION Don't think that *dependence* of two events means that one is the direct *cause* of the other. Having a working light in your kitchen and having a working light in your bedroom are dependent events because they share the same power source. One of the lights may stop working for many reasons, but if one light is out, there is a higher probability that the other light will be out (because of the common power source).

Example 4 illustrates the basic multiplication rule, with independent events in part (a) and dependent events in part (b).

EXAMPLE 4   **Drug Screening and the Basic Multiplication Rule**

Let's use only the 50 test results from the subjects who use drugs (from Table 4-1), as shown below:

Positive Test Results:	45
Negative Test Results:	5
Total:	50

a. If 2 of these 50 subjects are randomly selected *with replacement,* find the probability that the first selected person had a positive test result and the second selected person had a negative test result.

b. Repeat part (a) by assuming that the two subjects are selected *without* replacement.

continued

SOLUTION

a. *With Replacement:* First selection (with 45 positive results among 50 total results):

$$P(\text{positive test result}) = \frac{45}{50}$$

Second selection (with 5 negative test results among the same 50 total results):

$$P(\text{negative test result}) = \frac{5}{50}$$

We now apply the multiplication rule as follows: $P(A) \cdot P(B)$

$$P(\text{1st selection is positive and 2nd is negative}) = \frac{45}{50} \cdot \frac{5}{50} = 0.0900$$

b. *Without Replacement:* Without replacement of the first subject, the calculations are the same as in part (a), except that the second probability must be adjusted to reflect the fact that the first selection was positive and is not available for the second selection. After the first positive result is selected, we have 49 test results remaining, and 5 of them are negative. The second probability is therefore 5/49, as shown below: $P(A) \cdot P(B/A)$

$$P(\text{1st selection is positive and 2nd is negative}) = \frac{45}{50} \cdot \frac{5}{49} = 0.0918$$

The key point of part (b) in Example 4 is this: *We must adjust the probability of the second event to reflect the outcome of the first event.* Because selection of the second subject is made *without* replacement of the first subject, the second probability must take into account the fact that the first selection removed a subject who tested positive, so only 49 subjects are available for the second selection, and 5 of them had a negative test result. Part (a) of Example 4 involved sampling with replacement, so the events are independent; part (b) of Example 4 involved sampling without replacement, so the events are dependent. See the following.

Sampling In the wonderful world of statistics, sampling methods are critically important, and the following relationships hold:

- Sampling *with replacement*: Selections are *independent* events.
- Sampling *without replacement:* Selections are *dependent* events.

Exception: Treating Dependent Events as Independent

Some cumbersome calculations can be greatly simplified by using the common practice of treating events as independent when *small samples* are drawn without replacement from *large populations*. (In such cases, it is rare to select the same item twice.) Here is a common guideline routinely used with applications such as analyses of survey results:

TREATING DEPENDENT EVENTS AS INDEPENDENT:
5% GUIDELINE FOR CUMBERSOME CALCULATIONS

When sampling without replacement and the sample size is no more than 5% of the size of the population, treat the selections as being *independent* (even though they are actually dependent).

Example 5 illustrates use of the 5% guideline for cumbersome calculations and it also illustrates that the basic multiplication rule extends easily to three or more events.

EXAMPLE 5 Drug Screening and the 5% Guideline for Cumbersome Calculations

Assume that three adults are randomly selected *without replacement* from the 247,436,830 adults in the United States. Also assume that 10% of adults in the United States use drugs. Find the probability that the three selected adults all use drugs.

SOLUTION

Because the three adults are randomly selected without replacement, the three events are dependent, but here we can treat them as being independent by applying the 5% guideline for cumbersome calculations. The sample size of 3 is clearly no more than 5% of the population size of 247,436,830. We get

$$P(\text{all 3 adults use drugs}) = P(\text{first uses drugs } and \text{ second uses drugs } and$$
$$\text{third uses drugs})$$
$$= P(\text{first uses drugs}) \cdot P(\text{second uses drugs}) \cdot$$
$$P(\text{third uses drugs})$$
$$= (0.10)(0.10)(0.10) = 0.00100$$

There is a 0.00100 probability that all three selected adults use drugs.

In Example 5, if we treat the events as dependent without using the 5% guideline, we get the following cumbersome calculation that begins with 247,436,830 adults, with 10% of them (or 24,743,683) using drugs:

$$\left(\frac{24,743,683}{247,436,830}\right)\left(\frac{24,743,682}{247,436,829}\right)\left(\frac{24,743,681}{247,436,828}\right) = 0.0009999998909$$
$$= 0.00100 \text{ (rounded)}$$

Just imagine randomly selecting 1000 adults instead of just 3, as is commonly done in typical polls. Extending the above calculation to include 1000 factors instead of 3 factors would be what statisticians refer to as "painful."

CAUTION In any probability calculation, it is extremely important to carefully identify the event being considered. See Example 6, where parts (a) and (b) might seem quite similar but their solutions are very different.

EXAMPLE 6 Birthdays

When two different people are randomly selected from those in your class, find the indicated probability by assuming that birthdays occur on the days of the week with equal frequencies.

   a. Find the probability that the two people are born on the *same day of the week*.

   b. Find the probability that the two people are both born on *Monday*.

continued

SOLUTION

a. Because no particular day of the week is specified, the first person can be born on any one of the seven weekdays. The probability that the second person is born on the same day as the first person is $1/7$. The probability that two people are born on the same day of the week is therefore $1/7$.

b. The probability that the first person is born on Monday is $1/7$ and the probability that the second person is also born on Monday is $1/7$. Because the two events are independent, the probability that both people are born on Monday is

$$\frac{1}{7} \cdot \frac{1}{7} = \frac{1}{49}$$

WATCH YOUR LANGUAGE! Example 6 illustrates that finding correct or relevant probability values often requires greater language skills than computational skills. In Example 6, what exactly do we mean by "same day of the week"? See how parts (a) and (b) in Example 6 are very different.

Redundancy: Important Application of Multiplication Rule

The principle of *redundancy* is used to increase the reliability of many systems. Our eyes have passive redundancy in the sense that if one of them fails, we continue to see. An important finding of modern biology is that genes in an organism can often work in place of each other. Engineers often design redundant components so that the whole system will not fail because of the failure of a single component, as in the following example.

 EXAMPLE 7 **Airbus 310:** *Redundancy* **for Better Safety**

Modern aircraft are now highly reliable, and one design feature contributing to that reliability is the use of *redundancy,* whereby critical components are duplicated so that if one fails, the other will work. For example, the Airbus 310 twin-engine airliner has three independent hydraulic systems, so if any one system fails, full flight control is maintained with another functioning system. For this example, we will assume that for a typical flight, the probability of a hydraulic system failure is 0.002.

a. If the Airbus 310 were to have one hydraulic system, what is the probability that the aircraft's flight control would work for a flight?

b. Given that the Airbus 310 actually has three independent hydraulic systems, what is the probability that on a typical flight, control can be maintained with a working hydraulic system?

SOLUTION

a. The probability of a hydraulic system failure is 0.002, so the probability that it does *not* fail is 0.998. That is, the probability that flight control can be maintained is as follows:

$$P(1 \text{ hydraulic system } does\ not\ fail)$$
$$= 1 - P(\text{failure}) = 1 - 0.002 = 0.998$$

b. With three independent hydraulic systems, flight control will be maintained if the three systems do not all fail. The probability of all three hydraulic systems failing is $0.002 \cdot 0.002 \cdot 0.002 = 0.000000008$. It follows that the probability of maintaining flight control is as follows:

$$P(\text{it does } \textit{not} \text{ happen that all three hydraulic systems fail})$$
$$= 1 - 0.000000008 = 0.999999992$$

INTERPRETATION

With only one hydraulic system we have a 0.002 probability of failure, but with three independent hydraulic systems, there is only a 0.000000008 probability that flight control cannot be maintained because all three systems failed. By using three hydraulic systems instead of only one, risk of failure is decreased not by a factor of 1/3, but by a factor of 1/250,000. By using three independent hydraulic systems, risk is dramatically decreased and safety is dramatically increased.

Rationale for the Multiplication Rule

To see the reasoning that underlies the multiplication rule, consider a pop quiz consisting of these two questions:

1. True or false: A pound of feathers is heavier than a pound of gold.

2. Who said, "By a small sample, we may judge of the whole piece"? (a) Judge Judy; (b) Judge Dredd; (c) Miguel de Cervantes; (d) George Gallup; (e) Gandhi

The answers are T (true) and c. (The first answer is true, because weights of feathers are in avoirdupois units where a pound is 453.59 g, but weights of gold and other precious metals are in troy units where a pound is 373.24 g. The second answer is from *Don Quixote* by Cervantes.)

Here is the sample space for the different possible answers:

$$\text{Ta} \quad \text{Tb} \quad \text{Tc} \quad \text{Td} \quad \text{Te} \quad \text{Fa} \quad \text{Fb} \quad \text{Fc} \quad \text{Fd} \quad \text{Fe}$$

If both answers are random guesses, then the above 10 possible outcomes are equally likely, so

$$P(\text{both correct}) = P(T \text{ and } c) = \frac{1}{10} = 0.1$$

With $P(T \text{ and } c) = 1/10$, $P(T) = 1/2$, and $P(c) = 1/5$, we see that

$$\frac{1}{10} = \frac{1}{2} \cdot \frac{1}{5}$$

A *tree diagram* is a graph of the possible outcomes of a procedure, as in Figure 4-4. Figure 4-4 shows that if both answers are random guesses, all 10 branches are equally likely and the probability of getting the correct pair (T, c) is 1/10. For each response to the first question, there are 5 responses to the second. *The total number of outcomes is 5 taken 2 times, or 10.* The tree diagram in Figure 4-4 therefore provides a visual illustration for using multiplication.

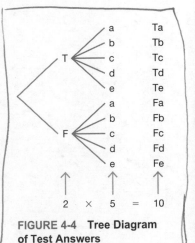

FIGURE 4-4   Tree Diagram of Test Answers

Summary of Addition Rule and Multiplication Rule

Addition Rule for P(A or B): The word *or* suggests addition, and when adding $P(A)$ and $P(B)$, we must add in such a way that every outcome is counted only once.

Multiplication Rule for P(A and B): The word *and* for two trials suggests multiplication, and when multiplying $P(A)$ and $P(B)$, we must be sure that the probability of event B takes into account the previous occurrence of event A.

4-2   Basic Skills and Concepts

Statistical Literacy and Critical Thinking

1. Notation When randomly selecting an adult, A denotes the event of selecting someone with blue eyes. What do $P(A)$ and $P(\overline{A})$ represent?

2. Notation When randomly selecting adults, let M denote the event of randomly selecting a male and let B denote the event of randomly selecting someone with blue eyes. What does $P(M|B)$ represent? Is $P(M|B)$ the same as $P(B|M)$?

3. Sample for a Poll There are 15,524,971 adults in Florida. If The Gallup organization randomly selects 1068 adults without replacement, are the selections independent or dependent? If the selections are dependent, can they be treated as being independent for the purposes of calculations?

4. Rule of Complements When randomly selecting an adult, let B represent the event of randomly selecting someone with Group B blood. Write a sentence describing what the rule of complements is telling us: $P(\text{B or }\overline{\text{B}}) = 1$.

Finding Complements. *In Exercises 5–8, find the indicated complements.*

5. LOL A U.S. Cellular survey of smartphone users showed that 26% of respondents answered "yes" when asked if abbreviations (such as LOL) are annoying when texting. What is the probability of randomly selecting a smartphone user and getting a response other than "yes"?

6. Color Blindness Women have a 0.25% rate of red/green color blindness. If a woman is randomly selected, what is the probability that she does *not* have red/green color blindness?

7. Clinical Test When the drug Viagra (sildenafil citrate) was clinically tested, 117 patients reported headaches and 617 did not. If one of these patients is randomly selected, find the probability of getting one who did not report a headache.

8. Sobriety Checkpoint When one of the authors observed a sobriety checkpoint conducted by the Dutchess County Sheriff Department, he saw that 676 drivers were screened and 6 were arrested for driving while intoxicated. Based on those results, we can estimate that $P(I) = 0.000888$, where I denotes the event of screening a driver and getting someone who is intoxicated. What does $P(\overline{I})$ denote, and what is its value?

In Exercises 9–20, use the data in the following table, which summarizes blood groups and Rh types for randomly selected subjects. Assume that subjects are randomly selected from those included in the table.

		O	A	B	AB
Type	Rh$^+$	59	53	12	6
	Rh$^-$	9	8	3	2

9. Blood Groups and Types If one person is selected, find the probability of getting someone who is not Group B.

10. Blood Groups and Types If one person is selected, find the probability of getting someone who is not type Rh⁻.

11. Blood Groups and Types If one person is selected, find the probability of getting someone who is Group B or type Rh⁻. Are the events of selecting someone who is Group B and the event of someone who is type Rh⁻ disjoint events?

12. Blood Groups and Types If one person is selected, find the probability of getting someone who is type Rh⁻ or Group AB. Are the events of selecting someone who is type Rh⁻ and the event of someone who is Group AB disjoint events?

13. Blood Groups and Types If two people are selected, find the probability that they are both Group O.

a. Assume that the selections are made without replacement. Are the events independent?

b. Assume that the selections are made with replacement. Are the events independent?

14. Blood Groups and Types If two people are selected, find the probability that they are both type Rh⁻.

a. Assume that the selections are made with replacement. Are the events independent?

b. Assume that the selections are made without replacement. Are the events independent?

15. Blood Groups and Types If two people are selected, find the probability that they are both type Rh⁺.

a. Assume that the selections are made with replacement. Are the events independent?

b. Assume that the selections are made without replacement. Are the events independent?

16. Blood Groups and Types If two people are selected, find the probability that none of them is group AB.

a. Assume that the selections are made without replacement. Are the events independent?

b. Assume that the selections are made with replacement. Are the events independent?

17. Blood Groups and Types If one person is selected, find the probability of getting someone who is Group A or Group B or type Rh⁻.

18. Blood Groups and Types If one person is selected, find the probability of getting someone who is Group O or Group AB or type Rh⁺.

19. Blood Groups and Types If three *different* people are selected, find the probability that they are all Group A.

20. Blood Groups and Types If three *different* people are selected, find the probability that they are all type Rh⁻.

In Exercises 21–24, use these results from the "1-Panel-THC" test for marijuana use, which is provided by the company Drug Test Success: Among 143 subjects with positive test results, there are 24 false positive results; among 157 negative results, there are 3 false negative results. (Hint: Construct a table similar to Table 4-1, which is included with the Chapter Problem.)

21. Testing for Marijuana Use

a. How many subjects are included in the study?

b. How many of the subjects had a true negative result?

c. What is the probability that a randomly selected test subject had a true negative result?

22. Testing for Marijuana Use If one of the test subjects is randomly selected, find the probability that the subject tested negative or used marijuana.

23. Testing for Marijuana Use If one of the test subjects is randomly selected, find the probability that the subject tested positive or did not use marijuana.

24. Testing for Marijuana Use If one of the test subjects is randomly selected, find the probability that the subject used marijuana. Do you think that the result reflects the general population rate of subjects who use marijuana?

Redundancy. *Exercises 25 and 26 involve redundancy.*

25. Redundancy in Computer Hard Drives It is generally recognized that it is wise to back up computer data. Assume that there is a 3% rate of disk drive failure in a year (based on data from various sources including lifehacker.com).

a. If you store all of your computer data on a single hard disk drive, what is the probability that the drive will fail during a year?

b. If all of your computer data are stored on a hard disk drive with a copy stored on a second hard disk drive, what is the probability that both drives will fail during a year?

c. If copies of all of your computer data are stored on three independent hard disk drives, what is the probability that all three will fail during a year?

d. Describe the improved reliability that is gained with backup drives.

26. Redundancy in Hospital Generators Hospitals typically require backup generators to provide electricity in the event of a power outage. Assume that emergency backup generators fail 22% of the times when they are needed (based on data from Arshad Mansoor, senior vice president with the Electric Power Research Institute). A hospital has two backup generators so that power is available if one of them fails during a power outage.

a. Find the probability that both generators fail during a power outage.

b. Find the probability of having a working generator in the event of a power outage. Is that probability high enough for the hospital?

Acceptance Sampling. *With one method of a procedure called acceptance sampling, a sample of items is randomly selected without replacement and the entire batch is accepted if every item in the sample is found to be okay (or conforming). Exercises 27 and 28 involve acceptance sampling.*

27. Defective Pacemakers Among 8834 cases of heart pacemaker malfunctions, 504 were found to be caused by firmware, which is software programmed into the device (based on data from "Pacemaker and ICD Generator Malfunctions," by Maisel et al., *Journal of the American Medical Association,* Vol. 295, No. 16). If the firmware is tested in three *different* pacemakers randomly selected from this batch of 8834 and the entire batch is accepted if there are no failures, what is the probability that the firmware in the entire batch will be accepted? Is this procedure likely to result in the entire batch being accepted?

28. Defective Ultrasound Transducers Among 676 ultrasound transducers tested, 269 were defective with transducer errors (based on data from "High Incidence of Defective Ultrasound Transducers in Use in Routine Clinical Practice," by Martensson et al., *European Journal of Cardiology,* Vol. 10). If four *different* units are randomly selected and tested, what is the probability that the entire batch will be accepted? Does that probability seem adequate?

In Exercises 29 and 30, find the probabilities and indicate when the "5% guideline for cumbersome calculations" is used.

29. Medical Helicopters In a study of helicopter usage and patient survival, results were obtained from 47,637 patients transported by helicopter and 111,874 patients transported by ground (based on data from "Association Between Helicopter vs Ground Emergency Medical

Services and Survival for Adults with Major Trauma," by Galvagno et al., *Journal of the American Medical Association,* Vol. 307, No. 15).

a. If 1 of the 159,511 patients in the study is randomly selected, what is the probability that the subject was transported by helicopter?

b. If 5 of the subjects in the study are randomly selected without replacement, what is the probability that all of them were transported by helicopter?

30. Medical Helicopters In the same study cited in the preceding exercise, among the 47,637 patients transported by helicopter, 188 of them left the treatment center against medical advice, and the other 47,449 did not leave against medical advice. If 40 of the subjects transported by helicopter are randomly selected without replacement, what is the probability that none of them left the treatment center against medical advice?

4-2 Beyond the Basics

31. MRI Reliability Refer to the accompanying figure showing surge protectors *p* and *q* used to protect an expensive magnetic resonance imaging (MRI) scanner used in a hospital. If there is a surge in the voltage, the surge protector reduces it to a safe level. Assume that each surge protector has a 0.985 probability of working correctly when a voltage surge occurs.

a. If the two surge protectors are arranged in series, what is the probability that a voltage surge will not damage the MRI? (Do not round the answer.)

b. If the two surge protectors are arranged in parallel, what is the probability that a voltage surge will not damage the MRI? (Do not round the answer.)

c. Which arrangement should be used for better protection?

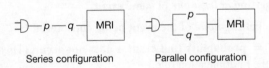

Series configuration   Parallel configuration

32. Same Birthdays If 25 people are randomly selected, find the probability that no 2 of them have the same birthday. Ignore leap years.

33. Exclusive Or The *exclusive or* means either one or the other events occurs, but not both.

a. For the formal addition rule, rewrite the formula for *P(A or B)* assuming that the addition rule uses the *exclusive or* instead of the *inclusive or.*

b. Repeat Exercise 11 "Blood Groups and Types" using the *exclusive or* instead of the *inclusive or.*

34. Complements and the Addition Rule Refer to the table of blood groups and types used for Exercises 9–20. Assume that one subject is randomly selected. Let *A* represent the event of getting someone with Group A blood and let *B* represent the event of getting someone with Group B blood. Find $P(\overline{A \text{ or } B})$, find $P(\overline{A} \text{ or } \overline{B})$, and then compare the results. In general, does $P(\overline{A \text{ or } B}) = P(\overline{A} \text{ or } \overline{B})$?

Complements, Conditional Probability, and Bayes' Theorem

4-3

Key Concept In Part 1 of this section we extend the use of the multiplication rule to include the probability that among several trials, we get *at least one* of some specified event. In Part 2 we consider *conditional probability*: the probability of an event occurring when we have additional information that some other event has already occurred. In Part 3 we provide a brief introduction to the use of Bayes' theorem.

PART 1   Complements: The Probability of "At Least One"

When finding the probability of some event occurring "at least once," we should understand the following:

- "At least one" has the same meaning as "one or more."
- The *complement* of getting "at least one" particular event is that you get *no* occurrences of that event.

For example, not getting at least 1 girl in 10 births is the same as getting no girls, which is also the same as getting 10 boys.

Not getting at least 1 girl in 10 births = Getting no girls = Getting 10 boys

The following steps describe the details of this backward method of finding the probability of getting at least one of some event:

Finding the probability of getting *at least one* of some event:

1. Let A = getting *at least one* of some event.
2. Then $\overline{A}$ = getting *none* of the event being considered.
3. Find $P(\overline{A})$ = probability that event A does not occur. (This is relatively easy using the multiplication rule.)
4. Subtract the result from 1. That is, evaluate this expression:

$$P(at\ least\ one\ \text{occurrence of event } A)$$
$$= 1 - P(no\ \text{occurrences of event } A)$$

EXAMPLE 1   **At Least One Subject with Group AB Blood**

The probability of randomly selecting someone with Group AB blood is 0.0526 (based on the table given with Exercises 9–20 in the preceding section). A researcher needs at least one subject having Group AB blood. If 20 subjects are randomly selected, find the probability of getting at least one with Group AB blood. Is the probability high enough so that the researcher can be reasonably sure of getting someone with Group AB blood?

SOLUTION

Step 1: Let A = at least 1 of the 20 subjects has Group AB blood.

Step 2: Identify the event that is the complement of A.

$\overline{A}$ = *not* getting at least 1 subject with Group AB blood among 20

= all 20 subjects have blood that is not Group AB

Step 3: Find the probability of the complement by evaluating $P(\overline{A})$ If there is a 0.0526 probability of a person having Group AB blood, it follows that there is a 0.9474 probability of a person not having Group AB blood, and we get the following:

$$
\begin{aligned}
P(\overline{A}) &= P(\text{all 20 subjects have blood that is not Group AB}) \\
&= 0.9474 \cdot 0.9474 \cdot \ \cdots \ \cdot 0.9474 \\
&= 0.9474^{20} = 0.339365436
\end{aligned}
$$

Step 4: Find $P(A)$ by evaluating $1 - P(\overline{A})$.

$$
P(A) = 1 - P(\overline{A}) = 1 - 0.339365436 = 0.661 \ (\text{rounded})
$$

INTERPRETATION

For a group of 20 subjects, there is a 0.661 probability of getting at least 1 person with Group AB blood. This probability is not *very* high, so if the researcher needs a person with Group AB blood, more than 20 subjects should be used.

PART 2 **Conditional Probability**

We now consider the principle that the probability of an event is often affected by knowledge that some other event has occurred. For example, the probability of a golfer making a hole in one is 1/12,000 (based on past results), but if you have the additional knowledge that the selected person is a professional golfer, the probability changes to 1/2375 (based on data from *USA Today*).

DEFINITION

A **conditional probability** of an event is a probability obtained with the additional information that some other event has already occurred.

Notation

$P(B|A)$ denotes the conditional probability of event B occurring, given that event A has already occurred.

INTUITIVE APPROACH FOR FINDING $P(B|A)$

The conditional probability of B occurring given that A has occurred can be found by *assuming that event A has occurred* and then calculating the probability that event B will occur, as illustrated in Example 2.

FORMAL APPROACH FOR FINDING $P(B|A)$

The probability $P(B|A)$ can be found by dividing the probability of events A and B both occurring by the probability of event A:

$$
P(B|A) = \frac{P(A \text{ and } B)}{P(A)}
$$

Prosecutor's Fallacy

The *prosecutor's fallacy* is misunderstanding or confusion of two different conditional probabilities: (1) the probability that a defendant is innocent, given that forensic evidence shows a match; (2) the probability that forensics shows a match, given that a person is innocent. The prosecutor's fallacy has led to wrong convictions and imprisonment of some innocent people.

Lucia de Berk was a nurse who was convicted of murder and sentenced to prison in the Netherlands. Hospital administrators observed suspicious deaths that occurred in hospital wards where de Berk had been present. An expert testified that there was only 1 chance in 342 million that her presence was a coincidence. However, mathematician Richard Gill calculated the probability to be closer to 1/150, or possibly as low as 1/5. The court used the probability that the suspicious deaths could have occurred with de Berk present, given that she was innocent. The court should have considered the probability that de Berk is innocent, given that the suspicious deaths occurred when she was present. This error of the prosecutor's fallacy is subtle and can be very difficult to understand and recognize, yet it can lead to the imprisonment of innocent people.

The preceding formula is a formal expression of conditional probability, but blind use of formulas is not recommended. Instead, we recommend the intuitive approach, as illustrated in Example 2.

 EXAMPLE 2 **Pre-Employment Drug Screening**

Refer to Table 4-1 to find the following:

a. If 1 of the 555 test subjects is randomly selected, find the probability that the subject had a positive test result, given that the subject actually uses drugs. That is, find P(positive test result | subject uses drugs).

b. If 1 of the 555 test subjects is randomly selected, find the probability that the subject actually uses drugs, given that he or she had a positive test result. That is, find P(subject uses drugs | positive test result).

TABLE 4-1 Results from Drug Tests of Job Applicants

	Positive Test Result (Test shows drug use.)	Negative Test Result (Test shows no drug use.)
Subject Uses Drugs	45 (True Positive)	5 (False Negative)
Subject Does Not Use Drugs	25 (False Positive)	480 (True Negative)

SOLUTION

a. *Intuitive Approach:* We want P(positive test result | subject uses drugs), the probability of getting someone with a positive test result, *given that the selected subject uses drugs*. Here is the key point: If we assume that the selected subject actually uses drugs, we are dealing only with the 50 subjects in the first row of Table 4-1. Among those 50 subjects, 45 had positive test results, so we get this result:

$$P(\text{positive test result} \mid \text{subject uses drugs}) = \frac{45}{50} = 0.900$$

Formal Approach: The same result can be found by using the formula for $P(B \mid A)$ given with the formal approach. We use the following notation.

$$P(B \mid A) = P(\text{positive test result} \mid \text{subject uses drugs})$$

where B = positive test result and A = subject uses drugs.

In the following calculation, we use P(subject uses drugs and had a positive test result) = 45/555 and P(subject uses drugs) = 50/555 to get the following results:

$$P(B \mid A) = \frac{P(A \text{ and } B)}{P(A)}$$

becomes

$$P(\text{positive test result} \mid \text{subject uses drugs})$$

$$= \frac{P(\text{subject uses drugs and had a positive test result})}{P(\text{subject uses drugs})}$$

$$= \frac{45/555}{50/555} = 0.900$$

By comparing the intuitive approach to the formal approach, it should be clear that the intuitive approach is much easier to use, and it is also less likely to result in errors. The intuitive approach is based on an *understanding* of conditional probability, instead of manipulation of a formula, and understanding is so much better.

b. Here we want P(subject uses drugs | positive test result). If we assume that the subject had a positive test result, we are dealing with the 70 subjects in the first column of Table 4-1. Among those 70 subjects, 45 use drugs, so

$$P(\text{subject uses drugs} \mid \text{positive test result}) = \frac{45}{70} = 0.643$$

Again, the same result can be found by applying the formula for conditional probability, but we will leave that for those with a special fondness for manipulations with formulas.

INTERPRETATION

The first result of P(positive test result | subject uses drugs) = 0.900 indicates that a subject who uses drugs has a 0.900 probability of getting a positive test result. The second result of P(subject uses drugs | positive test result) = 0.643 indicates that for a subject who gets a positive test result, there is a 0.643 probability that this subject actually uses drugs. Note that P(positive test result | subject uses drugs) P(subject uses drugs | positive test result). See "Confusion of the Inverse" that follows.

Confusion of the Inverse

Note that in Example 2, P(positive test result | subject uses drugs) $\neq$ P(subject uses drugs | positive test result). This example proves that in general, $P(B \mid A) \neq P(A \mid B)$. (There could be individual cases where $P(A \mid B)$ and $P(B \mid A)$ are equal, but they are generally not equal.) To incorrectly think that $P(B \mid A)$ and $P(A \mid B)$ are equal or to incorrectly use one value in place of the other is called *confusion of the inverse*.

EXAMPLE 3 **Confusion of the Inverse**

Consider these events:

D: It is dark outdoors.

M: It is midnight.

In the following, we conveniently ignore the Alaskan winter and other such anomalies.

$P(D \mid M) = 1$ (It is certain to be dark given that it is midnight.)

$P(M \mid D) = 0$ (The probability that it is exactly midnight given that it is dark is almost zero.)

Here, $P(D \mid M) \neq P(M \mid D)$. Confusion of the inverse occurs when we incorrectly switch those probability values or think that they are equal.

Group Testing

During World War II, the U.S. Army tested for syphilis by giving each soldier an individual blood test that was analyzed separately. One researcher suggested mixing pairs of blood samples. After the mixed pairs were tested, those with syphilis could be identified by retesting the few blood samples that were in the pairs that tested positive. Since the total number of analyses was reduced by pairing blood specimens, why not combine them in groups of three or four or more? This technique of combining samples in groups and retesting only those groups that test positive is known as *group testing* or *pooled testing,* or *composite testing.* University of Nebraska statistician Christopher Bilder wrote an article about this topic in *Chance* magazine, and he cited some real applications. He noted that the American Red Cross uses group testing to screen for specific diseases, such as hepatitis, and group testing is used by veterinarians when cattle are tested for the bovine viral diarrhea virus.

PART 3 Bayes' Theorem

In this section we extend the discussion of conditional probability to include applications of *Bayes' theorem* (or *Bayes' rule*), which we use for revising a probability value based on additional information that is later obtained.

Let's consider a study showing that physicians often give very misleading information when they experience confusion of the inverse. They tended to confuse $P(\text{cancer} \mid \text{positive test result})$ with $P(\text{positive test result} \mid \text{cancer})$. About 95% of physicians estimated $P(\text{cancer} \mid \text{positive test result})$ to be about 10 times too high, with the result that patients were given diagnoses that were very misleading, and patients were unnecessarily distressed by the incorrect information. Let's take a closer look at this classic example, and let's hope that we can give physicians information in a better format that is easy to understand.

EXAMPLE 4 **Interpreting Medical Test Results**

Assume cancer has a 1% prevalence rate, meaning that 1% of the population has cancer. Denoting the event of having a cancer by C, we have $P(C) = 0.01$ for a subject randomly selected from the population. This result is included with the following performance characteristics of the test for cancer (based on *Probabilistic Reasoning in Clinical Medicine,* by David Eddy, Cambridge University Press).

- There is a 1% prevalence rate of the cancer. That is, $P(C) = 0.01$.
- The false positive rate is 10%. That is, $P(\text{positive test result given that cancer is not present}) = 0.10$.
- The true positive rate is 80%. That is, $P(\text{positive test result given that cancer is present}) = 0.80$.

Find $P(C \mid \text{positive test result})$. That is, find the probability that a subject actually has cancer given that he or she has a positive test result.

SOLUTION

Using the given information, we can construct a hypothetical population with the above characteristics. We can find the entries in Table 4-2 on the next page, as follows.

- Assume that we have 1000 subjects. With a 1% prevalence rate, 10 of the subjects are expected to have cancer. The sum of the entries in the first row of values is therefore 10.
- The other 990 subjects do not have cancer. The sum of the entries in the second row of values is therefore 990.
- Among the 990 subjects without cancer, 10% get positive test results, so 10% of the 990 cancer-free subjects in the second row get positive test results. See the entry of 99 in the second row.
- For the 990 subjects in the second row, 99 test positive, so the other 891 must test negative. See the entry of 891 in the second row.
- Among the 10 subjects with cancer in the first row, 80% of the test results are positive, so 80% of the 10 subjects in the first row test positive. See the entry of 8 in the first row.
- The other 2 subjects in the first row test negative. See the entry of 2 in the first row.

To find $P(C|\text{positive test result})$, see that the first column of values includes the positive test results. In that first column, the probability of randomly selecting a subject with cancer is 8/107 or 0.0748, so $P(C|\text{positive test result}) = 0.0748$.

> **INTERPRETATION**

For the data given in this example, a randomly selected subject has a 1% chance of cancer, but for a randomly selected subject given a test with a positive result, the chance of cancer increases to 7.48%. Based on the data given in this example, a positive test result should not be devastating news, because there is still a good chance that the test is wrong.

TABLE 4-2 Test Results

	Positive Test Result (Test shows cancer.)	Negative Test Result (Test shows no cancer.)	Total
Cancer	8 (True Positive)	2 (False Negative)	10
No Cancer	99 (False Positive)	891 (True Negative)	990

$$P(C|+) = \frac{8}{99}$$

$$P(\text{true}|C) = \frac{8}{10}$$

The solution in Example 4 is not very difficult. Another approach is to compute the probability using this formula commonly given with Bayes' theorem:

$$P(A|B) = \frac{P(A)\cdot P(B|A)}{[P(A)\cdot P(B|A)] + [P(\overline{A})\cdot P(B|\overline{A})]}$$

	Positive	Negative
Cancer	$P(C \text{ and} +)$	$P(C \text{ and} -)$
Not cancer	$P(\overline{C} \text{ and} +)$	$P(\overline{C} \text{ and} -)$

If we replace A with C and replace B with "positive," we get this solution for Example 4:

$$P(C|\text{positive}) = \frac{P(C)\cdot P(\text{positive}|C)}{P(C)\cdot P(\text{positive}|C) + P(\overline{C})\cdot P(\text{Positive}|\overline{C})}$$

$$= \frac{0.01\cdot 0.80}{(0.01\cdot 0.80) + (0.99\cdot 0.10)} = 0.0748$$

$$P(C|\text{positive})$$
$$= \frac{P(C \text{ and Positive})}{P(C \text{ and Positive}) + P(\overline{C} \text{ and Positive})}$$

Study Results Here is a truly fascinating fact: When 100 physicians were given the information in Example 4, 95 of them estimated $P(C|\text{positive})$ to be around 0.70 to 0.80, so they were wrong by a factor of 10. Physicians are extremely intelligent, but here they likely suffered from confusion of the inverse. The given rate of 80% for positive test results among those who are true positives implies that $P(\text{positive}|C) = 0.80$, but this is very different from $P(C|\text{positive})$. The physicians would have done much better if they had seen the given information in the form of a table like Table 4-2.

The importance and usefulness of Bayes' theorem is that it can be used with *sequential* events, whereby new additional information is obtained for a subsequent event, and that new information is used to revise the probability of the initial event. In this context, the terms *prior probability* and *posterior probability* are commonly used.

> **DEFINITIONS**
>
> A **prior probability** is an initial probability value originally obtained before any additional information is obtained.
>
> A **posterior probability** is a probability value that has been revised by using additional information that is later obtained.

Relative to Example 4, $P(C) = 0.01$, which is the probability that a randomly selected subject has cancer. $P(C)$ is an example of a *prior probability*. Using the additional information that the subject has received a positive test result, we found that $P(C|\text{positive test result}) = 0.0748$, and this is a *posterior probability* because it uses that additional information of the positive test result.

4-3   Basic Skills and Concepts

Statistical Literacy and Critical Thinking

1. *Language:* **Complement of "At Least One"** Let A = the event of getting at least one defective pacemaker battery when 3 batteries are randomly selected with replacement from a batch. Write a statement describing event $\overline{A}$.

2. Probability of At Least One Let A = the event of getting at least 1 defective pacemaker battery when 3 batteries are randomly selected with replacement from a batch. If 5% of the batteries in a batch are defective and the other 95% are all good, which of the following are correct?

a. $P(\overline{A}) = (0.95)(0.95)(0.95) = 0.857$

b. $P(A) = 1 - (0.95)(0.95)(0.95) = 0.143$

c. $P(A) = (0.05)(0.05)(0.05) = 0.000125$

3. Notation Let event G = subject has glaucoma (disorder of the eye) and let event Y = test indicates that "yes," the subject has glaucoma. Use your own words to translate the notation $P(Y|G)$ into a verbal statement.

4. Confusion of the Inverse Using the same events G and Y described in Exercise 3, describe confusion of the inverse.

At Least One.   *In Exercises 5–12, find the probability.*

5. Four Boys Find the probability that when a couple has four children, at least one of them is a boy. (Assume that boys and girls are equally likely.)

6. Probability of a Girl Assuming that boys and girls are equally likely, find the probability of a couple having a boy when their third child is born, given that the first two children were both girls.

7. Births in the United States In the United States, the true probability of a baby being a boy is 0.512 (based on the data available at this writing). Among the next six randomly selected births in the United States, what is the probability that at least one of them is a girl?

8. Births in China In China, where many couples were allowed to have only one child, the probability of a baby being a boy was 0.545. Among six randomly selected births in China, what is the probability that at least one of them is a girl? Could this system continue to work indefinitely? (Phasing out of this policy was begun in 2015.)

9. Phone Survey Subjects for the California Health Interview Survey are contacted using telephone numbers in which the last four digits are randomly selected (with replacement). Find the probability that for one such phone number, the last four digits include at least one 0.

10. At Least One Correct Answer If you make random guesses for 10 multiple-choice MCAT test questions (each with five possible answers), what is the probability of getting at least 1 correct? If these questions are part of a practice test and an instructor says that you must get at least one correct answer before continuing, is there a good chance you will continue?

11. At Least One Defective Ultrasound Transducer A study showed that 39.8% of ultrasound transducers are defective (based on data from "High Incidence of Defective Ultrasound

Transducers in Use in Routine Clinical Practice," by Martensson et al., *European Journal of Echocardiography,* Vol. 10, No. 1093.) An engineer needs at least one defective ultrasound transducer so she can try to identify the problem. If she randomly selects 10 ultrasound transducers from a very large batch, what is the probability that she will get at least one that is defective? Is that probability high enough so that she can be reasonably sure of getting a defective transducer for her work?

12. Fruit Flies An experiment with fruit flies involves one parent with normal wings and one parent with vestigial wings. When these parents have an offspring, there is a 3/4 probability that the offspring has normal wings and a 1/4 probability of vestigial wings. If the parents give birth to five offspring, what is the probability that at least one of the offspring has vestigial wings? If researchers need at least one offspring with vestigial wings, can they be quite confident of getting one?

Identical and Fraternal Twins. *In Exercises 13–16, use the data in the following table. Instead of summarizing observed results, the entries reflect the actual probabilities based on births of twins (based on data from the Northern California Twin Registry and the article "Bayesians, Frequentists, and Scientists," by Bradley Efron, Journal of the American Statistical Association, Vol. 100, No. 469). Identical twins come from a single egg that splits into two embryos, and fraternal twins are from separate fertilized eggs. The table entries reflect the principle that among sets of twins, 1/3 are identical and 2/3 are fraternal. Also, identical twins must be of the same gender and the genders are equally likely (approximately), and genders of fraternal twins are equally likely.*

	Boy/boy	Boy/girl	Girl/boy	Girl/girl
Identical Twins	5	0	0	5
Fraternal Twins	5	5	5	5

13. Identical Twins

a. After having a sonogram, a pregnant woman learns that she will have twins. What is the probability that she will have identical twins?

b. After studying the sonogram more closely, the physician tells the pregnant woman that she will give birth to twin boys. What is the probability that she will have identical twins? That is, find the probability of identical twins given that the twins consist of two boys.

14. Fraternal Twins

a. After having a sonogram, a pregnant woman learns that she will have twins. What is the probability that she will have fraternal twins?

b. After studying the sonogram more closely, the physician tells the pregnant woman that she will give birth to twins consisting of one boy and one girl. What is the probability that she will have fraternal twins?

15. Fraternal Twins If a pregnant woman is told that she will give birth to fraternal twins, what is the probability that she will have one child of each gender?

16. Fraternal Twins If a pregnant woman is told that she will give birth to fraternal twins, what is the probability that she will give birth to two girls?

In Exercises 17–20, refer to the accompanying table showing results from a Chembio test for hepatitis C among HIV-infected patients (based on data from a variety of sources).

	Positive Test Result	Negative Test Result
Hepatitis C	335	10
No Hepatitis C	2	1153

17. False Positive Find the probability of selecting a subject with a positive test result, given that the subject does not have hepatitis C. Why is this case problematic for test subjects?

18. False Negative Find the probability of selecting a subject with a negative test result, given that the subject has hepatitis C. What would be an unfavorable consequence of this error?

19. Positive Predictive Value Find the positive predictive value for the test. That is, find the probability that a subject has hepatitis C, given that the test yields a positive result. Does the result make the test appear to be effective?

20. Negative Predictive Value Find the negative predictive value for the test. That is, find the probability that a subject does not have hepatitis C, given that the test yields a negative result. Does the result make the test appear to be effective?

21. Redundancy in Computer Hard Drives Assume that there is a 3% rate of disk drive failures in a year (based on data from various sources including lifehacker.com).

a. If all of your computer data are stored on a hard disk drive with a copy stored on a second hard disk drive, what is the probability that during a year, you can avoid catastrophe with at least one working drive? Express the result with four decimal places.

b. If copies of all of your computer data are stored on three independent hard disk drives, what is the probability that during a year, you can avoid catastrophe with at least one working drive? Express the result with six decimal places. What is wrong with using the usual round-off rule for probabilities in this case?

22. Redundancy in Hospital Generators Assume that emergency backup generators fail 22% of the times when they are needed (based on data from Arshad Mansoor, senior vice president with the Electric Power Research Institute). A hospital has three backup generators so that power is available if at least one of them works in a power failure. Find the probability of having at least one of the backup generators working, given that a power failure has occurred. Does the result appear to be adequate for the hospital's needs?

23. Composite Drug Test Based on the data in Table 4-1 on page 162, assume that the probability of a randomly selected person testing positive for drug use is 0.126. If drug screening samples are collected from 5 random subjects and combined, find the probability that the combined sample will reveal a positive result. Is that probability low enough so that further testing of the individual samples is rarely necessary?

24. Composite Water Samples The Fairfield County Department of Public Health tests water for the presence of *E. coli* (*Escherichia coli*) bacteria. To reduce laboratory costs, water samples from 10 public swimming areas are combined for one test, and further testing is done only if the combined sample tests positive. Based on past results, there is a 0.005 probability of finding *E. coli* bacteria in a public swimming area. Find the probability that a combined sample from 10 public swimming areas will reveal the presence of *E. coli* bacteria. Is that probability low enough so that further testing of the individual samples is rarely necessary?

4-3   Beyond the Basics

25. Shared Birthdays Find the probability that of 25 randomly selected people, at least 2 share the same birthday.

4-4   Risks and Odds

Key Concept This section introduces absolute risk reduction, relative risk, and odds ratio as measures helpful for comparing probability values and measuring risk. This section also introduces "number needed to treat" as a measure of the number of subjects that must be treated in order to prevent the single occurrence of some event, such as a disease.

One simple way to measure risk is to use a probability value. For example, in one of the largest medical experiments ever conducted, it was found that among 200,745 children injected with the Salk vaccine, 33 developed paralytic polio (poliomyelitis). It follows that for this treatment group, $P(\text{polio}) = 33/200,745 = 0.000164$. However, that single measure does not give us any information about the rate of polio for those children who were injected with a placebo. The risk of polio for children treated with the Salk vaccine should be somehow compared to the risk of polio for those children given a placebo. Let's consider the data summarized in Table 4-3.

TABLE 4-3 Prospective Study of Polio and the Salk Vaccine

	Polio	No polio	Total
Salk Vaccine	33	200,712	**200,745**
Placebo	115	201,114	**201,229**

Based on the data in Table 4-3, we can identify the following probabilities:

Polio rate for treatment group: $P(\text{polio} \mid \text{Salk vaccine}) = \dfrac{33}{200,745} = 0.000164$

Polio rate for placebo group: $P(\text{polio} \mid \text{placebo}) = \dfrac{115}{201,229} = 0.00571$

Informal comparison of the preceding two probabilities likely suggests that there is a substantial difference between the two polio rates. Later chapters will use more effective methods for determining whether the apparent difference is actually significant, but in this section we introduce some simple measures for comparing the two rates.

The preceding table can be generalized with the following format:

TABLE 4-4 Generalized Table Summarizing Results of a Prospective Study

	Disease	No Disease
Treatment	a	b
Placebo	c	d

We noted above that this section introduces some simple measures for comparing two rates, such as the polio rate for the Salk vaccine treatment group and the polio rate for the placebo group, as summarized in Table 4-3. We begin with the *absolute risk reduction*.

[Handwritten annotations in margin:]

Absolute Risk Reduction

$$= |P(D \mid T) - P(D \mid \bar{T})|$$

$$= \left| \frac{a}{a+b} - \frac{c}{c+d} \right|$$

[Handwritten next to Table 4-4: a+b, c+d, a+c, b+d]

Monkey Typists

A classical claim is that a monkey randomly hitting a keyboard would eventually produce the complete works of Shakespeare, assuming that it continues to type century after century. The multiplication rule for probability has been used to find such estimates. One result of 1,000,000,000,000,000, 000,000,000,000,000,000,000 years is considered by some to be too short. In the same spirit, Sir Arthur Eddington wrote this poem: "There once was a brainy baboon, who always breathed down a bassoon. For he said, 'It appears that in billions of years, I shall certainly hit on a tune.'"

Absolute Risk Reduction

DEFINITION

When comparing two probabilities or rates, the **absolute risk reduction** is simply the absolute value of the following difference.

Absolute risk reduction = |P(event occurring in treatment group)
  − P(event occurring in control group)|

If the data are in the generalized format of Table 4–4, we can express the absolute risk reduction as follows:

Absolute risk reduction = |P(event occurring in treatment group)
  − P(event occurring in control group)|

$$= \left| \frac{a}{a + b} - \frac{c}{c + d} \right|$$

(In the above expression, "treatment" might be replaced by the "presence of some condition" or some other equivalent description.)

CAUTION: The above definition of absolute risk reduction always results in the *positive* difference between a probability in the treatment group and a probability in the control group. Consider this when interpreting the effectiveness of the treatment in terms of being helpful or harmful. See Exercises 13–16, where those in an atorvastatin treatment group have a *higher* rate of infections than those in the placebo group. Be careful to interpret the results correctly.

EXAMPLE 1   Finding Absolute Risk Reduction

Using the data summarized in Table 4-3, find the absolute risk reduction, which can be used to measure the effectiveness of the Salk vaccine.

SOLUTION

Based on the data in Table 4-3, we have already found that P(polio | Salk vaccine) = 0.000164 and P(polio | placebo) = 0.000571. It follows that:

Absolute risk reduction = |P(polio | Salk vaccine) − P(polio | placebo)|
  = |0.000164 − 0.000571| = 0.000407

For a subject treated with the Salk vaccine, there is an absolute risk reduction of 0.000407 when compared to a subject given a placebo. That is, there are 0.0407% fewer events of polio for subjects treated with the Salk vaccine than for subjects given a placebo. This doesn't seem like much of a reduction, but when considered in the context of the number of polio events in a large population, it is a significant reduction.

Relative Risk

Section 1-3 included definitions of retrospective and prospective studies:

- Retrospective Study: Data are collected from a past time period by going back in time (through examinations of records, interviews, etc.).

- Prospective Study: Data are collected in the future from groups or "cohorts" that share common factors.

In a prospective study, a commonly used measure for comparing risk is *relative risk.* We first introduce the following notation, and then we define relative risk.

Notation

p_t = proportion (or incidence rate) of some characteristic in a *treatment group*

p_c = proportion (or incidence rate) of some characteristic in a *control group*

DEFINITION

In a *prospective study,* the **relative risk** (or **risk ratio** or **RR**) of a characteristic is the ratio p_t/p_c, where p_t is the proportion of the characteristic in the treatment (or exposed) group and p_c is the proportion in the control group (or group not exposed). If the data are in the same format as the generalized Table 4-4, then the relative risk is found by evaluating

$$\frac{p_t}{p_c} = \frac{\dfrac{a}{a+b}}{\dfrac{c}{c+d}}$$

treatment group
= exposed group

control group
= not exposed

Interpreting Relative Risk A relative risk value of 1 shows that the risk is the same for the treatment group and the control (or placebo) group. A relative risk value much greater than 1 shows that there is a much greater risk for the treatment group. The following example illustrates how the relative risk of 0.287 shows that the risk of polio in the treatment group is much less than the risk of polio in the placebo group.

EXAMPLE 2 Computing Relative Risk

Using the data in Table 4-3, find the relative risk.

SOLUTION

For the sample data in Table 4-3, we will consider the treatment group to be the group of children given the Salk vaccine, and the control group is the group of children given a placebo. Using the preceding notation, we have

$$p_t = \text{proportion of polio in } \textit{treatment group} = \frac{33}{33 + 200{,}712} = 0.000164$$

$$p_c = \text{proportion of polio in } \textit{control (placebo) group} = \frac{115}{115 + 201{,}114} = 0.000571$$

Using the above values, we can now find the relative risk as follows.

$$\text{Relative risk} = \frac{p_t}{p_c} = \frac{0.000164}{0.000571} = 0.287$$

INTERPRETATION

We can interpret this result as follows: The polio rate for children given the Salk vaccine is 0.287 of the polio rate for children given a placebo. (A relative risk less than 1 indicates that the treatment results in a reduced risk.) If we were to consider the reciprocal value of $0.000571/0.000164 = 3.48$, we see that children in the placebo group are 3.48 times more likely to get polio.

CAUTION: When interpreting relative risk, consider the incidence rates. If the probability of disease in an exposed group is 5/1,000,000 and the probability of disease in an unexposed group is 1/1,000,000, the relative risk is 5.0, which sounds really bad, but the very low incidence rates suggest that there isn't much risk in either group.

Number Needed to Treat

One problem with relative risk is that it may be misleading by suggesting that a treatment is superior or inferior, even when the absolute difference between rates is not very large. For example, if 3 out of 10,000 aspirin users were to experience an immediate cure of a cold compared to only 1 out of 10,000 placebo users, the relative risk of 3.00 correctly indicates that the incidence of immediate cold cures is *three times* as high for aspirin users, but the cure rates of 0.0003 and 0.0001 are so close that, for all practical purposes, aspirin should not be considered as a factor affecting the immediate cure of a cold. With cure rates of 0.0003 and 0.0001, the absolute risk reduction is 0.0002. Because the absolute risk reduction is so small, the effectiveness of the aspirin treatment would be negligible. In such a situation, the *number needed to treat* would be a more effective measure that is not so misleading.

DEFINITION

The **number needed to treat (NNT)** is the number of subjects that must be treated in order to prevent *one* event, such as a disease or adverse reaction. It is calculated by dividing 1 by the absolute risk reduction.

$$\text{number needed to treat} = \frac{1}{\text{absolute risk reduction}}$$

Round-Off Rule If the calculated value of the number needed to treat is not a whole number, round it *up* to the next larger whole number.

If the sample data are in the format of the generalized Table 4-4, then:

$$\text{Number needed to treat} = \frac{1}{\left|\dfrac{a}{a+b} - \dfrac{c}{c+d}\right|} \quad \text{(rounded up to the next larger whole number)}$$

If 3 out of 10,000 aspirin users were to experience an immediate cure of a cold compared to only 1 out of 10,000 placebo users, the absolute risk reduction is $|0.0003 - 0.0001| = 0.0002$, and the number needed to treat is $1/0.0002 = 5000$. This means that we would need to treat 5000 subjects with colds to get *one* person who experiences an immediate cure.

EXAMPLE 3 Computing the Number Needed to Treat

Using the polio data in Table 4-3, find the number needed to treat, then interpret the result.

SOLUTION

In Example 1 we found that the absolute risk reduction is 0.000407. It is now easy to find the number needed to treat.

$$\text{Number needed to treat} = \frac{1}{\text{absolute risk reduction}} = \frac{1}{0.000407} = 2457.002457$$

$$= 2458 \text{ (rounded up)}$$

INTERPRETATION

The result of 2458 can be interpreted as follows: We would need to vaccinate 2458 children with the Salk vaccine (instead of a placebo) to prevent *one* of the children from getting polio. Given the extremely serious consequences of polio, the Salk vaccine has been found to be very effective and important.

Odds

So far in this chapter, we have used probability values to express likelihood of various events. Probability values are numbers between 0 and 1 inclusive. However, expressions of likelihood are often given as *odds,* such as 50:1 (or "50 to 1").

DEFINITIONS

The **actual odds against** event A occurring are the ratio $P(\bar{A})/P(A)$, usually expressed in the form of $a:b$ (or "a to b"), where a and b are integers. (Reduce using the largest common factor; if $a = 16$ and $b = 4$, express the odds as 4:1 instead of 16:4.)

The **actual odds in favor** of event A occurring are the ratio $P(A)/P(\bar{A})$, which is the reciprocal of the actual odds against that event. If the odds against an event are $a:b$, then the odds in favor are $b:a$.

Note that in the two preceding definitions, the *actual odds against* and the *actual odds in favor* describe the actual likelihood of some event. (Gambling situations typically use *payoff odds,* which describe the amount of profit relative to the amount of a bet. For example, if you bet on the number 7 in roulette, the actual odds against winning are 37:1, but the payoff odds are 35:1. Racetracks and casinos are in business to make a profit, so the payoff odds will usually differ from the actual odds.)

EXAMPLE 4 **Rehospitalization and Discharge**

Consider the data in Table 4-5 (based on results from "The Safety of Newborn Early Discharge," by Liu, Clemens, Shay, Davis, and Novack, *Journal of the American Medical Association,* Vol. 278, No. 4).

a. For those babies discharged early, find the probability of being rehospitalized within a week.

b. For those babies discharged early, find the odds in favor of being rehospitalized early.

TABLE 4-5 Retrospective Study of Newborn Discharge and Rehospitalization

	Rehospitalized within a week	Not rehospitalized within a week	Total
Early discharge (<30 hours)	457	3199	3656
Late discharge (30 + hours)	260	2860	3120

continued

SOLUTION

a. There were 3656 babies discharged early, and 457 of them were rehospitalized within a week, so

$$P(\text{rehospitalized}) = \frac{457}{3656} = \frac{1}{8}$$

b. Because $P(\text{rehospitalized}) = 1/8$, it follows that $P(\overline{\text{rehospitalized}}) = 1 - 1/8 = 7/8$. We can now find the odds in favor of rehospitalization as follows:

Odds in favor of rehospitalization for the early discharge group

$$= \frac{P(\text{rehospitalized})}{P(\overline{\text{rehospitalized}})} = \frac{1/8}{7/8} = \frac{1}{7}$$

This result is often expressed as 1:7.

With odds of 1:7 in favor of rehospitalization for babies discharged early, it follows that the odds *against* rehospitalization for early discharge are 7:1.

Odds Ratio

For the data in Table 4-5, how does the likelihood of rehospitalization differ between the early discharge group and the late discharge group? One way to address that question is to use the *odds ratio*.

DEFINITION

In a *retrospective* or *prospective study*, the **odds ratio** (**OR** or **relative odds**) is a measure of risk found by evaluating the ratio of the odds in favor of the treatment group (or case group exposed to the risk factor) to the odds in favor of the control group, evaluated as follows:

$$\text{Odds ratio} = \frac{\text{odds in favor of treatment (or exposed) group}}{\text{odds in favor of control group}}$$

If the data are in the format of the generalized Table 4-4 on page 169, then the odds ratio can be computed as follows:

$$\text{Odds ratio} = \frac{ad}{bc}$$

 EXAMPLE 5 Computing Odds Ratio

Using the data in Table 4-5, find the odds ratio for rehospitalization.

SOLUTION

For this example, we consider the case group to be the babies discharged early, and we consider the control group to be the babies discharged late. The preceding example showed that for the early discharge group, the odds in favor of rehospitalization are 1:7. Using similar calculations for the late discharge group, we get odds in favor of rehospitalization of $1/11$ or 1:11. We can now find the odds ratio.

$$\text{Odds ratio} = \frac{\text{odds in favor of rehospitalization in early discharge group}}{\text{odds in favor of rehospitalization in late discharge group}} = \frac{1/7}{1/11}$$

$$= \frac{11}{7} \text{ or } 1.571$$

If we take advantage of the fact that Table 4-5 does correspond to the generalized Table 4-4 on page 169, then the odds ratio can also be calculated as follows:

$$\text{Odds ratio} = \frac{ad}{bc} = \frac{(457)(2860)}{(3199)(260)} = 1.571$$

> **INTERPRETATION**
>
> This result indicates that the odds in favor of rehospitalization are 1.571 times higher for babies discharged early when compared to those discharged late. This suggests that newborns discharged early are at substantially increased risk of rehospitalization.

Why Not Use Relative Risk for *Retrospective Studies*?

Relative risk makes sense only if the involved probabilities are good estimates of the actual incidence rates, as in a prospective study. Using relative risk for a retrospective study could incorrectly involve a situation in which researchers can choose disease cases that are very different from actual incidence rates, with the result that the relative risk can be very wrong. That is the reason that relative risk is defined for *prospective* studies only. The odds ratio is defined for *prospective* and *retrospective* studies.

> **Relative Risk: Prospective study**
>
> **Odds Ratio: Prospective study or retrospective study**

Table 4–6 includes the results from a *prospective* study of 1000 randomly selected subjects, which is conducted to investigate the risk of lung cancer from smoking. Table 4-6 contains entries that are realistic based on current incidence rates. However, Table 4-7 below is based on a *retrospective* study in which the researcher went back in time to find 985 subjects with lung cancer and 985 subjects without lung cancer, so Table 4-7 does *not* reflect actual incidence rates. See the following.

From Table 4-6: $P(\text{lung cancer} \mid \text{smoker}) = 13/180 = 0.0722$
From Table 4-7: $P(\text{lung cancer} \mid \text{smoker}) = 854/1021 = 0.836$

The above probabilities are very different, so both of them cannot be good estimates of the likelihood of getting lung cancer from smoking. The above probability of 0.0722 is a good estimate because it is based on a prospective study with realistic incidence rates, but the probability of 0.836 is a poor estimate because it is based on the retrospective study designed to include an equal number of subjects with lung cancer and subjects without lung cancer.

Now compare the relative risk values and the odds ratio values from Tables 4-6 and 4-7. See that the odds ratio values are approximately the same, but the relative risk values are dramatically different. The relative risk value of 29.6 from the prospective study is a good measure, but the relative risk of 6.1 from the retrospective study is a poor measure.

TABLE 4-6 Prospective Study

	RR = 29.6; OR = 31.8	
	Lung Cancer	No Lung Cancer
Smoker	13	167
Nonsmoker	2	818

TABLE 4-7 Retrospective Study

	RR = 6.1; OR = 31.9	
	Lung Cancer	No Lung Cancer
Smoker	854	167
Nonsmoker	131	818
Total	985	985

SUMMARY OF KEY POINTS

	Disease	No Disease
Treatment	a	b
Placebo	c	d

- **Absolute risk reduction** $= \left| \dfrac{a}{a + b} - \dfrac{c}{c + d} \right|$

- **Number Needed to Treat (NNT)** $= \dfrac{1}{\text{Absolute Risk Reduction}}$

- **Actual odds against event** $A = \dfrac{P(\bar{A})}{P(A)}$

- **Actual odds in favor of event** $A = \dfrac{P(A)}{P(\bar{A})}$

- Relative risk $(\text{RR}) = \dfrac{p_t}{p_c} = \dfrac{\dfrac{a}{a + b}}{\dfrac{c}{c + d}}$
  (for prospective only)

- Odds ratio $(\text{OR}) = \dfrac{ad}{bc} = \left(\dfrac{a}{b}\right) \Big/ \left(\dfrac{c}{d}\right)$

4-4   Basic Skills and Concepts

Statistical Literacy and Critical Thinking

1. Notation The relative risk of a characteristic is the ratio p_t / p_c. What do p_t and p_c represent?

2. Relative Risk Identify an important disadvantage of relative risk used with a relatively small difference between the rates in the treatment and control groups.

3. Number Needed to Treat A measure of the effectiveness of an influenza vaccine is the number needed to treat, which is 37 (under certain conditions). Interpret that number. Does the result apply to every particular group of 37 subjects?

4. Retrospective/Prospective The odds ratio is a measure used in retrospective or prospective studies. Describe retrospective and prospective studies.

Headaches and Viagra   *In Exercises 5–12, use the data in the accompanying table (based on data from Pfizer, Inc.). That table describes results from a clinical trial of the drug Viagra. Some subjects were treated with Viagra while others were given a placebo; then headache events were recorded.*

	Headache	No Headache
Viagra Treatment	117	617
Placebo	29	696

5. Type of Study Is the study retrospective or prospective?

6. Probability For those in the Viagra treatment group, find the probability that the subject experienced a headache.

7. Comparing Probabilities Compare P(headache | Viagra treatment) and P(headache | placebo).

8. Absolute Risk Reduction Find the value of the absolute risk reduction for headaches in the treatment and placebo groups.

9. Number Needed to Treat Find the number of Viagra users that would need to stop using Viagra in order to prevent a single headache.

10. Odds For those in the Viagra treatment group, find the odds in favor of a headache, then find the odds against a headache.

11. Relative Risk Find the relative risk of a headache for those in the treatment group compared to those in the placebo group. Interpret the result.

12. Odds Ratio Find the odds ratio for headaches in the treatment group compared to the placebo group, then interpret the result. Should Viagra users be concerned about headaches as an adverse reaction?

Clinical Trial of Atorvastatin (Lipitor). *In Exercises 13–16, use the data in the accompanying table that summarizes results from a clinical trial of atorvastatin (based on data from Parke-Davis).*

	Infection	No Infection
Atorvastatin (10 mg)	89	774
Placebo	27	243

13. Absolute Risk Reduction

a. What is the probability of infection in the atorvastatin treatment group?

b. What is the probability of infection in the placebo group?

c. Find the value of the absolute risk reduction for infection in the placebo group and the atorvastatin treatment group. Write a brief statement interpreting the result.

14. Number Needed to Treat Calculate the number needed to treat and interpret the result.

15. Odds For those who were treated with atorvastatin, find the odds in favor of an infection. Also find the odds in favor of an infection for those given a placebo. Is there much of a difference between these two results?

16. Odds Ratio and Relative Risk Find the odds ratio and relative risk for an infection in the group treated with atorvastatin compared to the placebo group. Based on this result, does atorvastatin appear to increase the risk of an infection? Why or why not?

17. Odds Ratio and Relative Risk In a clinical trial of 2103 subjects treated with Nasonex (mometasone), 26 reported headaches. In a control group of 1671 subjects given a placebo, 22 reported headaches. Find the relative risk and odds ratio for the headache data. What do the results suggest about the risk of a headache from the Nasonex treatment?

18. Design of Experiments You would like to conduct a study to determine the effectiveness of seat belts in saving lives in car crashes.

a. What would be wrong with randomly selecting 2000 drivers, then randomly assigning half of them to a group that uses seat belts and another group that does not wear seat belts?

b. If 2000 drivers are randomly selected and separated into two groups according to whether they use seat belts, what is a practical obstacle in conducting a prospective study of the effectiveness of seat belts in car crashes?

4-5   Rates of Mortality, Fertility, and Morbidity

In the biological and health sciences, *rates* are often used to describe the likelihood of an event. Rates are used by researchers and health professionals to monitor the health status of a community or population. Although any specific time interval could be used, we assume a time interval of *one year* throughout this section.

> **DEFINITION**
>
> A **rate** describes the frequency of occurrence of some event. It is the relative frequency of an event, multiplied by some number, typically a value such as 1000 or 100,000. A rate can be expressed as
>
> $$\left(\frac{a}{b}\right)k$$
>
> where
>
> a = frequency count of the number of people for whom the event occurred
>
> b = total number of people exposed to the risk of the event occurring
>
> k = multiplier number, such as 1000 or 100,000

The above general definition is commonly applied to measures of mortality, fertility, and morbidity. For the following rates, mortality refers to deaths, fertility refers to births, and morbidity refers to diseases. Here are additional terms and their meanings:

- *Infants:* Babies who were born alive
- *Neonates:* Infants under the age of 28 days
- *Fetal Death:* Occurs when a fetus is delivered without life after 20 weeks of gestation
- *Neonatal Death:* Occurs when an infant dies under 28 days of age

Mortality Rates

$$\text{Crude (or unadjusted) mortality rate} = \left(\frac{\text{deaths}}{\text{population size}}\right)k$$

$$\text{Infant mortality rate} = \left(\frac{\text{deaths of infants under 1 year of age}}{\text{number of live births}}\right)k$$

$$\text{Neonatal mortality rate} = \left(\frac{\text{deaths of infants under 28 days of age}}{\text{number of live births}}\right)k$$

$$\text{Fetal mortality rate} =$$
$$\left(\frac{\text{fetuses delivered without life after 20 weeks of gestation}}{\text{number of live births} + \text{fetuses delivered without life after 20 weeks of gestation}}\right)k$$

$$\text{Perinatal mortality rate} = \left(\frac{\text{fetal deaths} + \text{neonatal deaths}}{\text{live births} + \text{fetal deaths}}\right)k$$

Fertility Rates

$$\text{Crude birthrate} = \left(\frac{\text{live births}}{\text{population size}}\right)k$$

$$\text{General fertility rate} = \left(\frac{\text{live births}}{\text{number of women aged } 15 - 44}\right)k$$

Morbidity (Disease) Rates

$$\text{Incidence rate} = \left(\frac{\text{reported new cases of disease}}{\text{population size}}\right)k$$

$$\text{Prevalence rate} = \left(\frac{\text{number of people with disease at a given time}}{\text{population size at the given point in time}}\right)k$$

 EXAMPLE 1 **Crude Mortality Rate**

For a recent year in the United States, there were 2,515,458 deaths in a population of 312,799,495 people. Use those values with a multiplier of 1000 to find the crude mortality rate.

SOLUTION

With 2,515,458 people who died, with 312,799,495 people in the population, and letting $k = 1000$, we compute the crude mortality rate as follows:

$$\text{Crude mortality rate} = \left(\frac{\text{deaths}}{\text{population size}}\right)k = \left(\frac{2,515,458}{312,799,495}\right)1000$$

$$= 8.0 \text{ (rounded)}$$

INTERPRETATION

For this particular year, the death rate is 8.0 people for each 1000 people in the population. Using the relative frequency definition of probability given in Section 4-1, we might also say that for a randomly selected person, the probability of death in this year is $2,515,458/312,799,495 = 0.00804$. One important advantage of the mortality rate of 8.0 people (per 1000 people in the population) is that it results in a value that uses fewer decimal places and is generally easier to use and understand.

EXAMPLE 2 **Infant Mortality Rate**

The infant mortality rate is a very important measure of the health of a region. (According to the United Nations, the worldwide infant mortality rate is 49.4 per 1000 live births.) For a recent year, there were 3,953,590 live births in the United States, and there were 23,910 deaths of infants under 1 year of age. Using a multiplying factor of $k = 1000$, find the infant mortality rate of the United States and compare it to the rate of 2.1 for Japan.

SOLUTION

The infant mortality rate is computed as shown below.

$$\text{Infant mortality rate} = \left(\frac{\text{deaths of infants under 1 year of age}}{\text{number of live births}}\right)k$$

$$= \left(\frac{23,910}{3,953,590}\right)1000$$

$$= 6.0 \text{ (rounded)}$$

continued

> **INTERPRETATION**
>
> The infant mortality rate of 6.0 deaths per 1000 infants under 1 year of age is substantially greater than the infant mortality rate of 2.1 in Japan.

A *crude rate,* as defined, is a single value based on crude totals. When comparing two different regions, such as Florida and Colorado, a comparison of rates can be misleading because of differences in factors such as age that might affect the rates. In a recent year, the crude mortality rates (per 1000 population) were 9.1 in Florida and 6.4 in Colorado. This is not too surprising, considering that in Florida, roughly 18% of the population is over the age of 65, compared to only 11% for Colorado. The higher mortality rate for Florida does not mean that Florida is less healthy; in this case, it appears that Florida has a higher death rate largely because it has a higher proportion of older residents. Instead of using crude rates, we might use either *specific rates* or *adjusted rates*.

Specific rates are rates specific for some particular group, such as people aged 18–24, or rates specific for some particular cause of death, such as deaths due to myocardial infarction.

Adjusted rates involve calculations that can be quite complicated, but they basically make adjustments for important factors, such as age, gender, or race.

Because age is the characteristic that typically affects mortality the most, it is the most common factor used as the basis for adjustment. Calculations of adjusted rates involve the creation of a theoretical *standardized* population that is used for the regions being compared. A population of 1,000,000 people with the same composition as the United States is often used as the standardized population. Adjusted rates are valuable for comparing different regions, but they do not necessarily reflect the true crude death rates. Adjusted rates should not be used as death rates and they should not be compared to crude rates.

When assessing the accuracy of rates, we should consider the source. Mortality rates found in a source such as the *Statistical Abstract of the United States* (compiled by the U.S. Bureau of the Census) are likely to be quite accurate, because each state now has a mandatory death reporting system, although official government reports seem to take years to produce. However, morbidity rates are likely to be less accurate, because some diseases are known to be underreported or not reported at all. Some morbidity rates might be the result of very questionable surveys. However, some surveys, such as the annual National Health Survey, involve large samples of people who are very carefully chosen, so that results are likely to be very accurate.

4-5   Basic Skills and Concepts

Statistical Literacy and Critical Thinking

1. Death Rate The death rate in Germany is 11.6 per 1000. What exactly does that mean?

2. Rates Exercise 1 describes the death rate in Germany as 11.6 per 1000. Another way to describe the death rate is to give the rate as a proportion or probability of 0.0116. What advantage does the rate of "11.6 per 1000" have over the rate expressed as 0.0116?

3. Expected Deaths Given that Germany has a death rate of 11.6 per 1000 and a population of 80,722,792, about how many deaths are expected in a year?

4. Incidence and Prevalence What is the difference between a disease incidence rate and a disease prevalence rate?

Finding Rates. *In Exercises 5–12, use the data in the accompanying table (based on data for a recent year from various sources, including the U.S. Census Bureau and the National Institutes of Health) to find the indicated rates. Round results to one decimal place, and use a multiplying factor of* $k = 1000$ *unless indicated otherwise.*

Vital Statistics for the United States in One Year

Population: 312,799,495	Deaths: 2,515,458
Women aged 15–44: 61,488,227	Motor vehicle deaths: 33,783
Live births: 3,953,590	Fetuses delivered without life after 20 weeks of gestation: 26,148
Deaths of infants under 1 year of age: 23,910	Deaths of infants under 28 days of age: 15,973
HIV-infected persons: 1,155,792	Deaths from HIV infections: 7683

5. Find the neonatal mortality rate.

6. Find the fetal mortality rate.

7. Find the perinatal mortality rate.

8. Find the crude birth rate.

9. Find the general fertility rate.

10. Using a multiplier of $k = 100,000$, find the motor vehicle death incidence rate.

11. Find the HIV infection prevalence rate.

12. Find the HIV infection mortality rate for HIV-infected persons.

13. Finding Probability An example in this section involved the crude mortality rate, which was found to be 8.0 persons per 1000 population. Find the *probability* of randomly selecting someone and getting a person who died within the year. What advantage does the crude mortality rate have over the probability value?

14. Finding Probability The crude death rate for Brazil was recently 6.2, and that rate was computed using a multiplier of $k = 1000$.

a. Find the probability that a randomly selected Brazilian person died within the year.

b. If three Brazilians are randomly selected, find the probability that they all died within the year, and express the result using three significant digits.

c. If three Brazilians are randomly selected, find the probability that none of them died within the year, and express the result using three significant digits.

15. Finding Probability The crude death rate for South Africa was recently 12.4, and that rate was computed using a multiplier of $k = 1000$.

a. Find the probability that a randomly selected South African died within the year.

b. If three South Africans are randomly selected, find the probability that they all died within the year, and express the result using three significant digits.

c. If three South Africans are randomly selected, find the probability that at least one of them survived the year, and express the result using six decimal places. What would be wrong with expressing the answer using three significant digits?

continued

16. Finding Probability In a recent year in the United States, there were 787,650 deaths due to cardiovascular disease, and the population was 312,799,495.

a. Find the crude mortality rate for cardiovascular disease. (This result is sometimes called the *cause-specific death rate*.)

b. Find the probability that a randomly selected person died of cardiovascular disease and express the result using three significant digits.

c. Find the probability that when three people are randomly selected, none of them died because of cardiovascular disease.

17. Cause-of-Death Ratio In a recent year in the United States, there were 2,515,458 deaths, and 787,650 of them were due to cardiovascular disease. The **cause-of-death ratio** is expressed as follows:

$$\left(\frac{\text{deaths due to specific disease}}{\text{total number of deaths}} \right) k \quad \text{where } k = 100$$

a. Find the cause-of-death ratio for cardiovascular disease.

b. If three of the deaths are randomly selected, find the probability that none of them are due to cardiovascular disease.

18. Crude Mortality Rates The table below lists numbers of deaths and population sizes for different age groups for Florida and the United States for a recent year.

a. Find the crude mortality rate for Florida and the crude mortality rate for the United States. Although we should not compare crude mortality rates, what does the comparison suggest in this case?

b. Using only the age group of 65 and older, find the mortality rates for Florida and the United States. Compare the results.

c. What percentage of the Florida population is made up of people aged 65 and older? What is the percentage for the United States? What do the results suggest about the crude mortality for Florida compared to the United States?

	Age		
	0–24	25–64	65 and older
Florida deaths	3625	39,820	129,395
Florida population	5,716,861	9,842,031	3,375,303
U.S. deaths	63,208	619,982	1,832,268
U.S. population	103,542,603	163,960,163	45,296,729

19. Number of Deaths The number of deaths in the United States has been steadily increasing each year. Does this mean that the health of the nation is declining? Why or why not?

20. Comparing Rates In a recent year, the crude mortality rate of the United States was 8.0 (per 1000 population), and the corresponding crude mortality rate for China was 7.4. What is a major problem with comparing the crude mortality rates of the United States and China?

4-5   Beyond the Basics

21. Adjusted Mortality Rate Refer to the data listed in Exercise 18. Change the Florida population sizes for the three age categories so that they fit the same age distribution as the U.S. population. Next, adjust the corresponding numbers of deaths proportionately. (Use the same Florida mortality rates for the individual age categories, but apply those rates to the adjusted population sizes.) Finally, compute the Florida mortality rate using the adjusted values. The result is a mortality rate adjusted for the variable of age. (Better results could be obtained by using more age categories.) How does this adjusted mortality rate for Florida compare to the mortality rate for the United States? (*Note:* There are other methods for computing adjusted rates than the one used here.)

4-6 Counting

Key Concept Probability problems typically require that we know the total number of simple events, but finding that number often requires one of the five rules presented in this section. In Section 4-2, with the addition rule, multiplication rule, and conditional probability, we encouraged intuitive rules based on understanding and we discouraged blind use of formulas, but this section requires much greater use of formulas as we consider five different methods for counting the number of possible outcomes in a variety of situations. Not all counting problems can be solved with these five methods, but they do provide a strong foundation for the most common real applications.

1. Multiplication Counting Rule

The *multiplication counting rule* is used to find the total number of possibilities from some sequence of events.

> **MULTIPLICATION COUNTING RULE:** For a sequence of events in which the first event can occur n_1 ways, the second event can occur n_2 ways, the third event can occur n_3 ways, and so on, the total number of possibilities is $n_1 \cdot n_2 \cdot n_3 \ldots$.

 EXAMPLE 1 Multiplication Counting Rule: DNA

In a linear triplet of three DNA nucleotides, each of the nucleotides can be any one of these four bases (with repetition allowed): A (adenine); C (cytosine); G (guanine); T (thymine). Two different examples of triplets are CTA and TTG. What is the total number of different possible triplets? Given that the four nucleotides are equally likely, what is the probability of getting the triplet of AAA?

SOLUTION

There are 4 different possibilities for each of the three nucleotides, so the total number of different possible triplets is $n_1 \cdot n_2 \cdot n_3 = 4 \cdot 4 \cdot 4 = 64$.

If the four nucleotides are equally likely, the probability of getting the triplet of AAA is 1/64 or 0.0156.

2. Factorial Rule

The factorial rule is used to find the total number of ways that n different items can be rearranged with different arrangements of the same items counted separately. The factorial rule uses the following notation.

> **NOTATION**
>
> The **factorial symbol (!)** denotes the product of decreasing positive whole numbers. For example, $4! = 4 \cdot 3 \cdot 2 \cdot 1 = 24$. By special definition, $0! = 1$.

> **FACTORIAL RULE** The number of different *arrangements* (order matters) of n different items when all n of them are selected is $n!$.

The factorial rule is based on the principle that the first item may be selected n different ways, the second item may be selected $n - 1$ ways, and so on.

Routing problems often involve applications of the factorial rule, as in the following example.

EXAMPLE 2 **Factorial Rule: Travel Itinerary**

Quest Diagnostics collects blood specimens from different laboratories. A driver is dispatched to make collections at 5 different locations. How many different routes are possible?

SOLUTION

For those 5 different locations, the number of different routes is $5! = 5 \cdot 4 \cdot 3 \cdot 2 \cdot 1 = 120$.

Note that this solution could have been done by applying the multiplication counting rule. The first stop can be any one of the 5 locations, the second stop can be any one of the 4 remaining locations, and so on. The result is again $5 \cdot 4 \cdot 3 \cdot 2 \cdot 1 = 120$. Use of the factorial rule has the advantage of including the factorial symbol, which is sure to impress.

Permutations and Combinations: Does *Order* Count?

When using different counting methods, it is essential to know whether different arrangements of the same items are counted only once or are counted separately. The terms *permutations* and *combinations* are standard in this context, and they are defined as follows:

DEFINITIONS

Permutations of items are arrangements in which different sequences of the same items are counted *separately*. (The letter arrangements of abc, acb, bac, bca, cab, and cba are all counted *separately* as six different permutations.)

Combinations of items are arrangements in which different sequences of the same items are counted as being the *same*. (The letter arrangements of abc, acb, bac, bca, cab, and cba are all considered to be the *same* single combination.)

Mnemonics for Permutations and Combinations

- Remember "**P**ermutations **P**osition," where the alliteration reminds us that with permutations, the positions of the items makes a difference.

- Remember "**C**ombinations **C**ommittee," which reminds us that with members of a committee, rearrangements of the same members result in the same committee, so order does not count.

3. Permutations Rule (When All of the Items Are Different)

The permutations rule is used when there are n different items available for selection, we must select r of them without replacement, and the sequence of the items matters. The result is the total number of arrangements (or permutations) that are possible. (Remember: Rearrangements of the same items are counted as different permutations.)

PERMUTATIONS RULE: When n different items are available and r of them are selected without replacement, the number of different permutations (order counts) is given by

$$_nP_r = \frac{n!}{(n-r)!}$$

EXAMPLE 3 **Permutations Rule (with Different Items):**
                          Clinical Trial of New Drug

When testing a new drug, Phase I requires only 5 volunteers, and the objective is to assess the drug's safety. To be very cautious, we plan to treat the 5 subjects in sequence, so that any particularly adverse effect can allow us to stop the treatments before any other subjects are treated. If 8 volunteers are available, how many different sequences of 5 subjects are possible?

SOLUTION

We need to select $r = 5$ subjects from $n = 8$ volunteers that are available. The number of different sequences of arrangements is found as shown:

$$_nP_r = \frac{n!}{(n - r)!} = \frac{8!}{(8 - 5)!} = 6720$$

There are 6720 different possible arrangements of 5 subjects selected from the 8 that are available.

4. Permutations Rule (When Some Items Are Identical to Others)

When n items are all selected without replacement, but *some items are identical,* the number of possible permutations (order matters) is found by using the following rule.

> **PERMUTATIONS RULE (WHEN SOME ITEMS ARE IDENTICAL TO OTHERS)**
>
> The number of different permutations (order counts) when n items are available and all n of them are selected *without replacement,* but some of the items are identical to others, is found as follows:
>
> $$\frac{n!}{n_1! n_2! \ldots n_k!}$$ where n_1 are alike, n_2 are alike,..., and n_k are alike.

  EXAMPLE 4 **Permutations Rule (with Some Identical Items):**
                          Designing Surveys

When designing surveys, pollsters sometimes repeat a question to see if a subject is thoughtlessly providing answers just to finish quickly. For one particular survey with 10 questions, 2 of the questions are identical to each other, and 3 other questions are also identical to each other. For this survey, how many different arrangements are possible? Is it practical to survey enough subjects so that every different possible arrangement is used?

SOLUTION

We have 10 questions with 2 that are identical to each other and 3 others that are also identical to each other, and we want the number of permutations. Using the rule for permutations with some items identical to others, we get

$$\frac{n!}{n_1! n_2! \ldots n_k!} = \frac{10!}{2! 3!} = \frac{3,628,800}{2 \cdot 6} = 302,400$$

continued

INTERPRETATION

There are 302,400 different possible arrangements of the 10 questions. It is not practical to accommodate every possible permutation. For typical surveys, the number of respondents is somewhere around 1000.

5. Combinations Rule

The combinations rule is used when there are n different items available for selection, only r of them are selected without replacement, and *order does not matter*. The result is the total number of combinations that are possible. (Remember: Rearrangements of the same items are considered to be the same combination.)

COMBINATIONS RULE:

When n different items are available, but only r of them are selected *without replacement,* the number of different combinations (order does not matter) is found as follows:

$$_nC_r = \frac{n!}{(n-r)!r!}$$

  EXAMPLE 5 **Combinations Rule: Phase I of a Clinical Trial**

When testing a new drug on humans, a clinical test is normally done in three phases. Phase I is conducted with a relatively small number of healthy volunteers. Assume that we want to treat 20 healthy humans with a new drug, and we have 30 suitable volunteers available. If 20 subjects are selected from the 30 that are available, and the 20 selected subjects are all treated at the same time, how many different treatment groups are possible?

SOLUTION

Because all subjects are treated at the same time, order is irrelevant, so we need to find the number of different possible *combinations*. With $n = 30$ subjects available and with $r = 20$ subjects selected, the number of combinations is found as follows.

$$_nC_r = \frac{n!}{(n-r)!r!} = \frac{30!}{(30-20)!20!} = \frac{30!}{10! \cdot 20!} = 30{,}045{,}015$$

INTERPRETATION

There are 30,045,015 different possible combinations.

Permutations or Combinations? Because choosing between permutations and combinations can often be tricky, we provide the following example that emphasizes the difference between them.

  EXAMPLE 6 **Permutations and Combinations: Officers and Committees**

The Portland Medical Center must appoint three corporate officers: chief executive officer (CEO), executive chairperson, and chief operating officer (COO). It must also appoint a planning committee with three different members. There are eight qualified candidates, and officers can also serve on the planning committee.

a. How many different ways can the officers be appointed?

b. How many different ways can the committee be appointed?

SOLUTION

Note that in part (a), order is important because the officers have very different functions. However, in part (b), the order of selection is irrelevant because the committee members all serve the same function.

a. Because order *does* count, we want the number of *permutations* of $r = 3$ people selected from the $n = 8$ available people. We get

$$_nP_r = \frac{n!}{(n-r)!} = \frac{8!}{(8-3)!} = 336$$

b. Because order does *not* count, we want the number of *combinations* of $r = 3$ people selected from the $n = 8$ available people. We get

$$_nC_r = \frac{n!}{(n-r)!r!} = \frac{8!}{(8-3)!3!} = 56$$

With order taken into account, there are 336 different ways that the officers can be appointed, but without order taken into account, there are 56 different possible committees.

4-6 Basic Skills and Concepts

Statistical Literacy and Critical Thinking

1. Notation What does the symbol ! represent? Six different patients can be scheduled for X-ray films 6! different ways, so what is the actual number of ways that six people can be scheduled for X-ray films?

2. Permutations/Combinations What is the basic difference between permutations and combinations?

3. Notation Evaluate $_{11}C_6$. What does the result represent?

4. Notation Evaluate $_{11}P_6$. What does the result represent?

In Exercises 5–30, express all probabilities as fractions.

5. Pin Numbers The Kinsale Medical Supply Company issues pin numbers to its employees so that they can access an online database. A hacker must randomly guess the correct pin code for the Information Technology supervisor, and that pin code consists of four digits (each 0 through 9) that must be entered in the correct order. Repetition of digits is allowed. What is the probability of a correct guess on the first try?

6. Social Security Numbers A Social Security number consists of nine digits in a particular order, and repetition of digits is allowed. After seeing the last four digits printed on a receipt, if you randomly select the other digits, what is the probability of getting the correct Social Security number of the person who was given the receipt?

7. Assigning Shifts The staff supervisor at the Wellington Medical Center must assign a team of two physicians to work the emergency room on Saturday night. If there are 19 physicians available and two of them are randomly selected, what is the probability of getting the two youngest physicians?

8. Review Board The supervisor at the Wellington Medical Center must select three nurses from 11 who are available for a review board. How many different ways can that be done?

9. Blood Test Quest Diagnostics has just received 8 different blood samples. If they are tested in random order, what is the probability that they are tested in the alphabetical order of the subjects who provided the samples?

10. Radio Station Call Letters If radio station call letters must begin with either K or W and must contain a total of either three or four letters, how many different possibilities are there?

11. Scheduling Routes A new director of the Veterans Health Administration plans to visit one hospital in each of five different states. If the five states are randomly selected from all 50 states without replacement and the order is also random, what is the probability that she visits Idaho, Oregon, Alaska, New Jersey, and Ohio, in that order?

12. Survey Reliability A health survey with 12 questions is designed so that 3 of the questions are identical and 4 other questions are identical (except for minor changes in wording). How many different ways can the 12 questions be arranged?

13. Safety with Numbers A safe "combination" consists of four numbers between 0 and 99, and the safe is designed so that numbers can be repeated. If someone tries to gain access to the safe, what is the probability that he or she will get the correct combination on the first attempt? Assume that the numbers are randomly selected. Given the number of possibilities, does it seem feasible to try opening the safe by making random guesses for the combination?

14. Electricity The control panel for an MRI device uses five color-coded wires. If we troubleshoot by testing two wires at a time, how many different tests are required for every possible pairing of two wires?

15. Clinical Trial In a clinical trial of the drug atorvastatin (Lipitor), one group of subjects was given placebos, a second group was given treatments of 10 mg, a third group was given treatments of 20 mg, a fourth group was given treatments of 40 mg, and a fifth group was given treatments of 80 mg. If the Phase I trial involved 15 subjects randomly assigned to the five groups with three in each group, how many different ways can the groups be formed?

16. Emergency Room Instead of treating emergency room patients in the order that they arrive, it is common to treat those with more serious problems first. If an emergency room has seven different patients, how many ways can they be arranged in sequence?

17. ZIP Code If you randomly select five digits, each between 0 and 9, with repetition allowed, what is the probability you will get the ZIP code of the Secretary of Health and Human Services?

18. FedEx Deliveries With a short time remaining in the day, a FedEx driver has time to make deliveries of 5 locations among the 7 locations remaining. How many different routes are possible?

19. Phone Numbers Current rules for telephone *area codes* allow the use of digits 2–9 for the first digit and 0–9 for the second and third digits. How many different area codes are possible with these rules? That same rule applies to the *exchange* numbers, which are the three digits immediately preceding the last four digits of a phone number. Given both of those rules, how many ten-digit phone numbers are possible? Given that these rules apply to the United States and Canada and a few islands, are there enough possible phone numbers? (Assume that the combined population is about 400,000,000.)

20. Classic Counting Problem A classic counting problem is to determine the number of different ways that the letters of "Assassination" can be arranged. Find that number.

21. Corporate Officers and Committees The Newport Medical Supply Company must appoint a president, chief executive officer (CEO), chief operating officer (COO), and chief financial officer (CFO). It must also appoint a strategic planning committee with four different members. There are 10 qualified candidates, and officers can also serve on the committee.

a. How many different ways can the four officers be appointed?

b. How many different ways can a committee of four be appointed?

continued

c. What is the probability of randomly selecting the committee members and getting the four youngest of the qualified candidates?

22. Card Access You have an identification card used for access to a secure area of the Wellington Medical Center. It's dark and you can't see your card when you insert it. The card must be inserted with the front side up and the printing configured so that the beginning of your name enters first.

a. What is the probability of selecting a random position and inserting the card with the result that the card is inserted correctly?

b. What is the probability of randomly selecting the card's position and finding that it is incorrectly inserted on the first attempt, but it is correctly inserted on the second attempt?

c. How many random selections are required to be absolutely sure that the card works because it is inserted correctly?

23. Amino Acids With 10 different amino acids available, 4 are to be selected to form a chain (called a polypeptide chain) in which order counts. How many different chains are possible?

24. Identity Theft with Credit Cards Credit card numbers typically have 16 digits, but not all of them are random.

a. What is the probability of randomly generating 16 digits and getting *your* MasterCard number?

b. Receipts often show the last four digits of a credit card number. If only those last four digits are known, what is the probability of randomly generating the other digits of your MasterCard number?

c. Discover cards begin with the digits 6011. If you know that the first four digits are 6011 and you also know the last four digits of a Discover card, what is the probability of randomly generating the other digits and getting all of them correct? Is this something to worry about?

25. What a Word! One of the longest words in standard medical terminology is "lymphocytopenia". In how many ways can the letters in that word be arranged?

26. Phase I of a Clinical Trial A clinical test on humans of a new drug is normally done in three phases. Phase I is conducted with a relatively small number of healthy volunteers. For example, a Phase I test of bexarotene involved only 14 subjects. Assume that we want to treat 14 healthy humans with this new drug and we have 16 suitable volunteers available.

a. If the subjects are selected and treated one at a time *in sequence,* how many different sequential arrangements are possible if 14 people are selected from the 16 that are available?

b. If 14 subjects are selected from the 16 that are available, and the 14 selected subjects are all treated at the same time, how many different treatment groups are possible?

c. If 14 subjects are randomly selected and treated at the same time, what is the probability of selecting the 14 youngest subjects?

27. Lightning and Lottery As of this writing, the Mega Millions lottery is run in 44 states. Winning the jackpot requires that you select the correct five different numbers between 1 and 75 and, in a separate drawing, you must also select the correct single number between 1 and 15. Find the probability of winning the jackpot if you buy one ticket. How does the result compare to the probability of being struck by lightning in a year, which the National Weather Service estimates to be 1/960,000?

28. Designing Experiment Clinical trials of Nasonex involved a group given placebos and another group given treatments of Nasonex. Assume that a preliminary Phase I trial is to be conducted with 12 subjects, including 6 men and 6 women. If 6 of the 12 subjects are randomly selected for the treatment group, find the probability of getting 6 subjects of the same gender. Would there be a problem with having members of the treatment group all of the same gender?

29. Morse Codes The International Morse code is a way of transmitting coded text by using sequences of on/off tones. Each character is 1 or 2 or 3 or 4 or 5 segments long, and each segment is either a dot or a dash. For example, the letter G is transmitted as two dashes followed by a dot, as in — — •. How many different characters are possible with this scheme? Are there enough characters for the alphabet and numbers?

30. Mendel's Peas Mendel conducted some his famous experiments with peas that were either smooth yellow plants or wrinkly green plants. If four peas are randomly selected from a batch consisting of four smooth yellow plants and four wrinkly green plants, find the probability that the four selected peas are of the same type.

4-6   Beyond the Basics

31. Computer Variable Names A common computer programming rule is that names of variables must be between one and eight characters long. The first character can be any of the 26 letters, while successive characters can be any of the 26 letters or any of the 10 digits. For example, allowable variable names include A, BBB, and M3477K. How many different variable names are possible? (Ignore the difference between uppercase and lowercase letters.)

32. Handshakes

a. Five physicians gather for a meeting about a patient. If each physician shakes hands with each other physician exactly once, what is the total number of handshakes?

b. If n physicians shake hands with each other exactly once, what is the total number of handshakes?

c. How many different ways can five physicians be seated at a round table? (Assume that if everyone moves to the right, the seating arrangement is the same.)

d. How many different ways can n physicians be seated at a round table?

Chapter Quick Quiz

1. Standard Tests Standard tests, such as the MCAT, tend to make extensive use of multiple-choice questions because they are easy to grade using software. If one such multiple-choice question has possible correct answers of a, b, c, d, e, what is the probability of a wrong answer if the answer is a random guess?

2. Likelihood of Disease After obtaining a patient's positive test result, a physician concludes that there is a 30% chance that the subject has a disease. What is the probability that the subject does not have the disease?

3. Months If a month is randomly selected after mixing the pages from a calendar, what is the probability that it is a month containing the letter y?

4. Sigmoidoscopy/Colonoscopy Based on data from the Centers for Disease Control, 67.7% of males over the age of 50 have had a sigmoidoscopy or colonoscopy. If two males over the age of 60 are randomly selected, what is the probability that they both have had a sigmoidoscopy or colonoscopy?

5. Subjective Probability Estimate the probability that the next time you get a cut, it requires stitches.

In Exercises 6–10, use the following results from tests of an experiment to test the effectiveness of an experimental vaccine for children (based on data from USA Today). Express all probabilities in decimal form.

	Developed Flu	Did Not Develop Flu
Vaccine Treatment	14	1056
Placebo	95	437

6. If 1 of the 1602 subjects is randomly selected, find the probability of getting 1 that developed flu.

7. If 1 of the 1602 subjects is randomly selected, find the probability of getting 1 who had the vaccine treatment or developed flu.

8. If 1 of the 1602 subjects is randomly selected, find the probability of getting 1 who had the vaccine treatment and developed flu.

9. Find the probability of randomly selecting 2 subjects without replacement and finding that they both developed flu.

10. Find the probability of randomly selecting 1 of the subjects and getting 1 who developed flu, given that the subject was given the vaccine treatment.

Review Exercises

In Exercises 1–10, use the data in the accompanying table and express all results in decimal form. (The results are based on "Splinting vs Surgery in the Treatment of Carpal Tunnel Syndrome," by Gerritsen et al., Journal of the American Medical Association, Vol. 288, No. 10.)

Treatment for Carpal Tunnel Syndrome

	Successful Treatment	Unsuccessful Treatment
Splint Treatment	60	23
Surgery Treatment	67	6

1. Success If 1 of the patients is randomly selected, find the probability of selecting someone with a successful treatment.

2. Success Find the probability of randomly selecting a patient and getting one with a successful treatment, given that the patient was treated with splinting.

3. Success Find the probability of randomly selecting a patient and getting one with a successful treatment, given that the patient was treated with surgery.

4. Success or Surgery If 1 of the patients is randomly selected, find the probability of getting a patient who had a successful treatment or was treated with surgery.

5. No Success or Splint If 1 of the patients is randomly selected, find the probability of getting someone who had an unsuccessful treatment or was treated with a splint.

6. Both Successful If 2 patients are randomly selected *without replacement,* find the probability that they both had successful treatments.

7. Both Successful If 2 patients are randomly selected *with replacement,* find the probability that they both had successful treatments.

8. Complement If A represents the event of randomly selecting one patient included in the table and getting someone who was treated with surgery, what does $\overline{A}$ represent? Find the value of $P(\overline{A})$.

9. Complement If A represents the event of randomly selecting one patient included in the table and getting someone who had a successful treatment, what does $\overline{A}$ represent? Find the value of $P(\overline{A})$.

10. All Three Successful If 3 patients are randomly selected without replacement, find the probability that all three had successful treatments.

11. Overweight About 62% of the adults in England were classified as overweight or obese.

a. If someone is randomly selected, what is the probability that he or she is not overweight or obese?

b. If three different people are randomly selected, what is the probability that they all are not overweight or obese?

c. Would it be unlikely to randomly select three people and find that they all are not overweight or obese? Why or why not?

12. National Statistics Day

a. If a person is randomly selected, find the probability that his or her birthday is October 18, which is National Statistics Day in Japan. Ignore leap years.

b. If a person is randomly selected, find the probability that his or her birthday is in October. Ignore leap years.

c. Estimate a subjective probability for the event of randomly selecting an adult American and getting someone who knows that October 18 is National Statistics Day in Japan.

d. Is it unlikely to randomly select an adult American and get someone who knows that October 18 is National Statistics Day in Japan?

13. Composite Sampling for Diabetes Currently, the rate for new cases of diabetes in a year is 3.4 per 1000 (based on data from the Centers for Disease Control and Prevention). When testing for the presence of diabetes, the Portland Diagnostics Laboratory saves money by combining blood samples for tests. The combined sample tests positive if at least one person has diabetes. If the combined sample tests positive, then the individual blood tests are performed. In a test for diabetes, blood samples from 10 randomly selected subjects are combined. Find the probability that the combined sample tests positive with at least 1 of the 10 people having diabetes. Is it likely that such combined samples test positive?

14. Redundancy Using solar torches, it is estimated that the probability of failure on any given night is $1/600$.

a. What is the probability that the solar torch works on a particular night?

b. When using two solar torches, what is the probability that at least one of them works?

Cumulative Review Exercises

1. Fatal Drunk Driving Listed below are the blood alcohol concentrations (g/dL) of drivers convicted of drunk driving in fatal car crashes (based on data from the National Highway Traffic Safety Administration).

0.09   0.11   0.11   0.13   0.14   0.15   0.17   0.17   0.18   0.18   0.23   0.35

Find the value of the following statistics and include appropriate units.

a. mean   **b.** median   **c.** midrange   **d.** range

e. standard deviation   **f.** variance

2. Fatal Drunk Driving Use the same data given in Exercise 1.

a. Identify the 5-number summary and also identify any values that appear to be outliers.

b. Construct a boxplot.   **c.** Construct a stemplot.

3. Organ Donors *USA Today* provided information about a survey (conducted for Donate Life America) of 5100 adult Internet users. Of the respondents, 2346 said they are willing to donate organs after death. In this survey, 100 adults were surveyed in each state and the District of Columbia, and results were weighted to account for the different state population sizes.

a. What *percentage* of respondents said that they are willing to donate organs after death?

b. Based on the poll results, what is the *probability* of randomly selecting an adult who is willing to donate organs after death?

c. What term is used to describe the sampling method of randomly selecting 100 adults from each state and the District of Columbia?

4. Sampling Eye Color Based on a study by Dr. P. Sorita Soni, eye colors in the United States are as follows: 40% brown, 35% blue, 12% green, 7% gray, 6% hazel.

a. A statistics instructor collects eye color data from her students. What is the name for this type of sample?

b. Identify one factor that might make the sample from part (a) biased and not representative of the general population of people in the United States.

c. What is the probability that a randomly selected person will have brown or blue eyes?

d. If two people are randomly selected, what is the probability that at least one of them has brown eyes?

5. Tar and Nicotine Given below are the tar (mg) and nicotine contents (mg) in the king-size cigarettes of some popular brands of the first few subjects included in Data Set 15 "Cigarette Contents" in Appendix B. Construct a graph suitable for exploring an association between tar and nicotine content in cigarettes. What does the graph suggest about the association?

Tar	20	27	27	20	20	24	20	23	20	22
Nicotine	1.1	1.7	1.7	1.1	1.1	1.4	1.1	1.4	1.0	1.2

Technology Project

Simulations Calculating probabilities are sometimes painfully difficult, but *simulations* provide us with a very practical alternative to calculations based on formal rules. A **simulation** of a procedure is a process that behaves the same way as the procedure so that similar results are produced. Instead of calculating the probability of getting exactly 5 boys in 10 births, you could repeatedly toss 10 coins and count the number of times that exactly 5 heads (or simulated "boys") occur. Better yet, you could do the simulation with a random number generator on a computer or calculator to randomly generate 1s (or simulated "boys") and 0s (or simulated "girls"). Let's consider this probability exercise:

> **Find the probability that among 50 randomly selected people, at least 3 have the same birthday.**

For the above problem, a simulation begins by representing birthdays by integers from 1 through 365, where 1 represents a birthday of January 1, and 2 represents January 2, and so on. We can simulate 50 birthdays by using a calculator or computer to generate 50

continued

random numbers (with repetition allowed) between 1 and 365. Those numbers can then be sorted, so it becomes easy to examine the list to determine whether any 3 of the simulated birth dates are the same. (After sorting, equal numbers are adjacent.) We can repeat the process as many times as we wish, until we are satisfied that we have a good estimate of the probability. Use technology to simulate 20 different groups of 50 birthdays. Use the results to estimate the probability that among 50 randomly selected people, at least 3 have the same birthday.

Summary of Simulation Functions:

Statdisk: Select **Data** from the top menu, select **Uniform Generator** from the dropdown menu.

Excel: Click **Insert Function** f_x, select **Math & Trig**, select **RANDBETWEEN**. Copy to additional cells.

TI-83/84 Plus: Press **MATH**, select **PROB** from the top menu, select **randInt** from the menu.

StatCrunch: Select **Data** from the top menu, select **Simulate** from the dropdown menu, select **Discrete Uniform** from the submenu.

Minitab: Select **Calc** from the top menu, select **Random Data** from the dropdown menu, select **Integer** from the submenu.

FROM DATA TO DECISION

Critical Thinking:
Interpreting results from a test for smoking

It is estimated that roughly half of patients who smoke lie when asked if they smoke. Pulse CO-oximeters may be a way to get information about smoking without relying on patients' statements. Pulse CO-oximeters use light that shines through a fingernail, and it measures carboxyhemoglobin (carbon monoxide in blood). These devices are used by firemen and emergency departments to detect carbon monoxide poisoning, but they can also be used to identify smokers. The accompanying table lists results from people aged 18–44 when the pulse CO-oximeter is set to detect a 6% or higher level of carboxyhemoglobin (based on data from "Carbon Monoxide Test Can Be Used to Identify Smoker," by Patrice Wendling, *Internal Medicine News*, Vol. 40., No. 1, and Centers for Disease Control and Prevention).

CO-Oximetry Test for Smoking

	Positive Test Result	Negative Test Result
Smoker	49	57
Nonsmoker	24	370

Analyzing the Results

1. False Positive Based on the results in the table, find the probability that a subject is not a smoker, given that the test result is positive.

2. True Positive Based on the results in the table, find the probability that a subject smokes, given that the test result is positive.

3. False Negative Based on the results in the table, find the probability that a subject smokes, given that the test result is negative.

4. True Negative Based on the results in the table, find the probability that a subject does not smoke, given that the test result is negative.

5. Sensitivity Find the *sensitivity* of the test by finding the probability of a true positive, given that the subject actually smokes.

6. Specificity Find the *specificity* of the test by finding the probability of a true negative, given that the subject does not smoke.

7. Positive Predictive Value Find the *positive predictive value* of the test by finding the probability that the subject smokes, given that the test yields a positive result.

8. Negative Predictive Value Find the *negative predictive value* of the test by finding the probability that the subject does not smoke, given that the test yields a negative result.

9. Confusion of the Inverse Find the following values, then compare them. In this case, what is confusion of the inverse?

• $P(\text{smoker} \mid \text{positive test result})$

• $P(\text{positive test result} \mid \text{smoker})$

Cooperative Group Activities

1. In-class activity Divide into groups of three or four and use coin flipping to develop a simulation that emulates the kingdom that abides by this decree: After a mother gives birth to a son, she will not have any other children. If this decree is followed, does the proportion of girls increase?

2. In-class activity Divide into groups of three or four and use actual thumbtacks or Hershey's Kisses candies, or paper cups, to estimate the probability that when dropped, they will land with the point (or open side) up. How many trials are necessary to get a result that appears to be reasonably accurate when rounded to the first decimal place?

3. Out-of-class activity Marine biologists often use the *capture-recapture method* as a way to estimate the size of a population, such as the number of fish in a lake. This method involves capturing a sample from the population, tagging each member in the sample, and then returning it to the population. A second sample is later captured, and the tagged members are counted along with the total size of this second sample. The results can be used to estimate the size of the population.

Instead of capturing real fish, simulate the procedure using some uniform collection of items such as colored beads, M&Ms, or index cards. Start with a large collection of at least 200 of such items. Collect a sample of 50 and use a marker to "tag" each one. Replace the tagged items, mix the whole population, then select a second sample and proceed to estimate the population size. Compare the result to the actual population size obtained by counting all of the items.

4. Out-of-class activity In Cumulative Review Exercise 4, it was noted that eye colors in the United States are distributed as follows: 40% brown, 35% blue, 12% green, 7% gray, 6% hazel. That distribution can form the basis for probabilities. Conduct a survey by asking fellow students to identify the color of their eyes. Does the probability of 0.4 for brown eyes appear to be consistent with your results? Why would a large sample be required to confirm that P(hazel eyes) $= 0.06$?

5 Discrete Probability Distributions

 CHAPTER PROBLEM — **Is the XSORT Gender Selection Method Effective?**

We live in a time with incredible advances in technology, medicine, and health care. Cloning is no longer science fiction. We have iPads, iPhones, virtual-reality headsets, and self-driving cars. We carry calculators that can instantly execute many complex statistical calculations. Heart pacemakers have defibrillators capable of shocking and restarting stopped hearts. Couples use procedures that are claimed to greatly increase the chance of having a baby with a desired gender.

Some people argue that gender selection methods should be banned, regardless of the reason, while others enthusiastically support the use of such methods. Lisa Belkin asked in the *New York Times Magazine,* "If we allow parents to choose the sex of their child today, how long will it be before they order up eye color, hair color, personality traits, and IQ?" There are some convincing arguments in favor of at least limited use of gender selection. One such argument involves couples carrying

X-linked recessive genes. For some of these couples, any male children have a 50% chance of inheriting a disorder, but none of the female children will inherit the disorder. These couples may want to use gender selection as a way to ensure that they have baby girls, thereby guaranteeing that a disorder will not be inherited by any of their children.

The Genetics & IVF Institute in Fairfax, Virginia, developed a technique called MicroSort and claimed that it increases the chances of a couple having a baby with a desired gender. (Clinical trials of MicroSort have been discontinued.) The MicroSort XSORT method is claimed to increase the chances of a couple having a baby girl, and the MicroSort YSORT method is claimed to increase the chances of a baby boy. The latest results for the XSORT method consist of 945 couples who wanted to have baby girls. After using the XSORT technique, 879 of those couples had baby girls. (See Figure 5-1 for a bar graph illustrating these results.) We usually expect that in 945 births, the number of girls should be somewhere around 472 or 473. Given that 879 out of 945 couples had girls, can we conclude that the XSORT technique is effective, or might we explain the outcome as just a chance sample result? In answering that question, we will use principles of probability to determine whether the observed birth results differ significantly from results that we would expect from random chance. This is a common goal of inferential statistics: Determine whether results can be reasonably explained by random chance or whether random chance doesn't appear to be a feasible explanation, so that other factors are influencing results. In this chapter we present methods that allow us to find the probabilities we need for determining whether the XSORT results are significant, suggesting that the method is effective.

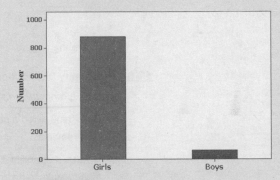

FIGURE 5-1   Results from the XSORT Method of Gender Selection

CHAPTER OBJECTIVES

Figure 5-2 on the next page provides a visual illustration of what this chapter accomplishes. When investigating the numbers of heads in two coin tosses, we can use the following two different approaches:

- **Use real sample data to find *actual* results:** The approach of Chapters 2 and 3 is to collect sample data from actual coin tosses, then summarize the results in a table representing the frequency distribution, and then find statistics, such as the sample mean $\bar{x}$ and the sample standard deviation s.

- **Use probabilities to find *expected* results:** Using principles of probability from Chapter 4, we can find the probability for each possible number of heads in two tosses. Then we could summarize the results in a table representing a probability distribution.

In this chapter we merge the above two approaches as we create a table describing what we *expect* to happen (instead of what did happen), then we find the population mean μ and population standard deviation σ. The table at the extreme right in Figure 5-2 is a *probability distribution,* because it describes the distribution using *probabilities* instead of frequency counts. The remainder of this book and the core of inferential statistics are based on some knowledge of probability distributions. In this chapter we focus on *discrete* probability distributions.

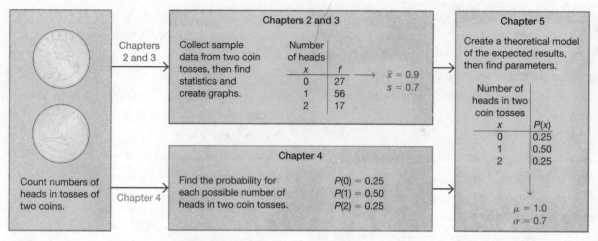

FIGURE 5-2

Here are the chapter objectives:

5-1 Probability Distributions

- Define *random variable* and *probability distribution*.

- Determine when a potential probability distribution actually satisfies the necessary requirements.

- Given a probability distribution, compute the mean and standard deviation, then use those results to determine whether results are *significantly low or significantly high*.

5-2 Binomial Probability Distributions

- Describe a binomial probability distribution and find probability values for a binomial distribution.

- Compute the mean and standard deviation for a binomial distribution, then use those results to determine whether results are *significantly low* or *significantly high*.

5-3 Poisson Probability Distributions

- Describe a Poisson probability distribution and find probability values for a Poisson distribution.

5-1   Probability Distributions

Key Concept This section introduces the concept of a *random variable* and the concept of a *probability distribution*. We illustrate how a *probability histogram* is a graph that visually depicts a probability distribution. We show how to find the important parameters of mean, standard deviation, and variance for a probability distribution. Most importantly, we describe how to determine whether outcomes are *significant* (significantly low or significantly high). We begin with the related concepts of *random variable* and *probability distribution*.

PART 1 Basic Concepts of a Probability Distribution

> **DEFINITIONS**
>
> A **random variable** is a variable (typically represented by x) that has a single numerical value, determined by chance, for each outcome of a procedure.
>
> A **probability distribution** is a description that gives the probability for each value of the random variable. It is often expressed in the format of a table, formula, or graph.

In Section 1-2 we made a distinction between discrete and continuous data. Random variables may also be discrete or continuous, and the following two definitions are consistent with those given in Section 1-2.

> **DEFINITIONS**
>
> A **discrete random variable** has a collection of values that is finite or countable. (If there are infinitely many values, the number of values is countable if it is possible to count them individually, such as the number of tosses of a coin before getting heads.)
>
> A **continuous random variable** has infinitely many values, and the collection of values is not countable. (That is, it is impossible to count the individual items because at least some of them are on a continuous scale, such as body temperatures.)

This chapter deals exclusively with discrete random variables, but the following chapters deal with continuous random variables.

Probability Distribution: Requirements

Every probability distribution must satisfy each of the following three requirements.

1. There is a *numerical* (not categorical) random variable x, and its number values are associated with corresponding probabilities.

2. $\Sigma P(x) = 1$ where x assumes all possible values. (The sum of all probabilities must be 1, but sums such as 0.999 or 1.001 are acceptable because they result from rounding errors.)

3. $0 \leq P(x) \leq 1$ for every individual value of the random variable x. (That is, each probability value must be between 0 and 1 inclusive.)

The second requirement comes from the simple fact that the random variable x represents all possible events in the entire sample space, so we are certain (with probability 1) that one of the events will occur. The third requirement comes from the basic principle that any probability value must be 0 or 1 or a value between 0 and 1.

 EXAMPLE 1 Genetics

Although the Chapter Problem involves 945 births, let's consider a simpler example that involves only two births with the following random variable:

$$x = \text{number of girls in two births}$$

The above x is a random variable because its numerical values depend on chance. With two births, the number of girls can be 0, 1, or 2, and Table 5-1 is a probability

continued

TABLE 5-1 Probability Distribution for the Number of Girls in Two Births

x: Number of Girls	P(x)
0	0.25
1	0.50
2	0.25

distribution because it gives the probability for each value of the random variable x and it satisfies the three requirements listed earlier:

1. The variable x is a numerical random variable and its values are associated with probabilities, as in Table 5-1.

2. $\Sigma P(x) = 0.25 + 0.50 + 0.25 = 1$

3. Each value of $P(x)$ is between 0 and 1. (Specifically, 0.25 and 0.50 and 0.25 are each between 0 and 1 inclusive.)

The random variable x in Table 5-1 is a discrete random variable, because it has three possible values (0, 1, 2), and 3 is a finite number, so this satisfies the requirement of being finite or countable.

Notation for 0+

In tables such as Table 5-1 or the binomial probabilities listed in Table A-1 in Appendix A, we sometimes use 0+ to represent a probability value that is positive but very small, such as 0.000000123. When rounding a probability value for inclusion in such a table, rounding to 0 would be misleading because it would incorrectly suggest that the event is impossible.

Probability Histogram: Graph of a Probability Distribution

There are various ways to graph a probability distribution, but for now we will consider only the **probability histogram.** Figure 5-3 is a probability histogram corresponding to Table 5-1. Notice that it is similar to a relative frequency histogram (described in Section 2-2), but the vertical scale shows *probabilities* instead of relative frequencies based on actual sample results.

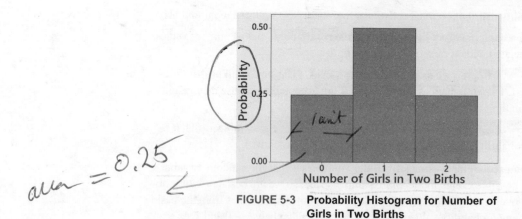

FIGURE 5-3   Probability Histogram for Number of Girls in Two Births

In Figure 5-3, we see that the values of 0, 1, 2 along the horizontal axis are located at the centers of the rectangles. This implies that the rectangles are each 1 unit wide, so the areas of the rectangles are 0.25, 0.50, and 0.25. The *areas* of these rectangles are the same as the *probabilities* in Table 5-1. We will see in Chapter 6 and future chapters that such a correspondence between areas and probabilities is very useful.

Probability Formula Example 1 involves a table, but a probability distribution could also be in the form of a formula. Consider the formula $P(x) = \dfrac{1}{2(2-x)!\,x!}$

(where x can be 0, 1, or 2). Using that formula, we find that $P(0) = 0.25$, $P(1) = 0.50$, and $P(2) = 0.25$. The probabilities found using this formula are the same as those in Table 5-1. This formula does describe a probability distribution because the three requirements are satisfied, as shown in Example 1.

EXAMPLE 2 **Hospital Job Interview Mistakes**

Hiring managers were asked to identify the biggest mistakes that job applicants make during an interview, and Table 5-2 is based on their responses (based on data from an Adecco survey). Does Table 5-2 describe a probability distribution?

TABLE 5-2 Hospital Job Interview Mistakes

x	$P(x)$
Inappropriate attire	0.50
Being late	0.44
Lack of eye contact	0.33
Checking phone or texting	0.30
Total	**1.57**

SOLUTION

Table 5-2 violates the first requirement because x is not a *numerical* random variable. Instead, the "values" of x are categorical data, not numbers. Table 5-2 also violates the second requirement because the sum of the probabilities is 1.57, but that sum should be 1. Because the three requirements are not all satisfied, we conclude that Table 5-2 does *not* describe a probability distribution.

Parameters of a Probability Distribution

Remember that with a probability distribution, we have a description of a *population* instead of a sample, so the values of the mean, standard deviation, and variance are *parameters,* not statistics. The mean, variance, and standard deviation of a discrete probability distribution can be found with the following formulas:

FORMULA 5-1 **Mean μ** for a probability distribution

$$\mu = \Sigma [x \cdot P(x)]$$

FORMULA 5-2 **Variance σ^2** for a probability distribution

$$\sigma^2 = \Sigma [(x - \mu)^2 \cdot P(x)] \text{ (This format is easier to understand.)}$$

FORMULA 5-3 **Variance σ^2** for a probability distribution

$$\sigma^2 = \Sigma [x^2 \cdot P(x)] - \mu^2 \text{ (This format is easier for manual calculations.)}$$

FORMULA 5-4 **Standard deviation σ** for a probability distribution

$$\sigma = \sqrt{\Sigma [x^2 \cdot P(x)] - \mu^2}$$

When applying Formulas 5-1 through 5-4, use the following rule for rounding results.

Round-Off Rule For μ, σ, And σ^2 From A Probability Distribution

Round results by carrying *one more decimal place* than the number of decimal places used for the random variable x. If the values of x are integers, round μ, σ, and σ^2 to one decimal place.

Exceptions to Round-Off Rule In some special cases, the above round-off rule results in values that are misleading or inappropriate. For example, with four-engine jets the mean number of jet engines working successfully throughout a flight is 3.999714286, which becomes 4.0 when rounded, but that is misleading because it suggests that all jet engines always work successfully. Here we need more precision to correctly reflect the true mean, such as the precision in 3.999714.

Expected Value

The mean of a discrete random variable x is the theoretical mean outcome for infinitely many trials. We can think of that mean as the *expected value* in the sense that it is the average value that we would expect to get if the trials could continue indefinitely.

DEFINITION

The **expected value** of a discrete random variable x is denoted by E, and it is the mean value of the outcomes, so $E = \mu$ and E can also be found by evaluating $\Sigma[x \cdot P(x)]$, as in Formula 5-1.

CAUTION An expected value need not be a whole number, even if the different possible values of x might all be whole numbers. The expected number of girls in five births is 2.5, even though five particular births can never result in 2.5 girls. If we were to survey many couples with five children, we *expect* that the mean number of girls will be 2.5.

 EXAMPLE 3 **Finding the Mean, Variance, and Standard Deviation**

Table 5-1 on page 200 describes the probability distribution for the number of girls in two births (assuming that boys and girls are equally likely). Find the mean, variance, and standard deviation for the probability distribution described in Table 5-1 from Example 1.

SOLUTION

In Table 5-3, the two columns at the left describe the probability distribution given earlier in Table 5-1. We create the two columns at the right for the purposes of the calculations required.

Using Formulas 5-1 and 5-2 and the table results, we get

Mean: $\mu = \Sigma[x \cdot P(x)] = 1.0$
Variance: $\sigma^2 = \Sigma[(x - \mu)^2 \cdot P(x)] = 0.5$

The standard deviation is the square root of the variance, so

$$\text{Standard deviation: } \sigma = \sqrt{0.5} = 0.707107 = 0.7 \text{ (rounded)}$$

Rounding: In Table 5-3, we use $\mu = 1.0$. If μ had been the value of 1.23456, we might round μ to 1.2, but we should use its *unrounded* value of 1.23456 in Table 5-3 calculations. Rounding in the middle of calculations can lead to results with errors that are too large.

TABLE 5-3 Calculating μ and σ for a Probability Distribution

x	$P(x)$	$x \cdot P(x)$	$(x - \mu)^2 \cdot P(x)$
0	0.25	$0 \cdot 0.25 = 0.00$	$(0 - 1)^2 \cdot 0.25 = 0.25$
1	0.50	$1 \cdot 0.50 = 0.50$	$(1 - 1)^2 \cdot 0.50 = 0.00$
2	0.25	$2 \cdot 0.25 = 0.50$	$(2 - 1)^2 \cdot 0.25 = 0.25$
Total		1.00	0.50
		$\uparrow$	$\uparrow$
		$\mu = \Sigma[x \cdot P(x)]$	$\sigma^2 = \Sigma[(x - \mu)^2 \cdot P(x)]$

INTERPRETATION

Assuming that boys and girls are equally likely in two births, the mean number of girls is 1.0, the variance is 0.50 girls^2, and the standard deviation is 0.7 girl. Also, the expected value for the number of girls in two births is 1.0 girl, which is the same value as the mean. If we were to collect data on a large number of trials with two births in each trial, we expect to get a mean of 1.0 girl.

Making Sense of Results: Significant Values

We present the following two different approaches for determining whether a value of a random variable x is significantly low or high.

Identifying Significant Results with the Range Rule of Thumb

The range rule of thumb (introduced in Section 3-2) may be helpful in interpreting the value of a standard deviation. According to the range rule of thumb, the vast majority of values should lie within 2 standard deviations of the mean, so we can consider a value to be *significant* if it is at least 2 standard deviations away from the mean. We can therefore identify "significant" values as follows:

Range Rule of Thumb for Identifying Significant Values

Significantly low values are $(\mu - 2\sigma)$ or lower.

Significantly high values are $(\mu + 2\sigma)$ or higher.

Values not significant: Between $(\mu - 2\sigma)$ and $(\mu + 2\sigma)$

Figure 3-3 from Section 3-2 illustrates the above criteria:

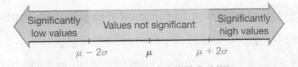

HINT Know that the use of the number 2 in the range rule of thumb is somewhat arbitrary, and this is a guideline, not an absolutely rigid rule.

EXAMPLE 4 **Identifying Significant Results with the Range Rule of Thumb**

In Example 3 we found that with two births, the mean number of girls is $\mu = 1.0$ girl and the standard deviation is $\sigma = 0.7$ girl. Use those results and the range rule of thumb to determine whether 2 girls is a significantly high number of girls.

SOLUTION

Using the range rule of thumb, the value of 2 girls is significantly high if it is greater than or equal to $\mu + 2\sigma$. With $\mu = 1.0$ girl and $\sigma = 0.7$ girl, we get

$$\mu + 2\sigma = 1 + 2(0.7) = 2.4 \text{ girls}$$

Significantly high numbers of girls are 2.4 and above.

INTERPRETATION

Based on these results, we conclude that 2 girls is not a significantly high number of girls (because 2 is not greater than or equal to 2.4).

Identifying Significant Results with Probabilities:

- **Significantly *high* number of successes:** x successes among n trials is a *significantly high* number of successes if the probability of x or more successes is 0.05 or less. That is, x is a significantly high number of successes if $P(x \text{ or more}) \leq 0.05$.*

- **Significantly *low* number of successes:** x successes among n trials is a *significantly low* number of successes if the probability of x or fewer successes is 0.05 or less. That is, x is a significantly low number of successes if $P(x \text{ or fewer}) \leq 0.05$.*

*The value 0.05 is not absolutely rigid. Other values, such as 0.01, could be used to distinguish between results that are significant and those that are not significant.

Identification of significantly low or significantly high numbers of successes is sometimes used for the purpose of rejecting assumptions, as stated in the following rare event rule.

The Rare Event Rule for Inferential Statistics

If, under a given assumption, the probability of a particular outcome is very small and the outcome occurs *significantly less than* or *significantly greater than* what we expect with that assumption, we conclude that the assumption is probably not correct.

For example, if testing the assumption that boys and girls are equally likely, the outcome of 20 girls in 100 births is significantly low and would be a basis for rejecting that assumption.

 EXAMPLE 5 **Identifying Significant Results with Probabilities**

Is 879 girls in 945 births a significantly high number of girls?

What does the result suggest about the Chapter Problem, which includes results from the XSORT method of gender selection? (Among 945 births from parents using the XSORT method, there were 879 girls. Is 879 girls in those 945 births *significantly high*?)

SOLUTION

A result of 879 girls in 945 births is greater than we expect with random chance, but we need to determine whether 879 girls is *significantly high*. Here, the relevant probability is the probability of getting *879 or more* girls in 945 births. Using methods covered later in Section 5-2, we can find that $P(879$ or more girls in 945 births$) = 0.0000$ (rounded). Because the probability of getting 879 or more girls is less than or equal to 0.05, we conclude that 879 girls in 945 births is a significantly high number of girls. See Figure 5-4, which is a probability histogram showing the probability for the different numbers of girls.

INTERPRETATION

It is unlikely that we would get 879 or more girls in 945 births by chance. It follows that 879 girls in 945 births is significantly high, so the XSORT method appears to be effective (but this does not *prove* that the XSORT method is responsible for the large number of girls).

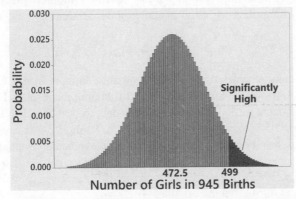

FIGURE 5-4   **Probability Histogram of Girls in 945 Births**

Do Boys or Girls Run in the Family?

One of the authors of this book, his siblings, and his siblings' children consist of 11 males and only 1 female. Is this an example of a phenomenon whereby one particular gender runs in a family? This issue was studied by examining a random sample of 8770 households in the United States. The results were reported in the *Chance* magazine article "Does Having Boys or Girls Run in the Family?" by Joseph Rodgers and Debby Doughty. Part of their analysis involves use of the binomial probability distribution discussed in this section. Their conclusion is that "We found no compelling evidence that sex bias runs in the family."

Not *Exactly*, but "At Least as Extreme"

It should be obvious that among 945 births, 879 girls is significantly high, whereas 475 girls is not significantly high. What makes 879 girls significant while 475 girls is not significant? It is not probabilities of *exactly* 879 girls and 475 girls (they are both less than 0.026). It is the fact that the probability of 879 or more girls is very low (0.0000), but the probability of 475 or more girls is not low (0.448).

PART 2   Expected Value and Rationale for Formulas

Expected Value

In Part 1 of this section we noted that the expected value of a random variable x is equal to the mean μ. We can therefore find the expected value by computing $\Sigma[x \cdot P(x)]$, just as we do for finding the value of μ.

EXAMPLE 6   **Births**

Assuming that boys and girls are equally likely, find the expected number of girls in 945 births. Instead of using Formula 5-1, just *think* about the number of girls expected in 945 births.

SOLUTION

The expected number of girls in 945 births is 472.5 girls.

continued

INTERPRETATION

In any specific sample of 945 births, we can never get 472.5 girls, but 472.5 girls is the expected value in the sense that it would be the mean from many samples of 945 births.

Rationale for Formulas 5-1 Through 5-4

Instead of blindly accepting and using formulas, it is much better to have some understanding of why they work. When computing the mean from a frequency distribution, f represents class frequency and N represents population size. In the expression below, we rewrite the formula for the mean of a frequency table so that it applies to a population. In the fraction f/N, the value of f is the frequency with which the value x occurs and N is the population size, so f/N is the probability for the value of x. When we replace f/N with $P(x)$, we make the transition from relative frequency based on a limited number of observations to probability based on infinitely many trials. This result shows why Formula 5-1 is as given earlier in this section.

$$\mu = \frac{\Sigma(f \cdot x)}{N} = \Sigma\left[\frac{f \cdot x}{N}\right] = \Sigma\left[x \cdot \frac{f}{N}\right] = \Sigma[x \cdot P(x)]$$

Similar reasoning enables us to take the variance formula from Chapter 3 and apply it to a random variable for a probability distribution; the result is Formula 5-2. Formula 5-3 is a shortcut version that will always produce the same result as Formula 5-2. Although Formula 5-3 is usually easier to work with, Formula 5-2 is easier to understand directly. Based on Formula 5-2, we can express the standard deviation as

$$\sigma = \sqrt{\Sigma[(x - \mu)^2 \cdot P(x)]}$$

or as the equivalent form given in Formula 5-4.

5-1 Basic Skills and Concepts

Statistical Literacy and Critical Thinking

Number of Girls in Four Births

Number of Girls x	$P(x)$
0	0.063
1	0.250
2	0.375
3	0.250
4	0.063

1. Random Variable The accompanying table lists probabilities for the corresponding numbers of girls in four births. What is the random variable, what are its possible values, and are its values numerical?

2. Discrete or Continuous? Is the random variable given in the accompanying table discrete or continuous? Explain.

3. Probability Distribution For the accompanying table, is the sum of the values of $P(x)$ equal to 1, as required for a probability distribution? Does the table describe a probability distribution?

4. Significant For 100 births, $P(\text{exactly 56 girls}) = 0.0390$ and $P(56 \text{ or more girls}) = 0.136$. Is 56 girls in 100 births a significantly high number of girls? Which probability is relevant to answering that question?

Identifying Discrete and Continuous Random Variables. *In Exercises 5 and 6, refer to the given values, then identify which of the following is most appropriate:* **discrete random variable, continuous random variable,** *or* **not a random variable.**

5. a. Exact weights of the next 100 babies born in the United States

b. Responses to the survey question "Which health plan do you have?"

continued

c. Numbers of families that must be surveyed before finding one with 10 children

d. Exact foot lengths of humans

e. Shoe sizes (such as 8 or 8½) of humans

6. a. Grades (A, B, C, D, F) earned in biostatistics classes

b. Heights of students in biostatistics classes

c. Numbers of students in biostatistics classes

d. Eye colors of biostatistics students

e. Numbers of times biostatistics students must toss a coin before getting heads

Identifying Probability Distributions. *In Exercises 7–14, determine whether a probability distribution is given. If a probability distribution is given, find its mean and standard deviation. If a probability distribution is not given, identify the requirements that are not satisfied.*

7. Genetic Disorder Five males with an X-linked genetic disorder have one child each. The random variable x is the number of children among the five who inherit the X-linked genetic disorder.

x	P(x)
0	0.031
1	0.156
2	0.313
3	0.313
4	0.156
5	0.031

8. Male Color Blindness When conducting research on color blindness in males, a researcher forms random groups with five males in each group. The random variable x is the number of males in the group who have a form of color blindness (based on data from the National Institutes of Health).

x	P(x)
0	0.659
1	0.287
2	0.050
3	0.004
4	0.001
5	0+

9. Genetics Experiment A genetics experiment involves offspring peas in groups of four. A researcher reports that for one group, the number of peas with white flowers has a probability distribution as given in the accompanying table.

x	P(x)
0	0.04
1	0.26
2	0.36
3	0.20
4	0.08

10. Mortality Study For a group of four men, the probability distribution for the number x who live through the next year is as given in the accompanying table.

x	P(x)
0	0.0000
1	0.0001
2	0.0006
3	0.0387
4	0.9606

11. Genetic Disorder Three males with an X-linked genetic disorder have one child each. The random variable x is the number of children among the three who inherit the X-linked genetic disorder.

x	P(x)
0	0.4219
1	0.4219
2	0.1406
3	0.0156

12. Diseased Seedlings An experiment involves groups of four seedlings grown under controlled conditions. The random variable x is the number of seedlings in a group that meet specific criteria for being classified as "diseased."

x	P(x)
0	0.805
1	0.113
2	0.057
3	0.009
4	0.002

Genetics. *In Exercises 13–18, refer to the accompanying table, which describes results from groups of 10 births from 10 different sets of parents. The random variable x represents the number of girls among 10 children.*

Number of Girls x	P(x)
0	0.001
1	0.010
2	0.044
3	0.117
4	0.205
5	0.246
6	0.205
7	0.117
8	0.044
9	0.010
10	0.001

13. Mean and Standard Deviation Find the mean and standard deviation for the number of girls in 10 births.

14. Range Rule of Thumb for Significant Events Use the range rule of thumb to determine whether 9 girls in 10 births is a significantly high number of girls.

15. Range Rule of Thumb for Significant Events Use the range rule of thumb to determine whether 1 girl in 10 births is a significantly low number of girls.

16. Using Probabilities for Significant Events

a. Find the probability of getting exactly 8 girls in 10 births.

b. Find the probability of getting 8 or more girls in 10 births.

c. Which probability is relevant for determining whether 8 is a significantly high number of girls in 10 births: the result from part (a) or part (b)?

d. Is 8 a significantly high number of girls in 10 births? Why or why not?

17. Using Probabilities for Significant Events

a. Find the probability of getting 6 or more girls in 10 births.

b. Find the probability of getting exactly 6 girls in 10 births.

c. Which probability is relevant for determining whether 6 is a significantly high number of girls in 10 births: the result from part (a) or part (b)?

d. Is 6 a significantly high number of girls in 10 births? Why or why not?

18. Using Probabilities for Significant Events

a. Find the probability of getting exactly 2 girls in 10 births.

b. Find the probability of getting 2 or fewer girls in 10 births.

c. Which probability is relevant for determining whether 2 is a significantly low number of girls in 10 births: the result from part (a) or part (b)?

d. Is 2 a significantly low number of girls in 10 births? Why or why not?

Sleepwalking. *In Exercises 19–23, refer to the accompanying table, which describes the numbers of adults in groups of five who reported sleepwalking (based on data from "Prevalence and Comorbidity of Nocturnal Wandering In the U.S. Adult General Population," by Ohayon et al., Neurology, Vol. 78, No. 20).*

x	P(x)
0	0.172
1	0.363
2	0.306
3	0.129
4	0.027
5	0.002

19. Mean and Standard Deviation Find the mean and standard deviation for the numbers of sleepwalkers in groups of five.

20. Range Rule of Thumb for Significant Events Use the range rule of thumb to determine whether 4 is a significantly high number of sleepwalkers in a group of 5 adults.

21. Range Rule of Thumb for Significant Events Use the range rule of thumb to determine whether 3 is a significantly high number of sleepwalkers in a group of 5 adults.

22. Using Probabilities for Identifying Significant Events

a. Find the probability of getting exactly 4 sleepwalkers among 5 adults.

b. Find the probability of getting 4 or more sleepwalkers among 5 adults.

c. Which probability is relevant for determining whether 4 is a significantly high number of sleepwalkers among 5 adults: the result from part (a) or part (b)?

d. Is 4 a significantly high number of sleepwalkers among 5 adults? Why or why not?

23. Using Probabilities for Identifying Significant Events

a. Find the probability of getting exactly 1 sleepwalker among 5 adults.

b. Find the probability of getting 1 or fewer sleepwalkers among 5 adults.

c. Which probability is relevant for determining whether 1 is a significantly low number of sleepwalkers among 5 adults: the result from part (a) or part (b)?

d. Is 1 a significantly low number of sleepwalkers among 5 adults? Why or why not?

5-2 Binomial Probability Distributions

Key Concept Section 5-1 introduced the important concept of a discrete probability distribution. Among the various discrete probability distributions that exist, the focus of this section is the *binomial probability distribution*. Part 1 of this section introduces the binomial probability distribution along with methods for finding probabilities. Part 2 presents easy methods for finding the mean and standard deviation of a binomial distribution. As in other sections, we stress the importance of *interpreting* probability values to determine whether events are *significantly low* or *significantly high*.

PART 1 Basics of Binomial Probability Distribution

Binomial probability distributions allow us to deal with circumstances in which the outcomes belong to *two* categories, such as cured/not cured or acceptable/defective or survived/died.

DEFINITION

A **binomial probability distribution** results from a procedure that meets these four requirements:

1. The procedure has a *fixed number of trials.* (A trial is a single observation.)

2. The trials must be *independent,* meaning that the outcome of any individual trial doesn't affect the probabilities in the other trials.

3. Each trial must have all outcomes classified into exactly *two categories,* commonly referred to as *success* and *failure.*

4. The probability of a success remains the same in all trials.

Notation For Binomial Probability Distributions

S and F (success and failure) denote the two possible categories of all outcomes.

$P(\text{S}) = p$ (p = probability of a success)

$P(\text{F}) = 1 - p = q$ (q = probability of a failure)

n the fixed number of trials

x a specific number of successes in n trials, so x can be any whole number between 0 and n, inclusive

p probability of *success* in *one* of the n trials

q probability of *failure* in *one* of the n trials

$P(x)$ probability of getting exactly x successes among the n trials

---

The word *success* as used here is arbitrary and does not necessarily represent something good. Either of the two possible categories may be called the success S as long as its probability is identified as p. (The value of q can always be found from $q = 1 - p$. If $p = 0.95$, then $q = 1 - 0.95 = 0.05$.)

CAUTION When using a binomial probability distribution, always be sure that x and p are *consistent* in the sense that they both refer to the *same* category being called a success.

 EXAMPLE 1 **Hybridization Experiments**

When Gregor Mendel conducted his famous hybridization experiments, he used peas with green pods and peas with yellow pods. Because green is dominant and yellow is recessive, when crossing two parents with the green/yellow pair of genes, we expect that 3/4 of the offspring peas should have green pods. That is, $P(\text{green pod}) = 3/4$. Assume that all parents have the green/yellow combination of genes, and we want to find the probability that exactly three of five offspring peas have green pods.

a. Does this procedure result in a binomial distribution?

b. If this procedure does result in a binomial distribution, identify the values of n, x, p, and q.

SOLUTION

a. This procedure does satisfy the requirements for a binomial distribution, as shown below.

   1. The number of trials (5) is fixed.

   2. The 5 trials are independent because the probability of any offspring pea having a green pod is not affected by the outcome of any other offspring pea.

   3. Each of the 5 trials has two categories of outcomes: The pea has a green pod or it does not.

   4. For each offspring pea, the probability that it has a green pod is $3/4$ or 0.75, and that probability remains the same for each of the 5 peas.

b. Having concluded that the given procedure does result in a binomial distribution, we now proceed to identify the values of n, x, p, and q.

   1. With 5 offspring peas, we have $n = 5$.

   2. We want the probability of exactly 3 peas with green pods, so $x = 3$.

   3. The probability of success (getting a pea with a green pod) for one selection is 0.75, so $p = 0.75$.

   4. The probability of failure (not getting a green pod) is 0.25, so $q = 0.25$.

Again, it is very important to be sure that x and p both refer to the same concept of "success." In this example, we use x to count the number of peas with green pods, so p must be the probability that a pea has a green pod. Therefore, x and p do use the same concept of success (green pod) here.

Not at Home

Pollsters cannot simply ignore those who were not at home when they were called the first time.  One solution is to make repeated callback attempts until the person can be reached. Alfred Politz and Willard Simmons describe a way to compensate for those missed calls without making repeated callbacks. They suggest weighting results based on how often people are not at home. For example, a person at home only two days out of six will have a 2/6 or 1/3 probability of being at home when called the first time. When such a person is reached the first time, his or her results are weighted to count three times as much as someone who is always home. This weighting is a compensation for the other similar people who are home two days out of six and were not at home when called the first time. This clever solution was first presented in 1949.

Treating Dependent Events as Independent

When selecting a sample (as in a survey), we usually sample without replacement. Sampling without replacement results in dependent events, which violates a requirement of a binomial distribution. However, we can often treat the events as if they were independent by applying the following 5% guideline introduced in Section 4-2:

5% Guideline for Cumbersome Calculations

When sampling without replacement and the sample size is no more than 5% of the size of the population, treat the selections as being *independent* (even though they are actually dependent).

Methods for Finding Binomial Probabilities

We now proceed with three methods for finding the probabilities corresponding to the random variable x in a binomial distribution. The first method involves calculations using the *binomial probability formula* and is the basis for the other two methods. The second method involves the use of software or a calculator, and the third method involves the use of the Appendix Table A-1. (With technology so widespread, such tables are becoming obsolete.) If using technology that automatically produces binomial probabilities, we recommend that you solve one or two exercises using Method 1 to better understand the basis for the calculations.

Method 1: Using the Binomial Probability Formula In a binomial probability distribution, probabilities can be calculated by using Formula 5-5.

FORMULA 5-5 Binomial Probability Formula

$$P(x) = \frac{n!}{(n-x)!x!} \cdot p^x \cdot q^{n-x} \qquad \text{for } x = 0, 1, 2, \ldots, n$$

where

n = number of trials
x = number of successes among n trials
p = probability of success in any one trial
q = probability of failure in any one trial $(q = 1 - p)$

Formula 5-5 can also be expressed as $P(x) = {}_nC_x \cdot p^x \cdot q^{n-x}$. With x items identical to themselves, and $n - x$ other items identical to themselves, the number of permutations is ${}_nC_x = n![(n-x)!x!]$, so the two sides of this equation are interchangeable. The factorial symbol !, introduced in Section 4-6, denotes the product of decreasing factors. Two examples of factorials are $3! = 3 \cdot 2 \cdot 1 = 6$ and $0! = 1$ (by definition).

 EXAMPLE 2 **Hybridization Experiment**

Assuming that the probability of a pea having a green pod is 0.75 (as in Example 1), use the binomial probability formula to find the probability of getting exactly 3 peas with green pods when 5 offspring peas are generated. That is, find $P(3)$ given that $n = 5, x = 3, p = 0.75$, and $q = 0.25$.

SOLUTION

Using the given values of n, x, p, and q in the binomial probability formula (Formula 5-5), we get

$$P(3) = \frac{5!}{(5-3)!3!} \cdot 0.75^3 \cdot 0.25^{5-3}$$

$$= \frac{5!}{2!3!} \cdot 0.421875 \cdot 0.0625$$

$$= (10)(0.421875)(0.0625) = 0.263671875$$

The probability of getting exactly 3 peas with green pods among 5 offspring peas is 0.264 (rounded to three significant digits).

Calculation hint: When computing a probability with the binomial probability formula, it's helpful to get a single number for $n![(n-x)!x!]$ or ${}_nC_x$, a single number for p^x, and a single number for q^{n-x}, and then simply multiply the three factors together as shown in the third line of the calculation in the preceding example. Don't round when you find those three factors; round only at the end, and round to three significant digits.

Method 2: Using Technology Technology can be used to find binomial probabilities. The screen displays listing binomial probabilities for $n = 5$ and $p = 0.75$, as in Example 2, are given. Notice that in each display, the probability distribution is given as a table.

Statdisk

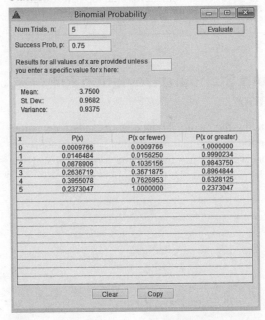

Excel

	A	B
1	0	0.000977
2	1	0.014648
3	2	0.087891
4	3	0.263672
5	4	0.395508
6	5	0.237305

Minitab

x	P(x)
0	0.000977
1	0.014648
2	0.087891
3	0.263672
4	0.395508
5	0.237305

TI-83/84 Plus

Method 3: Using Table A-1 in Appendix A This method can be skipped if technology is available. Table A-1 in Appendix A lists binomial probabilities for select values of n and p. It cannot be used if $n > 8$ or if the probability p is not one of the 13 values included in the table.

To use the table of binomial probabilities, we must first locate n and the desired corresponding value of x. At this stage, one row of numbers should be isolated. Now align that row with the desired probability of p by using the column across the top. The isolated number represents the desired probability. A very small probability, such as 0.000064, is indicated by 0+.

⊙─ **EXAMPLE 3** **Births**

Assuming that boys and girls are equally likely, find the probability of getting exactly 5 boys in 8 randomly selected births.

continued

SOLUTION

Because boys and girls are assumed to be equally likely, we have $p = 0.5$. Because there are 8 births we have $n = 8$. Because we want the probability of exactly 5 boys, we have $x = 5$.

Refer to Table A-1 with $n = 8$, $x = 0.5$, and $p = 0.5$. Locate $n = 8$ at the left, then find the row of probabilities for $x = 5$. Next, look across the top row to find the column of values under $p = 0.50$. Table A-1 shows that $P(5 \text{ boys}) = 0.219$.

PART 2 **Using Mean and Standard Deviation for Critical Thinking**

Section 5-1 included formulas for finding the mean, variance, and standard deviation from *any* discrete probability distribution. A binomial distribution is a particular type of discrete probability distribution, so we could use those same formulas, but if we know the values of n and p, it is much easier to use the following:

For Binomial Distributions

Formula 5-6   Mean: $\mu = np$

Formula 5-7   Variance: $\sigma^2 = npq$

Formula 5-8   Standard Deviation: $\sigma = \sqrt{npq}$

As in earlier sections, finding values for μ and σ can be great fun, but it is especially important to *interpret* and *understand* those values, so the range rule of thumb and the rare event rule for inferential statistics can be very helpful. Here is a brief summary of the range rule of thumb: Values are significantly low or high if they differ from the mean by more than 2 standard deviations, as described by the following:

Range Rule of Thumb

Significantly low values $\leq (\mu - 2\sigma)$

Significantly high values $\geq (\mu + 2\sigma)$

Values not significant: Between $(\mu - 2\sigma)$ and $(\mu + 2\sigma)$

EXAMPLE 4 **Hybridization Experiment**

Use Formulas 5-6 and 5-8 to find the mean and standard deviation for the numbers of peas with green pods when groups of 5 offspring peas are generated. Assume that there is a 0.75 probability that an offspring pea has a green pod.

SOLUTION

Using the values $n = 5$, $p = 0.75$, and $q = 0.25$, Formulas 5-6 and 5-8 can be applied as follows:

$$\mu = np = (5)(0.75) = 3.8$$
$$\sigma = \sqrt{npq} = \sqrt{(5)(0.75)(0.25)} = 1.0 \ (\text{rounded})$$

Formula 5-6 for the mean makes sense intuitively. If 75% of peas have green pods and five offspring peas are generated, we expect to get around $5 \cdot 0.75 = 3.8$ peas with green pods. This result can be generalized as $\mu = np$. The variance and standard deviation are not so easily justified, and we omit the complicated algebraic manipulations that lead to Formulas 5-7 and 5-8. Instead, refer again to the preceding example and Table 5-3 on page 203 to verify that for a binomial distribution, Formulas 5-6, 5-7, and 5-8 will produce the same results as Formulas 5-1, 5-3, and 5-4.

EXAMPLE 5 Genetics

In an actual experiment, Mendel generated 580 offspring peas. He claimed that 75%, or 435, of them would have green pods. The actual experiment resulted in 428 peas with green pods.

a. Assuming that groups of 580 offspring peas are generated, find the mean and standard deviation for the numbers of peas with green pods.

b. Use the range rule of thumb to find the numbers of peas with green pods that separate significantly low values and significantly high values from values that are not significant. Based on those numbers, can we conclude that Mendel's actual result of 428 peas with green pods is *significantly low* or *significantly high*? Does this suggest that Mendel's value of 75% is wrong?

SOLUTION

a. With $n = 580$ offspring peas, with $p = 0.75$, and $q = 0.25$, we can find the mean and standard deviation for the numbers of peas with green pods as follows:

$$\mu = np = (580)(0.75) = 435.0$$
$$\sigma = \sqrt{npq} = \sqrt{(580)(0.75)(0.25)} = 10.4$$

For groups of 580 offspring peas, the mean number of peas with green pods is 435.0 and the standard deviation is 10.4.

b. We must now interpret the results to determine whether Mendel's actual result of 428 peas is a result that could easily occur by chance, or whether that result is so unlikely that the assumed rate of 75% is wrong. We will use the range rule of thumb as follows:

Significantly low values $\leq (\mu - 2\sigma) = 435.0 - 2(10.4) = 414.2$

Significantly high values $\geq (\mu + 2\sigma) = 435.0 + 2(10.4) = 455.8$

INTERPRETATION

Based on these results, significantly low values are 414.2 or lower, and significantly high values are 455.8 or higher. That is, if Mendel generated many groups of 580 offspring peas and if his 75% rate is correct, the numbers of peas with green pods should usually fall between 414.2 and 455.8. Mendel actually got 428 peas with green pods, and that value is neither significantly low nor significantly high, so the experimental results are consistent with the 75% rate. The results do not suggest that Mendel's claimed rate of 75% is wrong.

Variation in Statistics Example 5 is a good illustration of the importance of variation in statistics. In a traditional algebra course, we might conclude that 428 is not 75% of 580 simply because 428 does not equal 435 (which is 75% of 580). However, in statistics we recognize that sample results vary. We don't expect to get *exactly* 75% of the peas with green pods. We recognize that as long as the results don't vary too far away from the claimed rate of 75%, they are consistent with that claimed rate of 75%.

In this section we presented easy procedures for finding values of the mean μ and standard deviation σ from a binomial probability distribution. However, it is really important to be able to *interpret* those values by using such tools as the range rule of thumb for distinguishing values that are significantly low or significantly high from values that are not significant.

Instead of the range rule of thumb, we could also use probabilities to determine when values are significantly high or significantly low.

Using Probabilities to Determine When Results Are Significantly High or Low

- **Significantly *high* number of successes:** x successes among n trials is a *significantly high* number of successes if the probability of x or more successes is 0.05 or less. That is, x is a significantly high number of successes if $P(x \text{ or more}) \leq 0.05$.*

- **Significantly *low* number of successes:** x successes among n trials is a *significantly low* number of successes if the probability of x or fewer successes is 0.05 or less. That is, x is a significantly low number of successes if $P(x \text{ or fewer}) \leq 0.05$.*

*The value 0.05 is not absolutely rigid. Other values, such as 0.01, could be used to distinguish between results that are significant and those that are not significant.

Rationale for the Binomial Probability Formula

The binomial probability formula is the basis for all three methods presented in this section. Instead of accepting and using that formula blindly, let's see why it works.

In Example 2, we used the binomial probability formula to find the probability of getting exactly 3 peas with green pods when 5 offspring peas are generated. With $P(\text{green pod}) = 0.75$, we can use the multiplication rule from Section 4-2 to find the probability that the first 3 peas have green pods while the last 2 peas do not have green pods. We get the following result:

$$P(3 \text{ peas with green pods followed by 2 peas with pods that are not green})$$
$$= 0.75 \cdot 0.75 \cdot 0.75 \cdot 0.25 \cdot 0.25$$
$$= 0.75^3 \cdot 0.25^2$$
$$= 0.0264$$

This result gives a probability of generating five offspring in which three have green pods. However, it does not give the probability of getting exactly three peas with green pods because it assumes a particular arrangement for three offspring peas with green pods. Other arrangements for generating three offspring peas with green pods are possible.

In Section 4-6 we saw that with three subjects identical to each other (such as peas with green pods) and two other subjects identical to each other (such as peas without green pods), the total number of arrangements, or permutations, is $5! / [\,(5 - 3)!3!\,]$, or 10. Each of those 10 different arrangements has a probability of $0.75^3 \cdot 0.25^2$, so the total probability is as follows:

$$P(3 \text{ peas with green pods among 5}) = \frac{5!}{(5 - 3)!3!} \cdot 0.75^3 \cdot 0.25^2$$

This particular result can be generalized as the binomial probability formula (Formula 5-5). That is, the binomial probability formula is a combination of the multiplication rule of probability and the counting rule for the number of arrangements of n items when x of them are identical to each other and the other $n - x$ are identical to each other.

The number of outcomes with exactly x successes among n trials

The probability of x successes among n trials for any one particular order

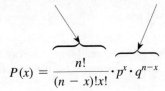

$$P(x) = \frac{n!}{(n - x)!x!} \cdot p^x \cdot q^{n-x}$$

TECH CENTER

Binomial Distributions
Access tech instructions, videos, and data sets at **www.TriolaStats.com**

5-2   Basic Skills and Concepts

Statistical Literacy and Critical Thinking

1. Hybridization Assume that 75% of offspring peas have green pods. Suppose we want to find the probability that when five offspring peas are randomly selected, exactly two of them are green. What is wrong with using the multiplication rule to find the probability of getting two peas with green pods followed by three peas with yellow pods: $(0.75)(0.75)(0.25)(0.25)(0.25) = 0.00879$?

2. Variation and Notation Assume that we want to find the probability that among five offspring peas, exactly two of them have green pods. Also assume that 75% of offspring peas have green pods (and the others have yellow pods).

a. Identify the values of n, x, p, and q.

b. For groups of 5 randomly selected offspring peas, find the mean, standard deviation, and variance for the numbers of peas among five that have green pods. Include appropriate units.

3. Independent Events Based on a KRC Research survey, when 1020 adults were asked about hand hygiene, 44% said that they wash their hands after using public transportation. Consider the probability that among 30 different adults randomly selected from the 1020 who were surveyed, there are at least 10 who wash their hands after using public transportation. Given that these subjects were selected without replacement, are the 30 selections independent? Can they be treated as being independent? Can the probability be found using the binomial probability formula?

4. Notation of 0+ Using the same survey from Exercise 3, the probability of randomly selecting 30 of the 1020 adults and getting exactly 24 who wash hands after using public transportation is represented as 0+. What does 0+ indicate? Does 0+ indicate that it is impossible to get exactly 24 adults who wash their hands after using public transportation?

Identifying Binomial Distributions.   *In Exercises 5–12, determine whether the given procedure results in a binomial distribution (or a distribution that can be treated as binomial). For those that are not binomial, identify at least one requirement that is not satisfied.*

5. Clinical Trial of YSORT The YSORT method of gender selection, developed by the Genetics & IVF Institute, was designed to increase the likelihood that a baby will be a boy. When 291 couples used the YSORT method and gave birth to 291 babies, the weights of the babies were recorded.

6. Clinical Trial of YSORT The YSORT method of gender selection, developed by the Genetics & IVF Institute, was designed to increase the likelihood that a baby will be a boy. When 291 couples use the YSORT method and give birth to 291 babies, the genders of the babies are recorded.

7. Clinical Trial of Lipitor Treating 863 subjects with Lipitor (atorvastatin) and recording whether there is a "yes" response when they are each asked if they experienced a headache (based on data from Pfizer, Inc.).

8. Clinical Trial of Lipitor Treating 863 subjects with Lipitor (atorvastatin) and asking each subject how their head feels (based on data from Pfizer, Inc.).

9. Nicorette Treating 50 smokers with Nicorette and asking them how their mouth and throat feel.

10. Nicorette Treating 50 smokers with Nicorette and recording whether there is a "yes" response when they are asked if they experience any mouth or throat soreness.

11. Defibrillators Determining whether each of 500 defibrillators is acceptable or defective.

12. Defibrillators Counting the numbers of defects in each of 500 defibrillators.

Binomial Probability Formula.   *In Exercises 13 and 14, answer the questions designed to help understand the rationale for the binomial probability formula.*

13. Guessing Answers Standard tests, such as the SAT, ACT, or Medical College Admission Test (MCAT) typically use multiple choice questions, each with five possible answers (a, b, c, d, e), one of which is correct. Assume that you guess the answers to the first three questions.

a. Use the multiplication rule to find the probability that the first two guesses are wrong and the third is correct. That is, find P(WWC), where W denotes a wrong answer and C denotes a correct answer.

b. Beginning with WWC, make a complete list of the different possible arrangements of two wrong answers and one correct answer; then find the probability for each entry in the list.

c. Based on the preceding results, what is the probability of getting exactly one correct answer when three guesses are made?

14. Vision Correction 53% of adults use eyeglasses for vision correction (based on data from a Vision Council survey). Four adults are randomly selected.

a. Use the multiplication rule to find the probability that the first three use eyeglasses and the fourth does not use eyeglasses. That is, find P(EEEN), where E denotes an adult who uses eyeglasses and N denotes an adult who does not use eyeglasses.

b. Beginning with EEEN, make a complete list of the different possible arrangements of three adults who use eyeglasses and one who does not use eyeglasses; then find the probability for each entry in the list.

c. Based on the preceding results, what is the probability of getting exactly three adults who use eyeglasses and one who does not?

MCAT Test.   *In Exercises 15–20, assume that random guesses are made for 7 multiple choice questions on an MCAT test, so that there are n = 7 trials, each with probability of success (correct) given by p = 0.20. Find the indicated probability for the number of correct answers.*

15. Find the probability that the number x of correct answers is exactly 6.

16. Find the probability that the number x of correct answers is at least 3.

17. Find the probability that the number x of correct answers is fewer than 4.

18. Find the probability that the number x of correct answers is no more than 5.

19. Find the probability of all correct answers.

20. Find the probability that at least two answers are correct.

In Exercises 21–24, assume that when adults are randomly selected, 21% do not require vision correction (based on data from a Vision Council survey).

21. If 8 adults are randomly selected, find the probability that exactly 2 of them do not require vision correction.

22. If 20 adults are randomly selected, find the probability that exactly 5 of them do not require vision correction.

23. If 10 adults are randomly selected, find the probability that at least 3 of them do not require vision correction.

24. If 12 adults are randomly selected, find the probability that fewer than 3 of them do not require vision correction.

Significance with Range Rule of Thumb.   *In Exercises 25 and 26, assume that different groups of couples use the XSORT method of gender selection and each couple gives birth to one baby. The XSORT method is designed to increase the likelihood that a baby will be a girl, but assume that the method has no effect, so the probability of a girl is 0.5.*

25. Gender Selection Assume that the groups consist of 36 couples.

a. Find the mean and standard deviation for the numbers of girls in groups of 36 births.

b. Use the range rule of thumb to find the values separating results that are significantly low or significantly high.

c. Is the result of 26 girls a result that is significantly high? What does it suggest about the effectiveness of the XSORT method?

26. Gender Selection Assume that the groups consist of 16 couples.

a. Find the mean and standard deviation for the numbers of girls in groups of 16 births.

b. Use the range rule of thumb to find the values separating results that are significantly low or significantly high.

c. Is the result of 11 girls a result that is significantly high? What does it suggest about the effectiveness of the XSORT method?

Significance with Range Rule of Thumb.   *In Exercises 27 and 28, assume that hybridization experiments are conducted with peas having the property that for offspring, there is a 0.75 probability that a pea has green pods (as in one of Mendel's famous experiments).*

27. Hybrids Assume that offspring peas are randomly selected in groups of 15.

a. Find the mean and standard deviation for the numbers of peas with green pods in the groups of 15.

continued

b. Use the range rule of thumb to find the values separating results that are significantly low or significantly high.

c. Is the result of 2 peas with green pods a result that is significantly low? Why or why not?

28. Hybrids Assume that offspring peas are randomly selected in groups of 22.

a. Find the mean and standard deviation for the numbers of peas with green pods in the groups of 22.

b. Use the range rule of thumb to find the values separating results that are significantly low or significantly high.

c. Is the result of 20 peas with green pods a result that is significantly high? Why or why not?

Composite Sampling.   *Exercises 29 and 30 involve the method of composite sampling, whereby a medical testing laboratory saves time and money by combining blood samples for tests so that only one test is conducted for several people. A combined sample tests positive if at least one person has the disease. If a combined sample tests positive, then individual blood tests are used to identify the individual with the disease.*

29. HIV It is estimated that worldwide, 1% of those aged 15–49 are infected with the human immunodeficiency virus (HIV) (based on data from the National Institutes of Health). In tests for HIV, blood samples from 36 people are combined. What is the probability that the combined sample tests positive for HIV? Is it unlikely for such a combined sample to test positive?

30. Blood Donor Testing The American Red Cross tests every unit of donated blood for several infectious diseases, including hepatitis B, hepatitis C, HIV, syphilis, and West Nile virus infection. Blood samples from 16 donors are combined and tested, and all 16 individual samples are approved only if the combined sample passes all tests. If there is 1.4% chance that a random individual fails any of the tests, find the probability that the combined sample is not approved.

Acceptance Sampling.   *Exercises 31 and 32 involve the method of acceptance sampling, whereby a shipment of a large number of items is accepted based on test results from a sample of the items.*

31. Aspirin The MedAssist Pharmaceutical Company receives large shipments of aspirin tablets and uses this acceptance sampling plan: Randomly select and test 40 tablets, and then accept the whole batch if there is only one or none that doesn't meet the required specifications. If one shipment of 5000 aspirin tablets actually has a 3% rate of defects, what is the probability that this whole shipment will be accepted? Will almost all such shipments be accepted, or will many be rejected?

32. AAA Batteries AAA batteries are made by companies including Duracell, Energizer, Eveready, and Panasonic, and they are used to power Prestige Medical Xenon pocket otoscopes (those things that physicians use to look in your ears). When purchasing bulk orders of AAA batteries, a manufacturer of otoscopes uses this acceptance sampling plan: Randomly select 50 batteries and determine whether each is within specifications. The entire shipment is accepted if at most 2 batteries do not meet specifications. A shipment contains 2000 AAA batteries, and 2% of them do not meet specifications. What is the probability that this whole shipment will be accepted? Will almost all such shipments be accepted, or will many be rejected?

Ultimate Binomial Exercises!   *Exercises 33–36 involve finding binomial probabilities, finding parameters, and determining whether values are significantly high or low by using the range rule of thumb and probabilities.*

33. Gender Selection At an early stage of clinical trials of the XSORT method of gender selection, 14 couples using that method gave birth to 13 girls and 1 boy.

a. Assuming that the XSORT method has no effect and boys and girls are equally likely, use the range rule of thumb to identify the limits separating values that are significantly low and those that are significantly high (for the number of girls in 14 births). Based on the results, is the result of 13 girls significantly high?

b. Find the probability of exactly 13 girls in 14 births, assuming that the XSORT method has no effect.

c. Find the probability of 13 or more girls in 14 births, assuming that the XSORT method has no effect.

d. Which probability is relevant for determining whether 13 girls is significantly high: the probability from part (b) or part (c)? Based on the relevant probability, is the result of 13 girls significantly high?

e. What do the results suggest about the effectiveness of the XSORT method?

34. Clinical Trial A treatment for hypertension has been found to be successful in 60% of the patient population. In a test of a new treatment, 40 subjects are treated for hypertension and 29 of these subjects experience success with the new treatment.

a. Assuming that the old success rate of 60% still applies, use the range rule of thumb to identify the limits separating numbers of successes that are significantly low or significantly high. Based on the results, is 29 successes among the 40 subjects significantly high?

b. Find the probability that exactly 29 of the 40 cases are successes, assuming that the general success rate is 60%.

c. Find the probability that 29 or more of the cases are successes, assuming that the general success rate is 60%.

d. Which probability is relevant for determining whether 29 successes is significantly high: the probability from part (b) or part (c)? Based on the relevant probability, is the result of 29 successes significantly high?

e. What do the results suggest about the effectiveness of the new treatment?

35. Hybrids One of Mendel's famous experiments with peas included 47 offspring, and 34 of them had long stems. Mendel claimed that under the same conditions, 75% of offspring peas would have long stems. Assume that Mendel's claim of 75% is true, and assume that a sample consists of 47 offspring peas.

a. Use the range rule of thumb to identify the limits separating values that are significantly low and those that are significantly high. Based on the results, is the result of 34 peas with long stems either significantly low or significantly high?

b. Find the probability of exactly 34 peas with long stems.

c. Find the probability of 34 or fewer peas with long stems.

d. Which probability is relevant for determining whether 34 peas with long stems is significantly low: the probability from part (b) or part (c)? Based on the relevant probability, is the result of 34 peas with long stems significantly low?

e. What do the results suggest about Mendel's claim of 75%?

36. Vaccine For a specific group of subjects, there is a 5% chance of influenza ("flu"). When 80 subjects were treated with a vaccine, only one of them presented with influenza.

a. Use the range rule of thumb to identify the limits separating values that are significantly low and those that are significantly high. Based on the results, is the result of one subject getting influenza either significantly low or significantly high?

b. Find the probability of exactly one subject experiencing influenza, assuming that the vaccine has no effect.

c. Find the probability of one or fewer subjects experiencing influenza, assuming that the vaccine has no effect.

continued

d. Which probability is relevant for determining whether one subject experiencing influenza is significantly low: the probability from part (b) or part (c)? Based on the relevant probability, is the result of one subject experiencing influenza significantly low?

e. What do the results suggest about the effectiveness of the vaccine?

5-2   Beyond the Basics

37. Geometric Distribution If a procedure meets all the conditions of a binomial distribution except that the number of trials is not fixed, then the **geometric distribution** can be used. The probability of getting the first success on the xth trial is given by $P(x) = p(1 - p)^{x-1}$, where p is the probability of success on any one trial. Subjects are randomly selected for the National Health and Nutrition Examination Survey conducted by the National Center for Health Statistics, Centers for Disease Control and Prevention. The probability that someone is a universal donor (with group O and type Rh negative blood) is 0.06. Find the probability that the first subject to be a universal blood donor is the fifth person selected.

38. Multinomial Distribution The binomial distribution applies only to cases involving two types of outcomes, whereas the **multinomial distribution** involves more than two categories. Suppose we have three types of mutually exclusive outcomes denoted by A, B, and C. Let $P(A) = p_1$, $P(B) = p_2$, and $P(C) = p_3$. In n independent trials, the probability of x_1 outcomes of type A, x_2 outcomes of type B, and x_3 outcomes of type C is given by

$$\frac{n!}{(x_1)!(x_2)!(x_3)!} \cdot p_1^{x_1} \cdot p_2^{x_2} \cdot p_3^{x_3}$$

Data Set 8 "IQ and Lead" in Appendix B includes 78 subjects from a low lead exposure group, 22 subjects from a medium lead exposure group, and 21 subjects from a high lead exposure group. Find the probability of randomly selecting 10 subjects for a follow-up study and getting 5 from the low lead group, 2 from the medium lead group, and 3 from the high lead group. Assume that the selections are made with replacement. Can we use the above expression for finding the probability if the sampling is done without replacement?

39. Hypergeometric Distribution If we sample from a small finite population *without replacement*, the binomial distribution should not be used because the events are not independent. If sampling is done without replacement and the outcomes belong to one of two types, we can use the **hypergeometric distribution.** If a population has A objects of one type, while the remaining B objects are of the other type, and if n objects are sampled without replacement, then the probability of getting x objects of type A and $n - x$ objects of type B is

$$P(x) = \frac{A!}{(A - x)!x!} \cdot \frac{B!}{(B - n + x)!(n - x)!} \div \frac{(A + B)!}{(A + B - n)!n!}$$

In a medical research project, there are 20 subjects available and 4 of them are infected with HIV, while the other 16 are not infected. If 8 of the subjects are randomly selected without replacement, what is the probability that 3 of the subjects are infected with HIV, while the other 5 are not infected? What is the probability if the sampling is done with replacement?

5-3   Poisson Probability Distributions

Key Concept In Section 5-1 we introduced general discrete probability distributions and in Section 5-2 we considered binomial probability distributions, which is one particular category of discrete probability distributions. In this section we introduce *Poisson probability distributions,* which are another category of discrete probability distributions.

The following definition states that Poisson distributions are used with occurrences of an event over a specified interval, and here are some applications:

- Number of Internet users logging onto WebMD in one day
- Number of patients arriving at an emergency room in one hour
- Number of Atlantic hurricanes in one year

DEFINITION

A **Poisson probability distribution** is a discrete probability distribution that applies to occurrences of some event *over a specified interval*. The random variable x is the number of occurrences of the event in an interval. The interval can be time, distance, area, volume, or some similar unit. The probability of the event occurring x times over an interval is given by Formula 5-9.

FORMULA 5-9 Poisson Probability Distribution

$$P(x) = \frac{\mu^x \cdot e^{-\mu}}{x!}$$

where

$$e \approx 2.71828$$

μ = mean number of occurrences of the event in the intervals

Requirements for the Poisson Probability Distribution

1. The random variable x is the number of occurrences of an event *in some interval.*
2. The occurrences must be *random.*
3. The occurrences must be *independent* of each other.
4. The occurrences must be *uniformly distributed* over the interval being used.

Parameters of the Poisson Probability Distribution

- The mean is μ.
- The standard deviation is $\sigma = \sqrt{\mu}$.

Properties of the Poisson Probability Distribution

1. A particular Poisson distribution is determined only by the mean μ.
2. A Poisson distribution has possible x values of 0, 1, 2, . . . with no upper limit.

EXAMPLE 1 **Hospital Births**

In a recent year, there were 4229 births at NYU Langone Medical Center (based on data from the NYU Langone website). Assume that the number of births each day is about the same, and assume that the Poisson distribution is a suitable model.

a. Find μ, the mean number of births per day.

b. Find the probability that on a randomly selected day, there are exactly 10 births. That is, find $P(10)$, where $P(x)$ is the probability of x births in a day.

continued

SOLUTION

a. The Poisson distribution applies because we are dealing with the occurrences of an event (births) over some interval (a day). The mean number of births per day is

$$\mu = \frac{\text{Number of births}}{\text{Number of days}} = \frac{4229}{365} = 11.5863$$

b. Using Formula 5-9, the probability of $x = 10$ births in a day is found as shown here (with $x = 10$, $\mu = 11.5863$, and $e = 2.71828$):

$$P(10) = \frac{\mu^x \cdot e^{-\mu}}{x!} = \frac{11.5863^{10} \cdot 2.71828^{-11.5863}}{10!} = 0.112$$

The probability of exactly 10 births in a day is 0.112.

Poisson Distribution as Approximation to Binomial

The Poisson distribution is sometimes used to approximate the binomial distribution when n is large and p is small. One rule of thumb is to use such an approximation when the following two requirements are both satisfied.

Requirements for Using Poisson as an Approximation to Binomial

1. $n \geq 100$

2. $np \leq 10$

If both requirements are satisfied and we want to use the Poisson distribution as an approximation to the binomial distribution, we need a value for μ. That value can be calculated by using Formula 5-6 (from Section 5-2):

FORMULA 5-6   Mean for Poisson as an Approximation to Binomial

$\mu = np$

 EXAMPLE 2 Influenza

In one year, the rate of influenza is 5%. If 120 people are randomly selected, find the probability of getting at least one who contracts influenza.

SOLUTION

The time interval is a year. With $n = 120$ and $p = 0.05$, the conditions $n \geq 100$ and $np \leq 10$ are both satisfied, so we can use the Poisson distribution as an approximation to the binomial distribution. We first need the value of μ, which is found as follows:

$$\mu = np = (120)(0.05) = 6$$

Having found the value of μ, we can proceed to find the probability for specific values of x. Because we want the probability that x is "at least 1," we will use the clever strategy of first finding $P(0)$, the probability of no subjects getting influenza.

The probability of at least one subject getting influenza can then be found by subtracting that result from 1. We find $P(0)$ by using $x = 0$, $\mu = 6$, and $e = 2.71828$, as shown here:

$$P(0) = \frac{\mu^x \cdot e^{-\mu}}{x!} = \frac{6^0 \cdot 2.71828^{-6}}{0!} = \frac{1 \cdot 0.00248}{1} = 0.00248$$

Using the Poisson distribution as an approximation to the binomial distribution, we find that there is a 0.00248 probability of no subjects with influenza, so the probability of at least one subject with influenza is $1 - 0.00248 = 0.998$. If we use the binomial distribution, we again get a probability of 0.998, so the Poisson approximation is quite good here.

TECH CENTER

Poisson Distributions
Access tech instructions, videos, and data sets at **www.TriolaStats.com**

5-3 Basic Skills and Concepts

Statistical Literacy and Critical Thinking

1. Notation In analyzing patient admissions at NYU Langone Medical Center, we find that 31,645 patients were admitted in a recent year (based on data from the NYU Langone website). Assume that we want to find the probability of exactly 85 patient admissions in a randomly selected day. In applying Formula 5-9, identify the values of μ, x, and e. Also, briefly describe what each of those symbols represents.

2. Patient Admissions Use the same patient admission data given in Exercise 1. Let the random variable x represent the number of patient admissions in one day, and assume that it has a Poisson distribution. What is the standard deviation for the values of the random variable x? What is the variance?

3. Poisson Probability Distribution The random variable x represents the number of patient admissions in a day, as described in Exercise 1. Assume that the random variable x has a Poisson distribution. What are the possible values of x? Is a value of $x = 90.3$ possible? Is x a discrete random variable or a continuous random variable?

4. Probability if 0 For Formula 5-9, what does $P(0)$ represent? Simplify Formula 5-9 for the case in which $x = 0$.

Births. *In Exercises 5–8, assume that the Poisson distribution applies, assume that the mean number of births at the NYU Langone Medical Center is 11.5863 per day, and proceed to find the probability that in a randomly selected day, the number of births is the value given.*

5. Births Find the probability that in a day, there will be exactly 12 births.

6. Births Find the probability that in a day, there will be exactly 9 births.

7. Births Find the probability that in a day, there will be at least 1 birth.

8. Births Find the probability that in a day, there will be at least 2 births.

9. Murders In a recent year, there were 333 murders in New York City. Find the mean number of murders per day; then use that result to find the probability that in a day, there are no murders. Does it appear that there are expected to be many days with no murders?

10. Deaths from Horse Kicks A classical example of the Poisson distribution involves the number of deaths caused by horse kicks to men in the Prussian Army between 1875 and 1894. Data for 14 corps were combined for the 20-year period, and the 280 corps-years included a total of 196 deaths. After finding the mean number of deaths per corps-year, find the probability that a randomly selected corps-year has the following numbers of deaths: (a) 0, (b) 1, (c) 2, (d) 3, (e) 4. The actual results consisted of these frequencies: 0 deaths (in 144 corps-years); 1 death (in 91 corps-years); 2 deaths (in 32 corps-years); 3 deaths (in 11 corps-years); 4 deaths (in 2 corps-years). Compare the actual results to those expected by using the Poisson probabilities. Does the Poisson distribution serve as a good tool for predicting the actual results?

11. World War II Bombs In analyzing hits by V-1 buzz bombs in World War II, South London was partitioned into 576 regions, each with an area of 0.25 km^2. A total of 535 bombs hit the combined area of 576 regions.

a. Find the probability that a randomly selected region had exactly 2 hits.

b. Among the 576 regions, find the expected number of regions with exactly 2 hits.

c. How does the result from part (b) compare to this actual result: There were 93 regions that had exactly 2 hits?

12. Disease Cluster Neuroblastoma, a rare form of cancer, occurs in 11 children in a million, so its probability is 0.000011. Four cases of neuroblastoma occurred in Oak Park, Illinois, which had 12,429 children.

a. Assuming that neuroblastoma occurs as usual, find the mean number of cases in groups of 12,429 children.

b. Using the unrounded mean from part (a), find the probability that the number of neuroblastoma cases in a group of 12,429 children is 0 or 1.

c. What is the probability of more than one case of neuroblastoma?

d. Does the cluster of four cases appear to be attributable to random chance? Why or why not?

13. Car Fatalities The recent rate of car fatalities was 33,561 fatalities for 2969 billion miles traveled (based on data from the National Highway Traffic Safety Administration). Find the probability that for the next billion miles traveled, there will be at least one fatality. What does the result indicate about the likelihood of at least one fatality?

14. Dandelions Dandelions are studied for their effects on crop production and lawn growth. In one region, the mean number of dandelions per square meter was found to be 7.0 (based on data from Manitoba Agriculture and Food).

a. Find the probability of no dandelions in an area of 1 m^2.

b. Find the probability of at least one dandelion in an area of 1 m^2.

c. Find the probability of at most two dandelions in an area of 1 m^2.

15. Rubella During the last 13 years in the United States, there were 138 cases of rubella.

a. Find the mean number of cases of rubella per year. Round the result to four decimal places.

b. Find the probability of no cases of rubella in a year.

c. Find the probability of exactly 9 cases of rubella in a year. How does it compare to the 2 years among 13 that had exactly 9 cases of rubella?

16. Diphtheria During the past 34 years, there were 56 cases of diphtheria in the United States.

a. Find the mean number of cases of diphtheria per year. Express the result with five decimal places.

b. Find the probability of no cases of diphtheria in a year.

c. Find the probability that the number of diphtheria cases in a year is 5 or fewer. If a year has more than 5 cases of diphtheria, is that a significantly high number?

5-3 Beyond the Basics

17. Probability Histogram for a Poisson Distribution Construct the probability histogram for Exercise 16. Is the Poisson probability distribution a normal distribution or is it skewed?

Chapter Quick Quiz

In Exercises 1–10, use the following: Based on data from the National Center for Health Statistics, 20.6% of adult males smoke. A random sample of 64 male adults is obtained.

1. Smoking Find the mean number of smokers in groups of 64 randomly selected adult males.

2. Smoking Find the standard deviation of the number of smokers in groups of 64 randomly selected adult males.

3. Smoking Are the results from Exercises 1 and 2 statistics or parameters?

4. Smoking For a random sample of 64 males, find the numbers separating the outcomes that are significantly high or significantly low.

5. Smoking Find the probability that the first 8 randomly selected males include exactly 3 who smoke.

In Exercises 6–10, use the following: Five male adults are randomly selected, and the table in the margin lists the probabilities for the number that are heavy drinkers (based on data from the National Center for Health Statistics). Males are considered to be heavy drinkers if they have at least 14 drinks per week "on average."

x	P(x)
0	0.762
1	0.213
2	0.024
3	0.001
4	0+
5	0+

6. Drinking Does the table describe a probability distribution? Why or why not?

7. Drinking Find the mean of the number of heavy drinkers in groups of five randomly selected adult males.

8. Drinking Based on the table, the standard deviation is 0.5 male. What is the variance? Include appropriate units.

9. Drinking What does the probability of 0+ indicate? Does it indicate that among five randomly selected adult males, it is impossible for all of them to be heavy drinkers?

10. Drinking What is the probability that fewer than three of the five adult males are heavy drinkers? If we were to find that among 5 randomly selected adult males, there are 4 heavy drinkers, is 4 significantly high?

Review Exercises

In Exercises 1–5, assume that 28% of randomly selected adults have high cholesterol (with a level of at least 240 mg/dL or are taking medicine to reduce cholesterol), based on results from the National Center for Health Statistics. Assume that a group of eight adults is randomly selected.

1. Cholesterol Find the probability that exactly three of the eight adults have high cholesterol.

2. Cholesterol Find the probability that at least two of the eight adults have high cholesterol. Does the result apply to eight adults from the same family? Why or why not?

3. Cholesterol Find the mean and standard deviation for the numbers of adults in groups of eight who have high cholesterol.

4. Cholesterol If the group of eight adults includes exactly 2 with high cholesterol, is that value of 2 significantly low?

5. Cholesterol If all eight of the adults have high cholesterol, is eight significantly high? Why or why not?

6. Security Survey In a *USA Today* poll, subjects were asked if passwords should be replaced with biometric security, such as fingerprints. The results from that poll have been used to create the accompanying table. Does this table describe a probability distribution? Why or why not?

Response	P(x)
Yes	0.53
No	0.17
Not sure	0.30

x	P(x)
0	0.304
1	0.400
2	0.220
3	0.064
4	0.011
5	0.001
6	0+

7. Condom Failure Rate According to the Department of Health and Human Services, the failure rate for male condoms is 18%. The accompanying table is based on the failure rate of 18%, where x represents the number of condoms that fail when six are tested.

a. Does the table describe a probability distribution? Why or why not?

b. Assuming that the table does describe a probability distribution, find its mean.

c. Assuming that the table does describe a probability distribution, find its standard deviation.

d. If 6 condoms are tested and 5 of them fail, is 5 a significantly high number of failures? Why or why not?

e. What does the symbol 0+ represent?

8. Poisson: Deaths Currently, an average of 143 residents of Madison, CT (population 17,858), die each year (based on data from the U.S. National Center for Health Statistics).

a. Find the mean number of deaths per day.

b. Find the probability that on a given day, there are no deaths.

c. Find the probability that on a given day, there are more than two deaths.

d. Based on the preceding results, should Madison have a contingency plan to handle more than two deaths per day? Why or why not?

Cumulative Review Exercises

1. Manatee Deaths Listed below are the annual numbers of manatee deaths from boats in Florida for each of the past 12 years, listed in chronological order.

$$73 \quad 69 \quad 79 \quad 92 \quad 73 \quad 90 \quad 97 \quad 83 \quad 88 \quad 81 \quad 73 \quad 68$$

a. Find the mean.

b. Find the median.

c. Find the range.

d. Find the standard deviation.

e. Find the variance.

f. Describe an important characteristic of the data that is not addressed by the statistics found in parts (a) through (e).

g. Use the range rule of thumb to identify the values separating significant values from those that are not significant.

h. Based on the results from part (f), do any of the years have a number of manatee deaths that is significantly low or significantly high?

i. What is the level of measurement of the data: nominal, ordinal, interval, or ratio?

j. Are the data discrete or continuous?

2. Analysis of Last Digits The accompanying table lists the last or rightmost digits of weights of the males listed in Data Set 1 "Body Data" in Appendix B. The last digits of a data set can sometimes be used to determine whether the data have been measured or simply reported. The presence of disproportionately more 0s and 5s is often a sure sign that the data have been reported instead of measured.

a. Using the table, find the mean and standard deviation of those last digits. Are the results statistics or parameters?

b. Examine the given table to determine if there is anything about the sample data (such as disproportionately more 0s and 5s) suggesting that the given last digits are not random? Or do they appear to be random?

c. Does the table describe a probability distribution? Why or why not?

x	f
0	9
1	20
2	14
3	18
4	15
5	15
6	16
7	13
8	20
9	13

3. Government Health Plan Fox News broadcast a graph similar to the one shown here. The graph is intended to compare the number of people actually enrolled in a government health plan (left bar) and the goal for the number of enrollees (right bar). Does the graph depict the data correctly or is it somehow misleading? Explain.

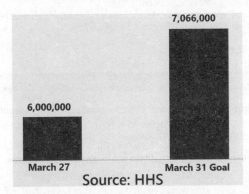

7,066,000

6,000,000

March 27   March 31 Goal
Source: HHS

4. Hypertension Among adults in Japan, 45% have hypertension (based on data from the National Survey of Circulatory Disorders in Japan).

a. Find the probability that a randomly selected adult does not have hypertension.

b. Find the probability that two randomly selected adults both have hypertension.

c. Find the probability that among three randomly selected adults, at least one has hypertension.

d. For groups of 50 randomly selected adults, find the mean and standard deviation for the number of adults having hypertension. Are these results statistics or parameters?

e. If 50 adults are randomly selected and 20 of them have hypertension, is 20 a result that is significantly low or significantly high? Why?

Technology Project

Mendel's Hybrid Experiments One of Mendel's famous experiments with peas included 1064 offspring, and 787 of them had long stems. Mendel claimed that under the same conditions, 75% of offspring peas would have long stems. Assume that Mendel's claim of 75% is true, and assume that a sample consists of 1064 offspring peas.

- Use the range rule of thumb to identify the limits separating values that are significantly low and those that are significantly high. Based on the results, is the result of 787 peas with long stems either significantly low or significantly high?

- Find the probability of exactly 787 peas with long stems.

- Find the probability of 787 or fewer peas with long stems.

- Which probability is relevant for determining whether 787 peas with long stems is significantly low: the probability from part (b) or part (c)? Based on the relevant probability, is the result of 787 peas with long stems significantly low?

- What do the results suggest about Mendel's claim of 75%?

FROM DATA TO DECISION

Critical Thinking: Determining criteria for concluding that a gender selection method is effective

You are responsible for analyzing results from a clinical trial of the effectiveness of a new method of gender selection. Assume that the sample size of $n = 75$ couples has already been established, and each couple will have one child. Further assume that each of the couples will be subjected to a treatment that supposedly increases the likelihood that the child will be a girl. Assume that with no treatment, the probability of a baby being a girl is 0.488, which is currently the correct value in the United States.

There is a danger in obtaining results first, then making conclusions about the results. If the results are close to showing the effectiveness of a treatment, it might be tempting to conclude that there is an effect when, in reality, there is no effect. It is better to establish criteria *before* obtaining results.

a. Using the methods of this chapter, identify the criteria that should be used for concluding that the treatment is effective in increasing the likelihood of a girl. Among the 75 births, how many girls would you require in order to conclude that the gender selection procedure is effective? Explain how you arrived at this result.

b. If 60% of the 75 babies are girls, is that result high enough to conclude that the gender selection method is effective? Why or why not?

c. If 64% of the 75 babies are girls, is that result high enough to conclude that the gender selection method is effective? Why or why not?

Cooperative Group Activities

1. In-class activity Win $1,000,000! The James Randi Educational Foundation offers a $1,000,000 prize to anyone who can show "under proper observing conditions, evidence of any paranormal, supernatural, or occult power or event." Divide into groups of three. Select one person who will be tested for extrasensory perception (ESP) by trying to correctly identify a digit (0–9) randomly selected by another member of the group. Conduct at least 20 trials. Another group member should record the randomly selected digit, the digit guessed by the subject, and whether the guess was correct or wrong. Construct the table for the probability distribution of randomly generated digits, construct the relative frequency table for the random digits that were actually obtained, and construct a relative frequency table for the guesses that were made. After comparing the three tables, what do you conclude? What proportion of guesses is correct? Does it seem that the subject has the ability to select the correct digit significantly more often than would be expected by chance?

2. In-class activity See the preceding activity and *design an experiment* that would be effective in testing someone's claim that he or she has the ability to identify the color of a card selected from a standard deck of playing cards. Describe the experiment with great detail. Because the prize of $1,000,000 is at stake, we want to be careful to avoid the serious mistake of concluding that the person has a paranormal power when that power is not actually present. There will likely be some chance that the subject could make random guesses and be correct every time, so identify a probability that is reasonable for the event of the subject passing the test with random guesses. Be sure that the test is designed so that this probability is equal to or less than the probability value selected.

3. In-class activity Suppose we want to identify the probability distribution for the number of children in families with at least one child. For each student in the class, find the number of brothers and sisters and record the total number of children (including the student) in each family. Construct the relative frequency table for the result obtained. (The values of the random variable x will be 1, 2, 3, ...) What is wrong with using this relative frequency table as an estimate of the probability distribution for the number of children in randomly selected families?

4. Out-of-class activity The analysis of the last digits of data can sometimes reveal whether the data have been collected through actual measurements or reported by the subjects. Refer to an almanac or the Internet and find a collection of data (such as lengths of rivers in the world), then analyze the distribution of last digits to determine whether the values were obtained through actual measurements.

5. Out-of-class activity The photos shown below depict famous statisticians with first names of David and John, not necessarily in the order shown. Conduct a survey by asking this question: "Which man is named David and which man is named John?" Do the respondents appear to give results significantly different from what is expected with random guesses? (See "Who Do You Look Like? Evidence of Facial Stereotypes for Male Names" by Lea, Thomas, Lamkin, and Bell, *Psychonomic Bulletin & Review,* Vol. 14, Issue 5.)

6 Normal Probability Distributions

 CHAPTER PROBLEM —— **What Is a *Normal* Pulse Rate?**

Exploring the pulse rates of adult males and females in Data Set 1 "Body Data" from Appendix B reveals the following:

- Adult males have pulse rates with a mean of 69.6 bpm (beats per minute), a standard deviation of 11.3 bpm, and a distribution that is approximately normal.

- Adult females have pulse rates with a mean of 74.0 bpm, a standard deviation of 12.5 bpm, and a distribution that is approximately normal.

- There appears to be a significant difference between pulse rates of males and females.

For the purposes of this chapter, we will use the above results as reasonable estimates of population parameters. See the following:

	μ	σ	Distribution
Male Adult Pulse Rates (bpm)	69.6	11.3	Normal
Female Adult Pulse Rates (bpm)	74.0	12.5	Normal

Physicians routinely measure pulse rates of patients, and the normal range is generally considered to be between 60 bpm and 100 bpm. Here are conditions for pulse rates outside that range:

Tachycardia: Pulse rate greater than 100 bpm.

Bradycardia: Pulse rate less than 60 bpm

An excessively high pulse rate (tachycardia) is generally more of a problem than an excessively low pulse rate (bradycardia). An excessively high pulse rate can indicate a high risk of stroke, heart disease, or can even cause death. An excessively low pulse can occur with an athlete in peak physical condition, and some drugs such as beta blockers can also cause an excessively low pulse rate.

Here are some questions that can be addressed with the methods of this chapter:

- What is the proportion of adult males who are expected to have pulse rates greater than 100 bpm?

- What is the proportion of adult males who are expected to have pulse rates less than 60 bpm.

- For males, if we introduce a criterion whereby the highest 1% of pulse rates are considered to be *significantly* high, what is the cutoff?

- For males, if we introduce a criterion whereby the lowest 1% of pulse rates are considered to be *significantly* low, what is the cutoff?

These same questions can be posed for adult females, and we will address such questions using the methods in this chapter.

CHAPTER OBJECTIVES

Chapter 5 introduced *discrete* probability distributions, but in this chapter we introduce *continuous* probability distributions, and most of this chapter focuses on *normal distributions*. Here are the chapter objectives:

 The Standard Normal Distribution

- Describe the characteristics of a standard normal distribution.

- Find the probability of some range of *z* values in a standard normal distribution.

- Find *z* scores corresponding to regions under the curve representing a standard normal distribution.

6-2 Real Applications of Normal Distributions

- Develop the ability to describe a normal distribution (not necessarily a standard normal distribution).

- Find the probability of some range of values in a normal distribution.

- Find *x* scores corresponding to regions under the curve representing a normal distribution.

6-3 Sampling Distributions and Estimators

- Develop the ability to describe a *sampling distribution of a statistic.*

- Determine whether a statistic serves as a good estimator of the corresponding population parameter.

 The Central Limit Theorem

- Describe what the central limit theorem states.

- Apply the central limit theorem by finding the probability that a sample mean falls within some specified range of values.

- Identify conditions for which it is appropriate to use a normal distribution for the distribution of sample means.

continued

Assessing Normality

- Develop the ability to examine histograms, outliers, and normal quantile plots to determine whether sample data appear to be from a population having a distribution that is approximately normal.

 Normal as Approximation to Binomial

- Identify conditions for which it is appropriate to use a normal distribution as an approximation to a binomial probability distribution.

- Use the normal distribution for approximating probabilities for a binomial distribution.

6-1 The Standard Normal Distribution

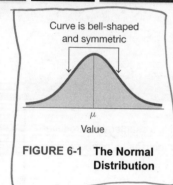

FIGURE 6-1 The Normal Distribution

Key Concept In this section we present the *standard normal distribution,* which is a specific normal distribution having the following three properties:

1. Bell-shaped: The graph of the standard normal distribution is bell-shaped (as in Figure 6-1).

2. $\mu = 0$: The standard normal distribution has a mean equal to 0.

3. $\sigma = 1$: The standard normal distribution has a standard deviation equal to 1.

In this section we develop the skill to find areas (or probabilities or relative frequencies) corresponding to various regions under the graph of the standard normal distribution. In addition, we find z scores that correspond to areas under the graph. These skills become important in the next section as we study nonstandard normal distributions and the real and important applications that they involve.

Normal Distributions

There are infinitely many different normal distributions, depending on the values used for the mean and standard deviation. We begin with a brief introduction to this general family of normal distributions.

> **DEFINITION**
>
> If a continuous random variable has a distribution with a graph that is symmetric and bell-shaped, as in Figure 6-1, and it can be described by the equation given as Formula 6-1, we say that it has a **normal distribution**.

> **FORMULA 6-1**
>
> $$y = \frac{e^{-\frac{1}{2}\left(\frac{x-\mu}{\sigma}\right)^2}}{\sigma\sqrt{2\pi}}$$

In this book, we won't actually use Formula 6-1, but examining the right side of the equation reveals that any particular normal distribution is determined by two parameters: the population mean, μ, and population standard deviation, σ. (In Formula 6-1, x is a variable that can change, $\pi = 3.14159$, and $e = 2.71828$.) Once specific values are selected for μ and σ, Formula 6-1 is an equation relating x and y, and we can graph that equation to get a result that will look like Figure 6-1. And that's about all we need to know about Formula 6-1!

Uniform Distributions

The major focus of this chapter is the concept of a normal probability distribution, but we begin with a *uniform distribution* so that we can see the following two very important properties:

1. The area under the graph of a continuous probability distribution is equal to 1.

2. There is a correspondence between area and probability, so *probabilities* can be found by identifying the corresponding *areas* in the graph using this formula for the area of a rectangle:

$$\text{Area} = \text{height} \times \text{width}$$

> **DEFINITION**
>
> A continuous random variable has a **uniform distribution** if its values are spread *evenly* over the range of possibilities. The graph of a uniform distribution results in a rectangular shape.

Density Curve The graph of any continuous probability distribution is called a **density curve,** and any density curve must satisfy the requirement that the total area under the curve is exactly 1. This requirement that the area must equal 1 simplifies probability problems, so the following statement is really important:

> **Because the total area under any density curve is equal to 1, there is a correspondence between *area* and *probability*.**

EXAMPLE 1 Waiting Times for Emergency Room Check-In

During certain time periods at a hospital in New York City, patients arriving at the emergency room have waiting times that are uniformly distributed between 0 minutes and 5 minutes, as illustrated in Figure 6-2.

Refer to Figure 6-2 to see these properties:

- All of the different possible waiting times are *equally likely*.

- Waiting times can be *any* value between 0 min and 5 min, so it is possible to have a waiting time of 1.234567 min.

- By assigning the probability of 0.2 to the height of the vertical line in Figure 6-2, the *enclosed area is exactly 1*. (In general, we should make the height of the vertical line in a uniform distribution equal to 1/range.)

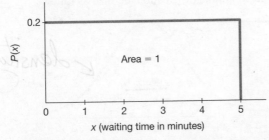

FIGURE 6-2 Uniform Distribution of Waiting Time

EXAMPLE 2 **Waiting Times at an Emergency Room**

Given the uniform distribution illustrated in Figure 6-2, find the probability that a randomly selected patient has a waiting time of at least 2 minutes.

SOLUTION

The shaded area in Figure 6-3 represents waiting times of at least 2 minutes. Because the total area under the density curve is equal to 1, there is a correspondence between area and probability. We can easily find the desired *probability* by using *areas* as follows:

$$P(\text{wait time of at least 2 min}) = \text{height} \times \text{width of shaded area in Figure 6-3}$$
$$= 0.2 \times 3$$
$$= 0.6$$

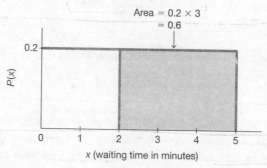

FIGURE 6-3   **Using Area to Find Probability**

INTERPRETATION

The probability of randomly selecting a patient with a waiting time of at least 2 minutes is 0.6.

Standard Normal Distribution

The density curve of a uniform distribution is a horizontal straight line, so we can find the area of any rectangular region by applying this formula:

$$\text{Area} = \text{height} \times \text{width}$$

Because the density curve of a normal distribution has a more complicated bell shape as shown in Figure 6-1, it is more difficult to find areas. However, the basic principle is the same: *There is a correspondence between area and probability.* In Figure 6-4 we show that for a standard normal distribution, the area under the density curve is equal to 1. In Figure 6-4, we use "z Score" as a label for the horizontal axis, and this is common for the standard normal distribution, defined as follows.

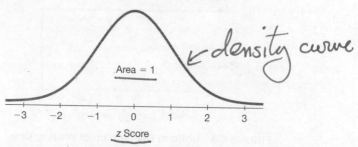

FIGURE 6-4   **Standard Normal Distribution**

DEFINITION

The **standard normal distribution** is a normal distribution with the parameters of $\mu = 0$ and $\sigma = 1$. The total area under its density curve is equal to 1 (as in Figure 6-4).

Finding Probabilities When Given z Scores

It is not easy to manually find areas in Figure 6-4, but we can find areas (or probabilities) for many different regions in Figure 6-4 by using technology, or we can also use Table A-2 (in Appendix A and the *Formulas and Tables* insert card). Key features of the different methods are summarized in Table 6-1, which follows. (StatCrunch provides options for a cumulative left region, a cumulative right region, or the region between two boundaries.) Because calculators and software generally give more accurate results than Table A-2, we *strongly* recommend using technology. (When there are discrepancies, answers in Appendix D will generally include results based on technology as well as answers based on Table A-2.)

TABLE 6-1 Formats Used for Finding Normal Distribution Areas

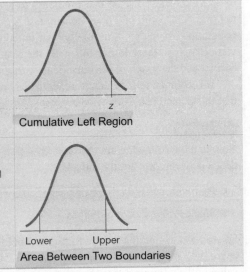

Cumulative Area from the Left
The following provide the *cumulative area from the left* up to a vertical line above a specific value of *z*:

- **Table A-2**
- **Statdisk**
- **Minitab**
- **Excel**
- **StatCrunch**

Cumulative Left Region

Area Between Two Boundaries
The following provide the area bounded on the left and bounded on the right by vertical lines above specific values.

- **TI-83/84 Plus calculator**
- **StatCrunch**

Lower   Upper
Area Between Two Boundaries

Table A-2: If using Table A-2, it is essential to understand these points:

1. Table A-2 is designed only for the *standard* normal distribution, which is a normal distribution with a mean of 0 and a standard deviation of 1.

2. Table A-2 is on two pages, with the left page for *negative z* scores and the right page for *positive z* scores.

3. Each value in the body of the table is a *cumulative area from the left* up to a vertical boundary above a specific z score.

continued

4. When working with a graph, avoid confusion between z scores and areas.

    z score: **_Distance_ along the horizontal scale of the standard normal distribution (corresponding to the number of standard deviations above or below the mean); refer to the leftmost column and top row of Table A-2.**

    Area: **_Region_ under the curve; refer to the values in the _body_ of Table A-2.**

5. The part of the z score denoting hundredths is found across the top row of Table A-2.

> **CAUTION** When working with a normal distribution, be careful to avoid confusion between z scores and areas.

The following examples illustrate procedures that can be used with real and important applications introduced in the following sections.

EXAMPLE 3 Bone Density Test

A bone mineral density test can be helpful in identifying the presence or likelihood of osteoporosis, a disease causing bones to become more fragile and more likely to break. The result of a bone density test is commonly measured as a z score. The population of z scores is normally distributed with a mean of 0 and a standard deviation of 1, so these test results meet the requirements of a standard normal distribution, and the graph of the bone density test scores is as shown in Figure 6-5.

    A randomly selected adult undergoes a bone density test. Find the probability that this person has a bone density test score less than 1.27.

SOLUTION

Note that the following are the *same* (because of the aforementioned correspondence between probability and area):

- *Probability* that the bone density test score is less than 1.27
- Shaded *area* shown in Figure 6-5

So we need to find the area in Figure 6-5 below $z = 1.27$. If using Table A-2, begin with the z score of 1.27 by locating 1.2 in the left column; next find the value in the adjoining row of probabilities that is directly below 0.07, as shown in the excerpt on the top of the following page. Table A-2 shows that there is an area of 0.8980 corresponding to $z = 1.27$. We want the area *below* 1.27, and Table A-2 gives the cumulative area from the left, so the desired area is 0.8980. Because of the correspondence between area and probability, we know that the probability of a z score below 1.27 is 0.8980.

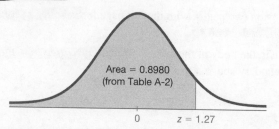

FIGURE 6-5   **Finding Area to the Left of $z = 1.27$**

TABLE A-2 *(continued)* Cumulative Area from the LEFT

z	.00	.01	.02	.03	.04	.05	.06	.07	.08	.09
0.0	.5000	.5040	.5080	.5120	.5160	.5199	.5239	.5279	.5319	.5359
0.1	.5398	.5438	.5478	.5517	.5557	.5596	.5636	.5675	.5714	.5753
0.2	.5793	.5832	.5871	.5910	.5948	.5987	.6026	.6064	.6103	.6141
1.0	.8413	.8438	.8461	.8485	.8508	.8531	.8554	.8577	.8599	.8621
1.1	.8643	.8665	.8686	.8708	.8729	.8749	.8770	.8790	.8810	.8830
1.2	.8849	.8869	.8888	.8907	.8925	.8944	.8962	.8980	.8997	.9015
1.3	.9032	.9049	.9066	.9082	.9099	.9115	.9131	.9147	.9162	.9177
1.4	.9192	.9207	.9222	.9236	.9251	.9265	.9279	.9292	.9306	.9319

INTERPRETATION

The *probability* that a randomly selected person has a bone density test result below 1.27 is 0.8980, shown as the shaded region in Figure 6-5. Another way to interpret this result is to conclude that 89.80% of people have bone density levels below 1.27.

EXAMPLE 4 Bone Density Test: Finding the Area to the *Right* of a Value

Using the same bone density test from Example 3, find the probability that a randomly selected person has a result above -1.00. A value above -1.00 is considered to be in the "normal" range of bone density readings.

SOLUTION

We again find the desired *probability* by finding a corresponding *area*. We are looking for the area of the region to the right of $z = -1.00$ that is shaded in Figure 6-6. The Statdisk display on the top of the following page shows that the area to the right of $z = -1.00$ is 0.841345.

If we use Table A-2, we should know that it is designed to apply only to cumulative areas from the *left*. Referring to the page with *negative z* scores, we find that the cumulative area from the left up to $z = -1.00$ is 0.1587, as shown in Figure 6-6. Because the total area under the curve is 1, we can find the shaded area by subtracting 0.1587 from 1. The result is 0.8413. Even though Table A-2 is designed only for cumulative areas from the left, we can use it to find cumulative areas from the right, as shown in Figure 6-6.

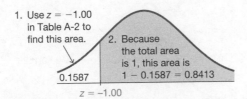

1. Use $z = -1.00$ in Table A-2 to find this area.

2. Because the total area is 1, this area is $1 - 0.1587 = 0.8413$

0.1587

$z = -1.00$

FIGURE 6-6 **Finding the Area to the Right of $z = -1$**

continued

Statdisk

Normal Distribution	

Enter one value, then click Evaluate
to find the other value:

z Value: [-1]

Cumulative area
from the left: [   ]

[Evaluate]

z Value: -1.000000
Prob Dens: 0.2419707

Cumulative Probs
Left: 0.158655
Right: 0.841345
2 Tailed: 0.317311
Central: 0.682689
As Table A-2: 0.158655

[Print]   [Copy]

INTERPRETATION

Because of the correspondence between probability and area, we conclude that the *probability* of randomly selecting someone with a bone density reading above -1 is 0.8413 (which is the *area* to the right of $z = -1.00$). We could also say that 84.13% of people have bone density levels above -1.00.

Example 4 illustrates a way that Table A-2 can be used indirectly to find a cumulative area from the right. The following example illustrates another way that we can find an area indirectly by using Table A-2.

EXAMPLE 5 Bone Density Test: Finding the Area Between Two Values

A bone density test reading between -1.00 and -2.50 indicates that the subject has osteopenia, which is some bone loss. Find the probability that a randomly selected subject has a reading between -1.00 and -2.50.

SOLUTION

We are again dealing with normally distributed values having a mean of 0 and a standard deviation of 1. The values between -1.00 and -2.50 correspond to the shaded region in the third graph included in Figure 6-7. Table A-2 cannot be used to find that area directly, but we can use this table to find the following:

1. The area to the left of $z = -1.00$ is 0.1587.
2. The area to the left of $z = -2.50$ is 0.0062.
3. The area *between* $z = -2.50$ and $z = -1.00$ (the shaded area at the far right in Figure 6-7) is the difference between the areas found in the preceding two steps:

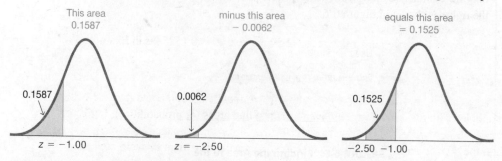

This area   minus this area   equals this area
0.1587 $-$ 0.0062   = 0.1525

0.1587   0.0062   0.1525

$z = -1.00$ $z = -2.50$ -2.50 -1.00

FIGURE 6-7   **Finding the Area Between Two z Scores**

INTERPRETATION

Using the correspondence between probability and area, we conclude that there is a probability of 0.1525 that a randomly selected subject has a bone density reading between −1.00 and −2.50. Another way to interpret this result is to state that 15.25% of people have osteopenia, with bone density readings between −1.00 and −2.50.

Example 5 can be generalized as the following rule:

The area corresponding to the region *between* two *z* scores can be found by finding the difference between the two areas found in Table A-2.

Figure 6-8 illustrates this general rule. The shaded region *B* can be found by calculating the *difference* between two areas found from Table A-2.

> **HINT** Don't try to memorize a rule or formula for this case. Focus on *understanding* by using a graph. Draw a graph, shade the desired area, and then get creative to think of a way to find the desired area by working with cumulative areas from the left.

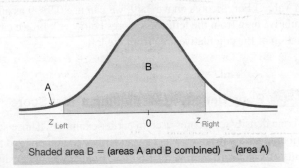

Shaded area B = (areas A and B combined) − (area A)

FIGURE 6-8   Finding the Area Between Two *z* Scores

Probabilities such as those in the preceding examples can also be expressed with the following notation.

Notation

$P(a < z < b)$	denotes the probability that the *z* score is between *a* and *b*.
$P(z > a)$	denotes the probability that the *z* score is greater than *a*.
$P(z < a)$	denotes the probability that the *z* score is less than *a*.

With this notation, $P(-2.50 < z < -1.00) = 0.1525$ states in symbols that the probability of a *z* score falling between −2.50 and −1.00 is 0.1525 (as in Example 5).

Finding *z* Scores from Known Areas

Examples 3, 4, and 5 all involved the standard normal distribution, and they were all examples with this same format: Given *z* scores, find areas (or probabilities). In many cases, we need a method for reversing the format: Given a known area (or probability), find the corresponding *z* score. In such cases, it is really important to avoid confusion between *z* scores and areas. Remember, *z* scores are *distances* along the horizontal scale, but areas (or probabilities) are regions under the density curve. (Table A-2 lists z-scores in the left column and across the top row, but areas are found in the *body* of the table.) We should also remember that z scores positioned in the left half of the curve are always negative. If we already know a probability and want to find the corresponding z score, we use the following procedure.

Procedure for Finding a z Score from a Known Area

1. Draw a bell-shaped curve and identify the region under the curve that corresponds to the given probability. If that region is not a cumulative region from the left, work instead with a known region that is a cumulative region from the left.

2. Use technology or Table A-2 to find the z score. With Table A-2, use the cumulative area from the left, locate the closest probability in the *body* of the table, and identify the corresponding z score.

Special Cases in Table A-2

z Score	Cumulative Area from the Left
1.645	0.9500
−1.645	0.0500
2.575	0.9950
−2.575	0.0050
Above 3.49	0.9999
Below −3.49	0.0001

Special Cases In the solution to Example 6 that follows, Table A-2 leads to a z score of 1.645, which is midway between 1.64 and 1.65. When using Table A-2, we can usually avoid interpolation by simply selecting the closest value. The accompanying table lists special cases that are often used in a wide variety of applications. (For one of those special cases, the value of z = 2.576 gives an area slightly closer to the area of 0.9950, but z = 2.575 has the advantage of being the value exactly midway between z = 2.57 and z = 2.58.) Except in these special cases, we can usually select the closest value in the table. (If a desired value is midway between two table values, select the larger value.) For z scores above 3.49, we can use 0.9999 as an approximation of the cumulative area from the left; for z scores below −3.49, we can use 0.0001 as an approximation of the cumulative area from the left.

EXAMPLE 6 Bone Density Test: Finding a Test Score

Use the same bone density test scores used in earlier examples. Those scores are normally distributed with a mean of 0 and a standard deviation of 1, so they meet the requirements of a standard normal distribution. Find the bone density score corresponding to P_{95}, the 95th percentile. That is, find the bone density score that separates the bottom 95% from the top 5%. See Figure 6-9.

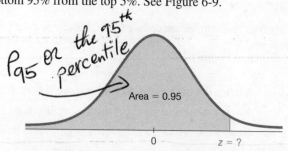

FIGURE 6-9   Finding the 95th Percentile

SOLUTION

Figure 6-9 shows the z score that is the 95th percentile, with 95% of the area (or 0.95) below it.

Technology: We could find the z score using technology. The following Excel display shows that the z score with an area of 0.95 to its left is z = 1.644853627, or 1.645 when rounded.

Excel

Function Arguments		? X

NORM.INV

Probability	0.95	= 0.95
Mean	0	= 0
Standard_dev	1	= 1

= 1.644853627

Returns the inverse of the normal cumulative distribution for the specified mean and standard deviation.

Standard_dev is the standard deviation of the distribution, a positive number.

Formula result = 1.644853627

Help on this function   OK   Cancel

Table A-2: If using Table A-2, search for the area of 0.95 *in the body* of the table and then find the corresponding z score. In Table A-2 we find the areas of 0.9495 and 0.9505, but there's an asterisk with a special note indicating that 0.9500 corresponds to a z score of 1.645. We can now conclude that the z score in Figure 6-9 is 1.645, so the 95th percentile is $z = 1.645$.

INTERPRETATION

For bone density test scores, 95% of the scores are less than or equal to 1.645, and 5% of them are greater than or equal to 1.645.

EXAMPLE 7 **Bone Density Test**

Using the same bone density test described in Example 3, we have a standard normal distribution with a mean of 0 and a standard deviation of 1. Find the bone density test score that separates the bottom 2.5% and find the score that separates the top 2.5%.

SOLUTION

The required z scores are shown in Figure 6-10. Those z scores can be found using technology. If using Table A-2 to find the z score located to the left, we search the *body of the table* for an area of 0.025. The result is $z = -1.96$. To find the z score located to the right, we search *the body of* Table A-2 for an area of 0.975. (Remember that Table A-2 always gives cumulative areas from the *left*.) The result is $z = 1.96$. The values of $z = -1.96$ and $z = 1.96$ separate the bottom 2.5% and the top 2.5%, as shown in Figure 6-10.

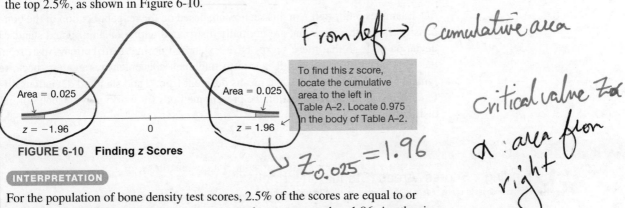

From left → Cumulative area

Area = 0.025   Area = 0.025

To find this z score, locate the cumulative area to the left in Table A-2. Locate 0.975 in the body of Table A-2.

$z = -1.96$ 0 $z = 1.96$

Critical value z_α

α : area from right

$z_{0.025} = 1.96$

FIGURE 6-10   Finding z Scores

INTERPRETATION

For the population of bone density test scores, 2.5% of the scores are equal to or less than -1.96 and 2.5% of the scores are equal to or greater than 1.96. Another interpretation is that 95% of all bone density test scores are between -1.96 and 1.96.

Critical Values For a normal distribution, a *critical value* is a z score on the borderline separating those z scores that are *significantly low* or *significantly high*. Common critical values are $z = -1.96$ and $z = 1.96$, and they are obtained as shown in Example 7. In Example 7, values of $z = -1.96$ or lower are significantly low because only 2.5% of the population have scores at or below -1.96, and the values at or above $z = 1.96$ are significantly high because only 2.5% of the population have scores at or above 1.96. Critical values will become extremely important in subsequent chapters. The following notation is used for critical z values found by using the standard normal distribution.

> **DEFINITION**
>
> For the standard normal distribution, a **critical value** is a z score on the borderline separating those z scores that are *significantly low* or *significantly high*.

Notation

The expression z_α denotes the z score with an area of α to its right. (α is the Greek letter alpha.)

EXAMPLE 8 **Finding the Critical Value z_α**

Find the value of $z_{0.025}$. (Let $\alpha = 0.025$ in the expression z_α.)

SOLUTION

The notation of $z_{0.025}$ is used to represent the z score with an area of 0.025 to its *right*. Refer to Figure 6-10 and note that the value of $z = 1.96$ has an area of 0.025 to its right, so $z_{0.025} = 1.96$. Note that $z_{0.025}$ corresponds to a cumulative left area of 0.975.

> **CAUTION** When finding a value of z_α for a particular value of α, note that α is the area to the *right* of z_α, but Table A-2 and some technologies give cumulative areas to the *left* of a given z score. To find the value of z_α, resolve that conflict by using the value of $1 - \alpha$. For example, to find $z_{0.1}$, refer to the z score with an area of 0.9 to its left.

Examples 3 through 7 in this section are based on the real application of the bone density test, with scores that are normally distributed with a mean of 0 and standard deviation of 1, so that these scores have a standard normal distribution. Apart from the bone density test scores, it is rare to find such convenient parameters, because typical normal distributions have means different from 0 and standard deviations different from 1. In the next section we present methods for working with such normal distributions.

TECH CENTER

Finding z Scores/Areas (Standard Normal)
Access tech instructions, videos, and data sets at **www.TriolaStats.com**

[handwritten in left margin: $z_{0.025} = 1.96$]

6-1 Basic Skills and Concepts

Statistical Literacy and Critical Thinking

1. Normal Distribution What's wrong with the following statement? "Because the digits 0, 1, 2, . . . , 9 are the normal results from lottery drawings, such randomly selected numbers have a normal distribution."

2. Normal Distribution A normal distribution is informally described as a probability distribution that is "bell-shaped" when graphed. Draw a rough sketch of a curve having the bell shape that is characteristic of a normal distribution.

3. Standard Normal Distribution Identify the two requirements necessary for a normal distribution to be a *standard* normal distribution.

4. Notation What does the notation z_α indicate?

Continuous Uniform Distribution. *In Exercises 5–8, refer to the continuous uniform distribution depicted in Figure 6-2 and described in Example 1. Assume that a patient is randomly selected, and find the probability that the waiting time is within the given range.*

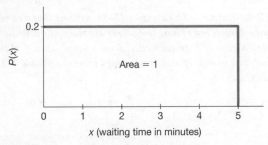

FIGURE 6-2   **Uniform Distribution of Waiting Time**

5. Greater than 3.00 minutes.

6. Less than 4.00 minutes.

7. Between 2 minutes and 3 minutes.

8. Between 2.5 minutes and 4.5 minutes.

Standard Normal Distribution. *In Exercises 9–12, find the area of the shaded region. The graph depicts the standard normal distribution of bone density scores with mean 0 and standard deviation 1.*

9.

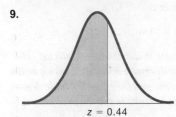

$z = 0.44$

10.

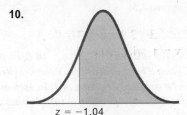

$z = -1.04$

11.

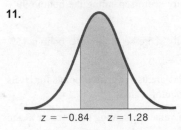

$z = -0.84$ $z = 1.28$

12.

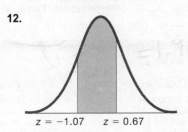

$z = -1.07$ $z = 0.67$

Standard Normal Distribution. *In Exercises 13–16, find the indicated z score. The graph depicts the standard normal distribution of bone density scores with mean 0 and standard deviation 1.*

13.

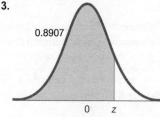

0.8907

14.

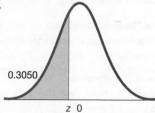

0.3050

15.

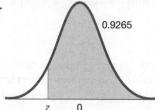

0.9265

16.

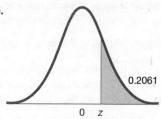

0.2061

Standard Normal Distribution. *In Exercises 17–36, assume that a randomly selected subject is given a bone density test. Those test scores are normally distributed with a mean of 0 and a standard deviation of 1. In each case, draw a graph, then find the probability of the given bone density test scores. If using technology instead of Table A-2, round answers to four decimal places.*

17. Less than −1.23.

18. Less than −1.96.

19. Less than 1.28.

20. Less than 2.25.

21. Greater than 0.25.

22. Greater than 0.18.

23. Greater than −2.55.

24. Greater than –3.05.

25. Between 2.00 and 3.00.

26. Between 1.50 and 2.50.

27. Between and −2.55 and −2.00.

28. Between −2.75 and –0.75.

29. Between −2.00 and 2.00.

30. Between −3.00 and 3.00.

31. Between −1.00 and 5.00.

32. Between −4.27 and 2.34.

33. Less than 4.55.

34. Greater than −3.75.

35. Greater than 0.

36. Less than 0.

Finding Bone Density Scores. *In Exercises 37–40 assume that a randomly selected subject is given a bone density test. Bone density test scores are normally distributed with a mean of 0 and a standard deviation of 1. In each case, draw a graph, and then find the bone density test score corresponding to the given information. Round results to two decimal places.*

37. Find P_{99}, the 99th percentile. This is the bone density score separating the bottom 99% from the top 1%.

38. Find P_{15}, the 15th percentile. This is the bone density score separating the bottom 15% from the top 85%.

39. If bone density scores in the bottom 2% and the top 2% are used as cutoff points for levels that are too low or too high, find the two readings that are cutoff values.

40. Find the bone density score that can be used as cutoff values separating the lowest 6% and highest 6%.

Critical Values.   *In Exercises 41–44, find the indicated critical value. Round results to two decimal places.*

41. $z_{0.10}$ **42.** $z_{0.02}$ **43.** $z_{0.04}$ **44.** $z_{0.15}$

Basis for the Range Rule of Thumb and the Empirical Rule.   *In Exercises 45–48, find the indicated area under the curve of the standard normal distribution; then convert it to a percentage and fill in the blank. The results form the basis for the range rule of thumb and the empirical rule introduced in Section 3-2.*

45. About _____ % of the area is between $z = -1$ and $z = 1$ (or within 1 standard deviation of the mean).

46. About % of the area is between $z = -2$ and $z = 2$ (or within 2 standard deviations of the mean).

47. About % _____ of the area is between $z = -3$ and $z = 3$ (or within 3 standard deviations of the mean).

48. About % _____ of the area is between $z = -3.5$ and $z = 3.5$ (or within 3.5 standard deviations of the mean).

6-1 Beyond the Basics

49. Significance For bone density scores that are normally distributed with a mean of 0 and a standard deviation of 1, find the *percentage* of scores that are

a. *significantly high* (or at least 2 standard deviations above the mean).

b. *significantly low* (or at least 2 standard deviations below the mean).

c. *not significant* (or less than 2 standard deviations away from the mean).

50. Distributions In a continuous uniform distribution,

$$\mu = \frac{\text{minimum } + \text{ maximum}}{2} \quad \text{and} \quad \sigma = \frac{\text{range}}{\sqrt{12}}$$

a. Find the mean and standard deviation for the distribution of the waiting times represented in Figure 6-2, which accompanies Exercises 5–8.

b. For a continuous uniform distribution with $\mu = 0$ and $\sigma = 1$, the minimum is $-\sqrt{3}$ and the maximum is $\sqrt{3}$. For this continuous uniform distribution, find the probability of randomly selecting a value between -1 and 1, and compare it to the value that would be obtained by incorrectly treating the distribution as a standard normal distribution. Does the distribution affect the results very much?

6-2 Real Applications of Normal Distributions

Key Concept Now we really get real as we extend the methods of the previous section so that we can work with any *nonstandard normal distribution* (with a mean different from 0 and/or a standard deviation different from 1). The key is a simple conversion (Formula 6-2) that allows us to "standardize" any normal distribution so that x values can be transformed to z scores; then the methods of the preceding section can be used.

FORMULA 6-2

$$z = \frac{x - \mu}{\sigma}$$ (round z scores to 2 decimal places)

Figure 6-11 illustrates the conversion from a nonstandard to a standard normal distribution. The area in *any* normal distribution bounded by some score x (as in Figure 6-11a) is the *same* as the area bounded by the corresponding z score in the standard normal distribution (as in Figure 6-11b).

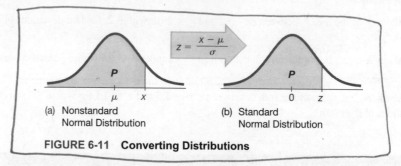

(a) Nonstandard
     Normal Distribution

(b) Standard
     Normal Distribution

FIGURE 6-11   Converting Distributions

Some calculators and software do not require the use of Formula 6-2 to convert to z scores because probabilities can be found directly. However, if using Table A-2, we must first convert values to standard z scores.

When finding areas with a nonstandard normal distribution, use the following procedure.

Procedure for Finding Areas with a Nonstandard Normal Distribution

1. Sketch a normal curve, label the mean and any specific x values, and then *shade* the region representing the desired probability.

2. For each relevant value x that is a boundary for the shaded region, use Formula 6-2 to convert that value to the equivalent z score. (With many technologies, this step can be skipped.)

3. Use technology (software or a calculator) or Table A-2 to find the area of the shaded region. This area is the desired probability.

The following example illustrates the above procedure.

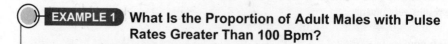

EXAMPLE 1   **What Is the Proportion of Adult Males with Pulse Rates Greater Than 100 Bpm?**

In the Chapter Problem we noted that pulse rates of adult males are normally distributed with a mean of 69.6 bpm and a standard deviation of 11.3 bpm. Find the proportion of adult males with a pulse rate greater than 100 bpm. These males are considered to be at a high risk of stroke, heart disease, or cardiac death.

SOLUTION

Step 1: See Figure 6-12, which incorporates this information: Men have pulse rates that are normally distributed with a mean of 69.6 bpm and a standard deviation of 11.3 bpm. The shaded region represents the men with pulse rates above 100 bpm.

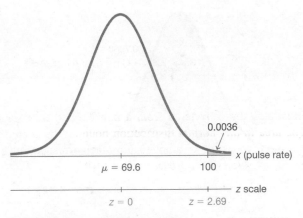

FIGURE 6-12   Pulse Rates of Men

Step 2: We can convert a pulse rate of 100 bpm to the z score of 2.69 by using Formula 6-2 as follows:

$$z = \frac{x - \mu}{\sigma} = \frac{100 - 69.6}{11.3} = 2.69 \text{ (rounded to two decimal places)}$$

Step 3: Technology: Technology can be used to find that the area to the right of 100 bpm in Figure 6-12 is 0.0036. (With many technologies, Step 2 can be skipped.)

Table A-2: Use Table A-2 to find that the cumulative area to the *left* of $z = 2.69$ is 0.9964. (Remember, Table A-2 is designed so that all areas are cumulative areas from the *left*.) Because the total area under the curve is 1, it follows that the shaded area in Figure 6-12 is $1 - 0.9964 = 0.0036$.

INTERPRETATION

The proportion of men with pulse rates above 100 bpm is 0.0036, which is roughly 4 men in a thousand. This is a very rare event, so an adult male presenting with a pulse rate above 100 bpm is extremely rare, or there is some medical condition that is causing the high pulse rate.

EXAMPLE 2 **Normal Pulse Rates**

Normal pulse rates are generally considered to be between 60 bpm and 100 bpm. Given that pulse rates of adult males are normally distributed with a mean of 69.6 bpm and a standard deviation of 11.3 bpm, find the *percentage* of males with normal pulse rates.

SOLUTION

Figure 6-13 shows the shaded region representing men with pulse rates between 60 bpm and 100 bpm.

Step 1: See Figure 6-13 on the next page, which incorporates this information: Men have pulse rates that are normally distributed with a mean of 69.6 bpm and a standard deviation of 11.3 bpm. The shaded region represents the men with pulse rates between 60 bpm and 100 bpm.

continued

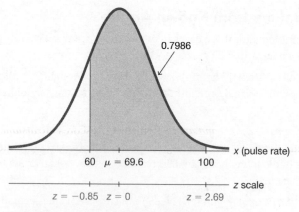

FIGURE 6-13 Pulse Rates of Men

Step 2: With some technologies, the shaded area in Figure 6-13 can be found directly and it is not necessary to convert the x scores of 60 bpm and 100 bpm to z scores. (See Step 3.)

If using Table A-2, we cannot find the shaded area directly, but we can find it indirectly by using the same procedures from Section 6-1, as follows: (1) Find the cumulative area from the left up to 100 bpm (or $z = 2.69$); (2) find the cumulative area from the left up to 60 bpm (or $z = -0.85$); (3) find the difference between those two areas. The pulse rates of 100 bpm and 60 bpm are converted to z scores by using Formula 6-2 as follows:

$$\text{For } x = 100 \text{ bpm: } z = \frac{x - \mu}{\sigma} = \frac{100 - 69.6}{11.3} = 2.69$$

$$(z = 2.69 \text{ yields an area of } 0.9964.)$$

$$\text{For } x = 60 \text{ bpm: } z = \frac{x - \mu}{11.3} = \frac{60 - 69.6}{11.3} = -0.85$$

$$(z = -0.85 \text{ yields an area of } 0.1977.)$$

Step 3: Technology: Technology will show that the shaded area in Figure 6-13 is 0.7986.

Table A-2: Refer to Table A-2 with $z = 2.69$ and find that the cumulative area to the *left* of $z = 2.69$ is 0.9964. (Remember, Table A-2 is designed so that all areas are cumulative areas from the *left*.) Table A-2 also shows that $z = -0.85$ corresponds to an area of 0.1977. Because the areas of 0.9964 and 0.1977 are *cumulative areas from the left,* we find the shaded area in Figure 6-13 as follows:

$$\text{Shaded area in Figure 6-13} = 0.9964 - 0.1977 = 0.7987$$

There is a small discrepancy between the area of 0.7986 found from technology and the area of 0.7987 found from Table A-2. The area obtained from technology is more accurate because it is based on unrounded z scores, whereas Table A-2 requires z scores rounded to two decimal places.

> **INTERPRETATION**

Expressing the result as a percentage, we conclude that about 80% of men have pulse rates between 60 bpm and 100 bpm.

Finding Values from Known Areas

Here are helpful hints for those cases in which the area (or probability or percentage) is known and we must find the relevant value(s):

1. Graphs are extremely helpful in visualizing, understanding, and successfully working with normal probability distributions, so they should always be used.

2. *Don't confuse z scores and areas.* Remember, z scores are *distances* along the horizontal scale, but areas are *regions* under the normal curve. Table A-2 lists z scores in the left columns and across the top row, but areas are found in the body of the table.

3. *Choose the correct (right/left) side of the graph.* A value separating the *top* 10% from the others will be located on the right side of the graph, but a value separating the *bottom* 10% will be located on the left side of the graph.

4. A z score must be *negative* whenever it is located in the *left* half of the normal distribution.

5. Areas (or probabilities) are always between 0 and 1, and they are never negative.

Procedure for Finding Values from Known Areas or Probabilities

1. Sketch a normal distribution curve, write the given probability or percentage in the appropriate region of the graph, and identify the x value(s) being sought.

2. Use technology. If technology is not available, use Table A-2 by referring to the *body* of Table A-2 to find the area to the left of x; then identify the z score corresponding to that area.

3. If you know z and must convert to the equivalent x value, use Formula 6-2 by entering the values for μ, σ, and the z score found in Step 2; then solve for x. Based on Formula 6-2, we can solve for x as follows:

$$x = \mu + (z \cdot \sigma) \qquad \text{(another form of Formula 6-2)}$$
$$\uparrow$$

(If z is located to the left of the mean, be sure that it is a negative number.)

4. Refer to the sketch of the curve to verify that the solution makes sense in the context of the graph and in the context of the problem.

The following example uses this procedure for finding a value from a known area.

EXAMPLE 3   Pulse Rates

Given that pulse rates of adult males are normally distributed with a mean of 69.6 bpm and a standard deviation of 11.3 bpm, find the pulse rate that separates the highest 1% from the lowest 99%. That is, find P_{99}.

SOLUTION

Step 1: Figure 6-14 on the next page shows the normal distribution with the pulse rate x that we want to identify. The shaded area represents the lowest 99% of the pulse rates.

continued

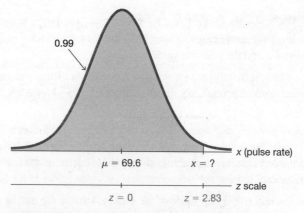

FIGURE 6-14   **Finding the 99th Percentile**

Step 2: Technology: Technology will provide the value of x in Figure 6-14. For example, see the accompanying Excel display showing that $x = 95.88773098$ bpm, or 95.9 bpm when rounded.

Excel

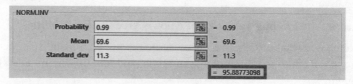

Table A-2: If using Table A-2, search for an area of 0.9900 *in the body* of the table. The area of 0.9900 corresponds to $z = 2.33$.

Step 3: With $z = 2.33$, $\mu = 69.6$ bpm, and $\sigma = 11.3$ bpm, we can solve for x by using Formula 6-2:

$$z = \frac{x - \mu}{\sigma} \quad \text{becomes} \quad 2.33 = \frac{x - 69.6}{11.3}$$

The result of $x = 95.929$ bpm can be found directly or by using the following version of Formula 6-2:

$$x = \mu + (z \cdot \sigma) = 69.6 + (2.33 \cdot 11.3) = 95.929 \text{ bpm}$$

Step 4: The solution of $x = 95.9$ bpm (rounded) in Figure 6-14 is reasonable because it is greater than the mean of 69.6 bpm.

> **INTERPRETATION**
>
> The male pulse rate of 95.9 (rounded) separates the top 1% from the bottom 99%.

Significance

In Chapter 4 we saw that probabilities can be used to determine whether values are *significantly high* or *significantly low*. Chapter 4 referred to x successes among n trials, but we can adapt those criteria to apply to continuous variables as follows:

Significantly high: The value x is *significantly high* if $P(x \text{ or greater}) \leq 0.05$.*

Significantly low: The value x is *significantly low* if $P(x \text{ or less}) \leq 0.05$.*

---

*The value of 0.05 is not absolutely rigid, and other values such as 0.01 could be used instead.

EXAMPLE 4 **Significantly Low or Significantly High Female Pulse Rates**

Use the preceding criteria to identify pulse rates of women that are significantly low or significantly high. Based on Data Set 1 "Body Data" in Appendix B, assume that women have normally distributed pulse rates with a mean of 74.0 beats per minute and a standard deviation of 12.5 beats per minute.

SOLUTION

Step 1: We begin with the graph shown in Figure 6-15. We have entered the mean of 74.0, and we have identified the x values separating the lowest 5% and the highest 5%.

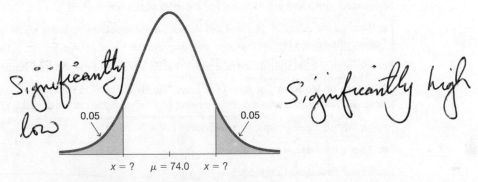

FIGURE 6-15   Pulse Rates of Women

Step 2: Technology: Technology will show that the values of x in Figure 6-15 are 53.4 beats per minute and 94.6 beats per minute when rounded.

Table A-2: If using Table A-2, we must work with cumulative areas from the left. For the leftmost value of x, the cumulative area from the left is 0.05, so search for an area of 0.05 *in the body* of the table to get $z = -1.645$ (identified by the asterisk between 0.0505 and 0.0495). For the rightmost value of x, the cumulative area from the left is 0.95, so search for an area of 0.9500 *in the body* of the table to get $z = 1.645$ (identified by the asterisk between 0.9495 and 0.9505). Having found the two z scores, we now proceed to convert them to pulse rates.

Step 3: We now solve for the two values of x by using Formula 6-2 directly or by using the following version of Formula 6-2:

Leftmost value of x: $x = \mu + (z \cdot \sigma) = 74.0 + (-1.645 \cdot 12.5) = 53.4$

Rightmost value of x: $x = \mu + (z \cdot \sigma) = 74.0 + (1.645 \cdot 12.5) = 94.6$

Step 4: Referring to Figure 6-15, we see that the leftmost value of $x = 53.4$ is reasonable because it is less than the mean of 74.0. Also, the rightmost value of 94.6 is reasonable because it is above the mean of 74.0.

INTERPRETATION

Here are the pulse rates of women that are significant:

- Significantly low: 53.4 beats per minute or lower
- Significantly high: 94.6 beats per minute or higher

Physicians could use these results to investigate health issues that could cause pulse rates to be significantly low or significantly high.

6-2   Basic Skills and Concepts

Statistical Literacy and Critical Thinking

1. Birth Weights Based on Data Set 3 "Births" in Appendix B, birth weights are normally distributed with a mean of 3152.0 g and a standard deviation of 693.4 g.

a. What are the values of the mean and standard deviation after converting all birth weights to *z* scores using $z = (x - \mu)/\sigma$?

b. The original birth weights are in grams. What are the units of the corresponding *z* scores?

2. Height of Mothers Based on Data Set 6 "Family Heights" in Appendix B, the heights of mothers are normally distributed with a mean of 64.2 inches and a standard deviation of 2.3 inches.

a. For the bell-shaped graph, what is the area under the curve?

b. What is the value of the median?

c. What is the value of the mode?

d. What is the value of the variance?

3. Normal Distributions What is the difference between a standard normal distribution and a nonstandard normal distribution?

4. Random Digits Computers are commonly used to randomly generate digits of telephone numbers to be called when conducting the California Health Survey. Can the methods of this section be used to find the probability that when one digit is randomly generated, it is less than 3? Why or why not? What is the probability of getting a digit less than 3?

IQ Scores. *In Exercises 5–8, find the area of the shaded region. The graphs depict IQ scores of adults, and those scores are normally distributed with a mean of 100 and a standard deviation of 15 (as on the Wechsler IQ test).*

5.

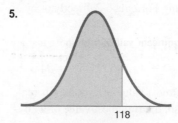

118

6.

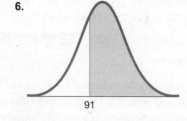

91

7.

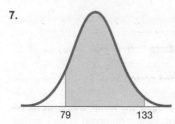

79   133

8.

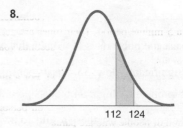

112   124

IQ Scores. *In Exercises 9–12, find the indicated IQ score and round to the nearest whole number. The graphs depict IQ scores of adults, and those scores are normally distributed with a mean of 100 and a standard deviation of 15 (as on the Wechsler IQ test).*

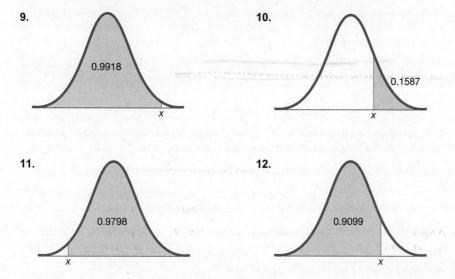

9. 0.9918

10. 0.1587

11. 0.9798

12. 0.9099

Male Pulse Rates. *In Exercises 13–20, assume that an adult male is randomly selected. Males have pulse rates that are normally distributed with a mean of 69.6 beats per minute and a standard deviation of 11.3 beats per minute (based on Data Set 1 "Body Data" in Appendix B). (Hint: Draw a graph in each case.)*

13. Find the probability of a pulse rate less than 95 beats per minute.

14. Find the probability of a pulse rate greater than 85 beats per minute.

15. Find the probability of a pulse rate between 65 beats per minute and 75 beats per minute.

16. Find the probability of a pulse rate between 75 beats per minute and 95 beats per minute.

17. Find P_{95}, which is the pulse rate separating the bottom 95% from the top 5%.

18. Find the third quartile Q_3, which is the pulse rate separating the top 75% from the bottom 25%.

19. Significance Instead of using 0.05 for identifying significant values, use the criteria that a value x is *significantly high* if $P(x$ or greater$) \leq 0.02$ and a value s is *significantly low* if $P(x$ or less$) \leq 0.02$. Find the pulse rates separating significant values from those that are not significant. Using these criteria, is a pulse rate of 100 beats per minute significantly high?

20. Significance Instead of using 0.05 for identifying significant values, use the criteria that a value x is *significantly high* if $P(x$ or greater$) \leq 0.033$ and a value is *significantly low* if $P(x$ or less$) \leq 0.033$. Find the pulse rates separating significant values from those that are not significant. Using these criteria, is a pulse rate of 55 beats per minute significantly low?

21. Eye Contact In a study of facial behavior, people in a control group are timed for eye contact in a 5-minute period. Their times are normally distributed with a mean of 184.0 seconds and a standard deviation of 55.0 seconds (based on data from "Ethological Study of Facial Behavior in Nonparanoid and Paranoid Schizophrenic Patients," by Pittman, Olk, Orr, and Singh, *Psychiatry,* Vol. 144, No. 1). For a randomly selected person from the control group, find the probability that the eye contact time is greater than 230.0 seconds, which is the mean for paranoid schizophrenics. Based on personal experience, does the result appear to be the proportion of people who are paranoid schizophrenics?

22. Body Temperatures Based on sample results in Data Set 2 "Body Temperatures" in Appendix B, assume that human body temperatures are normally distributed with a mean of 98.20°F and a standard deviation of 0.62°F.

a. According to emedicinehealth.com, a body temperature of 100.4°F or above is considered to be a fever. What percentage of normal and healthy persons would be considered to have a fever? Does this percentage suggest that a cutoff of 100.4°F is appropriate?

b. Physicians want to select a minimum temperature for requiring further medical tests. What should that temperature be if we want only 2.0% of healthy people to exceed it? (Such a result is a *false positive,* meaning that the test result is positive, but the subject is not really sick.)

23. Low Birth Weight The University of Maryland Medical Center considers "low birth weights" to be those less than 5.5 lb or 2495 g. Birth weights are normally distributed with a mean of 3152.0 g and a standard deviation of 693.4 g (based on Data Set 3 "Births" in Appendix B).

a. If a birth weight is randomly selected, what is the probability that it is a "low birth weight"?

b. Find the weights considered to be significantly low using the criterion of a probability of 0.05 or less. How do these results compare to the criterion of 2495 g?

c. Compare the results from parts (a) and (b).

24. Durations of Pregnancies The lengths of pregnancies are normally distributed with a mean of 268 days and a standard deviation of 15 days.

a. In a letter to "Dear Abby," a wife claimed to have given birth 308 days after a brief visit from her husband, who was working in another country. Find the probability of a pregnancy lasting 308 days or longer. What does the result suggest?

b. If we stipulate that a baby is *premature* if the duration of pregnancy is in the lowest 3%, find the duration that separates premature babies from those who are not premature. Premature babies often require special care, and this result could be helpful to hospital administrators in planning for that care.

Large Data Sets.   *In Exercises 25 and 26, refer to the data sets in Appendix B and use software or a calculator.*

25. Diastolic Blood Pressure of Males Refer to Data Set 1 in Appendix B and use the diastolic blood pressures of males.

a. Find the mean and standard deviation, and verify that the data have a distribution that is roughly normal. Round the results using three decimal places.

b. Treating the unrounded values of the mean and standard deviation as parameters, and assuming that male diastolic blood pressures are normally distributed, find diastolic blood pressures separating the lowest 2.5% and the highest 2.5%. These values could be helpful when physicians try to determine whether diastolic blood pressures are significantly low or significantly high.

26. Diastolic Blood Pressure of Females Repeat the preceding exercise using females instead of males.

6-2   Beyond the Basics

27. Outliers For the purposes of constructing modified boxplots as described in Section 3-3, outliers are defined as data values that are above Q_3 by an amount greater than $1.5 \times$ IQR or below Q_1 by an amount greater than $1.5 \times$ IQR, where IQR is the interquartile range. Using this definition of outliers, find the probability that when a value is randomly selected from a normal distribution, it is an outlier.

6-3   Sampling Distributions and Estimators

Key Concept We now consider the concept of a *sampling distribution of a statistic*. Instead of working with values from the original population, we want to focus on the values of *statistics* (such as sample proportions or sample means) obtained from the population. Figure 6-16 shows the key points that we need to know, so try really, really hard to understand the story that Figure 6-16 tells.

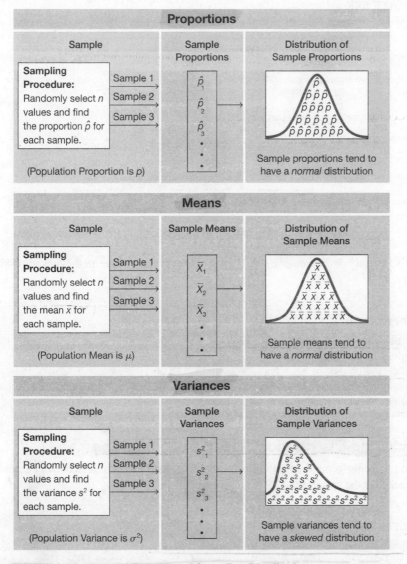

FIGURE 6-16   General Behavior of Sampling Distributions

A Short Story Among the population of all adults, exactly 40% have brown eyes (the authors just know this). In a survey of 1000 adults, 42% of the subjects were observed to have brown eyes. Being so intrigued by this, 50,000 people became so enthusiastic that they each conducted their own individual survey of 1000 randomly selected adults. Each of these 50,000 new surveyors reported the percentage that they found, with results such as 38%, 39%, and 43%. The authors obtained each of the 50,000

continued

sample percentages, changed them to proportions, and then they constructed the histogram shown in Figure 6-17. Notice anything about the *shape* of the histogram? It's *normal*. Notice anything about the mean of the sample proportions? They are centered about the value of 0.40, which happens to be the population proportion. Moral: When samples of the same size are taken from the same population, the following two properties apply:

1. Sample proportions tend to be normally distributed.
2. The mean of sample proportions is the same as the population mean. The implications of the preceding properties will be extensive in the chapters that follow.

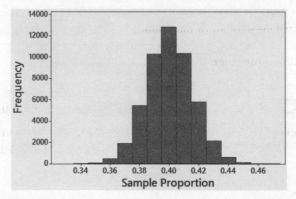

FIGURE 6-17   Histogram of 50,000 Sample Proportions

Let's formally define *sampling distribution,* the main character in the preceding short story.

DEFINITION

The **sampling distribution of a statistic** (such as a sample proportion or sample mean) is the distribution of all values of the statistic when all possible samples of the same size *n* are taken from the same population. (The sampling distribution of a statistic is typically represented as a probability distribution in the format of a probability histogram, formula, or table.)

Sampling Distribution of Sample Proportion

The preceding general definition of a sampling distribution of a statistic can now be restated for the specific case of a sample proportion:

DEFINITION

The **sampling distribution of the sample proportion** is the distribution of sample proportions (or the distribution of the variable $\hat{p}$), with all samples having the same sample size *n* taken from the same population. (The sampling distribution of the sample proportion is typically represented as a probability distribution in the format of a probability histogram, formula, or table.)

We need to distinguish between a population proportion p and a sample proportion, and the following notation is common and will be used throughout the remainder of this book, so it's very important.

Notation for Proportions

p = *population* proportion

$\hat{p}$ = *sample* proportion

HINT $\hat{p}$ is pronounced "p-hat." When symbols are used above a letter, as in $\bar{x}$ and $\hat{p}$, they represent *statistics*, not parameters.

Behavior of Sample Proportions

1. The distribution of sample proportions tends to approximate a normal distribution.

2. Sample proportions *target* the value of the population proportion in the sense that the mean of all of the sample proportions $\hat{p}$ is equal to the population proportion p; the expected value of the sample proportion is equal to the population proportion.

EXAMPLE 1 Sampling Distribution of the Sample Proportion

Consider repeating this process: Roll a die 5 times and find the proportion of *odd* numbers (1 or 3 or 5). What do we know about the behavior of all sample proportions that are generated as this process continues indefinitely?

SOLUTION

Figure 6-18 illustrates a process of rolling a die 5 times and finding the proportion of odd numbers. (Figure 6-18 shows results from repeating this process 10,000 times, but the true sampling distribution of the sample proportion involves repeating the process indefinitely.) Figure 6-18 shows that the sample proportions are approximately normally distributed. (Because the values of 1, 2, 3, 4, 5, 6 are all equally likely, the proportion of odd numbers in the population is 0.5, and Figure 6-18 shows that the sample proportions have a mean of 0.50.)

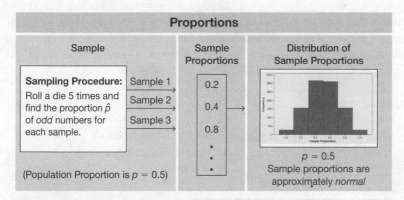

FIGURE 6-18   Sample Proportions from 10,000 Trials

Sampling Distribution of the Sample Mean

We now consider sample means.

> **DEFINITION**
>
> The **sampling distribution of the sample mean** is the distribution of all possible sample means (or the distribution of the variable $\bar{x}$), with all samples having the same sample size n taken from the same population. (The sampling distribution of the sample mean is typically represented as a probability distribution in the format of a probability histogram, formula, or table.)

Behavior of Sample Means

1. The distribution of sample means tends to be a normal distribution. (This will be discussed further in the following section, but the distribution tends to become closer to a normal distribution as the sample size increases.)

2. The sample means *target* the value of the population mean. (That is, the mean of the sample means is the population mean. The expected value of the sample mean is equal to the population mean.)

 EXAMPLE 2 **Sampling Distribution of the Sample Mean**

A pediatrician has three patients with measles and they are ages 4, 5, and 9. Consider the population of {4, 5, 9}. If two ages are randomly selected with replacement from the population {4, 5, 9}, identify the sampling distribution of the sample mean by creating a table representing the probability distribution of the sample mean. Do the values of the sample mean target the value of the population mean?

SOLUTION

If two values are randomly selected with replacement from the population {4, 5, 9}, the leftmost column of Table 6-2 lists the nine different possible samples. The second column lists the corresponding sample means. The nine samples are equally likely with a probability of 1/9. We saw in Section 5-1 that a probability distribution gives the probability for each value of a random variable, as in the second and third columns of Table 6-2. The second and third columns of Table 6-2 represent the sampling distribution of the sample mean. In Table 6-2, some of the sample mean values are repeated, so we combined them in Table 6-3.

TABLE 6-2 Sampling Distribution of Mean

Sample	Sample Mean $\bar{x}$	Probability
4, 4	4.0	1/9
4, 5	4.5	1/9
4, 9	6.5	1/9
5, 4	4.5	1/9
5, 5	5.0	1/9
5, 9	7.0	1/9
9, 4	6.5	1/9
9, 5	7.0	1/9
9, 9	9.0	1/9

TABLE 6-3 Sampling Distribution of Mean (Condensed)

Sample Mean $\bar{x}$	Probability
4.0	1/9
4.5	2/9
5.0	1/9
6.5	2/9
7.0	2/9
9.0	1/9

Because Table 6-3 lists the possible values of the sample mean along with their corresponding probabilities, Table 6-3 is an example of a sampling distribution of a sample mean.

The value of the mean of the population $\{4, 5, 9\}$ is $\mu = 6.0$. Using either Table 6-2 or 6-3, we could calculate the mean of the sample values and we get 6.0. Because the mean of the sample means (6.0) is equal to the mean of the population (6.0), we conclude that the values of the sample mean do *target* the value of the population mean. It's unfortunate that this sounds so much like doublespeak, but this illustrates that *the mean of the sample means is equal to the population mean μ.*

HINT Read the last sentence of the above paragraph a few times until it makes sense.

If we were to create a probability histogram from Table 6-2, it would not have the bell shape that is characteristic of a normal distribution, but that's because we are working with such small samples. If the population of $\{4, 5, 9\}$ were much larger and if we were selecting samples much larger than $n = 2$, as in this example, we would get a probability histogram that is much closer to being bell-shaped, indicating a normal distribution, as in Example 3.

EXAMPLE 3   Sampling Distribution of the Sample Mean

Consider repeating this process: Roll a die 5 times to randomly select 5 values from the population $\{1, 2, 3, 4, 5, 6\}$, then find the mean $\bar{x}$ of the results. What do we know about the behavior of all sample means that are generated as this process continues indefinitely?

SOLUTION

Figure 6-19 illustrates a process of rolling a die 5 times and finding the mean of the results. Figure 6-19 shows results from repeating this process 10,000 times, but the true sampling distribution of the mean involves repeating the process indefinitely. Because the values of 1, 2, 3, 4, 5, 6 are all equally likely, the population has a mean of $\mu = 3.5$. The 10,000 sample means included in Figure 6-19 have a mean of 3.5. If the process is continued indefinitely, the mean of the sample means will be 3.5. Also, Figure 6-19 shows that the distribution of the sample means is approximately a normal distribution.

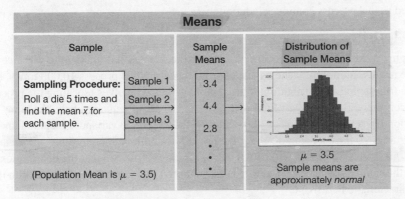

FIGURE 6-19   Sample Means from 10,000 Trials

Sampling Distribution of the Sample Variance

Let's now consider the sampling distribution of sample variances.

DEFINITION

The **sampling distribution of the sample variance** is the distribution of sample variances (the variable s^2), with all samples having the same sample size n taken from the same population. (The sampling distribution of the sample variance is typically represented as a probability distribution in the format of a table, probability histogram, or formula.)

CAUTION When working with population standard deviations or variances, be sure to evaluate them correctly. In Section 3-2 we saw that the computations for *population* standard deviations or variances involve division by the population size N instead of $n - 1$, as shown here.

$$\text{Population standard deviation:} \quad \sigma = \sqrt{\frac{\Sigma(x - \mu)^2}{N}}$$

$$\text{Population variance:} \quad \sigma^2 = \frac{\Sigma(x - \mu)^2}{N}$$

Because the calculations are typically performed with software or calculators, be careful to correctly distinguish between the variance of a sample and the variance of a population.

Behavior of Sample Variances

1. The distribution of sample variances tends to be a distribution skewed to the right.

2. The sample variances *target* the value of the population variance. (That is, the mean of the sample variances is the population variance. The expected value of the sample variance is equal to the population variance.)

EXAMPLE 4 Sampling Distribution of the Sample Variance

Consider repeating this process: Roll a die 5 times and find the variance s^2 of the results. What do we know about the behavior of all sample variances that are generated as this process continues indefinitely?

SOLUTION

Figure 6-20 illustrates a process of rolling a die 5 times and finding the variance of the results. Figure 6-20 shows results from repeating this process 10,000 times, but the true sampling distribution of the sample variance involves repeating the process indefinitely. Because the values of 1, 2, 3, 4, 5, 6 are all equally likely, the population has a variance of $\sigma^2 = 2.9$, and the 10,000 sample variances included in Figure 6-20 have a mean of 2.9. If the process is continued indefinitely, the mean of the sample variances will be 2.9. Also, Figure 6-20 shows that the distribution of the sample variances is a skewed distribution, not a normal distribution with its characteristic bell shape.

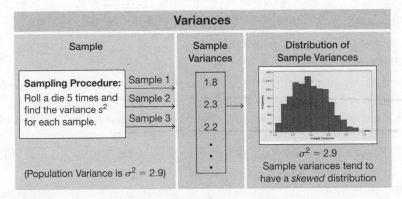

FIGURE 6-20   **Sample Variances from 10,000 Trials**

Estimators: Unbiased and Biased

The preceding examples show that sample proportions, means, and variances tend to *target* the corresponding population parameters. More formally, we say that sample proportions, means, and variances are *unbiased estimators*. See the following two definitions.

DEFINITIONS

An **estimator** is a statistic used to infer (or estimate) the value of a population parameter.

An **unbiased estimator** is a statistic that targets the value of the corresponding population parameter in the sense that the sampling distribution of the statistic has a mean that is equal to the corresponding population parameter.

Unbiased Estimators These statistics are unbiased estimators. That is, they each target the value of the corresponding population parameter (with a sampling distribution having a mean equal to the population parameter):

- Proportion $\hat{p}$
- Mean $\bar{x}$
- Variance s^2

Biased Estimators These statistics are biased estimators. That is, they do *not* target the value of the corresponding population parameter:

- Median
- Range
- Standard deviation s

Important Note: The sample standard deviations do not target the population standard deviation σ, but the bias is relatively small in large samples, so **s is often used to estimate σ** even though s is a biased estimator of σ.

EXAMPLE 5 **Sampling Distribution of the Sample Range**

As in Example 2, consider samples of size $n = 2$ randomly selected from the population $\{4, 5, 9\}$.

a. List the different possible samples along with the probability of each sample, then find the range for each sample.

b. Describe the sampling distribution of the sample range in the format of a table summarizing the probability distribution.

c. Based on the results, do the sample ranges target the population range, which is $9 - 4 = 5$?

d. What do these results indicate about the sample range as an estimator of the population range?

SOLUTION

a. In Table 6-4 we list the nine different possible samples of size $n = 2$ selected with replacement from the population $\{4, 5, 9\}$. The nine samples are equally likely, so each has probability $1/9$. Table 6-4 also shows the range for each of the nine samples.

TABLE 6-4 Sampling Distribution of Range

Sample	Sample Range	Probability
4, 4	0	1/9
4, 5	1	1/9
4, 9	5	1/9
5, 4	1	1/9
5, 5	0	1/9
5, 9	4	1/9
9, 4	5	1/9
9, 5	4	1/9
9, 9	0	1/9

b. The last two columns of Table 6-4 list the values of the range along with the corresponding probabilities, so the last two columns constitute a table summarizing the probability distribution. Table 6-4 therefore describes the *sampling distribution* of the sample range.

c. The mean of the sample ranges in Table 6-4 is $20/9$, or 2.2. The population of $\{4, 5, 9\}$ has a range of $9 - 4 = 5$. Because the mean of the sample ranges (2.2) is not equal to the population range (5), the sample ranges do *not* target the value of the population range.

d. Because the sample ranges do not target the population range, the sample range is a *biased estimator* of the population range.

INTERPRETATION

Because the sample range is a biased estimator of the population range, a sample range should generally not be used to estimate the value of the population range.

Why Sample with Replacement? All of the examples in this section involved sampling *with replacement*. Sampling *without replacement* would have the very practical advantage of avoiding wasteful duplication whenever the same item is selected more than once. Many of the statistical procedures discussed in the following chapters are based on the assumption that sampling is conducted with replacement because of these two very important reasons:

1. When selecting a relatively small sample from a large population, it makes no significant difference whether we sample with replacement or without replacement.

2. Sampling with replacement results in *independent* events that are unaffected by previous outcomes, and independent events are easier to analyze and result in simpler calculations and formulas.

6-3 Basic Skills and Concepts

Statistical Literacy and Critical Thinking

1. Births There are about 11,000 births each day in the United States, and the proportion of boys born in the United States is 0.512. Assume that each day, 100 births are randomly selected and the proportion of boys is recorded.

a. What do you know about the mean of the sample proportions?

b. What do you know about the shape of the distribution of the sample proportions?

2. Sampling with Replacement The Orangetown Medical Research Center randomly selects 100 births in the United States each day, and the proportion of boys is recorded for each sample.

a. Do you think the births are randomly selected with replacement or without replacement?

b. Give two reasons why statistical methods tend to be based on the assumption that sampling is conducted *with* replacement, instead of without replacement.

3. Unbiased Estimators Data Set 3 "Births" in Appendix B includes birth weights of 400 babies. If we compute the values of sample statistics from that sample, which of the following statistics are *unbiased* estimators of the corresponding population parameters: sample mean; sample median; sample range; sample variance; sample standard deviation; sample proportion?

4. Sampling Distribution Data Set 3 "Births" in Appendix B includes a sample of birth weights. If we explore this sample of 400 birth weights by constructing a histogram and finding the mean and standard deviation, do those results describe the sampling distribution of the mean? Why or why not?

5. Good Sample? A geneticist is investigating the proportion of boys born in the world population. Because she is based in China, she obtains sample data from that country. Is the resulting sample proportion a good estimator of the population proportion of boys born worldwide? Why or why not?

6. Physicians There are about 900,000 active physicians in the United States, and they have annual incomes with a distribution that is skewed instead of being normal. Many different samples of 40 physicians are randomly selected, and the mean annual income is computed for each sample.

a. What is the approximate shape of the distribution of the sample means (uniform, normal, skewed, other)?

b. What value do the sample means target? That is, what is the mean of all such sample means?

In Exercises 7–10, use the same population of {4, 5, 9} that was used in Examples 2 and 5. As in Examples 2 and 5, assume that samples of size n = 2 are randomly selected with replacement.

7. Sampling Distribution of the Sample Variance

a. Find the value of the population variance σ^2.

b. Table 6-2 describes the sampling distribution of the sample mean. Construct a similar table representing the sampling distribution of the sample variance s^2. Then combine values of s^2 that are the same, as in Table 6-3 (*Hint:* See Example 2 on page 260 for Tables 6-2 and 6-3, which describe the sampling distribution of the sample mean.)

c. Find the mean of the sampling distribution of the sample variance.

d. Based on the preceding results, is the sample variance an unbiased estimator of the population variance? Why or why not?

8. Sampling Distribution of the Sample Standard Deviation For the following, round results to three decimal places.

a. Find the value of the population standard deviation σ.

b. Table 6-2 describes the sampling distribution of the sample mean. Construct a similar table representing the sampling distribution of the sample standard deviation s. Then combine values of s that are the same, as in Table 6-3. (*Hint:* See Example 2 on page 260 for Tables 6-2 and 6-3, which describe the sampling distribution of the sample mean.)

c. Find the mean of the sampling distribution of the sample standard deviation.

d. Based on the preceding results, is the sample standard deviation an unbiased estimator of the population standard deviation? Why or why not?

9. Sampling Distribution of the Sample Median

a. Find the value of the population median.

b. Table 6-2 describes the sampling distribution of the sample mean. Construct a similar table representing the sampling distribution of the sample median. Then combine values of the median that are the same, as in Table 6-3. (*Hint:* See Example 2 on page 260 for Tables 6-2 and 6-3, which describe the sampling distribution of the sample mean.)

c. Find the mean of the sampling distribution of the sample median.

d. Based on the preceding results, is the sample median an unbiased estimator of the population median? Why or why not?

10. Sampling Distribution of the Sample Proportion

a. For the population, find the proportion of odd numbers.

b. Table 6-2 describes the sampling distribution of the sample mean. Construct a similar table representing the sampling distribution of the sample proportion of odd numbers. Then combine values of the sample proportion that are the same, as in Table 6-3. (*Hint:* See Example 2 on page 260 for Tables 6-2 and 6-3, which describe the sampling distribution of the sample mean.)

c. Find the mean of the sampling distribution of the sample proportion of odd numbers.

d. Based on the preceding results, is the sample proportion an unbiased estimator of the population proportion? Why or why not?

In Exercises 11–14, use the population of {34, 36, 41, 51} of the amounts of caffeine (mg / 12 oz) in Coca-Cola Zero, Diet Pepsi, Dr Pepper, and Mellow Yello Zero. Assume that random samples of size n = 2 are selected with replacement.

11. Sampling Distribution of the Sample Mean

a. After identifying the 16 different possible samples, find the mean of each sample, then construct a table representing the sampling distribution of the sample mean. In the table, combine values of the sample mean that are the same. (*Hint:* See Table 6-3 in Example 2 on page 260.)

b. Compare the mean of the population {34, 36, 41, 51} to the mean of the sampling distribution of the sample mean.

c. Do the sample means target the value of the population mean? In general, do sample means make good estimators of population means? Why or why not?

12. Sampling Distribution of the Median Repeat Exercise 11 using medians instead of means.

13. Sampling Distribution of the Range Repeat Exercise 11 using ranges instead of means.

14. Sampling Distribution of the Variance Repeat Exercise 11 using variances instead of means.

15. Births: Sampling Distribution of Sample Proportion When two births are randomly selected, the sample space for genders is bb, bg, gb, and gg (where b = boy and g = girl). Assume that those four outcomes are equally likely. Construct a table that describes the sampling distribution of the sample proportion of girls from two births. Does the mean of the sample proportions equal the proportion of girls in two births? Does the result suggest that a sample proportion is an unbiased estimator of a population proportion?

16. Births: Sampling Distribution of Sample Proportion For three births, assume that the genders are equally likely. Construct a table that describes the sampling distribution of the sample proportion of girls from three births. Does the mean of the sample proportions equal the proportion of girls in three births? (*Hint:* See Exercise 15 for two births.)

17. MCAT Tests Because they enable efficient procedures for evaluating answers, multiple choice questions are commonly used on standardized tests, such as the MCAT or the GRE Biology test. Such questions typically have five choices, one of which is correct. Assume that you must make random guesses for two such questions. Assume that both questions have correct answers of "a."

a. After listing the 25 different possible samples, find the proportion of correct answers in each sample; then construct a table that describes the sampling distribution of the sample proportions of correct responses.

b. Find the mean of the sampling distribution of the sample proportion.

c. Is the mean of the sampling distribution [from part (b)] equal to the population proportion of correct responses? Does the mean of the sampling distribution of proportions *always* equal the population proportion?

18. Hybridization A hybridization experiment begins with four peas having yellow pods and one pea having a green pod. Two of the peas are randomly selected *with replacement* from this population.

a. After identifying the 25 different possible samples, find the proportion of peas with yellow pods in each of them; then construct a table to describe the sampling distribution of the proportions of peas with yellow pods.

b. Find the mean of the sampling distribution.

c. Is the mean of the sampling distribution [from part (b)] equal to the population proportion of peas with yellow pods? Does the mean of the sampling distribution of proportions *always* equal the population proportion?

6-3 Beyond the Basics

19. Using a Formula to Describe a Sampling Distribution Exercise 15 "Births" requires the construction of a table that describes the sampling distribution of the proportions of girls from two births. Consider the formula shown here, and evaluate that formula using sample

continued

proportions (represented by x) of 0, 0.5, and 1. Based on the results, does the formula describe the sampling distribution? Why or why not?

$$P(x) = \frac{1}{2(2 - 2x)!(2x)!} \quad \text{where } x = 0, 0.5, 1$$

20. Mean Absolute Deviation Is the mean absolute deviation of a sample a good statistic for estimating the mean absolute deviation of the population? Why or why not? (*Hint:* See Example 5.)

6-4   The Central Limit Theorem

Key Concept In the preceding section we saw that the sampling distribution of sample means tends to be a normal distribution as the sample size increases. In this section we introduce and apply the *central limit theorem*. The central limit theorem allows us to use a normal distribution for some very meaningful and important applications.

> **CENTRAL LIMIT THEOREM**
>
> For all samples of the same size n with $n > 30$, the sampling distribution of $\bar{x}$ can be approximated by a normal distribution with mean μ and standard deviation $\sigma/\sqrt{n}$.

Given any population with *any* distribution (uniform, skewed, whatever), the distribution of sample means $\bar{x}$ can be approximated by a normal distribution when the samples are large enough with $n > 30$. (There are some special cases of very nonnormal distributions for which the requirement of $n > 30$ isn't quite enough, so the number 30 should be higher in those cases, but those cases are relatively rare.)

 EXAMPLE 1   HDL Cholesterol of Females

Figures 6-21 and 6-22 illustrate the central limit theorem.

- **Original data:** Figure 6-21 is a histogram of the high-density lipoprotein (HDL) cholesterol measures (mg/dL) of the 147 females listed in Data Set 1 "Body Data" in Appendix B, and those measures have a distribution that is skewed to the right instead of being normal.

- **Sample means:** Figure 6-22 is a histogram of 100 *sample means*. Each sample includes 100 HDL cholesterol measures of females, and this histogram shows that the sample means have a distribution that is very close to being normal.

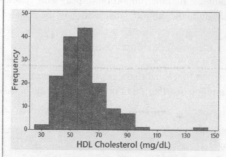

FIGURE 6-21   **Nonnormal Distribution: HDL Cholesterol from 147 Women**

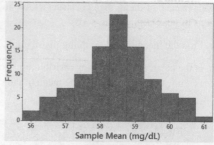

FIGURE 6-22   **Approximately Normal Distribution: Means from Samples of Size $n = 100$ of HDL Cholesterol from Females**

INTERPRETATION

The original HDL cholesterol measurements depicted in Figure 6-21 have a skewed distribution, but when we collect samples and compute their means, those sample means tend to have a distribution that is *normal*.

A Universal Truth Example 1 and the central limit theorem are truly remarkable because they describe a rule of nature that works throughout the universe. If we could send a spaceship to a distant planet "in a galaxy far, far away," and if we collect samples of rocks (all of the same large sample size) and weigh them, the sample means would have a distribution that is approximately normal. Think about the significance of that!

The following key points form the foundation for estimating population parameters and hypothesis testing—topics discussed at length in the following chapters.

KEY ELEMENTS

The Central Limit Theorem and the Sampling Distribution of $\bar{x}$

Given

1. Population (with any distribution) has mean μ and standard deviation σ.

2. Simple random samples all of the same size n are selected from the population.

Practical Rules for Real Applications Involving a Sample Mean $\bar{x}$

Requirements: Population has a normal distribution *or* $n > 30$:

Mean of all values of $\bar{x}$:	$\mu_{\bar{x}} = \mu$
Standard deviation of all values of $\bar{x}$:	$\sigma_{\bar{x}} = \dfrac{\sigma}{\sqrt{n}}$
z score conversion of $\bar{x}$:	$z = \dfrac{\bar{x} - \mu}{\dfrac{\sigma}{\sqrt{n}}}$

Original population is *not* normally distributed *and* $n \le 30$: The distribution of $\bar{x}$ might not be approximated well by a normal distribution, and the methods of this section might not apply. Use other methods, such as nonparametric methods or bootstrapping methods (Section 7-4).

Considerations for Practical Problem Solving

1. **Check Requirements:** When working with the mean from a sample, verify that the normal distribution can be used by confirming that the original population has a normal distribution or the sample size is $n > 30$.

2. **Individual Value or Mean from a Sample?** Determine whether you are using a normal distribution with a *single* value x or the mean $\bar{x}$ from a sample of n values. See the following.

- Individual value: When working with an *individual* value from a normally distributed population, use the methods of Section 6-2 with $z = \dfrac{x - \mu}{\sigma}$.

- Mean from a sample of values: When working with a mean for some *sample* of n values, be sure to use the value of $\sigma/\sqrt{n}$ for the standard deviation of the sample means, so use $z = \dfrac{\bar{x} - \mu}{\dfrac{\sigma}{\sqrt{n}}}$.

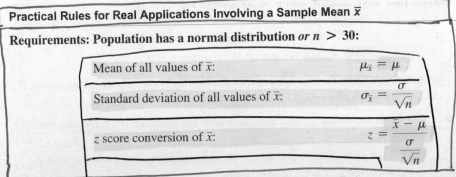 when n=1 $\longrightarrow$ $z = \dfrac{\bar{x} - \mu}{\sigma}$

The following new notation is used for the mean and standard deviation of the distribution of $\bar{x}$.

NOTATION FOR THE SAMPLING DISTRIBUTION OF $\bar{x}$

If all possible simple random samples of size n are selected from a population with mean μ and standard deviation σ, the mean of all sample means is denoted by $\mu_{\bar{x}}$ and the standard deviation of all sample means is denoted by $\sigma_{\bar{x}}$.

Mean of all values of $\bar{x}$: $\mu_{\bar{x}} = \mu$

Standard deviation of all values of $\bar{x}$: $\sigma_{\bar{x}} = \dfrac{\sigma}{\sqrt{n}}$

Note: $\sigma_{\bar{x}}$ is called the *standard error of the mean* and is sometimes denoted as SEM.

Applying the Central Limit Theorem

Many practical problems can be solved with the central limit theorem. Example 2 is a good illustration of the central limit theorem because we can see the difference between working with an *individual* value in part (a) and working with the *mean* for a sample in part (b). Study Example 2 carefully to understand the fundamental difference between the procedures used in parts (a) and (b). In particular, note that when working with an *individual* value, we use $z = \dfrac{x - \mu}{\sigma}$, but when working with the mean $\bar{x}$ for a collection of *sample* values, we use $z = \dfrac{\bar{x} - \mu}{\sigma/\sqrt{n}}$.

 EXAMPLE 2 **Pulse Rates of Women**

In the Chapter Problem it was noted that women have normally distributed pulse rates with a mean of 74.0 bpm and a standard deviation of 12.5 bpm.

   a. Find the probability that 1 randomly selected woman has a pulse rate greater than 80 bpm.

   b. Find the probability that a sample of 16 randomly selected women have a mean pulse rate greater than 80 bpm.

   c. Given that part (b) involves a sample size that is not larger than 30, why can the central limit theorem be used?

SOLUTION

   a. Approach Used for an Individual Value: Use the methods presented in Section 6-2 because we are dealing with an *individual* value from a normally distributed population. We seek the area of the green-shaded region in Figure 6-23(a).

   Technology: If using technology (as described at the end of Section 6-2), we find that the green-shaded area in the graph at the left is 0.3156.

   Table A-2: If using Table A-2, we convert the pulse rate of 80 bpm to the corresponding z score, as shown here:

$$z = \frac{x - \mu}{\sigma} = \frac{80 - 74.0}{12.5} = 0.48$$

    We refer to Table A-2 to find that the cumulative area to the *left* of $z = 0.48$ is 0.6844, so the green-shaded area in Figure 6-23(a) is $1 - 0.6844 = 0.3156$.

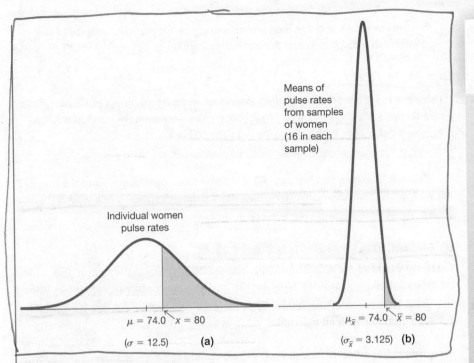

Means of
pulse rates
from samples
of women
(16 in each
sample)

Individual women
pulse rates

$\mu = 74.0$ $x = 80$
$(\sigma = 12.5)$ **(a)**

$\mu_{\bar{x}} = 74.0$ $\bar{x} = 80$
$(\sigma_{\bar{x}} = 3.125)$ **(b)**

FIGURE 6-23   Female Pulse Rates

The Fuzzy Central Limit Theorem

In *The Cartoon Guide to Statistics,* by Gonick and Smith, the authors describe the Fuzzy Central Limit Theorem as follows: "Data that are influenced by many small and unrelated random effects are approximately normally distributed. This explains why the normal is everywhere: stock market fluctuations, student weights, yearly temperature averages, SAT scores: All are the result of many different effects." People's heights, for example, are the results of hereditary factors, environmental factors, nutrition, health care, geographic region, and other influences, which, when combined, produce normally distributed values.

b. **Approach Used for the Mean of Sample Values:** Use the central limit theorem because we are dealing with the mean of a sample of 16 women, not an individual woman.

Requirement check for part b We can use the normal distribution if the original population is normally distributed or $n > 30$. The sample size is not greater than 30, but the original population of pulse rates of women has a normal distribution, so samples of *any* size will yield means that are normally distributed. ☑

Because we are now dealing with a distribution of sample means, we must use the parameters $\mu_{\bar{x}}$ and $\sigma_{\bar{x}}$, which are evaluated as follows:

$$\mu_{\bar{x}} = \mu = 74.0$$

$$\sigma_{\bar{x}} = \frac{\sigma}{\sqrt{n}} = \frac{12.5}{\sqrt{16}} = 3.125$$

We want to find the green-shaded area shown in Figure 6-23(b).

Technology: If using technology, the green-shaded area in Figure 6-23(b) is 0.0274.

Table A-2: If using Table A-2, we convert the value of $\bar{x} = 80$ bpm to the corresponding z score of $z = 1.92$, as shown here:

$$z = \frac{\bar{x} - \mu_{\bar{x}}}{\sigma_{\bar{x}}} = \frac{80 - 74.0}{\dfrac{12.5}{\sqrt{16}}} = \frac{6}{3.125} = 1.92$$

From Table A-2 we find that the cumulative area to the left of $z = 1.92$ is 0.9726, so the green-shaded area of Figure 6-23(b) is $1 - 0.9726 = 0.0274$.

c. Even though the sample size is not greater than 30, we can use the central limit theorem because the population of pulse rates of women is normally

continued

distributed. As noted in the requirement check for part (b), samples of *any* size will yield means that are normally distributed.

INTERPRETATION

There is a 0.3156 probability that an individual woman will have a pulse rate greater than 80 bpm, and there is a 0.0274 probability that 16 randomly selected women will have pulse rates with a mean greater than 80 bpm.

Example 2 shows that we can use the same basic procedures from Section 6-2, but we must remember to correctly adjust the standard deviation when working with a sample mean instead of an individual sample value.

Introduction to Hypothesis Testing

Carefully examine the conclusions that are reached in the next example illustrating the type of thinking that is the basis for the important procedure of hypothesis testing (formally introduced in Chapter 8). Example 3 uses the rare event rule for inferential statistics, first presented in Section 4-1:

Identifying Significant Results with Probabilities: The Rare Event Rule for Inferential Statistics

> If, under a given assumption, the probability of a particular observed event is very small and the observed event occurs *significantly less than* or *significantly greater than* what we typically expect with that assumption, we conclude that the assumption is probably not correct.

The following example illustrates the above rare event rule.

 EXAMPLE 3 Body Temperatures

Assume that the population of human body temperatures has a mean of 98.6°F, as is commonly believed. Also assume that the population standard deviation is 0.62°F (based on data from University of Maryland researchers). If a sample of size $n = 106$ is randomly selected, find the probability of getting a mean of 98.2°F or lower. (The value of 98.2°F was actually obtained from researchers; see the midnight temperatures for Day 2 in Data Set 2 "Body Temperatures" in Appendix B.)

SOLUTION

We work under the assumption that the population of human body temperatures has a mean of 98.6°F. We weren't given the distribution of the population, but because the sample size $n = 106$ exceeds 30, we use the central limit theorem and conclude that the distribution of sample means is a normal distribution with these parameters:

$$\mu_{\bar{x}} = \mu = 98.6 \ (\text{by assumption})$$

$$\sigma_{\bar{x}} = \frac{\sigma}{\sqrt{n}} = \frac{0.62}{\sqrt{106}} = 0.0602197$$

Figure 6-24 shows the shaded area (see the tiny left tail of the graph) corresponding to the probability we seek. Having already found the parameters that apply to the distribution shown in Figure 6-24, we can now find the shaded area by using the same procedures developed in Section 6-2.

Technology: If we use technology to find the shaded area in Figure 6-24, we get 0.0000000000155, which can be expressed as 0+.

Table A-2: If we use Table A-2 to find the shaded area in Figure 6-24, we must first convert the score of $x = 98.20°F$ to the corresponding z score:

$$z = \frac{\bar{x} - \mu_{\bar{x}}}{\sigma_{\bar{x}}} = \frac{98.20 - 98.6}{0.0602197} = -6.64$$

Referring to Table A-2 we find that $z = -6.64$ is off the chart, but for values of z below -3.49, we use an area of 0.0001 for the cumulative left area up to $z = -3.49$. We therefore conclude that the shaded region in Figure 6-24 is 0.0001.

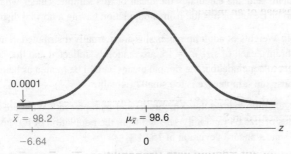

0.0001

$\bar{x} = 98.2$

$\mu_{\bar{x}} = 98.6$

z

-6.64

0

FIGURE 6-24   Means of Body Temperatures from Samples of Size $n = 106$

INTERPRETATION

The result shows that if the mean of our body temperatures is really 98.6°F, as we assumed, then there is an extremely small probability of getting a sample mean of 98.2°F or lower when 106 subjects are randomly selected. University of Maryland researchers did obtain such a sample mean, and after confirming that the sample is sound, there are two feasible explanations: (1) The population mean really is 98.6°F and their sample represents a chance event that is extremely rare; (2) the population mean is actually lower than the assumed value of 98.6°F and so their sample is typical. Because the probability is so low, it is more reasonable to conclude that the population mean is lower than 98.6°F. In reality it appears that the true mean body temperature is closer to 98.2°F!

This is the type of reasoning used in *hypothesis testing,* to be introduced in Chapter 8. For now, we should focus on the use of the central limit theorem for finding the probability of 0.0001, but we should also observe that this theorem will be used later in applying some very important concepts in statistics.

Correction for a Finite Population

In applying the central limit theorem, our use of $\sigma_{\bar{x}} = \sigma/\sqrt{n}$ assumes that the population has infinitely many members. When we sample with replacement, the population is effectively infinite. When sampling without replacement from a finite population, we may need to adjust $\sigma_{\bar{x}}$. Here is a common rule of thumb:

> **When sampling without replacement and the sample size n is greater than 5% of the finite population size N (that is, $n > 0.05N$), adjust the standard deviation of sample means $\sigma_{\bar{x}}$ by multiplying it by this *finite population correction factor*:**
>
> $$\sigma_{\bar{x}} \rightarrow \sigma_{\bar{x}} * \sqrt{\frac{N-n}{N-1}}$$

"members of population"

Except for Exercise 21 "Correcting for a Finite Population," the examples and exercises in this section assume that the finite population correction factor does *not* apply, because we are sampling with replacement, or the population is infinite, or the sample size doesn't exceed 5% of the population size.

6-4   Basic Skills and Concepts

Statistical Literacy and Critical Thinking

1. Requirements A researcher collects a simple random sample of grade-point averages of biostatistics students and she calculates the mean of this sample. Under what conditions can that sample mean be treated as a value from a population having a normal distribution?

2. Small Sample Weights of adult human brains are normally distributed. Samples of weights of adult human brains, each of size $n = 15$, are randomly collected and the sample means are found. Is it correct to conclude that the sample means cannot be treated as being from a normal distribution because the sample size is too small? Explain.

3. Notation In general, what do the symbols $\mu_{\bar{x}}$ and $\sigma_{\bar{x}}$ represent? What are the values of $\mu_{\bar{x}}$ and $\sigma_{\bar{x}}$ for samples of size 64 randomly selected from the population of IQ scores with population mean of 100 and standard deviation of 15?

4. Annual Incomes Annual incomes of physicians are known to have a distribution that is skewed to the right instead of being normally distributed. Assume that we collect a large ($n > 30$) random sample of annual incomes of physicians. Can the distribution of those incomes in that sample be approximated by a normal distribution because the sample is large? Why or why not?

Using the Central Limit Theorem.   *In Exercises 5–8, assume that males have pulse rates that are normally distributed with a mean of 69.6 beats per minute and a standard deviation of 11.3 beats per minute (based on Data Set 1 "Body Data" in Appendix B).*

5. a. If 1 adult male is randomly selected, find the probability that his pulse rate is less than 74 beats per minute.

b. If 25 adult males are randomly selected, find the probability that they have pulse rates with a mean less than 74 beats per minute.

c. Why can the normal distribution be used in part (b), even though the sample size does not exceed 30?

6. a. If 1 adult male is randomly selected, find the probability that his pulse rate is greater than 64 beats per minute.

b. If 36 adult males are randomly selected, find the probability that they have pulse rates with a mean greater than 64 beats per minute.

c. Why can the normal distribution be used in part (b), even though $n < 30$?

7. a. If 1 adult male is randomly selected, find the probability that his pulse rate is between 82 beats per minute and 86 beats per minute.

b. If 9 adult males are randomly selected, find the probability that they have pulse rates with a mean between 82 beats per minute and 86 beats per minute.

c. Why can the normal distribution be used in part (b), even though the sample size does not exceed 30?

8. a. If 1 adult male is randomly selected, find the probability that his pulse rate is between 66 beats per minute and 80 beats per minute.

b. If 16 adult males are randomly selected, find the probability that they have pulse rates with a mean between 66 beats per minute and 80 beats per minute.

c. Why can the normal distribution be used in part (b), even though $n < 30$?

9. Hemoglobin in Men Hemoglobin levels in adult males are normally distributed with a mean of 14.7 g/dL and a standard deviation of 1.3 g/dL (based on data from the National Health and Nutrition Examination Survey).

a. The normal hemoglobin range for men is 13.6 g/dL to 17.7 g/dL. What percentage of men have hemoglobin levels in the normal range?

b. If we randomly collect samples of men with 9 in each sample, what percentage of those samples have a mean hemoglobin level that is within the normal range?

10. Hemoglobin in Women Hemoglobin levels in adult females are normally distributed with a mean of 13.0 g/dL and a standard deviation of 1.3 g/dL (based on data from the National Health and Nutrition Examination Survey).

a. The normal hemoglobin range for women is 12.1 g/dL to 15.1 g/dL. What percentage of women have hemoglobin levels in the normal range?

b. If we randomly collect samples of women with 9 in each sample, what percentage of those samples have a mean hemoglobin level that is within the normal range?

11. Systolic BP in Women Systolic blood pressure is a measure of the pressure when heart pumps blood in arteries. Systolic blood pressure levels in women are normally distributed with a mean of 121.7 mm Hg and a standard deviation of 17.2 mm Hg (based on Data Set 1 "Body Data" in Appendix B).

a. A systolic blood pressure level above 130 mm Hg is considered to be hypertension. What percentage of women has hypertension?

b. If we randomly collect samples of women with 9 in each sample, what percentage of those samples have a mean above 130 mm Hg?

12. Systolic BP in Men Systolic blood pressure is a measure of the pressure when heart pumps blood in arteries. Systolic blood pressure levels in men are normally distributed with a mean of 124.2 mm Hg and a standard deviation of 14.4 mm Hg (based on Data Set 1 "Body Data" in Appendix B).

a. A systolic blood pressure level above 130 mm Hg is considered to be hypertension. What percentage of men has hypertension?

b. If we randomly collect samples of men with 9 in each sample, what percentage of those samples have a mean above 130 mm Hg?

13. Mensa Membership in Mensa requires a score in the top 2% on a standard intelligence test. The Wechsler IQ test is designed for a mean of 100 and a standard deviation of 15, and scores are normally distributed.

a. Find the minimum Wechsler IQ test score that satisfies the Mensa requirement.

b. If 4 randomly selected adults take the Wechsler IQ test, find the probability that their mean score is at least 131.

c. If 4 subjects take the Wechsler IQ test and they have a mean of 132, but the individual scores are lost, can we conclude that all 4 of them are eligible for Mensa?

14. Sleep The amounts of times that adults sleep are normally distributed with a mean of 6.8 hours and a standard deviation of 1.4 hours (based on data from multiple sources, including a Gallup poll and the *American Journal of Epidemiology*). A common recommendation is that we get between 7 and 9 hours of sleep each night.

a. For someone randomly selected, find the probability that they get between 7 and 9 hours of sleep in a night.

b. If we randomly collect a sample of 5 adults, what is the probability that the sample mean is between 7 hours and 9 hours?

Ergonomics. *Exercises 15–20 involve applications of ergonomics, which is a discipline focused on the design of tools and equipment so that they can be used safely, comfortably, and efficiently.*

15. Water Taxi Safety Passengers died when a water taxi sank in Baltimore's Inner Harbor. Men are typically heavier than women and children, so when loading a water taxi, assume a worst-case scenario in which all passengers are men. Assume that weights of men are normally distributed with a mean of 189 lb and a standard deviation of 39 lb (based on Data Set 1 "Body Data" in Appendix B). The water taxi that sank had a stated capacity of 25 passengers, and the boat was rated for a load limit of 3500 lb.

a. Given that the water taxi that sank was rated for a load limit of 3500 lb, what is the maximum mean weight of the passengers if the boat is filled to the stated capacity of 25 passengers?

b. If the water taxi is filled with 25 randomly selected men, what is the probability that their mean weight exceeds the value from part (a)?

c. After the water taxi sank, the weight assumptions were revised so that the new capacity became 20 passengers. If the water taxi is filled with 20 randomly selected men, what is the probability that their mean weight exceeds 175 lb, which is the maximum mean weight that does not cause the total load to exceed 3500 lb?

d. Is the new capacity of 20 passengers safe?

16. Designing Manholes According to the website www.torchmate.com, "manhole covers must be a minimum of 22 in. in diameter, but can be as much as 60 in. in diameter." Assume that a manhole is constructed to have a circular opening with a diameter of 22 in. Men have shoulder breadths that are normally distributed with a mean of 18.2 in. and a standard deviation of 1.0 in. (based on data from the National Health and Nutrition Examination Survey).

a. What percentage of men will fit into the manhole?

b. Assume that Connecticut's Eversource company employs 36 men who work in manholes. If 36 men are randomly selected, what is the probability that their mean shoulder breadth is less than 18.5 in.? Does this result suggest that money can be saved by making smaller manholes with a diameter of 18.5 in.? Why or why not?

17. Southwest Airlines Seats Southwest Airlines currently has a seat width of 17 in. Men have hip breadths that are normally distributed with a mean of 14.4 in. and a standard deviation of 1.0 in. (based on anthropometric survey data from Gordon, Churchill, et al.).

a. Find the probability that if an individual man is randomly selected, his hip breadth will be greater than 17 in.

b. Southwest Airlines uses a Boeing 737 for some of its flights, and that aircraft seats 122 passengers. If the plane is full with 122 randomly selected men, find the probability that these men have a mean hip breadth greater than 17 in.

c. Which result should be considered for any changes in seat design: the result from part (a) or part (b)?

18. Redesign of Ejection Seats When women were finally allowed to become pilots of fighter jets, engineers needed to redesign the ejection seats because they had been originally designed for men only. The ACES-II ejection seats were designed for men weighing between 140 lb and 211 lb. Weights of women are now normally distributed with a mean of 171 lb and a standard deviation of 46 lb (based on Data Set 1 "Body Data" in Appendix B).

a. If 1 woman is randomly selected, find the probability that her weight is between 140 lb and 211 lb.

b. If 25 different women are randomly selected, find the probability that their mean weight is between 140 lb and 211 lb.

c. When redesigning the fighter jet ejection seats to better accommodate women, which probability is more relevant: the result from part (a) or the result from part (b)? Why?

19. Doorway Height The Boeing 757-200 ER airliner carries 200 passengers and has doors with a height of 72 in. Heights of men are normally distributed with a mean of 68.6 in. and a standard deviation of 2.8 in. (based on Data Set 1 "Body Data" in Appendix B).

a. If a male passenger is randomly selected, find the probability that he can fit through the doorway without bending.

b. If half of the 200 passengers are men, find the probability that the mean height of the 100 men is less than 72 in.

c. When considering the comfort and safety of passengers, which result is more relevant: the probability from part (a) or the probability from part (b)? Why?

d. When considering the comfort and safety of passengers, why are women ignored in this case?

20. Loading Aircraft Before every flight, the pilot must verify that the total weight of the load is less than the maximum allowable load for the aircraft. The Bombardier Dash 8 aircraft can carry 37 passengers, and a flight has fuel and baggage that allows for a total passenger load of 6200 lb. The pilot sees that the plane is full and all passengers are women. The aircraft will be overloaded if the mean weight of the passengers is greater than $6200 \text{ lb}/37 = 167.6$ lb. What is the probability that the aircraft is overloaded? Should the pilot take any action to correct for an overloaded aircraft? Assume that weights of women are normally distributed with a mean of 171 lb and a standard deviation of 46 lb (based on Data Set 1 "Body Data" in Appendix B).

6-4 Beyond the Basics

21. Correcting for a Finite Population In a study of babies born with very low birth weights, 275 children were given IQ tests at age 8, and their scores approximated a normal distribution with $\mu = 95.5$ and $\sigma = 16.0$ (based on data from "Neurobehavioral Outcomes of School-Age Children Born Extremely Low Birth Weight or Very Preterm," by Anderson et al., *Journal of the American Medical Association,* Vol. 289, No. 24). Fifty of those children are to be randomly selected without replacement for a follow-up study.

a. When considering the distribution of the mean IQ scores for samples of 50 children, should $\sigma_{\bar{x}}$ be corrected by using the finite population correction factor? Why or why not? What is the value of $\sigma_{\bar{x}}$?

b. Find the probability that the mean IQ score of the follow-up sample is between 95 and 105.

6-5 Assessing Normality

Key Concept The following chapters include important statistical methods requiring that sample data are from a population having a *normal* distribution. In this section we present criteria for determining whether the requirement of a normal distribution is satisfied. The criteria involve (1) visual inspection of a histogram to see if it is roughly bell-shaped; (2) identifying any outliers; and (3) constructing a *normal quantile plot*.

PART 1 Basic Concepts of Assessing Normality

When trying to determine whether a collection of data has a distribution that is approximately normal, we can visually inspect a histogram to see if it is approximately bell-shaped (as discussed in Section 2-2), we can identify outliers, and we can also use a *normal quantile plot* (discussed briefly in Section 2-2).

> **DEFINITION**
>
> A **normal quantile plot** (or **normal probability plot**) is a graph of points (x, y) where each x value is from the original set of sample data, and each y value is the corresponding z score that is expected from the standard normal distribution.

Procedure for Determining Whether It Is Reasonable to Assume That Sample Data Are from a Population Having a Normal Distribution

1. *Histogram:* Construct a histogram. If the histogram departs dramatically from a bell shape, conclude that the data do not have a normal distribution.

2. *Outliers:* Identify outliers. If there is more than one outlier present, conclude that the data might not have a normal distribution. (Just one outlier could be an error or the result of chance variation, but be careful, because even a single outlier can have a dramatic effect on results.)

3. *Normal quantile plot:* If the histogram is basically symmetric and the number of outliers is 0 or 1, use technology to generate a *normal quantile plot*. Apply the following criteria to determine whether the distribution is normal. (These criteria can be used loosely for small samples, but they should be used more strictly for large samples.)

   Normal Distribution: The population distribution is normal if the pattern of the points is reasonably close to a straight line and the points do not show some systematic pattern that is not a straight-line pattern.

   Not a Normal Distribution: The population distribution is *not* normal if either or both of these two conditions apply:

   - The points do not lie reasonably close to a straight line.
   - The points show some *systematic pattern* that is not a straight-line pattern.

Histograms and Normal Quantile Plots

In Part 2 of this section we describe the process of constructing a normal quantile plot, but for now we focus on interpreting a normal quantile plot. The following displays show histograms of data along with the corresponding normal quantile plots.

Normal: The first case shows a histogram of IQ scores that is close to being bell-shaped, so the histogram suggests that the IQ scores are from a normal distribution. The corresponding normal quantile plot shows points that are reasonably close to a straight-line pattern, and the points do not show any other systematic pattern that is not a straight line. It is safe to assume that these IQ scores are from a population that has a normal distribution.

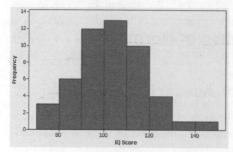
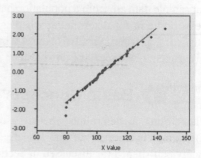

Uniform: The second case shows a histogram of data having a uniform (flat) distribution. The corresponding normal quantile plot suggests that the data are not normally distributed. Although the pattern of points is reasonably close to a straight-line pattern, *there is another systematic pattern that is not a straight-line pattern*. We conclude that these sample values are from a population having a distribution that is not normal.

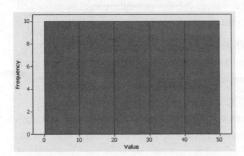 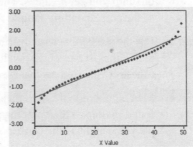

Skewed: The third case shows a histogram of the HDL cholesterol measurements. The shape of the histogram is skewed to the right. The corresponding normal quantile plot shows points that are not close to a straight-line pattern. These HDL cholesterol measurements are from a population having a distribution that is not normal.

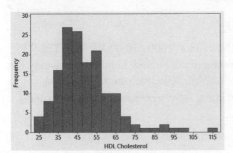 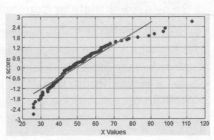

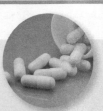
Tools for Determining Normality

- **Histogram/Outliers:** If the requirement of a normal distribution is not too strict, simply look at a histogram and find the number of outliers. If the histogram is roughly bell-shaped and the number of outliers is 0 or 1, treat the population as if it has a normal distribution.

- **Normal Quantile Plot:** Normal quantile plots can be difficult to construct on your own, but they can be generated with suitable technology.

- **Advanced Methods:** In addition to the procedures discussed in this section, there are other more advanced procedures for assessing normality, such as the chi-square goodness-of-fit test, the Lilliefors test, the Anderson-Darling test, the Jarque-Bera test, and the Ryan-Joiner test (discussed briefly in Part 2).

PART 2 Manual Construction of Normal Quantile Plots

The following is a relatively simple procedure for manually constructing a normal quantile plot, and it is the same procedure used by Statdisk and the TI-83/84 Plus calculator. Some statistical packages use various other approaches, but the interpretation of the graph is essentially the same.

Manual Construction of a Normal Quantile Plot

$n = \sqrt{\text{}}$

Step 1: First sort the data by arranging the values in order from lowest to highest.

Step 2: With a sample of size n, each value represents a proportion of $1/n$ of the sample. Using the known sample size n, find the values of $\frac{1}{2n}, \frac{3}{2n}, \frac{5}{2n}$, and so on, until you get n values. These values are the cumulative areas to the left of the corresponding sample values.

Step 3: Use the standard normal distribution (software or a calculator or Table A-2) to find the z scores corresponding to the cumulative left areas found in Step 2. (These are the z scores that are expected from a normally distributed sample.)

Step 4: Match the original sorted data values with their corresponding z scores found in Step 3; then plot the points (x, y), where each x is an original sample value and y is the corresponding z score.

Step 5: Examine the normal quantile plot and use the criteria given in Part 1. Conclude that the population has a normal distribution if the pattern of the points is reasonably close to a straight line and the points do not show some systematic pattern that is not a straight-line pattern.

EXAMPLE 1 Platelet Counts

Consider this sample of five patient platelet counts (1000 cells/μL): 125, 229, 236, 257, 234. With only five values, a histogram will not be very helpful in revealing the distribution of the data. Instead, construct a normal quantile plot for these five values and determine whether they appear to come from a population that is normally distributed.

SOLUTION

The following steps correspond to those listed in the procedure above for constructing a normal quantile plot.

Step 1: First, sort the data by arranging them in order. We get 125, 229, 234, 236, 257.

Step 2: With a sample of size $n = 5$, each value represents a proportion of $1/5$ of the sample, so we proceed to identify the cumulative areas to the left of the corresponding sample values. The cumulative left areas, which are expressed in general as $\frac{1}{2n}, \frac{3}{2n}, \frac{5}{2n}$, and so on, become these specific areas for this example with $n = 5$: $\frac{1}{10}, \frac{3}{10}, \frac{5}{10}, \frac{7}{10}, \frac{9}{10}$. These cumulative left areas expressed in decimal form are 0.1, 0.3, 0.5, 0.7, and 0.9.

Step 3: We now use technology (or Table A-2) with the cumulative left areas of 0.1000, 0.3000, 0.5000, 0.7000, and 0.9000 to find these corresponding z scores: $-1.28, -0.52, 0, 0.52$, and 1.28. (For example, the z score of -1.28 has an area of 0.1000 to its left.)

Step 4: We now pair the original sorted platelet counts with their corresponding z scores. We get these (x, y) coordinates, which are plotted in the following Statdisk display:

$$(125, -1.28), (229, -0.52), (234, 0), (236, 0.52), (257, 1.28)$$

Statdisk

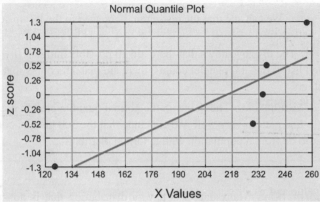

We examine the normal quantile plot in the Statdisk display. The points do not appear to lie reasonably close to the straight line, so we conclude that the sample of
five platelet counts does *not* appear to be from a normally distributed population.

Ryan-Joiner Test The Ryan-Joiner test is one of several formal tests of normality,
each having its own advantages and disadvantages. Statdisk has a feature of **Normality Assessment** that displays a histogram, normal quantile plot, the number of potential outliers, and results from the Ryan-Joiner test.

 EXAMPLE 2 Platelet Counts

Example 1 used a sample of five platelet counts. We can use the **Normality Assessment** feature of Statdisk with a different sample of the 300 platelet counts listed in
Data Set 1 "Body Data" in Appendix B.

Statdisk

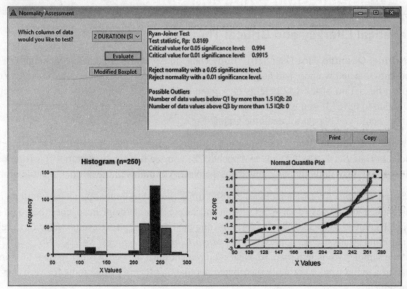

continued

Let's use the display with the three criteria for assessing normality.

1. *Histogram:* We can see that the histogram is *skewed* to the left instead of being bell-shaped.

2. *Outliers:* The display shows that there are 20 possible outliers. If we examine a sorted list of the 300 platelet counts, there are platelet counts that appear to be outliers.

3. *Normal quantile plot:* The points in the normal quantile plot do not fit a straight-line pattern very well. We conclude that the 300 platelet counts do *not* appear to be from a population with a normal distribution.

Data Transformations Many data sets have a distribution that is not normal, but we can *transform* the data so that the modified values have a normal distribution. One common transformation is to transform each value of x by taking its logarithm. (You can use natural logarithms or logarithms with base 10. If any original values are 0, take logarithms of values of $x + 1$). If the distribution of the logarithms of the values is a normal distribution, the distribution of the original values is called a **lognormal distribution.** (See Exercises 19 "Transformations" and 20 "Lognormal Distribution".) In addition to transformations with logarithms, there are other transformations, such as replacing each x value with $\sqrt{x}$, or $1/x$, or x^2. In addition to getting a required normal distribution when the original data values are not normally distributed, such transformations can be used to correct deficiencies, such as a requirement (found in later chapters) that different data sets have the same variance.

TECH CENTER

Normal Quantile Plots
Access tech instructions, videos, and data sets at **www.TriolaStats.com**

6-5   Basic Skills and Concepts

Statistical Literacy and Critical Thinking

1. Normal Quantile Plot Data Set 1 "Body Data" in Appendix B includes the heights of 147 randomly selected women, and heights of women are normally distributed. If you were to construct a histogram of the 147 heights of women in Data Set 1, what shape do you expect the histogram to have? If you were to construct a normal quantile plot of those same heights, what pattern would you expect to see in the graph?

2. Normal Quantile Plot After constructing a histogram of the ages of the 147 women included in Data Set 1 "Body Data" in Appendix B, you see that the histogram is far from being bell-shaped. What do you now know about the pattern of points in the normal quantile plot?

3. Small Sample An article includes elapsed times (hours) to lumbar puncture for 19 patients who entered emergency rooms with sudden and severe "thunderclap" headaches (based on data from "Thunderclap Headache and Normal Computed Tomographic Results: Value of Cerebrospinal Fluid Analysis," by DuPont et al., *Mayo Clinic Proceedings,* Vol. 83, No. 12). Given that the sample size is less than 30, what requirement must be met in order to treat the sample mean as a value from a normally distributed population? Identify three tools for verifying that requirement.

4. Assessing Normality The accompanying histogram is constructed from the diastolic blood pressure measurements of the 147 women included in Data Set 1 "Body Data" in Appendix B. If you plan to conduct further statistical tests and there is a loose requirement of a normally distributed population, what do you conclude about the population distribution based on this histogram?

Minitab

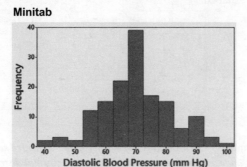

Interpreting Normal Quantile Plots. *In Exercises 5–8, examine the normal quantile plot and determine whether the sample data appear to be from a population with a normal distribution.*

5. Head Lengths of Bears The normal quantile plot represents the head lengths (in.) of bears listed in Data Set 11 "Bear Measurements."

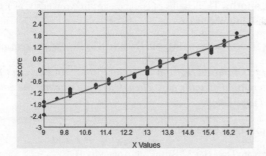

6. Diet Pepsi The normal quantile plot represents weights (pounds) of the contents of cans of Diet Pepsi.

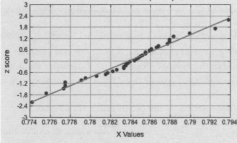

7. Patient Service Times The normal quantile plot represents service times (minutes) of randomly selected patients.

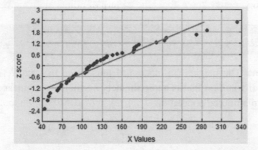

8. Visual Acuity Data Set 5 "Vision" includes measures of visual acuity. Shown here is the normal quantile plot resulting from the listed measurements from the right eye of the 300 subjects.

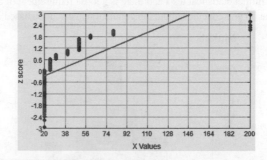

Determining Normality. *In Exercises 9–12, refer to the indicated sample data and determine whether they appear to be from a population with a normal distribution. Assume that this requirement is loose in the sense that the population distribution need not be exactly normal, but it must be a distribution that is roughly bell-shaped.*

9. Irises The petal lengths of irises, as listed in Data Set 16 "Iris Measurements" in Appendix B.

10. Births The lengths of stay (days) of newborn babies, as listed in Data Set 3 "Births" in Appendix B.

11. Cuckoo Egg Lengths The lengths of cuckoo eggs in wren nests, as listed in Data Set 17 "Cuckoo Egg Lengths" in Appendix B.

12. Bears The neck sizes of bears, as listed in Data Set 11 "Bear Measurements" in Appendix B.

Using Technology to Generate Normal Quantile Plots. *In Exercises 13–16, use technology to generate a normal quantile plot. Then determine whether the data come from a normally distributed population.*

13. Birth weights from Data Set 3 "Births" in Appendix B.

14. Lengths of stay from Data Set 3 "Births" in Appendix B.

15. White blood cell counts of females from Data Set 1 "Body Data" in Appendix B.

16. Red blood cell counts of females from Data Set 1 "Body Data" in Appendix B.

Constructing Normal Quantile Plots. *In Exercises 17 and 18, use the given data values to identify the corresponding z scores that are used for a normal quantile plot; then identify the coordinates of each point in the normal quantile plot. Construct the normal quantile plot, then determine whether the sample data appear to be from a population with a normal distribution.*

17. Male Arm Circumferences A sample of arm circumferences (cm) of males Data Set 1 "Body Data" in Appendix B: 37.0, 30.3, 34.0, 31.4, 27.4.

18. Brain Area A sample of human brain area (cm^2) is obtained from those listed in Data Set 9 "IQ and Brain Size" from Appendix B: 2216.40, 1866.99, 1850.64, 1743.04, 1709.30, 1689.60, 1806.31, 2136.37.

6-5 Beyond the Basics

19. Transformations The heights (in inches) of men listed in Data Set 1 "Body Data" in Appendix B have a distribution that is approximately normal, so it appears that those heights are from a normally distributed population.

continued

a. If 2 inches is added to each height, are the new heights also normally distributed?

b. If each height is converted from inches to centimeters, are the heights in centimeters also normally distributed?

c. Are the logarithms of normally distributed heights also normally distributed?

20. Lognormal Distribution The following are costs (dollars) of treating patients. Test these values for normality, then take the logarithm of each value and test for normality. What do you conclude?

  237,592 160,680 153,500 117,120 7304 6037 4483 4367 2658 1361 311

6-6   Normal as Approximation to Binomial

Key Concept Section 5-2 introduced binomial probability distributions, and this section presents a method for using a normal distribution as an approximation to a binomial probability distribution, so that some problems involving proportions can be solved by using a normal distribution. Here are the two main points of this section:

- Given probabilities p and q (where $q = 1 - p$) and sample size n, if the conditions $np \geq 5$ and $nq \geq 5$ are both satisfied, then probabilities from a binomial probability distribution can be approximated reasonably well by using a normal distribution having these parameters:

$$\mu = np$$
$$\sigma = \sqrt{npq}.$$

$$\sigma = \sqrt{n\,p\,(1-p)}$$

- The binomial probability distribution is *discrete* (with whole numbers for the random variable x), but the normal approximation is *continuous*. To compensate, we use a "continuity correction" with a whole number x represented by the interval from $x - 0.5$ to $x + 0.5$.

Brief Review of Binomial Probability Distribution In Section 5-2 we saw that a *binomial probability distribution* has (1) a fixed number of trials; (2) trials that are independent; (3) trials that are each classified into two categories commonly referred to as *success* and *failure*; and (4) trials with the property that the probability of success remains constant. Section 5-2 also introduced the following notation.

Notation

n = the fixed number of trials

x = the specific number of successes in n trials

p = probability of *success* in *one* of the n trials

q = probability of *failure* in *one* of the n trials (so $q = 1 - p$)

Rationale for Using a Normal Approximation We saw in Section 6-3 that the sampling distribution of a sample proportion tends to approximate a normal distribution. Also, see the probability histogram on the next page for the binomial distribution with $n = 580$ and $p = 0.25$. (In one of Mendel's famous hybridization experiments, he expected 25% of his 580 peas to be yellow.) The bell shape of this graph suggests that we can use a normal distribution to approximate the binomial distribution.

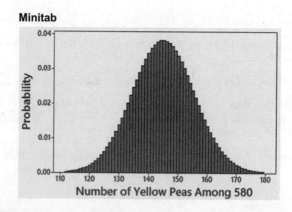

Minitab

Number of Yellow Peas Among 580

KEY ELEMENTS

Normal Distribution as an Approximation to the Binomial Distribution

Requirements

1. The sample is a simple random sample of size n from a population in which the proportion of successes is p, or the sample is the result of conducting n independent trials of a binomial experiment in which the probability of success is p.

2. $np \geq 5$ and $nq \geq 5$.

   (The requirements of $np \geq 5$ and $nq \geq 5$ are common, but some recommend using 10 instead of 5.)

Normal Approximation

If the above requirements are satisfied, then the probability distribution of the random variable x can be approximated by a normal distribution with these parameters:

- $\mu = np$
- $\sigma = \sqrt{npq}$

Continuity Correction

When using the normal approximation, adjust the discrete whole number x by using a *continuity correction* so that any individual value x is represented in the normal distribution by the interval from $x - 0.5$ to $x + 0.5$.

Procedure for Using a Normal Distribution to Approximate a Binomial Distribution

1. Check the requirements that $np \geq 5$ and $nq \geq 5$.

2. Find $\mu = np$ and $\sigma = \sqrt{npq}$ to be used for the normal distribution.

3. Identify the discrete whole number x that is relevant to the binomial probability problem being considered, and represent that value by the region bounded by $x - 0.5$ and $x + 0.5$.

4. Graph the normal distribution and shade the desired area bounded by $x - 0.5$ or $x + 0.5$ as appropriate.

EXAMPLE 1   Was Mendel Wrong?

In one of Mendel's famous hybridization experiments, he expected that among 580 offspring peas, 145 of them (or 25%) would be yellow, but he actually got 152 yellow peas. Assuming that Mendel's rate of 25% is correct, find the probability of getting 152 or more yellow peas by random chance. That is, given $n = 580$ and $p = 0.25$, find P(at least 152 yellow peas). Is 152 yellow peas *significantly high?*

SOLUTION

Step 1: Requirement check: With $n = 580$ and $p = 0.25$, we get $np = (580)(0.25) = 145$ and $nq = (580)(0.75) = 435$, so the requirements that $np \geq 5$ and $nq \geq 5$ are both satisfied.

Step 2: We now find μ and σ needed for the normal distribution:

$$\mu = np = 580 \cdot 0.25 = 145$$
$$\sigma = \sqrt{npq} = \sqrt{580 \cdot 0.25 \cdot 0.75} = 10.4283$$

Step 3: We want the probability of at least 152 yellow peas, so the discrete whole number relevant to this example is $x = 152$. We use the continuity correction as we represent the discrete value of 152 in the graph of the normal distribution by the interval between 151.5 and 152.5 (as shown in the top portion of Figure 6-25).

Step 4: See the bottom portion of Figure 6-25, which shows the normal distribution and the area to the right of 151.5 (representing "152 or more" yellow peas).

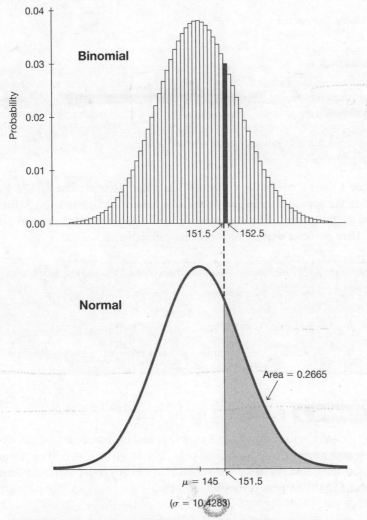

FIGURE 6-25   **Number of Yellow Peas Among 580**

continued

We want the area to the right of 151.5 in the bottom portion of Figure 6-25.

Technology: If using technology, we find that the shaded area is 0.2665.

Table A-2: If using Table A-2, we must first find the z score using $x = 151.5$, $\mu = 145$, and $\sigma = 10.4283$ as follows:

$$z = \frac{x - \mu}{\sigma} = \frac{151.5 - 145}{10.4283} = 0.62$$

Using Table A-2, we find that $z = 0.62$ corresponds to a cumulative left area of 0.7324, so the shaded region in the bottom portion of Figure 6-25 is $1 - 0.7324 = 0.2676$. (The result of 0.2665 from technology is more accurate.)

INTERPRETATION

Mendel's result of 152 yellow peas is greater than the 145 yellow peas he expected with his theory of hybrids, but with $P(152$ or more yellow peas$) = 0.2665$, we see that 152 yellow peas is *not significantly high*. That is a result that could easily occur with a true rate of 25% for yellow peas. This experiment does not contradict Mendel's theory.

Continuity Correction

DEFINITION

When we use the normal distribution (which is a *continuous* probability distribution) as an approximation to the binomial distribution (which is *discrete*), a **continuity correction** is made to a discrete whole number x in the binomial distribution by representing the discrete whole number x by the *interval* from $x - 0.5$ to $x + 0.5$ (that is, adding and subtracting 0.5).

Example 1 used a continuity correction when the discrete value of 152 was represented in the normal distribution by the area between 151.5 and 152.5. Because we wanted the probability of "152 or more" yellow peas, we used the area to the right of 151.5. Here are other uses of the continuity correction:

Statement About the *Discrete* Value	Area of the *Continuous* Normal Distribution
At least 152 (includes 152 and above)	To the *right* of 151.5
More than 152 (doesn't include 152)	To the *right* of 152.5
At most 152 (includes 152 and below)	To the *left* of 152.5
Fewer than 152 (doesn't include 152)	To the *left* of 151.5
Exactly 152	Between 151.5 and 152.5

EXAMPLE 2   Exactly 252 Yellow Peas

Using the same information from Example 1, find the probability of *exactly* 152 yellow peas among the 580 offspring peas. That is, given $n = 580$ and assuming that $p = 0.25$, find P(exactly 152 yellow peas). Is this result useful for determining whether 152 yellow peas is *significantly high*?

See Figure 6-26, which shows the normal distribution with $\mu = 145$ and $\sigma = 10.4283$. The shaded area approximates the probability of *exactly* 152 yellow peas. That region is the vertical strip between 151.5 and 152.5, as shown. We can find that area by using the same methods introduced in Section 6-2.

Technology: Using technology, the shaded area is 0.0305.

Table A-2: Using Table A-2, we convert 151.5 and 152.5 to $z = 0.62$ and $z = 0.72$, which yield cumulative left areas of 0.7324 and 0.7642. Because they are both cumulative left areas, the shaded region in Figure 6-26 is $0.7642 - 0.7324 = 0.0318$. The probability of exactly 152 yellow peas is 0.0318.

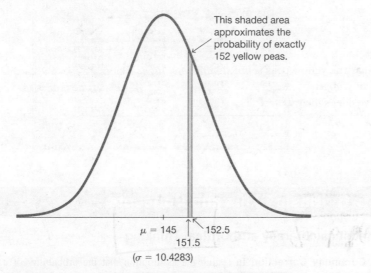

This shaded area approximates the probability of exactly 152 yellow peas.

$\mu = 145$ 152.5
151.5
$(\sigma = 10.4283)$

FIGURE 6-26   Probability of Exactly 152 Yellow Peas

In Section 4-1 we saw that x successes among n trials is significantly high if the probability of *x or more* successes is unlikely with a probability of 0.05 or less. In determining whether Mendel's result of 152 yellow peas contradicts his theory that 25% of the offspring should be yellow peas, we should consider the probability of *152 or more* yellow peas, not the probability of *exactly 152* peas. The result of 0.0305 is not the relevant probability; the relevant probability is 0.2665 found in Example 1. In general, the relevant result is the probability of getting a result *at least as extreme* as the one obtained.

Technology for Binomial Probabilities

This topic of using a normal distribution to approximate a binomial distribution was once quite important, but we can now use technology to find binomial probabilities that were once beyond our capabilities. For example, see the following Statdisk display on the next page showing that for Example 1, the probability of 152 or more yellow peas is 0.2650, and for Example 2, the probability of exactly 152 yellow peas is 0.0301, so there is no real need to use a normal approximation. However, there are cases where we need to use a normal approximation, and Section 8-3 uses a normal approximation to a binomial distribution for an important statistical method introduced in that section.

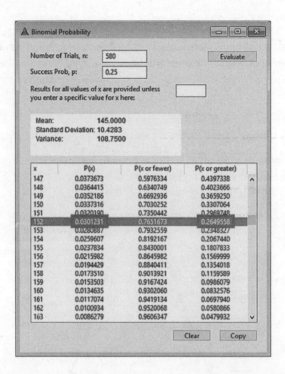

6-6   Basic Skills and Concepts

Statistical Literacy and Critical Thinking

1. Continuity Correction In testing the assumption that the probability of a baby boy is 0.512, a geneticist obtains a random sample of 1000 births and finds that 502 of them are boys. Using the continuity correction, describe the area under the graph of a normal distribution corresponding to the following. (For example, the area corresponding to "the probability of at least 502 boys" is this: the area to the right of 501.5.)

a. The probability of 502 or fewer boys

b. The probability of exactly 502 boys

c. The probability of more than 502 boys

2. Checking Requirements Common tests such as the SAT, ACT, LSAT (Law School Admissions Test), and MCAT (Medical College Admissions Test) use multiple choice test questions, each with possible answers of a, b, c, d, e, and each question has only one correct answer. We want to find the probability of getting at least 25 correct answers for someone who makes random guesses for answers to a block of 100 questions. If we plan to use the methods of this section with a normal distribution used to approximate a binomial distribution, are the necessary requirements satisfied? Explain.

3. Notation Common tests such as the SAT, ACT, LSAT, and MCAT tests use multiple choice test questions, each with possible answers of a, b, c, d, e, and each question has only one correct answer. For people who make random guesses for answers to a block of 100 questions, identify the values of p, q, μ, and σ. What do μ and σ measure?

4. Distribution of Proportions Each week, Nielsen Media Research conducts a survey of 5000 households and records the proportion of households tuned to *Sanjay Gupta MD*. If we obtain a large collection of those proportions and construct a histogram of them, what is the approximate shape of the histogram?

Using Normal Approximation. *In Exercises 5–8, do the following: If the requirements of np ≥ 5 and nq ≥ 5 are both satisfied, estimate the indicated probability by using the normal distribution as an approximation to the binomial distribution; if np < 5 or nq < 5, then state that the normal approximation should not be used.*

5. Births of Girls With $n = 7$ births and $p = 0.596$ for a girl, find P(exactly 6 girls).

6. Births of Girls With $n = 25$ births and $p = 0.596$ for a girl, find P(fewer than 10 girls).

7. Guessing on United States Medical Licensing Examinations With $n = 20$ guesses and $p = 0.2$ for a correct answer, find P(at least 6 correct answers).

8. Guessing on United States Medical Licensing Examinations With $n = 50$ guesses and $p = 0.2$ for a correct answer, find P(exactly 12 correct answers).

Eye Colors. *In Exercises 9–12, assume that eye colors are distributed as shown in the accompanying display (based on data from a study by Dr. P. Sorita at Indiana University), and also assume that 100 people are randomly selected.*

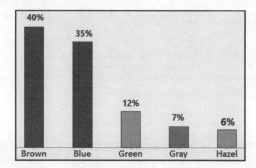

9. Blue Eyes Find the probability that at least 40 of the 100 subjects have blue eyes. Is 40 people with blue eyes significantly high?

10. Blue Eyes Find the probability that at least 49 of the 100 subjects have blue eyes. Is 49 people with blue eyes significantly high?

11. Green Eyes Find the probability that fewer than 5 of the 100 subjects have green eyes. Is 4 people with green eyes significantly low?

12. Brown Eyes Find the probability that among the 100 subjects, 33 or fewer have brown eyes. Is 33 people with brown eyes significantly low?

13. Tamiflu Assume that 10% of subjects treated with Tamiflu (oseltamivir) experienced the adverse reaction of nausea (based on clinical trials).

a. Find the probability that among 250 randomly selected subjects treated with Tamiflu, exactly 17 of them experience nausea.

b. Find the probability that among 250 randomly selected subjects treated with Tamiflu, the number who experience nausea is 17 or fewer.

c. Does it appear that 17 cases of nausea among the 250 subjects is significantly low?

14. Mendelian Genetics When Mendel conducted his famous genetics experiments with peas, one sample of offspring consisted of 929 peas, with 705 of them having red flowers. If we assume, as Mendel did, that under these circumstances, there is a 3/4 probability that a pea will have a red flower, we would expect that 696.75 (or about 697) of the peas would have red flowers, so the result of 705 peas with red flowers is more than expected.

a. If Mendel's assumed probability is correct, find the probability of getting 705 or more peas with red flowers.

continued

b. Is 705 peas with red flowers significantly high?

c. What do these results suggest about Mendel's assumption that 3/4 of peas will have red flowers?

15. Sleepwalking Assume that 29.2% of people have sleepwalked (based on "Prevalence and Comorbidity of Nocturnal Wandering in the U.S. Adult General Population," by Ohayon et al., *Neurology,* Vol. 78, No. 20). Assume that in a random sample of 1480 adults, 455 have sleepwalked.

a. Assuming that the rate of 29.2% is correct, find the probability that 455 or more of the 1480 adults have sleepwalked.

b. Is that result significantly high?

c. What does the result suggest about the rate of 29.2%?

16. Cell Phones and Brain Cancer In a study of 420,095 cell phone users in Denmark, it was found that 135 developed cancer of the brain or nervous system. For those not using cell phones, there is a 0.000340 probability of a person developing cancer of the brain or nervous system. We therefore expect about 143 cases of such cancers in a group of 420,095 randomly selected people.

a. Find the probability of 135 or fewer cases of such cancers in a group of 420,095 people.

b. What do these results suggest about media reports that indicate cell phones cause cancer of the brain or nervous system?

6-6   Beyond the Basics

17. Births The probability of a baby being born a boy is 0.512. Consider the problem of finding the probability of exactly 7 boys in 11 births. Solve that problem using (1) normal approximation to the binomial using Table A-2; (2) normal approximation to the binomial using technology instead of Table A-2; (3) using technology with the binomial distribution instead of using a normal approximation. Compare the results. Given that the requirements for using the normal approximation are just barely met, are the approximations off by very much?

Chapter Quick Quiz

Bone Density Test.   *In Exercises 1–4, assume that scores on a bone mineral density test are normally distributed with a mean of 0 and a standard deviation of 1.*

1. Bone Density Sketch a graph showing the shape of the distribution of bone density test scores.

2. Bone Density Find the score separating the lowest 9% of scores from the highest 91%.

3. Bone Density For a randomly selected subject, find the probability of a score greater than -2.93.

4. Bone Density For a randomly selected subject, find the probability of a score between 0.87 and 1.78.

5. Notation

a. Identify the values of μ and σ for the standard normal distribution.

b. What do the symbols $\mu_{\bar{x}}$ and $\sigma_{\bar{x}}$ represent?

In Exercises 6–10, assume that women have diastolic blood pressure measures that are normally distributed with a mean of 70.2 mm Hg and a standard deviation of 11.2 mm Hg (based on Data Set 1 "Body Data" in Appendix B).

6. Diastolic Blood Pressure Find the probability that a randomly selected woman has a normal diastolic blood pressure level, which is below 80 mm Hg.

7. Diastolic Blood Pressure Find the probability that a randomly selected woman has a diastolic blood pressure level between 60 mm Hg and 80 mm Hg.

8. Diastolic Blood Pressure Find P_{90}, the 90th percentile for the diastolic blood pressure levels of women.

9. Diastolic Blood Pressure If 16 women are randomly selected, find the probability that the mean of their diastolic blood pressure levels is less than 75 mm Hg.

10. Diastolic Blood Pressure The accompanying normal quantile plot was constructed from the diastolic blood pressure levels of a sample of women. What does this graph suggest about diastolic blood pressure levels of women?

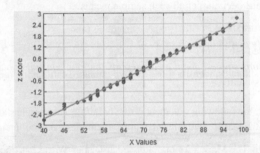

Review Exercises

1. Bone Density Test A bone mineral density test is used to identify a bone disease. The result of a bone density test is commonly measured as a z score, and the population of z scores is normally distributed with a mean of 0 and a standard deviation of 1.

a. For a randomly selected subject, find the probability of a bone density test score less than 1.23.

b. For a randomly selected subject, find the probability of a bone density test score greater than -1.23.

c. For a randomly selected subject, find the probability of a bone density test score between -1.01 and 2.01.

d. Find Q_3, the bone density test score separating the bottom 75% from the top 25%.

e. If the mean bone density test score is found for 16 randomly selected subjects, find the probability that the mean is greater than 0.50.

2. Biometric Security In designing a security system based on eye (iris) recognition, we must consider the standing eye heights of women, which are normally distributed with a mean of 59.7 in. and a standard deviation of 2.5 in. (based on anthropometric survey data from Gordon, Churchill, et al.).

a. If an eye recognition security system is positioned at a height that is uncomfortable for women with standing eye heights less than 54 in., what percentage of women will find that height uncomfortable?

b. In positioning the eye recognition security system, we want it to be suitable for the lowest 95% of standing eye heights of women. What standing eye height of women separates the lowest 95% of standing eye heights from the highest 5%?

3. Biometric Security Standing eye heights of men are normally distributed with a mean of 64.3 in. and a standard deviation of 2.6 in. (based on anthropometric survey data from Gordon, Churchill, et al.).

a. If an eye recognition security system is positioned at a height that is uncomfortable for men with standing eye heights greater than 70 in., what percentage of men will find that height uncomfortable?

b. In positioning the eye recognition security system, we want it to be suitable for the tallest 98% of standing eye heights of men. What standing eye height of men separates the tallest 98% of standing eye heights from the lowest 2%?

4. Sampling Distributions Scores on the Gilliam Autism Rating Scale (GARS) are normally distributed with a mean of 100 and a standard deviation of 15. A sample of 64 GARS scores is randomly selected and the sample mean is computed.

a. Describe the distribution of such sample means.

b. What is the mean of all such sample means?

c. What is the standard deviation of all such sample means?

5. Unbiased Estimators

a. What is an unbiased estimator?

b. For the following statistics, identify those that are unbiased estimators: mean, median, range, variance, proportion.

c. Determine whether the following statement is true or false: "The sample standard deviation is a biased estimator, but the bias is relatively small in large samples, so s is often used to estimate σ."

6. Disney Monorail The Mark VI monorail used at Disney World has doors with a height of 72 in. Heights of men are normally distributed with a mean of 68.6 in. and a standard deviation of 2.8 in. (based on Data Set 1 "Body Data" in Appendix B).

a. What percentage of adult men can fit through the doors without bending? Does the door design with a height of 72 in. appear to be adequate? Explain.

b. What doorway height would allow 99% of adult men to fit without bending?

7. Disney Monorail Consider the same Mark VI monorail described in the preceding exercise. Again assume that heights of men are normally distributed with a mean of 68.6 in. and a standard deviation of 2.8 in.

a. In determining the suitability of the monorail door height, why does it make sense to consider men while women are ignored?

b. Mark VI monorail cars have a capacity of 60 passengers. If a car is loaded with 60 randomly selected men, what is the probability that their mean height is less than 72 in.?

c. Why can't the result from part (b) be used to determine how well the doorway height accommodates men?

8. Assessing Normality of BMI Data Listed below are measures of body mass index (BMI) for women listed in Data Set 1 "Body Data."

a. Do these measures appear to come from a population that has a normal distribution? Why or why not?

b. Can the mean of this sample be treated as a value from a population having a normal distribution? Why or why not?

15.9   18.7   24.2   28.7   28.8   28.9   28.9   28.9   29.0   29.1   29.3   31.4   59.0

9. Hybridization Experiment In one of Mendel's experiments with plants, 1064 offspring consisted of 787 plants with long stems. According to Mendel's theory, 3/4 of the offspring plants should have long stems. Assuming that Mendel's proportion of 3/4 is correct, find the probability of getting 787 or fewer plants with long stems among 1064 offspring plants. Based on the result, is 787 offspring plants with long stems significantly low? What does the result imply about Mendel's claimed proportion of 3/4?

10. Tall Clubs The social organization Tall Clubs International has a requirement that women must be at least 70 in. tall. Assume that women have normally distributed heights with a mean of 63.7 in. and a standard deviation of 2.9 in. (based on Data Set 1 in Appendix B).

a. Find the percentage of women who satisfy the height requirement.

b. If the height requirement is to be changed so that the tallest 2.5% of women are eligible, what is the new height requirement?

Cumulative Review Exercises

In Exercises 1–3, use the following left threshold audiometry measures from females (from Data Set 4 "Audiometry" in Appendix B).

   15.9   18.7   24.2   28.7   28.8   28.9   28.9   28.9   29.0   29.1   29.3   31.4

1. Audiometry

a. Find the mean $\bar{x}$.

b. Find the median.

c. Find the standard deviation s.

d. Convert the highest measure to a z score.

e. What level of measurement (nominal, ordinal, interval, ratio) describes this data set?

f. Are the measures of hearing discrete data or continuous data?

2. Audiometry

a. Find Q_1, Q_2, and Q_3.

b. Construct a boxplot.

c. Based on the accompanying normal quantile plot of the audiometry measurements, what do you conclude about these sample data?

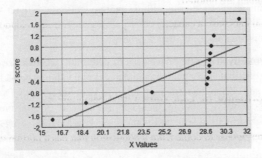

3. Left-Handedness According to data from the American Medical Association, 10% of us are left-handed.

a. If three people are randomly selected, find the probability that they are all left-handed.

b. If three people are randomly selected, find the probability that at least one of them is left-handed.

continued

c. Why can't we solve the problem in part (b) by using the normal approximation to the binomial distribution?

d. If groups of 50 people are randomly selected, what is the mean number of left-handed people in such groups?

e. If groups of 50 people are randomly selected, what is the standard deviation for the numbers of left-handed people in such groups?

f. Use the range rule of thumb to determine whether 8 left-handed people is a significantly high number of left-handed people in a randomly selected group of 50 people.

4. Blue Eyes Assume that 35% of us have blue eyes (based on a study by Dr. P. Soria at Indiana University).

a. Let B denote the event of selecting someone who has blue eyes. What does the event $\overline{B}$ denote?

b. Find the value of $P(\overline{B})$.

c. Find the probability of randomly selecting three different people and finding that all of them have blue eyes.

d. Find the probability that among 100 randomly selected people, at least 45 have blue eyes.

e. If 35% of us really do have blue eyes, is a result of 45 people with blue eyes among 100 randomly selected people a result that is significantly high?

5. Foot Lengths of Women Assume that foot lengths of women are normally distributed with a mean of 9.6 in. and a standard deviation of 0.5 in., based on data from the U.S. Army Anthropometry Survey (ANSUR).

a. Find the probability that a randomly selected woman has a foot length less than 10.0 in.

b. Find the probability that a randomly selected woman has a foot length between 8.0 in. and 11.0 in.

c. Find P_{95}.

d. Find the probability that 25 women have foot lengths with a mean greater than 9.8 in.

Technology Projects

Some methods in this chapter are easy with technology but very difficult without it. The two projects that follow illustrate how easy it is to use technology for assessing normality and finding binomial probabilities.

1. Assessing Normality It is often necessary to determine whether sample data appear to be from a normally distributed population, and that determination is helped with the construction of a histogram and normal quantile plot. Refer to Data Set 1 "Body Data" in Appendix B. For each of the 13 columns of data (not including age or gender), determine whether the data appear to be from a normally distributed population. Use Statdisk or any other technology. (Download a free copy of Statdisk from www.statdisk.org.)

2. Binomial Probabilities Section 6-6 described a method for using a normal distribution to approximate a binomial distribution. Many technologies are capable of generating probabilities for a binomial distribution. Instead of using a normal approximation to a binomial distribution, use technology to find the exact binomial probabilities in Exercises 9–12 of Section 6-6.

FROM DATA TO DECISION

Critical Thinking: Designing a campus dormitory elevator

An Ohio college student died when he tried to escape from a dormitory elevator that was overloaded with 24 passengers. The elevator was rated for a maximum weight of 2500 pounds. Let's consider this elevator with an allowable weight of 2500 pounds. Let's also consider parameters for weights of adults, as shown in the accompanying table (based on Data Set 1 "Body Data" in Appendix B).

Weights of Adults

	Males	Females
μ	189 lb	171 lb
σ	39 lb	46 lb
Distribution	Normal	Normal

We could consider design features such as the type of music that could be played on the elevator. We could select songs such as "Imagine" or "Daydream Believer." Instead, we will focus on the critical design feature of weight.

a. First, elevators commonly have a 25% margin of error, so they can safely carry a load that is 25% greater than the stated load. What amount is 25% greater than 2500 pounds? Let's refer to this amount as "the maximum safe load," while the 2500-pound limit is the "placard maximum load."

b. Now we need to determine the maximum number of passengers that should be allowed. Should we base our calculations on the maximum safe load or the 2500-pound placard maximum load?

c. The weights given in the accompanying table are weights of adults not including clothing or textbooks. Add another 10 pounds for each student's clothing and textbooks. What is the maximum number of elevator passengers that should be allowed?

d. Do you think that weights of college students are different from weights of adults from the general population? If so, how? How would that affect the elevator design?

Cooperative Group Activities

1. In-class activity Divide into groups of three or four students and address these issues affecting the design of manhole covers.

• Which of the following is most relevant for determining whether a manhole cover diameter of 24 in. is large enough: weights of men, weights of women, heights of men, heights of women, hip breadths of men, hip breadths of women, shoulder breadths of men, shoulder breadths of women?

• Why are manhole covers usually round? (This was once a popular interview question asked of applicants at IBM, and there are at least three good answers. One good answer is sufficient here.)

2. Out-of-class activity Divide into groups of three or four students. In each group, develop an original procedure to illustrate the central limit theorem. The main objective is to show that when you randomly select samples from a population, the means of those samples tend to be *normally* distributed, regardless of the nature of the population distribution. For this illustration, begin with some population of values that does not have a normal distribution.

3. In-class activity Divide into groups of three or four students. Using a coin to simulate births, each individual group member should simulate 25 births and record the number of simulated girls. Combine all results from the group and record $n = $ total number of births and $x = $ number of girls. Given batches of n births, compute the mean and standard deviation for the number of girls. Is the simulated result unusual? Why or why not?

4. In-class activity Divide into groups of three or four students. Select a set of data from Appendix B (excluding Data Sets that were used in examples or exercises in Section 6-5). Use the methods of Section 6-5 to construct a histogram and normal quantile plot, and then determine whether the data set appears to come from a normally distributed population.

CHAPTER PROBLEM — **Does Touch Therapy Work?**

Many patients pay $30 to $60 for a session of touch therapy in which the touch therapist moves his or her hands within a few inches of the patient's body without actually making physical contact. The objective is to cure a wide variety of medical conditions, including cancer, AIDS, asthma, heart disease, headaches, burns, and bone fractures. The intent is that a professionally trained touch therapist can detect poor alignments in the patient's energy field, and can then reposition energy fields to create an energy balance that fosters the healing process.

When she was in the fourth grade, nine-year old Emily Rosa chose the topic of touch therapy for a science fair project. She convinced 21 experienced touch therapists to participate in a simple test of their ability to detect a human energy field. Emily constructed a cardboard partition with two holes for hands. Each touch therapist would put both hands through the two holes, and Emily would place her hand just above one of the therapist's hands; then the therapist was asked to identify the hand that Emily had selected. Emily used a coin toss to randomly select the hand to be used. This test was repeated 280 times. If the touch therapists really did have the ability to sense a human energy field, they should have identified the correct hand significantly more than 50% of the time. If they did not have the ability to detect the energy field and they just guessed, they should have been correct about 50% of the time. Here are Emily's results: Among the 280 trials, the touch therapists identified the correct hand 123 times, for a success rate of 43.9%. Emily, with the help of her mother, a statistician, and a physician, submitted her findings for publication in the *Journal*

of the American Medical Association. After a careful and thorough review of the experimental design and results, the article "A Close Look at Therapeutic Touch" was published (*Journal of the American Medical Association*, Vol. 279, No. 13). Emily became the youngest researcher to be published in that journal. And she won a blue ribbon for her science fair project.

Let's consider the key results from Emily's project. Among the 280 trials, the touch therapists were correct 123 times. We have a sample proportion with $n = 280$ and $x = 123$ successes. Arguments against the validity of the study might include the claim that the number of trials is too small to be meaningful, or that the touch therapists just had a bad day and, because of chance, they were not as successful as the population of all touch therapists. We will consider such issues in this chapter.

CHAPTER OBJECTIVES

In this chapter we begin the study of methods of *inferential statistics*. Listed below are the major activities of inferential statistics, and this chapter introduces methods for the first activity of using sample data to estimate population parameters. Chapter 8 will introduce the basic methods for testing claims (or hypotheses) about population parameters.

Major Activities of Inferential Statistics

1. Use sample data to *estimate values of population parameters* (such as a population proportion or population mean).

2. Use sample data to *test hypotheses* (or claims) made about population parameters.

Here are the chapter objectives.

 Estimating a Population Proportion

- Construct a confidence interval estimate of a population proportion and interpret such confidence interval estimates.

- Identify the requirements necessary for the procedure that is used, and determine whether those requirements are satisfied.

- Develop the ability to determine the sample size necessary to estimate a population proportion.

 Estimating a Population Mean

- Construct a confidence interval estimate of a population mean, and be able to interpret such confidence interval estimates.

- Determine the sample size necessary to estimate a population mean.

 Estimating a Population Standard Deviation or Variance

- Develop the ability to construct a confidence interval estimate of a population standard deviation or variance, and be able to interpret such confidence interval estimates.

Bootstrapping: Using Technology for Estimates

- Develop the ability to use technology along with the bootstrapping method to construct a confidence interval estimate of a population proportion, population mean, and population standard deviation and population variance.

7-1 Estimating a Population Proportion

make an inference

Key Concept This section presents methods for using a sample proportion to make an inference about the value of the corresponding population proportion. This section focuses on the population proportion p, but we can also work with probabilities or percentages. When working with percentages, we will perform calculations with the equivalent proportion value. Here are the three main concepts included in this section:

- **Point Estimate:** The sample proportion (denoted by $\hat{p}$) is the best *point estimate* (or single value estimate) of the population proportion p.

- **Confidence Interval:** We can use a sample proportion to construct a *confidence interval* estimate of the true value of a population proportion, and we should know how to construct and interpret such confidence intervals.

- **Sample Size:** We should know how to find the sample size necessary to estimate a population proportion.

The concepts presented in this section are used in the following sections and chapters, so it is important to understand this section quite well.

PART 1 Point Estimate, Confidence Interval, and Sample Size

Point Estimate

If we want to estimate a population proportion with a single value, the best estimate is the sample proportion $\hat{p}$. Because $\hat{p}$ consists of a single value that is equivalent to a point on a line, it is called a *point estimate*.

> **DEFINITION**
>
> A **point estimate** is a single value used to estimate a population parameter.

> The sample proportion $\hat{p}$ is the best *point estimate* of the population proportion p.

Unbiased Estimator We use $\hat{p}$ as the point estimate of p because it is unbiased and it is the most consistent of the estimators that could be used. (An unbiased estimator is a statistic that targets the value of the corresponding population parameter in the sense that the sampling distribution of the statistic has a mean that is equal to the corresponding population parameter. The statistic $\hat{p}$ targets the population proportion p.) The sample proportion $\hat{p}$ is the most consistent estimator of p in the sense that the standard deviation of sample proportions tends to be smaller than the standard deviation of other unbiased estimators of p.

EXAMPLE 1 **Touch Therapy**

The Chapter Problem describes a test of touch therapy. If the touch therapists had the ability to sense a human energy field, they should have identified the correct hand significantly more than 50% of the time. If they made random guesses, their success rate should be around 50%. Using the result of 123 correct responses in the 280 trials, find the best point estimate of the proportion of correct responses.

SOLUTION

Because the sample proportion is the best point estimate of the population proportion, we conclude that the best point estimate of p is $123/280$ or 0.439. (If using the sample results to estimate the *percentage* of correct responses, the best point estimate is 43.9%.)

Confidence Interval

Why Do We Need Confidence Intervals? In Example 1 we saw that 0.439 is our *best* point estimate of the population proportion p, but we have no indication of how *good* that best estimate is. A confidence interval gives us a much better sense of how good an estimate is.

> **DEFINITION**
>
> A **confidence interval** (or **interval estimate**) is a range (or an interval) of values used to estimate the true value of a population parameter. A confidence interval is sometimes abbreviated as CI.

> **DEFINITION**
>
> The **confidence level** is the probability $1 - \alpha$ (such as 0.95, or 95%) that the confidence interval actually does contain the population parameter, assuming that the estimation process is repeated a large number of times. (The confidence level is also called the **degree of confidence,** or the **confidence coefficient.**)

The following table shows the relationship between the confidence level and the corresponding value of α. The confidence level of 95% is the value used most often.

Most Common Confidence Levels	Corresponding Values of α
90% (or 0.90) confidence level:	$\alpha = 0.10$
95% (or 0.95) confidence level:	$\alpha = 0.05$
99% (or 0.99) confidence level:	$\alpha = 0.01$

Here's an example of a confidence interval found later in Example 3:

The 0.95 (or 95%) confidence interval estimate of the population proportion p is $0.381 < p < 0.497$.

Interpreting a Confidence Interval

We must be careful to interpret confidence intervals correctly. There is a correct interpretation and many different and creative incorrect interpretations of the confidence interval $0.381 < p < 0.497$.

Correct: **"We are 95% confident that the interval from 0.381 to 0.497 actually does contain the true value of the population proportion p."**
This is a short and acceptable way of saying that if we were to select many different random samples of size 280 (as in the Chapter Problem) and construct the corresponding confidence intervals, 95% of them would contain the population proportion p. In this correct interpretation, the confidence level of 95% refers to the *success rate of the process* used to estimate the population proportion.

Wrong: **"There is a 95% chance that the true value of p will fall between 0.381 and 0.497."**
This is wrong because p is a population parameter with a fixed value; it is not a random variable with values that vary.

Wrong: **"95% of sample proportions will fall between 0.381 and 0.497."**
This is wrong because the values of 0.381 and 0.497 result from one sample; they are not parameters describing the behavior of all samples.

Confidence Level: The Process Success Rate A confidence level of 95% tells us that the *process* we are using should, in the long run, result in confidence interval limits that contain the true population proportion 95% of the time. Suppose that the true proportion of correct responses by the touch therapists is $p = 0.50$. See Figure 7-1, which shows that 19 out of 20 (or 95%) different confidence intervals contain the assumed value of $p = 0.50$. Figure 7-1 is trying to tell this story: With a 95% confidence level, we expect about 19 out of 20 confidence intervals (or 95%) to contain the true value of p.

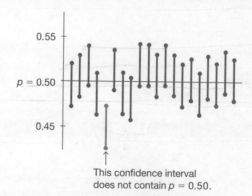

This confidence interval
does not contain $p = 0.50$.

FIGURE 7-1   Confidence Intervals from 20 Different Samples

Critical Values

Critical values are formally defined on the next page and they are based on the following observations:

1. When certain requirements are met, the sampling distribution of sample proportions can be approximated by a normal distribution, as shown in Figure 7-2.

2. A z score associated with a sample proportion has a probability of $\alpha/2$ of falling in the right tail portion of Figure 7-2.

3. The z score at the boundary of the right-tail region is commonly denoted by $z_{\alpha/2}$ and is referred to as a *critical value* because it is on the borderline separating z scores that are significantly high.

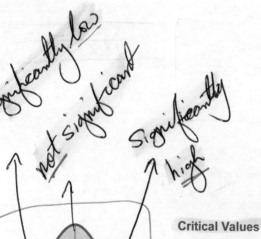

$\alpha/2$ $\alpha/2$

$z = 0$ $z_{\alpha/2}$

Found from technology or Table A-2

FIGURE 7-2   Critical Value $z_{\alpha/2}$ in the Standard Normal Distribution

DEFINITION

A **critical value** is the number on the borderline separating sample statistics that are significantly high or low from those that are not significant. The number $z_{\alpha/2}$ is a critical value that is a z score with the property that it is at the border that separates an area of $\alpha/2$ in the right tail of the standard normal distribution (as in Figure 7-2).

 EXAMPLE 2 **Finding a Critical Value**

Find the critical value $z_{\alpha/2}$ corresponding to a 95% confidence level.

SOLUTION

A 95% confidence level corresponds to $\alpha = 0.05$, so $\alpha/2 = 0.025$. Figure 7-3 shows that the area in each of the green-shaded tails is $\alpha/2 = 0.025$. We find $z_{\alpha/2} = 1.96$ by noting that the cumulative area to its left must be $1 - 0.025$, or 0.975. We can use technology or refer to Table A-2 to find that the cumulative left area of 0.9750 corresponds to $z = 1.96$. For a 95% confidence level, the critical value is therefore $z_{\alpha/2} = 1.96$.

Note that when finding the critical z score for a 95% confidence level, we use a cumulative left area of 0.9750 (*not* 0.95). Think of it this way:

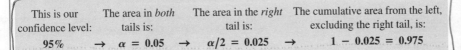

This is our confidence level:		The area in *both* tails is:		The area in the *right* tail is:		The cumulative area from the left, excluding the right tail, is:
95%	→	$\alpha = 0.05$	→	$\alpha/2 = 0.025$	→	$1 - 0.025 = 0.975$

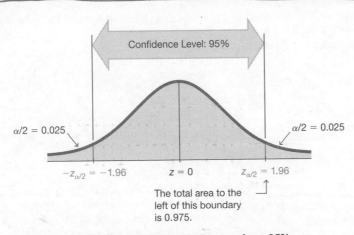

Confidence Level: 95%

$\alpha/2 = 0.025$ $\alpha/2 = 0.025$

$-z_{\alpha/2} = -1.96$ $z = 0$ $z_{\alpha/2} = 1.96$

The total area to the left of this boundary is 0.975.

FIGURE 7-3 **Finding the Critical Value $z_{\alpha/2}$ for a 95% Confidence Level**

Example 2 showed that a 95% confidence level results in a critical value of $z_{\alpha/2} = 1.96$. This is the most common critical value, and it is listed with two other common values in the table that follows.

Confidence Level	α	Critical Value, $z_{\alpha/2}$
90%	0.10	1.645
95%	0.05	1.96
99%	0.01	2.575

Simple Random Sample

$\hat{p} - p = error$

$E = z_{\alpha/2} \cdot \sigma_{\hat{p}}$

Margin of Error

We now formally define the *margin of error E* that we have all heard about so often in media reports.

DEFINITION

When data from a simple random sample are used to estimate a population proportion p, the difference between the sample proportion $\hat{p}$ and the population proportion p is an error. The maximum likely amount of that error is the **margin of error**, denoted by E. There is a probability of $1 - \alpha$ (such as 0.95) that the difference between $\hat{p}$ and p is E or less. The margin of error E is also called the *maximum error of the estimate* and can be found by multiplying the critical value and the estimated standard deviation of sample proportions, as shown in Formula 7-1.

FORMULA 7-1

$$E = z_{\alpha/2}\sqrt{\frac{\hat{p}\hat{q}}{n}} \quad \text{margin of error for proportions}$$

↑   ↑

Critical value   Estimated standard deviation of sample proportions

---

KEY ELEMENTS

Confidence Interval for Estimating a Population Proportion p

Objective

Construct a confidence interval used to estimate a population proportion p.

Notation

p = *population* proportion
$\hat{p}$ = *sample* proportion
n = number of sample values

E = margin of error
$z_{\alpha/2}$ = critical value: the z score separating an area of $\alpha/2$ in the right tail of the standard normal distribution

Requirements

1. The sample is a simple random sample.
2. The conditions for the binomial distribution are satisfied: There is a fixed number of trials, the trials are independent, there are two categories of outcomes, and the probabilities remain constant for each trial (as in Section 5-2).
3. There are at least 5 successes and at least 5 failures. (This requirement is a way to verify that $np \geq 5$ and $nq \geq 5$, so the normal distribution is a suitable approximation to the binomial distribution.)

Confidence Interval Estimate of p

$$\hat{p} - E < p < \hat{p} + E \quad \text{where} \quad E = z_{\alpha/2}\sqrt{\frac{\hat{p}\hat{q}}{n}}$$

The confidence interval is often expressed in the following two equivalent formats:

$$\hat{p} \pm E \quad \text{or} \quad (\hat{p} - E, \hat{p} + E)$$

Round-Off Rule for Confidence Interval Estimates of p

Round the confidence interval limits for p to three significant digits.

Procedure for Constructing a Confidence Interval for *p*

1. Verify that the requirements in the preceding Key Elements box are satisfied.

2. Use technology or Table A-2 to find the critical value $z_{\alpha/2}$ that corresponds to the desired confidence level.

3. Evaluate the margin of error $E = z_{\alpha/2}\sqrt{\hat{p}\hat{q}/n}$.

4. Using the value of the calculated margin of error E and the value of the sample proportion $\hat{p}$, find the values of the *confidence interval limits* $\hat{p} - E$ and $\hat{p} + E$. Substitute those values in the general format for the confidence interval.

5. Round the resulting confidence interval limits to three significant digits.

EXAMPLE 3 Constructing a Confidence Interval: Touch Therapy

In the Chapter Problem we noted that in an experiment with touch therapists, they made correct responses in 123 of the 280 trials. The sample results are $n = 280$ and $\hat{p} = 123/280$, or 0.439.

a. Find the margin of error E that corresponds to a 95% confidence level.

b. Find the 95% confidence interval estimate of the population proportion p.

c. Based on the results, can we safely conclude that the touch therapists had a success rate equivalent to tossing a coin?

SOLUTION

REQUIREMENT CHECK   (1) The experiment was examined and found to be sound, so we will treat the results as simple random samples. (2) The conditions for a binomial experiment are satisfied, because there is a fixed number of trials (280), the trials are independent (because the response from one touch therapist doesn't affect the probability of the response from another touch therapist), there are two categories of outcome (response was correct or incorrect), and the probability remains constant and is not changing over time. (3) The number of successes (123 correct responses) and the number of failures (157 incorrect responses) are both at least 5. The check of requirements has been successfully completed. ☑

Technology The confidence interval and margin of error can be easily found using technology. From the Statdisk display we can see the required entries on the left and the results displayed on the right. The results show that the margin of error is $E = 0.0581$ (rounded) and the confidence interval is $0.381 < p < 0.497$ (rounded). (The Wilson score confidence interval included in the display will be discussed later in Part 2 of this section.)

Statdisk

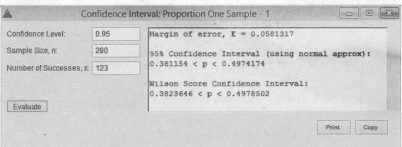

continued

Manual Calculation Here is how to find the confidence interval with manual calculations:

a. The margin of error is found by using Formula 7-1 with $z_{\alpha/2} = 1.96$ (as found in Example 2), $\hat{p} = 0.439$, $\hat{q} = 0.561$, and $n = 280$.

$$E = z_{\alpha/2}\sqrt{\frac{\hat{p}\hat{q}}{n}} = 1.96\sqrt{\frac{(0.439)(0.561)}{280}} = 0.058129$$

b. Constructing the confidence interval is really easy now that we know that $\hat{p} = 0.439$ and $E = 0.058129$. Simply substitute those values to obtain this result:

$$\hat{p} - E < p < \hat{p} + E$$
$$0.439 - 0.058129 < p < 0.439 + 0.058129$$
$$0.381 < p < 0.497 \quad \text{(rounded to three significant digits)}$$

This same result could be expressed in the format of 0.439 ± 0.058 or $(0.381, 0.497)$. If we want the 95% confidence interval for the true population *percentage,* we could express the result as $38.1\% < p < 49.7\%$.

c. Based on the confidence interval obtained in part (b), it appears that fewer than 50% of the touch therapist responses are correct (because the interval of values from 0.381 to 0.497 is an interval that is completely below 0.50).

Finding the Point Estimate and *E* from a Confidence Interval

Sometimes we want to better understand a confidence interval that might have been obtained from a journal article or technology. If we already know the confidence interval limits, the sample proportion (or the best point estimate) $\hat{p}$ and the margin of error E can be found as follows:

Point estimate of p:

$$\hat{p} = \frac{(\text{upper confidence interval limit}) + (\text{lower confidence interval limit})}{2}$$

Margin of error:

$$E = \frac{(\text{upper confidence interval limit}) - (\text{lower confidence interval limit})}{2}$$

EXAMPLE 4 **Finding the Sample Proportion and Margin of Error**

The article "High-Dose Nicotine Patch Therapy," by Dale, Hurt, et al. (*Journal of the American Medical Association,* Vol. 274, No. 17) includes this statement: "Of the 71 subjects, 70% were abstinent from smoking at 8 weeks (95% confidence interval [CI], 58% to 81%)." Use that statement to find the point estimate $\hat{p}$ and the margin of error E.

SOLUTION

We get the 95% confidence interval of $0.58 < p < 0.81$ from the given statement of "58% to 81%." The point estimate $\hat{p}$ is the value midway between the upper and lower confidence interval limits, so we get

$$\hat{p} = \frac{(\text{upper confidence limit}) + (\text{lower confidence limit})}{2}$$

$$= \frac{0.81 + 0.58}{2} = 0.695$$

The margin of error can be found as follows:

$$E = \frac{(\text{upper confidence limit}) - (\text{lower confidence limit})}{2}$$

$$= \frac{0.81 - 0.58}{2} = 0.115$$

Using Confidence Intervals for Hypothesis Tests

A confidence interval can be used to *informally* address some claim made about a population proportion p. For example, if sample results consist of 70 girls in 100 births, the resulting 95% confidence interval of $0.610 < p < 0.790$ can be used to *informally* support a claim that the proportion of girls is *different from* 50% (because 0.50 is not contained within the confidence interval).

Determining Sample Size

If we plan to collect sample data in order to estimate some population proportion, how do we know *how many* sample units we must get? If we solve the formula for the margin of error E (Formula 7-1) for the sample size n, we get Formula 7-2 that follows. Formula 7-2 requires $\hat{p}$ as an estimate of the population proportion p, but if no such estimate is known (as is often the case), we replace $\hat{p}$ by 0.5 and replace $\hat{q}$ by 0.5, with the result given in Formula 7-3. Replacing $\hat{p}$ and $\hat{q}$ with 0.5 results in the largest possible sample size, so we are sure that the sample size is adequate for estimating p.

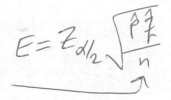

KEY ELEMENTS

Finding the Sample Size Required to Estimate a Population Proportion

Objective

Determine how large the sample size n should be in order to estimate the population proportion p.

Notation

p = population proportion
$\hat{p}$ = sample proportion
n = number of sample values
E = desired margin of error
$z_{\alpha/2}$ = z score separating an area of $\alpha/2$ in the right tail of the standard normal distribution

continued

Requirements

The sample must be a simple random sample of independent sample units.

When an estimate $\hat{p}$ is known: **Formula 7-2** $n = \dfrac{[z_{\alpha/2}]^2 \hat{p}\hat{q}}{E^2}$

When no estimate $\hat{p}$ is known: **Formula 7-3** $n = \dfrac{[z_{\alpha/2}]^2 0.25}{E^2}$

If a reasonable estimate of $\hat{p}$ can be made by using previous samples, a pilot study, or someone's expert knowledge, use Formula 7-2. If nothing is known about the value of $\hat{p}$, use Formula 7-3.

Round-Off Rule for Determining Sample Size

If the computed sample size n is not a whole number, round the value of n up to the next *larger* whole number, so the sample size is sufficient instead of being slightly insufficient. For example, round 384.16 to 385.

EXAMPLE 5 **What Percentage of Children Have Received Measles Vaccinations?**

If we were to conduct a survey to determine the percentage of children (older than 1 year) who have received measles vaccinations, how many children must be surveyed in order to be 95% confident that the sample percentage is in error by no more than three percentage points?

a. Assume that a recent survey showed that 90% of children have received measles vaccinations.

b. Assume that we have no prior information suggesting a possible value of the population proportion.

SOLUTION

a. With a 95% confidence level, we have $\alpha = 0.05$, so $z_{\alpha/2} = 1.96$. Also, the margin of error is $E = 0.03$, which is the decimal equivalent of "three percentage points." The prior survey suggests that $\hat{p} = 0.90$, so $\hat{q} = 0.10$ (found from $\hat{q} = 1 - 0.90$). Because we have an estimated value of $\hat{p}$, we use Formula 7-2 as follows:

$$n = \frac{[z_{\alpha/2}]^2 \hat{p}\hat{q}}{E^2} = \frac{[1.96]^2 (0.90)(0.10)}{0.03^2}$$

$$= 384.16 = 385 \text{ (rounded } up)$$

We must obtain a simple random sample that includes at least 385 children.

b. With no prior knowledge of $\hat{p}$ (or $\hat{q}$), we use Formula 7-3 as follows:

$$n = \frac{[z_{\alpha/2}]^2 \cdot 0.25}{E^2} = \frac{[1.96]^2 \cdot 0.25}{0.03^2}$$

$$= 1067.11 = 1068 \text{ (rounded up)}$$

We must obtain a simple random sample that includes at least 1068 children.

$CI = 95\%$

$\alpha = 0.05$

$z_{\alpha/2} = 1.96$

INTERPRETATION

To be 95% confident that our sample percentage is within three percentage points of the true percentage for all children, we should obtain a simple random sample of 1068 children, assuming no prior knowledge. By comparing this result to the sample size of 385 found in part (a), we can see that if we have no knowledge of a prior study, a larger sample is required to achieve the same results compared to when the value of $\hat{p}$ can be estimated.

CAUTION Try to avoid these three common errors when calculating sample size:

1. Don't make the mistake of using $E = 3$ as the margin of error corresponding to "three percentage points." If the margin of error is three percentage points, use $E = 0.03$.

2. Be sure to substitute the critical z score for $z_{\alpha/2}$. For example, when working with 95% confidence, be sure to replace $z_{\alpha/2}$ with 1.96. Don't make the mistake of replacing $z_{\alpha/2}$ with 0.95 or 0.05.

3. Be sure to round *up* to the next higher integer; don't round off using the usual round-off rules. Round 1067.11 to 1068.

Role of the Population Size N Formulas 7-2 and 7-3 are remarkable because they show that the sample size does not depend on the size (N) of the population; the sample size depends on the desired confidence level, the desired margin of error, and sometimes the known estimate of $\hat{p}$. (See Exercise 37 for dealing with cases in which a relatively large sample is selected without replacement from a finite population, so the sample size n does depend on the population size N.)

PART 2   Better-Performing Confidence Intervals

Disadvantage of Wald Confidence Interval

Coverage Probability The **coverage probability** of a confidence interval is the actual proportion of such confidence intervals that contain the true population proportion. If we select a specific confidence level, such as 0.95 (or 95%), we would like to get the *actual* coverage probability equal to our *desired* confidence level. However, for the confidence interval described in Part 1 (called a "Wald confidence interval"), the actual coverage probability is usually less than or equal to the confidence level that we select, and it could be substantially less. For example, if we select a 95% confidence level, we usually get 95% or *fewer* of confidence intervals containing the population proportion p. (This is sometimes referred to as being "too liberal.") For this reason, the Wald confidence interval is rarely used in professional applications and professional journals.

Better-Performing Confidence Intervals

Important note about exercises: Except for some Beyond the Basics exercises, the exercises for this Section 7-1 are based on the method for constructing a Wald confidence interval as described in Part 1, not the confidence intervals described here. It is recommended that students learn the methods presented earlier, but recognize that there are better methods available, and they can be used with suitable technology.

Plus Four Method The *plus four confidence interval* performs better than the Wald confidence interval in the sense that its coverage probability is closer to the confidence level that is used. The plus four confidence interval uses this very simple procedure: Add 2 to the number of successes x, add 2 to the number of failures (so that the number of trials n is increased by 4), and then find the Wald confidence interval as described in Part 1 of this section. The plus four confidence interval is very easy to calculate and it has coverage probabilities similar to those for the Wilson score confidence interval that follows.

Wilson Score Another confidence interval that performs better than the Wald CI is the *Wilson score confidence interval*:

$$\frac{\hat{p} + \frac{z_{\alpha/2}^2}{2n} \pm z_{\alpha/2} \sqrt{\frac{\hat{p}\hat{q} + \frac{z_{\alpha/2}^2}{4n}}{n}}}{1 + \frac{z_{\alpha/2}^2}{n}}$$

The Wilson score confidence interval performs better than the Wald CI in the sense that the coverage probability is closer to the confidence level. With a confidence level of 95%, the Wilson score confidence interval would get us closer to a 0.95 probability of containing the parameter p. The complexity of the above expression can be circumvented by using some technologies, such as Statdisk or XLSTAT, that provide Wilson score confidence interval results.

Clopper-Pearson Method The Clopper-Pearson method is an "exact" method in the sense that it is based on the exact binomial distribution instead of an approximation of a distribution. It is criticized for being *too conservative* in this sense: When we select a specific confidence level, the coverage probability is usually greater than or equal to the selected confidence level. Select a confidence level of 0.95, and the actual coverage probability is usually 0.95 or greater, so that 95% or more of such confidence intervals will contain p. Calculations with this method are too messy to consider here.

Which Method Is Best? There are other methods for constructing confidence intervals that are not discussed here. There isn't universal agreement on which method is best for constructing a confidence interval estimate of p.

- The Wald confidence interval is best as a teaching tool for introducing students to confidence intervals.

- The plus four confidence interval is almost as easy as Wald and it performs better than Wald by having a coverage probability closer to the selected confidence level.

Again, note that except for some Beyond the Basic exercises, the exercises that follow are based on the Wald confidence interval given earlier, not the better-performing confidence intervals discussed here.

TECH CENTER

Proportions: Confidence Intervals & Sample Size Determination

Access tech instructions, videos, and data sets at **www.TriolaStats.com**

7-1   Basic Skills and Concepts

Statistical Literacy and Critical Thinking

1. Reporting Results Here is a result stated in a format commonly used in the media: "In a clinical trial of 227 subjects treated with OxyContin (oxycodone), 13% of the subjects reported dizziness. The margin of error is ± 4 percentage points." What important feature of the poll is omitted?

2. Margin of Error For the poll described in Exercise 1, describe what is meant by the statement that "the margin of error was given as ± 4 percentage points."

3. Notation For the poll described in Exercise 1, what values do $\hat{p}$, $\hat{q}$, n, E, and p represent? If the confidence level is 95%, what is the value of α?

4. Confidence Levels Given specific sample data, such as the data given in Exercise 1, which confidence interval is wider: the 95% confidence interval or the 80% confidence interval? Why is it wider?

Finding Critical Values.   *In Exercises 5–8, find the critical value $z_{\alpha/2}$ that corresponds to the given confidence level.*

5. 90%   **6.** 99%   **7.** 99.5%   **8.** 95%

Formats of Confidence Intervals.   *In Exercises 9–12, express the confidence interval using the indicated format. (The confidence intervals are based on proportions of eye colors.)*

9. Brown Eyes Express $0.375 < p < 0.425$ in the form of $\hat{p} \pm E$.

10. Blue Eyes Express $0.320 < p < 0.450$ in the form of $\hat{p} \pm E$.

11. Green Eyes Express the confidence interval (0.0780, 0.162) in the form of $\hat{p} - E < p < \hat{p} + E$.

12. Gray Eyes Express the confidence interval 0.070 ± 0.021 in the form of $\hat{p} - E < p < \hat{p} + E$.

Constructing and Interpreting Confidence Intervals.   *In Exercises 13–16, use the given sample data and confidence level. In each case, (a) find the best point estimate of the population proportion p; (b) identify the value of the margin of error E; (c) construct the confidence interval; (d) write a statement that correctly interprets the confidence interval.*

13. OxyContin In a clinical trial of OxyContin (oxycodone), 16 subjects experienced headaches among the 227 subjects treated with OxyContin. Construct a 95% confidence interval for the proportion of treated subjects who experience headaches.

14. Eliquis The drug Eliquis (apixaban) is used to help prevent blood clots in certain patients. In clinical trials, among 5924 patients treated with Eliquis, 153 developed the adverse reaction of nausea (based on data from Bristol-Myers Squibb Co.). Construct a 99% confidence interval for the proportion of adverse reactions.

15. Survey Return Rate In a study of cell phone use and brain hemispheric dominance, an Internet survey was e-mailed to 5000 subjects randomly selected from an online group whose focus is related to ears. 717 surveys were returned. Construct a 90% confidence interval for the proportion of returned surveys.

16. Medical Malpractice In a study of 1228 randomly selected medical malpractice lawsuits, it was found that 856 of them were dropped or dismissed (based on data from the Physicians Insurers Association of America). Construct a 95% confidence interval for the proportion of medical malpractice lawsuits that are dropped or dismissed.

Critical Thinking. *In Exercises 17–28, use the data and confidence level to construct a confidence interval estimate of p, then address the given question.*

17. Births A random sample of 860 births in New York State included 426 boys. Construct a 95% confidence interval estimate of the proportion of boys in all births. It is believed that among all births, the proportion of boys is 0.512. Do these sample results provide strong evidence against that belief?

18. Mendelian Genetics One of Mendel's famous genetics experiments yielded 580 peas, with 428 of them green and 152 yellow.

a. Find a 99% confidence interval estimate of the *percentage* of green peas.

b. Based on his theory of genetics, Mendel expected that 75% of the offspring peas would be green. Given that the percentage of offspring green peas is not 75%, do the results contradict Mendel's theory? Why or why not?

19. OxyContin The drug OxyContin (oxycodone) is used to treat pain, but it is dangerous because it is addictive and can be lethal. In clinical trials, 227 subjects were treated with OxyContin and 52 of them developed nausea (based on data from Purdue Pharma L.P.).

a. Construct a 95% confidence interval estimate of the *percentage* of OxyContin users who develop nausea.

b. Compare the result from part (a) to this 95% confidence interval for 5 subjects who developed nausea among the 45 subjects given a placebo instead of OxyContin: $1.93\% < p < 20.3\%$. What do you conclude?

20. Medication Usage In a survey of 3005 adults aged 57 through 85 years, it was found that 81.7% of them used at least one prescription medication (based on data from "Use of Prescription and Over-the-Counter Medications and Dietary Supplements Among Older Adults in the United States," by Qato et al., *Journal of the American Medical Association,* Vol. 300, No. 24).

a. How many of the 3005 subjects used at least one prescription medication?

b. Construct a 90% confidence interval estimate of the *percentage* of adults aged 57 through 85 years who use at least one prescription medication.

c. What do the results tell us about the proportion of college students who use at least one prescription medication?

21. Cell Phones and Cancer A study of 420,095 Danish cell phone users found that 0.0321% of them developed cancer of the brain or nervous system. Prior to this study of cell phone use, the rate of such cancer was found to be 0.0340% for those not using cell phones. The data are from the *Journal of the National Cancer Institute*.

a. Use the sample data to construct a 90% confidence interval estimate of the *percentage* of cell phone users who develop cancer of the brain or nervous system.

b. Do cell phone users appear to have a rate of cancer of the brain or nervous system that is different from the rate of such cancer among those not using cell phones? Why or why not?

22. Lipitor In clinical trials of the drug Lipitor (atorvastatin), 270 subjects were given a placebo and 7 of them had allergic reactions. Among 863 subjects treated with 10 mg of the drug, 8 experienced allergic reactions. Construct the two 95% confidence interval estimates of the percentages of allergic reactions. Compare the results. What do you conclude?

23. Gender Selection Before its clinical trials were discontinued, the Genetics & IVF Institute conducted a clinical trial of the XSORT method designed to increase the probability of conceiving a girl and, among the 945 babies born to parents using the XSORT method, there were 879 girls. Construct the 95% confidence interval estimate of the percentage of success. What do you conclude?

24. Gender Selection Before its clinical trials were discontinued, the Genetics & IVF Institute conducted a clinical trial of the YSORT method designed to increase the probability of conceiving a boy and, among the 291 babies born to parents using the YSORT method, there were 239 boys. What do you conclude?

25. Postponing Death An interesting hypothesis is that individuals can temporarily postpone their death to survive a major holiday or important event such as a birthday. In a study of this phenomenon, it was found that in the week before and the week after Thanksgiving, there were 12,000 total deaths, and 6062 of them occurred in the week before Thanksgiving (based on data from "Holidays, Birthdays, and Postponement of Cancer Death," by Young and Hade, *Journal of the American Medical Association,* Vol. 292, No. 24.) Construct a 95% confidence interval estimate of the proportion of number of deaths in the week before Thanksgiving to the total deaths in the week before and the week after Thanksgiving. Based on the result, does there appear to be any indication that people can temporarily postpone their death to survive the Thanksgiving holiday? Why or why not?

26. Cloning Survey A Gallup poll included 1012 randomly selected adults who were asked whether "cloning of humans should or should not be allowed." Results showed that 901 of those surveyed indicated that cloning should *not* be allowed. A news reporter wants to determine whether these survey results constitute strong evidence that the majority (more than 50%) of people are opposed to such cloning. Construct a 99% confidence interval estimate of the proportion of adults believing that cloning of humans should not be allowed. Is there strong evidence supporting the claim that the majority is opposed to such cloning?

27. Smoking Cessation In a program designed to help patients stop smoking, 198 patients were given *sustained* care, and 82.8% of them were no longer smoking after one month. Among 199 patients given *standard* care, 62.8% were no longer smoking after one month (based on data from "Sustained Care Intervention and Postdischarge Smoking Cessation Among Hospitalized Adults," by Rigotti et al., *Journal of the American Medical Association,* Vol. 312, No. 7). Construct the two 95% confidence interval estimates of the percentages of success. Compare the results. What do you conclude?

28. Measured Results vs. Reported Results The same study cited in the preceding exercise produced these results after six months for the 198 patients given sustained care: 25.8% were no longer smoking, and these results were biochemically confirmed, but 40.9% of these patients *reported* that they were no longer smoking. Construct the two 95% confidence intervals. Compare the results. What do you conclude?

Determining Sample Size. *In Exercises 29–36, use the given data to find the minimum sample size required to estimate a population proportion or percentage.*

29. Ambidextrous Find the sample size needed to estimate the percentage of Lyon residents who are ambidextrous. Use a margin of error of four percentage points, and use a confidence level of 95%.

a. Assume that $\hat{p}$ and $\hat{q}$ are unknown.

b. Assume that based on prior studies, about 2% of the residents of Lyon are ambidextrous.

c. How do the results from parts (a) and (b) change if the entire France is used instead of Lyon?

30. Polio You plan to conduct a survey to estimate the percentage of adults who have had polio. Find the number of people who must be surveyed if you want to be 99% confident that the sample percentage is within three percentage points of the true percentage for the population of all adults.

a. Assume that nothing is known about the prevalence of polio.

b. Assume that about 15% of adults have had polio.

c. Does the added knowledge in part (b) have much of an effect on the sample size?

31. Bachelor's Degree in Four Years In a study of government financial aid for college students, it becomes necessary to estimate the percentage of full-time college students who earn a bachelor's degree in four years or less. Find the sample size needed to estimate that percentage. Use a 0.05 margin of error, and use a confidence level of 95%.

a. Assume that nothing is known about the percentage to be estimated.

b. Assume that prior studies have shown that about 40% of full-time students earn bachelor's degrees in four years or less.

c. Does the added knowledge in part (b) have much of an effect on the sample size?

32. Astrology A sociologist plans to conduct a survey to estimate the percentage of health care professionals who believe in astrology. How many health care professionals must be surveyed if we want a confidence level of 99% and a margin of error of four percentage points?

a. Assume that nothing is known about the percentage to be estimated.

b. Use the information from a previous Harris survey in which 26% of respondents said that they believed in astrology.

33. Biometric Security In considering the use of biometric security (such as fingerprints) to replace passwords, you want to estimate the percentage of adults who believe that passwords should be replaced with biometric security. How many randomly selected adults must you survey? Assume that you want to be 95% confident that the sample percentage is within 2.5 percentage points of the true population percentage.

a. Assume that nothing is known about the percentage of adults who believe that passwords should be replaced with biometric security.

b. Assume that a prior survey suggests that about 53% of adults believe that biometric security should replace passwords (based on a *USA Today* report).

c. Does the additional survey information from part (b) have much of an effect on the sample size that is required?

34. Nicotine Patches You plan to conduct a clinical trial to test the effectiveness of nicotine patch therapy in helping smokers to stop smoking. How many smokers must be included in order to be 99% confident that the estimate is in error by no more than two percentage points?

a. Assume that nothing is known about the effectiveness of nicotine patch therapy.

b. Assume that a prior clinical trial suggests that nicotine patch therapy has a success rate of about 45% (based on data from "High-Dose Nicotine Patch Therapy," by Dale et al., *Journal of the American Medical Association,* Vol. 274, No. 17).

c. Does the additional survey information from part (b) have much of an effect on the sample size that is required?

35. Vision Correction A manufacturing company is considering entering the new market of eyeglasses. How many people must be surveyed in order to be 90% confident that the estimated percentage of adults who wear eyeglasses is within three percentage points of the true population percentage?

a. Assume that nothing is known about the percentage of adults who wear eyeglasses.

b. Assume that about 53% of adults wear eyeglasses (based on a Vision Council prior survey).

c. Given that the required sample size is relatively small, could you simply survey the adults that you know?

36. Women Who Give Birth An epidemiologist plans to conduct a survey to estimate the percentage of women who give birth. How many women must be surveyed in order to be 99% confident that the estimated percentage is in error by no more than two percentage points?

a. Assume that nothing is known about the percentage to be estimated.

continued

b. Assume that a prior study conducted by the U.S. Census Bureau showed that 82% of women give birth.

c. What is wrong with surveying randomly selected adult women?

7-1   Beyond the Basics

37. Finite Population Correction Factor For Formulas 7-2 and 7-3 we assume that the population is infinite or very large and that we are sampling with replacement. When we sample without replacement from a relatively small population with size N, we modify E to include the *finite population correction factor* shown here, and we can solve for n to obtain the result shown below. Use this result to repeat part (b) of Exercise 36, assuming that we limit our population to a county with 2500 women who have completed the time during which they can give birth.

$$E = z_{\alpha/2}\sqrt{\frac{\hat{p}\hat{q}}{n}}\sqrt{\frac{N-n}{N-1}} \qquad n = \frac{N\hat{p}\hat{q}[z_{\alpha/2}]^2}{\hat{p}\hat{q}[z_{\alpha/2}]^2 + (N-1)E^2}$$

38. One-Sided Confidence Interval A one-sided claim about a population proportion is a claim that the proportion is less than (or greater than) some specific value. Such a claim can be formally addressed using a *one-sided confidence interval* for p, which can be expressed as $p < \hat{p} + E$ or $p > \hat{p} - E$, where the margin of error E is modified by replacing $z_{\alpha/2}$ with z_α. (Instead of dividing α between two tails of the standard normal distribution, put all of it in one tail.) Use the data given in Exercise 13 "OxyContin" to construct a one-sided 95% confidence interval that would be suitable for addressing the claim that the rate of headaches among OxyContin users is less than 10%.

39. Coping with No Success According to the *Rule of Three,* when we have a sample size n with $x = 0$ successes, we have 95% confidence that the true population proportion has an upper bound of $3/n$. (See "A Look at the Rule of Three," by Jovanovic and Levy, *American Statistician,* Vol. 51, No. 2.)

a. If n independent trials result in no successes, why can't we find confidence interval limits by using the methods described in this section?

b. If 40 couples use a method of gender selection and each couple has a baby girl, what is the 95% upper bound for p, the proportion of all babies who are boys?

7-2   Estimating a Population Mean

Key Concept The main goal of this section is to present methods for using a sample mean $\bar{x}$ to make an inference about the value of the corresponding population mean μ. There are three main concepts included in this section:

- **Point Estimate:** The sample mean $\bar{x}$ is the best *point estimate* (or single value estimate) of the population mean μ.

- **Confidence Interval:** Use sample data to construct and interpret a *confidence interval* estimate of the true value of a population mean μ.

- **Sample Size:** Find the sample size necessary to estimate a population mean.

Part 1 of this section deals with the very realistic and commonly used case in which we want to estimate μ and the population standard deviation σ is not known. Part 2 includes a brief discussion of the procedure used when σ is known, which is very rare.

PART 1 Estimating a Population Mean When σ Is Not Known

It's rare that we want to estimate the unknown value of a population mean μ but we somehow know the value of the population standard deviation σ, so Part 1 focuses on the realistic situation in which σ is not known.

Point Estimate As discussed in Section 6-3, the sample mean $\bar{x}$ is an *unbiased estimator* of the population mean μ. Also, for many populations, sample means tend to vary less than other measures of center. For these reasons, the sample mean $\bar{x}$ is usually the best point estimate of the population mean μ.

> **The sample mean $\bar{x}$ is the best *point estimate* of the population mean μ.**

Because even the best point estimate gives us no indication of how accurate it is, we use a *confidence interval* (or *interval estimate*), which consists of a range (or an interval) of values instead of just a single value.

Confidence Interval The accompanying Key Elements box includes the key elements for constructing a confidence interval estimate of a population mean μ in the common situation where σ is not known.

KEY ELEMENTS

Confidence Interval for Estimating a Population Mean with σ Not Known

Objective

Construct a confidence interval used to estimate a population mean.

Notation

μ = population mean	n = number of sample values
$\bar{x}$ = sample mean	E = margin of error
s = sample standard deviation	

Requirements

1. The sample is a simple random sample.

2. Either or both of these conditions are satisfied: The population is normally distributed or $n > 30$.

Confidence Interval

Formats: $\bar{x} - E < \mu < \bar{x} + E$ or $\bar{x} \pm E$ or $(\bar{x} - E, \bar{x} + E)$

- **Margin of Error:** $E = t_{\alpha/2} \cdot \dfrac{s}{\sqrt{n}}$ (Use df $= n - 1$.)

- **Confidence Level:** The confidence interval is associated with a confidence level, such as 0.95 (or 95%), and α is the complement of the confidence level. For a 0.95 (or 95%) confidence level, $\alpha = 0.05$.

- **Critical Value:** $t_{\alpha/2}$ is the critical t value separating an area of $\alpha/2$ in the right tail of the Student t distribution.

- **Degrees of Freedom:** df $= n - 1$ is the number of degrees of freedom. Used when finding the critical value.

Round-Off Rule

1. *Original Data:* When using an *original set of data* values, round the confidence interval limits to one more decimal place than is used for the original set of data.

2. *Summary Statistics:* When using the *summary statistics* of n, $\bar{x}$, and s, round the confidence interval limits to the same number of decimal places used for the sample mean.

Requirement of "Normality or $n > 30$"

Normality The method for finding a confidence interval estimate of μ is *robust* against a departure from normality, which means that the normality requirement is loose. The distribution need not be perfectly bell-shaped, but it should appear to be somewhat symmetric with one mode and no outliers.

Sample Size $n > 30$ This is a common guideline, but sample sizes of 15 to 30 are adequate if the population appears to have a distribution that is not far from being normal and there are no outliers. For some population distributions that are extremely far from normal, the sample size might need to be larger than 30. This text uses the simplified criterion of $n > 30$ as justification for treating the distribution of sample means as a normal distribution.

Student t Distribution

In this section we use a *Student t distribution*, which is commonly referred to as a t distribution. It was developed by William Gosset (1876–1937), who was a Guinness Brewery employee who needed a distribution that could be used with small samples. The brewery prohibited publication of research results, but Gosset got around this by publishing under the pseudonym "Student." Here are some key points about the Student t distribution:

- **Student t Distribution** If a population has a normal distribution, then the distribution of

$$t = \frac{\bar{x} - \mu}{\frac{s}{\sqrt{n}}}$$

is a **Student t distribution** for all samples of size n. A Student t distribution is commonly referred to as a t **distribution**.

- **Degrees of Freedom** Finding a critical value $t_{\alpha/2}$ requires a value for the **degrees of freedom** (or **df**). In general, the number of degrees of freedom for a collection of sample data is the number of sample values that can vary after certain restrictions have been imposed on all data values. (*Example:* If 10 test scores have the restriction that their mean is 80, then their sum must be 800, and we can freely assign values to the first 9 scores, but the 10th score would then be determined, so in this case there are 9 degrees of freedom.) For the methods of this section, the number of degrees of freedom is the sample size minus 1.

$$\text{Degrees of freedom} = n - 1$$

- **Finding Critical Value $t_{\alpha/2}$** A critical value $t_{\alpha/2}$ can be found using technology or Table A-3. Technology can be used with any number of degrees of freedom, but Table A-3 can be used for select numbers of degrees of freedom only. If using Table A-3 to find a critical value of $t_{\alpha/2}$, but the table does not include the exact number of degrees of freedom, you could use the closest value, or you could be conservative by using the next lower number of degrees of freedom found in the table, or you could interpolate.

- The Student t distribution is different for different sample sizes. (See Figure 7-4 on the next page for the cases $n = 3$ and $n = 12$.)

- The Student t distribution has the same general symmetric bell shape as the standard normal distribution, but has more variability (with wider distributions), as we expect with small samples.

- The Student t distribution has a mean of $t = 0$ (just as the standard normal distribution has a mean of $z = 0$).

- The standard deviation of the Student t distribution varies with the sample size, but it is greater than 1 (unlike the standard normal distribution, which has $\sigma = 1$).

- As the sample size n gets larger, the Student t distribution gets closer to the standard normal distribution.

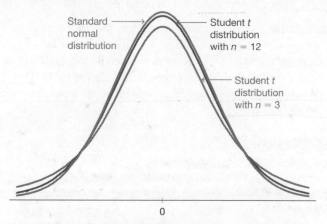

FIGURE 7-4   Student t Distributions for $n = 3$ and $n = 12$
The Student t distribution has the same general shape and symmetry as the standard normal distribution, but it has the greater variability that is expected with small samples.

Procedure for Constructing a Confidence Interval for μ

Confidence intervals can be easily constructed with technology or they can be manually constructed by using the following procedure.

1. Verify that the two requirements are satisfied: The sample is a simple random sample and the population is normally distributed or $n > 30$.

2. With σ unknown (as is usually the case), use $n - 1$ degrees of freedom and use technology or a t distribution table (such as Table A-3) to find the critical value $t_{\alpha/2}$ that corresponds to the desired confidence level.

3. Evaluate the margin of error using $E = t_{\alpha/2} \cdot s/\sqrt{n}$.

4. Using the value of the calculated margin of error E and the value of the sample mean $\bar{x}$, substitute those values in one of the formats for the confidence interval: $\bar{x} - E < \mu < \bar{x} + E$ or $\bar{x} \pm E$ or $(\bar{x} - E, \bar{x} + E)$.

5. Round the resulting confidence interval limits as follows: With an *original set of data* values, round the confidence interval limits to one more decimal place than is used for the original set of data, but when using the *summary statistics* of n, $\bar{x}$, and s, round the confidence interval limits to the same number of decimal places used for the sample mean.

EXAMPLE 1   Finding a Critical Value $t_{\alpha/2}$

Find the critical value $t_{\alpha/2}$ corresponding to a 95% confidence level given that the sample has size $n = 15$.

SOLUTION

Because $n = 15$, the number of degrees of freedom is $n - 1 = 14$. The 95% confidence level corresponds to $\alpha = 0.05$, so there is an area of 0.025 in each of the two tails of the t distribution, as shown in Figure 7-5.

continued

Using Technology Technology can be used to find that for 14 degrees of freedom and an area of 0.025 in each tail, the critical value is $t_{\alpha/2} = t_{0.025} = 2.145$.

Using Table A-3 To find the critical value using Table A-3, use the column with 0.05 for the "Area in Two Tails" (or use the same column with 0.025 for the "Area in One Tail"). The number of degrees of freedom is df $= n - 1 = 14$. We get $t_{\alpha/2} = t_{0.025} = 2.145$.

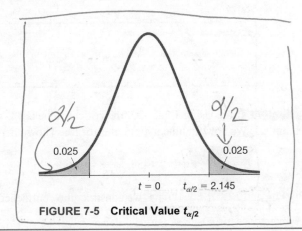

$$df = n - 1$$
$$\alpha = 0.05$$
$$CI = 95\%$$
$$t\alpha/_2 = t_{0.025}$$

FIGURE 7-5   **Critical Value $t_{\alpha/2}$**

EXAMPLE 2   **Confidence Interval Using Birth Weights**

Listed below are weights (hectograms, or hg) of randomly selected girls at birth, based on data from the National Center for Health Statistics. Here are the summary statistics: $n = 15$, $\bar{x} = 30.9$ hg, $s = 2.9$ hg. Use the sample data to construct a 95% confidence interval for the mean birth weight of girls.

33   28   33   37   31   32   31   28   34   28   33   26   30   31   28

SOLUTION

REQUIREMENT CHECK   We must first verify that the requirements are satisfied.
(1) The sample is a simple random sample. (2) Because the sample size is $n = 15$, the requirement that "the population is normally distributed or the sample size is greater than 30" can be satisfied only if the sample data appear to be from a normally distributed population, so we need to investigate normality. The accompanying normal quantile plot shows that the sample data appear to be from a normally distributed population, so this second requirement is satisfied. ✓

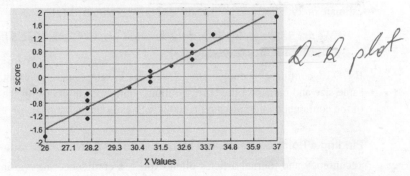

Q-Q plot

continued

Estimating Sugar in Oranges

In Florida, members of the citrus industry make extensive use of statistical methods. One particular application involves the way in which growers are paid for oranges used to make orange juice. An arriving truckload of oranges is first weighed at the receiving plant, and then a sample of about a dozen oranges is randomly selected. The sample is weighed and then squeezed, and the amount of sugar in the juice is measured. Based on the sample results, an estimate is made of the total amount of sugar in the entire truckload. Payment for the load of oranges is based on the estimate of the amount of sugar because sweeter oranges are more valuable than those less sweet, even though the amounts of juice may be the same.

Using Technology Technology can be used to automatically construct the confidence interval. Shown here is the StatCrunch display resulting from the 15 birth weights. The display shows the lower confidence interval limit (29.247163) and the upper confidence interval limit (32.486171). After rounding to one decimal place (as in the sample mean), we can express the 95% confidence interval as 29.2 hg $< \mu <$ 32.5 hg.

StatCrunch

95% confidence interval results:
μ : Mean of variable

Variable	Sample Mean	Std. Err.	DF	L. Limit	U. Limit
BirthWt	30.866667	0.75508856	14	29.247163	32.486171

Using t Distribution Table Using Table A-3, the critical value is $t_{0.025} = 2.145$ as shown in Example 1. We now find the margin of error E as shown here:

$$E = t_{\alpha/2} \frac{s}{\sqrt{n}} = 2.145 \cdot \frac{2.9}{\sqrt{15}} = 1.606126$$

With $\bar{x} = 30.9$ hg and $E = 1.606126$ hg, we construct the confidence interval as follows:

$$\bar{x} - E < \mu < \bar{x} + E$$
$$30.9 - 1.606126 < \mu < 30.9 + 1.606126$$
$$29.3 \text{ hg} < \mu < 32.5 \text{ hg} \quad (\text{rounded to one decimal place})$$

The lower confidence interval limit of 29.3 hg is actually 29.2 hg if we use technology or if we use summary statistics with more decimal places than the one decimal place used in the preceding calculation.

INTERPRETATION

We are 95% confident that the limits of 29.2 hg and 32.5 hg actually do contain the value of the population mean μ. If we were to collect many different random samples of 15 newborn girls and find the mean weight in each sample, about 95% of the resulting confidence intervals should contain the value of the mean weight of all newborn girls.

Interpreting the Confidence Interval The confidence interval is associated with a **confidence level,** such as 0.95 (or 95%). When interpreting a confidence interval estimate of μ, know that the confidence level gives us the *success rate of the procedure used to construct the confidence interval.* For example, the 95% confidence interval estimate of 29.2 hg $< \mu <$ 32.5 hg can be interpreted as follows:

> **"We are 95% confident that the interval from 29.2 hg to 32.5 hg actually does contain the true value of μ."**

By "95% confident" we mean that if we were to select many different samples of the same size and construct the corresponding confidence intervals, in the long run, 95% of the confidence intervals should actually contain the value of μ.

Finding a Point Estimate and Margin of Error E from a Confidence Interval

Technology and journal articles often express a confidence interval in a format such as (10.0, 30.0). The sample mean $\bar{x}$ is the value midway between those limits, and the margin of error E is one-half the difference between those limits (because the upper limit is $\bar{x} + E$ and the lower limit is $\bar{x} - E$, the distance separating them is $2E$).

Point estimate of μ: $\bar{x} = \dfrac{(\text{upper confidence limit}) + (\text{lower confidence limit})}{2}$

Margin of error: $E = \dfrac{(\text{upper confidence limit}) - (\text{lower confidence limit})}{2}$

For example, the confidence interval (10.0, 30.0) yields $\bar{x} = 20.0$ and $E = 10.0$.

Using Confidence Intervals to Describe, Explore, or Compare Data

In some cases, confidence intervals might be among the different tools used to describe, explore, or compare data sets, as in the following example.

EXAMPLE 3   **Second-Hand Smoke**

Figure 7-6 shows graphs of confidence interval estimates of the mean cotinine level in each of three samples: (1) people who smoke; (2) people who don't smoke but are exposed to tobacco smoke at home or work; (3) people who don't smoke and are not exposed to smoke. (The sample data are listed in Data Set 14 "Passive and Active Smoke" in Appendix B.) Because cotinine is produced by the body when nicotine is absorbed, cotinine is a good indication of nicotine intake. Figure 7-6 helps us see the effects of second-hand smoke. In Figure 7-6, we see that the confidence interval for smokers does not overlap the other confidence intervals, so it appears that the mean cotinine level of smokers is different from that of the other two groups. The two nonsmoking groups have confidence intervals that do overlap, so it is possible that they have the same mean cotinine level. It is helpful to compare confidence intervals or their graphs, but such comparisons should not be used for making formal and final conclusions about equality of means. Chapters 9 and 12 introduce better methods for formal comparisons of means.

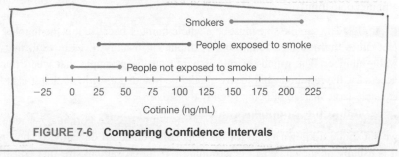

FIGURE 7-6   **Comparing Confidence Intervals**

> **CAUTION** Confidence intervals can be used *informally* to compare different data sets, but *the overlapping of confidence intervals should not be used for making formal and final conclusions about equality of means.*

Determining Sample Size

If we want to collect a sample to be used for estimating a population mean μ, *how many* sample values do we need? When determining the sample size needed to estimate a population mean, we must have an estimated or known value of the population standard deviation σ, so that we can use Formula 7-4 shown in the accompanying Key Elements box.

KEY ELEMENTS

Finding the Sample Size Required to Estimate a Population Mean

Objective

Determine the sample size n required to estimate the value of a population mean μ.

Notation

μ = population mean
σ = population standard deviation
$\bar{x}$ = sample mean

E = desired margin of error
$z_{\alpha/2}$ = z score separating an area of $\alpha/2$ in the right tail of the standard normal distribution

Requirement

The sample must be a simple random sample.

Sample Size

The required sample size is found by using Formula 7-4.

FORMULA 7-4
$$n = \left[\frac{z_{\alpha/2}\sigma}{E} \right]^2$$

Round-Off Rule

If the computed sample size n is not a whole number, round the value of n up to the next *larger* whole number.

Population Size Formula 7-4 does not depend on the size (N) of the population (except for cases in which a relatively large sample is selected without replacement from a finite population).

Rounding The sample size must be a whole number because it is the number of sample values that must be found, but Formula 7-4 usually gives a result that is not a whole number. The round-off rule is based on the principle that when rounding is necessary, the required sample size should be rounded *upward* so that it is at least adequately large instead of being slightly too small.

Dealing with Unknown σ When Finding Sample Size Formula 7-4 requires that we substitute a known value for the population standard deviation σ, but in reality, it is usually unknown. When determining a required sample size (not constructing a confidence interval), here are some ways that we can work around the problem of not knowing the value of σ:

1. Use the range rule of thumb (see Section 3-2) to estimate the standard deviation as follows: $\sigma \approx$ range$/4$, where the range is determined from sample data. (With a sample of 87 or more values randomly selected from a normally distributed population, range$/4$ will yield a value that is greater than or equal to σ at least 95% of the time.)

2. Start the sample collection process without knowing σ and, using the first several values, calculate the sample standard deviation s and use it in place of σ. The estimated value of σ can then be improved as more sample data are

obtained, and the required sample size can be adjusted as you collect more sample data.

3. Estimate the value of σ by using the results of some other earlier study. In addition, we can sometimes be creative in our use of other known results. For example, Wechsler IQ tests are designed so that the standard deviation is 15. Biostatistics students have IQ scores with a standard deviation less than 15, because they are a more homogeneous group than people randomly selected from the general population. We do not know the specific value of σ for Biostatistics students, but we can be safe by using $\sigma = 15$. Using a value for σ that is larger than the true value will make the sample size larger than necessary, but using a value for σ that is too small would result in a sample size that is inadequate. *When determining the sample size n, any errors should always be conservative in the sense that they make the sample size too large instead of too small.*

EXAMPLE 4 IQ Scores of Smokers

Assume that we want to estimate the mean IQ score for the population of adults who smoke. How many smokers must be randomly selected for IQ tests if we want 95% confidence that the sample mean is within 3 IQ points of the population mean?

SOLUTION

For a 95% confidence interval, we have $\alpha = 0.05$, so $z_{\alpha/2} = 1.96$. Because we want the sample mean to be within 3 IQ points of μ, the margin of error is $E = 3$. Also, we can assume that $\sigma = 15$ (see the discussion that immediately precedes this example). Using Formula 7-4, we get

$$n = \left[\frac{z_{\alpha/2}\sigma}{E} \right]^2 = \left[\frac{1.96 \cdot 15}{3} \right]^2 = 96.04 = 97 \text{ (rounded } up\text{)}$$

INTERPRETATION

Among the thousands of adults who smoke, we need to obtain a simple random sample of at least 97 of their IQ scores. With a simple random sample of only 97 adult smokers, we will be 95% confident that the sample mean $\bar{x}$ is within 3 IQ points of the true population mean μ.

PART 2 Estimating a Population Mean When σ Is Known

In the real world of professional statisticians and professional journals and reports, it is extremely rare that we want to estimate an unknown value of a population mean μ but we somehow know the value of the population standard deviation σ. If we somehow do know the value of σ, the confidence interval is constructed using the standard normal distribution instead of the Student t distribution, so the same procedure from Part 1 can be used with this margin of error:

$$\text{Margin of error: } E = z_{\alpha/2} \cdot \frac{\sigma}{\sqrt{n}} \quad \text{(used with known } \sigma\text{)}$$

EXAMPLE 5 **Confidence Interval Estimate of μ with Known σ**

Use the same 15 birth weights of girls given in Example 2, for which $n = 15$ and $\bar{x} = 30.9$ hg. Construct a 95% confidence interval estimate of the mean birth weight of all girls by assuming that σ is known to be 2.9 hg.

SOLUTION

REQUIREMENT CHECK The requirements were checked in Example 2. The requirements are satisfied. ✓

With a 95% confidence level, we have $\alpha = 0.05$, and we get $z_{\alpha/2} = 1.96$ (as in Example 2 from Section 7-1). Using $z_{\alpha/2} = 1.96$, $\sigma = 2.9$ hg, and $n = 15$, we find the value of the margin of error E:

$$E = z_{\alpha/2} \cdot \frac{\sigma}{\sqrt{n}}$$

$$= 1.96 \cdot \frac{2.9}{\sqrt{15}} = 1.46760$$

With $\bar{x} = 30.9$ and $E = 1.46760$, we find the 95% confidence interval as follows:

$$\bar{x} - E < \mu < \bar{x} + E$$

$$30.9 - 1.46760 < \mu < 30.9 + 1.46760$$

$$29.4 \text{ hg} < \mu < 32.4 \text{ hg (rounded to one decimal place)}$$

The confidence interval found here using the normal distribution is slightly narrower than the confidence interval found using the t distribution in Example 2. Because $z_{\alpha/2} = 1.96$ is smaller than $t_{\alpha/2} = 2.145$, the margin of error E is smaller and the confidence interval is narrower. The critical value $t_{\alpha/2}$ is larger because the t distribution incorporates the greater amount of variation that we get with smaller samples.

Remember, this example illustrates the situation in which the population standard deviation σ is known, which is rare. The more realistic situation with σ unknown is considered in Part 1 of this section.

Choosing the Appropriate Distribution

When constructing a confidence interval estimate of the population mean μ, it is important to use the correct distribution. Table 7-1 summarizes the key points to consider.

TABLE 7-1 Choosing Between Student t and z (Normal) Distributions

Conditions	Method
σ not known and normally distributed population *or* σ not known and $n > 30$	Use Student t distribution.
σ known and normally distributed population *or* σ known and $n > 30$ (In reality, σ is rarely known.)	Use normal (z) distribution.
Population is not normally distributed and $n \leq 30$.	Use the bootstrapping method (Section 7-4) or a nonparametric method.

TECH CENTER

Means: Confidence Intervals & Sample Size Determination
Access tech instructions, videos, and data sets at **www.TriolaStats.com**

7-2   Basic Skills and Concepts

Statistical Literacy and Critical Thinking

In Exercises 1–3, refer to the accompanying screen display that results from measured hemoglobin levels (g/dL) in 100 randomly selected adult females. The confidence level of 95% was used.

TI-83/84 Plus

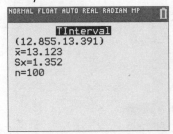

```
NORMAL FLOAT AUTO REAL RADIAN MP
        TInterval
(12.855,13.391)
x̄=13.123
Sx=1.352
n=100
```

1. Hemoglobin Refer to the accompanying screen display.

a. Express the confidence interval in the format that uses the "less than" symbol. If the original listed data use two decimal places, round the confidence interval limits accordingly.

b. Identify the best point estimate of μ and the margin of error.

c. In constructing the confidence interval estimate of μ, why is it not necessary to confirm that the sample data appear to be from a population with a normal distribution?

2. Degrees of Freedom

a. What is the number of degrees of freedom that should be used for finding the critical value $t_{\alpha/2}$?

b. Find the critical value $t_{\alpha/2}$ corresponding to a 95% confidence level.

c. Give a brief general description of the number of degrees of freedom.

3. Interpreting a Confidence Interval The results in the screen display are based on a 95% confidence level. Write a statement that correctly interprets the confidence interval.

4. Normality Requirement What does it mean when we say that the confidence interval methods of this section are *robust* against departures from normality?

Using Correct Distribution.   *In Exercises 5–8, assume that we want to construct a confidence interval. Do one of the following, as appropriate: (a) Find the critical value $t_{\alpha/2}$, (b) find the critical value $z_{\alpha/2}$, (c) state that neither the normal distribution nor the t distribution applies.*

5. Audiometry Confidence level is 95%, σ is not known, and the normal quantile plot of measured right-ear hearing thresholds from 10 randomly selected adult females is shown on the top of the next page.

continued

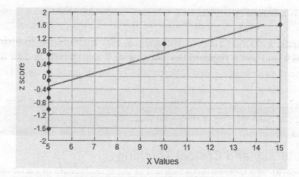

6. Vision Confidence level is 90%, σ is not known, and the histogram of right-eye vision measurements is obtained from a random sample of 61 adult males.

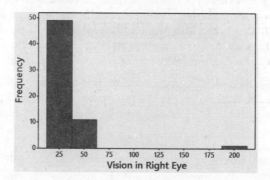

7. Vision Confidence level is 99%, $\sigma = 24.8$, and the histogram of 61 right-eye vision measurements from a random sample of 61 adult males is shown in Exercise 6.

8. Birth Weights Here are summary statistics for randomly selected weights of newborn girls: $n = 205$, $\bar{x} = 30.4$ hg, $s = 7.1$ hg (based on Data Set 3 "Births" in Appendix B). The confidence level is 95%.

Confidence Intervals. *In Exercises 9–24, construct the confidence interval estimate of the mean.*

9. Birth Weights of Girls Use these summary statistics given in Exercise 8: $n = 205$, $\bar{x} = 30.4$ hg, $s = 7.1$ hg. Use a 95% confidence level. Are the results very different from those found in Example 2 with only 15 sample values?

10. Birth Weights of Boys Use these summary statistics for birth weights of 195 boys: $\bar{x} = 32.7$ hg, $s = 6.6$ hg (based on Data Set 3 "Births" in Appendix B). Use a 95% confidence level. Are the results very different from those found in Exercise 9? Does it appear that boys and girls have very different birth weights?

11. Mean Body Temperature Data Set 2 "Body Temperatures" in Appendix B includes a sample of 106 body temperatures having a mean of 98.20°F and a standard deviation of 0.62°F. Construct a 95% confidence interval estimate of the mean body temperature for the entire population. What does the result suggest about the common belief that 98.6°F is the mean body temperature?

12. Atkins Weight Loss Program In a test of weight loss programs, 40 adults used the Atkins weight loss program. After 12 months, their mean weight *loss* was found to be 2.1 lb, with a standard deviation of 4.8 lb. Construct a 90% confidence interval estimate of the mean weight loss for all such subjects. Does the Atkins program appear to be effective? Does it appear to be practical?

13. Insomnia Treatment A clinical trial was conducted to test the effectiveness of the drug zopiclone for treating insomnia in older subjects. Before treatment with zopiclone, 16 subjects had a mean wake time of 102.8 min. After treatment with zopiclone, the 16 subjects had a mean wake time of 98.9 min and a standard deviation of 42.3 min (based on data from "Cognitive Behavioral Therapy vs Zopiclone for Treatment of Chronic Primary Insomnia in Older Adults," by Sivertsen et al., *Journal of the American Medical Association,* Vol. 295, No. 24). Assume that the 16 sample values appear to be from a normally distributed population and construct a 98% confidence interval estimate of the mean wake time for a population with zopiclone treatments. What does the result suggest about the mean wake time of 102.8 min before the treatment? Does zopiclone appear to be effective?

14. Garlic for Reducing Cholesterol In a test of the effectiveness of garlic for lowering cholesterol, 49 subjects were treated with raw garlic. Cholesterol levels were measured before and after the treatment. The changes (before minus after) in their levels of low-density lipoprotein (LDL) cholesterol (in mg/dL) had a mean of 0.4 and a standard deviation of 21.0 (based on data from "Effect of Raw Garlic vs Commercial Garlic Supplements on Plasma Lipid Concentrations in Adults with Moderate Hypercholesterolemia," by Gardner et al., *Archives of Internal Medicine,* Vol. 167). Construct a 98% confidence interval estimate of the mean net change in LDL cholesterol after the garlic treatment. What does the confidence interval suggest about the effectiveness of garlic in reducing LDL cholesterol?

15. Genes Samples of DNA are collected, and the four DNA bases of A, G, C, and T are coded as 1, 2, 3, and 4, respectively. The results are listed below. Construct a 95% confidence interval estimate of the mean. What is the practical use of the confidence interval?

2 2 1 4 3 3 3 3 4 1

16. Mercury in Tuna Listed below are amounts of mercury (μg, or or micrograms, per serving) in samples of tuna served as sashimi in Chicago (based on data from the Food and Drug Administration). Use a 95% confidence level. The Food and Drug Administration also measured amounts of mercury in samples of tuna from Tokyo. Can the confidence interval be used to describe mercury levels in Tokyo?

1.5   1.3   0.8   0.9   0.75   1.4   0.9   1.8   0.95   1.1

17. Cell Phone Radiation Listed below are the measured radiation emissions (in W/kg) corresponding to these cell phones: Samsung SGH-tss9, Blackberry Storm, Blackberry Curve, Motorola Moto, T-Mobile Sidekick, Sanyo Katana Eclipse, Palm Pre, Sony Ericsson, Nokia 6085, Apple iPhone 3GS, Kyocera Neo E1100. The data are from the Environmental Working Group. The media often present reports about the dangers of cell phone radiation as a cause of cancer. Construct a 90% confidence interval estimate of the population mean. What does the result suggest about the Federal Communications Commission (FCC) standard that cell phone radiation must be 1.6 W/kg or less?

0.38   0.55   1.54   1.55   0.50   0.60   0.92   0.96   1.00   0.86   1.46

18. Lead in Medicine Listed below are the lead concentrations (in μg/g) measured in different Ayurveda medicines. Ayurveda is a traditional medical system commonly used in India. The lead concentrations listed here are from medicines manufactured in the United States. The data are based on the article "Lead, Mercury, and Arsenic in US and Indian Manufactured Ayurvedic Medicines Sold via the Internet," by Saper et al., *Journal of the American Medical Association,* Vol. 300, No. 8. Use the sample data to construct a 95% confidence interval estimate of the mean of the lead concentrations for the population of all such medicines. If a safety standard requires lead concentrations less than 7 μg/g, does it appear that the population mean is less than that level?

3.0   6.5   6.0   5.5   20.5   7.5   12.0   20.5   11.5   17.5

19. Mercury in Sushi A Food and Drug Administration (FDA) guideline is that the mercury in fish should be below 1 part per million (ppm). Listed below are the amounts of mercury (ppm) found in tuna sushi sampled at different stores in New York City. The study was

continued

sponsored by the *New York Times,* and the stores (in order) are D'Agostino, Eli's Manhattan, Fairway, Food Emporium, Gourmet Garage, Grace's Marketplace, and Whole Foods. Construct a 98% confidence interval estimate of the mean amount of mercury in the population. Given that the FDA guideline is that fish should have a maximum of 1 ppm of mercury, what does the confidence interval suggest?

0.56   0.75   0.10   0.95   1.25   0.54   0.88

20. Years in College Listed below are the numbers of years it took for a random sample of college students to earn bachelor's degrees (based on data from the National Center for Education Statistics). Construct a 95% confidence interval estimate of the mean time required for all college students to earn bachelor's degrees. Does it appear that college students typically earn bachelor's degrees in four years? Is there anything about the data that would suggest that the confidence interval might not be a good result?

4   4   4   4   4   4   4.5   4.5   4.5   4.5   4.5   4.5   6   6   8   9   9   13   13   15

21. Caffeine in Soft Drinks Listed below are measured amounts of caffeine (mg per 12 oz of drink) obtained in one can from each of 20 brands (7-UP, A&W Root Beer, Cherry Coke,…, TaB). Use a confidence level of 99%. Does the confidence interval give us good information about the population of all cans of the same 20 brands that are consumed? Does the sample appear to be from a normally distributed population? If not, how are the results affected?

0   0   34   34   34   45   41   51   55   36   47   41   0   0   53   54   38   0   41   47

22. Shoveling Heart Rates Because cardiac deaths appear to increase after heavy snowfalls, an experiment was designed to compare cardiac demands of snow shoveling to those of using an electric snow thrower. Ten subjects cleared tracts of snow using both methods, and their maximum heart rates (beats per minute, or BPM) were recorded during both activities. The following results were obtained (based on data from "Cardiac Demands of Heavy Snow Shoveling," by Franklin et al., *Journal of the American Medical Association,* Vol. 273, No. 11):

Manual Snow Shoveling Maximum Heart Rates: $n = 10$, $\bar{x} = 175$ BPM, $s = 15$ BPM
Electric Snow Thrower Maximum Heart Rates: $n = 10$, $\bar{x} = 124$ BPM, $s = 18$ BPM

a. Find the 95% confidence interval estimate of the population mean for those people who shovel snow manually.

b. Find the 95% confidence interval estimate of the population mean for those people who use the electric snow thrower.

c. If you are a physician with concerns about cardiac deaths fostered by manual snow shoveling, what single value in the confidence interval from part (a) would be of greatest concern?

d. Compare the confidence intervals from parts (a) and (b) and interpret your findings.

23. Echinacea Treatment In a study designed to test the effectiveness of echinacea for treating upper respiratory tract infections in children, 337 children were treated with echinacea and 370 other children were given a placebo. The numbers of days of peak severity of symptoms for the echinacea treatment group had a mean of 6.0 and a standard deviation of 2.3. The numbers of days of peak severity of symptoms for the placebo group had a mean of 6.1 days and a standard deviation of 2.4 days (based on data from "Efficacy and Safety of Echinacea in Treating Upper Respiratory Tract Infections in Children," by Taylor et al., *Journal of the American Medical Association,* Vol. 290, No. 21).

a. Construct the 95% confidence interval for the mean number of days of peak severity of symptoms for those who receive echinacea treatment.

b. Construct the 95% confidence interval for the mean number of days of peak severity of symptoms for those who are given a placebo.

c. Compare the two confidence intervals. What do the results suggest about the effectiveness of echinacea?

24. Acupuncture for Migraines In a study designed to test the effectiveness of acupuncture for treating migraine, 142 subjects were treated with acupuncture and 80 subjects were given a sham treatment. The numbers of migraine attacks for the acupuncture treatment group had a mean of 1.8 and a standard deviation of 1.4. The numbers of migraine attacks for the sham treatment group had a mean of 1.6 and a standard deviation of 1.2.

a. Construct the 95% confidence interval estimate of the mean number of migraine attacks for those treated with acupuncture.

b. Construct the 95% confidence interval estimate of the mean number of migraine attacks for those given a sham treatment.

c. Compare the two confidence intervals. What do the results suggest about the effectiveness of acupuncture?

Appendix B Data Sets. *In Exercises 25 and 26, use the Appendix B data sets to construct the confidence interval estimates of the mean.*

25. Pulse Rates Refer to Data Set 1 "Body Data" in Appendix B and construct a 95% confidence interval estimate of the mean pulse rate of adult females; then do the same for adult males. Compare the results.

26. Nicotine in Cigarettes Refer to Data Set 15 "Cigarette Contents" in Appendix B and assume that the samples are simple random samples obtained from normally distributed populations.

a. Construct a 95% confidence interval estimate of the mean amount of nicotine in cigarettes that are king size, non-filtered, non-menthol, and non-light.

b. Construct a 95% confidence interval estimate of the mean amount of nicotine in cigarettes that are 100 mm, filtered, non-menthol, and non-light.

c. Compare the results. Do filters on cigarettes appear to be effective?

Sample Size. *In Exercises 27–34, find the sample size required to estimate the population mean.*

27. Mean IQ of Nurses The Wechsler IQ test is designed so that the mean is 100 and the standard deviation is 15 for the population of normal adults. Find the sample size necessary to estimate the mean IQ score of nurses. We want to be 99% confident that our sample mean is within 4 IQ points of the true mean. The mean for this population is clearly greater than 100. The standard deviation for this population is less than 15 because it is a group with less variation than a group randomly selected from the general population; therefore, if we use $\sigma = 15$ we are being conservative by using a value that will make the sample size at least as large as necessary. Assume then that $\sigma = 15$ and determine the required sample size. Does the sample size appear to be practical?

28. Mean IQ of Psychologists See the preceding exercise, in which we can assume that $\sigma = 15$ for the IQ scores. Psychologists are a group with IQ scores that vary less than the IQ scores of the general population. Find the sample size needed to estimate the mean IQ of psychologists, given that we want 98% confidence that the sample mean is within 3 IQ points of the population mean. Does the sample size appear to be practical?

29. Mean Grade-Point Average Assume that all grade-point averages are to be standardized on a scale between 0 and 4. How many grade-point averages must be obtained so that the sample mean is within 0.03 of the population mean? Assume that a 99% confidence level is desired. If we use the range rule of thumb, we can estimate σ to be range$/4 = (4 - 0)/4 = 1$. Does the sample size seem practical?

30. Mean Height of Male Medical Students Data Set 1 "Body Data" in Appendix B includes heights of 153 randomly selected adult males, and those heights have a standard deviation of 7.10 cm. Because it is reasonable to assume that heights of male medical students

continued

have less variation than heights of the population of adult males, we can be conservative by letting $s = 7.10$ cm. How many male medical students must be measured in order to estimate the mean height of all male medical students? Assume that we want 95% confidence that the sample mean is within 3 cm of the population mean. Does it seem reasonable to assume that heights of male medical students have less variation than heights of the population of adult males?

31. Mean Age of Female Medical Students Data Set 1 "Body Data" in Appendix B includes ages of 147 randomly selected adult females, and those ages have a standard deviation of 17.7 years. Assume that ages of female medical students have less variation than ages of females in the general population, so let $\sigma = 17.7$ years for the sample size calculation. How many female medical student ages must be obtained in order to estimate the mean age of all female medical students? Assume that we want 95% confidence that the sample mean is within one-half year of the population mean. Does it seem reasonable to assume that ages of female medical students have less variation than ages of females in the general population?

32. Mean Systolic Blood Pressure of Females Data Set 1 "Body Data" in Appendix B includes systolic blood pressures of 147 randomly selected adult females, and those systolic blood pressures vary from a low of 88 mm Hg to a high of 186 mm Hg. Find the minimum sample size required to estimate the mean systolic blood pressure of adult females. Assume that we want 95% confidence that the sample mean is within 5 mm Hg of the population mean.

a. Find the sample size using the range rule of thumb to estimate s.

b. Assume that $s = 17.22$ mm Hg, based on the value of $s = 17.2$ mm Hg for the sample of 147 female systolic blood pressures.

c. Compare the results from parts (a) and (b). Which result is likely to be better?

33. Mean Systolic Blood Pressure of Males Data Set 1 "Body Data" in Appendix B includes systolic blood pressures of 153 randomly selected adult males, and those systolic blood pressures vary from a low of 94 mm Hg to a high of 168 mm Hg. Find the minimum sample size required to estimate the mean systolic blood pressure of adult males. Assume that we want 95% confidence that the sample mean is within 5 mm Hg of the population mean.

a. Find the sample size using the range rule of thumb to estimate s.

b. Assume that $s = 14.35$ mm Hg, based on the value of $s = 14.35$ mm Hg for the sample of 153 male systolic blood pressures.

c. Compare the results from parts (a) and (b). Which result is likely to be better?

34. Mean Body Temperature Data Set 2 "Body Temperatures" in Appendix B includes 106 body temperatures of adults for day 2 at 12 AM, and they vary from a low of 96.5°F to a high of 99.6°F. Find the minimum sample size required to estimate the mean body temperature of all adults. Assume that we want 98% confidence that the sample mean is within 0.1°F of the population mean.

a. Find the sample size using the range rule of thumb to estimate σ.

b. Assume that $\sigma = 0.62$°F, based on the value of $s = 0.62$°F for the sample of 106 body temperatures.

c. Compare the results from parts (a) and (b). Which result is likely to be better?

7-2 Beyond the Basics

35. Finite Population Correction Factor If a simple random sample of size n is selected without replacement from a finite population of size N, and the sample size is more than 5% of the population size $(n > 0.05N)$, better results can be obtained by using the finite population correction factor, which involves multiplying the margin of error E by $\sqrt{(N - n)/(N - 1)}$.

continued

For a sample of 40 platelet counts of females from Data Set 1 "Body Data" in Appendix B, we get $\bar{x} = 255.1$ and $s = 65.4$. All platelet counts are in 1000 cells/μL.

a. Construct a 95% confidence interval estimate of μ assuming that the population is large.

b. Construct a 95% confidence interval estimate of μ assuming that the sample is selected without replacement from a population of 500 females.

c. Compare the results.

7-3 Estimating a Population Standard Deviation or Variance

Key Concept This section presents methods for using a sample standard deviation s (or a sample variance s^2) to estimate the value of the corresponding population standard deviation σ (or population variance σ^2). Here are the main concepts included in this section:

- **Point Estimate:** The sample variance s^2 is the best *point estimate* (or single value estimate) of the population variance σ^2. The sample standard deviation s is commonly used as a point estimate of σ, even though it is a biased estimator, as described in Section 6-3.

- **Confidence Interval:** When constructing a *confidence interval* estimate of a population standard deviation (or population variance), we construct the confidence interval using the χ^2 *distribution*. (The Greek letter χ is pronounced "kigh.")

Chi-Square Distribution

Here are key points about the χ^2 (chi-square or chi-squared) distribution:

- In a normally distributed population with variance σ^2, if we randomly select independent samples of size n and, for each sample, compute the sample variance s^2, the sample statistic $\chi^2 = (n-1)s^2/\sigma^2$ has a sampling distribution called the **chi-square distribution,** as shown in Formula 7-5.

FORMULA 7-5

$$\chi^2 = \frac{(n-1)s^2}{\sigma^2}$$

- **Critical Values of χ^2** We denote a right-tailed critical value by χ^2_R and we denote a left-tailed critical value by χ^2_L. Those critical values can be found by using technology or Table A-4, and they require that we first determine a value for the number of *degrees of freedom*.

- **Degrees of Freedom** For the methods of this section, the number of degrees of freedom is the sample size minus 1.

Degrees of freedom: df $= n - 1$

continued

- The chi-square distribution is skewed to the right, unlike the normal and Student *t* distributions (see Figure 7-7).

- The values of chi-square can be zero or positive, but they cannot be negative, as shown in Figure 7-7.

- The chi-square distribution is different for each number of degrees of freedom, as illustrated in Figure 7-8. As the number of degrees of freedom increases, the chi-square distribution approaches a normal distribution.

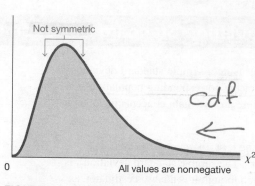

FIGURE 7-7   Chi-Square Distribution

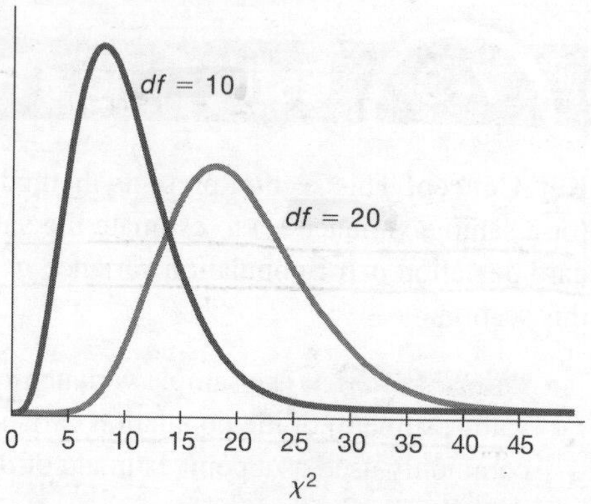

FIGURE 7-8   Chi-Square Distribution for df = 10 and df = 20

Because the chi-square distribution is not symmetric, a confidence interval estimate of σ^2 does not fit a format of $s^2 - E < \sigma^2 < s^2 + E$, so we must do separate calculations for the upper and lower confidence interval limits. If using Table A-4 for finding critical values, note the following design feature of that table:

In Table A-4, each critical value of χ^2 in the body of the table corresponds to an area given in the top row of the table, and each area in that top row is a *cumulative area to the right* of the critical value.

CAUTION Table A-2 for the standard normal distribution provides cumulative areas from the *left*, but Table A-4 for the chi-square distribution uses cumulative areas from the *right*.

○━━ **EXAMPLE 1**   **Finding Critical Values of χ^2**

A simple random sample of 22 IQ scores is obtained (as in Example 2, which follows). Construction of a confidence interval for the population standard deviation σ requires the left and right critical values of χ^2 corresponding to a confidence level of 95% and a sample size of $n = 22$. Find χ_L^2 (the critical value of χ^2 separating an area of 0.025 in the left tail), and find χ_R^2 (the critical value of χ^2 separating an area of 0.025 in the right tail).

SOLUTION

With a sample size of $n = 22$, the number of degrees of freedom is df = $n - 1 = 21$. See Figure 7-9.

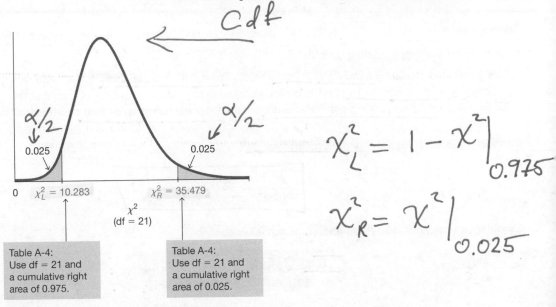

FIGURE 7-9   Finding Critical Values of χ^2

The critical value to the right ($\chi_R^2 = 35.479$) is obtained from Table A-4 in a straightforward manner by locating 21 in the degrees-of-freedom column at the left and 0.025 across the top row. The leftmost critical value of $\chi_L^2 = 10.283$ also corresponds to 21 in the degrees-of-freedom column, but we must locate 0.975 (or $1 - 0.025$) across the top row because the values in the top row are always *areas to the right* of the critical value. Refer to Figure 7-9 and see that the total area to the right of $\chi_L^2 = 10.283$ is 0.975.

When obtaining critical values of χ^2 from Table A-4, if a number of degrees of freedom is not found in the table, you can be conservative by using the next lower number of degrees of freedom, or you can use the closest critical value in the table, or you can get an approximate result with interpolation. For numbers of degrees of freedom greater than 100, use the equation given in Exercise 23 on page 340, or use a more extensive table, or use technology.

Although s^2 is the best point estimate of σ^2, there is no indication of how good it is, so we use a confidence interval that gives us a range of values associated with a confidence level.

KEY ELEMENTS

Confidence Interval for Estimating a Population Standard Deviation or Variance

Objective

Construct a confidence interval estimate of a population standard deviation or variance.

Notation

σ = population standard deviation	σ^2 = population variance
s = sample standard deviation	s^2 = sample variance
n = number of sample values	E = margin of error
χ_L^2 = left-tailed critical value of χ^2	χ_R^2 = right-tailed critical value of χ^2

continued

Requirements

1. The sample is a simple random sample.

2. The population must have normally distributed values (even if the sample is large). The requirement of a normal distribution is much stricter here than in earlier sections, so large departures from normal distributions can result in large errors. (If the normality requirement is not satisfied, use the bootstrap method described in Section 7-4.)

Confidence Interval for the Population Variance σ^2

$$\frac{(n-1)s^2}{\chi_R^2} < \sigma^2 < \frac{(n-1)s^2}{\chi_L^2}$$

Confidence Interval for the Population Standard Deviation σ

$$\sqrt{\frac{(n-1)s^2}{\chi_R^2}} < \sigma < \sqrt{\frac{(n-1)s^2}{\chi_L^2}}$$

Round-Off Rule

1. *Original Data:* When using the *original set of data* values, round the confidence interval limits to one more decimal place than is used for the original data.

2. *Summary Statistics:* When using the *summary statistics (n, s)*, round the confidence interval limits to the same number of decimal places used for the sample standard deviation.

CAUTION A confidence interval can be expressed in a format such as $11.0 < \sigma < 20.4$ or a format of $(11.0, 20.4)$, but *it cannot be expressed in a format of $s \pm E$.*

Procedure for Constructing a Confidence Interval for σ or σ^2

Confidence intervals can be easily constructed with technology or they can be constructed by using Table A-4 with the following procedure.

1. Verify that the two requirements are satisfied: The sample is a random sample from a normally distributed population.

2. Using $n - 1$ degrees of freedom, find the critical values χ_R^2 and χ_L^2 that correspond to the desired confidence level (as in Example 1).

3. Construct a confidence interval estimate of σ^2 by using the following:

$$\frac{(n-1)s^2}{\chi_R^2} < \sigma^2 < \frac{(n-1)s^2}{\chi_L^2}$$

4. To get a confidence interval estimate of σ, take the square root of each component of the above confidence interval.

5. Round the confidence interval limits using the round-off rule given in the preceding Key Elements box.

Using Confidence Intervals for Comparisons or Hypothesis Tests

Comparisons Confidence intervals can be used *informally* to compare the variation in different data sets, but *the overlapping of confidence intervals should not be* used for making formal and final conclusions about equality of variances or standard deviations.

EXAMPLE 2 **Confidence Interval for Estimating σ of IQ Scores**

Data Set 8 "IQ and Lead" in Appendix B lists IQ scores for subjects in three different lead exposure groups. The 22 full IQ scores for the group with medium exposure to lead (Group 2) have a standard deviation of 14.29263. Consider the sample to be a simple random sample and construct a 95% confidence interval estimate of σ, the standard deviation of the population from which the sample was obtained.

SOLUTION

REQUIREMENT CHECK

Step 1: Check requirements. (1) The sample can be treated as a simple random sample. (2) The accompanying histogram has a shape very close to the bell shape of a normal distribution, so the requirement of normality is satisfied. ✅

Minitab

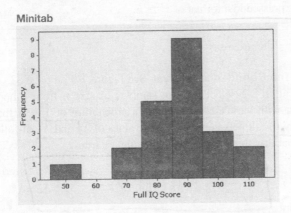

Step 2: Using Technology The confidence interval can be found using technology. The StatCrunch display shows the lower and upper confidence interval limits for the 95% confidence interval estimate of σ^2, so we get $120.9 < \sigma^2 < 417.2$. Taking square roots, we get $11.0 < \sigma < 20.4$

StatCrunch

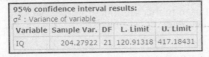

95% confidence interval results:
σ^2 : Variance of variable

Variable	Sample Var.	DF	L. Limit	U. Limit
IQ	204.27922	21	120.91318	417.18431

Using Table A-4 If using Table A-4, we first use the sample size of $n = 22$ to find degrees of freedom: df $= n - 1 = 21$. In Table A-4, refer to the row corresponding to 21 degrees of freedom, and refer to the columns with areas of 0.975 and 0.025. (For a 95% confidence level, we divide $\alpha = 0.05$ equally between the two tails of the chi-square distribution, and we refer to the values of 0.975 and 0.025 across the top row of Table A-4.) The critical values are $\chi_L^2 = 10.283$ and $\chi_R^2 = 35.479$ (as shown in Example 1).

continued

Step 3: Using the critical values of 10.283 and 35.479, the sample standard deviation of $s = 14.29263$, and the sample size of $n = 22$, we construct the 95% confidence interval by evaluating the following:

$$\frac{(n-1)s^2}{\chi_R^2} < \sigma^2 < \frac{(n-1)s^2}{\chi_L^2}$$

$$\frac{(22-1)(14.29263)^2}{35.479} < \sigma^2 < \frac{(22-1)(14.29263)^2}{10.283}$$

Step 4: Evaluating the expression above results in $120.9 < \sigma^2 < 417.2$. Finding the square root of each part (before rounding), then rounding to one decimal place, yields this 95% confidence interval estimate of the population standard deviation: $11.0 < \sigma < 20.4$.

INTERPRETATION

Based on this result, we have 95% confidence that the limits of 11.0 and 20.4 contain the true value of σ. The confidence interval can also be expressed as (11.0, 20.4), but it cannot be expressed in a format of $s \pm E$.

TABLE 7-2 Finding Sample Size

	σ
To be 95% confident that s is within . . .	of the value of σ, the sample size n should be at least
1%	19,205
5%	768
10%	192
20%	48
30%	21
40%	12
50%	8
To be 99% confident that s is within . . .	of the value of σ, the sample size n should be at least
1%	33,218
5%	1,336
10%	336
20%	85
30%	38
40%	22
50%	14

Rationale for the Confidence Interval See Figure 7-9 on page 333 to make sense of this statement: If we select random samples of size n from a normally distributed population with variance σ^2, there is a probability of $1 - \alpha$ that the statistic $(n-1)s^2/\sigma^2$ will fall between the critical values of χ_L^2 and χ_R^2. It follows that there is a $1 - \alpha$ probability that both of the following are true:

$$\frac{(n-1)s^2}{\sigma^2} < \chi_R^2 \quad \text{and} \quad \frac{(n-1)s^2}{\sigma^2} > \chi_L^2$$

Multiply both of the preceding inequalities by σ^2, then divide each inequality by the appropriate critical value of χ^2, so the two preceding inequalities can be expressed in these equivalent forms:

$$\frac{(n-1)s^2}{\chi_R^2} < \sigma^2 \quad \text{and} \quad \frac{(n-1)s^2}{\chi_L^2} > \sigma^2$$

The two preceding inequalities can be combined into one inequality to get the format of the confidence interval used in this section:

$$\frac{(n-1)s^2}{\chi_R^2} < \sigma^2 < \frac{(n-1)s^2}{\chi_L^2}$$

Determining Sample Size

The procedures for finding the sample size necessary to estimate σ are much more complex than the procedures given earlier for means and proportions. For normally distributed populations, Table 7-2 or the formula given in Exercise 24 "Finding Sample Size" on page 340 can be used.

EXAMPLE 3 **Finding Sample Size for Estimating σ**

We want to estimate the standard deviation σ of all IQ scores of people with exposure to lead. We want to be 99% confident that our estimate is within 5% of the true value of σ. How large should the sample be? Assume that the population is normally distributed.

SOLUTION

From Table 7-2, we can see that 99% confidence and an error of 5% for σ correspond to a sample of size 1336. We should obtain a simple random sample of 1336 IQ scores from the population of subjects exposed to lead.

TECH CENTER

 Confidence Interval Estimate for Standard Deviation or Variance
Access tech instructions, videos, and data sets at **www.TriolaStats.com**

7-3 Basic Skills and Concepts

Statistical Literacy and Critical Thinking

1. Brain Volume Using all of the brain volumes listed in Data Set 9 "IQ and Brain Size," we get this 95% confidence interval estimate: $9027.8 < \sigma^2 < 33{,}299.8$, and the units of measurement are $(cm^3)^2$. Identify the corresponding confidence interval estimate of σ and include the appropriate units. Given that the original values are whole numbers, round the limits using the round-off rule given in this section. Write a statement that correctly interprets the confidence interval estimate of σ.

2. Expressing Confidence Intervals Example 2 showed how the statistics of $n = 22$ and $s = 14.3$ result in this 95% confidence interval estimate of σ: $11.0 < \sigma < 20.4$. That confidence interval can also be expressed as $(11.0, 20.4)$, but it cannot be expressed as 15.7 ± 4.7. Given that 15.7 ± 4.7 results in values of 11.0 and 20.4, why is it wrong to express the confidence interval as 15.7 ± 4.7?

3. Last Digit Analysis The accompanying dotplot depicts the last digits of the weights of 153 males in Data Set 1 "Body Data." Do those digits appear to be from a normally distributed population? If not, does the large sample size of $n = 153$ justify treating the values as if they were from a normal distribution? Can the sample be used to construct a 95% confidence interval estimate of σ for the population of all such digits?

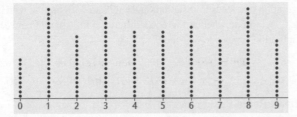

4. Normality Requirement What is different about the normality requirement for a confidence interval estimate of σ and the normality requirement for a confidence interval estimate of μ?

Finding Critical Values and Confidence Intervals. *In Exercises 5–8, use the given information to find the number of degrees of freedom, the critical values χ_L^2 and χ_R^2, and the confidence interval estimate of σ. The samples are from Appendix B and it is reasonable to assume that a simple random sample has been selected from a population with a normal distribution.*

5. Nicotine in Menthol Cigarettes 95% confidence; $n = 25$, $s = 0.24$ mg.

6. White Blood Cell Counts of Men 95% confidence; $n = 153$, $s = 1.86$.

7. Red Blood Cell Counts of Women 97% confidence; $n = 138$, $s = 1.2$.

8. Weights of men 97% confidence; $n = 164$, $s = 52$ kg.

Finding Confidence Intervals. *In Exercises 9–16, assume that each sample is a simple random sample obtained from a population with a normal distribution.*

9. Body Data Data Set 1 "Body Data" in Appendix B includes a sample of 300 pulses having a mean of 71.77 and a standard deviation of 12.13. Construct a 99% confidence interval estimate of the standard deviation of the pulse for the entire population.

10. Atkins Weight Loss Program In a test of weight loss programs, 40 adults used the Atkins weight loss program. After 12 months, their mean weight *loss* was found to be 2.1 lb, with a standard deviation of 4.8 lb. Construct a 90% confidence interval estimate of the standard deviation of the weight loss for all such subjects. Does the confidence interval give us information about the effectiveness of the diet?

11. Insomnia Treatment A clinical trial was conducted to test the effectiveness of the drug zopiclone for treating insomnia in older subjects. After treatment with zopiclone, 16 subjects had a mean wake time of 98.9 min and a standard deviation of 42.3 min (based on data from "Cognitive Behavioral Therapy vs Zopiclone for Treatment of Chronic Primary Insomnia in Older Adults," by Sivertsen et al., *Journal of the American Medical Association,* Vol. 295, No. 24). Assume that the 16 sample values appear to be from a normally distributed population and construct a 98% confidence interval estimate of the standard deviation of the wake times for a population with zopiclone treatments. Does the result indicate whether the treatment is effective?

12. Garlic for Reducing Cholesterol In a test of the effectiveness of garlic for lowering cholesterol, 49 subjects were treated with raw garlic. Cholesterol levels were measured before and after the treatment. The changes (before minus after) in their levels of LDL cholesterol (in mg/dL) had a mean of 0.4 and a standard deviation of 21.0 (based on data from "Effect of Raw Garlic vs Commercial Garlic Supplements on Plasma Lipid Concentrations in Adults with Moderate Hypercholesterolemia," by Gardner et al., *Archives of Internal Medicine,* Vol. 167). Construct a 98% confidence interval estimate of the standard deviation of the changes in LDL cholesterol after the garlic treatment. Does the result indicate whether the treatment is effective?

13. World's Fastest Mammal The world's fastest mammal is the cheetah, also known as *Acinonyx jubatus*, an animal indigenous to South Western Asia and Africa. Listed below are speeds (in kmph) from a sample of these cheetahs. Construct a 99% confidence interval estimate of the standard deviation of speeds for all such cheetahs.

110 112 120 105 108 107 111 119 114 112 100 102 101 99 117

14. Queues A Providence Hospital experiment involves two different waiting line configurations for patients arriving for admission. The waiting times (in seconds) are recorded with a single-line configuration that feeds four stations and another configuration with individual lines at the four stations. Determine whether there is a difference in variation between the two data sets. Which configuration appears to be better?

Single Line	390	396	402	408	426	438	444	462	462	462
Individual Lines	252	324	348	372	402	462	462	510	558	600

15. Shoveling Heart Rates Because cardiac deaths appear to increase after heavy snowfalls, an experiment was designed to compare cardiac demands of snow shoveling to those of using an electric snow thrower. Ten subjects cleared tracts of snow using both methods, and their maximum heart rates (beats per minute, or BPM) were recorded during both activities. The results shown below were obtained (based on data from "Cardiac Demands of Heavy Snow Shoveling," by Franklin et al., *Journal of the American Medical Association,* Vol. 273, No. 11).

Manual Snow Shoveling: $n = 10$, $\bar{x} = 175$ BPM, $s = 15$ BPM

Electric Snow Thrower: $n = 10$, $\bar{x} = 124$ BPM, $\bar{x} = 124$, $s = 18$ BPM

continued

a. Construct a 95% confidence interval estimate of the population standard deviation σ for those who did manual snow shoveling.

b. Construct a 95% confidence interval estimate of the population standard deviation σ for those who used the automated electric snow thrower.

c. Compare the results. Does the variation appear to be different for the two groups?

16. Acupuncture for Migraines In a study designed to test the effectiveness of acupuncture for treating migraine headaches, 142 subjects were treated with acupuncture and 80 subjects were given a sham treatment. The numbers of migraine attacks for the acupuncture treatment group had a mean of 1.8 and a standard deviation of 1.4. The numbers of migraine attacks for the sham treatment group had a mean of 1.6 and a standard deviation of 1.2. Construct a 95% confidence interval estimate of σ for each of the two groups, and then compare the results.

Large Data Sets from Appendix B. *In Exercises 17 and 18, use the data set in Appendix B. Assume that each sample is a simple random sample obtained from a population with a normal distribution.*

 17. Birth Length of Stay Refer to Data Set 3 "Births" in Appendix B.

a. Use the lengths of stay (days) for the 205 girls to construct a 95% confidence interval estimate of the standard deviation of the population from which the sample was obtained. For critical values, use $\chi_L^2 = 166.337$ and $\chi_R^2 = 245.449$. Does the distribution of those data appear to be approximately normal? How does that affect the results?

b. Repeat part (a) using the 195 boys and, for critical values, use $\chi_L^2 = 157.321$ and $\chi_R^2 = 234.465$.

c. Compare the results from part (a) and part (b).

 18. Birth Weights Refer to Data Set 3 "Births" in Appendix B

a. Use the 205 birth weights of girls to construct a 95% confidence interval estimate of the standard deviation of the population from which the sample was obtained. For critical values, use $\chi_L^2 = 166.337$ and $\chi_R^2 = 245.449$.

b. Repeat part (a) using the 195 birth weights of boys and, for critical values, use $\chi_L^2 = 157.321$ and $\chi_R^2 = 234.465$.

c. Compare the results from part (a) and part (b).

Determining Sample Size. *In Exercises 19–22, assume that each sample is a simple random sample obtained from a normally distributed population. Use Table 7-2 on page 336 to find the indicated sample size.*

19. IQ of Biostatistics Professors You want to estimate σ for the population of IQ scores of biostatistics professors. Find the minimum sample size needed to be 95% confident that the sample standard deviation s is within 1% of σ. Is this sample size practical?

20. Surgery Times You want to estimate σ for the population of surgery times for appendectomy. You want to be 95% confident that the sample standard deviation is within 5% of σ. Find the minimum sample size. Is this sample size practical?

21. Statistics Student Incomes You want to estimate the standard deviation of the annual incomes of all current statistics students. Find the minimum sample size needed to be 99% confident that the sample standard deviation is within 5% of the population standard deviation. Are those incomes likely to satisfy the requirement of a normal distribution?

22. Aspirin Quality When attempting to verify the aspirin contents in manufactured tablets, you must estimate the standard deviation of the population of aspirins in use. Find the minimum sample size needed to be 99% confident that the sample standard deviation is within 10% of the population standard deviation.

7-3 Beyond the Basics

23. Finding Critical Values In constructing confidence intervals for σ or σ^2, Table A-4 can be used to find the critical values χ_L^2 and χ_R^2 only for select values of n up to 101, so the number of degrees of freedom is 100 or smaller. For larger numbers of degrees of freedom, we can approximate χ_L^2 and χ_R^2 by using

$$\chi^2 = \frac{1}{2}[\pm z_{\alpha/2} + \sqrt{2k-1}]^2$$

where k is the number of degrees of freedom and $z_{\alpha/2}$ is the critical z score described in Section 7-1. Use this approximation to find the 95% critical values χ_L^2 and χ_R^2 for the acupuncture treatment group in Exercise 16 "Acupuncture for Migraines" where $n = 142$. How do the results compare to the actual critical values of $\chi_L^2 = 110.020$ and $\chi_R^2 = 175.765$?

24. Finding Sample Size Instead of using Table 7-2 for determining the sample size required to estimate a population standard deviation σ, the following formula can be used:

$$n = \frac{1}{2}\left(\frac{z_{\alpha/2}}{d}\right)^2$$

where $z_{\alpha/2}$ corresponds to the confidence level and d is the decimal form of the percentage error. For example, to be 95% confident that s is within 15% of the value of σ, use $z_{\alpha/2} = 1.96$ and $d = 0.15$ to get a sample size of $n = 86$. Find the sample size required to estimate σ, assuming that we want 98% confidence that s is within 15% of σ.

7-4 Bootstrapping: Using Technology for Estimates

Key Concept The preceding sections presented methods for estimating population proportions, means, and standard deviations (or variances). All of those methods have certain requirements that limit the situations in which they can be used. When some of the requirements are not satisfied, we can often use the bootstrap method to estimate a parameter with a confidence interval. The bootstrap method typically requires the use of software.

Sampling Requirement The preceding methods of this chapter all have a requirement that the sample must be a simple random sample. If the sample is not collected in an appropriate way, there's a good chance that *nothing* can be done to get a usable confidence interval estimate of a parameter. *Bootstrap methods do not correct for poor sampling methods.*

Requirements Listed below are important requirements from the preceding sections of this chapter:

- **CI for Proportion (Section 7-1):** There are at least 5 successes and at least 5 failures, or $np \geq 5$ and $nq \geq 5$.
- **CI for Mean (Section 7-2):** The population is normally distributed or $n > 30$.
- **CI for σ or σ^2 (Section 7-3):** The population must have normally distributed values, even if the sample is large.

When the above requirements are not satisfied, we should not use the methods presented in the preceding sections of this chapter, but we can use the bootstrap method instead. The bootstrap method does not require large samples. This method does not require the sample to be collected from a normal or any other particular distribution, and so it is called a **nonparametric** or **distribution-free method;** other nonparametric methods are included in Chapter 13.

DEFINITION

Given a simple random sample of size *n*, a **bootstrap sample** is another random sample of *n* values obtained *with replacement* from the original sample.

Without replacement, every sample would be the same as the original sample, so the proportions or means or standard deviations or variances would all be the same, and there would be no confidence "interval."

CAUTION Note that a bootstrap sample involves sampling *with replacement,* so that when a sample value is selected, it is replaced before the next selection is made.

 EXAMPLE 1   Bootstrap Sample of Incomes

When one of the authors collected annual incomes of current statistics students, he obtained these results (in thousands of dollars): 0, 2, 3, 7.

Original Sample   Bootstrap Sample

The sample of {7, 2, 2, 3} is one bootstrap sample obtained from the original sample. Other bootstrap samples may be different.

Incomes tend to have distributions that are skewed instead of being normal, so we should not use the methods of Section 7-2 with a small sample of incomes. This is a situation in which the bootstrap method comes to the rescue.

Why Is It Called "Bootstrap"? The term "bootstrap" is used because the data "pull themselves up by their own bootstraps" to generate new data sets. In days of yore, "pulling oneself up by one's bootstraps" meant that an impossible task was somehow accomplished, and the bootstrap method described in this section might seem impossible, but it works!

How Many? In the interest of providing manageable examples that don't occupy multiple pages each, the examples in this section involve very small data sets and no more than 20 bootstrap samples, but we should use at least 1000 bootstrap samples when we use bootstrap methods in serious applications. Professional statisticians commonly use 10,000 or more bootstrap samples.

Bootstrap Procedure for a Confidence Interval Estimate of a Parameter

1. Given a simple random sample of size *n*, obtain many (such as 1000 or more) bootstrap samples of the same size *n*.

2. For the parameter to be estimated, find the corresponding statistic for each of the bootstrap samples. (Example: For a confidence estimate of μ, find the *sample mean* $\bar{x}$ from each bootstrap sample.)

3. Sort the list of sample statistics from low to high.

continued

4. Using the sorted list of the statistics, create the confidence interval by finding corresponding percentile values. Procedures for finding percentiles are given in Section 3-3. (Example: Using a list of sorted sample means, the 90% confidence interval limits are P_5 and P_{95}. The 90% confidence interval estimate of μ is $P_5 < \mu < P_{95}$.)

Usefulness of Results For the purpose of illustrating the bootstrap procedure, Examples 2, 3, and 4 all involve very small samples with only 20 bootstrap samples. Consequently, the resulting confidence intervals include almost the entire range of sample values, and those confidence intervals are not very useful. Larger samples with 1000 or more bootstrap samples will provide much better results than those from Examples 2, 3, and 4.

Proportions

When working with proportions, it is very helpful to represent the data from the two categories by using 0's and 1's, as in the following example.

EXAMPLE 2 Eye Color Survey: Bootstrap CI for Proportion

In a survey, four randomly selected subjects were asked if they have brown eyes, and here are the results: 0, 0, 1, 0 (where 0 = no and 1 = yes). Use the bootstrap resampling procedure to construct a 90% confidence interval estimate of the population proportion p, the proportion of people with brown eyes in the population.

SOLUTION

REQUIREMENT CHECK The sample is a simple random sample. (There is no requirement of at least 5 successes and at least 5 failures, or $np \geq 5$ and $nq \geq 5$. There is no requirement that the sample must be from a normally distributed population.) ☑

Step 1: In Table 7-3, we created 20 bootstrap samples from the original sample of 0, 0, 1, 0.

Step 2: Because we want a confidence interval estimate of the population proportion p, we want the sample proportion $\hat{p}$ for each of the 20 bootstrap samples, and those sample proportions are shown in the column to the right of the bootstrap samples.

Step 3: The column of data shown farthest to the right is a list of the 20 sample proportions arranged in order ("sorted") from lowest to highest.

Step 4: Because we want a confidence level of 90%, we want to find the percentiles P_5 and P_{95}. Recall that P_5 separates the lowest 5% of values, and P_{95} separates the top 5% of values. Using the methods from Section 3-3 for finding percentiles, we use the *sorted* list of bootstrap sample proportions to find that $P_5 = 0.00$ and $P_{95} = 0.75$. The 90% confidence interval estimate of the population proportion is $0.00 < p < 0.75$.

TABLE 7-3 Bootstrap Samples for p

Bootstrap Sample				$\hat{p}$	Sorted $\hat{p}$	
1	0	0	1	0.50	0.00	$P_5 = 0.00$
1	0	1	0	0.50	0.00	
0	1	1	1	0.75	0.00	
0	0	0	0	0.00	0.00	
0	1	0	0	0.25	0.25	
1	0	0	0	0.25	0.25	
0	1	0	1	0.50	0.25	
1	0	0	0	0.25	0.25	
0	0	0	0	0.00	0.25	
0	0	1	1	0.50	0.25	90% Confidence Interval:
0	0	0	1	0.25	0.25	$0.00 < p < 0.75$
0	0	1	0	0.25	0.25	
1	1	1	0	0.75	0.50	
0	0	0	0	0.00	0.50	
0	0	0	0	0.00	0.50	
0	1	1	0	0.50	0.50	
0	0	1	0	0.25	0.50	
1	0	0	0	0.25	0.75	
1	1	1	0	0.75	0.75	$P_{95} = 0.75$
0	0	0	1	0.25	0.75	

INTERPRETATION

The confidence interval of $0.00 < p < 0.75$ is quite wide. After all, every confidence interval for every proportion must fall between 0 and 1, so the 90% confidence interval of $0.00 < p < 0.75$ doesn't seem to be helpful, but it is based on only four sample values.

> **HINT** Example 2 uses only 20 bootstrap samples, but effective use of the bootstrap method typically requires the use of software to generate 1000 or more bootstrap samples.

Means

In Section 7-2 we noted that when constructing a confidence interval estimate of a population mean, there is a requirement that the sample is from a normally distributed population or the sample size is greater than 30. The bootstrap method can be used when this requirement is not satisfied.

EXAMPLE 3 Incomes: Bootstrap CI for Mean

When one of the authors collected a simple random sample of annual incomes of his statistics students, he obtained these results (in thousands of dollars): 0, 2, 3, 7. Use the bootstrap resampling procedure to construct a 90% confidence interval estimate of the mean annual income of the population of all of the author's statistics students.

SOLUTION

REQUIREMENT CHECK   The sample is a simple random sample and there is no requirement that the sample must be from a normally distributed population. Because distributions of incomes are typically skewed instead of normal, we should not use the methods of Section 7-2 for finding the confidence interval, but the bootstrap method can be used. ☑

Step 1: In Table 7-4, we created 20 bootstrap samples (with replacement!) from the original sample of 0, 2, 3, 7. (Here we use only 20 bootstrap samples, so we have a manageable example that doesn't occupy many pages of text, but we usually want at least 1000 bootstrap samples.)

Step 2: Because we want a confidence interval estimate of the population mean μ, we want the sample mean $\bar{x}$ for each of the 20 bootstrap samples, and those sample means are shown in the column to the right of the bootstrap samples.

Step 3: The column of data shown farthest to the right is a list of the 20 sample means arranged in order ("sorted") from lowest to highest.

Step 4: Because we want a confidence level of 90%, we want to find the percentiles P_5 and P_{95}. Again, P_5 separates the lowest 5% of values, and P_{95} separates the top 5% of values. Using the methods from Section 3-3 for finding percentiles, we use the *sorted* list of bootstrap sample means to find that $P_5 = 1.75$ and $P_{95} = 4.875$. The 90% confidence interval estimate of the population mean is $1.75 < \mu < 4.875$, where the values are in thousands of dollars.

TABLE 7-4 Bootstrap Samples for μ

Bootstrap Sample				$\bar{x}$	Sorted $\bar{x}$	
3	3	0	2	2.00	1.75	→ $P_5 = 1.75$
0	3	2	2	1.75	1.75	
7	0	2	7	4.00	1.75	
3	2	7	3	3.75	2.00	
0	0	7	2	2.25	2.00	
7	0	0	3	2.50	2.25	
3	0	3	2	2.00	2.50	
3	7	3	7	5.00	2.50	
0	3	2	2	1.75	2.50	
0	3	7	0	2.50	2.75	**90% Confidence Interval:**
0	7	2	2	2.75	3.00	$1.75 < \mu < 4.875$
7	2	2	3	3.50	3.25	
7	2	3	7	4.75	3.25	
2	7	2	7	4.50	3.50	
0	7	2	3	3.00	3.75	
7	3	7	2	4.75	4.00	
3	7	0	3	3.25	4.50	
0	0	3	7	2.50	4.75	
3	3	7	0	3.25	4.75	→ $P_{95} = 4.875$
2	0	2	3	1.75	5.00	

Standard Deviations

In Section 7-3 we noted that when constructing confidence interval estimates of population standard deviations or variances, there is a requirement that the sample must be from a population with normally distributed values. Even if the sample is large, this normality requirement is much stricter than the normality requirement used for estimating population means. Consequently, the bootstrap method becomes more important for confidence interval estimates of σ or σ^2.

 EXAMPLE 4 **Incomes: Bootstrap CI for Standard Deviation**

Use these same incomes (thousands of dollars) from Example 3: 0, 2, 3, 7. Use the bootstrap resampling procedure to construct a 90% confidence interval estimate of the population standard deviation σ, the standard deviation of the annual incomes of the population of the author's statistics students.

SOLUTION

REQUIREMENT CHECK   The same requirement check used in Example 3 applies here. ☑

The same basic procedure used in Example 3 is used here. Example 3 already includes 20 bootstrap samples, so here we find the *standard deviation* of each bootstrap sample, and then we sort them to get this sorted list of sample standard deviations:

1.26	1.26	1.26	1.41	1.41	2.22	2.31	2.38	2.63	2.63
2.87	2.87	2.89	2.94	2.99	3.30	3.32	3.32	3.32	3.56

The 90% confidence interval limits are found from this sorted list of standard deviations by finding P_5 and P_{95}. Using the methods from Section 3-3, we get $P_5 = 1.26$ and $P_{95} = 3.44$. The 90% confidence interval estimate of the population standard deviation σ is $1.26 < \sigma < 3.44$, where the values are in thousands of dollars.

Again, know that for practical reasons, the examples of this section involved very small data sets and no more than 20 bootstrap samples, but use at least 1000 bootstrap samples. The use of 10,000 or more bootstrap samples is common.

TECH CENTER

 Bootstrap Resampling
Access tech instructions, videos, and data sets at **www.TriolaStats.com**

7-4 Basic Skills and Concepts

Statistical Literacy and Critical Thinking

1. Replacement Why does the bootstrap method require sampling with replacement? What would happen if we used the methods of this section but sampled without replacement?

2. Bootstrap Sample Here is a random sample of numbers of students in a day that required book from the library: 14, 16, 18, 15, 13, 10. For this sample, what is a bootstrap sample?

3. Bootstrap Sample Given the sample data from Exercise 2, which of the following are *not* possible bootstrap samples?

a. 16, 16, 18, 18, 18   **b.** 14, 16, 15, 18, 18, 13, 10, 14, 15   **c.** 14, 16, 18, 15, 13, 10

d. 14, 15, 10, 16   **e.** 14, 15, 10, 16, 9, 17

4. How Many? The examples in this section all involved no more than 20 bootstrap samples. How many should be used in real applications?

In Exercises 5–8, use the relatively small number of given bootstrap samples to construct the confidence interval.

5. Survey Responses In a hospital's canteen, four attendants are asked if they would be willing to complete a survey before leaving. Responses included these: yes, no, no, yes. Letting "yes" = 1 and letting "no" = 0, here are ten bootstrap samples for those responses: {0, 0, 1, 0}, {1, 0, 0, 0}, {0, 1, 1, 0}, {1, 0, 0, 1}, {1, 1, 0, 1}, {0, 0, 0, 1}, {1, 1, 0, 1}, {1, 1, 0, 0}, {0, 0, 1, 0}, {0, 0, 0, 1}. Using only the ten given bootstrap samples, construct a 90% confidence interval estimate of the proportion of patients who said that they would be willing to complete the survey.

6. OR Hygiene An operating room official records whether hygiene is maintained in OR, and the results include these: hygienic, unhygienic, hygienic, and unhygienic. Letting "hygienic" = 1 and letting "unhygienic" = 0, here are ten bootstrap samples for these ORs: {0, 0, 0, 0}, {0, 0, 1, 0}, {0, 1, 0, 0}, {0, 0, 0, 0}, {1, 0, 0, 0}, {0, 0, 0, 0}, {0, 0, 0, 0}, {0, 0, 0, 1}, {0, 1, 0, 1}, {0, 0, 0, 0}. Using only the ten given bootstrap samples, construct an 80% confidence interval estimate of the proportion of ORs observing hygiene.

7. Freshman 15 Here is a sample of amounts of weight change (kg) of college students in their freshman year (from Data Set 10 "Freshman 15" in Appendix B): 11, 3, 0, −2, where −2 represents a *loss* of 2 kg and positive values represent weight gained. Here are ten bootstrap samples: {11, 11, 11, 0}, {11, −2, 0, 11}, {11, −2, 3, 0}, {3, −2, 0, 11}, {0, 0, 0, 3}, {3, −2, 3, −2}, {11, 3, −2, 0}, {−2, 3, −2, 3}, {−2, 0, −2, 3}, {3, 11, 11, 11}.

a. Using only the ten given bootstrap samples, construct an 80% confidence interval estimate of the mean weight change for the population.

b. Using only the ten given bootstrap samples, construct an 80% confidence interval estimate of the standard deviation of the weight changes for the population.

8. Cell Phone Radiation Here is a sample of measured radiation emissions (cW/kg) for cell phones (based on data from the Environmental Working Group): 38, 55, 86, 145. Here are ten bootstrap samples: {38, 145, 55, 86}, {86, 38, 145, 145}, {145, 86, 55, 55}, {55, 55, 55, 145}, {86, 86, 55, 55}, {38, 38, 86, 86}, {145, 38, 86, 55}, {55, 86, 86, 86}, {145, 86, 55, 86}, {38, 145, 86, 55}.

a. Using only the ten given bootstrap samples, construct an 80% confidence interval estimate of the population mean.

b. Using only the ten given bootstrap samples, construct an 80% confidence interval estimate of the population standard deviation.

In Exercises 9–22, use technology to create the large number of bootstrap samples.

9. Freshman 15 Repeat Exercise 7 "Freshman 15" using a confidence level of 90% for parts (a) and (b) and using 1000 bootstrap samples instead of the 10 that were given in Exercise 7.

10. Cell Phone Radiation Repeat Exercise 8 "Cell Phone Radiation" using a confidence level of 90% for parts (a) and (b), using 1000 bootstrap samples instead of the 10 that were given in Exercise 8.

11. ER Wait Times The District of Columbia has some of the longest emergency room waiting times in the United States. Here are times (minutes) patients waited in District of Columbia emergency rooms before seeing a physician: 40, 68, 72, 67, 54, 59, 68, 47, 55, 74, 63, 73. Use the bootstrap method with 1000 bootstrap samples.

a. Construct a 99% confidence interval estimate of the population mean. Is the result dramatically different from the 99% confidence interval that would be found using the confidence interval constructed by using the *t* distribution, as in Section 7-2?

continued

b. Construct a 95% confidence interval estimate of the population standard deviation. Is the result dramatically different from the 95% confidence interval that would be found using the χ^2 distribution, as in Section 7-3?

12. ER Wait Times Repeat Exercise 11 "ER Wait Times" using these emergency room waiting times (minutes) from Florida: 29, 49, 31, 24, 14, 37, 43, 40, 35, 34, 10, 38, 2, 54.

13. Lipitor In clinical trials of the drug Lipitor (atorvastatin), 863 subjects were treated with 10 mg of the drug, and 8 of them experienced allergic reactions. Use the bootstrap method to construct a 95% confidence interval estimate of the *percentage* of treated subjects who experience allergic reactions. Use 1000 bootstrap samples. How does the result compare to the confidence interval found in Exercise 22 from Section 7-1 on page 312?

14. Eliquis The drug Eliquis (apixaban) is used to help prevent blood clots in certain patients. In clinical trials, among 5924 patients treated with Eliquis, 153 developed the adverse reaction of nausea (based on data from Bristol-Myers Squibb Co.). Use the bootstrap method to construct a 99% confidence interval estimate of the proportion of patients who experience nausea. Use 1000 bootstrap samples. How does the result compare to the confidence interval found in Exercise 14 "Eliquis" from Section 7-1 on page 311?

15. Survey Return Rate In a study of cell phone use and brain hemispheric dominance, an Internet survey was e-mailed to 5000 subjects randomly selected from an online otological group (focused on ears), and 717 surveys were returned. Use the bootstrap method to construct a 90% confidence interval estimate of the proportion of returned surveys. Use 1000 bootstrap samples. How does the result compare to the confidence interval found in Exercise 15 "Survey Return Rate" from Section 7-1 on page 311?

16. Medical Malpractice In a study of 1228 randomly selected medical malpractice lawsuits, it was found that 856 of them were dropped or dismissed (based on data from the Physicians Insurers Association of America). Use the bootstrap method to construct a 95% confidence interval estimate of the proportion of lawsuits that are dropped or dismissed. Use 1000 bootstrap samples. How does the result compare to the confidence interval found in Exercise 16 "Medical Malpractice" from Section 7-1 on page 311?

17. Student Evaluations Listed below are student evaluation ratings of courses, where a rating of 5 is for "excellent." The ratings were obtained at the University of Texas at Austin. Using the bootstrap method with 1000 bootstrap samples, construct a 90% confidence interval estimate of μ. How does the result compare to the result that would be obtained by using the methods from Section 7-2?

3.8   3.0   4.0   4.8   3.0   4.2   3.5   4.7   4.4   4.2   4.3   3.8   3.3   4.0   3.8

18. Caffeine in Soft Drinks Listed below are measured amounts of caffeine (mg per 12 oz of drink) obtained in one can from each of 20 brands. Using the bootstrap method with 1000 bootstrap samples, construct a 99% confidence interval estimate of μ. How does the result compare to the confidence interval found in Exercise 21 "Caffeine in Soft Drinks" in Section 7-2 on page 328?

0   0   34   34   34   45   41   51   55   36   47   41   0   0   53   54   38   0   41   47

19. Cell Phone Radiation Here are the measured radiation emissions (in W/kg) from different cell phones: 0.38, 0.55, 1.54, 1.55, 0.50, 0.60, 0.92, 0.96, 1.00, 0.86, 1.46. Use the bootstrap method with 1000 bootstrap samples to find a 90% confidence interval estimate of μ. How does the result compare to the confidence interval found for Exercise 17 in Section 7-2 on page 327?

20. Cell Phone Radiation Repeat Exercise 19 using the standard deviation instead of the mean. Compare the confidence interval to the one that would be found using the methods of Section 7-3.

21. Analysis of Last Digits Weights of respondents were recorded as part of the California Health Interview Survey. The last digits of weights from 50 randomly selected respondents are listed below.

5   0   1   0   2   0   5   0   5   0   3   8   5   0   5   0   5   6   0   0   0   0   0   0   8
5   5   0   4   5   0   0   4   0   0   0   0   0   8   0   9   5   3   0   5   0   0   0   5   8

continued

a. Use the bootstrap method with 1000 bootstrap samples to find a 95% confidence interval estimate of σ.

b. Find the 95% confidence interval estimate of σ found by using the methods of Section 7-3.

c. Compare the results. If the two confidence intervals are different, which one is better? Why?

22. Analysis of Last Digits Repeat Exercise 21 "Analysis of Last Digits" using the mean instead of the standard deviation. Compare the confidence interval to the one that would be found using the methods of Section 7-2.

7-4   Beyond the Basics

23. Effect of the Number of Bootstrap Samples Repeat Exercise 21 "Analysis of Last Digits" using 10,000 bootstrap samples instead of 1000. What happens?

24. Distribution Shapes Use the sample data given in Exercise 21 "Analysis of Last Digits."

a. Do the original sample values appear to be from a normally distributed population? Explain.

b. Do the 1000 bootstrap samples appear to have means that are from a normally distributed population? Explain.

c. Do the 1000 bootstrap samples appear to have standard deviations that are from a normally distributed population? Explain.

Chapter Quick Quiz

1. Vision Correction Here is a 95% confidence interval estimate of the proportion of adults who correct their vision by wearing contact lenses: $0.110 < p < 0.150$ (based on data from a Vision Council survey). What is the best point estimate of the proportion of adults in the population who correct their vision by wearing contact lenses?

2. Interpreting CI Write a brief statement that correctly interprets the confidence interval given in Exercise 1.

3. Critical Value For the survey described in Exercise 1, find the critical value that would be used for constructing a 99% confidence interval estimate of the population proportion.

4. Vision Correction From the same survey results cited in Exercise 1 "Vision Correction," it was reported that 3% of adults correct their vision with surgery, and the margin of error is ± 1.0 percentage points. Identify the confidence interval.

5. Sample Size for Proportion Find the sample size required to estimate the percentage of college students who take a statistics course. Assume that we want 95% confidence that the proportion from the sample is within four percentage points of the true population percentage.

6. Sample Size for Mean Find the sample size required to estimate the mean IQ of surgeons. Assume that we want 98% confidence that the mean from the sample is within three IQ points of the true population mean. Also assume that $\sigma = 15$.

7. Requirements A quality control analyst has collected a random sample of 12 batteries used in heart pacemakers and she plans to test their voltage level and construct a 95% confidence interval estimate of the mean voltage level for the population of batteries. What requirements must be satisfied in order to construct the confidence interval using the method with the t distribution?

8. Degrees of Freedom In general, what does "degrees of freedom" refer to? For the sample data described in Exercise 7, find the number of degrees of freedom, assuming that you want to construct a confidence interval estimate of μ using the t distribution.

9. Critical Value Refer to Exercise 7 and assume that the requirements are satisfied. Find the critical value that would be used for constructing a 95% confidence interval estimate of μ using the t distribution.

10. Which Method? Refer to Exercise 7 and assume that a sample of 12 voltage levels appears to be from a population with a distribution that is substantially far from being normal. Should a 95% confidence interval estimate of σ be constructed using the χ^2 distribution? If not, what other method could be used to find a 95% confidence interval estimate of σ?

Review Exercises

1. Brain Cancer Cluster In a study designed to determine whether there was a cluster of brain cancer cases at a Pratt & Whitney plant, records from 223,000 employees were studied and 723 employees with brain tumors were found. Treat those employees as a random sample and construct a 95% confidence interval estimate of the proportion of all adults who develop such tumors. Write a brief statement interpreting that confidence interval.

2. Medicare A hospital wants to estimate the percentage of admitted patients who receive Medicare benefits. If we want to estimate that percentage based on examination of randomly selected patient payment records, how many patient records must be examined in order to be 90% confident that we are within four percentage points of the population percentage?

3. Syringe Diameters Listed below are outer diameters (mm) of syringes.

a. Identify the best point estimate of the population mean μ.

b. Construct a 95% confidence interval estimate of the mean diameters of all syringes.

c. Write a statement that interprets the confidence interval.

10.80   10.80   10.80   10.80   10.80   10.80   10.80   10.80   11.10   11.10   11.10   11.10

4. Lefties There have been several studies conducted in an attempt to identify ways in which left-handed people are different from those who are right handed. Assume that you want to estimate the mean IQ of all left-handed adults. How many random left-handed adults must be tested in order to be 99% confident that the mean IQ of the sample group is within four IQ points of the mean IQ of all left-handed adults? Assume that σ is known to be 15.

5. Distributions Identify the distribution (normal, Student t, chi-square) that should be used in each of the following situations. If none of the three distributions can be used, what other method could be used?

a. In constructing a confidence interval of μ, you have 75 sample values and they appear to be from a population with a skewed distribution. The population standard deviation is not known.

b. In constructing a confidence interval estimate of μ, you have 75 sample values and they appear to be from a population with a skewed distribution. The population standard deviation is known to be 18.2 cm.

c. In constructing a confidence interval estimate of σ, you have 75 sample values and they appear to be from a population with a skewed distribution.

d. In constructing a confidence interval estimate of σ, you have 75 sample values and they appear to be from a population with a normal distribution.

e. In constructing a confidence interval estimate of p, you have 1200 survey respondents and 5% of them answered "yes" to the first question.

6. Sample Size You have been assigned the task of conducting a survey to study diet habits of high-school students.

a. If you want to estimate the percentage of students who stick to diet recommendations during the past 30 days, how many students must you survey if you want 99% confidence that your percentage has a margin of error of four percentage points?

continued

b. If you want to estimate the mean number of students who stick to diet recommendations during the past 30 days, how many students must you survey if you want 99% confidence that your sample mean is in error by no more than 4? (Based on results from a pilot study, assume that the standard deviation of number of students who stick to diet recommendations in the past 30 days is 12.)

c. If you plan to obtain the estimates described in parts (a) and (b) with a single survey having several questions, how many students must be surveyed?

7. Paracetamol Generic paracetamol tablets are supposed to contain 500 mg of paracetamol. Listed below are the measured amounts of paracetamol (mg) found in randomly selected tablets. Construct a 95% confidence interval estimate of the mean amount of paracetamol in tablets. Do these tablets appear to be acceptable?

> 510   525   480   465   570   525   445   480   490   500   520   490

8. Paracetamol

a. Use the sample data from Exercise 7 and construct a 95% confidence interval estimate of σ.

b. Assume that we want almost all of the tablets to contain between 450 mg and 550 mg of paracetamol. Find the range, then use the range rule of thumb to estimate the desired standard deviation.

c. Based on the results from parts (a) and (b), what do you conclude?

9. Bootstrap for Paracetamol Repeat Exercise 7 using 1000 bootstrap samples. How does the result compare to the confidence interval found in Exercise 7?

10. CI for Proportion In a TE Connectivity survey of 1000 randomly selected adults, 2% said that they "did not know" when asked if they felt comfortable being in a self-driving vehicle. There is a need to construct a 95% confidence interval estimate of the proportion of all adults in the population who don't know.

a. Find the confidence interval using the normal distribution as an approximation to the binomial distribution.

b. Find the confidence interval using 1000 bootstrap samples.

c. Compare the results.

Cumulative Review Exercises

Stride.   *Listed below are lengths (cm) of walking stride of adult males. Use these values for Exercises 1–5.*

> 76.2   74.5   76.5   78.2   73.8   75.7   75.1   76.4   77.1   74.3

1. Statistics Find the mean, median, standard deviation, and range. Are the results statistics or parameters?

2. Range Rule of Thumb Use the results from Exercise 1 with the range rule of thumb to find the limits separating those that are significantly low and those that are significantly high. Is a walking stride of 72 cm significantly low (or small)?

3. Level of Measurement What is the level of measurement of the walking strides (nominal, ordinal, interval, ratio)? Are the original unrounded walking strides continuous data or discrete data?

4. Distribution Do the given data appear to be from a normally distributed population? Explain.

5. Confidence Interval Construct a 99% confidence interval estimate of the mean walking stride for the population of all adult males.

6. Sample Size Find the sample size necessary to estimate the mean walking stride for the population of adult females. Assume that we want 99% confidence that the sample mean is in error by no more than 0.25 cm. Based on a prior study, assume that adult females have walking stride with a deviation of 1.18 cm.

7. Foot Lengths Based on Data Set 7 "Foot and Height," assume that women have foot lengths that are normally distributed with a mean of 24.20 cm and a standard deviation of 1.12 cm.

a. Find the probability that a randomly selected woman has a foot length greater than 25.00 cm.

b. Find the probability that 25 randomly selected women have foot lengths with a mean greater than 25.00 cm.

c. For the population of foot lengths of women, find the 95th percentile.

8. Piercing, Tattoos, Infections Survey subjects were asked if they knew that body piercings and tattoos can transmit infectious disease. There were 1440 responses of "yes" and 48 responses of "no" (based on data from "Body Piercing and Tattoos: A Survey on Young Adults' Knowledge of the Risks and Practices in Body Art," by Quaranta et al., *BioMed Central Public Health,* published online). Find the 99% confidence interval estimate of the *percentage* of those who know that body piercings and tattoos can transmit infectious disease. Does the population appear to be well informed about the risk of infectious disease?

Technology Project

Body Temperatures Data Set 2 "Body Temperatures" in Appendix B includes body temperatures (°F) of a sample of healthy adults. Use technology for the following.

a. Find the mean and standard deviation of the body temperatures at 8 AM on day 2.

b. Generate a histogram and normal quantile plot of the body temperatures at 8 AM on day 2. Does it appear that the temperatures are from a population having a normal distribution? Explain.

c. In obtaining a 95% confidence interval estimate of the body temperatures of all adults, are the requirements for using a *t* distribution satisfied? Explain.

d. Find a 95% confidence interval estimate of the mean body temperature of all adults.

e. Find a 95% confidence interval estimate of the mean body temperature of all adults, using 1000 bootstrap samples.

f. What do you conclude about the common belief that the mean body temperature is 98.6°F?

FROM DATA TO DECISION

Critical Thinking: What does the survey tell us?

Surveys have become an integral part of our lives. Because it is so important that every citizen has the ability to interpret survey results, surveys are the focus of this project.

Four researchers conducted a survey of 717 subjects. Here are some findings (based on data from "Hemispheric Dominance and Cell Phone Use," by Seidman et al., *JAMA Otolaryngology - Head Neck Surgery,* Vol. 139, No. 5):

- The respondents include 642 right-handed subjects, 69 left-handed subjects, and 6 ambidextrous subjects.

- Among the 642 right-handed subjects, 436 prefer to use their right ear for cell phone use, 166 prefer their left ear, and 40 have no preference.

- Among the 69 left-handed subjects, 16 prefer to use their right ear for cell phone use, 50 prefer their left ear, and 3 have no preference.

Analyzing the Data

1. Use the survey results to construct a 95% confidence interval estimate of the proportion of all right-handed people who prefer their right ear for cell phone use.

2. Use the result from part (a) and identify the margin of error.

3. A common criticism of surveys is that they poll only a very small percentage of the population and therefore cannot be accurate. Is a sample of only 717 people taken from a large population a sample size that is too small? Write a brief explanation of why the sample size of 717 is or is not too small.

4. Does it appear that most right-handed people prefer their right ear for cell phone use? Does it appear that most left-handed people prefer their left ear for cell phone use?

5. The survey was e-mailed to 5000 people and 717 surveys were returned. What does the response rate suggest about the results? What does the sampling method suggest about the results?

Cooperative Group Activities

1. Out-of-class activity Collect sample data, and use the methods of this chapter to construct confidence interval estimates of population parameters. Here are some suggestions for parameters:

• Proportion of students at your college who can raise one eyebrow without raising the other eyebrow.

• Mean pulse rate of male college students, or mean pulse rate of female college students.

• Mean length of words in *New York Times* editorials and mean length of words in a professional journal, such as *Journal of the American Medical Association*.

• Proportion of students at your college who have consumed an alcoholic beverage within the last seven days.

• Mean number of hours that students at your college study each week.

2. In-class activity Without using any measuring device, each student should draw a line believed to be 3 in. long and another line believed to be 3 cm long. Then use rulers to measure and record the lengths of the lines drawn. Find the means and standard deviations of the two sets of lengths. Use the sample data to construct a confidence interval for the length of the line estimated to be 3 in., and then do the same for the length of the line estimated to be 3 cm. Do the confidence interval limits actually contain the correct length? Compare the results. Do the estimates of the 3-in. line appear to be more accurate than those for the 3-cm line?

3. In-class activity Assume that a method of gender selection can affect the probability of a baby being a girl, so that the probability becomes $1/4$. Each student should simulate 20 births by drawing 20 cards from a shuffled deck. Replace each card after it has been drawn, then reshuffle. Consider the hearts to be girls and consider all other cards to be boys. After making 20 selections and recording the "genders" of the babies, construct a confidence interval estimate of the proportion of girls. Does the result appear to be effective in identifying the true value of the population proportion? (If decks of cards are not available, use some other way to simulate the births, such as using the random number generator on a calculator or using digits from phone numbers or Social Security numbers.)

4. Out-of-class activity Groups of three or four students should go to the library and collect a sample consisting of the ages of books (based on copyright dates). Plan and describe the sampling procedure, execute the sampling procedure, and then use the results to construct a confidence interval estimate of the mean age of all books in the library.

5. In-class activity Each student should estimate the length of the classroom. The values should be based on visual estimates, with no actual measurements being taken. After the estimates have been collected, construct a confidence interval, then measure the length of the room. Does the confidence interval contain the actual length of the classroom? Is there a "collective wisdom," whereby the class mean is approximately equal to the actual room length?

6. In-class activity Divide into groups of three or four. Examine a sample of different issues of a current magazine and find the proportion of pages that include advertising. Based on the results, construct a 95% confidence interval estimate of the percentage of all such pages that have advertising. Compare results with other groups.

7. Out-of-class activity Identify a topic of general interest and coordinate with all members of the class to conduct a survey. Instead of conducting a "scientific" survey using sound principles of random selection, use a convenience sample consisting of respondents who are readily available, such as friends, relatives, and other students. Analyze and interpret the results. Identify the population. Identify the shortcomings of using a convenience sample, and try to identify how a sample of subjects randomly selected from the population might be different.

8. Out-of-class activity Each student should find an article in a professional journal that includes a confidence interval of the type discussed in this chapter. Write a brief report describing the confidence interval and its role in the context of the article.

Hypothesis Testing

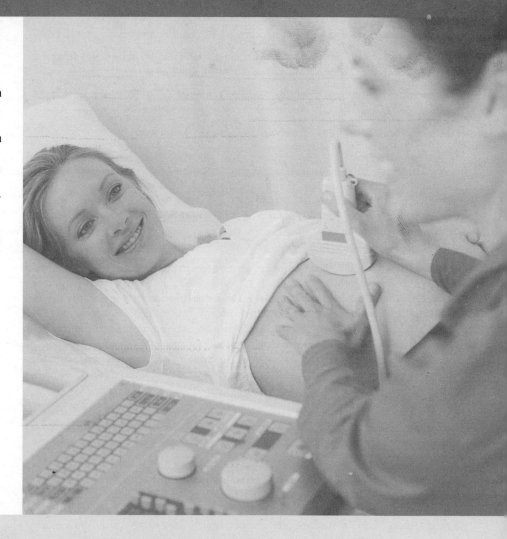

 CHAPTER PROBLEM

Does the MicroSort Method of Gender Selection Increase the Likelihood That a Baby Will Be a Girl?

Gender selection methods are somewhat controversial. Some people believe that use of such methods should be prohibited, regardless of the reason. Others believe that limited use should be allowed for medical reasons, such as to prevent gender-specific hereditary disorders. For example, some couples carry X-linked recessive genes, so that a male child has a 50% chance of inheriting a serious disorder and a female child

has no chance of inheriting the disorder. These couples may want to use a gender selection method to increase the likelihood of having a baby girl so that none of their children inherit the disorder.

Methods of gender selection have been around for many years. In the 1980s, ProCare Industries sold a product called Gender Choice. It cost only $49.95, but the Food and Drug

352

Administration told the company to stop distributing Gender Choice because there was no evidence to support the claim that it was 80% reliable.

The Genetics & IVF Institute developed a newer gender selection method called MicroSort. Clinical trials for this method were never completed and MicroSort was not brought to market. The MicroSort XSORT method was designed to increase the likelihood of a baby girl, and the YSORT method was designed to increase the likelihood of a boy. The MicroSort website included this statement: "The Genetics & IVF Institute is offering couples the ability to increase the chance of having a child of the desired gender to reduce the probability of X-linked diseases or for family balancing." For a cost exceeding $3000, the Genetics & IVF Institute claimed that it could increase the probability of having a baby of the gender that a couple prefers. In clinical trials, among 945 babies born to parents who used the XSORT method in trying to have a baby girl, 879 couples did have baby girls, for a success rate of 93%. Under normal circumstances with no special treatment, girls occur in about 50% of births. (Actually, the current birth rate of girls is 48.8%, but we will use 50% to keep things simple.) These results provide us with an interesting question: Given that 879 out of 945 couples had girls, can we actually support the claim that the XSORT technique is effective in increasing the probability of a girl? When the Genetics & IVF Institute chose to discontinue the clinical trials, does it appear that a major reason was ineffectiveness of their methods?

CHAPTER OBJECTIVES

Here are the chapter objectives:

 Basics of Hypothesis Testing

- Develop the ability to identify the null and alternative hypotheses when given some claim about a population parameter (such as a proportion, mean, standard deviation, or variance).

- Develop the ability to calculate a test statistic, find critical values, calculate *P*-values, and state a final conclusion that addresses the original claim. Here are the components that should be included in the hypothesis test:

  - Statements of the null and alternative hypotheses expressed in symbolic form
  - Value of the test statistic
  - Selection of the sampling distribution to be used for the hypothesis test
  - Identification of a *P*-value and/or critical value(s)
  - Statement of a conclusion rejecting the null hypothesis or failing to reject the null hypothesis
  - Statement of a final conclusion that uses simple and nontechnical terms to address the original claim

 Testing a Claim About a Proportion

- Develop the ability to conduct a formal hypothesis test of a claim about a population proportion. The procedure should include the components listed above with the objectives for Section 8-1.

 Testing a Claim About a Mean

- Develop the ability to use sample data to conduct a formal hypothesis test of a claim made about a population mean. The procedure should include the same components listed above with the objectives for Section 8-1.

8-4   Testing a Claim About a Standard Deviation or Variance

- Develop the ability to use sample data to conduct a formal hypothesis test of a claim made about a population standard deviation or variance. The procedure should include the same components listed with the objectives for Section 8-1.

8-1   Basics of Hypothesis Testing

Key Concept In this section we present key components of a formal hypothesis test. The concepts in this section are general and apply to hypothesis tests involving proportions, means, or standard deviations or variances. In Part 1, we begin with the "big picture" to understand the basic underlying approach to hypothesis tests. Then we describe null and alternative hypotheses, significance level, types of tests (two-tailed, left-tailed, right-tailed), test statistic, *P*-value, critical values, and statements of conclusions. In Part 2 we describe types of errors (type I and type II). In Part 3 we describe the *power* of a hypothesis test.

PART 1   Basic Concepts of Hypothesis Testing

We begin with two very basic definitions.

> **DEFINITIONS**
>
> In statistics, a **hypothesis** is a claim or statement about a property of a population.
>
> A **hypothesis test** (or **test of significance**) is a procedure for testing a claim about a property of a population.

The "property of a population" referred to in the preceding definitions is often the value of a population parameter, so here are some examples of typical hypotheses (or claims):

- $\mu < 98.6°F$ "The mean body temperature of humans is less than 98.6°F."

- $p > 0.5$ "The proportion of girls born to parents using the XSORT method of gender selection is greater than 0.5."

- $\sigma = 15$ "The population of nurses has IQ scores with a standard deviation equal to 15."

 EXAMPLE 1   XSORT Method of Gender Selection

Consider the claim from the Chapter Problem that "the XSORT technique is effective in increasing the probability of a girl." Using p to denote the proportion of girls born to parents using the XSORT method of gender selection, the "effective" claim is equivalent to the claim that the proportion is significantly greater than half, or $p > 0.5$. The expression $p > 0.5$ is the symbolic form of the original claim.

The Big Picture In Example 1, we have the claim that the proportion p is such that $p > 0.5$. Among 945 babies, how many do we need to get a *significantly high* number of girls?

- A result of 473 girls (or 50.1%) could easily occur by chance under normal circumstances with no treatment, so 473 is *not significantly high.*
- The actual result of 879 girls (or 93.0%) appears to be *significantly high.*

The method of hypothesis testing gives us a standard and widely accepted procedure for deciding whether such results are significant.

Using Technology It is easy to obtain hypothesis-testing results using technology. The accompanying screen displays show results from different technologies, so *we can use computers or calculators to do all of the computational heavy lifting.* Examining the screen displays, we see some common elements. They all display a "test statistic" of $z = 26.45$ (rounded), and they all include a "*P*-value" of 0.0000 (rounded). These two results are important, but *understanding* the hypothesis-testing procedure is critically important. Focus on *understanding* how the hypothesis-testing procedure works and learn the associated terminology. Only then will results from technology make sense.

Statdisk

Alternative Hypothesis:
p > p(hyp)
Sample proportion: 0.9301587
Test Statistic, z: 26.4469
Critical z: 1.6449
P-Value: 0.0000

Minitab

Test of p = 0.5 vs p > 0.5

Sample	X	N	Sample p	95% Lower Bound	Z-Value	P-Value
1	879	945	0.930159	0.916521	26.45	0.000

TI-83/84 Plus

```
NORMAL FLOAT AUTO REAL RADIAN MP

        1-PropZTest
prop>.5
z=26.44689198
p=0
p̂=.9301587302
n=945
```

XLSTAT

Difference	0.4302
z (Observed value)	26.4469
z (Critical value)	1.6449
p-value (one-tailed)	< 0.0001
alpha	0.05

StatCrunch

Hypothesis test results:
p : Proportion of successes
H_0 : p = 0.5
H_A : p > 0.5

Proportion	Count	Total	Sample Prop.	Std. Err.	Z-Stat	P-value
p	879	945	0.93015873	0.016265001	26.446892	<0.0001

Significance Hypothesis tests are also called *tests of significance*. In Section 4-1 we used probabilities to determine when sample results are *significantly low* or *significantly high.* This chapter formalizes those concepts in a unified procedure that is used often throughout many different fields of application. Figure 8-1 on the next page summarizes the procedures used in two slightly different methods for conducting a formal hypothesis test. We will proceed to conduct a formal test of the claim from Example 1 that $p > 0.5$. In testing that claim, we will use the sample data from the results cited in the Chapter Problem, with $x = 879$ girls among $n = 945$ births.

FIGURE 8-1
Procedure for Hypothesis Tests

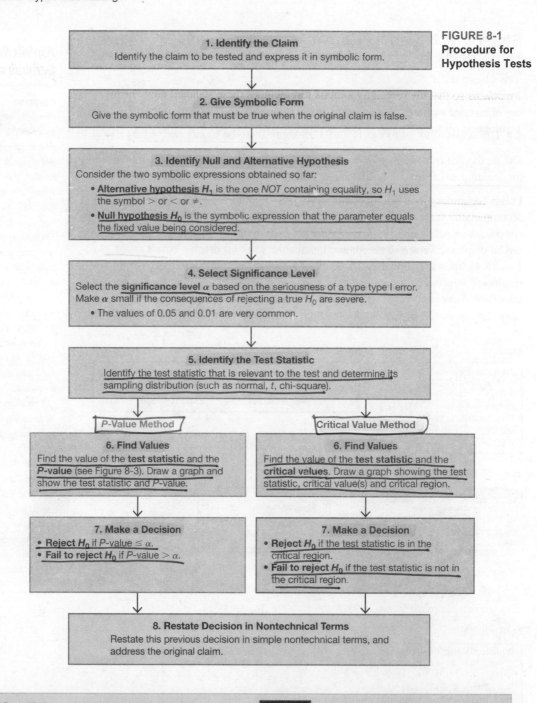

1. Identify the Claim
Identify the claim to be tested and express it in symbolic form.

2. Give Symbolic Form
Give the symbolic form that must be true when the original claim is false.

3. Identify Null and Alternative Hypothesis
Consider the two symbolic expressions obtained so far:
- **Alternative hypothesis H_1** is the one *NOT* containing equality, so H_1 uses the symbol $>$ or $<$ or $\neq$.
- **Null hypothesis H_0** is the symbolic expression that the parameter equals the fixed value being considered.

4. Select Significance Level
Select the **significance level** α based on the seriousness of a type type I error. Make α small if the consequences of rejecting a true H_0 are severe.
- The values of 0.05 and 0.01 are very common.

5. Identify the Test Statistic
Identify the test statistic that is relevant to the test and determine its sampling distribution (such as normal, t, chi-square).

P-Value Method

6. Find Values
Find the value of the **test statistic** and the **P-value** (see Figure 8-3). Draw a graph and show the test statistic and *P*-value.

7. Make a Decision
- **Reject H_0** if *P*-value $\leq \alpha$.
- **Fail to reject H_0** if *P*-value $> \alpha$.

Critical Value Method

6. Find Values
Find the value of the **test statistic** and the **critical values**. Draw a graph showing the test statistic, critical value(s) and critical region.

7. Make a Decision
- **Reject H_0** if the test statistic is in the critical region.
- **Fail to reject H_0** if the test statistic is not in the critical region.

8. Restate Decision in Nontechnical Terms
Restate this previous decision in simple nontechnical terms, and address the original claim.

Confidence Interval Method

Construct a confidence interval with a confidence level selected as in Table 8-1.

Because a confidence interval estimate of a population parameter contains the likely values of that parameter, reject a claim that the population parameter has a value that is not included in the confidence interval.

Table 8-1   Confidence Level for Confidence Interval

		Two-Tailed Test	One-Tailed Test
Significance	0.01	99%	98%
Level for	0.05	95%	90%
Hypothesis	0.10	90%	80%
Test			

Steps 1, 2, 3: Use the Original Claim to Create a Null Hypothesis H_0 and an Alternative Hypothesis H_1

The objective of Steps 1, 2, 3 is to identify the *null hypothesis* and *alternative hypothesis* so that the formal hypothesis test includes these standard components that are often used in many different disciplines. The null hypothesis includes the working assumption for the purposes of conducting the test.

DEFINITIONS

The **null hypothesis** (denoted by H_0) is a statement that the value of a population parameter (such as proportion, mean, or standard deviation) is *equal to* some claimed value.

The **alternative hypothesis** (denoted by H_1 or H_a or H_A) is a statement that the parameter has a value that somehow differs from the null hypothesis. For the methods of this chapter, the symbolic form of the alternative hypothesis must use one of these symbols: $<, >, \neq$.

The term *null* is used to indicate *no* change or no effect or no difference. We conduct the hypothesis test by assuming that the parameter is *equal to* some specified value so that we can work with a single distribution having a specific value.

Example: Here is an example of a null hypothesis involving a proportion:

$$H_0\text{: } p = 0.5$$

Example: Here are different examples of alternative hypotheses involving proportions:

$$H_1\text{: } p > 0.5 \qquad H_1\text{: } p < 0.5 \qquad H_1\text{: } p \neq 0.5$$

Given the claim from Example 1 that the gender selection method is effective in increasing the probability that a baby will be a girl, we can apply Steps 1, 2, and 3 in Figure 8-1 as follows.

Step 1: Identify the claim to be tested and express it in symbolic form. Using p to denote the probability of selecting a girl, the claim that the gender selection is effective can be expressed in symbolic form as $p > 0.5$.

Step 2: Give the symbolic form that must be true when the original claim is false. If the original claim of $p > 0.5$ is false, then $p \leq 0.5$ must be true.

Step 3: This step is in two parts: Identify the alternative hypothesis H_1 and identify the null hypothesis H_0.

- Identify H_1: Using the two symbolic expressions $p > 0.5$ and $p \leq 0.5$, the alternative hypothesis H_1 is the one that does not contain equality. Of those two expressions, $p > 0.5$ does not contain equality, so we get

$$H_1\text{: } p > 0.5$$

- Identify H_0: The null hypothesis H_0 is the symbolic expression that the parameter *equals* the fixed value being considered, so we get

$$H_0\text{: } p = 0.5$$

The result of the first three steps is the identification of the null and alternative hypotheses:

$$H_0\text{: } p = 0.5 \text{ (null hypothesis)}$$
$$H_1\text{: } p > 0.5 \text{ (alternative hypothesis)}$$

Note About Forming Your Own Claims (Hypotheses): If you are conducting a study and want to use a hypothesis test to *support* your claim, your claim must be worded so that it becomes the alternative hypothesis (and can be expressed using only the symbols $<$, $>$, or $\neq$). You can never support a claim that a parameter is *equal to* a specified value.

Step 4: Select the Significance Level α

> **DEFINITION**
>
> The **significance level α** for a hypothesis test is the probability value used as the cutoff for determining when the sample evidence constitutes significant evidence against the null hypothesis. By its nature, the significance level α is the probability of mistakenly rejecting the null hypothesis when it is true:
>
> $$\text{Significance level } \alpha = P(\text{rejecting } H_0 \text{ when } H_0 \text{ is true})$$

The significance level α is the same α introduced in Section 7-1, where we defined "critical value." Common choices for α are 0.05, 0.01, and 0.10; 0.05 is the most common choice.

Step 5: Identify the Statistic Relevant to the Test and Determine Its Sampling Distribution (such as normal, t, or X^2)

Table 8-2 lists parameters along with the corresponding sampling distributions.

Example: The claim $p > 0.5$ is a claim about the population proportion p, so use the normal distribution provided that the requirements are satisfied. (With $n = 945$, $p = 0.5$, and $q = 0.5$ from Example 1, $np \geq 5$ and $nq \geq 5$ are both true.)

TABLE 8-2

Parameter	Sampling Distribution	Requirements	Test Statistic
Proportion p	Normal (z)	$np \geq 5$ and $nq \geq 5$	$z = \dfrac{\hat{p} - p}{\sqrt{\frac{pq}{n}}}$
Mean μ	t	σ not known and normally distributed population or σ not known and $n > 30$	$t = \dfrac{\bar{x} - \mu}{\frac{s}{\sqrt{n}}}$
Mean μ	Normal (z)	σ known and normally distributed population or σ known and $n > 30$	$z = \dfrac{\bar{x} - \mu}{\frac{\sigma}{\sqrt{n}}}$
St. dev. σ or variance σ^2	X^2	Strict requirement: normally distributed population	$X^2 = \dfrac{(n - 1)s^2}{\sigma^2}$

Step 6: Find the Value of the Test Statistic, Then Find Either the P-Value or the Critical Value(s)

> **DEFINITION**
>
> The **test statistic** is a value used in making a decision about the null hypothesis. It is found by converting the sample statistic (such as $\hat{p}$, $\bar{x}$, or s) to a score (such as z, t, or X^2) with the assumption that the null hypothesis is true.

In this chapter we use the test statistics listed in the last column of Table 8-2.

Example: Preliminary results from the XSORT method of gender selection involved 14 babies, with 13 of them being girls. Here we have $n = 14$ and $x = 13$, so $\hat{p} = x/n = 13/14 = 0.929$. With the null hypothesis of H_0: $p = 0.5$, we are working with the assumption that $p = 0.5$, and it follows that $q = 1 - p = 0.5$. We can evaluate the test statistic as shown below (or technology can find the test statistic for us).

$$z = \frac{\hat{p} - p}{\sqrt{\dfrac{pq}{n}}} = \frac{\dfrac{13}{14} - 0.5}{\sqrt{\dfrac{(0.5)(0.5)}{14}}} = 3.21$$

Finding the *P*-value and/or critical value(s) requires that we first consider whether the hypothesis test is two-tailed, left-tailed, or right-tailed, which are described as follows.

Two-Tailed, Left-Tailed, Right-Tailed

> **DEFINITION**
>
> The **critical region** (or **rejection region**) is the area corresponding to all values of the test statistic that cause us to reject the null hypothesis.

Depending on the claim being tested, the critical region could be in the two extreme tails, it could be in the left tail, or it could be in the right tail.

- **Two-tailed test:** The critical region is in the two extreme regions (tails) under the curve (as in the top graph in Figure 8-2).
- **Left-tailed test:** The critical region is in the extreme left region (tail) under the curve (as in the middle graph in Figure 8-2).
- **Right-tailed test:** The critical region is in the extreme right region (tail) under the curve (as in the bottom graph in Figure 8-2).

> **HINT** Look at the symbol used in the alternative hypothesis H_1.
> - The symbol $>$ points to the right and the test is right-tailed.
> - The symbol $<$ points to the left and the test is left-tailed.
> - The symbol $\neq$ is used for a two-tailed test.
>
> *Example:* With H_0: $p = 0.5$ and H_1: $p > 0.5$, we reject the null hypothesis and support the alternative hypothesis only if the sample proportion is greater than 0.5 by a significant amount, so the hypothesis test in this case is *right-tailed*.

P-Value Method

With the ***P*-value method** of testing hypotheses, we make a decision by comparing the *P*-value to the significance level.

> **DEFINITION**
>
> In a hypothesis test, the ***P*-value** is the probability of getting a value of the test statistic that is *at least as extreme* as the test statistic obtained from the sample data, assuming that the null hypothesis is true.

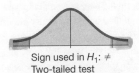

Sign used in H_1: $\neq$
Two-tailed test

Sign used in H_1: $<$
Left-tailed test

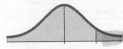

Sign used in H_1: $>$
Right-tailed test

FIGURE 8-2 Critical Region in Two-Tailed, Left-Tailed, and Right-Tailed Tests

To find the *P*-value, first <u>find the area beyond the test statistic</u>, then use the procedure given in Figure 8-3. That procedure can be summarized as follows:

- Critical region in left tail: *P*-value = area to the *left* of the test statistic
- Critical region in right tail: *P*-value = area to the *right* of the test statistic
- Critical region in two tails: *P*-value = *twice* the area in the tail beyond the test statistic

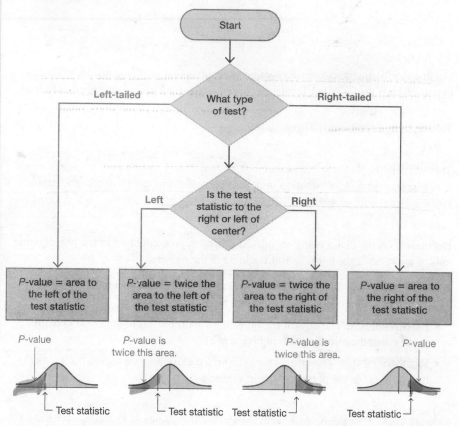

FIGURE 8-3 Finding *P*-Values

Example: Using only the preliminary results of the XSORT method of gender selection, we have 13 girls in 14 births and the test statistic is $z = 3.21$ and it has a normal distribution area of 0.0007 to its right, so a right-tailed test with test statistic $z = 3.21$ has a *P*-value of 0.0007.

CAUTION Don't confuse a *P*-value with the parameter *p* or the statistic $\hat{p}$. Know the following notation:

P-value = probability of a test statistic at least as extreme as the one obtained

p = population proportion

$\hat{p}$ = sample proportion

P-Value and Hypothesis Testing Controversy

The standard method of testing hypotheses and the use of *P*-values have very widespread acceptance and use, but not everyone is convinced that these methods are sound. Editors of the *Journal of Basic and Applied Social Psychology* took a strong stand when they said that they would no longer publish articles that included *P*-values. They said that *P*-values are an excuse for lower-quality research and the *P*-value criterion is too easy to pass. In the past, *P*-values have been misinterpreted and misused, so a serious and important statistical analysis should not rely solely on *P*-value results. Instead, it would be wise to consider other aspects, such as the following.

- *Sample Size:* Very large samples could result in small *P*-values suggesting that results are significant when the results don't really make much of a practical difference.
- *Power:* Part 3 of this section discusses the concept of *power,* and it is often helpful to analyze power as part of an analysis.
- *Other Factors:* Instead of relying on just one outcome such as the *P*-value, it is generally better to also consider other results, such as a confidence interval, results from simulations, practical significance, design of the study, quality of the sample, consequences of type I and type II errors (discussed in Part 2 of this section), and replication of results.

This chapter presents the same methods of hypothesis testing and the same use of *P*-values that are currently being used, but again, it should be stressed that important applications should also consider other factors, such as those listed above.

Critical Value Method

With the **critical value method** (or traditional method) of testing hypotheses, we make a decision by comparing the test statistic to the critical value(s).

> **DEFINITION**
>
> In a hypothesis test, the **critical value(s)** separates the critical region (where we reject the null hypothesis) from the values of the test statistic that do not lead to rejection of the null hypothesis.

Critical values depend on the null hypothesis, the sampling distribution, and the significance level α.

Example: The critical region in Figure 8-4 is shaded in green. Figure 8-4 shows that with a significance level of $\alpha = 0.05$, the critical value is $z = 1.645$.

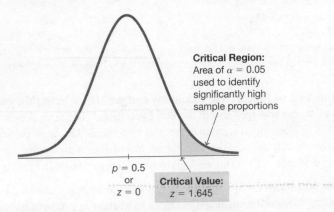

Critical Region: Area of $\alpha = 0.05$ used to identify significantly high sample proportions

$p = 0.5$ or $z = 0$

Critical Value: $z = 1.645$

FIGURE 8-4   Critical Value and Critical Region

Step 7: Make a Decision to Either Reject H_0 or Fail to Reject H_0.

Decision Criteria for the *P*-Value Method:

- If P-value $\leq \alpha$, reject H_0. ("If the P is low, the null must go.")
- If P-value $> \alpha$, fail to reject H_0.

Example: With significance level $\alpha = 0.05$ and P-value $= 0.0007$, we have P-value $\leq \alpha$, so reject H_0. Remember, the P-value is the probability of getting a sample result at least as extreme as the one obtained, so if the P-value is low (less than or equal to α), the sample statistic is significantly low or significantly high.

Decision Criteria for the Critical Value Method:

- If the test statistic is in the critical region, reject H_0.
- If the test statistic is not in the critical region, fail to reject H_0.

Example: With test statistic $z = 3.21$ and the critical region from $z = 1.645$ to infinity, the test statistic falls within the critical region, so reject H_0.

Step 8: Restate the Decision Using Simple and Nontechnical Terms

Without using technical terms not understood by most people, state a final conclusion that addresses the original claim with wording that can be understood by those without knowledge of statistical procedures.

Example: There is sufficient evidence to support the claim that with the XSORT method of gender selection, the probability of getting a baby girl is greater than 0.5.

Wording the Final Conclusion For help in wording the final conclusion, refer to Table 8-3, which lists the four possible circumstances and their corresponding conclusions. Note that only the first case leads to wording indicating *support* for the original conclusion. If you want to support some claim, state it in such a way that it becomes the alternative hypothesis, and then hope that the null hypothesis gets rejected.

TABLE 8-3 Wording of the Final Conclusion

Condition	Conclusion
Original claim does not include equality, and you reject H_0.	"There is sufficient evidence to *support* the claim that . . . (original claim)."
Original claim does not include equality, and you fail to reject H_0.	"There is not sufficient evidence to support the claim that . . . (original claim)."
Original claim includes equality, and you reject H_0.	"There is sufficient evidence to warrant *rejection* of the claim that . . . (original claim)."
Original claim includes equality, and you fail to reject H_0.	"There is not sufficient evidence to warrant rejection of the claim that . . . (original claim)."

Accept or Fail to Reject? We should say that we "fail to reject the null hypothesis" instead of saying that we "accept the null hypothesis." The term *accept* is misleading, because it implies incorrectly that the null hypothesis has been proved, but we can never prove a null hypothesis. The phrase *fail to reject* says more correctly that the available evidence isn't strong enough to warrant rejection of the null hypothesis.

Multiple Negatives Final conclusions can include as many as three negative terms. (*Example:* "There is *not* sufficient evidence to warrant *rejection* of the claim of *no* difference between 0.5 and the population proportion.") For such confusing conclusions, it is better to restate them to be understandable. Instead of saying that "there is not sufficient evidence to warrant rejection of the claim of no difference between 0.5 and the population proportion," a better statement would be this: "Until stronger evidence is obtained, continue to assume that the population proportion is equal to 0.5."

CAUTION Never conclude a hypothesis test with a statement of "reject the null hypothesis" or "fail to reject the null hypothesis." Always make sense of the conclusion with a statement that uses simple nontechnical wording that addresses the original claim.

Confidence Intervals for Hypothesis Tests

In this section we have described the individual components used in a hypothesis test, but the following sections will combine those components in comprehensive procedures. We can test claims about population parameters by using the *P*-value method or the critical value method summarized in Figure 8-1, or we can use confidence intervals.

A confidence interval estimate of a population parameter contains the likely values of that parameter. If a confidence interval does not include a claimed value of a population parameter, reject that claim. For two-tailed hypothesis tests, construct a confidence interval with a confidence level of $1 - \alpha$, but for a one-tailed hypothesis test with significance level α, construct a confidence interval with a confidence level of $1 - 2\alpha$. (See Table 8-1 on page 356 for common cases.) For a left-tailed test or a right-tailed test, we could also use a one-sided confidence interval; see Exercise 38 in Section 7-1. After constructing the confidence interval, use this criterion:

A confidence interval estimate of a population parameter contains the likely values of that parameter. We should therefore reject a claim that the population parameter has a value that is not included in the confidence interval.

Equivalent Methods

In some cases, a conclusion based on a confidence interval may be different from a conclusion based on a hypothesis test. The *P*-value method and critical value method are equivalent in the sense that they always lead to the same conclusion. The following table shows that for the methods included in this chapter, a confidence interval estimate of a proportion might lead to a conclusion different from that of a hypothesis test.

Parameter	Is a confidence interval *equivalent* to a hypothesis test in the sense that they always lead to the same conclusion?
Proportion	No
Mean	Yes
Standard Deviation or Variance	Yes

PART 2 Type I and Type II Errors

When testing a null hypothesis, we arrive at a conclusion of rejecting it or failing to reject it. Our conclusions are sometimes correct and sometimes wrong (even if we apply all procedures correctly). Table 8-4 includes two different types of errors and we distinguish between them by calling them type I and type II errors, as described here:

- **Type I error:** The mistake of rejecting the null hypothesis when it is actually true. The symbol α (alpha) is used to represent the probability of a type I error.

$$\alpha = P(\text{type I error}) = P(\text{rejecting } H_0 \text{ when } H_0 \text{ is true})$$

- **Type II error:** The mistake of failing to reject the null hypothesis when it is actually false. The symbol β (beta) is used to represent the probability of a type II error.

$$\beta = P(\text{type II error}) = P(\text{failing to reject } H_0 \text{ when } H_0 \text{ is false})$$

TABLE 8-4 Type I and Type II Errors

		True State of Nature	
		Null hypothesis is true	Null hypothesis is false
Preliminary Conclusion	Reject H_0	Type I error: Reject a true H_0. P (type I error) $= \alpha$	Correct decision
	Fail to reject H_0	Correct decision	Type II error: Fail to reject a false H_0. P(type II error) $= \beta$

Memory Hint for Type I and Type II Errors Remember "routine for fun," and use the consonants from those words (**R**ou**T**i**N**e **F**o**R** **F**u**N**) to remember that a type I error is RTN: Reject True Null (hypothesis), and a type II error is FRFN: Fail to Reject a False Null (hypothesis).

Hint for Describing Type I and Type II Errors Descriptions of a type I error and a type II error refer to the *null hypothesis* being true or false, but when wording a statement representing a type I error or a type II error, *be sure that the conclusion addresses the original claim* (which may or may not be the null hypothesis). See Example 2.

EXAMPLE 2 Describing Type I and Type II Errors

Consider the claim that the XSORT gender selection method is effective in increasing the likelihood of a baby girl, so that the probability of a baby girl is $p > 0.5$. Given the following null and alternative hypotheses, write statements describing (a) a type I error, and (b) a type II error.

$H_0: p = 0.5$

$H_1: p > 0.5$ (original claim that will be addressed in the final conclusion)

SOLUTION

a. **Type I Error:** A type I error is the mistake of rejecting a true null hypothesis, so the following is a type I error: In reality $p = 0.5$, but sample evidence leads us to conclude that $p > 0.5$.

- In this case, a type I error is to conclude that the XSORT gender selection method is effective when in reality it has no effect.

b. **Type II Error:** A type II error is the mistake of failing to reject the null hypothesis when it is false, so the following is a type II error: In reality $p > 0.5$, but we fail to support that conclusion.

- In this case, a type II error is to conclude that the XSORT gender selection method has no effect, when it really is effective in increasing the likelihood of a baby girl.

Controlling Type I and Type II Errors Step 4 in our standard procedure for testing hypotheses is to select a significance level α (such as 0.05), which is the probability of a type I error. The values of α, β, and the sample size n are all related, so if you choose any two of them, the third is automatically determined (although β can't be determined until an alternative value of the population parameter has been specified along with α and n). One common practice is to select the significance level α, then select a sample size that is practical, so the value of β is determined. Generally, try to use the largest α that you can tolerate, but for type I errors with more serious consequences, select smaller values of α. Then choose a sample size n as large as is reasonable, based on considerations of time, cost, and other relevant factors. Another common practice is to select α and β so the required sample size n is automatically determined. (See Example 4 in Part 3 of this section.)

PART 3 Power of a Hypothesis Test

We use β to denote the probability of failing to reject a false null hypothesis, so $P(\text{type II error}) = \beta$. It follows that $1 - \beta$ is the probability of rejecting a false null hypothesis, so $1 - \beta$ is a probability that is one measure of the effectiveness of a hypothesis test.

> **DEFINITION**
>
> The **power** of a hypothesis test is the probability $1 - \beta$ of rejecting a false null hypothesis. The value of the power is computed by using a particular significance level α and a *particular* value of the population parameter that is an alternative to the value assumed true in the null hypothesis.

Because determination of power requires a particular value that is an alternative to the value assumed in the null hypothesis, a hypothesis test can have many different values of power, depending on the particular values of the population parameter chosen as alternatives to the null hypothesis.

EXAMPLE 3 Power of a Hypothesis Test

Consider these preliminary results from the XSORT method of gender selection: There were 13 girls among the 14 babies born to couples using the XSORT method. If we want to test the claim that girls are more likely ($p > 0.5$) with the XSORT method, we have the following null and alternative hypotheses:

$$H_0: p = 0.5 \qquad H_1: p > 0.5$$

Let's use a significance level of $\alpha = 0.05$. In addition to all given test components, finding power requires that we select a particular value of p that is an alternative to

continued

the value assumed in the null hypothesis H_0: $p = 0.5$. Find the values of power corresponding to these alternative values of p: 0.6, 0.7, 0.8, and 0.9.

SOLUTION

The values of power in the following table were found by using Minitab, and exact calculations are used instead of a normal approximation to the binomial distribution.

Specific Alternative Value of p	β	Power of Test = $1 - \beta$
0.6	0.820	0.180
0.7	0.564	0.436
0.8	0.227	0.773
0.9	0.012	0.988

INTERPRETATION

On the basis of the power values listed above, we see that this hypothesis test has a power of 0.180 (or 18.0%) of rejecting H_0: $p = 0.5$ when the population proportion p is actually 0.6. That is, if the true population proportion is actually equal to 0.6, there is an 18.0% chance of making the correct conclusion of rejecting the false null hypothesis that $p = 0.5$. That low power of 18.0% is not so good.

There is a 0.436 probability of rejecting $p = 0.5$ when the true value of p is actually 0.7. It makes sense that this test is more effective in rejecting the claim of $p = 0.5$ when the population proportion is actually 0.7 than when the population proportion is actually 0.6. (When identifying animals assumed to be horses, there's a better chance of rejecting an elephant as a horse—because of the greater difference—than rejecting a mule as a horse.) In general, increasing the difference between the assumed parameter value and the actual parameter value results in an increase in power, as shown in the table above.

Because the calculations of power are quite complicated, the use of technology is strongly recommended. (In this section, only Exercises 33–35 involve power.)

Power and the Design of Experiments

Just as 0.05 is a common choice for a significance level, a power of at least 0.80 is a common requirement for determining that a hypothesis test is effective. (Some statisticians argue that the power should be higher, such as 0.85 or 0.90.) When designing an experiment, we might consider how much of a difference between the claimed value of a parameter and its true value is an important amount of difference. If testing the effectiveness of the XSORT gender selection method, a change in the proportion of girls from 0.5 to 0.501 is not very important, whereas a change in the proportion of girls from 0.5 to 0.9 would be very important. Such magnitudes of differences affect power. When designing an experiment, a goal of having a power value of at least 0.80 can often be used to determine the minimum required sample size, as in the following example.

 **EXAMPLE 4** **Finding the Sample Size Required to Achieve 80% Power**

Here is a statement similar to one in an article from the *Journal of the American Medical Association:* "The trial design assumed that with a 0.05 significance level, 153 randomly selected subjects would be needed to achieve 80% power to detect a reduction in the coronary heart disease rate from 0.5 to 0.4." From that statement we know the following:

- Before conducting the experiment, the researchers selected a significance level of 0.05 and a power of at least 0.80.

- The researchers decided that a reduction in the proportion of coronary heart disease from 0.5 to 0.4 is an important and clinically significant difference that they wanted to detect (by correctly rejecting the false null hypothesis).

- Using a significance level of 0.05, power of 0.80, and the alternative proportion of 0.4, technology such as Minitab is used to find that the required minimum sample size is 153.

The researchers can then proceed by obtaining a sample of at least 153 randomly selected subjects. Because of factors such as dropout rates, the researchers are likely to need somewhat more than 153 subjects. (See Exercise 35.)

8-1   Basic Skills and Concepts

Statistical Literacy and Critical Thinking

1. Vitamin C and Aspirin A bottle contains a label stating that it contains Spring Valley pills with 500 mg of vitamin C, and another bottle contains a label stating that it contains Bayer pills with 325 mg of aspirin. When testing claims about the mean contents of the pills, which would have more serious implications: rejection of the Spring Valley vitamin C claim or rejection of the Bayer aspirin claim? Is it wise to use the same significance level for hypothesis tests about the mean amount of vitamin C and the mean amount of aspirin?

2. Estimates and Hypothesis Tests Data Set 2 "Body Temperatures" in Appendix B includes sample body temperatures. We could use methods of Chapter 7 for making an estimate, or we could use those values to test the common belief that the mean body temperature is 98.6°F. What is the difference between estimating and hypothesis testing?

3. Mean Height of Women A formal hypothesis test is to be conducted using the claim that the mean height of women is equal to 161.7 cm.

a. What is the null hypothesis, and how is it denoted?

b. What is the alternative hypothesis, and how is it denoted?

c. What are the possible conclusions that can be made about the null hypothesis?

d. Is it possible to conclude that "there is sufficient evidence to support the claim that the mean height of women is equal to 161.7 cm"?

4. Interpreting P-value The Ericsson method is one of several methods claimed to increase the likelihood of a baby girl. In a clinical trial, results could be analyzed with a formal hypothesis test with the alternative hypothesis of $p > 0.5$, which corresponds to the claim that the method increases the likelihood of having a girl, so that the proportion of girls is greater than 0.5. If you have an interest in establishing the success of the method, which of the following P-values would you prefer: 0.999, 0.5, 0.95, 0.05, 0.01, 0.001? Why?

Identifying H_0 and H_1.   *In Exercises 5–8, do the following:*

a. Express the original claim in symbolic form.

b. Identify the null and alternative hypotheses.

5. Hypertension Claim: Most adults do not have hypertension. When 983 randomly selected adults were tested, it was found that 70.9% of them do not have hypertension.

6. Cell Phones Claim: Fewer than 95% of nurses have a cell phone. In a survey of 1128 nurses, 87% said that they have a cell phone.

7. Pulse Rates Claim: The mean pulse rate (in beats per minute, or bpm) of adult females is equal to 73 bpm. For the random sample of 147 adult females in Data Set 1 "Body Data" from Appendix B, the mean pulse rate is 74.0 bpm and the standard deviation is 12.5 bpm.

8. Pulse Rates Claim: The standard deviation of pulse rates of adult females is less than 13 bpm. For the random sample of 147 adult females in Data Set 1 "Body Data" from Appendix B, the pulse rates have a standard deviation of 12.5 bpm.

Conclusions. *In Exercises 9–12, refer to the exercise identified. Make subjective estimates to decide whether results are significantly low or significantly high, then state a conclusion about the original claim. For example, if the claim is that a coin favors heads and sample results consist of 11 heads in 20 flips, conclude that there is not sufficient evidence to support the claim that the coin favors heads (because it is easy to get 11 heads in 20 flips by chance with a fair coin).*

9. Exercise 5 "Hypertension"

10. Exercise 6 "Cell Phone"

11. Exercise 7 "Pulse Rates"

12. Exercise 8 "Pulse Rates"

Test Statistics. *In Exercises 13–16, refer to the exercise identified and find the value of the test statistic. (Refer to Table 8-2 on page 358 to select the correct expression for evaluating the test statistic.)*

13. Exercise 5 "Hypertension"

14. Exercise 6 "Cell Phone"

15. Exercise 7 "Pulse Rates"

16. Exercise 8 "Pulse Rates"

P-Values. *In Exercises 17–20, do the following:*

a. Identify the hypothesis test as being two-tailed, left-tailed, or right-tailed.

b. Find the P-value. (See Figure 8-3 on page 360.)

c. Using a significance level of $\alpha = 0.05$, should we reject H_0 or should we fail to reject H_0?

17. The test statistic of $z = 1.00$ is obtained when testing the claim that $p > 0.3$.

18. The test statistic of $z = -2.26$ is obtained when testing the claim that $p = 0.68$.

19. The test statistic of $z = 2.01$ is obtained when testing the claim that $p \neq 0.345$.

20. The test statistic of $z = -1.58$ is obtained when testing the claim that $p < 2/5$.

Critical Values. *In Exercises 21–24, refer to the information in the given exercise and do the following.*

a. Find the critical value(s).

b. Using a significance level of $\alpha = 0.05$, should we reject H_0 or should we fail to reject H_0?

21. Exercise 17

22. Exercise 18

23. Exercise 19

24. Exercise 20

Final Conclusions. *In Exercises 25–28, use a significance level of $\alpha = 0.05$ and use the given information for the following:*

a. State a conclusion about the null hypothesis. (Reject H_0 or fail to reject H_0.)

b. Without using technical terms or symbols, state a final conclusion that addresses the original claim.

25. Original claim: More than 70% of adults do not have hypertension. The hypothesis test results in a P-value of 0.2678.

26. Original claim: Fewer than 90% of nurses have a cell phone. The hypothesis test results in a *P*-value of 0.0003.

27. Original claim: The mean pulse rate (in beats per minute) of adult males is 72 bpm. The hypothesis test results in a *P*-value of 0.0095.

28. Original claim: The standard deviation of pulse rates of adult males is more than 11 bpm. The hypothesis test results in a *P*-value of 0.3045.

Type I and Type II Errors. *In Exercises 29–32, provide statements that identify the type I error and the type II error that correspond to the given claim. (Although conclusions are usually expressed in verbal form, the answers here can be expressed with statements that include symbolic expressions such as* $p = 0.1$.)

29. The proportion of people who write with their left hand is equal to 0.1.

30. The proportion of people with blue eyes is equal to 0.35.

31. The proportion of adults who use the Internet is greater than 0.87.

32. The proportion of people who require no vision correction is less than 0.25.

8-1 Beyond the Basics

33. Interpreting Power Chantix (varenicline) tablets are used as an aid to help people stop smoking. In a clinical trial, 129 subjects were treated with Chantix twice a day for 12 weeks, and 16 subjects experienced abdominal pain (based on data from Pfizer, Inc.). If someone claims that more than 8% of Chantix users experience abdominal pain, that claim is supported with a hypothesis test conducted with a 0.05 significance level. Using 0.18 as an alternative value of *p*, the power of the test is 0.96. Interpret this value of the power of the test.

34. Calculating Power Consider a hypothesis test of the claim that the Ericsson method of gender selection is effective in increasing the likelihood of having a baby girl, so that the claim is $p > 0.5$. Assume that a significance level of $\alpha = 0.05$ is used, and the sample is a simple random sample of size $n = 64$.

a. Assuming that the true population proportion is 0.65, find the power of the test, which is the probability of rejecting the null hypothesis when it is false. (*Hint:* With a 0.05 significance level, the critical value is $z = 1.645$, so any test statistic in the right tail of the accompanying top graph is in the rejection region where the claim is supported. Find the sample proportion $\hat{p}$ in the top graph, and use it to find the power shown in the bottom graph.)

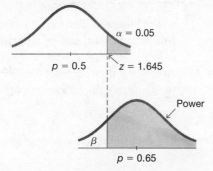

b. Explain why the green-shaded region of the bottom graph represents the power of the test.

35. Finding Sample Size to Achieve Power Researchers plan to conduct a test of a gender selection method. They plan to use the alternative hypothesis of $H_1: p > 0.5$ and a significance level of $\alpha = 0.05$. Find the sample size required to achieve at least 80% power in detecting an increase in *p* from 0.50 to 0.55. (This is a very difficult exercise. *Hint:* See Exercise 34.)

8-2   Testing a Claim About a Proportion

Key Concept This section describes a complete procedure for testing a claim made about a population proportion p. We illustrate hypothesis testing with the P-value method, the critical value method, and the use of confidence intervals. The methods of this section can be used with claims about population proportions, probabilities, or the decimal equivalents of percentages.

There are different methods for testing a claim about a population proportion. Part 1 of this section is based on the use of a normal approximation to a binomial distribution, and this method serves well as an introduction to basic concepts, but it is not a method used by professional statisticians. Part 2 discusses other methods that might require the use of technology.

PART 1   Normal Approximation Method

The following box includes the key elements used for testing a claim about a population proportion by using a normal distribution as an approximation to a binomial distribution. The test statistic does not include a correction for continuity (as described in Section 6-6), because its effect tends to be very small with large samples.

KEY ELEMENTS

Testing a Claim About a Population Proportion (Normal Approximation Method)

Objective

Conduct a formal hypothesis test of a claim about a population proportion p.

Notation

n = sample size or number of trials

$\hat{p} = \dfrac{x}{n}$ (*sample* proportion)

p = population proportion (p is the value used in the statement of the null hypothesis)

$q = 1 - p$

Requirements

1. The sample observations are a simple random sample.

2. The conditions for a *binomial distribution* are satisfied:

   - There is a fixed number of trials.

   - The trials are independent.

   - Each trial has two categories of "success" and "failure."

   - The probability of a success remains the same in all trials.

3. The conditions $np \geq 5$ and $nq \geq 5$ are both satisfied, so **the binomial distribution of sample proportions can be approximated by a normal distribution with** $\mu = np$ and $\sigma = \sqrt{npq}$ (as described in Section 6-6). Note that p used here is the *assumed* proportion used in the claim, not the sample proportion $\hat{p}$.

Test Statistic for Testing a Claim About a Proportion

$$z = \frac{\hat{p} - p}{\sqrt{\dfrac{pq}{n}}}$$

P-Values: P-values are automatically provided by technology. If technology is not available, use the standard normal distribution (Table A-2) and refer to Figure 8-1 on page 356.

Critical Values: Use the standard normal distribution (Table A-2).

Equivalent Methods

When testing claims about proportions, the confidence interval method is not equivalent to the *P*-value and critical value methods, so the confidence interval method could result in a different conclusion. (Both the *P*-value method and the critical value method use the same standard deviation based on the *claimed proportion p*, so they are equivalent to each other, but the confidence interval method uses an estimated standard deviation based on the *sample proportion*.) *Recommendation:* Use a confidence interval to *estimate* a population proportion, but use the *P*-value method or critical value method for *testing a claim* about a proportion. See Exercise 30.

Claim: The XSORT Method of Gender Selection Is Effective

Let's use the preliminary results from tests of the XSORT method of gender selection. Those preliminary results consisted of 14 babies born to couples using the XSORT method of gender selection, and 13 of the babies were girls. Use these results to test the claim that most babies born to couples using the XSORT method are girls. We interpret "most" to mean "more than half" or "greater than 0.5."

REQUIREMENT CHECK   We first check the three requirements.

1. The 14 babies are not randomly selected, but based on the design of the clinical trial, they can be treated as being random.

2. There is a fixed number (14) of independent trials with two categories (the baby is a girl or is not).

3. The requirements $np \geq 5$ and $nq \geq 5$ are both satisfied with $n = 14$, $p = 0.5$, and $q = 0.5$. [The value of $p = 0.5$ comes from the claim. We get $np = (14)(0.5) = 7$, which is greater than or equal to 5, and we get $nq = (14)(0.5) = 7$, which is also greater than or equal to 5.]

The three requirements are satisfied. ☑

Solution: *P*-Value Method

Technology Computer programs and calculators usually provide a *P*-value, so the *P*-value method is used. Different technologies will display the test statistic of $z = 3.21$ and the *P*-value of 0.0007.

Table A-2 If technology is not available, Figure 8-1 on page 356 in the preceding section lists the steps for using the *P*-value method. Using those steps from Figure 8-1, we can test the claim that "most babies born to couples using the XSORT method are girls" as follows.

Step 1: The original claim is that the XSORT method is effective in increasing the likelihood of a baby girl, and that claim can be expressed in symbolic form as $p > 0.5$.

Step 2: The opposite of the original claim is $p \leq 0.5$.

Step 3: Of the preceding two symbolic expressions, the expression $p > 0.5$ does not contain equality, so it becomes the alternative hypothesis. The null hypothesis is the statement that p equals the fixed value of 0.5. We can therefore express H_0 and H_1 as follows:

$$H_0: p = 0.5$$
$$H_1: p > 0.5 \text{ (original claim)}$$

continued

Process of Drug Approval

Gaining Food and Drug Administration (FDA) approval for a new drug is expensive and time-consuming. Here are the different stages of getting approval for a new drug:

- **Phase I study:** The safety of the drug is tested with a small (20–100) group of volunteers.
- **Phase II:** The drug is tested for effectiveness in randomized trials involving a larger (100–300) group of subjects. This phase often has subjects randomly assigned to either a treatment group or a placebo group.
- **Phase III:** The goal is to better understand the effectiveness of the drug as well as its adverse reactions. This phase typically involves 1,000–3,000 subjects, and it might require several years of testing.

Lisa Gibbs wrote in *Money* magazine that "the (drug) industry points out that for every 5,000 treatments tested, only 5 make it to clinical trials and only 1 ends up in drugstores." Total cost estimates vary from a low of $40 million to as much as $1.5 billion.

Step 4: For the significance level, we select $\alpha = 0.05$, which is a very common choice.

Step 5: Because we are testing a claim about a population proportion p, the sample statistic $\hat{p}$ is relevant to this test. The sampling distribution of sample proportions $\hat{p}$ can be approximated by a normal distribution in this case (as described in Section 6-3).

Step 6: The test statistic $z = 3.21$ can be found by using technology, or it can be calculated by using $\hat{p} = 13/14$ (sample proportion), $n = 14$ (sample size), $p = 0.5$ (assumed in the null hypothesis), and $q = 1 - 0.5 = 0.5$.

$$z = \frac{\hat{p} - p}{\sqrt{\dfrac{pq}{n}}} = \frac{\dfrac{13}{14} - 0.5}{\sqrt{\dfrac{(0.5)(0.5)}{14}}} = 3.21$$

The P-value can be found from technology, or it can be found by using the following procedure, which is shown in Figure 8-3 on page 360:

Left-tailed test: P-value = area to left of test statistic z

Right-tailed test: P-value = area to right of test statistic z

Two-tailed test: P-value = *twice* the area of the extreme region bounded by the test statistic z

Because this hypothesis test is right-tailed with a test statistic of $z = 3.21$, the P-value is the area to the right of $z = 3.21$. Referring to Table A-2, we see that the cumulative area to the *left* of $z = 3.21$ is 0.9993, so the area to the right of that test statistic is $1 - 0.9993 = 0.0007$. We get P-value = 0.0007. Figure 8-5 shows the test statistic and P-value for this example.

Step 7: Because the P-value of 0.0007 is less than or equal to the significance level of $\alpha = 0.05$, we reject the null hypothesis.

Step 8: Because we reject H_0: $p = 0.5$, we support the alternative hypothesis of $p > 0.5$. We conclude that there is sufficient sample evidence to support the claim that the XSORT method is effective in increasing the likelihood of a baby girl. (See Table 8-3 on page 362 for help with wording this final conclusion.)

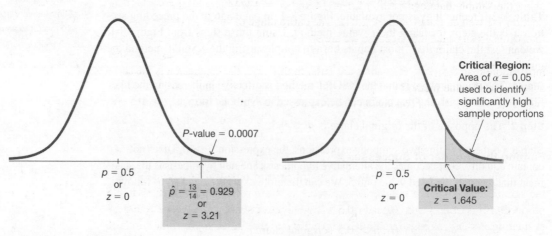

FIGURE 8-5 *P*-Value Method   FIGURE 8-6   Critical Value Method

CAUTION: Don't confuse the following notation.

- P-value = probability of getting a test statistic at least as extreme as the one representing the sample data, assuming that the null hypothesis H_0 is true
- p = population proportion
- $\hat{p}$ = sample proportion

Solution: Critical Value Method

The critical value method of testing hypotheses is summarized in Figure 8-1 on page 356 in Section 8-1. When using the critical value method with the claim that "most babies born to couples using the XSORT method are girls," Steps 1 through 5 are the same as Steps 1 through 5 for the P-value method, as shown. We continue with Step 6 of the critical value method.

Step 6: The test statistic is computed to be $z = 3.21$, as shown for the preceding P-value method. With the critical value method, we now find the critical values (instead of the P-value). This is a right-tailed test, so the area of the critical region is an area of $\alpha = 0.05$ in the right tail. Referring to Table A-2 and applying the methods of Section 6-1, we find that the critical value is $z = 1.645$, which is at the boundary of the critical region, as shown in Figure 8-6.

Step 7: Because the test statistic does fall within the critical region, we reject the null hypothesis.

Step 8: Because we reject H_0: $p = 0.5$, we conclude that there is sufficient sample evidence to support the claim that for couples using the XSORT gender selection method, most (more than half) of their babies are girls.

Solution: Confidence Interval Method

The claim that "with the XSORT method of gender selection, most babies are girls" is a claim that can be tested with a 0.05 significance level by constructing a 90% confidence interval. (See Table 8-1 on page 356 to see why the 0.05 significance level corresponds to a 90% confidence interval.)

The 90% confidence interval estimate of the population proportion p is found using the sample data consisting of $n = 14$ and $\hat{p} = 13/14$. Using the methods of Section 7-1 we get: $0.815 < p < 1.042$. The entire range of values in this confidence interval is greater than 0.5. Because we are 90% confident that the limits of 0.815 and 1.042 contain the true value of p, the sample data appear to support the claim that most (more than 0.5) XSORT babies are girls. In this case, the conclusion is the same as with the P-value method and the critical value method, but that is not always the case. It is possible that a conclusion based on the confidence interval can be different from the conclusion based on the P-value method or critical value method.

Finding the Number of Successes x

When using technology for hypothesis tests of proportions, we must usually enter the sample size n and the number of successes x, but in real applications the sample proportion $\hat{p}$ is often given instead of x. The number of successes x can be found by evaluating $x = n\hat{p}$, as illustrated in Example 1. Note that in Example 1, the result of 5587.712 adults must be rounded to the nearest whole number of 5588.

Is 0.05 a Bad Choice?

The value of 0.05 is a very common choice for serving as the cutoff separating results considered to be significant from those that are not. Science writer John Timmer wrote in *Ars Technica* that some problems with conclusions in science are attributable to the fact that statistics is sometimes weak because of the common use of 0.05 for a significance level. He gives examples of particle physics and genetics experiments in which P-values must be much lower than 0.05. He cites a study by statistician Valen Johnson, who suggested that we should raise standards by requiring that experiments use a P-value of 0.005 or lower. We do know that the choice of 0.05 is largely arbitrary, and lowering the significance level will result in fewer conclusions of significance, along with fewer wrong conclusions.

EXAMPLE 1   Finding the Number of Successes *x*

A study of sleepwalking or "nocturnal wandering" was described in the journal *Neurology,* and it included information that 29.2% of 19,136 American adults have sleepwalked. What is the actual number of adults who have sleepwalked?

SOLUTION

The number of adults who have sleepwalked is 29.2% of 19,136, or $0.292 \times 19,136 = 5587.712$, but the result must be a whole number, so we round the product to the nearest whole number of 5588.

> **CAUTION** When conducting hypothesis tests of claims about proportions, slightly different results can be obtained when calculating the test statistic using a given sample proportion instead of using a rounded value of *x* found by using $x = n\hat{p}$.

EXAMPLE 2   Fewer Than 30% of Adults Have Sleepwalked

Using the same sleepwalking data from Example 1 ($n = 19,136$ and $\hat{p} = 29.2\%$), would a reporter be justified in stating that "fewer than 30% of adults have sleepwalked"? Let's use a 0.05 significance level to test the claim that for the adult population, the proportion of those who have sleepwalked is less than 0.30.

SOLUTION

REQUIREMENT CHECK   (1) The sample is a simple random sample. (2) There is a fixed number (19,136) of independent trials with two categories (a subject has sleepwalked or has not). (3) The requirements $np \geq 5$ and $nq \geq 5$ are both satisfied with $n = 19,136$ and $p = 0.30$. [We get $np = (19,136)(0.30) = 5740.8$, which is greater than or equal to 5, and we also get $nq = (19,136)(0.70) = 13,395.2$, which is greater than or equal to 5.] The three requirements are all satisfied.

Step 1: The original claim is expressed in symbolic form as $p < 0.30$.

Step 2: The opposite of the original claim is $p \geq 0.30$.

Step 3: Because $p < 0.30$ does not contain equality, it becomes H_1. We get

$$H_0: p = 0.30 \text{ (null hypothesis)}$$
$$H_1: p < 0.30 \text{ (alternative hypothesis and original claim)}$$

Step 4: The significance level is $\alpha = 0.05$.

Step 5: Because the claim involves the proportion p, the statistic relevant to this test is the sample proportion $\hat{p}$ and the sampling distribution of sample proportions can be approximated by the normal distribution.

Step 6: Technology If using technology, the test statistic and the P-value will be provided. See the following results from StatCrunch showing that the test statistic is $z = -2.41$ (rounded) and the P-value $= 0.008$.

StatCrunch

Hypothesis test results:
p : Proportion of successes
$H_0 : p = 0.3$
$H_A : p < 0.3$

Proportion	Count	Total	Sample Prop.	Std. Err.	Z-Stat	P-value
p	5588	19136	0.29201505	0.0033127149	-2.4103945	0.008

Table A-2 If technology is not available, proceed as follows to conduct the hypothesis test using the *P*-value method summarized in Figure 8-1 on page 356.

The test statistic $z = -2.41$ is calculated as follows:

$$z = \frac{\hat{p} - p}{\sqrt{\dfrac{pq}{n}}} = \frac{\dfrac{5588}{19{,}136} - 0.30}{\sqrt{\dfrac{(0.30)(0.70)}{19{,}136}}} = -2.41$$

Refer to Figure 8-3 on page 360 for the procedure for finding the *P*-value. Figure 8-3 shows that for this left-tailed test, the *P*-value is the area to the left of the test statistic. Using Table A-2, we see that the area to the left of $z = -2.41$ is 0.0080, so the *P*-value is 0.0080.

Step 7: Because the *P*-value of 0.0080 is less than or equal to the significance level of 0.05, we reject the null hypothesis.

INTERPRETATION

Because we reject the null hypothesis, we support the alternative hypothesis. We therefore conclude that there is sufficient evidence to support the claim that fewer than 30% of adults have sleepwalked.

Lefties Die Sooner?

A study by psychologists Diane Halpern and Stanley Coren received considerable media attention and generated considerable interest when it concluded that left-handed people don't live as long as right-handed people. Based on their study, it appeared that left-handed people live an average of nine years less than righties. The Halpern/Coren study has been criticized for using flawed data. They used second-hand data by surveying relatives about people who had recently died. The myth of lefties dying younger became folklore that has survived many years. However, more recent studies show that left-handed people do *not* have shorter lives than those who are right-handed.

Critical Value Method If we were to repeat Example 2 using the critical value method of testing hypotheses, we would see that in Step 6 the critical value is $z = -1.645$, which can be found from technology or Table A-2. In Step 7 we would reject the null hypothesis because the test statistic of $z = -2.41$ would fall within the critical region bounded by $z = -1.645$. We would then reach the same conclusion given in Example 2.

Confidence Interval Method If we were to repeat Example 2 using the confidence interval method, we would use a 90% confidence level because we have a left-tailed test. (See Table 8-1.) We get this 90% confidence interval: $0.287 < p < 0.297$. Because the entire range of the confidence interval falls below 0.30, there is sufficient evidence to support the claim that fewer than 30% of adults have sleepwalked.

PART 2 Exact Methods for Testing Claims About a Population Proportion *p*

Instead of using the normal distribution as an *approximation* to the binomial distribution, we can get *exact* results by using the binomial probability distribution itself. Binomial probabilities are a real nuisance to calculate manually, but technology makes this approach quite simple. Also, this exact approach does not require that $np \geq 5$ and $nq \geq 5$, so we have a method that applies when that requirement is not satisfied. To test hypotheses using the exact method, find P-values as follows:

Exact Method Identify the sample size n, the number of successes x, and the claimed value of the population proportion p (used in the null hypothesis); then find the P-value by using technology for finding binomial probabilities as follows:

Left-tailed test: P-value $= P(x$ or fewer successes among n trials$)$

Right-tailed test: P-value $= P(x$ or more successes among n trials$)$

Two-tailed test: P-value $=$ twice the smaller of the preceding left-tailed and right-tailed values

Note: There is no universally accepted method for the above two-tailed exact case, so this case can be treated with other different approaches, some of which are quite complex. For example, Minitab uses a "likelihood ratio test" that is different from the above approach that is commonly used.

EXAMPLE 3   Using the Exact Method

In testing a method of gender selection, 10 randomly selected couples are treated with the method, they each have a baby, and 9 of the babies are girls. Use a 0.05 significance level to test the claim that with this method, the probability of a baby being a girl is greater than 0.75.

SOLUTION

REQUIREMENT CHECK   The normal approximation method described in Part 1 of this section requires that $np \geq 5$ and $nq \geq 5$, but $nq = (10)(0.25) = 2.5$, so the requirement is violated. The exact method has only the requirements of being a simple random sample and satisfying the conditions for binomial distribution, and those two requirements are satisfied. ☑

Here are the null and alternative hypotheses:

$$H_0: p = 0.75 \text{ (null hypothesis)}$$
$$H_1: p > 0.75 \text{ (alternative hypothesis and original claim)}$$

Instead of using the normal distribution, we use technology to find probabilities in a binomial distribution with $p = 0.75$. Because this is a right-tailed test, the P-value is the probability of 9 or more successes among 10 trials, assuming that $p = 0.75$. See the following Statdisk display of exact probabilities from the binomial distribution. This Statdisk display shows that the probability of 9 or more successes is 0.2440252 when rounded to seven decimal places, so the P-value is 0.2440252. The P-value is high (greater than 0.05), so we fail to reject the null hypothesis. There is not sufficient evidence to support the claim that with the gender selection method, the probability of a girl is greater than 0.75.

Statdisk

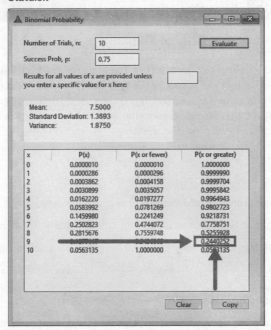

Improving the Exact Method A criticism of the exact method is that it is *too conservative* in the sense that the actual probability of a type I error is typically less than or equal to α, and it could be much lower than α.

> With the exact method, the *actual* probability of a type I error is less than or equal to α, which is the *desired* probability of a type I error.

A **simple continuity correction** improves the conservative behavior of the exact method with an adjustment to the P-value that is obtained by subtracting from it the value that is one-half the binomial probability at the boundary, as shown below. (See Exercise 33.) This method is easy to apply if technology is available for finding binomial probabilities.

Simple Continuity Correction to the Exact Method

Left-tailed test: $P\text{-value} = P(x \text{ or fewer}) - \dfrac{1}{2}P(\text{exactly } x)$

Right-tailed test: $P\text{-value} = P(x \text{ or more}) - \dfrac{1}{2}P(\text{exactly } x)$

Two-tailed test: $P\text{-value} = $ twice the smaller of the preceding left-tailed and right-tailed values

The above "simple continuity correction" is described in "Modifying the Exact Test for a Binomial Proportion and Comparisons with Other Approaches," by Alan Huston, *Journal of Applied Statistics,* Vol. 33, No. 7. For another improvement that uses weighted tail areas based on a measure of skewness, see the preceding article by Alan Huston.

TECH CENTER

Hypothesis Test: Proportion

Access tech instructions, videos, and data sets at **www.TriolaStats.com**

8-2 Basic Skills and Concepts

Statistical Literacy and Critical Thinking

In Exercises 1–4, use these results from a **USA Today** *survey in which 510 people chose to respond to this question that was posted on the* **USA Today** *website: "Should Americans replace passwords with biometric security (fingerprints, etc)?" Among the respondents, 53% said yes. We want to test the claim that more than half of the population believes that passwords should be replaced with biometric security.*

1. Number and Proportion

a. Identify the actual number of respondents who answered yes.

b. Identify the sample proportion and the symbol used to represent it.

2. Null and Alternative Hypotheses Identify the null hypothesis and alternative hypothesis.

3. Equivalence of Methods If we use the same significance level to conduct the hypothesis test using the *P*-value method, the critical value method, and a confidence interval, which method is not equivalent to the other two?

4. Requirements and Conclusions

a. Are any of the three requirements violated? Can the methods of this section be used to test the claim?

b. It was stated that we can easily remember how to interpret *P*-values with this: "If the *P* is low, the null must go." What does this mean?

c. Another memory trick commonly used is this: "If the *P* is high, the null will fly." Given that a hypothesis test never results in a conclusion of proving or supporting a null hypothesis, how is this memory trick misleading?

d. Common significance levels are 0.01 and 0.05. Why would it be unwise to use a significance level with a number like 0.0483?

Using Technology. *In Exercises 5–8, identify the indicated values or interpret the given display. Use the normal distribution as an approximation to the binomial distribution as described in Part 1 of this section. Use a 0.05 significance level and answer the following:*

a. Is the test two-tailed, left-tailed, or right-tailed?

b. What is the test statistic?

c. What is the *P*-value?

d. What is the null hypothesis, and what do you conclude about it?

e. What is the final conclusion?

TI-83/84 Plus

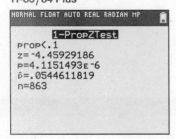

5. Adverse Reactions to Drug The drug Lipitor (atorvastatin) is used to treat high cholesterol. In a clinical trial of Lipitor, 47 of 863 treated subjects experienced headaches (based on data from Pfizer). The accompanying TI-83/84 Plus calculator display shows results from a test of the claim that fewer than 10% of treated subjects experience headaches.

6. Self-Driving Vehicles In a TE Connectivity survey of 1000 adults, 29% said that they would feel comfortable in a self-driving vehicle. The accompanying StatCrunch display results from testing the claim that more than $1/4$ of adults feel comfortable in a self-driving vehicle.

StatCrunch

Hypothesis test results:
p : Proportion of successes
$H_0 : p = 0.25$
$H_A : p > 0.25$

Proportion	Count	Total	Sample Prop.	Std. Err.	Z-Stat	P-value
p	290	1000	0.29	0.013693064	2.921187	0.0017

7. Hygiene A KRC Research poll of 1020 randomly selected adults showed that 65% of them wash their hands after touching an animal. The following Minitab display results from a test of the claim that 67% of adults wash their hands after touching an animal.

Minitab

Test of $p = 0.67$ vs $p \neq 0.67$

Sample	X	N	Sample p	95% CI	Z-Value	P-Value
1	663	1020	0.650000	(0.620729, 0.679271)	-1.36	0.174

8. Biometric Security In a *USA Today* survey of 510 people, 53% said that we should replace passwords with biometric security, such as fingerprints. The accompanying Statdisk display results from a test of the claim that half of us say that we should replace passwords with biometric security.

Statdisk

Sample proportion: 0.5294118
Test Statistic, z: 1.3284
Critical z: ±1.9600
P-Value: 0.1840

Testing Claims About Proportions. *In Exercises 9–28, test the given claim. Identify the null hypothesis, alternative hypothesis, test statistic, P-value, or critical value(s), then state the conclusion about the null hypothesis, as well as the final conclusion that addresses the original claim. Use the P-value method unless your instructor specifies otherwise. Use the normal distribution as an approximation to the binomial distribution, as described in Part 1 of this section.*

9. Gender Selection The Genetics & IVF Institute conducted a clinical trial of the YSORT method designed to increase the probability of conceiving a boy. 291 babies were born to parents using the YSORT method, and 239 of them were boys. Use a 0.01 significance level to test the claim that the YSORT method is effective in increasing the likelihood that a baby will be a boy.

10. Eliquis The drug Eliquis (apixaban) is used to help prevent blood clots in certain patients. In clinical trials, among 5924 patients treated with Eliquis, 153 developed the adverse reaction of nausea (based on data from Bristol-Myers Squibb Co.). Use a 0.05 significance level to test the claim that 3% of Eliquis users develop nausea. Does nausea appear to be a problematic adverse reaction?

11. Stem Cell Survey Adults were randomly selected for a *Newsweek* poll. They were asked if they "favor or oppose using federal tax dollars to fund medical research using stem cells obtained from human embryos." Of those polled, 481 were in favor, 401 were opposed, and 120 were unsure. A politician claims that people don't really understand the stem cell issue and their responses to such questions are random responses equivalent to a coin toss. Exclude the 120 subjects who said that they were unsure, and use a 0.01 significance level to test the claim that the proportion of subjects who respond in favor is equal to 0.5. What does the result suggest about the politician's claim?

12. Clinical Trial of Tamiflu Clinical trials involved treating flu patients with Tamiflu (oseltamivir phosphate), which is a medicine intended to attack the influenza virus and stop it from causing flu symptoms. Among 724 patients treated with Tamiflu, 72 experienced nausea as an adverse reaction. Use a 0.05 significance level to test the claim that the rate of nausea is greater than the 6% rate experienced by flu patients given a placebo. Does nausea appear to be a concern for those given the Tamiflu treatment?

13. OxyContin The drug OxyContin (oxycodone) is used to treat pain, but it is dangerous because it is addictive and can be lethal. In clinical trials, 227 subjects were treated with OxyContin and 52 of them developed nausea (based on data from Purdue Pharma L.P.). Use a 0.05 significance level to test the claim that more than 20% of OxyContin users develop nausea. Does the rate of nausea appear to be too high?

14. Medical Malpractice In a study of 1228 randomly selected medical malpractice lawsuits, it was found that 856 of them were dropped or dismissed (based on data from the Physicians Insurers Association of America). Use a 0.01 significance level to test the claim that most medical malpractice lawsuits are dropped or dismissed. Should this be comforting to physicians?

15. Survey Return Rate In a study of cell phone use and brain hemispheric dominance, an Internet survey was e-mailed to 5000 subjects randomly selected from an online group involved with ears. 717 surveys were returned. Use a 0.01 significance level to test the claim that the return rate is less than 15%.

16. Drug Screening The company Drug Test Success provides a "1-Panel-THC" test for marijuana usage. Among 300 tested subjects, results from 27 subjects were wrong (either a false positive or a false negative). Use a 0.05 significance level to test the claim that less than 10% of the test results are wrong. Does the test appear to be good for most purposes?

17. Births A random sample of 860 births in New York State included 426 boys. Use a 0.05 significance level to test the claim that 51.2% of newborn babies are boys. Do the results support the belief that 51.2% of newborn babies are boys?

18. Mendelian Genetics When Mendel conducted his famous genetics experiments with peas, one sample of offspring consisted of 428 green peas and 152 yellow peas. Use a 0.01 significance level to test Mendel's claim that under the same circumstances, 25% of offspring peas will be yellow. What can we conclude about Mendel's claim?

19. Predicting Gender of Baby A study addressed the issue of whether pregnant women can correctly guess the gender of their baby. Among 104 recruited subjects, 55% correctly guessed the gender of the baby (based on data from "Are Women Carrying 'Basketballs' Really Having Boys? Testing Pregnancy Folklore," by Perry, DiPietro, and Constigan, *Birth,* Vol. 26, No. 3). Use these sample data to test the claim that the success rate of such guesses is no different from the 50% success rate expected with random chance guesses. Use a 0.05 significance level.

20. Predicting Gender of Baby In the same study cited in the preceding exercise, 45 of the pregnant women had more than 12 years of education, and 32 of them made correct predictions. Use these results to test the claim that women with more than 12 years of education have a proportion of correct predictions that is greater than the 0.5 proportion expected with random guesses. Use a 0.01 significance level. Do these women appear to have an ability to correctly predict the gender of their babies?

21. Touch Therapy When she was 9 years of age, Emily Rosa did a science fair experiment in which she tested professional touch therapists to see if they could sense her energy field. She flipped a coin to select either her right hand or her left hand, and then she asked the therapists to identify the selected hand by placing their hand just under Emily's hand without seeing it and without touching it. Among 280 trials, the touch therapists were correct 123 times (based on data in "A Close Look at Therapeutic Touch," *Journal of the American Medical Association,* Vol. 279, No. 13). Use a 0.10 significance level to test the claim that touch therapists use a method equivalent to random guesses. Do the results suggest that touch therapists are effective?

22. Touch Therapy Repeat the preceding exercise using a 0.01 significance level. Does the conclusion change?

23. Cell Phones and Cancer In a study of 420,095 Danish cell phone users, 135 subjects developed cancer of the brain or nervous system (based on data from the *Journal of the National Cancer Institute* as reported in *USA Today*). Test the claim of a somewhat common belief that such cancers are affected by cell phone use. That is, test the claim that cell phone users develop cancer of the brain or nervous system at a rate that is different from the rate of 0.0340% for people who do not use cell phones. Because this issue has such great importance, use a 0.005 significance level. Based on these results, should cell phone users be concerned about cancer of the brain or nervous system?

24. Lie Detectors Trials in an experiment with a polygraph yield 98 results that include 24 cases of wrong results and 74 cases of correct results (based on data from experiments conducted by researchers Charles R. Honts of Boise State University and Gordon H. Barland of the Department of Defense Polygraph Institute). Use a 0.05 significance level to test the claim that such polygraph results are correct less than 80% of the time. Based on the results, should polygraph test results be prohibited as evidence in trials?

25. Testing Effectiveness of Nicotine Patches In one study of smokers who tried to quit smoking with nicotine patch therapy, 39 were smoking one year after the treatment and 32 were not smoking one year after the treatment (based on data from "High-Dose Nicotine Patch Therapy," by Dale et al., *Journal of the American Medical Association,* Vol. 274, No. 17). Use a 0.05 significance level to test the claim that among smokers who try to quit with nicotine patch therapy, the majority are smoking a year after the treatment. What do these results suggest about the effectiveness of nicotine patch therapy for those trying to quit smoking?

26. Postponing Death An interesting and popular hypothesis is that individuals can temporarily postpone death to survive a major holiday or important event such as a birthday. In a study, it was found that there were 6062 deaths in the week before Thanksgiving, and 5938 deaths the week after Thanksgiving (based on data from "Holidays, Birthdays, and Postponement of Cancer Death," by Young and Hade, *Journal of the American Medical Association,* Vol. 292, No. 24). If people can postpone death until after Thanksgiving, then the proportion of deaths in the week before should be less than 0.5. Use a 0.05 significance level to test the claim that the proportion of deaths in the week before Thanksgiving is less than 0.5. Based on the result, does there appear to be any indication that people can temporarily postpone death to survive the Thanksgiving holiday?

27. Smoking Stopped In a program designed to help patients stop smoking, 198 patients were given *sustained* care, and 82.8% of them were no longer smoking after one month (based on data from "Sustained Care Intervention and Postdischarge Smoking Cessation Among Hospitalized Adults," by Rigotti et al., *Journal of the American Medical Association,* Vol. 312, No. 7). Use a 0.01 significance level to test the claim that 80% of patients stop smoking when given sustained care. Does sustained care appear to be effective?

28. Medication Usage In a survey of 3005 adults aged 57 through 85 years, it was found that 81.7% of them used at least one prescription medication (based on data from "Use of Prescription and Over-the-Counter Medications and Dietary Supplements Among Older Adults in the United States," by Qato et al., *Journal of the American Medical Association,* Vol. 300, No. 24). Use a 0.01 significance level to test the claim that more than 3/4 of adults use at least one prescription medication. Does the rate of prescription use among adults appear to be high?

8-2   Beyond the Basics

29. Exact Method For each of the three different methods of hypothesis testing (identified in the column at the left), enter the *P*-values corresponding to the given alternative hypothesis and sample data. Comment on the results.

	$H_1: p \neq 0.5$ $n = 10, x = 9$	$H_1: p \neq 0.4$ $n = 10, x = 9$	$H_1: p > 0.5$ $n = 1009, x = 545$
Normal approximation			
Exact			
Exact with simple continuity correction			

30. Using Confidence Intervals to Test Hypotheses When analyzing the last digits of telephone numbers of hospital patients, it is found that among 1000 randomly selected digits, 119 are zeros. If the digits are randomly selected, the proportion of zeros should be 0.1.

a. Use the critical value method with a 0.05 significance level to test the claim that the proportion of zeros equals 0.1.

b. Use the P-value method with a 0.05 significance level to test the claim that the proportion of zeros equals 0.1.

c. Use the sample data to construct a 95% confidence interval estimate of the proportion of zeros. What does the confidence interval suggest about the claim that the proportion of zeros equals 0.1?

d. Compare the results from the critical value method, the P-value method, and the confidence interval method. Do they all lead to the same conclusion?

31. Power For a hypothesis test with a specified significance level α, the probability of a type I error is α, whereas the probability β of a type II error depends on the particular value of p that is used as an alternative to the null hypothesis.

a. Using an alternative hypothesis of $p < 0.4$, using a sample size of $n = 50$, and assuming that the true value of p is 0.25, find the power of the test. See Exercise 34 "Calculating Power" in Section 8-1. [*Hint:* Use the values $p = 0.25$ and $pq/n = (0.25)(0.75)/50.$]

b. Find the value of β, the probability of making a type II error.

c. Given the conditions cited in part (a), find the power of the test. What does the power tell us about the effectiveness of the test?

8-3 Testing a Claim About a Mean

Key Concept Testing a claim about a population mean is one of the most important methods presented in this book. This section deals with the very realistic and commonly used case in which the population standard deviation σ is not known.

In reality, it is very rare that we test a claim about an unknown value of a population mean μ but we somehow know the value of the population standard deviation σ. The realistic situation is that we test a claim about a population mean and the value of the population standard deviation σ is not known. When σ is not known, we estimate it with the sample standard deviation s. From the central limit theorem (Section 6-4), we know that the distribution of sample means $\bar{x}$ is approximately a normal distribution with mean $\mu_{\bar{x}} = \mu$ and standard deviation $\sigma_{\bar{x}} = \sigma/\sqrt{n}$, but if σ is unknown, we estimate $\sigma/\sqrt{n}$ with $s/\sqrt{n}$, which is used in the test statistic for a "t test." This test statistic has a distribution called the Student t distribution. The requirements, test statistic, P-value, and critical values are summarized in the Key Elements box that follows.

Equivalent Methods

For the t test described in this section, the P-value method, the critical value method, and the confidence interval method are all equivalent in the sense that they all lead to the same conclusions.

Testing Claims About a Population Mean with σ Not Known

Objective

Use a formal hypothesis test to test a claim about a population mean μ.

Notation

n = sample size

s = *sample* standard deviation

$\bar{x}$ = *sample* mean

$\mu_{\bar{x}}$ = *population* mean (this value is taken from the claim and is used in the statement of the null hypothesis H_0)

Requirements

1. The sample is a simple random sample.

2. Either or both of these conditions are satisfied: The population is normally distributed or $n > 30$.

Test Statistic for Testing a Claim About a Mean

$$t = \frac{\bar{x} - \mu_{\bar{x}}}{\frac{s}{\sqrt{n}}}$$ (Round t to three decimal places, as in Table A-3.)

P-Values: Use technology or use the Student t distribution (Table A-3) with degrees of freedom given by df = $n - 1$. (Figure 8-3 in Section 8-1 on page 360 summarizes the procedure for finding P-values.)

Critical Values: Use the Student t distribution (Table A-3) with degrees of freedom given by df = $n - 1$. (When Table A-3 doesn't include the number of degrees of freedom, you could be conservative by using the next lower number of degrees of freedom found in the table, you could use the closest number of degrees of freedom in the table, or you could interpolate.)

Requirement of Normality or $n > 30$ This t test is *robust* against a departure from normality, meaning that the test works reasonably well if the departure from normality is not too extreme. Verify that there are no outliers and that the histogram or dotplot has a shape that is not very far from a normal distribution.

If the original population is not itself normally distributed, we use the condition $n > 30$ for justifying use of the normal distribution, but there is no exact specific minimum sample size that works for all cases. Sample sizes of 15 to 30 are sufficient if the population has a distribution that is not far from normal, but some populations have distributions that are extremely far from normal, and sample sizes greater than 30 might be necessary. In this text we use the simplified criterion of $n > 30$ as justification for treating the distribution of sample means as a normal distribution, regardless of how far the distribution departs from a normal distribution.

Important Properties of the Student t Distribution

Here is a brief review of important properties of the Student t distribution first presented in Section 7-2:

1. The Student t distribution is different for different sample sizes (see Figure 7-4 in Section 7-2).

2. The Student t distribution has the same general bell shape as the standard normal distribution; its wider shape reflects the greater variability that is expected when s is used to estimate σ.

continued

3. The Student t distribution has a mean of $t = 0$ (just as the standard normal distribution has a mean of $z = 0$).

4. The standard deviation of the Student t distribution varies with the sample size and is greater than 1 (unlike the standard normal distribution, which has $\sigma = 1$).

5. As the sample size n gets larger, the Student t distribution gets closer to the standard normal distribution.

P-Value Method with Technology

If suitable technology is available, the P-value method of testing hypotheses is the way to go.

 EXAMPLE 1 Adult Sleep: *P*-Value Method with Technology

The authors obtained times of sleep for randomly selected adult subjects included in the National Health and Nutrition Examination Study, and those times (hours) are listed below. Here are the unrounded statistics for this sample: $n = 12$, $\bar{x} = 6.83333333$ hours, $s = 1.99240984$ hours. A common recommendation is that adults should sleep between 7 hours and 9 hours each night. Use the P-value method with a 0.05 significance level to test the claim that the mean amount of sleep for adults is less than 7 hours.

$$4 \quad 8 \quad 4 \quad 4 \quad 8 \quad 6 \quad 9 \quad 7 \quad 7 \quad 10 \quad 7 \quad 8$$

SOLUTION

REQUIREMENT CHECK (1) The sample is a simple random sample. (2) The second requirement is that "the population is normally distributed or $n > 30$." The sample size is $n = 12$, which does not exceed 30, so we must determine whether the sample data appear to be from a normally distributed population. The accompanying histogram and normal quantile plot, along with the apparent absence of outliers, indicate that the sample appears to be from a population with a distribution that is approximately normal. Both requirements are satisfied. ☑

Statdisk

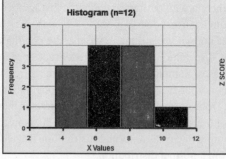
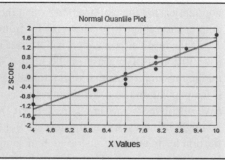

Here are the steps that follow the procedure summarized in Figure 8-1 on page 356.

Step 1: The claim that "the mean amount of adult sleep is less than 7 hours" becomes $\mu < 7$ hours when expressed in symbolic form.

Step 2: The alternative (in symbolic form) to the original claim is $\mu \geq 7$ hours.

Step 3: Because the statement $\mu < 7$ hours does not contain the condition of equality, it becomes the alternative hypothesis H_1. The null hypothesis H_0 is the statement that $\mu = 7$ hours.

$H_0: \mu = 7$ hours (null hypothesis)

$H_1: \mu < 7$ hours (alternative hypothesis and original claim)

Step 4: As specified in the statement of the problem, the significance level is $\alpha = 0.05$.

Step 5: Because the claim is made about the *population mean μ*, the sample statistic most relevant to this test is the *sample mean $\bar{x}$*, and we use the *t* distribution.

Step 6: The sample statistics of $n = 12$, $\bar{x} = 6.83333333$ hours, $s = 1.99240984$ hours are used to calculate the test statistic as follows, but technologies provide the test statistic of $t = -0.290$. In calculations such as the following, it is good to carry extra decimal places and not round.

$$t = \frac{\bar{x} - \mu_{\bar{x}}}{\frac{s}{\sqrt{n}}} = \frac{6.83333333 - 7}{\frac{1.99240984}{\sqrt{12}}} = -0.290$$

P-Value with Technology We could use technology to obtain the *P*-value. Shown here are results from several technologies, and we can see that the *P*-value is 0.3887 (rounded). (SPSS shows a two-tailed *P*-value of 0.777, so it must be halved for this one-tailed test.)

Step 7: Because the *P*-value of 0.3887 is greater than the significance level of $\alpha = 0.05$, we fail to reject the null hypothesis.

INTERPRETATION

Step 8: Because we fail to reject the null hypothesis, we conclude that there is not sufficient evidence to support the claim that the mean amount of adult sleep is less than 7 hours.

TI-83/84 Plus

```
NORMAL FLOAT AUTO REAL RADIAN MP

          T-Test
μ<7
t=-.2897748534
p=.3886888459
x̄=6.833333333
Sx=1.99240984
n=12
```

JMP

Hypothesized Value	7
Actual Estimate	6.83333
DF	11
Std Dev	1.99241
t Test	
Test Statistic	-0.2898
Prob > |t|	0.7774
Prob > t	0.6113
Prob < t	0.3887

Excel (XLSTAT)

Difference	-0.1667
t (Observed value)	-0.2898
t (Critical value)	-1.7959
DF	11
p-value (one-tailed)	0.3887
alpha	0.05

Minitab

Test of μ = 7 vs < 7

Variable	N	Mean	StDev	SE Mean	95% Upper Bound	T	P
Sleep	12	6.833	1.992	0.575	7.866	−0.29	0.389

StatCrunch

Hypothesis test results:
μ : Mean of variable
$H_0 : \mu = 7$
$H_A : \mu < 7$

Variable	Sample Mean	Std. Err.	DF	T-Stat	P-value
Sleep	6.8333333	0.57515918	11	-0.28977485	0.3887

Statdisk

t Test
Test Statistic, t: -0.2898
Critical t: -1.7959
P-Value: 0.3887

90% Confidence interval:
5.800414 < μ < 7.866252

SPSS

	Test Value = 7					
					95% Confidence Interval of the Difference	
	t	df	Sig. (2-tailed)	Mean Difference	Lower	Upper
SLEEP	-.290	11	.777	-.16667	-1.4326	1.0993

Examine the technology displays to see that only two of them include critical values, but they all include *P*-values. This is a major reason why the *P*-value method of testing hypotheses has become so widely used in recent years.

P-Value Method Without Technology

If suitable technology is not available, we can use Table A-3 to identify a *range of values* containing the *P*-value. In using Table A-3, keep in mind that it is designed for positive values of *t* and right-tail areas only, but left-tail areas correspond to the same *t* values with negative signs.

EXAMPLE 2 **Adult Sleep: *P*-Value Method Without Technology**

Example 1 is a left-tailed test with a test statistic of $t = -0.290$ (rounded) and a sample size of $n = 12$, so the number of degrees of freedom is df $= n - 1 = 11$. Using the test statistic of $t = -0.290$ with Table A-3, examine the values of *t* in the row for df $= 11$ to see that 0.290 is less than all of the listed *t* values in the row, which indicates that the area in the left tail below the test statistic of $t = -0.290$ is greater than 0.10. In this case, Table A-3 allows us to conclude that the *P*-value > 0.10, but technology provided the *P*-value of 0.3887. With a *P*-value > 0.10, the conclusions are the same as in Example 1.

HINT: Because using Table A-3 to find a range of values containing the *P*-value can be a bit tricky, the critical value method (see Example 3) might be easier than the *P*-value method if suitable technology is not available.

Critical Value Method

EXAMPLE 3 **Adult Sleep: Critical Value Method**

Example 1 is a left-tailed test with test statistic $t = -0.290$ (rounded). The sample size is $n = 12$, so the number of degrees of freedom is df $= n - 1 = 11$. Given the significance level of $\alpha = 0.05$, refer to the row of Table A-3 corresponding to 11 degrees of freedom, and refer to the column identifying an "area in one tail" of 0.05 (the significance level). The intersection of the row and column yields the critical value of $t = 1.796$, but this test is left-tailed, so the actual critical value is $t = -1.796$. Figure 8-7 shows that the test statistic of $t = -0.290$ does not fall within the critical region bounded by the critical value $t = -1.796$, so we fail to reject the null hypothesis. The conclusions are the same as those given in Example 1.

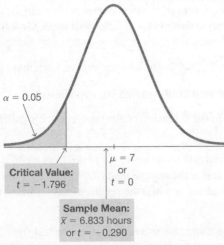

$\alpha = 0.05$

Critical Value:
$t = -1.796$

$\mu = 7$
or
$t = 0$

Sample Mean:
$\bar{x} = 6.833$ hours
or $t = -0.290$

FIGURE 8-7   *t* Test: Critical Value Method

Confidence Interval Method

 EXAMPLE 4 **Adult Sleep: Confidence Interval Method**

Example 1 is a left-tailed test with significance level $\alpha = 0.05$, so we should use 90% as the confidence level (as indicated by Table 8-1 on page 356). For the sample data given in Example 1, here is the 90% confidence interval estimate of μ: 5.80 hours $< \mu <$ 7.87 hours. In testing the claim that $\mu < 7$ hours, we use $H_0: \mu = 7$ hours, but the assumed value of $\mu = 7$ hours is contained within the confidence interval limits, so the confidence interval is telling us that 7 hours could be the value of μ. We don't have sufficient evidence to reject $H_0: \mu = 7$ hours, so we fail to reject this null hypothesis and we get the same conclusions given in Example 1.

 EXAMPLE 5 **Is the Mean Body Temperature Really 98.6°F?**

Data Set 2 "Body Temperatures" in Appendix B includes measured body temperatures with these statistics for 12 AM on day 2: $n = 106$, $\bar{x} = 98.20°F$, $s = 0.62°F$. Use a 0.05 significance level to test the common belief that the population mean is 98.6°F.

SOLUTION

REQUIREMENT CHECK   (1) With the study design used, we can treat the sample as a simple random sample. (2) The second requirement is that "the population is normally distributed or $n > 30$." The sample size is $n = 106$, so the second requirement is satisfied and there is no need to investigate the normality of the data. Both requirements are satisfied. ✓
Here are the steps that follow the procedure summarized in Figure 8-1.

Step 1: The claim that "the population mean is 98.6°F" becomes $\mu = 98.6°F$ when expressed in symbolic form.

Step 2: The alternative (in symbolic form) to the original claim is $\mu \neq 98.6°F$.

continued

Step 3: Because the statement $\mu \neq 98.6°F$ does not contain the condition of equality, it becomes the alternative hypothesis H_1. The null hypothesis H_0 is the statement that $\mu = 98.6°F$.

$$H_0: \mu = 98.6°F \text{ (null hypothesis and original claim)}$$

$$H_1: \mu \neq 98.6°F \text{ (alternative hypothesis)}$$

Step 4: As specified in the statement of the problem, the significance level is $\alpha = 0.05$.

Step 5: Because the claim is made about the *population mean* μ, the sample statistic most relevant to this test is the *sample mean* $\bar{x}$. We use the t distribution because the relevant sample statistic is $\bar{x}$ and the requirements for using the t distribution are satisfied.

Step 6: The sample statistics are used to calculate the test statistic as follows, but technologies use unrounded values to provide the test statistic of $t = -6.61$.

$$t = \frac{\bar{x} - \mu_{\bar{x}}}{\frac{s}{\sqrt{n}}} = \frac{98.20 - 98.6}{\frac{0.62}{\sqrt{106}}} = -6.64$$

P-Value: The P-value is 0.0000 or 0+ (or "less than 0.01" if using Table A-3).

Critical Values: The critical values are ± 1.983 (or ± 1.984 if using Table A-3).

Confidence Interval: The 95% confidence interval is $98.08°F < \mu < 98.32°F$.

Step 7: All three approaches lead to the same conclusion: Reject H_0.

- **P-Value:** The P-value of 0.0000 is less than the significance level of $\alpha = 0.05$.
- **Critical Values:** The test statistic $t = -6.64$ falls in the critical region bounded by ± 1.983.
- **Confidence Interval:** The claimed mean of 98.6°F does not fall within the confidence interval of $98.08°F < \mu < 98.32°F$.

INTERPRETATION

Step 8: There is sufficient evidence to warrant *rejection* of the common belief that the population mean body temperature is 98.6°F.

Alternative Methods Used When Population Is Not Normal and $n \leq 30$

The methods of this section include two requirements: (1) The sample is a simple random sample; (2) either the population is normally distributed or $n > 30$. If we have sample data that are not collected in an appropriate way, such as a voluntary response sample, it is likely that there is nothing that can be done to salvage the data, and the methods of this section should not be used. If the data are a simple random sample but the second condition is violated, there are alternative methods that could be used, including these three alternative methods:

- **Bootstrap Resampling** Use the confidence interval method of testing hypotheses, but obtain the confidence interval using bootstrap resampling, as described in Section 7-4. Be careful to use the appropriate confidence level, as indicated by Table 8-1 on page 356. Reject the null hypothesis if the confidence interval limits do not contain the value of the mean claimed in the null hypothesis. See Example 6.

- **Sign Test** See Section 13-2.
- **Wilcoxon Signed-Ranks Test** See Section 13-3.

 EXAMPLE 6 **Bootstrap Resampling**

Listed below is a random sample of times (seconds) of tobacco use in animated children's movies (from Data Set 13 "Alcohol and Tobacco in Movies"). Use a 0.05 significance level to test the claim that the sample is from a population with a mean greater than 1 minute (or 60 seconds).

0 223 0 176 0 548 0 37 158 51 0 0 299 37 0 11 0 0 0 0

SOLUTION

REQUIREMENT CHECK The t test described in this section requires that the population is normally distributed or $n > 30$, but we have $n = 20$ and the accompanying normal quantile plot shows that the sample does not appear to be from a normally distributed population. The t test should *not* be used. ☑

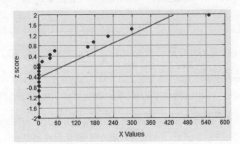

SOLUTION

Instead of incorrectly using the t test, we use the bootstrap resampling method described in Section 7-4. After obtaining 1000 bootstrap samples and finding the mean of each sample, we sort the means. Because the test is right-tailed with a 0.05 significance level, we use the 1000 sorted sample means to find the 90% confidence interval limits of $P_5 = 29.9$ seconds and $P_{95} = 132.9$ seconds. The 90% confidence interval is 29.9 seconds $< \mu <$ 132.9 seconds. (These values can vary somewhat.) Because the assumed mean of 60 seconds is contained within those confidence interval limits, we fail to reject H_0: $\mu = 60$ seconds. There is not sufficient evidence to support H_1: $\mu > 60$ seconds.

INTERPRETATION

There is not sufficient evidence to support the claim that the given sample is from a population with a mean greater than 60 seconds.

TECH CENTER

 Hypothesis Test: Mean
Access tech instructions, videos, and data sets at **www.TriolaStats.com**

8-3   Basic Skills and Concepts

Statistical Literacy and Critical Thinking

1. Alcohol Use and Video Games: Checking Requirements Twelve different video games showing alcohol use were observed. The duration times of alcohol use were recorded, with the times (seconds) listed below (based on data from "Content and Ratings of Teen-Rated Video Games," by Haninger and Thompson, *Journal of the American Medical Association,* Vol. 291, No. 7). What requirements must be satisfied to test the claim that the sample is from a population with a mean greater than 90 sec? Are the requirements all satisfied?

84   14   583   50   0   57   207   43   178   0   2   57

2. df If we are using the sample data from Exercise 1 for a *t* test of the claim that the population mean is greater than 90 sec, what does df denote, and what is its value?

3. *t* Test Exercise 2 refers to a *t* test. What is a *t* test? Why is the letter *t* used?

4. Confidence Interval Assume that we will use the sample data from Exercise 1 "Alcohol Use and Video Games" with a 0.05 significance level in a test of the claim that the population mean is greater than 90 sec. If we want to construct a confidence interval to be used for testing that claim, what confidence level should be used for the confidence interval? If the confidence interval is found to be 21.1 sec $< \mu <$ 191.4 sec, what should we conclude about the claim?

Finding *P*-values. *In Exercises 5–8, either use technology to find the P-value or use Table A-3 to find a range of values for the P-value.*

5. Body Temperature The claim is that for 12 AM body temperatures, the mean is $\mu < 98.6°F$. The sample size is $n = 4$ and the test statistic is $t = -2.503$.

6. Body Temperature Data Set 2 "Body Temperatures" in Appendix B includes measured human body temperatures with these statistics for 12 AM on day 1: $n = 93$, $\bar{x} = 98.12°F$, $s = 0.65°F$. In testing the claim that the mean body temperature is 98.6°F, the test statistic $t = -7.122$ is obtained.

7. Platelets The claim is that for the population of adult females, the mean platelet count is $\mu < 300$. The sample size is $n = 15$ and the test statistic is $t = -0.666$.

8. Platelets The claim is that for the population of adult males, the mean platelet count is $\mu > 210$. The sample size is $n = 53$ and the test statistic is $t = 1.368$.

Testing Hypotheses. *In Exercises 9–24, assume that a simple random sample has been selected and test the given claim. Unless specified by your instructor, use either the P-value method or the critical value method for testing hypotheses. Identify the null and alternative hypotheses, test statistic, P-value (or range of P-values), or critical value(s), and state the final conclusion that addresses the original claim.*

Difference	-0.4737
t (Observed value)	-3.8654
|t| (Critical value)	2.0262
DF	37
p-value (Two-tailed)	0.0004
alpha	0.05

9. Body Temperatures Data Set 2 "Body Temperatures" in Appendix B includes 38 body temperatures measured at 8 AM on day 1 of a study, and the accompanying XLSTAT display results from using those data to test the claim that the mean body temperature is equal to 98.6°F. Conduct the hypothesis test using these results.

	t Test
Test Statistic	-13.272
Prob > |t|	<.0001*
Prob > t	1.0000
Prob < t	<.0001*

10. Body Temperatures Data Set 2 "Body Temperatures" in Appendix B includes 70 body temperatures measured at 8 AM on day 2 of a study, and the accompanying JMP display results from using those data to test the claim that the mean body temperature is equal to 98.6°F. Conduct the hypothesis test using these results.

11. Platelets Data Set 1 "Body Data" in Appendix B includes platelet counts (1000 cells/μL) measured from 147 adult females. In testing the claim that the population of adult females has a mean platelet count less than 270, the accompanying Statdisk display is obtained by assuming a 0.05 significance level.

Test Statistic, t:	−2.7637
Critical t:	−1.6554
P-Value:	0.0032

12. Platelets Data Set 1 "Body Data" in Appendix B includes platelet counts (1000 cells/μL) measured from 153 adult males. In testing the claim that the population of adult males has a mean platelet count greater than 220, the accompanying Minitab display is obtained.

Test of $\mu = 220$ vs > 220

Variable	N	Mean	StDev	SE Mean	95% Lower Bound	T	P
Platelet	153	224.27	59.46	4.81	216.32	0.89	0.188

13. Waist Size Data Set 1 "Body Data" in Appendix B includes waist size of 147 females, and the summary statistics are $\bar{x} = 98.24$ cm and $s = 17.94$ cm. Use a 0.01 significance level to test that claim that the population of waist size of females is less than 100 cm.

14. Waist Size Data Set 1 "Body Data" in Appendix B includes waist size of 153 males, and the summary statistics are $\bar{x} = 100.1$ cm and $s = 14.94$ cm. Use a 0.01 significance level to test that claim that the population of waist size of males is greater than 98 cm.

15. Garlic for Reducing Cholesterol In a test of the effectiveness of garlic for lowering cholesterol, 49 subjects were treated with raw garlic. Cholesterol levels were measured before and after the treatment. The changes (before minus after) in their levels of low-density lipoprotein (LDL) cholesterol (in mg/dL) have a mean of 0.4 and a standard deviation of 21.0 (based on data from "Effect of Raw Garlic vs Commercial Garlic Supplements on Plasma Lipid Concentrations in Adults with Moderate Hypercholesterolemia," by Gardner et al., *Archives of Internal Medicine*, Vol. 167, No. 4). Use a 0.05 significance level to test the claim that with garlic treatment, the mean change in LDL cholesterol is greater than 0. What do the results suggest about the effectiveness of the garlic treatment?

16. Insomnia Treatment A clinical trial was conducted to test the effectiveness of the drug zopiclone for treating insomnia in older subjects. Before treatment with zopiclone, 16 subjects had a mean wake time of 102.8 min. After treatment with zopiclone, the 16 subjects had a mean wake time of 98.9 min and a standard deviation of 42.3 min (based on data from "Cognitive Behavioral Therapy vs Zopiclone for Treatment of Chronic Primary Insomnia in Older Adults," by Sivertsen et al., *Journal of the American Medical Association*, Vol. 295, No. 24). Assume that the 16 sample values appear to be from a normally distributed population, and test the claim that after treatment with zopiclone, subjects have a mean wake time of less than 102.8 min. Does zopiclone appear to be effective?

17. Is the Diet Practical? When 40 people used the Weight Watchers diet for one year, their mean weight loss was 3.0 lb and the standard deviation was 4.9 lb (based on data from "Comparison of the Atkins, Ornish, Weight Watchers, and Zone Diets for Weight Loss and Heart Disease Reduction," by Dansinger et al., *Journal of the American Medical Association*, Vol. 293, No. 1). Use a 0.01 significance level to test the claim that the mean weight loss is greater than 0. Based on these results, does the diet appear to have statistical significance? Does the diet appear to have practical significance?

18. Conductor Life Span A *New York Times* article noted that the mean life span for 35 male symphony conductors was 73.4 years, in contrast to the mean of 69.5 years for males in the general population. Assuming that the 35 males have life spans with a standard deviation of 8.7 years, use a 0.05 significance level to test the claim that male symphony conductors have a mean life span that is greater than 69.5 years. Does it appear that male symphony conductors live longer than males from the general population? Why doesn't the experience of being a male symphony conductor cause men to live longer? (*Hint*: Are male symphony conductors born as conductors, or do they become conductors at a much later age?)

19. Course Evaluations Data from student course evaluations were obtained from the University of Texas at Austin. The summary statistics are $n = 436$, $\bar{x} = 3.97$, $s = 0.55$. Use a 0.05 significance level to test the claim that the population of student course evaluations has a mean equal to 4.00. Do the results apply to the population of all students?

20. Treating Chronic Fatigue Syndrome Patients with chronic fatigue syndrome were tested, and then retested after being treated with fludrocortisone. A standard scale from -7 to $+7$ is used to measure fatigue before and after the treatment. The changes are summarized with these statistics: $n = 21$, $\bar{x} = 4.00$, $s = 2.17$ (based on data from "The Relationship Between Neurally Mediated Hypotension and the Chronic Fatigue Syndrome," by Bou-Holaigah, Rowe, Kan, and Calkins, *Journal of the American Medical Association,* Vol. 274, No. 12). The changes were computed in a way that makes positive values represent improvements. Use a 0.01 significance level to test the claim that the mean change is positive. Does the treatment appear to be effective?

21. Lead in Medicine Listed below are the lead concentrations (in $\mu g/g$) measured in different Ayurveda medicines. Ayurveda is a traditional medical system commonly used in India. The lead concentrations listed here are from medicines manufactured in the United States (based on data from "Lead, Mercury, and Arsenic in US and Indian Manufactured Ayurvedic Medicines Sold via the Internet," by Saper et al., *Journal of the American Medical Association,* Vol. 300, No. 8). Use a 0.05 significance level to test the claim that the mean lead concentration for all such medicines is less than 14 $\mu g/g$.

3.0   6.5   6.0   5.5   20.5   7.5   12.0   20.5   11.5   17.5

22. Got a Minute? Students of one of the authors estimated the length of one minute without reference to a watch or clock, and the times (seconds) are listed below. Use a 0.05 significance level to test the claim that these times are from a population with a mean equal to 60 seconds. Does it appear that students are reasonably good at estimating one minute?

69   81   39   65   42   21   60   63   66   48   64   70   96   91   65

23. Car Booster Seats The National Highway Traffic Safety Administration conducted crash tests of child booster seats for cars. Listed below are results from those tests, with the measurements given in hic (standard "head injury condition" units). The safety requirement is that the hic measurement should be less than 1000 hic. Use a 0.01 significance level to test the claim that the sample is from a population with a mean less than 1000 hic. Do the results suggest that all of the child booster seats meet the specified requirement?

774   649   1210   546   431   612

24. Heights of Supermodels Listed below are the heights (cm) for the simple random sample of female supermodels Lima, Bundchen, Ambrosio, Ebanks, Iman, Rubik, Kurkova, Kerr, Kroes, Swanepoel, Prinsloo, Hosk, Kloss, Robinson, Heatherton, and Refaeli. Use a 0.01 significance level to test the claim that supermodels have heights with a mean that is greater than the mean height of 162 cm for women in the general population. Given that there are only 16 heights represented, can we really conclude that supermodels are taller than the typical woman?

178   177   176   174   175   178   175   178   178   177   180   176   180   178   180   176

Large Data Sets from Appendix B. *In Exercises 25–28, use the data set in Appendix B to test the given claim. Use the P-value method unless your instructor specifies otherwise.*

25. Pulse Rates Use the pulse rates of adult females listed in Data Set 1 "Body Data" in Appendix B to test the claim that the mean is less than 75 bpm. Use a 0.05 significance level.

26. Pulse Rates Use the pulse rates of adult males listed in Data Set 1 "Body Data" in Appendix B to test the claim that the mean is less than 75 bpm. Use a 0.05 significance level.

27. Diastolic Blood Pressure for Women Use the diastolic blood pressure measurements for adult females listed in Data Set 1 "Body Data" in Appendix B and test the claim that the adult female population has a mean diastolic blood pressure level less than 90 mm Hg. A diastolic blood pressure above 90 is considered to be hypertension. Use a 0.05 significance level. Based on the result, can we conclude that none of the adult females in the sample have hypertension?

28. Diastolic Blood Pressure for Men Repeat the preceding exercise for adult males instead of adult females.

8-3 Beyond the Basics

29. Finding Critical t Values When finding critical values, we often need significance levels other than those available in Table A-3. One approach is to approximate critical t values by calculating $t = \sqrt{\text{df} \cdot (e^{A^2/\text{df}} - 1)}$ where $\text{df} = n - 1$, $e = 2.718$, $A = z(8 \cdot \text{df} + 3)/(8 \cdot \text{df} + 1)$, and z is the critical z score. Use this approximation to find the critical t score for Exercise 11 "Platelets," using a significance level of 0.05. Compare the result to the critical t value shown in the Statdisk display. Does this approximation appear to work reasonably well?

30. Interpreting Power For the sample data in Example 1 "Adult Sleep" from this section, Minitab and StatCrunch show that the hypothesis test has a power of 0.4943 of supporting the claim that $\mu < 7$ hours of sleep when the actual population mean is 6.0 hours of sleep. Interpret this value of the power, then identify the value of β and interpret that value. (For the t test in this section, a "noncentrality parameter" makes calculations of power much more complicated than the process described in Section 8-1, so software is recommended for power calculations.)

8-4   Testing a Claim About a Standard Deviation or Variance

Key Concept This section presents methods for conducting a formal hypothesis test of a claim made about a population standard deviation σ or population variance σ^2. The methods of this section use the chi-square distribution that was first introduced in Section 7-3.

> **CAUTION** The X^2 (chi-square) test of this section is *not robust* against a departure from normality, meaning that the test does not work well if the population has a distribution that is far from normal. The condition of a normally distributed population is therefore a much stricter requirement when testing claims about σ or σ^2 than when testing claims about a population mean μ.

Equivalent Methods

When testing claims about σ or σ^2, the P-value method, the critical value method, and the confidence interval method are all equivalent in the sense that they will always lead to the same conclusion.

KEY ELEMENTS

Testing Claims About σ or σ^2

Objective:

Conduct a hypothesis test of a claim made about a population standard deviation σ or population variance σ^2.

Notation

n = sample size s = *sample* standard deviation
σ = *population* standard deviation s^2 = *sample* variance
σ^2 = *population* variance

Requirements

1. The sample is a simple random sample.

2. The population has a normal distribution. (This is a fairly strict requirement.)

Test Statistic

$$\chi^2 = \frac{(n-1)s^2}{\sigma^2} \text{ (round to three decimal places, as in Table A-4)}$$

P-Values: Use technology or Table A-4 with degrees of freedom of df $= n - 1$.
Critical Values: Use Table A-4 with degrees of freedom df $= n - 1$.

Properties of the Chi-Square Distribution

The chi-square distribution was introduced in Section 7-3, where we noted the following important properties.

1. All values of χ^2 are nonnegative, and the distribution is not symmetric (see Figure 8-8).

2. There is a different χ^2 distribution for each number of degrees of freedom (see Figure 8-9).

3. The critical values are found in Table A-4 using

$$\text{degrees of freedom} = n - 1$$

Here is an important note if using Table A-4 for finding critical values:

In Table A-4, each critical value of χ^2 in the body of the table corresponds to an area given in the top row of the table, and each area in that top row is a *cumulative area to the right* of the critical value.

> **CAUTION** Table A-4 for the chi-square distribution uses cumulative areas from the *right* (unlike Table A-2 for the standard normal distribution, which provides cumulative areas from the *left*.) See Example 1 in Section 7-3.

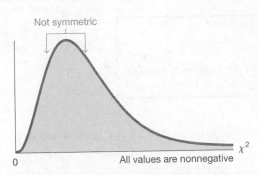

FIGURE 8-8   **Properties of the Chi-Square Distribution**

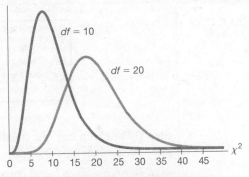

FIGURE 8-9   **Chi-Square Distribution for df = 10 and df = 20**

EXAMPLE 1   *P*-Value Method: Do Supermodel Heights Vary Less?

Listed below are the heights (cm) for the simple random sample of female super-models: Lima, Bundchen, Ambrosio, Ebanks, Iman, Rubik, Kurkova, Kerr, Kroes, Swanepoel, Prinsloo, Hosk, Kloss, Robinson, Heatherton, and Refaeli. Use a 0.01 significance level to test the claim that supermodels have heights with a standard deviation that is less than $\sigma = 7.5$ cm for the population of women. Does it appear that heights of supermodels vary less than heights of women from the population?

178 177 176 174 175 178 175 178 178 177 180 176 180 178 180 176

SOLUTION

REQUIREMENT CHECK   (1) The sample is a simple random sample. (2) In checking for normality, we see that the sample has no outliers, the accompanying normal quantile plot shows points that are reasonably close to a straight-line pattern, and there is no other pattern that is not a straight line. Both requirements are satisfied. ✓

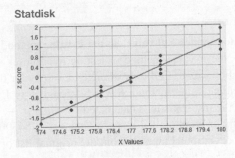

Statdisk

Technology Technology capable of conducting this test will typically display the *P*-value. The StatCrunch result is shown on the top of the next page. (Instead of using the assumed value of σ for H_0 and H_1, StatCrunch uses σ^2. For the null hypothesis, $\sigma = 7.5$ is equivalent to $\sigma^2 = 7.5^2 = 56.25$.) The display shows that the test statistic is $\chi^2 = 0.907$ (rounded) and the *P*-value is less than 0.0001.

continued

StatCrunch

Hypothesis test results:
σ^2 : Variance of population
$H_0 : \sigma^2 = 56.25$
$H_A : \sigma^2 < 56.25$

Variance	Sample Var.	DF	Chi-Square Stat	P-value
σ2	3.4000004	15	0.90666677	<0.0001

Step 1: The claim that "the standard deviation is less than 7.5 cm" is expressed in symbolic form as $\sigma < 7.5$ cm.

Step 2: If the original claim is false, then $\sigma \geq 7.5$ cm.

Step 3: The expression $\sigma < 7.5$ cm does not contain equality, so it becomes the alternative hypothesis. The null hypothesis is the statement that $\sigma = 7.5$ cm.

$$H_0: \sigma = 7.5 \text{ cm}$$
$$H_1: \sigma < 7.5 \text{ cm (original claim)}$$

Step 4: The significance level is $\alpha = 0.01$.

Step 5: Because the claim is made about σ, we use the χ^2 (chi-square) distribution.

Step 6: The StatCrunch display shows the test statistic of $\chi^2 = 0.907$ (rounded), and it shows that the P-value is less than 0.0001.

Step 7: Because the P-value is less than the significance level of $\alpha = 0.01$, we reject H_0.

`INTERPRETATION`

Step 8: There is sufficient evidence to support the claim that female supermodels have heights with a standard deviation that is less than 7.5 cm for the population of women. It appears that heights of supermodels do vary less than heights of women in the general population.

Critical Value Method

Technology typically provides a P-value, so the P-value method is used. If technology is not available, the P-value method of testing hypotheses is a bit challenging, because Table A-4 allows us to find only a range of values for the P-value. Instead, we could use the critical value method. Steps 1 through 5 in Example 1 would be the same. In Step 6, the test statistic is calculated by using $\sigma = 7.5$ cm (as assumed in the null hypothesis in Example 1); $n = 16$, and $s = 1.843909$ cm, which is the unrounded standard deviation computed from the original list of 16 heights. We get this test statistic:

$$\chi^2 = \frac{(n-1)s^2}{\sigma^2} = \frac{(16-1)(1.843909)^2}{7.5^2} = 0.907$$

The critical value of $\chi^2 = 5.229$ is found from Table A-4, and it corresponds to 15 degrees of freedom and an "area to the right" of 0.99 (based on the significance level of 0.01 for a left-tailed test). See Figure 8-10. In Step 7 we reject the null hypothesis because the test statistic of $\chi^2 = 0.907$ falls in the critical region, as shown in Figure 8-10. We conclude that there is sufficient evidence to support the claim that supermodels have heights with a standard deviation that is less than 7.5 cm for the population of women.

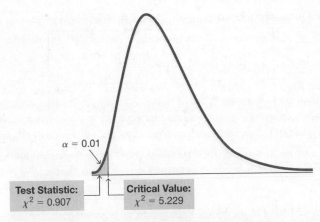

FIGURE 8-10   Testing the Claim That $\sigma < 7.5$ cm

Confidence Interval Method

As stated earlier, when testing claims about σ or σ^2, the P-value method, the critical value method, and the confidence interval method are all equivalent in the sense that they will always lead to the same conclusion. See Example 2.

EXAMPLE 2   Supermodel Heights: Confidence Interval Method

Repeat the hypothesis test in Example 1 by constructing a suitable confidence interval.

SOLUTION

First, we should be careful to select the correct confidence level. Because the hypothesis test is left-tailed and the significance level is 0.01, we should use a confidence level of 98%, or 0.98. (See Table 8-1 on page 356 for help in selecting the correct confidence level.)

Using the methods described in Section 7-3, we can use the sample data listed in Example 1 to construct a 98% confidence interval estimate of σ. We use $n = 16$, $s = 1.843909$ cm, $\chi_L^2 = 5.229$, and $\chi_R^2 = 30.578$. (The critical values χ_L^2 and χ_R^2 are found in Table A-4. Use the row with df $= n - 1 = 15$. The 0.98 confidence level corresponds to $\alpha = 0.02$, and we divide that area of 0.02 equally between the two tails so that the areas to the *right* of the critical values are 0.99 and 0.01. Refer to Table A-4 and use the columns with areas of 0.99 and 0.01 and use the 15th row.)

$$\sqrt{\frac{(n-1)s^2}{\chi_R^2}} < \sigma < \sqrt{\frac{(n-1)s^2}{\chi_L^2}}$$

$$\sqrt{\frac{(16-1)(1.843909^2)}{30.578}} < \sigma < \sqrt{\frac{(16-1)(1.843909^2)}{5.229}}$$

$$1.3 \text{ cm} < \sigma < 3.1 \text{ cm}$$

With this confidence interval, we can support the claim that $\sigma < 7.5$ cm because all values of the confidence interval are less than 7.5 cm. We reach the same conclusion found with the P-value method and the critical value method.

Alternative Method Used When Population Is Not Normal

The methods of this section include two requirements: (1) The sample is a simple random sample; (2) the population is normally distributed. If sample data are not collected in a random manner, the methods of this section do not apply. If the sample appears to be from a population not having a normal distribution, we could use the confidence interval method of testing hypotheses, but obtain the confidence interval using bootstrap resampling, as described in Section 7-4. Be careful to use the appropriate confidence level, as indicated by Table 8-1 on page 356. Reject the null hypothesis if the confidence interval limits do not contain the value of the mean claimed in the null hypothesis. See the Technology Project near the end of this chapter.

TECH CENTER

Hypothesis Test: Standard Deviation or Variance

Access tech instructions, videos, and data sets at www.TriolaStats.com

8-4   Basic Skills and Concepts

Statistical Literacy and Critical Thinking

1. Birth Weights Shown below are birth weights (in kilograms) of male babies born to mothers taking a special vitamin supplement (based on data from the New York State Department of Health). Assume that we want to use the sample data to test the claim that the sample is from a population with a standard deviation equal to 0.470 kg, which is the standard deviation for the population not given the special vitamin supplement. What requirements must be satisfied? How does the normality requirement for a hypothesis test of a claim about a standard deviation differ from the normality requirement for a hypothesis test of a claim about a mean?

3.73   4.37   3.73   4.33   3.39   3.68   4.68   3.52
3.02   4.09   2.47   4.13   4.47   3.22   3.43   2.54

2. Birth Weights Use the data and the claim given in Exercise 1 to identify the null and alternative hypotheses and the test statistic. What is the sampling distribution of the test statistic?

3. Birth Weights For the sample data from Exercise 1, we get a P-value of 0.0291 when testing the claim that the sample is from a population with a standard deviation equal to 0.470 kg. Assume that the test is conducted with a significance level given by $\alpha = 0.05$.

a. What should we conclude about the null hypothesis?

b. What should we conclude about the original claim?

c. Does the vitamin supplement appear to affect the variation among birth weights?

4. Birth Weights: Confidence Interval If we use the data given in Exercise 1, we get this 95% confidence interval estimate of the standard deviation of birth weights: 0.486 kg $< \sigma <$ 1.017 kg. When testing the claim that the sample is from a population with a standard deviation equal to 0.470 kg, what do we conclude from the confidence interval?

Testing Claims About Variation. *In Exercises 5–16, test the given claim. Identify the null hypothesis, alternative hypothesis, test statistic, P-value, or critical value(s), then state the conclusion about the null hypothesis, as well as the final conclusion that addresses the original claim. Assume that a simple random sample is selected from a normally distributed population.*

5. Pulse Rates of Men A simple random sample of 153 men results in a standard deviation of 11.3 beats per minute (based on Data Set 1 "Body Data" in Appendix B). The normal range of pulse rates of adults is typically given as 60 to 100 beats per minute. If the range rule of thumb is applied to that normal range, the result is a standard deviation of 10 beats per minute. Use the sample results with a 0.05 significance level to test the claim that pulse rates of men have a standard deviation equal to 10 beats per minute; see the accompanying StatCrunch display for this test. What do the results indicate about the effectiveness of using the range rule of thumb with the "normal range" from 60 to 100 beats per minute for estimating σ in this case?

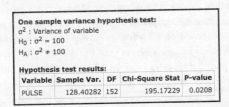

One sample variance hypothesis test:
σ^2 : Variance of variable
$H_0 : \sigma^2 = 100$
$H_A : \sigma^2 \neq 100$

Hypothesis test results:

Variable	Sample Var.	DF	Chi-Square Stat	P-value
PULSE	128.40282	152	195.17229	0.0208

6. Pulse Rates of Women Repeat the preceding exercise using the pulse rates of women listed in Data Set 1 "Body Data" in Appendix B. For the sample of pulse rates of women, $n = 147$ and $s = 12.5$. See the accompanying JMP display that results from using the original list of pulse rates instead of the summary statistics. (*Hint:* The bottom three rows of the display provide P-values for a two-tailed test, a left-tailed test, and a right-tailed test, respectively.) What do the results indicate about the effectiveness of using the range rule of thumb with the "normal range" from 60 to 100 beats per minute for estimating σ in this case?

△ **Test Standard Deviation**

Hypothesized Value	10
Actual Estimate	12.5436
DF	146
Test	ChiSquare
Test Statistic	229.7176
Min PValue	<.0001*
Prob < ChiSq	1.0000
Prob > ChiSq	<.0001*

7. Body Temperature Example 5 in Section 8-3 involved a test of the claim that humans have body temperatures with a mean equal to 98.6°F. The sample of 106 body temperatures has a standard deviation of 0.62°F. The conclusion in that example would change if the sample standard deviation s were 2.08°F or greater. Use a 0.01 significance level to test the claim that the sample of 106 body temperatures is from a population with a standard deviation less than 2.08°F. What does the result tell us about the validity of the hypothesis test in Example 5 in Section 8-3?

8. Birth Weights A simple random sample of birth weights of 30 girls has a standard deviation of 829.5 hg. Use a 0.01 significance level to test the claim that birth weights of girls have the same standard deviation as the birth weights of boys, which is 660.2 hg (based on Data Set 3 "Births" in Appendix B).

9. Physician IQ Scores For a random sample of IQ scores of 18 physicians, the mean is 124.2 and the standard deviation is 9.6 (based on data from a study conducted at the University of Wisconsin at Madison). Use a 0.05 significance level to test the claim that because physicians are a more homogeneous population than the general population, their IQ scores have a standard deviation less than 15, which is the standard deviation for the general population.

10. Statistics Test Scores Tests in one of the author's statistics classes have scores with a standard deviation equal to 14.1. One of his last classes had 27 test scores with a standard deviation of 9.3. Use a 0.01 significance level to test the claim that this class has less variation than other past classes. Does a lower standard deviation suggest that this last class is doing better?

11. New Filling Process The Orange Machine Company supplies a tool for pouring cold medicine into bottles in such a way that the standard deviation of the contents is 4.25 g. A new filling process is tested on 71 bottles and the standard deviation for this sample is 3.87 g. Use a 0.05 significance level to test the claim that the new process dispenses amounts with a standard deviation less than the standard deviation of 4.25 g for the old process. Is the new process better in the sense of dispensing amounts that are more consistent?

12. Spoken Words Couples were recruited for a study of how many words people speak in a day. A random sample of 56 males resulted in a mean of 16,576 words and a standard deviation of 7871 words. Use a 0.01 significance level to test the claim that males have a standard deviation that is greater than the standard deviation of 7460 words for females (based on data from "Are Women Really More Talkative Than Men?" by Mehl et al., *Science,* Vol. 317, No. 5834).

13. Weight Loss from Diet When 40 people used the Weight Watchers diet for one year, their weight *losses* had a standard deviation of 4.9 lb (based on data from "Comparison of the Atkins, Ornish, Weight Watchers, and Zone Diets for Weight Loss and Heart Disease Reduction," by Dansinger, et al., *Journal of the American Medical Association,* Vol. 293, No. 1). Use a 0.01 significance level to test the claim that the amounts of weight loss have a standard deviation equal to 6.0 lb, which appears to be the standard deviation for the amounts of weight loss with the Zone diet.

14. Sphygmomanometers An aneroid sphygmomanometer is a mechanical device used to measure blood pressure. A random sample of these devices is tested for accuracy and the errors (mm Hg) are listed below (based on data from "How Accurate Are Sphygmomanometers?" by Mion and Pierin, *Journal of Human Hypertension,* Vol. 12, No. 4). One of the devices is considered to be unacceptable if its error is more than 3 mm Hg. We will use this criterion for concluding that the sample is from a population of unacceptable devices: $\sigma > 1.5$ mm Hg. Use a 0.05 significance level with the sample data to test the claim that the sample is from a population with a standard deviation greater than 1.5 mm Hg. What does the result suggest about the accuracy of aneroid sphygmomanometers?

$$-4 \quad -11 \quad 5 \quad 5 \quad 8 \quad 14 \quad -16 \quad -12 \quad 4 \quad 6 \quad -6$$

15. Queues Providence Hospital once had separate waiting lines for patients arriving for admission, but it now has a single waiting line that feeds the processing stations as vacancies occur. The standard deviation of waiting times with the old multiple-line configuration was 109.3 sec. Listed below is a simple random sample of waiting times (minutes) with the single waiting line. Use a 0.05 significance level to test the claim that with a single waiting line, the waiting times have a standard deviation less than 109.3 sec. What improvement occurred when multiple waiting lines were replaced by a single waiting line?

$$390 \quad 396 \quad 402 \quad 408 \quad 426 \quad 438 \quad 444 \quad 462 \quad 462 \quad 462$$

16. World's Smallest Mammal The world's smallest mammal is the bumblebee bat, also known as the Kitti's hog-nosed bat (or *Craseonycteris thonglongyai*). Such bats are roughly the size of a large bumblebee. Listed below are weights (in grams) from a sample of these bats. Using a 0.05 significance level, test the claim that these weights come from a population with a standard deviation equal to 0.30 g, which is the standard deviation of weights of the bumblebee bats from one region in Thailand. Do these bats appear to have weights with the same variation as the bats from that region in Thailand?

$$1.7 \quad 1.6 \quad 1.5 \quad 2.0 \quad 2.3 \quad 1.6 \quad 1.6 \quad 1.8 \quad 1.5 \quad 1.7 \quad 2.2 \quad 1.4 \quad 1.6 \quad 1.6 \quad 1.6$$

8-4 Beyond the Basics

17. Finding Critical Values of X^2 For large numbers of degrees of freedom, we can approximate critical values of X^2 as follows:

$$\chi^2 = \frac{1}{2}\left(z + \sqrt{2k-1}\right)^2$$

Here k is the number of degrees of freedom and z is the critical value(s) found from technology or Table A-2. In Exercise 12 "Spoken Words," we have df = 55, so Table A-4 does not list an exact critical value. If we want to approximate a critical value of X^2 in the right-tailed hypothesis test with $\alpha = 0.01$ and a sample size of 56, we let $k = 55$ with $z = 2.33$ (or the more accurate value of $z = 2.326348$ found from technology). Use this approximation to estimate the critical value of χ^2 for Exercise 12. How close is it to the critical value of $\chi^2 = 82.292$ obtained by using Statdisk and Minitab?

18. Finding Critical Values of χ^2 Repeat Exercise 17 using this approximation (with k and z as described in Exercise 19):

$$\chi^2 = k\left(1 - \frac{2}{9k} + z\sqrt{\frac{2}{9k}}\right)^3$$

Chapter Quick Quiz

1. Distributions Using the methods of this chapter, identify the distribution that should be used for testing a claim about the given population parameter.

a. Mean

b. Proportion

c. Standard deviation

2. Tails Determine whether the given claim involves a hypothesis test that is left-tailed, two-tailed, or right-tailed.

a. $p \neq 0.5$

b. $\mu < 98.6$

c. $\sigma > 15$

3. Instagram Poll In a Pew Research Center poll of Internet users aged 18–29, 53% said that they use Instagram. We want to use a 0.05 significance level to test the claim that the majority of Internet users aged 18–29 use Instagram.

a. Identify the null and alternative hypotheses.

b. Using a sample size of 532, find the value of the test statistic.

c. Technology is used to find that the P-value for the test is 0.0827. What should we conclude about the null hypothesis?

d. What should we conclude about the original claim?

4. P-Value Find the P-value in a test of the claim that the mean annual income of a nurse is greater than $60,000 (based on data from the Bureau of Labor Statistics) given that the test statistic is $t = 2.462$ for a sample of 30 nurses.

5. Conclusions True or false: In hypothesis testing, it is *never* valid to form a conclusion of supporting the null hypothesis.

6. Conclusions True or false: The conclusion of "fail to reject the null hypothesis" has exactly the same meaning as "accept the null hypothesis."

7. Uncertainty True or false: If correct methods of hypothesis testing are used with a large simple random sample that satisfies the test requirements, the conclusion will always be true.

8. Chi-Square Test In a test of the claim that $\sigma = 10$ for the population of IQ scores of nurses, we find that the rightmost critical value is $\chi^2_R = 40.646$. Is the leftmost critical χ^2_L value equal to -40.646?

9. Robust Explain what is meant by the statements that the t test for a claim about μ is robust, but the χ^2 test for a claim about σ^2 is not robust.

10. Equivalent Methods Which of the following statements are true?

a. When testing a claim about a population mean μ, the P-value method, critical value method, and confidence interval method are all equivalent in the sense that they always yield the same conclusions.

b. When testing a claim about a population proportion p, the P-value method, critical value method, and confidence interval method are all equivalent in the sense that they always yield the same conclusions.

c. When testing a claim about any population parameter, the P-value method, critical value method, and confidence interval method are all equivalent in the sense that they always yield the same conclusions.

Review Exercises

1. True/False Characterize each of the following statements as being true or false.

a. In a hypothesis test, a very high P-value indicates strong support of the alternative hypothesis.

b. The Student t distribution can be used to test a claim about a population mean whenever the sample data are randomly selected from a normally distributed population.

c. When using a χ^2 distribution to test a claim about a population standard deviation, there is a very loose requirement that the sample data are from a population having a normal distribution.

d. When conducting a hypothesis test about the claimed proportion of surgeons who have current passports, the problems with a convenience sample can be overcome by using a larger sample size.

e. When repeating the same hypothesis test with different random samples of the same size, the conclusions will all be the same.

2. Is Nessie Real? This question was posted on the America Online website: Do you believe the Loch Ness monster exists? Among 21,346 responses, 64% were "yes." Use a 0.01 significance level to test the claim that most people believe that the Loch Ness monster exists. How is the conclusion affected by the fact that Internet users who saw the question could decide whether to respond?

3. White Blood Cell Count A simple random sample of 50 adult females is obtained, and the white blood cell count (in cells per microliter) is measured for each of them, with these results: $n = 50$, $\bar{x} = 6.889$ million cells per microliter, $s = 2.021$ million cells per microliter (from Data Set 1 "Body Data" in Appendix B). Use a 0.01 significance level to test that claim that the sample is from a population with a mean less than 8.3 million cells per microliter, which is often used as the upper limit of the range of normal values. Does the result suggest that each of the 50 females has a white blood cell count below 8.3 million cells per microliter?

4. Smoking Recently, a simple random sample of 572 adult males showed that 124 of them smoke (based on data from the Centers for Disease Control and Prevention). It has been established that in 2008, 20.4% of adult males smoke. Use a 0.05 significance level to test the claim that the rate of smoking by adult males is now the same as in 2008.

5. Controlling Cholesterol The Westbrook Pharmaceutical Company manufactures atorvastatin pills, designed to lower cholesterol levels. Listed below are the amounts (in mg) of atorvastatin in a random sample of the pills. Use a 0.05 significance level to test the claim that the pills come from a population in which the mean amount of atorvastatin is equal to 25 mg.

24.1 24.4 24.3 24.9 24.1 26.2 25.1 24.7 24.4 25.0 24.7 25.1 25.3 25.5 25.5

6. BMI for Miss America A claimed trend of thinner Miss America winners has generated charges that the contest encourages unhealthy diet habits among young women. Listed below are body mass indexes (BMI) for recent Miss America winners. Use a 0.01 significance level to test the claim that recent winners are from a population with a mean BMI less than 20.16, which was the BMI for winners from the 1920s and 1930s. Given that BMI is a measure of the relative amounts of body fat and height, do recent winners appear to be significantly smaller than those from the 1920s and 1930s?

$$19.5 \quad 20.3 \quad 19.6 \quad 20.2 \quad 17.8 \quad 17.9 \quad 19.1 \quad 18.8 \quad 17.6 \quad 16.8$$

7. BMI for Miss America Use the same BMI indexes given in Exercise 6. Use a 0.01 significance level to test the claim that recent Miss America winners are from a population with a standard deviation equal to 1.34, which was the standard deviation of BMI for winners from the 1920s and 1930s. Do recent winners appear to have variation that is different from that of the 1920s and 1930s?

8. Type I Error and Type II Error

a. In general, what is a type I error? In general, what is a type II error?

b. For the hypothesis test in Exercise 6 "BMI for Miss America," write a statement that would be a type I error, and write another statement that would be a type II error.

Cumulative Review Exercises

1. Lightning Deaths Listed below are the numbers of deaths from lightning strikes in the United States each year for a sequence of 14 recent and consecutive years. Find the values of the indicated statistics.

$$51 \quad 44 \quad 51 \quad 43 \quad 32 \quad 38 \quad 48 \quad 45 \quad 27 \quad 34 \quad 29 \quad 26 \quad 28 \quad 23$$

a. Mean   **b.** Median   **c.** Standard deviation   **d.** Variance   **e.** Range

f. What important feature of the data is not revealed from an examination of the statistics, and what tool would be helpful in revealing it?

2. Lightning Deaths Refer to the sample data in Cumulative Review Exercise 1.

a. What is the level of measurement of the data (nominal, ordinal, interval, ratio)?

b. Are the values discrete or continuous?

c. Are the data categorical or quantitative?

d. Is the sample a simple random sample?

3. Confidence Interval for Lightning Deaths Use the sample values given in Cumulative Review Exercise 1 to construct a 99% confidence interval estimate of the population mean. Assume that the population has a normal distribution. Write a brief statement that interprets the confidence interval.

4. Hypothesis Test for Lightning Deaths Refer to the sample data given in Cumulative Review Exercise 1 and consider those data to be a random sample of annual lightning deaths from recent years. Use those data with a 0.01 significance level to test the claim that the mean number of annual lightning deaths is less than the mean of 72.6 deaths from the 1980s. If the mean is now lower than in the past, identify one of the several factors that could explain the decline.

5. Lightning Deaths The accompanying bar chart shows the numbers of lightning strike deaths broken down by gender for a recent period of nine years. What is wrong with the graph?

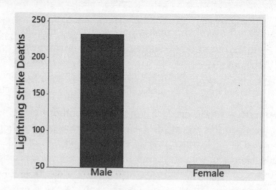

6. Lightning Deaths The graph in Cumulative Review Exercise 5 was created by using data consisting of 232 male deaths from lightning strikes and 55 female deaths from lightning strikes. Assume that these data are randomly selected lightning deaths and proceed to test the claim that the proportion of male deaths is greater than $1/2$. Use a 0.01 significance level. Any explanation for the result?

7. Lightning Deaths The graph in Cumulative Review Exercise 5 was created by using data consisting of 232 male deaths from lightning strikes and 55 female deaths from lightning strikes. Assume that these data are randomly selected lightning deaths and proceed to construct a 95% confidence interval estimate of the proportion of males among all lightning deaths. Based on the result, does it seem feasible that males and females have equal chances of being killed by lightning?

8. Lightning Deaths Based on the results given in Cumulative Review Exercise 6, assume that for a randomly selected lightning death, there is a 0.8 probability that the victim is a male.

a. Find the probability that three random people killed by lightning strikes are all males.

b. Find the probability that three random people killed by lightning strikes are all females.

c. Find the probability that among three people killed by lightning strikes, at least one is a male.

d. If five people killed by lightning strikes are randomly selected, find the probability that exactly three of them are males.

e. A study involves random selection of different groups of 50 people killed by lightning strikes. For those groups, find the mean and standard deviation for the numbers of male victims.

f. For the same groups described in part (e), would 46 be a significantly high number of males in a group? Explain.

9. Odds Ratio In a study of the relationship between headaches and body weight, there were 4489 overweight subjects, and 331 of them experienced migraine headaches. Among 5487 subjects with normal weight, 358 experienced migraine headaches (based on data from "Body Mass Index and Episodic Headaches," by Bigal et al., *Archives of Internal Medicine,* Vol. 167, No. 18). Find the odds ratio and interpret the result.

Technology Project

1. Bootstrapping and Robustness Consider the probability distribution defined by the formula $P(x) = \dfrac{3x^2}{1000}$ where x can be any value between 0 and 10 inclusive (not just integers). The accompanying graph of this probability distribution shows that its shape is very far from the bell shape of a normal distribution. This probability distribution has parameters $\mu = 7.5$ and $\sigma = 1.93649$. Listed below is a simple random sample of values from this distribution, and the normal quantile plot for this sample is shown. Given the very non-normal shape of the distribution, it is not surprising to see the normal quantile plot with points that are far from a straight-line pattern, confirming that the sample does not appear to be from a normally distributed population.

$$8.69 \quad 2.03 \quad 9.09 \quad 7.15 \quad 9.05 \quad 9.40 \quad 6.30 \quad 7.89 \quad 7.98 \quad 7.67$$
$$7.77 \quad 7.17 \quad 8.86 \quad 8.29 \quad 9.21 \quad 7.80 \quad 7.70 \quad 8.12 \quad 9.11 \quad 7.64$$

$P(x) = \dfrac{3x^2}{1000}$ defined on [0, 10]

Normal Quantile Plot of 20 Sample Values

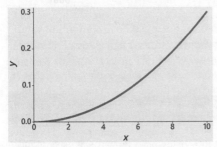
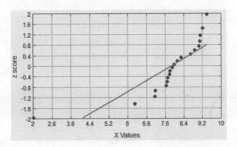

a. Mean Test the claim that the 20 given sample values are from a population having a mean equal to 7.5, which is the known population mean. Because the sample is not from a normally distributed population and because $n = 20$ does not satisfy the requirement of $n > 30$, we should not use the methods of Section 8-3. Instead, test the claim by using the confidence interval method based on a bootstrap sample of size 1000 (See Section 7-4). Use a 0.05 significance level. Does the bootstrap confidence interval contain the known population mean of 7.5? Is the bootstrap method effective for this test? What happens if we conduct this test by throwing all caution to the wind and constructing the 95% confidence interval by using the t distribution as described in Section 7-2?

b. Standard Deviation Test the claim that the 20 sample values are from a population with a standard deviation equal to 1.93649, which is the known population standard deviation. Use the confidence interval method based on a bootstrap sample of size 1000. (See Section 7-4.) Use a 0.05 significance level. Does the bootstrap confidence interval contain the known population standard deviation of 1.93649? Is the bootstrap method effective for this test? What happens if we conduct the test by throwing all caution to the wind and constructing the 95% confidence interval by using the χ^2 distribution as described in Section 7-3?

FROM DATA TO DECISION

Critical Thinking: Testing the Salk Vaccine

The largest health experiment ever conducted involved a test of the Salk vaccine designed to protect children from the devastating effects of polio. The test included 201,229 children who were given the Salk vaccine, and 33 of them developed polio. The claim that the Salk vaccine is effective is equivalent to the claim that the proportion of vaccinated children who develop polio is less than 0.0000573, which was the rate of polio among children not given the Salk vaccine. (*Note:* The actual Salk vaccine experiment involved another group of 200,745 children who were injected with an ineffective salt solution instead of the Salk vaccine. This study design with a treatment group and placebo group is very common and very effective. Methods for comparing two proportions are presented in Chapter 9.)

Analyzing the Results

a. Test the given claim using a 0.05 significance level. Does the Salk vaccine appear to be effective?

b. For the hypothesis test from part (a), consider the following two errors:

• Concluding that the Salk vaccine is effective when it is not effective.

• Concluding that the Salk vaccine is not effective when it is effective.

Determine which of the above two errors is a type I error and determine which is a type II error. Which error would have worse consequences? How could the hypothesis test be conducted in order to reduce the chance of making the more serious error?

Cooperative Group Activities

1. Out-of-class activity In the United States, 40% of us have brown eyes, according to Dr. P. Sorita Soni at Indiana University. Groups of three or four students should randomly select people and identify the color of their eyes. The claim that 40% of us have brown eyes can then be tested.

2. In-class activity After dividing into groups of between 10 and 20 people, each group member should record the number of heartbeats in a minute. After calculating the sample mean and standard deviation, each group should proceed to test the claim that the mean is greater than 48 beats per minute, which is the result for one of the authors. (When people exercise, they tend to have lower pulse rates.)

3. In-class activity Without using any measuring device, each student should draw a line believed to be 3 in. long and another line believed to be 3 cm long. Then use rulers to measure and record the lengths of the lines drawn. Find the means and standard deviations of the two sets of lengths. Test the claim that the lines estimated to be 3 in. have a mean length that is equal to 3 in. Test the claim that the lines estimated to be 3 cm have a mean length that is equal to 3 cm. Compare the results. Do the estimates of the 3-in. line appear to be more accurate than those for the 3-cm line? What do these results suggest?

4. In-class activity Assume that a method of gender selection can affect the probability of a baby being a girl so that the probability becomes 1/4. Each student should simulate 20 births by drawing 20 cards from a shuffled deck. Replace each card after it has been drawn, then reshuffle. Consider the hearts to be girls and consider all other cards to be boys. After making 20 selections and recording the "genders" of the babies, use a 0.10 significance level to test the claim that the proportion of girls is equal to 1/4. How many students are expected to get results leading to the wrong conclusion that the proportion is not 1/4? How does that relate to the probability of a type I error? Does this procedure appear to be effective in identifying the effectiveness of the gender selection method? (If decks of cards are not available, use some other way to simulate the births, such as using the random number generator on a calculator or using digits from phone numbers or Social Security numbers.)

5. Out-of-class activity Groups of three or four students should go to the library and collect a sample consisting of the ages of books (based on copyright dates). Plan and describe the sampling plan, execute the sampling procedure, and then use the results to test the claim that the mean age of books in the library is greater than 20 years.

6. In-class activity A class project should be designed to conduct a test in which each student is given a taste of Coke and a taste of Pepsi. The student is then asked to identify which sample is Coke. After all of the results are collected, test the claim that the success rate is better than the rate that would be expected with random guesses.

7. In-class activity Each student should estimate the length of the classroom. The values should be based on visual estimates, with no actual measurements being taken. After the estimates have been collected, measure the length of the room, then test the claim that the sample mean is equal to the actual length of the classroom. Is there a "collective wisdom," whereby the class mean is approximately equal to the actual room length?

8. Out-of-class activity Using one wristwatch that is reasonably accurate, set the time to be exact. Visit www.time.gov to set the exact time. If you cannot set the time to the nearest second, record the error for the watch you are using. Now compare the time on this watch to the time on other watches that have not been set to the exact time. Record the errors with negative signs for watches that are ahead of the actual time and positive signs for those watches that are behind the actual time. Use the data to test the claim that the mean error of all wristwatches is equal to 0. Do we collectively run on time, or are we early or late? Also test the claim that the standard deviation of errors is less than 1 min. What are the practical implications of a standard deviation that is excessively large?

9. In-class activity In a group of three or four people, conduct an extrasensory perception (ESP) experiment by selecting one of the group members as the subject. Draw a circle on one small piece of paper and draw a square on another sheet of the same size. Repeat this experiment 20 times: Randomly select the circle or the square and place it in the subject's hand behind his or her back so that it cannot be seen, then ask the subject to identify the shape (without seeing it); record whether the response is correct. Test the claim that the subject has ESP because the proportion of correct responses is greater than 0.5.

10. Out-of-class activity Each student should find an article in a professional journal that includes a hypothesis test of the type discussed in this chapter. Write a brief report describing the hypothesis test and its role in the context of the article.

9 Inferences from Two Samples

CHAPTER PROBLEM — Is the "Freshman 15" Real, or Is It a Myth?

There is a common and popular belief that college students typically gain 15 lb (or 6.8 kg) during their freshman year. This 15-lb weight gain has been dubbed the "Freshman 15." Reasonable explanations for this phenomenon include the new stresses of college life (not including a statistics class, which is just plain fun); new eating habits; less free time for physical activities; cafeteria food with an abundance of fat and carbohydrates; the new freedom to choose among a variety of foods (including sumptuous pizzas that are just a phone call away); and a lack of sleep that results in lower levels of leptin, which helps regulate appetite and metabolism. But is the Freshman 15 real, or is it a myth that has been perpetuated through anecdotal evidence and/or flawed data?

Several studies have focused on the credibility of the Freshman 15 belief. We will consider one reputable study with results published in the article "Changes in Body Weight and Fat Mass of Men and Women in the First Year of College: A Study of the 'Freshman 15'," by Daniel Hoffman, Peggy Policastro, Virginia Quick, and Soo-Kyung Lee, *Journal of American College Health,* Vol. 55, No. 1. The authors of that article have provided the data from their study, and much of it is listed in Data Set 10 "Freshman 15" in Appendix B. If you examine the weights in Data Set 10, you should note the following:

- The weights in Data Set 10 are in *kilograms*, not pounds, and 15 lb is equivalent to 6.8 kg. The "Freshman 15 (pounds)" is equivalent to the "Freshman 6.8 kilograms."

- Data Set 10 includes two weights for each of the 67 study subjects. Each subject was weighed in September of the freshman year, and again in April of the freshman year. These two measurements were made at the beginning and end of the seven months of campus life that passed between the measurements. It is important to recognize that each individual pair of before and after measurements is from the same student, so the lists of 67 "before" weights and 67 "after" weights constitute *paired* data from the 67 subjects in the study.

- Because the Freshman 15 refers to weight *gained,* we will use weight changes in this format:

(April weight) − (September weight). If a student does gain 15 lb, the value of (April weight) − (September weight) is 15 lb, or 6.8 kg. (A negative weight "gain" indicates that the student lost weight.)

- The published article about the Freshman 15 study is marked by some limitations, including these:

  1. All subjects volunteered for the study.

  2. All of the subjects were attending Rutgers, the State University of New Jersey.

The Freshman 15 constitutes a *claim* made about the population of college students. If we use μ_d to denote the mean of all (April weight) − (September weight) differences for college students during their freshman year, the Freshman 15 is the claim that $\mu_d = 15$ lb or $\mu_d = 6.8$ kg. Because the sample weights are measured in kilograms, we will consider the claim to be $\mu_d = 6.8$ kg. Later in this chapter, a formal hypothesis test will be used to test this claim. We will then be able to reach one of two possible conclusions: Either there is sufficient evidence to warrant rejection of the claim that $\mu_d = 6.8$ kg (so the Freshman 15 is rejected), or we will conclude that there is not sufficient evidence to warrant rejection of the claim that $\mu_d = 6.8$ kg (so the Freshman 15 cannot be rejected). We will then be better able to determine whether the Freshman 15 is a myth.

CHAPTER OBJECTIVES

Inferential statistics involves forming conclusions (or inferences) about a population parameter. Two major activities of inferential statistics are estimating values of population parameters using confidence intervals (as in Chapter 7) and testing claims made about population parameters (as in Chapter 8). Chapters 7 and 8 both involved methods for dealing with a sample from *one* population, but this chapter extends those methods to situations involving *two* populations. Here are the chapter objectives:

9-1   Two Proportions

- Conduct a formal hypothesis test of a claim made about two population proportions.

- Construct a confidence interval estimate of the difference between two population proportions.

9-2   Two Means: Independent Samples

- Distinguish between a situation involving two independent samples and a situation involving two samples that are not independent.

- Conduct a formal hypothesis test of a claim made about two independent populations.
- Construct a confidence interval estimate of the difference between the means of two independent populations.

9-3 Two Dependent Samples (Matched Pairs)

- Identify sample data consisting of matched pairs.
- Conduct a formal hypothesis test of a claim made about the mean of the differences between matched pairs.
- Construct a confidence interval estimate of the mean difference between matched pairs.

9-4 Two Variances or Standard Deviations

- Develop the ability to conduct a formal hypothesis test of a claim made about two population standard deviations or variances.

9-1 Two Proportions

Key Concept In this section we present methods for (1) testing a claim made about two population proportions and (2) constructing a confidence interval estimate of the difference between two population proportions. The methods of this chapter can also be used with probabilities or the decimal equivalents of percentages.

KEY ELEMENTS

Inferences About Two Proportions

Objectives

1. **Hypothesis Test:** Conduct a hypothesis test of a claim about two population proportions.

2. **Confidence Interval:** Construct a confidence interval estimate of the difference between two population proportions.

Notation for Two Proportions

For population 1 we let

p_1 = *population* proportion $\hat{p}_1 = \dfrac{x_1}{n_1}$ (*sample* proportion)

n_1 = size of the first sample $\hat{q}_1 = 1 - \hat{p}_1$ (complement of $\hat{p}_1$)

x_1 = number of successes in the first sample

The corresponding notations p_2, n_2, x_2, $\hat{p}_2$, and $\hat{q}_2$ apply to population 2.

Two population

$\hat{p}_1 - \hat{p}_2$ Vs

$p_1 - p_2$

Pooled Sample Proportion

The **pooled sample proportion** is denoted by $\bar{p}$ and it combines the two sample proportions into one proportion, as shown here:

$$\bar{p} = \frac{x_1 + x_2}{n_1 + n_2}$$

$$\bar{q} = 1 - \bar{p}$$

continued

Requirements

1. The sample proportions are from two simple random samples.

2. The two samples are *independent*. (Samples are *independent* if the sample values selected from one population are not related to or somehow naturally paired or matched with the sample values selected from the other population.)

3. For each of the two samples, there are at least 5 successes and at least 5 failures. (That is, $n\hat{p} \geq 5$ and $n\hat{q} \geq 5$ for each of the two samples).

Test Statistic for Two Proportions (with H_0: $p_1 = p_2$)

$$z = \frac{(\hat{p}_1 - \hat{p}_2) - (p_1 - p_2)}{\sqrt{\frac{\bar{p}\bar{q}}{n_1} + \frac{\bar{p}\bar{q}}{n_2}}} \quad \text{where } p_1 - p_2 = 0 \text{ (assumed in the null hypothesis)}$$

$$\text{where } \bar{p} = \frac{x_1 + x_2}{n_1 + n_2} \quad (pooled \text{ sample proportion}) \text{ and } \bar{q} = 1 - \bar{p}$$

P-Value: *P*-values are automatically provided by technology. If technology is not available, use Table A-2 (standard normal distribution) and find the *P*-value using the procedure given in Figure 8-3 on page 360 from Section 8-1.

Critical Values: Use Table A-2. (Based on the significance level α, find critical values by using the same procedures introduced in Section 8-1.)

Confidence Interval Estimate of $p_1 - p_2$

The confidence interval estimate of the difference $p_1 - p_2$ is

$$(\hat{p}_1 - \hat{p}_2) - E < (p_1 - p_2) < (\hat{p}_1 - \hat{p}_2) + E$$

where the margin of error E is given by

$$E = z_{\alpha/2}\sqrt{\frac{\hat{p}_1\hat{q}_1}{n_1} + \frac{\hat{p}_2\hat{q}_2}{n_2}}$$

Rounding: Round the confidence interval limits to three significant digits.

Equivalent Methods

When testing a claim about two population proportions:

- The *P*-value method and the critical value method are equivalent.
- The confidence interval method is *not* equivalent to the *P*-value method or the critical value method.

Recommendation: If you want to *test a claim* about two population proportions, use the *P*-value method or critical value method; if you want to *estimate* the difference between two population proportions, use the confidence interval method.

Hypothesis Tests

For tests of hypotheses made about two population proportions, we consider only tests having a null hypothesis of $p_1 = p_2$ (so the null hypothesis is H_0: $p_1 = p_2$). With the assumption that $p_1 = p_2$, the estimates of $\hat{p}_1$ and $\hat{p}_2$ are combined to provide the best estimate of the common value of $\hat{p}_1$ and $\hat{p}_2$, and that combined value is the pooled sample proportion $\bar{p}$ given in the preceding Key Elements box. The following example will help clarify the roles of x_1, n_1, $\hat{p}_1$, $\bar{p}$, and so on. Note that with the assumption of equal population proportions, the best estimate of the common population proportion is obtained by pooling both samples into one big sample, so that $\bar{p}$ is the estimator of the common population proportion.

P-Value Method

 EXAMPLE 1   Do Airbags Save Lives?

The table below lists results from a simple random sample of front-seat occupants involved in car crashes (based on data from "Who Wants Airbags?" by Meyer and Finney, *Chance,* Vol. 18, No. 2). Use a 0.05 significance level to test the claim that the fatality rate of occupants is lower for those in cars equipped with airbags.

	Airbag Available	No Airbag Available
Occupant Fatalities	41	52
Total number of occupants	11,541	9,853

P_1 P_2

SOLUTION

REQUIREMENT CHECK   We first verify that the three necessary requirements are satisfied. (1) The data are from two simple random samples. (2) The two samples are *independent* of each other. (3) The airbag group includes 41 occupants who were killed and 11,500 occupants who were not killed, so the number of successes is at least 5 and the number of failures is at least 5. The second group includes 52 occupants who were killed and 9801 who were not killed, so the number of successes is at least 5 and the number of failures is at least 5. The requirements are satisfied. ☑

We will use the *P*-value method of hypothesis testing, as summarized in Figure 8-1 on page 356. In the following steps we stipulate that the group *with* airbags is Sample 1, and the group *without* airbags is Sample 2.

Step 1: The claim that the fatality rate is lower for those with airbags can be expressed as $p_1 < p_2$.

Step 2: If $p_1 < p_2$ is false, then $p_1 \geq p_2$.

Step 3: Because the claim of $p_1 < p_2$ does not contain equality, it becomes the alternative hypothesis. The null hypothesis is the statement of equality, so we have

$$H_0: p_1 = p_2 \qquad H_1: p_1 < p_2 \text{ (original claim)}$$

Step 4: The significance level is $\alpha = 0.05$.

Step 5: This step and the following step can be circumvented by using technology; see the display that follows this example. If not using technology, we use the normal distribution (with the test statistic given earlier in the Key Elements box) as an approximation to the binomial distribution. We estimate the common value of p_1 and p_2 with the pooled sample estimate $\bar{p}$ calculated as shown below, with extra decimal places used to minimize rounding errors in later calculations.

$$\bar{p} = \frac{x_1 + x_2}{n_1 + n_2} = \frac{41 + 52}{11{,}541 + 9{,}853} = 0.004347$$

With $\bar{p} = 0.004347$, it follows that $\bar{q} = 1 - 0.004347 = 0.995653$.

Step 6: We can now find the value of the test statistic. Note that the null hypothesis assumption of $p_1 = p_2$ implies that $p_1 - p_2 = 0$ in the following calculation.

$$z = \frac{(\hat{p}_1 - \hat{p}_2) - (p_1 - p_2)}{\sqrt{\dfrac{\overline{p}\,\overline{q}}{n_1} + \dfrac{\overline{p}\,\overline{q}}{n_2}}} \longrightarrow pooled$$

$$= \frac{\left(\dfrac{41}{11{,}541} - \dfrac{52}{9{,}853}\right) - 0}{\sqrt{\dfrac{(0.004347)\,(0.995653)}{11{,}541} + \dfrac{(0.004347)\,(0.995653)}{9{,}853}}}$$

$$= -1.91$$

This is a left-tailed test, so the P-value is the area to the left of the test statistic $z = -1.91$ (as indicated by Figure 8-3 on page 360). Refer to Table A-2 and find that the area to the left of the test statistic $z = -1.91$ is 0.0281, so the P-value is 0.0281. (Technology provides a more accurate P-value of 0.0280.) The test statistic and P-value are shown in Figure 9-1(a).

Step 7: Because the P-value of 0.0281 is less than the significance level of $\alpha = 0.05$, we reject the null hypothesis of $p_1 = p_2$. ("If the P is *low,* the null must go.")

INTERPRETATION

We must address the original claim that the fatality rate is lower for occupants in cars equipped with airbags. Because we reject the null hypothesis, we conclude that there is sufficient evidence to support the claim that the proportion of accident fatalities for occupants in cars with airbags is less than the proportion of fatalities for occupants in cars without airbags. (See Table 8-3 on page 362 for help in wording the final conclusion.) Based on these results, there appears to be strong evidence that drivers in cars with airbags are at lower risk of a fatality.

The sample data used in this example are only part of the data given in the article cited in the statement of the problem. If all of the available data are used, the test statistic becomes $z = -57.76$, and the P-value is very close to 0, so using all of the data provides even more compelling evidence of the effectiveness of airbags in saving lives.

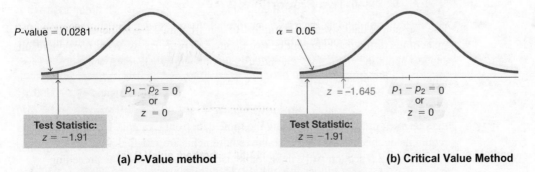

(a) *P*-Value method   (b) Critical Value Method

FIGURE 9-1   Testing the Claim of a Lower Fatality Rate with Airbags

Technology Software and calculators usually provide a P-value, so the P-value method is typically used for testing a claim about two proportions. See the accompanying Statdisk results from Example 1 showing the test statistic of $z = -1.91$ (rounded) and the P-value of 0.0280.

Statdisk

Pooled proportion: 0.004347
Test Statistic, z: −1.9116
Critical z: −1.6449
P-Value: 0.0280
90% Confidence interval:
−0.0032321 < p1-p2 < −0.0002179

Critical Value Method

The critical value method of testing hypotheses can also be used for Example 1. In Step 6, instead of finding the P-value, find the critical value. With a significance level of $\alpha = 0.05$ in a left-tailed test based on the normal distribution, we refer to Table A-2 and find that an area of $\alpha = 0.05$ in the left tail corresponds to the critical value of $z = -1.645$. In Figure 9-1(b) we can see that the test statistic of $z = -1.91$ falls within the critical region beyond the critical value of -1.645. We again reject the null hypothesis. The conclusions are the same as in Example 1.

Confidence Intervals

Using the format given in the preceding Key Elements box, we can construct a confidence interval estimate of the difference between population proportions $(p_1 - p_2)$. If a confidence interval estimate of $p_1 - p_2$ does not include 0, we have evidence suggesting that p_1 and p_2 have different values. The confidence interval uses a standard deviation based on the use of *sample* proportions, whereas a hypothesis test uses a standard deviation based on the *assumption* that the two population proportions are equal and their common value is estimated by pooling the sample proportions. Consequently, a conclusion based on a confidence interval might be different from a conclusion based on a hypothesis test. See the caution that follows Example 2.

EXAMPLE 2 Confidence Interval for Claim About Two Proportions

Use the sample data given in Example 1 to construct a 90% confidence interval estimate of the difference between the two population proportions. What does the result suggest about the claim that "the fatality rate of occupants is lower for those in cars equipped with airbags"?

SOLUTION

REQUIREMENT CHECK   We are using the same data from Example 1, and the same requirement check applies here, so the requirements are satisfied. ☑

The confidence interval can be found using technology; see the preceding Statdisk display. If not using technology, proceed as follows.

not pooled

With a 90% confidence level, $z_{\alpha/2} = 1.645$ (from Table A-2). We first calculate the value of the margin of error E as shown here.

$$E = z_{\alpha/2}\sqrt{\frac{\hat{p}_1\hat{q}_1}{n_1} + \frac{\hat{p}_2\hat{q}_2}{n_2}} = 1.645\sqrt{\frac{\left(\frac{41}{11{,}541}\right)\left(\frac{11{,}500}{11{,}541}\right)}{11{,}541} + \frac{\left(\frac{52}{9{,}853}\right)\left(\frac{9801}{9{,}853}\right)}{9{,}853}}$$

$$= 0.001507$$

With $\hat{p}_1 - \hat{p}_2 = 41/11{,}541 - 52/9{,}853 = -0.001725$ and $E = 0.001507$, the confidence interval is evaluated as follows, with the confidence interval limits rounded to three significant digits:

$$(\hat{p}_1 - \hat{p}_2) - E < (p_1 - p_2) < (\hat{p}_1 - \hat{p}_2) + E$$

$$-0.001725 - 0.001507 < (p_1 - p_2) < -0.001725 + 0.001507$$

$$-0.00323 < (p_1 - p_2) < -0.000218$$

See the preceding Statdisk display showing the same confidence interval obtained here.

INTERPRETATION

The confidence interval limits do not contain 0, suggesting that there is a significant difference between the two proportions. The confidence interval suggests that the fatality rate is lower for occupants in cars with airbags than for occupants in cars without airbags. The confidence interval also provides an estimate of the amount of the difference between the two fatality rates.

A confidence interval provides additional information beyond just a decision on whether or not to reject a hypothesis. It also provides information about the range of plausible values of the true risk difference. In this example, the range of values in the confidence interval is roughly -0.003 to -0.002. We can translate these numbers into rates by multiplying by some population size, say, 1000. Using the 90% confidence interval, we estimate that drivers without airbags are at increased risk of a fatal car accident by somewhere between 2 and 3 additional fatalities per 1000 occupants.

> **CAUTION Use of One Confidence Interval** Don't test for equality of two population proportions by determining whether there is an overlap between two individual confidence interval estimates of the two individual population proportions. When compared to the confidence interval estimate of $p_1 - p_2$, the analysis of overlap between two individual confidence intervals is more conservative (by rejecting equality less often), and it has less power (because it is less likely to reject $p_1 - p_2$ when in reality $p_1 \neq p_2$). See Exercise 25 "Overlap of Confidence Intervals."

What Can We Do When the Requirements Are Not Satisfied?

Bad Samples If we violate the requirement that we have two simple random samples, we could be in big trouble. For example, if we have two convenience samples, there is probably nothing that can be done to salvage them.

Fewer Than 5 Successes or Fewer Than 5 Failures in a Hypothesis Test If we violate the requirement that each of the two samples has at least 5 successes and at least 5

Fisher's Exact test

failures, we can use *Fisher's exact test*, which provides an *exact P*-value instead of using the method based on a normal distribution approximation. Fisher's exact test involves very complicated calculations, so the use of technology is strongly recommended. Statdisk, Minitab, XLSTAT, and StatCrunch all have the ability to perform Fisher's exact test. (See Section 11-2.)

Fewer Than 5 Successes or Fewer Than 5 Failures in a Confidence Interval If we violate the requirement that each of the two samples has at least 5 successes and at least 5 failures, we can use bootstrap resampling methods to construct a confidence interval. See Section 7-4.

$CI \rightarrow Bootstrapping$

Rationale: Why Do the Procedures of This Section Work?

Hypothesis Tests With $n_1\hat{p}_1 \geq 5$ and $n_1\hat{q}_1 \geq 5$, the distribution of $\hat{p}_1$ can be approximated by a normal distribution with mean p_1, standard deviation $\sqrt{p_1q_1/n_1}$, and variance p_1q_1/n_1 (based on Sections 6-6 and 7-1). This also applies to the second sample. The distributions of $\hat{p}_1$ and $\hat{p}_2$ are each approximated by a normal distribution, so the difference $\hat{p}_1 - \hat{p}_2$ will also be approximated by a normal distribution with mean $p_1 - p_2$ and variance

$$\sigma^2_{(\hat{p}_1-\hat{p}_2)} = \sigma^2_{\hat{p}_1} + \sigma^2_{\hat{p}_2} = \frac{p_1q_1}{n_1} + \frac{p_2q_2}{n_2} \quad —(\alpha)$$

(The result above is based on this property: The variance of the *differences* between two independent random variables is the *sum* of their individual variances.)

The pooled estimate of the common value of p_1 and p_2 is $\bar{p} = (x_1 + x_2)/(n_1 + n_2)$. If we replace p_1 and p_2 by $\bar{p}$ and replace q_1 and q_2 by $\bar{q} = 1 - \bar{p}$, the variance above leads to the following standard deviation:

$$(\alpha) \implies \sigma_{(\hat{p}_1-\hat{p}_2)} = \sqrt{\frac{\bar{p}\bar{q}}{n_1} + \frac{\bar{p}\bar{q}}{n_2}}$$

We now know that the distribution of $\hat{p}_1 - \hat{p}_2$ is approximately normal, with mean $p_1 - p_2$ and standard deviation as shown above, so the z test statistic has the form given in the Key Elements box near the beginning of this section.

Confidence Interval The form of the confidence interval requires an expression for the variance different from the one given above. When constructing a confidence interval estimate of the difference between two proportions, we don't assume that the two proportions are equal, and we estimate the standard deviation as

$$\sqrt{\frac{\hat{p}_1\hat{q}_1}{n_1} + \frac{\hat{p}_2\hat{q}_2}{n_2}}$$

In the test statistic

$$z = \frac{(\hat{p}_1 - \hat{p}_2) - (p_1 - p_2)}{\sqrt{\frac{\hat{p}_1\hat{q}_1}{n_1} + \frac{\hat{p}_2\hat{q}_2}{n_2}}}$$

use the positive and negative values of z (for two tails) and solve for $p_1 - p_2$. The results are the limits of the confidence interval given in the Key Elements box near the beginning of this section.

TECH CENTER

Inferences with Two Proportions
Access tech instructions, videos, and data sets at **www.TriolaStats.com**

9-1   Basic Skills and Concepts

Statistical Literacy and Critical Thinking

1. Verifying Requirements In the largest clinical trial ever conducted, 401,974 children were randomly assigned to two groups. The treatment group consisted of 201,229 children given the Salk vaccine for polio, and 33 of those children developed polio. The other 200,745 children were given a placebo, and 115 of those children developed polio. If we want to use the methods of this section to test the claim that the rate of polio is less for children given the Salk vaccine, are the requirements for a hypothesis test satisfied? Explain.

2. Notation For the sample data given in Exercise 1, consider the Salk vaccine treatment group to be the first sample. Identify the values of n_1, $\hat{p}_1$, $\hat{q}_1$, n_2, $\hat{p}_2$, $\hat{q}_2$, $\bar{p}$, and $\bar{q}$. Round all values so that they have six significant digits.

3. Hypotheses and Conclusions Refer to the hypothesis test described in Exercise 1.

a. Identify the null hypothesis and the alternative hypothesis.

b. If the P-value for the test is reported as "less than 0.001," what should we conclude about the original claim?

4. Using Confidence Intervals

a. Assume that we want to use a 0.05 significance level to test the claim that $p_1 < p_2$. Which is better: a hypothesis test or a confidence interval?

b. In general, when dealing with inferences for two population proportions, which two of the following are equivalent: confidence interval method; P-value method; critical value method?

c. If we want to use a 0.05 significance level to test the claim that $p_1 < p_2$, what confidence level should we use for the confidence interval?

d. If we test the claim in part (c) using the sample data in Exercise 1, we get this confidence interval: $-0.000508 < p_1 - p_2 < -0.000309$. What does this confidence interval suggest about the claim?

Interpreting Displays.   *In Exercises 5 and 6, use the results from the given displays.*

5. Testing Laboratory Gloves The *New York Times* published an article about a study in which Professor Denise Korniewicz and other Johns Hopkins researchers subjected laboratory gloves to stress. Among 240 vinyl gloves, 63% leaked viruses. Among 240 latex gloves, 7% leaked viruses. See the accompanying display of the Statdisk results. Using a 0.01 significance level, test the claim that vinyl gloves have a greater virus leak rate than latex gloves.

Statdisk

Pooled proportion: 0.35
Test Statistic, z: 12.8231
Critical z: 2.3264
P-Value: 0.0000
98% Confidence interval:
0.4762035 < p1-p2 < 0.6404632

6. Treating Carpal Tunnel Syndrome Carpal tunnel syndrome is a common wrist complaint resulting from a compressed nerve, and it is often the result of extended use of repetitive wrist movements, such as those associated with the use of a keyboard. In a randomized controlled trial, 73 patients were treated with surgery and 67 were found to have successful treatments. Among 83 patients treated with splints, 60 were found to have successful treatments (based on data from "Splinting vs Surgery in the Treatment of Carpal Tunnel Syndrome," by Gerritsen

StatCrunch

Difference	0.1949
z (Observed value)	3.1226
z (Critical value)	2.3263
p-value (one-tailed)	0.0009
alpha	0.01

continued

et al., *Journal of the American Medical Association,* Vol. 288, No. 10). Use the accompanying StatCrunch display with a 0.01 significance level to test the claim that the success rate is better with surgery.

Testing Claims About Proportions.   *In Exercises 7–22, test the given claim. Identify the null hypothesis, alternative hypothesis, test statistic, P-value or critical value(s), then state the conclusion about the null hypothesis, as well as the final conclusion that addresses the original claim.*

7. Ginkgo for Dementia The herb ginkgo biloba is commonly used as a treatment to prevent dementia. In a study of the effectiveness of this treatment, 1545 elderly subjects were given ginkgo and 1524 elderly subjects were given a placebo. Among those in the ginkgo treatment group, 246 later developed dementia, and among those in the placebo group, 277 later developed dementia (based on data from "Ginkgo Biloba for Prevention of Dementia," by DeKosky et al., *Journal of the American Medical Association,* Vol. 300, No. 19). We want to use a 0.01 significance level to test the claim that ginkgo is effective in preventing dementia.

a. Test the claim using a hypothesis test.

b. Test the claim by constructing an appropriate confidence interval.

c. Based on the results, is ginkgo effective in preventing dementia?

8. Clinical Trials of Lipitor Lipitor (atorvastatin) is a drug used to control cholesterol. In clinical trials of Lipitor, 94 subjects were treated with Lipitor and 270 subjects were given a placebo. Among those treated with Lipitor, 7 developed infections. Among those given a placebo, 27 developed infections. We want to use a 0.05 significance level to test the claim that the rate of infections was the same for those treated with Lipitor and those given a placebo.

a. Test the claim using a hypothesis test.

b. Test the claim by constructing an appropriate confidence interval.

c. Based on the results, is the rate of infections different for those treated with Lipitor?

9. Smoking Cessation Programs Among 198 smokers who underwent a "sustained care" program, 51 were no longer smoking after six months. Among 199 smokers who underwent a "standard care" program, 30 were no longer smoking after six months (based on data from "Sustained Care Intervention and Postdischarge Smoking Cessation Among Hospitalized Adults," by Rigotti et al., *Journal of the American Medical Association,* Vol. 312, No. 7). We want to use a 0.01 significance level to test the claim that the rate of success for smoking cessation is greater with the sustained care program.

a. Test the claim using a hypothesis test.

b. Test the claim by constructing an appropriate confidence interval.

c. Does the difference between the two programs have practical significance?

10. Are Radiation Effects the Same for Men and Women? Among 2739 female atom bomb survivors, 1397 developed thyroid diseases. Among 1352 male atom bomb survivors, 436 developed thyroid diseases (based on data from "Radiation Dose-Response Relationships for Thyroid Nodules and Autoimmune Thyroid Diseases in Hiroshima and Nagasaki Atomic Bomb Survivors 55–58 Years After Radiation Exposure," by Imaizumi et al., *Journal of the American Medical Association,* Vol. 295, No. 9).

a. Use a 0.01 significance level to test the claim that female survivors and male survivors have different rates of thyroid diseases.

b. Construct the confidence interval corresponding to the hypothesis test conducted with a 0.01 significance level. What conclusion does the confidence interval suggest?

11. Dreaming in Black and White A study was conducted to determine the proportion of people who dream in black and white instead of color. Among 306 people over the age of 55, 68 dream in black and white, and among 298 people under the age of 25, 13 dream in black and white (based on data from "Do We Dream in Color?" by Eva Murzyn, *Consciousness and Cognition,* Vol. 17, No. 4). We want to use a 0.01 significance level to test the claim that the proportion of people over 55 who dream in black and white is greater than the proportion of those under 25.

a. Test the claim using a hypothesis test.

b. Test the claim by constructing an appropriate confidence interval.

c. An explanation given for the results is that those over the age of 55 grew up exposed to media that were mostly displayed in black and white. Can the results from parts (a) and (b) be used to verify that explanation?

12. Clinical Trials of OxyContin OxyContin (oxycodone) is a drug used to treat pain, but it is well known for its addictiveness and danger. In a clinical trial, among subjects treated with OxyContin, 52 developed nausea and 175 did not develop nausea. Among other subjects given placebos, 5 developed nausea and 40 did not develop nausea (based on data from Purdue Pharma L.P.). Use a 0.05 significance level to test for a difference between the rates of nausea for those treated with OxyContin and those given a placebo.

a. Use a hypothesis test.

b. Use an appropriate confidence interval.

c. Does nausea appear to be an adverse reaction resulting from OxyContin?

13. Are Seat Belts Effective? A simple random sample of front-seat occupants involved in car crashes is obtained. Among 2823 occupants not wearing seat belts, 31 were killed. Among 7765 occupants wearing seat belts, 16 were killed (based on data from "Who Wants Airbags?" by Meyer and Finney, *Chance,* Vol. 18, No. 2). We want to use a 0.05 significance level to test the claim that seat belts are effective in reducing fatalities.

a. Test the claim using a hypothesis test.

b. Test the claim by constructing an appropriate confidence interval.

c. What does the result suggest about the effectiveness of seat belts?

14. Cardiac Arrest at Day and Night A study investigated survival rates for in-hospital patients who suffered cardiac arrest. Among 58,593 patients who had cardiac arrest during the day, 11,604 survived and were discharged. Among 28,155 patients who suffered cardiac arrest at night, 4139 survived and were discharged (based on data from "Survival from In-Hospital Cardiac Arrest During Nights and Weekends," by Peberdy et al., *Journal of the American Medical Association,* Vol. 299, No. 7). We want to use a 0.01 significance level to test the claim that the survival rates are the same for day and night.

a. Test the claim using a hypothesis test.

b. Test the claim by constructing an appropriate confidence interval.

c. Based on the results, does it appear that for in-hospital patients who suffer cardiac arrest, the survival rate is the same for day and night?

15. Is Echinacea Effective for Colds? Rhinoviruses typically cause common colds. In a test of the effectiveness of echinacea, 40 of the 45 subjects treated with echinacea developed rhinovirus infections. In a placebo group, 88 of the 103 subjects developed rhinovirus infections (based on data from "An Evaluation of *Echinacea angustifolia* in Experimental Rhinovirus Infections," by Turner et al., *New England Journal of Medicine,* Vol. 353, No. 4). We want to use a 0.05 significance level to test the claim that echinacea has an effect on rhinovirus infections.

a. Test the claim using a hypothesis test.

b. Test the claim by constructing an appropriate confidence interval.

c. Based on the results, does echinacea appear to have any effect on the infection rate?

16. Bednets to Reduce Malaria In a randomized controlled trial in Kenya, insecticide-treated bednets were tested as a way to reduce malaria. Among 343 infants using bednets, 15 developed malaria. Among 294 infants not using bednets, 27 developed malaria (based on data from "Sustainability of Reductions in Malaria Transmission and Infant Mortality in Western Kenya with Use of Insecticide-Treated Bednets," by Lindblade et al., *Journal of the American Medical Association,* Vol. 291, No. 21). We want to use a 0.01 significance level to test the claim that the incidence of malaria is lower for infants using bednets.

a. Test the claim using a hypothesis test.

b. Test the claim by constructing an appropriate confidence interval.

c. Based on the results, do the bednets appear to be effective?

17. Cell Phones and Handedness A study was conducted to investigate the association between cell phone use and hemispheric brain dominance. Among 216 subjects who prefer to use their left ear for cell phones, 166 were right-handed. Among 452 subjects who prefer to use their right ear for cell phones, 436 were right-handed (based on data from "Hemispheric Dominance and Cell Phone Use," by Seidman et al., *JAMA Otolaryngology—Head & Neck Surgery,* Vol. 139, No. 5). We want to use a 0.01 significance level to test the claim that the rate of right-handedness for those who prefer to use their left ear for cell phones is less than the rate of right-handedness for those who prefer to use their right ear for cell phones. (Try not to get too confused here.)

a. Test the claim using a hypothesis test.

b. Test the claim by constructing an appropriate confidence interval.

18. Denomination Effect A trial was conducted with 75 women in China given a 100-yuan bill, while another 75 women in China were given 100 yuan in the form of smaller bills (a 50-yuan bill plus two 20-yuan bills plus two 5-yuan bills). Among those given the single bill, 60 spent some or all of the money. Among those given the smaller bills, 68 spent some or all of the money (based on data from "The Denomination Effect," by Raghubir and Srivastava, *Journal of Consumer Research,* Vol. 36). We want to use a 0.05 significance level to test the claim that when given a single large bill, a smaller proportion of women in China spend some or all of the money when compared to the proportion of women in China given the same amount in smaller bills.

a. Test the claim using a hypothesis test.

b. Test the claim by constructing an appropriate confidence interval.

c. If the significance level is changed to 0.01, does the conclusion change?

19. Headache Treatment In a study of treatments for very painful "cluster" headaches, 150 patients were treated with oxygen and 148 other patients were given a placebo consisting of ordinary air. Among the 150 patients in the oxygen treatment group, 116 were free from headaches 15 minutes after treatment. Among the 148 patients given the placebo, 29 were free from headaches 15 minutes after treatment (based on data from "High-Flow Oxygen for Treatment of Cluster Headache," by Cohen, Burns, and Goadsby, *Journal of the American Medical Association,* Vol. 302, No. 22). We want to use a 0.01 significance level to test the claim that the oxygen treatment is effective.

a. Test the claim using a hypothesis test.

b. Test the claim by constructing an appropriate confidence interval.

c. Based on the results, is the oxygen treatment effective?

20. Does Aspirin Prevent Heart Disease? In a trial designed to test the effectiveness of aspirin in preventing heart disease, 11,037 male physicians were treated with aspirin and 11,034 male physicians were given placebos. Among the subjects in the aspirin treatment group, 139 experienced myocardial infarctions (heart attacks). Among the subjects given placebos, 239 experienced myocardial infarctions (based on data from "Final Report on the Aspirin Component of the Ongoing Physicians' Health Study," *New England Journal of Medicine,* Vol. 321: 129–135). Use a 0.05 significance level to test the claim that aspirin has no effect on myocardial infarctions.

a. Test the claim using a hypothesis test.

b. Test the claim by constructing an appropriate confidence interval.

c. Based on the results, does aspirin appear to be effective?

21. Lefties In a random sample of males, it was found that 23 write with their left hands and 217 do not. In a random sample of females, it was found that 65 write with their left hands and 455 do not (based on data from "The Left-Handed: Their Sinister History," by Elaine Fowler Costas, Education Resources Information Center, Paper 399519). We want to use a 0.01 significance level to test the claim that the rate of left-handedness among males is less than that among females.

a. Test the claim using a hypothesis test.

b. Test the claim by constructing an appropriate confidence interval.

c. Based on the results, is the rate of left-handedness among males less than the rate of left-handedness among females?

22. Ground vs. Helicopter for Serious Injuries A study investigated rates of fatalities among patients with serious traumatic injuries. Among 61,909 patients transported by helicopter, 7813 died. Among 161,566 patients transported by ground services, 17,775 died (based on data from "Association Between Helicopter vs Ground Emergency Medical Services and Survival for Adults with Major Trauma," by Galvagno et al., *Journal of the American Medical Association,* Vol. 307, No. 15). Use a 0.01 significance level to test the claim that the rate of fatalities is higher for patients transported by helicopter.

a. Test the claim using a hypothesis test.

b. Test the claim by constructing an appropriate confidence interval.

c. Considering the test results and the actual sample rates, is one mode of transportation better than the other? Are there other important factors to consider?

9-1   Beyond the Basics

23. Determining Sample Size The sample size needed to estimate the difference between two population proportions to within a margin of error E with a confidence level of $1 - \alpha$ can be found by using the following expression:

$$E = z_{\alpha/2}\sqrt{\frac{p_1 q_1}{n_1} + \frac{p_2 q_2}{n_2}}$$

Replace n_1 and n_2 by n in the formula above (assuming that both samples have the same size) and replace each of p_1, q_1, p_2, and q_2 by 0.5 (because their values are not known). Solving for n results in this expression:

$$n = \frac{z_{\alpha/2}^2}{2E^2}$$

Use this expression to find the size of each sample if you want to estimate the difference between the proportions of men and women who consume medication daily. Assume that you want 95% confidence that your error is no more than 0.03.

24. Yawning and Fisher's Exact Test In one segment of the TV series *Mythbusters,* an experiment was conducted to test the common belief that people are more likely to yawn when they see others yawning. In one group, 34 subjects were exposed to yawning, and 10 of them

continued

yawned. In another group, 16 subjects were not exposed to yawning, and 4 of them yawned. We want to test the belief that people are more likely to yawn when they are exposed to yawning.

a. Why can't we test the claim using the methods of this section?

b. If we ignore the requirements and use the methods of this section, what is the P-value? How does it compare to the P-value of 0.5128 obtained by using Fisher's exact test?

c. Comment on the conclusion of the *Mythbusters* segment that yawning is contagious.

25. Overlap of Confidence Intervals In the article "On Judging the Significance of Differences by Examining the Overlap Between Confidence Intervals," by Schenker and Gentleman (*American Statistician*, Vol. 55, No. 3), the authors consider sample data in this statement: "Independent simple random samples, each of size 200, have been drawn, and 112 people in the first sample have the attribute, whereas 88 people in the second sample have the attribute."

a. Use the methods of this section to construct a 95% confidence interval estimate of the difference $p_1 - p_2$. What does the result suggest about the equality of p_1 and p_2?

b. Use the methods of Section 7-1 to construct individual 95% confidence interval estimates for each of the two population proportions. After comparing the overlap between the two confidence intervals, what do you conclude about the equality of p_1 and p_2?

c. Use a 0.05 significance level to test the claim that the two population proportions are equal. What do you conclude?

d. On the basis of the preceding results, what should you conclude about the equality of p_1 and p_2? Which of the three preceding methods is least effective in testing for the equality of p_1 and p_2?

26. Equivalence of Hypothesis Test and Confidence Interval Two different simple random samples are drawn from two different populations. The first sample consists of 20 people, with 10 having a common attribute. The second sample consists of 2000 people, with 1404 of them having the same common attribute. Compare the results from a hypothesis test of $p_1 = p_2$ (with a 0.05 significance level) and a 95% confidence interval estimate of $p_1 - p_2$.

Two Means: Independent Samples

Key Concept This section presents methods for using sample data from two independent samples to test hypotheses made about two population means or to construct confidence interval estimates of the difference between two population means. In Part 1 we discuss situations in which the standard deviations of the two populations are unknown and are not assumed to be equal. In Part 2 we briefly discuss two other situations: (1) The two population standard deviations are unknown but are assumed to be equal; (2) the unrealistic case in which two population standard deviations are both known.

PART 1   Independent Samples: σ_1 and σ_2 Unknown and Not Assumed Equal

This section involves two *independent* samples, and the following section deals with samples that are *dependent*. It is important to know the difference between independent samples and dependent samples.

DEFINITIONS

Two samples are **independent** if the sample values from one population are not related to or somehow naturally paired or matched with the sample values from the other population.

Two samples are **dependent** (or consist of **matched pairs**) if the sample values are somehow matched, where the matching is based on some inherent relationship. (That is, each pair of sample values consists of two measurements from the same subject—such as before/after data—or each pair of sample values consists of matched pairs—such as husband/wife data—where the matching is based on some meaningful relationship. *Caution:* "Dependence" does not require a direct cause/effect relationship.)

HINT If the two samples have different sample sizes with no missing data, they must be independent. If the two samples have the same sample size, the samples may or may not be independent.

Here is an example of independent samples and another example of dependent samples:

- *Independent Samples:* **Heights of Men and Women** Data Set 1 "Body Data" in Appendix B includes the following heights (cm) of samples of men and women, and the two samples are not matched according to some inherent relationship. They are actually two independent samples that just happen to be listed in a way that might cause us to incorrectly think that they are matched.

Heights (cm) of Men	172	154	156	158	169
Heights (cm) of Women	186	161	179	167	179

- *Dependent Samples:* **Heights of Husbands and Wives** Students of one of the authors collected data consisting of the heights (cm) of husbands and the heights (cm) of their wives. Five of those pairs of heights are listed below. These two samples are dependent, because the height of each husband is *matched* with the height of his wife.

Height (cm) of Husband	175	180	173	176	178
Height (cm) of Wife	160	165	163	162	166

For inferences about means from two independent populations, the following box summarizes key elements of a hypothesis test and a confidence interval estimate of the difference between the population means.

KEY ELEMENTS

Inferences About Two Means: Independent Samples

Objectives

1. **Hypothesis Test:** Conduct a hypothesis test of a claim about two independent population means.

2. **Confidence Interval:** Construct a confidence interval estimate of the difference between two independent population means.

continued

Notation

For population 1 we let

$\mu_1 =$ *population* mean $\qquad\qquad \bar{x}_1 =$ *sample* mean

$\sigma_1 =$ *population* standard deviation $\qquad s_1 =$ *sample* standard deviation

$n_1 =$ size of the first sample

The corresponding notations μ_2, σ_2, $\bar{x}_2$, s_2, and n_2, apply to population 2.

Requirements

1. The values of σ_1 and σ_2 are unknown and we do not assume that they are equal.

2. The two samples are *independent*.

3. Both samples are *simple random samples*.

4. Either or both of these conditions are satisfied: The two sample sizes are both *large* (with $n_1 > 30$ and $n_2 > 30$) or both samples come from populations having normal distributions. (The methods used here are *robust* against departures from normality, so for small samples, the normality requirement is loose in the sense that the procedures perform well as long as there are no outliers and departures from normality are not too extreme.)

Hypothesis Test Statistic for Two Means: Independent Samples (with H_0: $\mu_1 = \mu_2$)

$$t = \frac{(\bar{x}_1 - \bar{x}_2) - (\mu_1 - \mu_2)}{\sqrt{\dfrac{s_1^2}{n_1} + \dfrac{s_2^2}{n_2}}} \quad \text{(where } \mu_1 - \mu_2 \text{ is often assumed to be 0)}$$

Degrees of Freedom: When finding critical values or P-values, use the following for determining the number of degrees of freedom, denoted by df. (Although these two methods typically result in different numbers of degrees of freedom, the conclusion of a hypothesis test is rarely affected by the choice.)

1. Use this simple and <u>conservative estimate</u>:

   df = smaller of $n_1 - 1$ and $n_2 - 1$

2. Technologies typically use the more accurate but more difficult estimate given in Formula 9-1.

FORMULA 9-1

$$df = \frac{(A + B)^2}{\dfrac{A^2}{n_1 - 1} + \dfrac{B^2}{n_2 - 1}}$$

where $A = \dfrac{s_1^2}{n_1}$ and $B = \dfrac{s_2^2}{n_2}$

For hypothesis Testing

Note: Answers in Appendix D include technology answers based on Formula 9-1 along with "Table" answers based on using Table A-3 with the simple estimate of df given in option 1 above.

P-Values: P-values are automatically provided by technology. If technology is not available, refer to the t distribution in Table A-3. Use the procedure summarized in Figure 8-3 on page 360.

Critical Values: Refer to the t distribution in Table A-3.

Confidence Interval Estimate of $\mu_1 - \mu_2$: Independent Samples

The confidence interval estimate of the difference $\mu_1 - \mu_2$ is

$$(\bar{x}_1 - \bar{x}_2) - E < (\mu_1 - \mu_2) < (\bar{x}_1 - \bar{x}_2) + E$$

where

$$E = t_{\alpha/2}\sqrt{\frac{s_1^2}{n_1} + \frac{s_2^2}{n_2}}$$

and the number of degrees of freedom df is as described above for hypothesis tests. (In this book, we use df = smaller of $n_1 - 1$ and $n_2 - 1$.)

for CI
$$\sigma_1 = \frac{S_1}{\sqrt{n_1}}$$
$$\sigma_2 = \frac{S_2}{\sqrt{n_2}}$$
$$\sigma_{12} = \sqrt{\sigma_1^2 + \sigma_2^2}$$

Equivalent Methods

The *P*-value method of hypothesis testing, the critical value method of hypothesis testing, and confidence intervals all use the same distribution and standard error, so they are all equivalent in the sense that they result in the same conclusions.

P-Value Method

 EXAMPLE 1 **Second-Hand Smoke**

Data Set 14 "Passive and Active Smoke" includes measures of cotinine (ng/mL) in subjects from different groups. Cotinine is produced when nicotine is absorbed by the body, so cotinine is a good indicator of nicotine. Listed below are the summary statistics from a group of smokers and another group of subjects who do not smoke but are exposed to environmental tobacco smoke at home or work. Use a 0.05 significance level to test the claim that the population of smokers has a higher mean cotinine level than the nonsmokers exposed to smoke. Do smokers appear to have higher of levels of cotinine than nonsmokers who are exposed to smoke?

> Smokers $n = 40, \bar{x} = 172.5 \text{ ng/mL}, s = 119.5 \text{ ng/mL}$
>
> Nonsmokers Exposed to Smoke $n = 40, \bar{x} = 60.6 \text{ ng/mL}, s = 138.1 \text{ ng/mL}$

SOLUTION

REQUIREMENT CHECK (1) The values of the two population standard deviations are not known and we are not making an assumption that they are equal. (2) The two samples are independent. They are not matched or paired in any way. (3) The samples are simple random samples. (4) Both samples are large, with more than 30 subjects. The requirements are all satisfied. ☑

Using the *P*-value method summarized in Figure 8-1 on page 356, we can test the claim as follows.

Step 1: The claim that "the population of smokers has a higher mean cotinine level than the nonsmokers exposed to smoke" can be expressed as $\mu_1 > \mu_2$.

Step 2: If the original claim is false, then $\mu_1 \leq \mu_2$.

Step 3: The alternative hypothesis is the expression not containing equality, and the null hypothesis is an expression of equality, so we have

$$H_0: \mu_1 = \mu_2 \qquad H_1: \mu_1 > \mu_2$$

We now proceed with the assumption that $\mu_1 = \mu_2$, or $\mu_1 - \mu_2 = 0$.

Step 4: The significance level is $\alpha = 0.05$.

Step 5: Because we have two independent samples and we are testing a claim about the two population means, we use a *t* distribution with the test statistic given earlier in this section.

Step 6: The test statistic is calculated using the statistics given in the statement of the problem:

$$t = \frac{(\bar{x}_1 - \bar{x}_2) - (\mu_1 - \mu_2)}{\sqrt{\dfrac{s_1^2}{n_1} + \dfrac{s_2^2}{n_2}}} = \frac{(172.5 - 60.6) - 0}{\sqrt{\dfrac{119.5^2}{40} + \dfrac{138.1^2}{40}}} = 3.875$$

continued

P-Value With test statistic $t = 3.875$, we refer to Table A-3 (t Distribution). The number of degrees of freedom is the smaller of $n_1 - 1$ and $n_2 - 1$, or the smaller of $(40 - 1)$ and $(40 - 1)$, which is 39. With df = 39 and a right-tailed test, Table A-3 indicates that the test statistic $t = 3.875$ results in a P-value that is less than 0.005. Technology will provide the P-value of 0.0001 when using the original data or unrounded sample statistics.

Step 7: Because the P-value is less than the significance level of 0.05, we reject the null hypothesis. ("If the P is *low,* the null must go.")

> **INTERPRETATION**

Step 8: There is sufficient evidence to support the claim that the population of smokers has a higher mean cotinine level than the nonsmokers exposed to smoke. It appears that smoking is associated with higher levels of cotinine than nonsmokers exposed to smoke.

XLSTAT

Difference	111.9000
t (Observed value)	3.8755
t (Critical value)	1.6650
DF	76
p-value (one-tailed)	0.0001
alpha	0.05

Technology The tricky part about the preceding P-value approach is that Table A-3 can only give a range for the P-value, and determining that range is often a bit tricky. Technology automatically provides the P-value, so technology makes the P-value method quite easy. See the accompanying XLSTAT display showing the test statistic of $t = 3.8755$ and the P-value of 0.0001.

Critical Value Method

If technology is not available, the critical value method of testing a claim about two means is generally easier than the P-value method. Example 1 can be solved using the critical value method. When finding critical values in Table A-3, we use df = smaller of $n_1 - 1$ and $n_2 - 1$ as a relatively easy way to avoid using the really messy calculation required with Formula 9-1. In Example 1 with sample sizes of $n_1 = 40$ and $n_2 = 40$, the number of degrees of freedom is 39, so using Table A-3 with df = 39 and $\alpha = 0.05$ in the right tail, we get the critical value of $t = 1.685$. Technology uses Formula 9-1 to find the more accurate critical value of $t = 1.665$. See Figure 9-2. The test statistic of $t = 3.875$ falls in the critical region, so we reject the null hypothesis, as we did in Example 1.

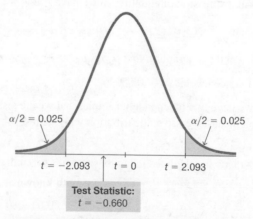

$\alpha/2 = 0.025$ $\alpha/2 = 0.025$

$t = -2.093$ $t = 0$ $t = 2.093$

Test Statistic:
$t = -0.660$

FIGURE 9-2   Hypothesis Test of Means from Two Independent Populations

Confidence Intervals

 EXAMPLE 2 Confidence Interval for Second-Hand Smoke

Using the sample data given in Example 1, construct a 90% confidence interval estimate of the difference between the mean cotinine level of smokers and the mean cotinine level of nonsmokers exposed to smoke.

SOLUTION

REQUIREMENT CHECK Because we are using the same data from Example 1, the same requirement check applies here, so the requirements are satisfied. ✓

We first find the value of the margin of error E. In Table A-3 with df = 39 and $\alpha = 0.10$ in two tails, we get critical values of $t = \pm 1.685$. (Technology can be used to find the more accurate critical values of $t = \pm 1.665$.)

$$E = t_{\alpha/2}\sqrt{\frac{s_1^2}{n_1} + \frac{s_2^2}{n_2}} = 1.685\sqrt{\frac{119.5^2}{40} + \frac{138.1^2}{40}} = 48.655276$$

Using $E = 48.655276$, $\bar{x}_1 = 172.5$, and $\bar{x}_2 = 60.6$, we can now find the confidence interval as follows:

$$(\bar{x}_1 - \bar{x}_2) - E < (\mu_1 - \mu_2) < (\bar{x}_1 - \bar{x}_2) + E$$
$$63.2 \text{ ng/mL} < (\mu_1 - \mu_2) < 160.6 \text{ ng/mL}$$

If we use technology to obtain more accurate results, we get the confidence interval of 63.8 ng/mL $< (\mu_1 - \mu_2) <$ 160.0 ng/mL, so we can see that the confidence interval above is quite good, even though we used a simplified method for finding the number of degrees of freedom (instead of getting more accurate results by using Formula 9-1).

INTERPRETATION

We are 90% confident that the limits of 63.2 ng/mL and 160.6 ng/mL actually do contain the difference between the two population means. Because those limits do not contain 0, this confidence interval suggests that the mean cotinine level of smokers is greater than the mean cotinine level of nonsmokers exposed to smoke.

PART 2 Alternative Methods

Part 1 of this section dealt with situations in which the two population standard deviations are unknown and are not assumed to be equal. In Part 2 we address two other situations:

1. The two population standard deviations are unknown but are assumed to be equal.

2. The two population standard deviations are both known.

Alternative Method: Assume That $\sigma_1 = \sigma_2$ and *Pool* the Sample Variances

Even when the specific values of σ_1 and σ_2 are not known, if it can be assumed that they have the *same* value, the sample variances s_1^2 and s_2^2 can be *pooled* to obtain an

estimate of the common population variance σ^2. The **pooled estimate of σ^2** is denoted by s_p^2 and is a weighted average of s_1^2 and s_2^2, which is used in the test statistic for this case:

$$\textbf{Test Statistic} \quad t = \frac{(\bar{x}_1 - \bar{x}_2) - (\mu_1 - \mu_2)}{\sqrt{\dfrac{s_p^2}{n_1} + \dfrac{s_p^2}{n_2}}}$$

where $s_p^2 = \dfrac{(n_1 - 1)s_1^2 + (n_2 - 1)s_2^2}{(n_1 - 1) + (n_2 - 1)}$ (pooled sample variance)

and the number of degrees of freedom is $\mathrm{df} = n_1 + n_2 - 2$.

The requirements for this case are the same as in Part 1, except the first requirement is that σ_1 and σ_2 are not known but they are assumed to be equal. Confidence intervals are found by evaluating $(\bar{x}_1 - \bar{x}_2) - E < (\mu_1 - \mu_2) < (\bar{x}_1 - \bar{x}_2) + E$ with the following margin of error E.

$$\textbf{Margin of Error for Confidence Interval} \quad E = t_{\alpha/2}\sqrt{\frac{s_p^2}{n_1} + \frac{s_p^2}{n_2}}$$

where s_p^2 is as given in the test statistic above, and $\mathrm{df} = n_1 + n_2 - 2$.

When Should We Assume That $\sigma_1 = \sigma_2$? If we use randomness to assign subjects to treatment and placebo groups, we know that the samples are drawn from the same population. So if we conduct a hypothesis test assuming that two population means are equal, it is not unreasonable to also assume that the samples are from populations with the same standard deviations (but we should still check that assumption).

Advantage of Pooling The advantage of this alternative method of pooling sample variances is that the number of degrees of freedom is a little higher, so hypothesis tests have more power and confidence intervals are a little narrower.

In the article "Homogeneity of Variance in the Two-Sample Means Test" (by Moser and Stevens, *American Statistician,* Vol. 46, No. 1), the authors note that we rarely know that $\sigma_1 = \sigma_2$. They analyze the performance of the different tests by considering sample sizes and powers of the tests. They conclude that more effort should be spent learning the method given in Part 1, and less emphasis should be placed on the method based on the assumption of $\sigma_1 = \sigma_2$.

Alternative Method Used When σ_1 and σ_2 Are Known

In reality, the population standard deviations σ_1 and σ_2 are almost never known, but if they are somehow known, the test statistic and confidence interval are based on the normal distribution instead of the t distribution. The requirements are the same as those given in Part 1, except for this first requirement: σ_1 and σ_2 are known. Critical values and P-values are found using technology or Table A-2, and the test statistic for this case is as follows:

$$\textbf{Test Statistic} \quad z = \frac{(\bar{x}_1 - \bar{x}_2) - (\mu_1 - \mu_2)}{\sqrt{\dfrac{\sigma_1^2}{n_1} + \dfrac{\sigma_2^2}{n_2}}}$$

Confidence intervals are found by evaluating
$(\bar{x}_1 - \bar{x}_2) - E < (\mu_1 - \mu_2) < (\bar{x}_1 - \bar{x}_2) + E$, where:

$$\textbf{Margin of Error for Confidence Interval} \quad E = z_{\alpha/2}\sqrt{\frac{\sigma_1^2}{n_1} + \frac{\sigma_2^2}{n_2}}$$

What if One Standard Deviation Is Known and the Other Is Unknown? If σ_1 is known but σ_2 is unknown, use the procedures in Part 1 of this section with these changes: Replace s_1 with the known value of σ_1 and use the number of degrees of freedom found from the expression below. (See "The Two-Sample t Test with One Variance Unknown," by Maity and Sherman, *The American Statistician,* Vol. 60, No. 2.)

$$df = \frac{\left(\dfrac{\sigma_1^2}{n_1} + \dfrac{s_2^2}{n_2}\right)^2}{\dfrac{\left(s_2^2/n_2\right)^2}{n_2 - 1}}$$

Recommended Strategy for Two Independent Means

Here is the recommended strategy for the methods of this section:

> **Assume that σ_1 and σ_2 are unknown, do *not* assume that $\sigma_1 = \sigma_2$, and use the test statistic and confidence interval given in Part 1 of this section.**

TECH CENTER

Inferences with Two Means: Independent Samples

Access tech instructions, videos, and data sets at **www.TriolaStats.com**

9-2   Basic Skills and Concepts

Statistical Literacy and Critical Thinking

1. Independent and Dependent Samples Which of the following involve independent samples?

a. Data Set 1 "Body Data" includes systolic and diastolic blood pressures of subjects.

b. Data Set 7 "Foot and Height Data" includes feet lengths of 19 males and 21 females.

c. Data Set 6 "Family Heights" includes heights of mothers and heights of their sons.

2. Confidence Interval for Hemoglobin Large samples of women and men are obtained and the hemoglobin level is measured in each subject. Here is the 95% confidence interval for the difference between the two population means, where the measures from women correspond to population 1 and the measures from men correspond to population 2: $-1.76 \text{ g/dL} < \mu_1 - \mu_2 < -1.62 \text{ g/dL}$.

a. What does the confidence interval suggest about equality of the mean hemoglobin level in women and the mean hemoglobin level in men?

b. Write a brief statement that interprets that confidence interval.

c. Express the confidence interval with measures from men being population 1 and measures from women being population 2.

3. Hypothesis Tests and Confidence Intervals for Hemoglobin

a. Exercise 2 includes a confidence interval. If you use the P-value method or the critical value method from Part 1 of this section to test the claim that women and men have the same mean

continued

hemoglobin levels, will the hypothesis tests and the confidence interval result in the same conclusion?

b. In general, if you conduct a hypothesis test using the methods of Part 1 of this section, will the P-value method, the critical value method, and the confidence interval method result in the same conclusion?

c. Assume that you want to use a 0.01 significance level to test the claim that the mean hemoglobin amount in women is *less* than the mean hemoglobin amount in men. What *confidence level* should be used if you want to test that claim using a confidence interval?

4. Degrees of Freedom For Example 1 on page 425, we used df = smaller of $n_1 - 1$ and $n_2 - 1$, we got df = 39, and the corresponding critical value is $t = 1.685$. If we calculate df using Formula 9-1, we get df = 76.423, and the corresponding critical value is $t = 1.665$. How is using a critical value of $t = 1.685$ more "conservative" than using the critical value of $t = 1.665$? (*Hint:* What magnitude of difference between the two sample means is required when using a critical value of $t = 1.685$ compared to the critical value of 1.665?)

In Exercises 5–22, assume that the two samples are independent simple random samples selected from normally distributed populations, and do not assume that the population standard deviations are equal. (Note: Answers in Appendix D include technology answers based on Formula 9-1 along with "Table" answers based on Table A-3 with df equal to the smaller of $n_1 - 1$ and $n_2 - 1$.)

5. Hypothesis Test of Effectiveness of Humidity in Treating Croup In a randomized controlled trial conducted with children suffering from viral croup, 46 children were treated with low humidity while 46 other children were treated with high humidity. Researchers used the Westley Croup Score to assess the results after one hour. The low-humidity group had a mean score of 0.98 with a standard deviation of 1.22, while the high-humidity group had a mean score of 1.09 with a standard deviation of 1.11 (based on data from "Controlled Delivery of High vs Low Humidity vs Mist Therapy for Croup Emergency Departments," by Scolnik et al., *Journal of the American Medical Association,* Vol. 295, No. 11). Use a 0.05 significance level to test the claim that the two groups are from populations with the same mean. What does the result suggest about the common treatment of humidity?

6. Effectiveness of Echinacea In a randomized, double-blind, placebo-controlled trial of children, echinacea was tested as a treatment for upper respiratory infections in children. "Days of fever" was one criterion used to measure effects. Among 337 children treated with echinacea, the mean number of days with fever was 0.81, with a standard deviation of 1.50 days. Among 370 children given a placebo, the mean number of days with fever was 0.64 with a standard deviation of 1.16 days (based on data from "Efficacy and Safety of Echinacea in Treating Upper Respiratory Tract Infections in Children," by Taylor et al., *Journal of the American Medical Association,* Vol. 290, No. 21). Use a 0.05 significance level to test the claim that echinacea affects the number of days with fever. Based on these results, does echinacea appear to be effective?

7. Effects of Cocaine on Children A study was conducted to assess the effects that occur when children are exposed to cocaine before birth. Children were tested at age 4 for object assembly skill, which was described as "a task requiring visual-spatial skills related to mathematical competence." The 190 children born to cocaine users had a mean of 7.3 and a standard deviation of 3.0. The 186 children not exposed to cocaine had a mean score of 8.2 with a standard deviation of 3.0. (The data are based on "Cognitive Outcomes of Preschool Children with Prenatal Cocaine Exposure," by Singer et al., *Journal of the American Medical Association,* Vol. 291, No. 20.)

a. Use a 0.05 significance level to test the claim that prenatal cocaine exposure is associated with lower scores of four-year-old children on the test of object assembly.

b. Test the claim in part (a) by using a confidence interval.

8. Magnet Treatment of Pain People spend around $5 billion annually for the purchase of magnets used to treat a wide variety of pains. Researchers conducted a study to determine whether magnets are effective in treating back pain. Pain was measured using the visual analog scale, and the results given below are among the results obtained in the study (based on data from "Bipolar Permanent Magnets for the Treatment of Chronic Lower Back Pain: A Pilot Study," by Collacott, Zimmerman, White, and Rindone, *Journal of the American Medical Association,* Vol. 283, No. 10).

a. Use a 0.05 significance level to test the claim that those treated with magnets have a greater mean reduction in pain than those given a sham treatment (similar to a placebo).

b. Construct the confidence interval appropriate for the hypothesis test in part (a).

c. Does it appear that magnets are effective in treating back pain? Is it valid to argue that magnets might appear to be effective if the sample sizes are larger?

Reduction in Pain Level After Magnet Treatment: $n = 20, \bar{x} = 0.49, s = 0.96$

Reduction in Pain Level After Sham Treatment: $n = 20, \bar{x} = 0.44, s = 1.4$

9. Cigarette Nicotine The mean nicotine content of a simple random sample of 25 unfiltered king-size cigarettes is 1.26 mg, with a standard deviation of 0.23 mg. The mean nicotine content of a simple random sample of 25 filtered 100-mm cigarettes is 0.92 mg with a standard deviation of 0.25 mg (from Data Set 15 "Cigarette Contents" in Appendix B).

a. Use a 0.05 significance level to test the claim that unfiltered king-size cigarettes have a mean nicotine content greater than that of filtered 100-mm cigarettes. What does the result suggest about the effectiveness of cigarette filters?

b. Construct a 90% confidence interval estimate of the difference between the mean nicotine content of unfiltered king-size cigarettes and the mean nicotine content of filtered 100-mm cigarettes. Does the result suggest that 100-mm filtered cigarettes have less nicotine than unfiltered king-size cigarettes?

10. Bipolar Depression Treatment In clinical experiments involving different groups of independent samples, it is important that the groups be similar in the important ways that affect the experiment. In an experiment designed to test the effectiveness of paroxetine for treating bipolar depression, subjects were measured using the Hamilton depression scale, with the results given below (based on data from "Double-Blind, Placebo-Controlled Comparison of Imipramine and Paroxetine in the Treatment of Bipolar Depression," by Nemeroff et al., *American Journal of Psychiatry,* Vol. 158, No. 6). Use a 0.05 significance level to test the claim that the treatment group and placebo group come from populations with the same mean. What does the result of the hypothesis test suggest about paroxetine as a treatment for bipolar depression?

Placebo group: $n = 43, \bar{x} = 21.57, s = 3.87$

Paroxetine treatment group: $n = 33, \bar{x} = 20.38, s = 3.91$

11. Effects of Alcohol An experiment was conducted to test the effects of alcohol. The errors were recorded in a test of visual and motor skills for a treatment group of people who drank ethanol and another group given a placebo. The results are shown in the accompanying table (based on data from "Effects of Alcohol Intoxication on Risk Taking, Strategy, and Error Rate in Visuomotor Performance," by Streufert et al., *Journal of Applied Psychology,* Vol. 77, No. 4).

Treatment Group	Placebo Group
$n_1 = 22$	$n_2 = 22$
$\bar{x}_1 = 4.20$	$\bar{x}_2 = 1.71$
$s_1 = 2.20$	$s_2 = 0.72$

a. Use a 0.05 significance level to test the claim that there is a difference between the treatment group and control group. If there is a significant difference, can we conclude that the treatment causes a decrease in visual and motor skills?

b. Construct a 95% confidence interval estimate of the difference between the two population means. Do the results support the common belief that drinking is hazardous for drivers, pilots, ship captains, and so on? Why or why not?

12. Effect of Marijuana Use on College Students Many studies have been conducted to test the effects of marijuana use on mental abilities. In one such study, groups of light and heavy users of marijuana in college were tested for memory recall, with the results given below (based on data from "The Residual Cognitive Effects of Heavy Marijuana Use in College Students," by Pope and Yurgelun-Todd, *Journal of the American Medical Association*, Vol. 275, No. 7).

a. Use a 0.01 significance level to test the claim that the population of heavy marijuana users has a lower mean than the light users. Should marijuana use be of concern to college students?

b. Construct a 98% confidence interval for the difference between the two population means. Does the confidence interval include zero? What does the confidence interval suggest about the equality of the two population means?

> Items sorted correctly by light marijuana users: $n = 64, \bar{x} = 53.3, s = 3.6$
> Items sorted correctly by heavy marijuana users: $n = 65, \bar{x} = 51.3, s = 4.5$

13. Second-Hand Smoke Data Set 14 "Passive and Active Smoke" includes cotinine levels measured in a group of nonsmokers exposed to tobacco smoke ($n = 40$, $\bar{x} = 60.58$ ng/mL, $s = 138.09$ ng/mL) and a group of nonsmokers not exposed to tobacco smoke ($n = 40$, $\bar{x} = 16.35$ ng/mL, $s = 62.53$ ng/mL). Cotinine is a metabolite of nicotine, meaning that when nicotine is absorbed by the body, cotinine is produced.

a. Use a 0.01 significance level to test the claim that nonsmokers exposed to tobacco smoke have a higher mean cotinine level than nonsmokers not exposed to tobacco smoke.

b. Construct the confidence interval appropriate for the hypothesis test in part (a).

c. What do you conclude about the effects of second-hand smoke?

14. BMI We know that the mean weight of men is greater than the mean weight of women, and the mean height of men is greater than the mean height of women. A person's body mass index (BMI) is computed by dividing weight (kg) by the square of height (m). Given below are the BMI statistics for random samples of females and males taken from Data Set 1 "Body Data" in Appendix B.

a. Use a 0.01 significance level to test the claim that females and males have the same mean BMI.

b. Construct the confidence interval that is appropriate for testing the claim in part (a).

c. Do females and males appear to have the same mean BMI?

> Female BMI: $n = 80, \bar{x} = 29.29, s = 7.29$
> Male BMI: $n = 85, \bar{x} = 28.31, s = 5.29$

15. IQ and Lead Exposure Data Set 8 "IQ and Lead" in Appendix B lists verb IQ scores for a random sample of subjects with low lead levels in their blood and another random sample of subjects with high lead levels in their blood. The statistics are summarized below.

a. Use a 0.01 significance level to test the claim that the mean verb IQ score of people with low blood lead levels is higher than the mean verb IQ score of people with high blood lead levels.

b. Construct a confidence interval appropriate for the hypothesis test in part (a).

c. Does exposure to lead appear to have an effect on verb IQ scores?

> Low Blood Lead Level: $n = 78, \bar{x} = 85.14103, s = 14.68609$
> High Blood Lead Level: $n = 21, \bar{x} = 82.52381, s = 8.31636$

16. Seat Belts A study of seat belt use involved children who were hospitalized after motor vehicle crashes. For a group of 123 children who were wearing seat belts, the number of days in intensive care units (ICU) has a mean of 0.83 and a standard deviation of 1.77. For a group of 290 children who were not wearing seat belts, the number of days spent in ICUs has a mean of 1.39 and a standard deviation of 3.06 (based on data from "Morbidity Among Pediatric Motor Vehicle Crash Victims: The Effectiveness of Seat Belts," by Osberg and Di Scala, *American Journal of Public Health,* Vol. 82, No. 3).

a. Use a 0.05 significance level to test the claim that children wearing seat belts have a lower mean length of time in an ICU than the mean for children not wearing seat belts.

b. Construct a confidence interval appropriate for the hypothesis test in part (a).

c. What important conclusion do the results suggest?

17. Bad Stuff in Children's Movies Data Set 13 "Alcohol and Tobacco in Movies" includes lengths of times (seconds) of alcohol use shown in animated children's movies. For the Disney movies, $n = 33$, $\bar{x} = 40.4$ sec, $s = 78.3$ sec. For the other movies, $n = 17$, $\bar{x} = 17.1$ sec, $s = 28.9$ sec. The sorted times for the non-Disney movies are listed below.

a. Use a 0.05 significance level to test the claim that Disney animated children's movies and other animated children's movies have the same mean time showing alcohol use.

b. Construct a confidence interval appropriate for the hypothesis test in part (a).

c. Conduct a quick visual inspection of the listed times for the non-Disney movies and comment on the normality requirement. How does the normality of the 17 non-Disney times affect the results?

$$0\quad 0\quad 0\quad 0\quad 0\quad 0\quad 0\quad 0\quad 0\quad 0\quad 0\quad 5\quad 28\quad 39\quad 72\quad 73\quad 74$$

18. Radiation in Baby Teeth Listed below are amounts of strontium-90 (in millibecquerels, or mBq, per gram of calcium) in a simple random sample of baby teeth obtained from Pennsylvania residents and New York residents born after 1979 (based on data from "An Unexpected Rise in Strontium-90 in U.S. Deciduous Teeth in the 1990s," by Mangano et al., *Science of the Total Environment,* Vol. 317).

a. Use a 0.05 significance level to test the claim that the mean amount of strontium-90 from Pennsylvania residents is greater than the mean amount from New York residents.

b. Construct a confidence interval for testing the claim in part (a).

Pennsylvania:	155	142	149	130	151	163	151	142	156	133	138	161
New York:	133	140	142	131	134	129	128	140	140	140	137	143

19. Longevity Listed below are the numbers of years that popes and British monarchs (since 1690) lived after their election or coronation (based on data from *Computer-Interactive Data Analysis,* by Lunn and McNeil, John Wiley & Sons). Treat the values as simple random samples from a larger population.

a. Use a 0.01 significance level to test the claim that the mean longevity for popes is less than the mean for British monarchs after coronation.

b. Construct a confidence interval for testing the claim in part (a).

Popes:	2	9	21	3	6	10	18	11	6	25	23	6
	2	15	32	25	11	8	17	19	5	15	0	26
Kings and Queens:	17	6	13	12	13	33	59	10	7	63	9	25	36	15

20. Blanking Out on Tests Many students have had the unpleasant experience of panicking on a test because the first question was exceptionally difficult. The arrangement of test items was studied for its effect on anxiety. The following scores are measures of "debilitating test anxiety," which most of us call panic or blanking out (based on data from "Item Arrangement, Cognitive Entry Characteristics, Sex and Test Anxiety as Predictors of Achievement in Examination Performance," by Klimko, *Journal of Experimental Education,* Vol. 52, No. 4.) Is

continued

there sufficient evidence to support the claim that the two populations of scores have different means? Is there sufficient evidence to support the claim that the arrangement of the test items has an effect on the score?

Questions Arranged from Easy to Difficult						Questions Arranged from Difficult to Easy			
24.64	39.29	16.32	32.83	28.02		33.62	34.02	26.63	30.26
33.31	20.60	21.13	26.69	28.90		35.91	26.68	29.49	35.32
26.43	24.23	7.10	32.86	21.06		27.24	32.34	29.34	33.53
28.89	28.71	31.73	30.02	21.96		27.62	42.91	30.20	32.54
25.49	38.81	27.85	30.29	30.72					

21. Do Men and Women Have the Same Mean Diastolic Blood Pressure? Refer to Data Set 1 "Body Data" and use a 0.05 significance level to test the claim that women and men have the same mean diastolic blood pressure.

22. Birth Weights Refer to Data Set 3 "Births" and use the birth weights of boys and girls. Test the claim that at birth, girls have a lower mean weight than boys.

9-2 Beyond the Basics

23. Repeat Exercise 15 "IQ and Lead Exposure" by assuming that the two population standard deviation are equal, so $\sigma_1 = \sigma_2$. Use the appropriate method from Part 2 of this section. Does pooling the standard deviations yield results showing greater significance?

24. Degrees of Freedom In Exercise 20 "Blanking Out on Tests," using the "smaller of $n_1 - 1$ and $n_2 - 1$" for the number of degrees of freedom results in df = 15. Find the number of degrees of freedom using Formula 9-1. In general, how are hypothesis tests and confidence intervals affected by using Formula 9-1 instead of the "smaller of $n_1 - 1$ and $n_2 - 1$"?

25. No Variation in a Sample An experiment was conducted to test the effects of alcohol. Researchers measured the breath alcohol levels for a treatment group of people who drank ethanol and another group given a placebo. The results are given below (based on data from "Effects of Alcohol Intoxication on Risk Taking, Strategy, and Error Rate in Visuomotor Performance," by Streufert et al., *Journal of Applied Psychology*, Vol. 77, No. 4). Use a 0.05 significance level to test the claim that the two sample groups come from populations with the same mean.

$$\text{Treatment Group:} \quad n_1 = 22, \ \bar{x}_1 = 0.049, \ s_1 = 0.015$$
$$\text{Placebo Group:} \quad n_2 = 22, \ \bar{x}_2 = 0.000, \ s_2 = 0.000$$

9-3 Two Dependent Samples (Matched Pairs)

Key Concept This section presents methods for testing hypotheses and constructing confidence intervals involving the mean of the differences of the values from two populations that are dependent in the sense that the data consist of matched pairs. The pairs must be matched according to some relationship, such as before/after measurements from the same subjects or husbands and wives.

Good Experimental Design

Suppose we want to test the effectiveness of a drug designed to lower blood pressure. It would be better to use before/after measurements from a single group of subjects treated with the drug than to use measurements from one group of subjects who were not treated with the drug and a separate group who were treated. The advantage of using matched pairs (before/after measurements) is that we reduce extraneous variation, which could occur with the two different independent samples. This strategy for designing an experiment can be generalized by the following design principle:

> **When designing an experiment or planning an observational study, using dependent samples with matched pairs is generally better than using two independent samples.**

Déjà Vu All Over Again The methods of hypothesis testing in this section are the *same methods* for testing a claim about a population mean (Part 1 of Section 8-3), except that here we use the *differences* from the matched pairs of sample data.

There are no exact procedures for dealing with dependent samples, but the following approximation methods are commonly used.

KEY ELEMENTS

Inferences About Differences from Matched Pairs

Objectives

1. **Hypothesis Test:** Use the differences from two dependent samples (matched pairs) to test a claim about the mean of the population of all such differences.

2. **Confidence Interval:** Use the differences from two dependent samples (matched pairs) to construct a confidence interval estimate of the mean of the population of all such differences.

Notation for Dependent Samples

d = individual difference between the two values in a single matched pair
μ_d = mean value of the differences d for the *population* of all matched pairs of data
$\bar{d}$ = mean value of the differences d for the paired *sample* data
s_d = standard deviation of the differences d for the paired *sample* data
n = number of *pairs* of sample data

Requirements

1. The sample data are dependent (matched pairs).

2. The matched pairs are a simple random sample.

3. Either or both of these conditions are satisfied: The number of pairs of sample data is large ($n > 30$) or the pairs of values have differences that are from a population having a distribution that is approximately normal. These methods are *robust* against departures for normality, so the normality requirement is loose.

Test Statistic for Dependent Samples (with H_0: $\mu_d = 0$)

$$t = \frac{\bar{d} - \mu_d}{\frac{s_d}{\sqrt{n}}}$$

P-Values: P-values are automatically provided by technology or the t distribution in Table A-3 can be used. Use the procedure given in Figure 8-3 on page 360.

Critical Values: Use Table A-3 (t distribution). For degrees of freedom, use df = $n - 1$.

Confidence Intervals for Dependent Samples

$$\bar{d} - E < \mu_d < \bar{d} + E$$

where $E = t_{\alpha/2} \dfrac{s_d}{\sqrt{n}}$ (Degrees of freedom: df = $n - 1$.)

Procedures for Inferences with Dependent Samples

1. Verify that the sample data consist of dependent samples (or matched pairs), and verify that the requirements in the preceding Key Elements box are satisfied.

2. Find the difference d for each pair of sample values. (*Caution:* Be sure to subtract in a consistent manner, such as "before − after.")

3. Find the value of $\bar{d}$ (mean of the differences) and s_d (standard deviation of the differences).

4. For hypothesis tests and confidence intervals, use the same t test procedures used for a single population mean (described in Part 1 of Section 8-3).

Equivalent Methods

Because the hypothesis test and confidence interval in this section use the same distribution and standard error, they are *equivalent* in the sense that they result in the same conclusions. Consequently, a null hypothesis that the mean difference equals 0 can be tested by determining whether the confidence interval includes 0.

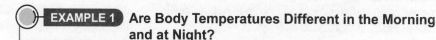

EXAMPLE 1 Are Body Temperatures Different in the Morning and at Night?

Table 9-1 lists body temperatures of five subjects at 8 AM and at 12 AM. The data are matched pairs because each pair of temperatures is measured in the same person. Data Set 2 in Appendix B lists 69 pairs of such data for Day 2 of the observations, but we use only 5 of those pairs so that we can easily show the steps in the procedure.

Use the data in Table 9-1 with a 0.05 significance level to test the claim that there is no difference in body temperatures measured at 8 AM and at 12 AM.

TABLE 9-1 Body Temperatures of Five Subjects on the Same Day

Temperature (°F) at 8 AM	98.0	97.6	97.2	97.0	98.0
Temperature (°F) at 12 AM	97.0	98.8	97.6	97.7	98.8
Difference d	1.0	−1.2	−0.4	−0.7	−0.8

SOLUTION

REQUIREMENT CHECK We address the three requirements listed earlier in the Key Elements box. (1) The samples are dependent, since each pair of temperatures is matched because the two values are from the same person. (2) The pairs of data are randomly selected. We will consider the data to be a simple random sample. (3) Because the number of pairs of data is $n = 5$, which is not large, we should check for normality of the differences and we should check for outliers. There are no outliers, and a normal quantile plot would show that the points approximate a straight-line pattern with no other pattern, so the differences satisfy the loose requirement of being from a normally distributed population. All requirements are satisfied. ✔

We will follow the same method of hypothesis testing that we used for testing a claim about a mean (see Figure 8-1 on page 356), but we use *differences* instead of raw sample data.

Step 1: The claim that there is *no difference* in body temperatures measured at 8 AM and at 12 AM can be expressed as $\mu_d = 0$.

Step 2: If the original claim is not true, then $\mu_d \neq 0$.

Step 3: The null hypothesis must express equality and the alternative hypothesis cannot include equality, so we have

$$H_0: \mu_d = 0 \text{ (original claim)} \qquad H_1: \mu_d \neq 0$$

Step 4: The significance level is $\alpha = 0.05$.

Step 5: We use the Student t distribution.

Step 6: Before finding the value of the test statistic, we must first find the values of $\bar{d}$ and s_d. We use the differences from Table 9-1 ($1, -1.2, -0.4, -0.7, -0.8$) to find these sample statistics: $\bar{d} = -0.42°$F and $s_d = 0.84°$F. Using these sample statistics and the assumption from the null hypothesis that $\mu_d = 0$, we can now find the value of the test statistic. (The value of $t = -1.113$ is obtained if unrounded values of $\bar{d}$ and s_d are used; technology will provide a test statistic of $t = -1.113$.)

$$t = \frac{\bar{d} - \mu_d}{\frac{s_d}{\sqrt{n}}} = \frac{-0.42 - 0}{\frac{0.84}{\sqrt{5}}} = -1.118$$

P-Value Method

Technology Technology will provide a P-value of 0.3281

Table Because we are using a t distribution, we refer to Table A-3 for the row with df = 4 and we see that the test statistic $t = -1.118$ corresponds to an "Area in Two Tails" that is greater than 0.20, so P-value > 0.20. See Figure 9-3(a).

Critical Value Method Refer to Table A-3 to find the critical values of $t = \pm 2.776$ as follows: Use the column for 0.05 (Area in Two Tails), and use the row with degrees of freedom of $n - 1 = 4$. Table A-3 shows a t value of 2.776, but this test is two-tailed so there are two critical values: $t = \pm 2.776$. See Figure 9-3(b).

Step 7: If we use the P-value method, we fail to reject H_0 because the P-value of 0.3281 is greater than the significance level of 0.05. If we use the critical value method, we fail to reject H_0 because the test statistic does not fall in the critical region.

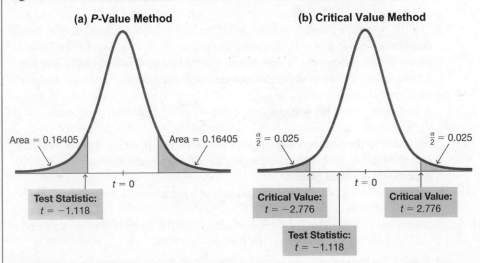

FIGURE 9-3   Hypothesis Test with Dependent Samples

continued

INTERPRETATION

We conclude that there is not sufficient evidence to warrant rejection of the null hypothesis that $\mu_d = 0$. There is not sufficient evidence to warrant rejection of the claim of no difference in body temperatures measured at 8 AM and at 12 AM.

Technology Software and calculators typically provide a P-value, so the P-value method of testing hypotheses is usually used. See the accompanying Statdisk results showing the test statistic of $t = -1.113$ and the P-value of 0.3281. Because the P-value of 0.3281 is greater than the significance level of 0.05, we fail to reject the null hypothesis and we conclude that there is not sufficient evidence to warrant rejection of the claim of no difference in body temperatures measured at 8 AM and at 12 AM.

Statdisk

Sample size, n:	5
Difference Mean, d:	−0.42
Difference St. Dev., sd:	0.8438009
Test Statistic, t:	−1.1130
Critical t:	±2.7764
P-Value:	0.3281

95% Confidence interval:
-1.467718 < µd < 0.6277183

EXAMPLE 2 **Confidence Interval for Estimating the Mean of the Temperature Differences**

Using the same sample data in Table 9-1, construct a 95% confidence interval estimate of μ_d, which is the mean of the temperature differences. By using a confidence level of 95%, we get a result that could be used for the hypothesis test in Example 1.

SOLUTION

REQUIREMENT CHECK   The solution for Example 1 includes verification that the requirements are satisfied.

The preceding Statdisk display shows the 95% confidence interval. It is found using the values of $\bar{d} = -0.42$, $s_d = 0.84$, and $t_{\alpha/2} = 2.776$ (found from Table A-3 with $n - 1 = 4$ degrees of freedom and an area of 0.05 divided equally between the two tails). We first find the value of the margin of error E.

$$E = t_{\alpha/2}\frac{s_d}{\sqrt{n}} = 2.776 \cdot \frac{0.84}{\sqrt{5}} = 1.042831$$

We now find the confidence interval as shown below. If we use the unrounded $s_d = 0.8438009$, we get the more accurate confidence interval of $-1.47°F < \mu_d < 0.63°F$.

$$\bar{d} - E < \mu_d < \bar{d} + E$$
$$-0.42 - 1.042831 < \mu_d < -0.42 + 1.042831$$
$$-1.46°F < \mu_d < 0.62°F$$

INTERPRETATION

We have 95% confidence that the limits of $-1.47°F$ and $0.63°F$ contain the true value of the mean of the difference between body temperatures at 8 AM and 12 AM. In the long run, 95% of such samples will lead to confidence interval limits that actually do contain the true population mean of the differences. See that the confidence interval includes the value of 0, so it is very possible that the mean of the differences is equal to 0, indicating that there is no significant difference between the 8 AM body temperatures and the 12 AM body temperatures. Keep in mind that this conclusion is based on the very small sample included in Table 9-1.

EXAMPLE 3   Is the "Freshman 15" Real, or Is It a Myth?

The Chapter Problem states that according to the "Freshman 15," college students typically gain 15 lb (or 6.8 kg) during their freshman year. Data Set 10 "Freshman 15" includes results from a study designed to test that common belief. Test that claim using a 0.05 significance level.

SOLUTION

REQUIREMENT CHECK   We address the three requirements. (1) The samples are dependent, since each pair of weights is matched because the two values are from the same person. (2) Although the sample isn't really a simple random sample, we will treat it as a simple random sample for the purposes of this example. (3) Because the number of pairs of data is $n = 67$, which is large, we satisfy the third requirement. All requirements are satisfied. ✅

The claim is that college students "typically" gain 15 lb (or 6.8 kg) during their freshman year. Using differences in the format of "April weight $-$ September weight," that claim is expressed as $\mu_d = 6.8$ kg, so we use the following null and alternative hypotheses:

$$H_0: \mu_d = 6.8 \text{ kg} \quad H_1: \mu_d \neq 6.8 \text{ kg}$$

Using technology, we can easily find that the 95% confidence interval estimate of the difference is $0.2 \text{ kg} < \mu_d < 2.1 \text{ kg}$. That confidence interval does not include the value of 6.8 kg, so there is sufficient evidence to warrant rejection of the null hypothesis. That confidence interval consists of positive values only, so there does appear to be weight gain, but it is likely to be between 0.4 lb (or 0.2 kg) and 4.6 lb (or 2.1 kg), not 15 lb. The concept of the "Freshman 15" appears to greatly exaggerate the typical freshman weight gain. The "Freshman 15" is therefore a myth, but we should qualify that conclusion by noting that the sample of 67 subjects includes volunteers from Rutgers University and it is not a simple random sample, so it is possible that the conclusion is not correct.

Alternative Method Used When Population Is Not Normal and $n \leq 30$

Bootstrap   The Key Elements box near the beginning of this section included the following requirement: The number of pairs of sample data is large ($n > 30$) or the pairs of values have differences that are from a population having a distribution that is approximately normal. If that condition is violated, we can use the "Bootstrap Procedure for a Confidence Interval Estimate of a Parameter" included in Section 7-4. For each pair of data values, find the difference d, then use the list of differences and apply the bootstrap method described in Section 7-4. Use percentiles to find the confidence interval that can be used for hypothesis tests. See Exercise 22 "Bootstrap."

Twins in Twinsburg

During the first weekend in August of each year, Twinsburg, Ohio, celebrates its annual "Twins Days in Twinsburg" festival. Thousands of twins from around the world have attended this festival in the past. Scientists saw the festival as an opportunity to study identical twins. Because they have the same basic genetic structure, identical twins are ideal for studying the different effects of heredity and environment on a variety of traits, such as male baldness, heart disease, and deafness—traits that were recently studied at one Twinsburg festival. A study of twins showed that myopia (near-sightedness) is strongly affected by hereditary factors, not by environmental factors such as watching television, surfing the Internet, or playing computer or video games.

Inferences with Two Means: Dependent Samples
Access tech instructions, videos, and data sets at www.TriolaStats.com

9-3   Basic Skills and Concepts

Statistical Literacy and Critical Thinking

1. True Statements? For the methods of this section, which of the following statements are true?

a. When testing a claim using a simple random sample of ten matched pairs of heights, hypothesis tests using the *P*-value method, critical value method, and confidence interval method will all result in the same conclusion.

b. The methods of this section are *robust* against departures from normality, which means that the distribution of sample differences must be very close to a normal distribution.

c. If we want to use a confidence interval to test the claim that $\mu_d < 0$ with a 0.01 significance level, the confidence interval should have a confidence level of 98%.

d. The methods of this section can be used with annual incomes of 50 randomly selected nurses in North Carolina and 50 randomly selected nurses in South Carolina.

e. If we have ten matched pairs of heights of nurses, the methods of this section require that we use a sample size of $n = 20$.

2. Notation Listed below are body temperatures from five different subjects measured at 8 AM and again at 12 AM (from Data Set 2 "Body Temperatures"). Find the values of $\bar{d}$ and s_d. In general, what does μ_d represent?

Temperature (°F) at 8 AM	97.0	98.0	97.0	96.4	96.1
Temperature (°F) at 12 AM	97.7	98.8	98.0	98.0	98.3

3. Units of Measure If the values listed in Exercise 2 are changed so that they are expressed in Celsius degrees instead of Fahrenheit degrees, how are hypothesis test results affected?

4. Degrees of Freedom If we use the sample data in Exercise 2 for constructing a 99% confidence interval, what is the number of degrees of freedom that should be used for finding the critical value of $t_{\alpha/2}$? What is the critical value $t_{\alpha/2}$?

In Exercises 5–16, use the listed paired sample data, and assume that the samples are simple random samples and that the differences have a distribution that is approximately normal.

5. Is Blood Pressure the Same for Both Arms? Listed below are systolic blood pressure measurements (mm Hg) taken from the right and left arms of the same woman (based on data from "Consistency of Blood Pressure Differences Between the Left and Right Arms," by Eguchi et al., *Archives of Internal Medicine,* Vol. 167). Use a 0.01 significance level to test for a difference between the measurements from the two arms. What do you conclude?

Right arm	102	101	94	79	79
Left arm	175	169	182	146	144

6. Heights of Presidents A popular theory is that presidential candidates have an advantage if they are taller than their main opponents. Listed below are heights (cm) of presidents along with the heights of their main opponents.

a. Use the sample data with a 0.05 significance level to test the claim that for the population of heights of presidents and their main opponents, the differences have a mean greater than 0 cm (so presidents tend to be taller than their opponents).

b. Construct the confidence interval that could be used for the hypothesis test described in part (a). What feature of the confidence interval leads to the same conclusion reached in part (a)?

Height (cm) of President	185	178	175	183	193	173
Height (cm) of Main Opponent	171	180	173	175	188	178

7. Body Temperatures Listed below are body temperatures from seven different subjects measured at two different times in a day (from Data Set 2 "Body Temperatures" in Appendix B).

a. Use a 0.10 significance level to test the claim that there is no difference between body temperatures measured at 8 AM and at 12 AM.

b. Construct the confidence interval that could be used for the hypothesis test in part (a). What feature of the confidence interval leads to the same conclusion reached in part (a)?

Body Temperature (°F) at 8 AM	97.0	97.4	98.2	96.6	97.4	97.4	98.4
Body Temperature (°F) at 12 AM	97.6	98.0	98.8	98.6	98.8	98.2	98.0

8. The Spoken Word Listed below are the numbers of words spoken in a day by each member of six different couples.

a. Use a 0.05 significance level to test the claim that among couples, males speak fewer words in a day than females.

b. Construct the confidence interval that could be used for the hypothesis test described in part (a). What feature of the confidence interval leads to the same conclusion reached in part (a)?

Male	15,684	26,429	1,411	7,771	18,876	15,477	14,069	25,835
Female	24,625	13,397	18,338	17,791	12,964	16,937	16,255	18,667

9. Heights of Fathers and Sons Listed below are heights (in.) of fathers and their first sons. The data are from a journal kept by Francis Galton. (See Data Set 6 "Family Heights"). Use a 0.10 significance level to test the claim that there is no difference in heights between fathers and their first sons.

Height of Father	69.0	65.5	67.0	69.0	71.0	72.0	70.5	70.0	69.0	66.0
Height of Son	70.5	68.0	70.0	69.0	68.0	73.0	74.0	68.0	71.0	66.0

10. Heights of Mothers and Daughters Listed below are heights (in.) of mothers and their first daughters. The data are from a journal kept by Francis Galton. (See Data Set 6 "Family Heights") Use a 0.10 significance level to test the claim that there is no difference in heights between mothers and their first daughters.

Height of Mother	65.5	66.0	60.0	63.0	63.0	60.0	62.0	64.0	68.0	69.0
Height of Daughter	66.0	66.5	62.0	65.0	66.0	61.7	68.0	65.0	68.5	67.0

11. Friday the 13th Researchers collected data on the numbers of hospital admissions resulting from motor vehicle crashes, and results are given below for Fridays on the 6th of a month and Fridays on the following 13th of the same month (based on data from "Is Friday the 13th Bad for Your Health?" by Scanlon et al., *British Medical Journal*, Vol. 307, as listed in the *Data and Story Line* online resource of data sets). Construct a 95% confidence interval estimate of the mean of the population of differences between hospital admissions on days that are Friday

continued

the 6th of a month and days that are Friday the 13th of a month. Use the confidence interval to test the claim that when the 13th day of a month falls on a Friday, the numbers of hospital admissions from motor vehicle crashes are not affected.

Friday the 6th	9	6	11	11	3	5
Friday the 13th	13	12	14	10	4	12

12. Before/After Treatment Results Captopril is a drug designed to lower systolic blood pressure. When subjects were treated with this drug, their systolic blood pressure readings (in mm Hg) were measured before and after the drug was taken. Results are given in the accompanying table (based on data from "Essential Hypertension: Effect of an Oral Inhibitor of Angiotensin-Converting Enzyme," by MacGregor et al., *British Medical Journal,* Vol. 2). Using a 0.01 significance level, is there sufficient evidence to support the claim that captopril is effective in lowering systolic blood pressure?

Subject	A	B	C	D	E	F	G	H	I	J	K	L
Before	200	174	198	170	179	182	193	209	185	155	169	210
After	191	170	177	167	159	151	176	183	159	145	146	177

13. Two Heads Are Better Than One Listed below are brain volumes (cm^3) of twins from Data Set 9 "IQ and Brain Size" in Appendix B. Construct a 99% confidence interval estimate of the mean of the differences between brain volumes for the first-born and the second-born twins. What does the confidence interval suggest?

First Born	1005	1035	1281	1051	1034	1079	1104	1439	1029	1160
Second Born	963	1027	1272	1079	1070	1173	1067	1347	1100	1204

14. Hypnotism for Reducing Pain A study was conducted to investigate the effectiveness of hypnotism in reducing pain. Results for randomly selected subjects are given in the accompanying table (based on "An Analysis of Factors That Contribute to the Efficacy of Hypnotic Analgesia," by Price and Barber, *Journal of Abnormal Psychology,* Vol. 96, No. 1). The values are before and after hypnosis; the measurements are in centimeters on a pain scale, with higher values representing greater pain. Construct a 95% confidence interval for the mean of the "before/after" differences. Does hypnotism appear to be effective in reducing pain?

Subject	A	B	C	D	E	F	G	H
Before	6.6	6.5	9.0	10.3	11.3	8.1	6.3	11.6
After	6.8	2.4	7.4	8.5	8.1	6.1	3.4	2.0

15. Self-Reported and Measured Male Heights As part of the National Health and Nutrition Examination Survey, the Department of Health and Human Services obtained self-reported heights (in.) and measured heights (in.) for males aged 12–16. Listed below are sample results. Construct a 99% confidence interval estimate of the mean difference between reported heights and measured heights. Interpret the resulting confidence interval, and comment on the implications of whether the confidence interval limits contain 0.

Reported	68	71	63	70	71	60	65	64	54	63	66	72
Measured	67.9	69.9	64.9	68.3	70.3	60.6	64.5	67.0	55.6	74.2	65.0	70.8

16. Historical Data Set In 1908, "Student" (William Gosset) published the article "The Probable Error of a Mean" (*Biometrika,* Vol. 6, No. 1). He included the data listed below for two different types of straw seed (regular and kiln dried) that were used on adjacent plots of land. The listed values are the yields of straw in cwt (100 lb, or hundredweight) per acre, and the yields are paired by the plot of land that they share.

continued

a. Using a 0.05 significance level, test the claim that there is no difference between the yields from the two types of seed.

b. Construct a 95% confidence interval estimate of the mean difference between the yields from the two types of seed.

c. Does it appear that either type of seed is better?

Regular	19.25	22.75	23	23	22.5	19.75	24.5	15.5	18	14.25	17
Kiln dried	25	24	24	28	22.5	19.5	22.25	16	17.25	15.75	17.25

Larger Data Sets. *In Exercises 17–20, use the indicated Data Sets from Appendix B. The complete data sets can be found at www.TriolaStats.com. Assume that the paired sample data are simple random samples and the differences have a distribution that is approximately normal.*

17. Body Temperatures Repeat Exercise 7 "Body Temperatures" using all of the 8 AM and 12 AM body temperatures on Day 2 as listed in Data Set 2 "Body Temperatures" in Appendix B. Use a significance level of 0.05.

18. Heights of Mothers and Daughters Repeat Exercise 9 "Heights of Mothers and Daughters" using all of the heights of mothers and daughters listed in Data Set 6 "Family Heights" in Appendix B.

19. Heights of Fathers and Sons Repeat Exercise 10 "Heights of Fathers and Sons" using all of the heights of fathers and sons listed in Data Set 6 "Family Heights" in Appendix B.

20. Tobacco and Alcohol in Children's Movies Refer to Data Set 13 "Alcohol and Tobacco in Movies" in Appendix B and use the times (seconds) that animated Disney movies showed the use of tobacco and the times that they showed the use of alcohol. Use a 0.05 significance level to test the claim that the mean of the differences is greater than 0 sec so that more time is devoted to showing tobacco than alcohol.

9-3 Beyond the Basics

21. Body Temperatures Refer to Data Set 2 "Body Temperatures" in Appendix B and use all of the matched pairs of body temperatures at 8 AM and 12 AM on Day 1. When using a 0.05 significance level for testing a claim of a difference between the temperatures at 8 AM and at 12 AM on Day 1, how are the hypothesis test results and confidence interval results affected if the temperatures are converted from degrees Fahrenheit to degrees Celsius? What is the relationship between the confidence interval limits for the body temperatures in degrees Fahrenheit and the confidence interval limits for the body temperatures in degrees Celsius?

Hint: $C = \dfrac{5}{9}(F - 32)$.

22. Bootstrap

a. If paired sample data (x, y) are such that the values of x do not appear to be from a population with a normal distribution, and the values of y do not appear to be from a population with a normal distribution, does it follow that the values of $\bar{d}$ will not appear to be from a population with a normal distribution?

b. For the hypothesis test described in Exercise 21, use the temperatures in degrees Fahrenheit and find the 95% confidence interval estimate of μ_d based on 1000 bootstrap samples. Generate the bootstrap samples using the values of $\bar{d}$.

9-4   Two Variances or Standard Deviations

Key Concept In this section we present the F test for testing claims made about two population variances (or standard deviations). The F test (named for statistician Sir Ronald Fisher) uses the F distribution introduced in this section. The F test requires that both populations have normal distributions. Instead of being robust, this test is *very* sensitive to departures from normal distributions, so the normality requirement is quite strict. Part 1 describes the F test procedure for conducting a hypothesis test, and Part 2 gives a brief description of two alternative methods for comparing variation in two samples.

PART 1   *F* Test as a Hypothesis Test with Two Variances or Standard Deviations

The following Key Elements box includes elements of a hypothesis test of a claim about two population variances or two population standard deviations. The procedure is based on using two sample variances, but the *same procedure* is used for claims made about two population standard deviations.

The actual F test could be two-tailed, left-tailed, or right-tailed, but we can make computations much easier by stipulating that the larger of the two sample variances is denoted by s_1^2. It follows that the smaller sample variance is denoted as s_2^2. This stipulation of denoting the larger sample variance by s_1^2 allows us to avoid the somewhat messy problem of finding a critical value of F for the left tail.

KEY ELEMENTS

Hypothesis Test with Two Variances or Standard Deviations

Objective

Conduct a hypothesis test of a claim about two population variances or standard deviations. (Any claim made about two population standard deviations can be restated with an equivalent claim about two population variances, so the same procedure is used for two population standard deviations or two population variances.)

Notation

$s_1^2 = $ *larger* of the two sample variances
$n_1 = $ size of the sample with the *larger* variance
$\sigma_1^2 = $ variance of the population from which the sample with the *larger* variance was drawn

The symbols s_2^2, n_2, and σ_2^2 are used for the other sample and population.

Requirements

1. The two populations are *independent*.

2. The two samples are simple random samples.

3. Each of the two populations must be *normally distributed*, regardless of their sample sizes. This F test is *not* *robust* against departures from normality, so it performs poorly if one or both of the populations have a distribution that is not normal. The requirement of normal distributions is quite strict for this F test.

continued

Test Statistic for Hypothesis Tests with Two Variances (with $H_0: \sigma_1^2 = \sigma_2^2$)

$F = \dfrac{s_1^2}{s_2^2}$ (where s_1^2 is the *larger* of the two sample variances)

P-Values: *P*-values are automatically provided by technology. If technology is not available, use the computed value of the *F* test statistic with Table A-5 to find a range for the *P*-value.

Critical Values: Use Table A-5 to find critical *F* values that are determined by the following:

1. The significance level α (Table A-5 includes critical values for $\alpha = 0.025$ and $\alpha = 0.05$.)

2. **Numerator degrees of freedom** $= n_1 - 1$ (determines *column* of Table A-5)

3. **Denominator degrees of freedom** $= n_2 - 1$ (determines *row* of Table A-5). For significance level $\alpha = 0.05$, refer to Table A-5 and use the right-tail

area of 0.025 or 0.05 depending on the type of test, as shown here:

- *Two-tailed test:* Use Table A-5 with 0.025 in the right tail. (The significance level of 0.05 is divided between the two tails, so the area in the right tail is 0.025.)

- *One-tailed test:* Use Table A-5 with $\alpha = 0.05$ in the right tail.

Find the critical F value for the right tail: Because we are stipulating that the larger sample variance is s_1^2, all one-tailed tests will be right-tailed and all two-tailed tests will require that we find only the critical value located to the right. (We have no need to find the critical value at the left tail, which is not very difficult. See Exercise 19 "Finding Lower Critical *F* Values.")

Explore the Data! Because the *F* test requirement of normal distributions is quite strict, be sure to examine the distributions of the two samples using histograms and normal quantile plots, and confirm that there are no outliers. (See "Assessing Normality" in Section 6-5.)

F Distribution

For two normally distributed populations with equal variances $(\sigma_1^2 = \sigma_2^2)$, the sampling distribution of the test statistic $F = s_1^2/s_2^2$ is the **F distribution** shown in Figure 9-4 (provided that we have not yet imposed the stipulation that the larger sample variance is s_1^2). If you repeat the process of selecting samples from two normally distributed populations with equal variances, the distribution of the ratio s_1^2/s_2^2 is the *F* distribution.

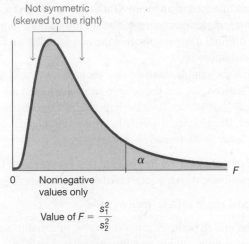

FIGURE 9-4 *F* Distribution

There is a different F distribution for each different pair of degrees of freedom for the numerator and denominator.

See Figure 9-4 and note these properties of the F distribution:

- The F distribution is not symmetric.
- Values of the F distribution cannot be negative.
- The exact shape of the F distribution depends on the two different degrees of freedom.

Interpreting the Value of the F Test Statistic

If the two populations have equal variances, the ratio s_1^2/s_2^2 will tend to be close to 1. Because we are stipulating that s_1^2 is the larger sample variance, the ratio s_1^2/s_2^2 will be a *large* number whenever s_1^2 and s_2^2 are far apart in value. Consequently, a value of F near 1 will be evidence in favor of $\sigma_1^2 = \sigma_2^2$, but a large value of F will be evidence against $\sigma_1^2 = \sigma_2^2$.

Large values of F are evidence *against* $\sigma_1^2 = \sigma_2^2$.

> **EXAMPLE 1** **Effect of Birth Weight on IQ Score**

When investigating a relationship between birth weight and IQ, researchers found that 258 subjects with extremely low birth weights (less than 1000 g) had Wechsler IQ scores at age 8 with a mean of 95.5 and a standard deviation of 16.0. For 220 subjects with normal birth weights, the mean IQ score at age 8 is 104.9 and the standard deviation is 14.1. (Based on data from "Neurobehavioral Outcomes of School-Age Children Born Extremely Low Birth Weight or Very Preterm in the 1990s," by Anderson et al., *Journal of the American Medical Association,* Vol. 289, No. 24.) Using a 0.05 significance level, test the claim that babies with extremely low birth weights and babies with normal birth weights have different amounts of variation.

> **SOLUTION**

REQUIREMENT CHECK (1) The two populations are independent of each other. The two samples are not matched in any way. (2) Given the design for the study, we assume that the two samples can be treated as simple random samples. (3) Based on an analysis of the original data, assume that the two samples are from populations having normal distributions.

Instead of using the sample standard deviations to test the claim of equal population standard deviations, we use the sample variances to test the claim of equal population variances, but we can state the hypotheses and conclusions in terms of standard deviations. Because we stipulate in this section that the larger variance is denoted by s_1^2, we let $s_1^2 = 16.0^2$ and $s_2^2 = 14.1^2$.

Step 1: The claim of different amounts of variation is equivalent to a claim of different standard deviations, which is expressed symbolically as $\sigma_1 \neq \sigma_2$.

Step 2: If the original claim is false, then $\sigma_1 = \sigma_2$.

Step 3: Because the null hypothesis is the statement of equality and because the alternative hypothesis cannot contain equality, we have

$$H_0: \sigma_1 = \sigma_2 \quad H_1: \sigma_1 \neq \sigma_2 \text{ (original claim)}$$

Step 4: The significance level is $\alpha = 0.05$.

Step 5: Because this test involves two population variances, we use the F distribution.

Step 6: The test statistic is

$$F = \frac{s_1^2}{s_2^2} = \frac{16.0^2}{14.1^2} = 1.2877$$

P-Value Method

Technology Using technology, we can find that the P-value is 0.0537, so we fail to reject H_0. (See the accompanying Statdisk display.)

Table The format and limitations of Table A-5 make the P-value method a bit tricky without technology, but here goes. For a two-tailed test with significance level 0.05, there is an area of 0.025 in the right tail, so we use the two pages for the F distribution (Table A-5) with "0.025 in the right tail." With numerator degrees of freedom $= n_1 - 1 = 257$ and denominator degrees of freedom $= n_2 - 1 = 219$, Table A-5 tells us that the critical value of F is somewhere between 1.0000 and 1.4327. The test statistic of $F = 1.2877$ is between 1.000 and 1.4327, so Table A-5 is no help for this example.

Critical Value Method Using technology, we find that the critical values are 0.7755 and 1.2928. (See the accompanying Statdisk display.) The test statistic $F = 1.2877$ falls between those two critical values, so the test statistic does not fall in the critical region and we fail to reject H_0.

> Statdisk
>
> | | |
> |---|---|
> | Test Statistic, F: | 1.2877 |
> | Lower Critical F: | 0.7755348 |
> | Upper Critical F: | 1.292841 |
> | P-Value: | 0.0537 |
>
> 95% Confidence interval:
> 0.9979949 < SD1/SD2 < 1.288547

INTERPRETATION

There is not sufficient evidence to support the claim that the two populations have different amounts of variation.

Caution: Part 2 of Section 9-2 includes methods for testing claims about two population means, and one of those methods has a requirement that $\sigma_1 = \sigma_2$. Using the F test is *not* recommended as a way to decide whether this requirement is met. For Section 9-2, using the F test runs the risk of using differences that are too small to have an effect on the t test for two independent samples. That approach is often described as being analogous to sending someone out to sea in a rowboat (the preliminary F test) to determine whether the sea is safe for an ocean liner (the t test).

PART 2 Alternative Methods

Part 1 of this section presents the F test for testing claims made about the standard deviations (or variances) of two independent populations. Because that test is so sensitive to departures from normality, we now briefly describe two alternative methods that are not so sensitive to departures from normality.

Count Five

The *count five* method is a relatively simple alternative to the F test, and it does not require normally distributed populations. (See "A Quick, Compact, Two-Sample Dispersion Test: Count Five," by McGrath and Yeh, *American Statistician,* Vol. 59,

No. 1.) If the two sample sizes are equal, and if one sample has at least five of the largest mean absolute deviations (MAD), then we conclude that its population has a larger variance. See Exercise 17 "Count Five Test" for the specific procedure.

Levene-Brown-Forsythe Test

The *Levene-Brown-Forsythe test* (or modified Levene's test) is another alternative to the F test, and it is much more robust against departures from normality. This test begins with a transformation of each set of sample values. Within the first sample, replace each x value with $|x - \text{median}|$, and apply the same transformation to the second sample. Using the transformed values, conduct a t test of equality of means for independent samples, as described in Part 1 of Section 9-2. Because the transformed values are now deviations, the t test for equality of means is actually a test comparing variation in the two samples. See Exercise 18 "Levene-Brown-Forsythe Test."

There are other alternatives to the F test, as well as adjustments that improve the performance of the F test. See "Fixing the F Test for Equal Variances," by Shoemaker, *American Statistician,* Vol. 57, No. 2.

TECH CENTER

Inferences from Two Standard Deviations

Access tech instructions, videos, and data sets at **www.TriolaStats.com**

9-4 Basic Skills and Concepts

Statistical Literacy and Critical Thinking

1. *F* Test Statistic

a. If s_1^2 represents the larger of two sample variances, can the F test statistic ever be less than 1?

b. Can the F test statistic ever be a negative number?

c. If testing the claim that $\sigma_1^2 \neq \sigma_2^2$, what do we know about the two samples if the test statistic F is very close to 1.

d. Is the F distribution symmetric, skewed left, or skewed right?

2. *F* Test Using the sample data in Data Set 1 "Body Data" in Appendix B for a test of the claim that weights of men and weights of women have different variances, we find that $s = 20.8856$ pounds for women and $s = 17.6514$ pounds for men.

a. Find the values of s_1^2 and s_2^2 and express them with appropriate units of measure.

b. Identify the null and alternative hypotheses.

c. Find the value of the F test statistic and round it to four decimal places.

d. The P-value for this test is 0.405. What do you conclude about the stated claim?

3. Testing Normality For the hypothesis test described in Exercise 2, the sample sizes are $n_1 = 147$ and $n_2 = 153$. When using the F test with these data, is it correct to reason that there is no need to check for normality because $n_1 > 30$ and $n_2 > 30$?

4. Robust What does it mean when we say that the F test described in this section is *not robust* against departures from normality?

In Exercises 5–16, test the given claim.

5. Testing Effects of Alcohol Researchers conducted an experiment to test the effects of alcohol. Errors were recorded in a test of visual and motor skills for a treatment group of 22 people who drank ethanol and another group of 22 people given a placebo. The errors for the treatment group have a standard deviation of 2.20, and the errors for the placebo group have a standard deviation of 0.72 (based on data from "Effects of Alcohol Intoxication on Risk Taking, Strategy, and Error Rate in Visuomotor Performance," by Streufert et al., *Journal of Applied Psychology,* Vol. 77, No. 4). Use a 0.05 significance level to test the claim that the treatment group has errors that vary significantly more than the errors of the placebo group.

6. Second-Hand Smoke Data Set 14 "Passive and Active Smoke" includes cotinine levels measured in a group of smokers ($n = 40$, $\bar{x} = 172.48$ ng/mL, $s = 119.50$ ng/mL) and a group of nonsmokers not exposed to tobacco smoke ($n = 40$, $\bar{x} = 16.35$ ng/mL, $s = 62.53$ ng/mL). Cotinine is a metabolite of nicotine, meaning that when nicotine is absorbed by the body, cotinine is produced.

a. Use a 0.05 significance level to test the claim that the variation of cotinine in smokers is greater than the variation of cotinine in nonsmokers not exposed to tobacco smoke.

b. The 40 cotinine measurements from the nonsmoking group consists of these values (all in ng/mL): 1, 1, 90, 244, 309, and 35 other values that are all 0. Does this sample appear to be from a normally distributed population? If not, how are the results from part (a) affected?

7. Baseline Characteristics In journal articles about clinical experiments, it is common to include *baseline characteristics* of the different treatment groups so that they can be compared. In an article about the effects of different diets, a table of baseline characteristics showed that 40 subjects treated with the Atkins diet had a mean age of 47 years with a standard deviation of 12 years. Also, 40 subjects treated with the Zone diet had a mean age of 51 years with a standard deviation of 9 years. Use a 0.05 significance level to test the claim that subjects from both treatment groups have ages with the same amount of variation. How are comparisons of treatments affected if the treatment groups have different characteristics?

8. IQ and Lead Exposure Data Set 8 "IQ and Lead" in Appendix B lists verb IQ scores for a random sample of subjects with low lead levels in their blood and another random sample of subjects with high lead levels in their blood. The statistics are summarized below. Use a 0.025 significance level to test the claim that verb IQ scores of people with low lead levels vary more than verb IQ scores of people with high lead levels.

Low Lead Level: $n = 78, \bar{x} = 85.14103, s = 14.68609$

High Lead Level: $n = 21, \bar{x} = 82.52381, s = 8.31636$

9. Magnet Treatment of Pain Researchers conducted a study to determine whether magnets are effective in treating back pain, with results given below (based on data from "Bipolar Permanent Magnets for the Treatment of Chronic Lower Back Pain: A Pilot Study," by Collacott, Zimmerman, White, and Rindone, *Journal of the American Medical Association*, Vol. 283, No. 10). The values represent measurements of pain using the visual analog scale. Use a 0.05 significance level to test the claim that those given a sham treatment (similar to a placebo) have pain reductions that vary more than the pain reductions for those treated with magnets.

Reduction in Pain Level After Sham Treatment: $n = 20, \bar{x} = 0.44, s = 1.4$

Reduction in Pain Level After Magnet Treatment: $n = 20, \bar{x} = 0.49, s = 0.96$

10. Humidity in Treating Croup In a randomized controlled trial conducted with children suffering from viral croup, 46 children were treated with low humidity while 46 other children were treated with high humidity. Researchers used the Westley Croup Score to assess the results after one hour. The low-humidity group had a mean score of 0.98 with a standard deviation of 1.22, while the high-humidity group had a mean score of 1.09 with a standard deviation of 1.11 (based on data from "Controlled Delivery of High vs Low Humidity vs Mist Therapy

continued

for Croup Emergency Departments," by Scolnik et al., *Journal of the American Medical Association,* Vol. 295, No. 11). Use a 0.05 significance level to test the claim that the two groups are from populations with the same standard deviation.

11. Cigarette Filters and Nicotine Listed below are statistics from measured nicotine contents of randomly selected filtered and non-filtered king-size cigarettes (based on data from the Federal Trade Commission). Use a 0.05 significance level to test the claim that king-size cigarettes with filters have amounts of nicotine that vary more than the amounts of nicotine in non-filtered king-size cigarettes.

$$\text{Filtered Kings} \quad n = 21, \bar{x} = 0.94 \text{ mg}, s = 0.31 \text{ mg}$$
$$\text{Non-filtered Kings} \quad n = 8, \bar{x} = 1.65 \text{ mg}, s = 0.16 \text{ mg}$$

12. Zinc Treatment Use a 0.05 significance level to test the claim that weights of babies born to mothers given placebos vary more than weights of babies born to mothers given zinc supplements. Use the following statistics (based on data from "The Effect of Zinc Supplementation on Pregnancy Outcome," by Goldenberg et al., *Journal of the American Medical Association,* Vol. 274, No. 6).

$$\text{Placebo group:} \quad n = 16, \bar{x} = 3088 \text{ g}, s = 728 \text{ g}$$
$$\text{Treatment group:} \quad n = 16, \bar{x} = 3214 \text{ g}, s = 669 \text{ g}$$

13. Body Temperatures of Men and Women Listed below are the body temperatures (°F) measured in males at 8 AM on Day 1 as listed in Data Set 2 "Body Temperatures" in Appendix B. For the body temperatures of females measured at the same time, we get $n = 59, \bar{x} = 97.45°F$, and $s = 0.66°F$. Use a 0.10 significance level to test the claim that men have body temperatures that vary more than the body temperatures of women.

$$98.0 \quad 97.0 \quad 98.6 \quad 97.4 \quad 98.2 \quad 98.2 \quad 98.2 \quad 96.6 \quad 97.4 \quad 97.4 \quad 98.2$$

14. Radiation in Baby Teeth Listed below are amounts of strontium-90 (in millibecquerels, or mBq, per gram of calcium) in a simple random sample of baby teeth obtained from Pennsylvania residents and New York residents born after 1979 (based on data from "An Unexpected Rise in Strontium-90 in U.S. Deciduous Teeth in the 1990s," by Mangano et al., *Science of the Total Environment,* Vol. 317). Use a 0.05 significance level to test the claim that amounts of strontium-90 from Pennsylvania residents vary more than amounts from New York residents.

Pennsylvania:	155	142	149	130	151	163	151	142	156	133	138	161
New York:	133	140	142	131	134	129	128	140	140	140	137	143

15. Longevity Listed below are the numbers of years that popes and British monarchs (since 1690) lived after their election or coronation. Treat the values as simple random samples from a larger population. Use a 0.05 significance level to test the claim that both populations of longevity times have the same variation.

Popes:	2	9	21	3	6	10	18	11	6	25	23	6	2
	15	32	25	11	8	17	19	5	15	0	26		
Kings and Queens:	17	6	13	12	13	33	59	10	7	63	9	25	36	15

16. Blanking Out on Tests Many students have had the unpleasant experience of panicking on a test because the first question was exceptionally difficult. The arrangement of test items was studied for its effect on anxiety. The following scores are measures of "debilitating test anxiety," which most of us call panic or blanking out (based on data from "Item Arrangement, Cognitive Entry Characteristics, Sex and Test Anxiety as Predictors of Achievement in Examination Performance," by Klimko, *Journal of Experimental Education,* Vol. 52, No. 4.) Using a 0.05 significance level, test the claim that the two populations of scores have different amounts of variation. The data are listed on the top of the next page.

Questions Arranged from Easy to Difficult				
24.64	39.29	16.32	32.83	28.02
33.31	20.60	21.13	26.69	28.90
26.43	24.23	7.10	32.86	21.06
28.89	28.71	31.73	30.02	21.96
25.49	38.81	27.85	30.29	30.72

Questions Arranged from Difficult to Easy			
33.62	34.02	26.63	30.26
35.91	26.68	29.49	35.32
27.24	32.34	29.34	33.53
27.62	42.91	30.20	32.54

9-4   Beyond the Basics

17. Count Five Test for Comparing Variation in Two Populations Repeat Exercise 16 "Blanking Out on Tests," but instead of using the F test, use the following procedure for the "count five" test of equal variations (which is not as complicated as it might appear).

a. For each value x in the first sample, find the absolute deviation $|x - \bar{x}|$, then sort the absolute deviation values. Do the same for the second sample.

b. Let c_1 be the count of the number of absolute deviation values in the first sample that are greater than the largest absolute deviation value in the second sample. Also, let c_2 be the count of the number of absolute deviation values in the second sample that are greater than the largest absolute deviation value in the first sample. (One of these counts will always be zero.)

c. If the sample sizes are equal $(n_1 = n_2)$, use a critical value of 5. If $n_1 \neq n_2$, calculate the critical value shown below.

$$\frac{\log(\alpha/2)}{\log\left(\dfrac{n_1}{n_1 + n_2}\right)}$$

d. If $c_1 \geq$ critical value, then conclude that $\sigma_1^2 > \sigma_2^2$. If $c_2 \geq$ critical value, then conclude that $\sigma_2^2 > \sigma_1^2$. Otherwise, fail to reject the null hypothesis of $\sigma_1^2 = \sigma_2^2$.

18. Levene-Brown-Forsythe Test Repeat Exercise 16 "Blanking Out on Tests" using the Levene-Brown-Forsythe test.

19. Finding Lower Critical F Values For hypothesis tests that are two-tailed, the methods of Part 1 require that we need to find only the upper critical value. Let's denote the upper critical value by F_R, where the subscript indicates the critical value for the right tail. The lower critical value F_L (for the left tail) can be found as follows: (1) Interchange the degrees of freedom used for finding F_R; (2) then, using the degrees of freedom found in Step 1, find the F value from Table A-5; (3) take the reciprocal of the F value found in Step 2, and the result is F_L. Find the critical values F_L and F_R for Exercise 16 "Blanking Out on Tests."

Chapter Quick Quiz

In Exercises 1–5, use the following survey results: Randomly selected subjects were asked if they were aware that the earth has lost half of its wildlife population during the past 50 years. Among 1121 women, 23% said that they were aware. Among 1084 men, 26% said that they were aware (based on data from a Harris poll).

1. Biodiversity Identify the null and alternative hypotheses resulting from the claim that for the people who were aware of the statement, the proportion of women is equal to the proportion of men.

2. Biodiversity Find the values of x_1 (the number of women who were aware of the statement), x_2 (the number of men who were aware of the statement), $\hat{p}_1$, $\hat{p}_2$, and the pooled proportion $\bar{p}$ obtained when testing the claim given in Exercise 1.

3. Biodiversity When testing the claim that $p_1 = p_2$, a test statistic of $z = -1.64$ is obtained. Find the P-value for the hypothesis test.

4. Biodiversity When using the given sample data to construct a 95% confidence interval estimate of the difference between the two population proportions, the result of $(-0.0659, 0.00591)$ is obtained from technology.

a. Express that confidence interval in a format that uses the symbol $<$.

b. What feature of the confidence interval is a basis for deciding whether there is a significant difference between the proportion of women aware of the statement and the proportion of men who are aware?

5. Biodiversity Assume that a P-value of 0.1 is obtained when testing the claim given in Exercise 1 "Biodiversity." What should be concluded about the null hypothesis? What should be the final conclusion?

6. True? Determine whether the following statement is true: When random samples of 50 male nurses and 50 female nurses are obtained and we want to test the claim that male nurses and female nurses have different mean annual incomes, there is no need to confirm that the samples are from populations with normal distributions.

7. True? When we collect random samples to test the claim that the proportion of female surgeons in the United States is equal to the proportion of female surgeons outside the United States, there is a requirement that $np \geq 30$ and $nq \geq 30$.

8. Dependent or Independent? Listed below are measures of visual acuity of the right and left eyes of five subjects (from Data Set 5 "Vision" in Appendix B). Are the data dependent or independent?

Right eye	60	25	20	50	30
Left eye	80	20	25	50	25

9. Hypotheses Identify the null and alternative hypotheses for using the sample data from Exercise 8 in testing the claim that for differences between right-eye measurements and left-eye measurements, those differences are from a population with a mean equal to 0.

10. Test Statistics Identify the test statistics that should be used for testing the following claims.

a. The mean of the differences between platelet counts of husbands and platelet counts of their wives is equal to 0.

b. The mean platelet count of adult Californians is equal to the mean platelet count of adult Texans.

c. The proportion of men with diabetes is equal to the proportion of women with diabetes.

d. The variation among pulse rates of women is equal to the variation among pulse rates of men.

Review Exercises

1. Blinding Among 13,200 submitted abstracts that were blindly evaluated (with authors and institutions not identified), 26.7% were accepted for publication. Among 13,433 abstracts that were not blindly evaluated, 29.0% were accepted (based on data from "Effect of Blinded Peer Review on Abstract Acceptance," by Ross et al., *Journal of the American Medical Association,* Vol. 295, No. 14). Use a 0.01 significance level to test the claim that the acceptance rate is the same with or without blinding. How might the results be explained?

2. Blinding Construct the confidence interval that could be used to test the claim in Exercise 1. What feature of the confidence interval leads to the same conclusion from Exercise 1?

3. Heights Listed below are heights (cm) randomly selected from the sample of women and heights (cm) randomly selected from the sample of men (from Data Set 1 "Body Data" in Appendix B). Use a 95% confidence level to estimate the magnitude of the difference between the mean height of women and the mean height of men.

| Women: | 160.3 | 167.7 | 166.9 | 153.3 | 160.0 | 177.3 | 169.1 | 134.5 | 163.3 | 171.1 |
| Men: | 190.3 | 169.8 | 179.8 | 179.8 | 177.0 | 178.5 | 173.5 | 178.7 | 179.0 | 181.3 |

4. Heights Use a 0.01 significance level with the sample data from Exercise 3 to test the claim that women have heights with a mean that is less than the mean height of men.

5. Effects of Physical Training A study was conducted to investigate effects of physical training. Sample data from ten subjects are listed below, with all weights given in kilograms. (See "Effect of Endurance Training on Possible Determinants of VO_2 During Heavy Exercise," by Casaburi et al., *Journal of Applied Physiology,* Vol. 62, No. 1.)

a. Is there sufficient evidence to conclude that there is a difference between the pre-training and post-training weights? What do you conclude about the effect of training on weight?

b. Construct a 95% confidence interval for the mean of the differences between pre-training and post-training weights.

| Pre-training: | 99 | 57 | 62 | 69 | 74 | 77 | 59 | 92 | 70 | 85 |
| Post-training: | 94 | 57 | 62 | 69 | 66 | 76 | 58 | 88 | 70 | 84 |

6. Variation of Heights Use the sample data given in Exercise 3 "Heights" and test the claim that women and men have heights with the same variation. Use a 0.05 significance level.

Cumulative Review Exercises

Family Heights. *In Exercises 1–5, use the following heights (in.) of fathers, mothers, and their adult sons (from Data Set 6 "Family Heights"). The data are matched so that each column consists of heights from the same family.*

Father	68.0	68.0	65.5	66.0	67.5	70.0	68.0	71.0
Mother	64.0	60.0	63.0	59.0	62.0	69.0	65.5	66.0
Son	71.0	64.0	71.0	68.0	70.0	71.0	71.7	71.0

1. a. Are the three samples independent or dependent? Why?

b. Find the mean, median, range, standard deviation, and variance of the heights of the sons. Express results with the appropriate units.

c. What is the level of measurement of the sample data (nominal, ordinal, interval, ratio)?

d. Are the original unrounded heights discrete data or continuous data?

2. Scatterplot Construct a scatterplot of the paired father/son heights. What does the graph suggest?

3. Confidence Interval Construct a 95% confidence interval estimate of the mean height of sons. Write a brief statement that interprets the confidence interval.

4. Hypothesis Test Use a 0.05 significance level to test the claim that differences between heights of fathers and their sons have a mean of 0 in.

5. Assessing Normality Refer to the accompanying normal quantile plot to determine whether the sample of heights of fathers appears to be from a normally distributed population.

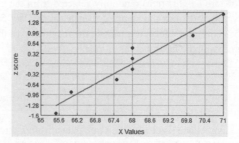

6. Braking Reaction Times: Histogram Listed below are sorted braking reaction times (in 1/10,000 sec) for male and female subjects (based on data from the RT-2S Brake Reaction Time Tester). Construct a histogram for the reaction times of males. Use a class width of 8 and use 28 as the lower limit of the first class. Instead of using class boundaries for the horizontal axis, use class midpoint values. Does it appear that the data are from a population with a normal distribution?

Male	28	30	31	34	34	36	36	36	36	38	39	40	40	40	40	41	41	41
	42	42	44	46	47	48	48	49	51	53	54	54	56	57	60	61	61	63
Female	22	24	34	36	36	37	39	41	41	43	43	45	45	47	53	54	54	55
	56	57	57	57	58	61	62	63	66	67	68	71	72	76	77	78	79	80

7. Braking Reaction Times: Normal? The accompanying normal quantile plot is obtained by using the braking reaction times of females listed in Exercise 6. Interpret this graph.

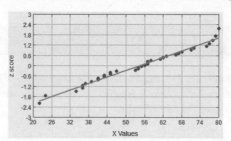

8. Braking Reaction Times: Boxplots Use the same data from Exercise 6 and use the same scale to construct a boxplot of the braking reaction times of males and another boxplot for the braking reaction times of females. What do the boxplots suggest?

9. Braking Reaction Times: Hypothesis Test Use the sample data from Exercise 6 with a 0.01 significance level to test the claim that males and females have the same mean braking reaction time.

10. Braking Reaction Times: Confidence Intervals

a. Construct a 99% confidence interval estimate of the mean braking reaction time of males, construct a 99% confidence interval estimate of the mean braking reaction time of females, and then compare the results.

b. Construct a 99% confidence interval estimate of the difference between the mean braking reaction time of males and the mean braking reaction time of females.

c. Which is better for comparing the mean reaction times of males and females: the results from part (a) or the results from part (b)?

Technology Project

Many technologies are capable of generating normally distributed data drawn from a population with a specified mean and standard deviation. In Example 3 of Section 6-1, we noted that bone density test scores are measured as z scores having a normal distribution with a mean of 0 and a standard deviation of 1. Generate two sets of sample data that represent simulated bone density scores, as shown below.

• **Treatment Group:** Generate 10 sample values from a normally distributed population of bone density scores with mean 0 and standard deviation 1.

• **Placebo Group:** Generate 15 sample values from a normally distributed population of bone density scores with mean 0 and standard deviation 1.

Statdisk:	Select **Data,** then **Normal Generator.**
Minitab:	Select **Calc, Random Data, Normal.**
Excel:	Select **Data Analysis, Random Number Generation.**
TI-83/84 Plus:	Press **MATH,** select **PROB,** then use **randNorm** function with the format of $(\bar{x}, s, n)$.
StatCrunch:	Click on **Data,** select **Simulate,** select **Normal.**

Because each of the two samples consists of random selections from a normally distributed population with a mean of 0 and a standard deviation of 1, the data are generated so that both data sets really come from the same population, so there should be no difference between the two sample means.

a. After generating the two data sets, use a 0.10 significance level to test the claim that the two samples come from populations with the same mean.

b. If this experiment is repeated many times, what is the expected percentage of trials leading to the conclusion that the two population means are different? How does this relate to a type I error?

c. If your generated data lead to the conclusion that the two population means are different, would this conclusion be correct or incorrect in reality? How do you know?

d. If part (a) is repeated 20 times, what is the probability that none of the hypothesis tests leads to rejection of the null hypothesis?

e. Repeat part (a) 20 times. How often was the null hypothesis of equal means rejected? Is this the result you expected?

FROM DATA TO DECISION

Critical Thinking: Ages of workers killed in the Triangle Factory fire

Listed below are the ages (years) of the 146 employees who perished in the Triangle Factory fire that occurred on March 25, 1911, in Manhattan (based on data from the Kheel Center and the *New York Times*). One factor contributing to the large number of deaths is that almost all exits were locked so that employees could be checked for theft when they finished work at the end of the day. That fire revealed grossly poor and unsafe working conditions that led to changes in building codes and labor laws.

Analyzing the Results

1. First *explore* the combined male and female ages using suitable statistics and graphs. What is the mean age? What are the minimum and maximum ages? What is the standard deviation of the ages? Are there any outliers? Describe the distribution of the ages.

2. Examination of the two lists shows that relatively few men perished in the fire. Treat the ages as sample data and determine whether there is sufficient evidence to support the claim that among the workers who perish in such circumstances, the majority are women.

3. Construct a 95% confidence interval estimate of the mean age of males and construct another 95% confidence interval estimate of the mean age of females. Compare the results.

4. Treat the ages as sample data and determine whether there is sufficient evidence to support the claim that female workers have a mean age that is less than that of male workers.

5. Treat the ages as sample data and determine whether there is sufficient evidence to support the claim that ages of males and females have different standard deviations.

6. Based on the preceding results, identify any particularly notable features of the data.

Males

38	19	30	24	23	23	19	18	19	33	17	22	33	25	20	23	22

Females

24	16	25	31	22	18	19	22	16	23	17	15	21	18	17	17	17	31	20	36
18	25	30	16	25	25	21	19	17	18	20	18	26	26	16	18	18	17	22	17
20	22	18	20	16	25	18	40	21	18	19	19	18	18	19	16	19	16	16	21
33	21	14	22	19	19	23	19	18	21	39	20	14	27	22	15	19	16	16	19
18	21	18	19	19	20	18	43	16	20	18	30	21	22	18	21	35	22	21	22
21	22	17	24	25	20	18	32	20	21	19	24	17	18	30	18	16	22	22	17
22	20	15	20	17	21	21	18	17											

Cooperative Group Activities

1. Out-of-class activity Collect sample data and test the claim that people who exercise tend to have pulse rates that are lower than those who do not exercise.

2. Out-of-class activity Collect sample data and test the claim that the proportion of female students who smoke is equal to the proportion of male students who smoke.

3. Out-of-class activity Measure and record the height of the man and woman from each of several different couples. Estimate the mean of the differences between the heights of men and the heights of their partners. Compare the result to the difference between the mean height of men and the mean height of women included in Data Set 1 "Body Data" in Appendix B. Do the results suggest that height is a factor when people select partners?

4. In-class activity Divide into groups according to gender, with about 10 or 12 students in each group. Each group member should record his or her pulse rate by counting the number of heartbeats in 1 minute, and then the group statistics $(n, \bar{x}, s)$ should be calculated. The groups should test the null hypothesis of no difference between their mean pulse rate and the mean of the pulse rates for the population from which subjects of the same gender were selected for Data Set 1 "Body Data" in Appendix B.

5. Out-of-class activity Randomly select a sample of male students and a sample of female students and ask each selected person a yes/no question, such as whether the federal government should fund stem cell research. Record the response, the gender of the respondent, and the gender of the person asking the question. Use a formal hypothesis test to determine whether there is a difference between the proportions of *yes* responses from males and females. Also, determine whether the responses appear to be influenced by the gender of the interviewer.

6. Out-of-class activity Construct a short survey of just a few questions, including a question asking the subject to report his or her height. After the subject has completed the survey, measure the subject's height (without shoes) using an accurate measuring system. Record the gender, reported height, and measured height of each subject. Do male subjects appear to exaggerate their heights? Do female subjects appear to exaggerate their heights? Do the errors for males appear to have the same mean as the errors for females?

7. In-class activity Without using any measuring device, ask each student to draw a line believed to be 3 in. long and another line believed to be 3 cm long. Then use rulers to measure and record the lengths of the lines drawn. Record the errors along with the genders of the students making the estimates. Test the claim that when estimating the length of a 3-in. line, the mean error from males is equal to the mean error from females. Also, do the results show that we have a better understanding of the British system of measurement (inches) than the SI system (centimeters)?

8. Out-of-class activity Obtain sample data and test the claim that husbands are older than their wives.

9. Out-of-class activity Survey married couples and record the number of credit cards each person has. Analyze the paired data to determine whether husbands have more credit cards, wives have more credit cards, or they both have about the same number of credit cards. Try to identify reasons for any discrepancy.

10. Out-of-class activity Obtain sample data to test the claim that in the college library, science books have a mean age that is less than the mean age of novels.

11. Out-of-class activity Conduct experiments and collect data to test the claim that there are no differences in taste between ordinary tap water and different brands of bottled water.

10 Correlation and Regression

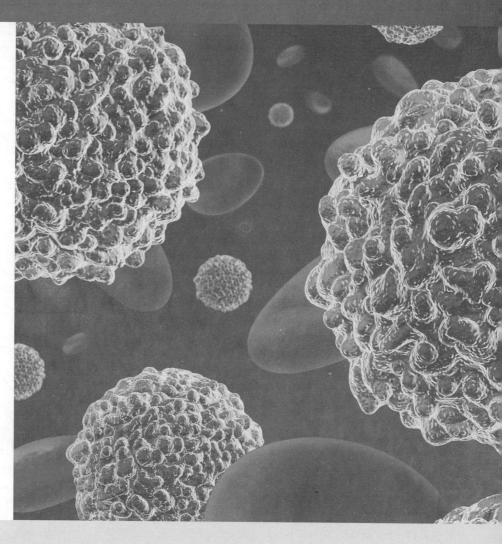

 CHAPTER PROBLEM

Save Money and Time (or Not?) with a Simpler Health Test?

When assessing the health of a person, some body measurements are relatively easy, quick, and inexpensive, while others are more expensive and time consuming. Measuring pulse rate takes only a minute and requires only a clock or watch, but measuring a person's white blood cell count requires drawing a blood sample that must be sent to a laboratory. Monitoring the white blood cell count is important because those white blood cells help fight infections. If there is a strong correlation between pulse rate and white blood cell count, we could use the pulse rate to predict the white blood cell count and thereby save money and time. In this chapter, we will investigate the correlation between the pulse rate and white blood cell count of females. We will begin with the data in Table 10-1, which uses only five of the pairs of data available in Data Set 1

"Body Data" in Appendix B. We consider this smaller data set for the purposes of illustrating the methods of this chapter. Pulse rates are measured in beats per minute, and the white blood cell count gives the number of white blood cells expressed in units of 1000 cells/μL.

TABLE 10-1 Pulse Rates and White Blood Cell Counts of Adult Females

Pulse Rate	56.0	82.0	78.0	86.0	88.0
White Blood Cell Count	6.9	8.1	6.4	6.3	10.9

Using the methods of this chapter, we can address questions such as these:

- Is there a *correlation* between pulse rates of females and their white blood cell counts?

- If there is a correlation between pulse rates of females and their white blood cell counts, can we describe it with an equation so that we can predict white blood cell count given a pulse rate? If so, how *accurate* is the prediction likely to be?

CHAPTER OBJECTIVES

A major focus of this chapter is to analyze *paired* sample data. In Section 9-3 we considered sample data consisting of matched pairs, but the goal in Section 9-3 was to make inferences about the *mean of the differences* from the matched pairs. In this chapter we again consider paired sample data, but the objective is fundamentally different from that of Section 9-3. In this chapter we present methods for determining whether there is a *correlation*, or association, between two variables. For linear correlations, we can identify an equation of a straight line that best fits the data, and we can use that equation to predict the value of one variable given the value of the other variable. Here are the chapter objectives:

 Correlation

- Use paired data to find the value of the linear correlation coefficient r.

- Determine whether there is sufficient evidence to support a conclusion that there is a linear correlation between two variables.

 Regression

- Use paired sample data to find the equation of the regression line.

- Find the best predicted value of a variable given some value of the other variable.

 Prediction Intervals and Variation

- Use paired sample data to determine the value of the coefficient of determination r^2, and to interpret that value.

- Use paired sample data to use a given value of one variable to find a predicted value and a prediction interval for a second variable.

10-4 **Multiple Regression**

- Interpret results from technology to determine whether a multiple regression equation is suitable for making predictions.

- Compare results from different combinations of predictor variables and identify the combination that results in the best multiple regression equation.

Dummy Variables and Logistic Regression

- Find regression equations that include a dummy variable, which has only two possible discrete values.

- Apply methods of logistic regression when a dummy variable is the response (*y*) variable.

 Correlation

Key Concept In Part 1 we introduce the *linear correlation coefficient r*, which is a number that measures how well paired sample data fit a straight-line pattern when graphed. We use the sample of paired data (sometimes called **bivariate data**) to find the value of *r* (usually found using technology), then we use that value to decide whether there is a linear correlation between the two variables. In this section we consider only *linear* relationships, which means that when graphed in a scatterplot, the points approximate a *straight-line* pattern. In Part 2, we discuss methods for conducting a formal hypothesis test that can be used to decide whether there is a linear correlation between all population values for the two variables.

PART 1   Basic Concepts of Correlation

We begin with the basic definition of *correlation,* a term commonly used in the context of an association between two variables.

> **DEFINITIONS**
>
> A **correlation** exists between two variables when the values of one variable are somehow associated with the values of the other variable.
>
> A **linear correlation** exists between two variables when there is a correlation and the plotted points of paired data result in a pattern that can be approximated by a straight line.

Table 10-1, for example, includes paired sample data consisting of pulse rates and white blood cell counts for five adult females. We will determine whether there is a linear correlation between the variable *x* (pulse rate) and the variable *y* (white blood cell count). Instead of blindly jumping into the calculation of the linear correlation coefficient *r*, it is wise to first *explore* the data.

Explore!

Because it is always wise to explore sample data before applying a formal statistical procedure, we should use a scatterplot to explore the paired data visually. Figure 10-1 shows a scatterplot of the data. The plotted points do not appear to follow a straight-line pattern very well, so it might appear that there is no linear correlation.

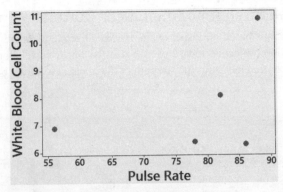

FIGURE 10-1   Scatterplot of Pulse Rates and
White Blood Cell Counts

Interpreting Scatterplots

Figure 10-2 shows four scatterplots with different characteristics.

- Figure 10-2(a): Distinct straight-line, or linear, pattern. We say that there is a *positive* linear correlation between x and y, since as the x values increase, the corresponding y values also increase.

- Figure 10-2(b): Distinct straight-line, or linear pattern. We say that there is a *negative* linear correlation between x and y, since as the x values increase, the corresponding y values decrease.

- Figure 10-2(c): No distinct pattern which suggests that there is no correlation between x and y.

- Figure 10-2(d): Distinct pattern suggesting a correlation between x and y, but the pattern is not that of a straight line.

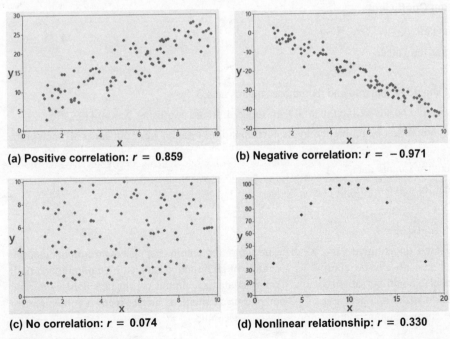

(a) Positive correlation: $r = 0.859$

(b) Negative correlation: $r = -0.971$

(c) No correlation: $r = 0.074$

(d) Nonlinear relationship: $r = 0.330$

FIGURE 10-2   Scatterplots

Measure the Strength of the Linear Correlation with r

Because conclusions based on visual examinations of scatterplots are largely subjective, we need more objective measures. We use the linear correlation coefficient r, which is a number that measures the strength of the linear association between the two variables.

DEFINITION

The **linear correlation coefficient** r measures the strength of the linear correlation between the paired quantitative x values and y values in a *sample*. The linear correlation coefficient r is computed by using Formula 10-1 or Formula 10-2, included in the following Key Elements box. [The linear correlation coefficient is sometimes referred to as the **Pearson product moment correlation coefficient** in honor of Karl Pearson (1857–1936), who originally developed it.]

Because the linear correlation coefficient r is calculated using sample data, it is a sample statistic used to measure the strength of the linear correlation between x and y. If we had every pair of x and y values from an entire population, the result of Formula 10-1 or Formula 10-2 would be a population parameter, represented by ρ (Greek letter rho).

KEY ELEMENTS

Calculating and Interpreting the Linear Correlation Coefficient r

Objective

Determine whether there is a linear correlation between two variables.

Notation for the Linear Correlation Coefficient

n	number of *pairs* of sample data.
Σ	denotes addition of the items indicated.
Σx	sum of all x values.
Σx^2	indicates that each x value should be squared and then those squares added.
$(\Sigma x)^2$	indicates that the x values should be added and the total then squared. Avoid confusing Σx^2 and $(\Sigma x)^2$.
Σxy	indicates that each x value should first be multiplied by its corresponding y value. After obtaining all such products, find their sum.
r	linear correlation coefficient for *sample* data.
ρ	linear correlation coefficient for a *population* of paired data.

Requirements

Given any collection of sample paired quantitative data, the linear correlation coefficient r can always be computed, but the following requirements should be satisfied when using the sample paired data to make a conclusion about the linear correlation in the corresponding population of paired data.

1. The sample of paired (x, y) data is a simple random sample of quantitative data. (It is important that the sample data have not been collected using some inappropriate method, such as using a voluntary response sample.)

continued

2. Visual examination of the scatterplot must confirm that the points approximate a straight-line pattern.*

3. Because results can be strongly affected by the presence of outliers, any outliers must be removed if they are known to be errors. The effects of any other outliers should be considered by calculating r with and without the outliers included.*

Note: Requirements 2 and 3 above are simplified attempts at checking this formal requirement: The pairs of (x, y) data must have a **bivariate normal distribution.** Normal distributions are discussed in Chapter 6, but this assumption basically requires that for any fixed value of x, the corresponding values of y have a distribution that is approximately normal, and for any fixed value of y, the values of x have a distribution that is approximately normal. This requirement is usually difficult to check, so for now, we will use Requirements 2 and 3 as listed above.

Formulas for Calculating r

FORMULA 10-1 $r = \dfrac{n(\Sigma xy) - (\Sigma x)(\Sigma y)}{\sqrt{n(\Sigma x^2) - (\Sigma x)^2}\sqrt{n(\Sigma y^2) - (\Sigma y)^2}}$ (Good format for calculations)

FORMULA 10-2 $r = \dfrac{\Sigma(z_x z_y)}{n - 1}$ (Good format for understanding)

where z_x denotes the z score for an individual sample value x and z_y is the z score for the corresponding sample value y.

Rounding the Linear Correlation Coefficient r

Round the linear correlation coefficient r to three decimal places so that its value can be directly compared to critical values in Table A-6.

Interpreting the Linear Correlation Coefficient r

- *Using P-Value from Technology to Interpret r:* Use the *P*-value and significance level α as follows:

    P-value $\leq \alpha$: Supports the claim of a linear correlation.
    P-value $> \alpha$: Does not support the claim of a linear correlation.

- *Using Table A-6 to Interpret r:* Consider critical values from Table A-6 or technology as being both positive and negative, draw a graph similar to Figure 10-3 that accompanies Example 4 on page 467, and then use the following decision criteria:

    Correlation If the computed linear correlation coefficient r lies in the left tail beyond the leftmost critical value or if it lies in the right tail beyond the rightmost critical value (that is, $|r| \geq$ critical value), conclude that there is sufficient evidence to support the claim of a linear correlation.

    No Correlation If the computed linear correlation coefficient lies *between* the two critical values (that is, $|r| <$ critical value), conclude that there is not sufficient evidence to support the claim of a linear correlation.

CAUTION Remember, the methods of this section apply to a *linear* correlation. If you conclude that there does not appear to be a linear correlation, it is possible that there might be some other association that is not linear, as in Figure 10-2(d) on page 461. Always create a scatterplot to see relationships that might not be linear.

Properties of the Linear Correlation Coefficient r

1. The value of r is always between -1 and 1 inclusive. That is, $-1 \leq r \leq 1$.

2. If all values of either variable are converted to a different scale, the value of r does not change.

3. The value of r is not affected by the choice of x or y. Interchange all x values and y values, and the value of r will not change.

4. r measures the strength of a *linear* relationship. It is not designed to measure the strength of a relationship that is not linear, as in Figure 10-2(d).

5. r is very sensitive to outliers in the sense that a single outlier could dramatically affect its value.

Calculating the Linear Correlation Coefficient r

The following three examples illustrate three different methods for finding the value of the linear correlation coefficient r, but you need to use only one method. *The use of technology (as in Example 1) is strongly recommended.* If manual calculations are absolutely necessary, Formula 10-1 is recommended (as in Example 2). If a better understanding of r is desired, Formula 10-2 is recommended (as in Example 3).

EXAMPLE 1 **Finding r Using Technology**

To better illustrate the calculation of r, we use the data from Table 10-1 reproduced here. Use technology to find the value of the correlation coefficient r for the data in Table 10-1.

TABLE 10-1 Pulse Rates and White Blood Cell Counts of Adult Females

Pulse Rate	56.0	82.0	78.0	86.0	88.0
White Blood Cell Count	6.9	8.1	6.4	6.3	10.9

SOLUTION

The value of r will be automatically calculated with software or a calculator. See the accompanying technology displays showing that $r = 0.405$ (rounded).

Statdisk

```
Correlation Results:
Correlation coeff, r:  0.4050369
Critical r:            ±0.8783393
P-value (two-tailed): 0.49876
```

Minitab

```
Pearson correlation of Pulse and White = 0.405
P-Value = 0.499
```

StatCrunch

```
Correlation between Pulse and White is:
0.40503693
```

XLSTAT

Variables	Pulse	White
Pulse	1	0.4050
White	0.4050	1

TI-83/84 Plus

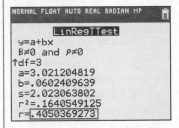

```
NORMAL FLOAT AUTO REAL RADIAN MP
        LinRegTTest
y=a+bx
β≠0 and ρ≠0
↑df=3
 a=3.021204819
 b=.0602409639
 s=2.023063802
 r²=.1640549125
 r=.4050369273
```

SPSS

		Pulse	White
Pulse	Pearson Correlation	1	.405
	Sig. (2-tailed)		.499
	N	5	5
White	Pearson Correlation	.405	1
	Sig. (2-tailed)	.499	
	N	5	5

JMP

△ **Correlations**

	Pulse	White
Pulse	1.0000	0.4050
White	0.4050	1.0000

△ **Correlation Probability**

	Pulse	White
Pulse	<.0001	0.4988
White	0.4988	<.0001

EXAMPLE 2 **Finding *r* Using Formula 10-1**

Use Formula 10-1 to find the value of the linear correlation coefficient *r* for the five pairs of data listed in Table 10-1.

SOLUTION

Using Formula 10-1, the value of *r* is calculated as shown below. Here, the variable *x* is used for the pulse rate, and the variable *y* is used for the white blood cell count. Because there are five pairs of data, $n = 5$. Other required values are computed in Table 10-2.

TABLE 10-2 Calculating *r* with Formula 10-1

x (Pulse Rate)	y (White Blood Cell Count)	x^2	y^2	xy
56	6.9	3136	47.61	386.4
82	8.1	6724	65.61	664.2
78	6.4	6084	40.96	499.2
86	6.3	7396	39.69	541.8
88	10.9	7744	118.81	959.2
$\Sigma x = 390$	$\Sigma y = 38.6$	$\Sigma x^2 = 31{,}084$	$\Sigma y^2 = 312.68$	$\Sigma xy = 3050.8$

Using Formula 10-1 with the paired data in Table 10-2, *r* is calculated as follows:

$$r = \frac{n\Sigma xy - (\Sigma x)(\Sigma y)}{\sqrt{n(\Sigma x^2) - (\Sigma x)^2}\sqrt{n(\Sigma y^2) - (\Sigma y)^2}}$$

$$= \frac{5(3050.8) - (390)(38.6)}{\sqrt{5(31{,}084) - (390)^2}\sqrt{5(312.68) - (38.6)^2}}$$

$$= \frac{200}{\sqrt{3320}\sqrt{73.44}} = 0.405$$

EXAMPLE 3 Finding *r* Using Formula 10-2

Use Formula 10-2 to find the value of the linear correlation coefficient *r* for the five pairs of data listed in Table 10-1.

SOLUTION

If manual calculations are absolutely necessary, Formula 10-1 is much easier than Formula 10-2, but Formula 10-2 has the advantage of making it easier to *understand* how *r* works. (See the *rationale* for *r* discussed later in this section.) As in Example 2, the variable *x* is used for the pulse rates, and the variable *y* is used for the white blood cell counts. In Formula 10-2, each sample value is replaced by its corresponding *z* score. For example, using unrounded numbers, the pulse rates have a mean of $\bar{x} = 78.0$ and a standard deviation of $s_x = 12.884099$, so the first pulse rate of 56 is converted to a *z* score of -1.707531 as shown here:

$$z_x = \frac{x - \bar{x}}{s_x} = \frac{56 - 78.0}{12.884099} = -1.707531$$

Table 10-3 lists the *z* scores for all of the pulse rates (see the third column) and the *z* scores for all of the white blood cell counts (see the fourth column). The last column of Table 10-3 lists the products $z_x \cdot z_y$.

TABLE 10-3 Calculating *r* with Formula 10-2

x (Pulse Rate)	*y* (White Blood Cell Count)	z_x	z_y	$z_x \cdot z_y$
56	6.9	−1.707531	−0.427920	0.730687
82	8.1	0.310460	0.198304	0.061566
78	6.4	0	−0.688847	0
86	6.3	0.620920	−0.741032	−0.460122
88	10.9	0.776151	1.659495	1.288018
				$\Sigma(z_x \cdot z_y) = 1.620148$

Using $\Sigma(z_x \cdot z_y) = 1.620148$ from Table 10-3, the value of *r* is calculated by using Formula 10-2 as shown below.

$$r = \frac{\Sigma(z_x \cdot z_y)}{n - 1} = \frac{1.620148}{4} = 0.405$$

Is There a Linear Correlation?

We know from the preceding three examples that the value of the linear correlation coefficient is $r = 0.405$ for the five pairs of sample data in Table 10-1. We now proceed to interpret the meaning of $r = 0.405$ found from the five pairs of sample data, and our goal is to decide whether there appears to be a linear correlation between pulse rates and white blood cell counts of all adult females. Using the criteria given in the preceding box, we can base our interpretation on a *P*-value or a critical value from Table A-6. See the criteria for "Interpreting the Linear Correlation Coefficient *r*" given in the preceding Key Elements box.

)─ **EXAMPLE 4** **Is There a Linear Correlation?**

Using the value of $r = 0.405$ for the five pairs of values in Table 10-1 and using a significance level of 0.05, is there sufficient evidence to support a claim that there is a linear correlation between pulse rates and white blood cell counts?

SOLUTION

REQUIREMENT CHECK   The first requirement of a simple random sample is satisfied by the design of the study. The data are quantitative. The second requirement of a scatterplot showing a straight-line pattern is very questionable; see the scatterplot in Figure 10-1 on page 461. The scatterplot of Figure 10-1 also shows that the third requirement of no outliers is questionable because the leftmost points appear to be relatively far from the other points. We will proceed as if the requirements are satisfied. ✅

We can base our conclusion about correlation on either the P-value obtained from technology or the critical value found in Table A-6. (See the criteria for "Interpreting the Linear Correlation Coefficient r" given in the preceding Key Elements box.)

- ***Using P-Value from Technology to Interpret r:*** Use the P-value and significance level α as follows:

  P-value $\leq \alpha$: Supports the claim of a linear correlation.

  P-value $> \alpha$: Does not support the claim of a linear correlation.

  For the data in Table 10-1, technology can be used to find that the P-value is 0.4988. Because that P-value is greater than the significance level of 0.05, we conclude that *there is not sufficient evidence to support the conclusion of a linear correlation between pulse rates and white blood cell counts for all adult females.*

- ***Using Table A-6 to Interpret r:*** Consider critical values from Table A-6 as being both positive and negative, and draw a graph similar to Figure 10-3. For the data in Table 10-1, Table A-6 yields a critical value of 0.878 (for a 0.05 significance level). We now compare the computed value of $r = 0.405$ to the critical values of $r = \pm 0.878$ as shown in Figure 10-3.

Correlation If the computed linear correlation coefficient r lies in the left or right tail region beyond the critical value for that tail, conclude that there is sufficient evidence to support the claim of a linear correlation.

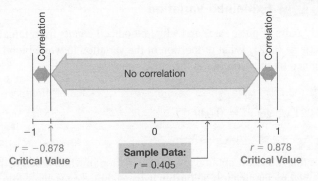

FIGURE 10-3   Critical *r* Values and the Computed *r* Value

continued

No Correlation If the computed linear correlation coefficient lies between the two critical values, conclude that there is not sufficient evidence to support the claim of a linear correlation.

Because Figure 10-3 shows that the computed value of $r = 0.405$ lies between the two critical values, we conclude that *there is not sufficient evidence to support the claim of a linear correlation between pulse rates and white blood cell counts for adult females.*

INTERPRETATION

Based on the five pairs of data in Table 10-1, we do not have sufficient evidence to conclude that there is a linear correlation between pulse rates and white blood cell counts (but a larger data set might lead to a different conclusion).

Example 4 led to the conclusion of no linear correlation, but if we use the 147 pairs of pulse rates and white blood cell counts for all of the females included in Data Set 1 "Body Data" in Appendix B, we get $r = 0.221$ and a P-value of 0.007, so the larger data set leads to the conclusion that there is sufficient evidence to support the claim that there is a linear correlation. But even though we have evidence to support the claim of a linear correlation, the low value of $r = 0.221$ suggests that the correlation is not very strong. See the following interpretation based on the value of r^2.

Interpreting *r*: Explained Variation

If we conclude that there is a linear correlation between x and y, we can find a linear equation that expresses y in terms of x, and that equation can be used to predict values of y for given values of x. In Section 10-2 we will describe a procedure for finding such equations and show how to predict values of y when given values of x. But a predicted value of y will not necessarily be the exact result that occurs because in addition to x, there are other factors affecting y, such as random variation and other characteristics not included in the study. In Section 10-3 we will present a rationale and more details about this principle:

The value of r^2 is the proportion of the variation in y that is explained by the linear relationship between x and y.

 EXAMPLE 5 **Explained Variation**

Using the 147 pairs of pulse rates and white blood cell counts from females in Data Set 1, we get $r = 0.221$. What proportion of the variation in white blood cell counts can be explained by the variation in the pulse rates?

SOLUTION

With $r = 0.221$ we get $r^2 = 0.049$.

INTERPRETATION

We conclude that 0.049 (or about 5%) of the variation in white blood cell counts can be explained by the linear relationship between pulse rates and white blood cell counts. That's not much. This also implies that about 95% of the variation in white blood cell counts cannot be explained by pulse rates.

Interpreting *r* with Causation: Don't Go There!

Using the 147 pairs of pulse rates and white blood cell counts from females in Data Set 1 "Body Data" in Appendix B, we conclude that there is a linear correlation. We should *not* make any conclusion that includes a statement about a cause-effect relationship between the two variables. We should not conclude that higher pulse rates *cause* higher white blood cell counts. See the first of the following common errors, and know this:

Correlation does not imply causality!

Common Errors Involving Correlation

Here are three of the most common errors made in interpreting results involving correlation:

1. *Assuming that correlation implies causality.* One classic example involves paired data consisting of the stork population in Copenhagen and the number of human births. For several years, the data suggested a linear correlation. *Bulletin:* Storks do not actually cause births, and births do not cause storks. Both variables were affected by another variable lurking in the background. (A **lurking variable** is one that affects the variables being studied but is not included in the study.) Here, an increasing human population resulted in more births and increased construction of thatched roofs that attracted storks!

2. *Using data based on averages.* Averages suppress individual variation and may inflate the correlation coefficient. One study produced a 0.4 linear correlation coefficient for paired data relating income and education among individuals, but the linear correlation coefficient became 0.7 when regional averages were used.

3. *Ignoring the possibility of a nonlinear relationship.* If there is no linear correlation, there might be some other correlation that is not linear, as in Figure 10-2(d) on page 461.

PART 2 Formal Hypothesis Test

Hypotheses If conducting a formal hypothesis test to determine whether there is a significant linear correlation between two variables, use the following null and alternative hypotheses that use ρ to represent the linear correlation coefficient of the population:

Null Hypothesis $H_0: \rho = 0$ (No correlation)

Alternative Hypothesis $H_1: \rho \neq 0$ (Correlation)

Test Statistic The same methods of Part 1 can be used with the test statistic *r*, or the *t* test statistic can be found using the following:

Test Statistic $t = \dfrac{r}{\sqrt{\dfrac{1 - r^2}{n - 2}}}$ (with $n - 2$ degrees of freedom)

If the above *t* test statistic is used, *P*-values and critical values can be found using technology or Table A-3 as described in earlier chapters. See the following example.

EXAMPLE 6 Hypothesis Test Using the *P*-Value from the *t* Test

Use the paired pulse rates and white blood cell counts from Table 10-1 on page 459 to conduct a formal hypothesis test of the claim that there is a linear correlation between the two variables. Use a 0.05 significance level with the *P*-value method of testing hypotheses.

SOLUTION

REQUIREMENT CHECK The requirements were addressed in Example 4. ✓

To claim that there is a linear correlation is to claim that the population linear correlation coefficient ρ is different from 0. We therefore have the following hypotheses:

$$H_0: \rho = 0 \quad \text{(There is no linear correlation.)}$$

$$H_1: \rho \neq 0 \quad \text{(There is a linear correlation.)}$$

The linear correlation coefficient is $r = 0.405$ and $n = 5$ (because there are 5 pairs of sample data), so the test statistic is

$$t = \frac{r}{\sqrt{\dfrac{1 - r^2}{n - 2}}} = \frac{0.405}{\sqrt{\dfrac{1 - 0.405^2}{5 - 2}}} = 0.767$$

With $n - 2 = 3$ degrees of freedom, Table A-3 shows that the test statistic of $t = 0.767$ yields a *P*-value that is greater than 0.20. Technologies show that the *P*-value is 0.499 when rounded. Because the *P*-value of 0.499 is greater than the significance level of 0.05, we fail to reject H_0. ("If the *P* is low, the null must go." The *P*-value of 0.499 is not low.)

INTERPRETATION

We conclude that there is not sufficient evidence to support the claim of a linear correlation between pulse rates and white blood cell counts of adult females.

One-Tailed Tests The examples and exercises in this section generally involve two-tailed tests, but one-tailed tests can occur with a claim of a positive linear correlation or a claim of a negative linear correlation. In such cases, the hypotheses will be as shown below.

Claim of Negative Correlation (Left-Tailed Test)	Claim of Positive Correlation (Right-Tailed Test)
$H_0: \rho = 0$	$H_0: \rho = 0$
$H_1: \rho < 0$	$H_1: \rho > 0$

For these one-tailed tests, the *P*-value method can be used as in earlier chapters.

Rationale for Methods of This Section We have presented Formulas 10-1 and 10-2 for calculating *r* and have illustrated their use. Those formulas are given on the next page, along with some other formulas that are "equivalent," in the sense that they all produce the same values.

FORMULA 10-1 $r = \dfrac{n\Sigma xy - (\Sigma x)(\Sigma y)}{\sqrt{n(\Sigma x^2) - (\Sigma x)^2}\sqrt{n(\Sigma y^2) - (\Sigma y)^2}}$

FORMULA 10-2 $r = \dfrac{\Sigma(z_x z_y)}{n - 1}$

$$r = \dfrac{\Sigma(x - \bar{x})(y - \bar{y})}{(n - 1)s_x s_y} \qquad r = \dfrac{\Sigma\left[\dfrac{(x - \bar{x})}{s_x}\dfrac{(y - \bar{y})}{s_y}\right]}{n - 1}$$

$$r = \dfrac{s_{xy}}{\sqrt{s_{xx}}\sqrt{s_{yy}}}$$

We will use Formula 10-2 to help us understand the reasoning that underlies the development of the linear correlation coefficient. Because Formula 10-2 uses z scores, the value of $\Sigma(z_x z_y)$ does not depend on the scale that is used for the x and y values. Figure 10-1 on page 461 shows the scatterplot of the pulse rate and white blood cell count data from Table 10-1, and Figure 10-4 shows the scatterplot of the z scores from the same sample data. Compare Figure 10-1 to Figure 10-4 and see that they are essentially the same scatterplots with different scales. Figure 10-4 shows the same coordinate axes that we have all come to know and love from earlier mathematics courses. Figure 10-4 shows the scatterplot partitioned into four quadrants.

If the points of the scatterplot approximate an uphill line, individual values of the product $z_x \cdot z_y$ tend to be positive (because most of the points are found in the first and third quadrants, where the values of z_x and z_y are either both positive or both negative), so $\Sigma(z_x z_y)$ tends to be positive. If the points of the scatterplot approximate a downhill line, most of the points are in the second and fourth quadrants, where z_x and z_y are opposite in sign, so $\Sigma(z_x z_y)$ tends to be negative. Points that follow no linear pattern tend to be scattered among the four quadrants, so the value of $\Sigma(z_x z_y)$ tends to be close to 0.

We can therefore use $\Sigma(z_x z_y)$ as a measure of how the points are configured among the four quadrants. A large positive sum suggests that the points are predominantly in the first and third quadrants (corresponding to a positive linear correlation), a large negative sum suggests that the points are predominantly in the second and fourth

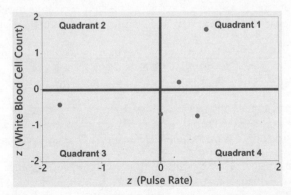

FIGURE 10-4   Scatterplot of z Scores from Pulse Rates and White Blood Cell Counts in Table 10-1

quadrants (corresponding to a negative linear correlation), and a sum near 0 suggests that the points are scattered among the four quadrants (with no linear correlation). We divide $\Sigma(z_x z_y)$ by $n - 1$ to get an average instead of a statistic that becomes larger simply because there are more data values. (The reasons for dividing by $n - 1$ instead of n are essentially the same reasons that relate to the standard deviation.) The end result is Formula 10-2, which can be algebraically manipulated into any of the other expressions for r.

TECH CENTER

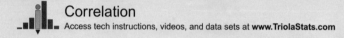

Correlation
Access tech instructions, videos, and data sets at www.TriolaStats.com

10-1   Basic Skills and Concepts

Statistical Literacy and Critical Thinking

1. Notation Twenty different statistics students are randomly selected. For each of them, their body temperature (°C) is measured and their head circumference (cm) is measured.

a. For this sample of paired data, what does r represent, and what does ρ represent?

b. Without doing any research or calculations, estimate the value of r.

c. Does r change if the body temperatures are converted to Fahrenheit degrees?

2. Interpreting r For the same two variables described in Exercise 1, if we find that $r = 0$, does that indicate that there is no association between those two variables?

3. Global Warming If we find that there is a linear correlation between the concentration of carbon dioxide (CO_2) in our atmosphere and the global mean temperature, does that indicate that changes in CO_2 cause changes in the global mean temperature? Why or why not?

4. Scatterplots Match these values of r with the five scatterplots shown here and on the top of the next page: 0.268, 0.992, −1, 0.746, and 1.

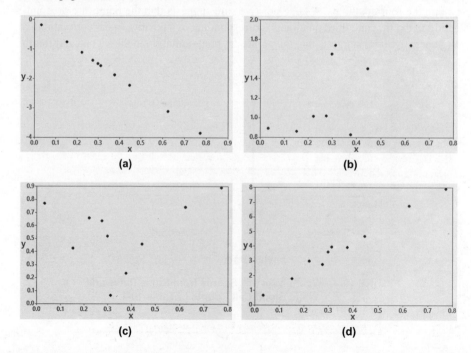

(a)

(b)

(c)

(d)

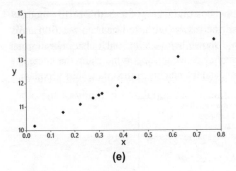

(e)

Interpreting r. *In Exercises 5–8, use a significance level of* $\alpha = 0.05$ *and refer to the accompanying displays.*

5. Bear Weight and Chest Size Fifty-four wild bears were anesthetized, and then their weights and chest sizes were measured and listed in Data Set 11 "Bear Measurements." Results are shown in the accompanying Statdisk display. Is there sufficient evidence to support the claim that there is a linear correlation between the weights of bears and their chest sizes? When measuring an anesthetized bear, is it easier to measure chest size than weight? If so, does it appear that a measured chest size can be used to predict the weight?

Correlation Results:	
Correlation coeff, r: 0.963141	
Critical r:	±0.2680855
P-value (two-tailed): 0.000	

6. Cereal Killers The amounts of sugar (grams of sugar per gram of cereal) and calories (per gram of cereal) were recorded for a sample of 16 different cereals. TI-83/84 Plus calculator results are shown here. Is there sufficient evidence to support the claim that there is a linear correlation between sugar and calories in a gram of cereal? Explain.

TI-83/84 Plus

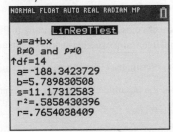

```
NORMAL FLOAT AUTO REAL RADIAN MP
         LinRegTTest
y=a+bx
β≠0 and ρ≠0
↑df=14
 a=-188.3423729
 b=5.789830508
 s=11.17312583
 r²=.5858430396
 r=.7654038409
```

7. Heights of Fathers and Sons The heights (in inches) of a sample of 134 father/son pairs of subjects were measured and the results are listed in Data Set 6 "Family Heights" in Appendix B. XLSTAT results are shown below. Is there sufficient evidence to support the claim that there is a linear correlation between the heights of fathers and the heights of their sons? Explain.

Correlation matrix (Pearson):						
Variables	Father	Son				
Father	1	0.5516				
Son	0.5516	1				
Values in bold are different from 0 with a significance level alpha=0.05						
p-values:						
Variables	Father	Son				
Father	0	0.0000				
Son	<0.0001	0				
Values in bold are different from 0 with a significance level alpha=0.05						

8. Heights of Mothers and Daughters The heights (in inches) of a sample of 134 mother/daughter pairs of subjects were measured and the results are listed in Data Set 6 "Family Heights" in Appendix B. StatCrunch results are shown below. StatCrunch also indicates that the *P*-value is less than 0.0001. Is there sufficient evidence to support the claim that there is a linear correlation between the heights of mothers and the heights of their daughters? Explain.

> **Simple linear regression results:**
> Dependent Variable: Daughter
> Independent Variable: Mother
> Daughter = 42.020798 + 0.35953064 Mother
> Sample size: 134
> R (correlation coefficient) = 0.35352441
> R-sq = 0.12497951
> Estimate of error standard deviation: 2.19515

Explore! *Exercises 9 and 10 provide two data sets from "Graphs in Statistical Analysis," by F. J. Anscombe,* **The American Statistician,** *Vol. 27. For each exercise,*

a. Construct a scatterplot.

b. Find the value of the linear correlation coefficient *r*, then determine whether there is sufficient evidence to support the claim of a linear correlation between the two variables.

c. Identify the feature of the data that would be missed if part (b) was completed without constructing the scatterplot.

9.

x	10	8	13	9	11	14	6	4	12	7	5
y	9.14	8.14	8.74	8.77	9.26	8.10	6.13	3.10	9.13	7.26	4.74

10.

x	10	8	13	9	11	14	6	4	12	7	5
y	7.46	6.77	12.74	7.11	7.81	8.84	6.08	5.39	8.15	6.42	5.73

11. Outlier Refer to the accompanying Minitab-generated scatterplot.

a. Examine the pattern of all 10 points and subjectively determine whether there appears to be a correlation between *x* and *y*.

b. After identifying the 10 pairs of coordinates corresponding to the 10 points, find the value of the correlation coefficient *r* and determine whether there is a linear correlation.

c. Now remove the point with coordinates (10, 10) and repeat parts (a) and (b).

d. What do you conclude about the possible effect from a single pair of values?

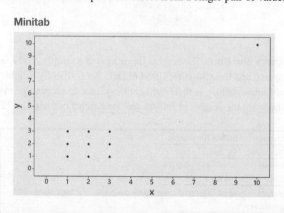

Minitab

12. Clusters Refer to the following Minitab-generated scatterplot. The four points in the lower left corner are measurements from women, and the four points in the upper right corner are from men.

a. Examine the pattern of the four points in the lower left corner (from women) only, and subjectively determine whether there appears to be a correlation between *x* and *y* for women.

b. Examine the pattern of the four points in the upper right corner (from men) only, and subjectively determine whether there appears to be a correlation between *x* and *y* for men.

c. Find the linear correlation coefficient using only the four points in the lower left corner (for women). Will the four points in the upper left corner (for men) have the same linear correlation coefficient?

d. Find the value of the linear correlation coefficient using all eight points. What does that value suggest about the relationship between *x* and *y*?

e. Based on the preceding results, what do you conclude? Should the data from women and the data from men be considered together, or do they appear to represent two different and distinct populations that should be analyzed separately?

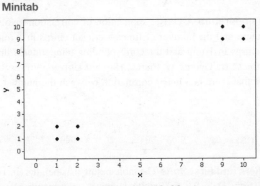

Minitab

Testing for a Linear Correlation.   *In Exercises 13–28, construct a scatterplot, and find the value of the linear correlation coefficient r. Also find the P-value or find the critical values of r from Table A-6. Use a significance level of α = 0.05. Determine whether there is sufficient evidence to support a claim of a linear correlation between the two variables. (Save your work because the same data sets will be used in Section 10-2 exercises.)*

13. Pulse Rate and Systolic Blood Pressure The table below lists pulse rates and systolic and diastolic blood pressures (mm Hg) of subjects (from Data Set 1 "Body Data" in Appendix B). Is there sufficient evidence to conclude that there is a linear correlation between pulse rates and systolic blood pressures? Does it appear that people with higher pulse rates have high systolic blood pressure?

Pulse Rates	80	84	94	74	50	60	52	58	66	62	52
Systolic Blood Pressure	100	112	134	126	114	134	118	138	114	124	138
Diastolic Blood Pressure	70	70	94	64	68	60	64	80	66	70	58

14. Pulse Rate and Diastolic Blood Pressure Use the paired pulse rates and diastolic blood pressure data from the preceding exercise. Is there sufficient evidence to conclude that there is a linear correlation between pulse rates and diastolic blood pressures?

15. CSI Statistics Police sometimes measure shoe prints at crime scenes so that they can learn a few things about criminals. Listed below are shoe print lengths, foot lengths, and heights of females (from Data Set 7 "Foot and Height" in Appendix B). Is there sufficient evidence to conclude that there is a linear correlation between shoe print lengths and heights of females? Based on these results, does it appear that police can use a shoe print length to estimate the height of a female?

Shoe Print (cm)	26.5	26.0	27.0	25.1	27.9
Foot Length (cm)	23.3	23.5	25.1	24.1	23.8
Height (cm)	167.6	165.1	172.7	157.5	167.6

16. CSI Statistics Use the paired foot length and height data from the preceding exercise. Is there sufficient evidence to conclude that there is a linear correlation between foot lengths and heights of females? Based on these results, does it appear that police can use foot length to estimate the height of a female?

17. Lemons and Car Crashes Listed below are annual data for various years. The data are weights (metric tons) of lemons imported from Mexico and U.S. car crash fatality rates per 100,000 population [based on data from "The Trouble with QSAR (or How I Learned to Stop Worrying and Embrace Fallacy)," by Stephen Johnson, *Journal of Chemical Information and Modeling,* Vol. 48, No. 1]. Is there sufficient evidence to conclude that there is a linear correlation between weights of lemon imports from Mexico and U.S. car fatality rates? Do the results suggest that imported lemons cause car fatalities?

Lemon Imports	230	265	358	480	530
Crash Fatality Rate	15.9	15.7	15.4	15.3	14.9

18. Crickets and Temperature A classic application of correlation involves the association between the temperature and the number of times a cricket chirps in 1 minute. Listed below are the numbers of chirps in 1 min and the corresponding temperatures in °F (based on data from *The Song of Insects,* by George W. Pierce, Harvard University Press). Is there sufficient evidence to conclude that there is a linear correlation between the number of chirps in 1 min and the temperature?

Chirps in 1 min	882	1188	1104	864	1200	1032	960	900
Temperature (°F)	69.7	93.3	84.3	76.3	88.6	82.6	71.6	79.6

19. Heights of Fathers and First Sons The table below lists heights (in.) of fathers, mothers and their first sons (from Data Set 6 "Family Heights" in Appendix B). Is there sufficient evidence to conclude that there is a linear correlation between heights of fathers and first sons?

Height of father (in.)	70	69	70	71	74	70.5	69	70	68	65	66	71
Height of mother (in.)	74	63.5	58	63	62	64	61	63	60	67	66	63.5
Height of son (in.)	68	70.5	72	61	74	74	68	68	67.5	66.5	66	71

20. Heights of Mothers and First Sons Use the paired heights of mothers and their first sons data from the preceding exercise. Is there sufficient evidence to conclude that there is a linear correlation between heights of mothers and their first sons?

21. Weighing Seals with a Camera Listed below are the overhead widths (cm) of seals measured from photographs and the weights (kg) of the seals (based on "Mass Estimation of Weddell Seals Using Techniques of Photogrammetry," by R. Garrott of Montana State University). The purpose of the study was to determine if weights of seals could be determined from overhead photographs. Is there sufficient evidence to conclude that there is a linear correlation between overhead widths of seals from photographs and the weights of the seals?

Overhead Width	7.2	7.4	9.8	9.4	8.8	8.4
Weight	116	154	245	202	200	191

22. Manatees Listed below are numbers of registered pleasure boats in Florida (tens of thousands) and the numbers of manatee fatalities from encounters with boats in Florida for each of several years. The values are from Data Set 12 "Manatee Deaths." Is there sufficient evidence to conclude that there is a linear correlation between numbers of registered pleasure boats and numbers of manatee boat fatalities?

Pleasure Boats	68	68	67	70	71	73	76	81	83
Manatee Fatalities	53	38	35	49	42	60	54	67	82

23. POTUS Media periodically discuss the issue of heights of winning presidential candidates and heights of their main opponents. Listed below are those heights (cm) from several recent presidential elections. Is there sufficient evidence to conclude that there is a linear correlation between heights of winning presidential candidates and heights of their main opponents? Should there be such a correlation?

President	178	182	188	175	179	183	192	182	177	185	188	188	183	188
Opponent	180	180	182	173	178	182	180	180	183	177	173	188	185	175

24. Tree Circumference and Height Listed below are the circumferences (in feet) and the heights (in feet) of trees in Marshall, Minnesota (based on data from "Tree Measurements," by Stanley Rice, *American Biology Teacher,* Vol. 61, No. 9). Is there sufficient evidence to support the claim of a linear correlation between circumferences and heights of trees? Why should there be a correlation?

Circumference	1.8	1.9	1.8	2.4	5.1	3.1	5.5	5.1	8.3	13.7	5.3	4.9
Height	21.0	33.5	24.6	40.7	73.2	24.9	40.4	45.3	53.5	93.8	64.0	62.7

Appendix B Data Sets. *In Exercises 25–32, use the data in Appendix B to construct a scatterplot, find the value of the linear correlation coefficient r, and find either the P-value or the critical values of r using α = 0.05. Determine whether there is sufficient evidence to support the claim of a linear correlation between the two variables. (Save your work because the same data sets will be used in Section 10-2 exercises.)*

25. IQ and Brain Volume Use all of the paired IQ scores and brain volumes in Data Set 9 "IQ and Brain Size" in Appendix B.

26. IQ and Weight Use all of the paired IQ scores and body weights in Data Set 9 "IQ and Brain Size" in Appendix B.

27. CSI Statistics Use the paired shoe print lengths and heights of the 19 males from Data Set 7 "Foot and Height."

28. CSI Statistics Use the paired foot lengths and heights of the 19 males from Data Set 7 "Foot and Height."

29. Pulse Rate and Blood Pressure Use all of the paired pulse rates and systolic blood pressure amounts for adult females from Data Set 1 "Body Data" in Appendix B.

30. Blood Pressure Use all of the paired systolic and diastolic data for adult females as listed in Data Set 1 "Body Data" in Appendix B. Is there sufficient evidence to conclude that there is a linear correlation between systolic blood pressures and diastolic blood pressures of adult females?

31. Audiometry Use the right ear threshold measurements and the corresponding left ear threshold measurements from Data Set 4 "Audiometry" in Appendix B. Is there sufficient evidence to support the claim of a linear correlation?

32. Vision Use the measurements of visual acuity from the right eye and left eye as listed in Data Set 5 "Vision" in Appendix B. Is there sufficient evidence to support the claim of a linear correlation?

10-1 Beyond the Basics

33. Transformed Data In addition to testing for a linear correlation between x and y, we can often use *transformations* of data to explore other relationships. For example, we might replace each x value by x^2 and use the methods of this section to determine whether there is a linear correlation between y and x^2. Given the paired data in the accompanying table, construct the scatterplot and then test for a linear correlation between y and each of the following. Which case results in the largest value of r?

a. x **b.** x^2 **c.** $\log x$ **d.** $\sqrt{x}$ **e.** $1/x$

x	2	3	20	50	95
y	0.3	0.5	1.3	1.7	2.0

34. Finding Critical *r* Values Table A-6 lists critical values of *r* for selected values of *n* and α. More generally, critical *r* values can be found by using the formula

$$r = \frac{t}{\sqrt{t^2 + n - 2}}$$

where the *t* value is found from the table of critical *t* values (Table A-3) assuming a two-tailed case with $n - 2$ degrees of freedom. Use the formula for *r* given here and Table A-3 (with $n - 2$ degrees of freedom) to find the critical *r* values corresponding to $H_1 : \rho \neq 0$, $\alpha = 0.02$, and $n = 27$.

10-2   Regression

Key Concept This section presents methods for finding the equation of the straight line that best fits the points in a scatterplot of paired sample data. That best-fitting straight line is called the *regression line,* and its equation is called the *regression equation.* We can use the regression equation to make predictions for the value of one of the variables, given some specific value of the other variable. In Part 2 of this section we discuss marginal change, influential points, and residual plots as tools for analyzing correlation and regression results.

PART 1   Basic Concepts of Regression

In some cases, two variables are related in a *deterministic* way, meaning that given a value for one variable, the value of the other variable is exactly determined without any error, as in the equation $y = 2.54x$ for converting a distance *x* from inches to centimeters. Such equations are considered in algebra courses, but statistics courses focus on *probabilistic* models, which are equations with a variable that is not determined completely by the other variable. For example, the height of a child cannot be determined completely by the height of the father and/or mother. Sir Francis Galton (1822–1911) studied the phenomenon of heredity and showed that when tall or short couples have children, the heights of those children tend to *regress,* or revert to the more typical mean height for people of the same gender. We continue to use Galton's "regression" terminology, even though our data do not always involve the same height phenomena studied by Galton.

DEFINITIONS

Given a collection of paired sample data, the **regression line** (or *line of best fit*, or *least-squares line*) is the straight line that "best" fits the scatterplot of the data. (The specific criterion for the "best-fitting" straight line is the "least-squares" property described later.)

The **regression equation**

$$\hat{y} = b_0 + b_1 x$$

algebraically describes the regression line. The regression equation expresses a relationship between *x* (called the **explanatory variable**, or **predictor variable**, or **independent variable**) and $\hat{y}$ (called the **response variable** or **dependent variable**).

The preceding definition shows that in statistics, the typical equation of a straight line $y = mx + b$ is expressed in the form $\hat{y} = b_0 + b_1 x$, where b_0 is the *y*-intercept and b_1 is the slope. The values of the slope b_1 and *y*-intercept b_0 can be easily found by using any one of the many computer programs and calculators designed to provide those values, as illustrated in Example 1. The values of b_1 and b_0 can also be found with manual calculations, as shown in Example 2.

KEY ELEMENTS

Finding the Equation of the Regression Line

Objective

Find the equation of a regression line.

Notation for the Equation of a Regression Line

	Sample Statistic	Population Parameter
y-intercept of regression equation	b_0	β_0
Slope of regression equation	b_1	β_1
Equation of the regression line	$\hat{y} = b_0 + b_1 x$	$y = \beta_0 + \beta_1 x$

Requirements

1. The sample of paired (x, y) data is a *random* sample of quantitative data.

2. Visual examination of the scatterplot shows that the points approximate a straight-line pattern.*

3. Outliers can have a strong effect on the regression equation, so remove any outliers if they are known to be errors. Consider the effects of any outliers that are not known errors.*

Note: Requirements 2 and 3 above are simplified attempts at checking the following formal requirements for regression analysis:

- For each fixed value of x, the corresponding values of y have a normal distribution.

- For the different fixed values of x, the distributions of the corresponding y values all have the same standard deviation. (This is violated if part of the scatterplot shows points very close to the regression line while another portion of the scatterplot shows points that are much farther away from the regression line. See the discussion of residual plots in Part 2 of this section.)

- For the different fixed values of x, the distributions of the corresponding y values have means that lie along the same straight line.

The methods of this section are not seriously affected if departures from normal distributions and equal standard deviations are not too extreme.

Formulas for Finding the Slope b_1 and y-Intercept b_0 in the Regression Equation $\hat{y} = b_0 + b_1 x$

FORMULA 10-3   **Slope:** $b_1 = r \dfrac{s_y}{s_x}$ where r is the linear correlation coefficient, s_y is the standard deviation of the y values, and s_x is the standard deviation of the x values.

FORMULA 10-4   **y-intercept:** $b_0 = \bar{y} - b_1 \bar{x}$

The slope b_1 and y-intercept b_0 can also be found using the following formulas that are useful for manual calculations or computer programs:

$$b_1 = \frac{n(\Sigma xy) - (\Sigma x)(\Sigma y)}{n(\Sigma x^2) - (\Sigma x)^2} \qquad b_0 = \frac{(\Sigma y)(\Sigma x^2) - (\Sigma x)(\Sigma xy)}{n(\Sigma x^2) - (\Sigma x)^2}$$

Rounding the Slope b_1 and the y-Intercept b_0

Round b_1 and b_0 to three significant digits. It's difficult to provide a simple universal rule for rounding values of b_1 and b_0, but this rule will work for most situations in this book. (Depending on how you round, this book's answers to examples and exercises may be slightly different from your answers.)

Postponing Death

Several stud-ies addressed the ability of people to postpone their death until after an impor-tant event. For example, sociolo-gist David Phillips analyzed death rates of Jewish men who died near Passover, and he found that the death rate dropped dramatically in the week before Passover, but rose the week after. Other researchers of cancer patients concluded that there is "no pattern to support the con-cept that 'death takes a holiday.'" (See "Holidays, Birthdays, and Postponement of Cancer Death," by Young and Hade, *Journal of the American Medical Associa-tion*, Vol. 292, No. 24.) Based on records of 1.3 million deaths, this more recent study found no relationship between the time of death and Christmas, Thanksgiv-ing, or the person's birthday. The findings were disputed by David Phillips, who said that the study focused on cancer patients, but they are least likely to have psychosomatic effects.

> **EXAMPLE 1** Using Technology to Find the Regression Equation

Refer to the sample data given in Table 10-1 on page 459 in the Chapter Problem. Use technology to find the equation of the regression line in which the explanatory variable (or *x* variable) is pulse rate and the response variable (or *y* variable) is the corresponding white blood cell count.

> **SOLUTION**

REQUIREMENT CHECK   (1) The data are assumed to be a simple random sample. (2) Figure 10-1 is a scatterplot of the data. It is very questionable whether the points roughly follow a straight-line pattern. (3) There are no outliers. We will proceed as if the requirements are satisfied. ☑

Technology The use of technology is recommended for finding the equation of a regression line. Shown below are the results from different technologies. Some tech-nologies provide the actual equation, and some technologies list the values of the *y*-intercept and the slope. All of these technologies show that the regression equa-tion can be expressed as $\hat{y} = 3.02 + 0.0602x$, where $\hat{y}$ is the predicted white blood cell count and *x* is the pulse rate.

Statdisk

```
Regression Results:
Y= b0 + b1x:
Y Intercept, b0:    3.021205
Slope, b1:          0.060241
```

Excel (XLSTAT)

```
Equation of the model:

White BCC = 3.02120+0.06024*Pulse
```

Minitab

```
Regression Equation
White BCC = 3.02 + 0.0602 Pulse
```

TI-83/84 Plus

```
NORMAL FLOAT AUTO REAL RADIAN MP
          LinRegTTest
y=a+bx
β>0 and ρ>0
t=.767302074
P=.2493804256
df=3
a=3.021204819
b=.0602409639
↓s=2.023063802
```

StatCrunch

```
Simple linear regression results:
Dependent Variable: White BCC
Independent Variable: Pulse
White BCC = 3.0212048 + 0.060240964 Pulse
```

SPSS

Model		Unstandardized Coefficients		Standardized Coefficients	t	Sig.
		B	Std. Error	Beta		
1	(Constant)	3.021	6.190		.488	.659
	Pulse	.060	.079	.405	.767	.499

JMP

```
⊿ Linear Fit
WhiteBCC = 3.0212048 + 0.060241*Pulse
```

We should know that the regression equation is an *estimate* of the true regression equation for the population of paired data. This estimate is based on one particular set of sample data, but another sample drawn from the same population would probably lead to a slightly different equation.

EXAMPLE 2 **Using Manual Calculations to Find the Regression Equation**

Refer to the sample data given in Table 10-1 on page 459 in the Chapter Problem. Use Formulas 10-3 and 10-4 to find the equation of the regression line in which the explanatory variable (or x variable) is pulse rate and the response variable (or y variable) is the corresponding white blood cell count.

SOLUTION

REQUIREMENT CHECK The requirements are addressed in Example 1. ✅

We begin by finding the slope b_1 using Formula 10-3 as follows (with extra digits included for greater accuracy). Remember, r is the linear correlation coefficient, s_y is the standard deviation of the sample y values, and s_x is the standard deviation of the sample x values.

$$b_1 = r \frac{s_y}{s_x} = 0.405037 \cdot \frac{1.916246}{12.884099} = 0.060241$$

After finding the slope b_1, we can now use Formula 10-4 to find the y-intercept as follows:

$$b_0 = \bar{y} - b_1 \bar{x} = 7.72 - (0.060241)(78.0) = 3.021202$$

After rounding, the slope is $b_1 = 0.0602$ and the y-intercept is $b_0 = 3.02$. We can now express the regression equation as $\hat{y} = 3.02 + 0.0602x$, where $\hat{y}$ is the predicted white blood cell count and x is the pulse rate.

EXAMPLE 3 **Graphing the Regression Line**

Graph the regression equation $\hat{y} = 3.02 + 0.0602x$ (found in Examples 1 and 2) on the scatterplot of the pulse and white blood cell count data from Table 10-1 and examine the graph to subjectively determine how well the regression line fits the data.

SOLUTION

Shown below is the Minitab display of the scatterplot with the graph of the regression line included. We can see that the regression line does not fit the points very well.

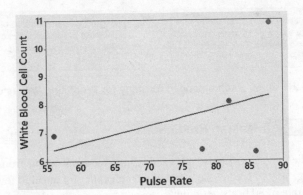

Making Predictions

Regression equations are often useful for *predicting* the value of one variable, given some specific value of the other variable. When making predictions, we should consider the following:

1. **Bad Model:** If the regression equation does not appear to be useful for making predictions, *don't* use the regression equation for making predictions. For bad models, the best predicted value of a variable is simply its sample mean.

2. **Good Model:** Use the regression equation for predictions only if the graph of the regression line on the scatterplot confirms that the regression line fits the points reasonably well.

3. **Correlation:** Use the regression equation for predictions only if the linear correlation coefficient r indicates that there is a linear correlation between the two variables (as described in Section 10-1).

4. **Scope:** Use the regression line for predictions only if the data do not go much beyond the scope of the available sample data. (Predicting too far beyond the scope of the available sample data is called *extrapolation,* and it could result in bad predictions.)

Figure 10-5 summarizes a strategy for predicting values of a variable y when given some value of x. Figure 10-5 shows that if the regression equation is a good model, then we substitute the value of x into the regression equation to find the predicted value of y. However, if the regression equation is not a good model, the best predicted value of y is simply $\bar{y}$, the mean of the y values. Remember, this strategy applies to *linear* patterns of points in a scatterplot. If the scatterplot shows a pattern that is nonlinear (not a straight-line) pattern, other methods apply.

Strategy for Predicting Values of y

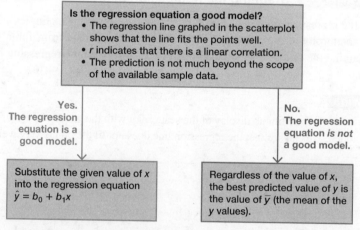

FIGURE 10-5   Recommended Strategy for Predicting Values of y

---

EXAMPLE 4   **Making Predictions**

a. Use the five pairs of pulse rates and white blood cell counts from Table 10-1 on page 459 to predict the white blood cell count for an adult female with a pulse rate of 80 beats per minute.

b. Use the pulse rates and white blood cell counts for females in Data Set 1 "Body Data" in Appendix B to predict the white blood cell count for an adult female with a pulse rate of 80 beats per minute. This data set includes 147 pairs of values, and the linear correlation coefficient is $r = 0.221$ with a P-value of 0.007. Also, the regression equation is $\hat{y} = 4.06 + 0.0345x$.

SOLUTION

a. **Bad Model: Use $\bar{y}$ for Predictions.** The regression line does not fit the points well, as shown in Example 3. Also, there does not appear to be a linear correlation between pulse rates and white blood cell counts as shown in Section 10-1. Because the regression equation is not a good model, the best predicted white blood cell count is $\bar{y} = 7.72$, which is the mean of the five white blood cell counts from Table 10-1.

b. **Good Model: Use the Regression Equation for Predictions.** Because the regression equation $\hat{y} = 4.06 + 0.0345x$ is a good model, substitute $x = 80$ into the equation to get the predicted white blood cell count of 6.8.

INTERPRETATION

Note that in part (a), the paired data result in a poor regression model, so the best predicted white blood cell count is the sample mean of the five white blood cell counts: $\bar{y} = 7.72$. However, in part (b) there is a linear correlation between pulse rates and white blood cell counts, so the best predicted value is found by substituting $x = 80$ into the regression equation.

Key point: Use the regression equation for predictions only if it is a good model. If the regression equation is not a good model, use the predicted value of $\bar{y}$.

PART 2 Beyond the Basics of Regression

In Part 2 we consider the concept of marginal change, which is helpful in interpreting a regression equation; then we consider the effects of outliers and special points called *influential points*. We also consider residual plots.

Interpreting the Regression Equation: Marginal Change

We can use the regression equation to see the effect on one variable when the other variable changes by some specific amount.

> **DEFINITION**
>
> In working with two variables related by a regression equation, the **marginal change** in a variable is the amount that it changes when the other variable changes by exactly one unit. The slope b_1 in the regression equation represents the marginal change in y that occurs when x changes by one unit.

Let's consider the 147 pairs of pulse rates and white blood cell counts for females from Data Set 1 "Body Data" in Appendix B. Those 147 pairs of data result in this regression equation: $\hat{y} = 4.06 + 0.0345x$. The slope of 0.0345 tells us that if we increase x (pulse rate) by 1 (beat per minute), the predicted white blood cell count will increase by 0.0345. That is, for every additional 1 beat per minute increase in pulse rate, we expect the white blood cell count to increase by 0.0345.

Outliers and Influential Points

A correlation/regression analysis of bivariate (paired) data should include an investigation of *outliers* and *influential points,* defined as follows.

DEFINITIONS

In a scatterplot, an **outlier** is a point lying far away from the other data points.

Paired sample data may include one or more **influential points,** which are points that strongly affect the graph of the regression line.

To determine whether a point is an outlier, examine the scatterplot to see if the point is far away from the others. Here's how to determine whether a point is an influential point: First graph the regression line resulting from the data with the point included, then graph the regression line resulting from the data with the point excluded. If the regression line changes by a considerable amount, the point is influential.

EXAMPLE 5 Influential Point

Consider the 147 pairs of pulse rates and white blood cell counts for adult females from Data Set 1 "Body Data" in Appendix B. The scatterplot located to the left below shows the regression line. If we include an additional pair of data, $x = 30$ and $y = 100$, we get the regression line shown to the right below. The additional point (30, 100) is an influential point because the graph of the regression line did change considerably, as shown by the regression line located to the right below. Compare the two graphs to see clearly that the addition of this one pair of values has a very dramatic effect on the regression line, so that the additional point (30, 100) is an influential point. The additional point is also an outlier because it is far from the other points.

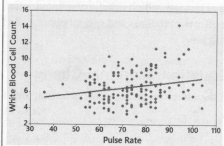

Pulse Rates and White Blood Cell Counts for Females from Table 10-1

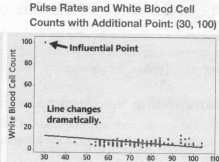

Pulse Rates and White Blood Cell Counts with Additional Point: (30, 100)

Residuals and the Least-Squares Property

We stated that the regression equation represents the straight line that "best" fits the data. The criterion to determine the line that is better than all others is based on the vertical distances between the original data points and the regression line. Such distances are called *residuals.*

DEFINITION

For a pair of sample x and y values, the **residual** is the difference between the *observed* sample value of y and the y value that is *predicted* by using the regression equation. That is,

$$\text{Residual} = (\text{observed } y - \text{predicted } y) = y - \hat{y}$$

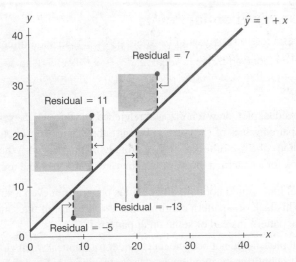

FIGURE 10-6   Residuals and Squares of Residuals

So far, this definition hasn't yet won any prizes for simplicity, but you can easily understand residuals by referring to Figure 10-6, which corresponds to the paired sample data shown in the margin. In Figure 10-6, the residuals are represented by the dashed lines. The paired data are plotted as points in Figure 10-6.

x	8	12	20	24
y	4	24	8	32

Consider the sample point with coordinates of (8, 4). If we substitute $x = 8$ into the regression equation $\hat{y} = 1 + x$, we get a predicted value of $\hat{y} = 9$. But for $x = 8$, the actual observed sample value is $y = 4$. The difference $y - \hat{y} = 4 - 9 = -5$ is a residual.

The regression equation represents the line that "best" fits the points according to the following least-squares property.

> **DEFINITION**
> A straight line satisfies the **least-squares property** if the sum of the squares of the residuals is the smallest sum possible.

From Figure 10-6, we see that the residuals are $-5, 11, -13$, and 7, so the sum of their squares is

$$(-5)^2 + 11^2 + (-13)^2 + 7^2 = 364$$

We can visualize the least-squares property by referring to Figure 10-6, where the squares of the residuals are represented by the shaded square areas. The sum of the shaded square areas is 364, which is the smallest sum possible. Use any other straight line, and the shaded squares will combine to produce an area larger than the combined shaded area of 364.

Fortunately, we need not deal directly with the least-squares property when we want to find the equation of the regression line. Calculus has been used to build the least-squares property into Formulas 10-3 and 10-4. Because the derivations of these formulas require calculus, we don't include the derivations in this text.

Residual Plots

In this section and the preceding section we listed simplified requirements for the effective analyses of correlation and regression results. We noted that we should always begin with a scatterplot, and we should verify that the pattern of points is approximately a straight-line pattern. We should also consider outliers. A *residual plot* can be another helpful tool for analyzing correlation and regression results and for checking the requirements necessary for making inferences about correlation and regression.

> **DEFINITION**
>
> A **residual plot** is a scatterplot of the (x, y) values after each of the y-coordinate values has been replaced by the residual value $y - \hat{y}$ (where $\hat{y}$ denotes the predicted value of y). That is, a residual plot is a graph of the points $(x, y - \hat{y})$.

To construct a residual plot, draw a horizontal reference line through the residual value of 0, then plot the paired values of $(x, y - \hat{y})$. Because the manual construction of residual plots can be tedious, the use of technology is strongly recommended. When analyzing a residual plot, look for a pattern in the way the points are configured, and use these criteria:

- The residual plot should not have any obvious pattern (not even a straight-line pattern). (This lack of a pattern confirms that a scatterplot of the sample data is a straight-line pattern instead of some other pattern.)

- The residual plot should not become much wider (or thinner) when viewed from left to right. (This confirms the requirement that for the different fixed values of x, the distributions of the corresponding y values all have the same standard deviation.)

EXAMPLE 6 Residual Plot

The 147 pairs of pulse rates and white blood cell counts for females in Data Set 1 "Body Data" in Appendix B are used to obtain the accompanying Minitab-generated residual plot. When the first sample x value of 80 is substituted into the regression equation of $\hat{y} = 4.06 + 0.0345x$ (found in Examples 1 and 2), we get the predicted value of $\hat{y} = 6.8$. For the first x value of 80, the actual corresponding y value is 8.7, so the value of the residual is

$$(\text{Observed } y - \text{predicted } y) = y - \hat{y} = 8.7 - 6.8 = 1.9$$

Using the x value of 80 and the residual of 1.9, we get the coordinates of the point (80, 1.9), which is one of the points in the residual plot shown here.

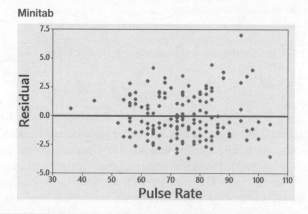

Minitab

See the three residual plots on the top of the next page.

- **Leftmost Residual Plot:** This graph suggests that the regression equation is a good model.

- **Middle Residual Plot:** This graph shows a distinct pattern, suggesting that the sample data do not follow a straight-line pattern as required.

- **Rightmost Residual Plot:** This graph becomes thicker, which suggests that the requirement of equal standard deviations is violated.

Residual Plot Suggesting That the Regression Equation Is a Good Model

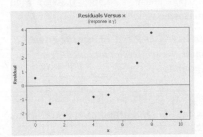

Residual Plot with an Obvious Pattern, Suggesting That the Regression Equation Is Not a Good Model

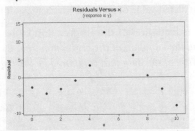

Residual Plot That Becomes Wider, Suggesting That the Regression Equation Is Not a Good Model

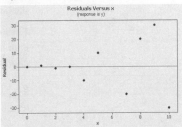

TECH CENTER

Regression
Access tech instructions, videos, and data sets at **www.TriolaStats.com**

10-2 Basic Skills and Concepts

Statistical Literacy and Critical Thinking

1. Notation Different patients are randomly selected and their red blood cell and white blood cell counts are measured. Using technology with x representing the red blood cell and y representing white blood cell, we find that the regression equation has a slope of 0.3585 and a y-intercept of 4.915.

a. What is the equation of the regression line?

b. What does the symbol $\hat{y}$ represent?

2. Notation What is the difference between the regression equation $\hat{y} = b_0 + b_1 x$ and the regression equation $y = \beta_0 + \beta_1 x$?

3. Best-Fit Line

a. What is a residual?

b. In what sense is the regression line the straight line that "best" fits the points in a scatterplot?

4. Correlation and Slope What is the relationship between the linear correlation coefficient r and the slope b_1 of a regression line?

Making Predictions. *In Exercises 5–8, let the predictor variable x be the first variable given. Use the given data to find the regression equation and the best predicted value of the response variable. Be sure to follow the prediction procedure summarized in Figure 10-5 on page 482. Use a 0.05 significance level.*

5. Waist Size and BMI Waist size (cm) and BMI are measured from randomly selected adult males (from Data Set 1 "Body Data"). The 153 pairs of measurements yield $\bar{x} = 100.8$ cm, $\bar{y} = 28.161$ cm, $r = 0.926$, P-value $= 0.0000$, and $\hat{y} = -4.898 + 0.3303x$. Find the best predicted value of $\hat{y}$ (BMI) given an adult male with a waist size of 120 cm.

6. Bear Measurements Head lengths (in.) and chests (in.) were measured for 20 randomly selected bears (from Data Set 11 "Bear Measurements"). The 20 pairs of measurements yield $\bar{x} = 13.525$ in., $\bar{y} = 36.95$ in., $r = 0.872$, P-value $= 0.000$, and $\hat{y} = -13.84 + 3.755x$. Find the best predicted value of $\hat{y}$ (chest) given a bear with a head length of 14.5 in.

7. Pulse Rates and Arm Circumference Pulse rates and arm circumferences are measured for 50 randomly selected adult females (from Data Set 1 "Body Data"). The 50 pairs of measurements yield $\bar{x} = 75.52$ BPM, $\bar{y} = 32.036$ cm, $r = -0.059$, P-value $= 0.682$, and $\hat{y} = 33.92 - 0.025x$. Find the best predicted value of $\hat{y}$ (arm circumference) given an adult female with pulse rate of 82 BPM.

8. Weights and Waists Weights (kg) and waists (cm) are measured for 100 randomly selected adult females (from Data Set 1 "Body Data"). The 100 pairs of measurements yield $\bar{x} = 77.17$ kg, $\bar{y} = 98.15$ cm, $r = 0.916$, P-value $= 0.000$, and $\hat{y} = 36.36 + 0.8006x$. Find the best predicted value of $\hat{y}$ (waist) given an adult female who weighs 94.6 kg.

Finding the Equation of the Regression Line. *In Exercises 9 and 10, use the given data to find the equation of the regression line. Examine the scatterplot and identify a characteristic of the data that is ignored by the regression line.*

9.

x	10	8	13	9	11	14	6	4	12	7	5
y	9.14	8.14	8.74	8.77	9.26	8.10	6.13	3.10	9.13	7.26	4.74

10.

x	10	8	13	9	11	14	6	4	12	7	5
y	7.46	6.77	12.74	7.11	7.81	8.84	6.08	5.39	8.15	6.42	5.73

11. Effects of an Outlier Refer to the Minitab-generated scatterplot given in Exercise 11 of Section 10-1 on page 474.

a. Using the pairs of values for all 10 points, find the equation of the regression line.

b. After removing the point with coordinates (10, 10), use the pairs of values for the remaining 9 points and find the equation of the regression line.

c. Compare the results from parts (a) and (b).

12. Effects of Clusters Refer to the Minitab-generated scatterplot given in Exercise 12 of Section 10-1 on page 475.

a. Using the pairs of values for all 8 points, find the equation of the regression line.

b. Using only the pairs of values for the 4 points in the lower left corner, find the equation of the regression line.

c. Using only the pairs of values for the 4 points in the upper right corner, find the equation of the regression line.

d. Compare the results from parts (a), (b), and (c).

Regression and Predictions. *Exercises 13–24 use the same data sets as Exercises 13–24 in Section 10-1. In each case, find the regression equation, letting the first variable be the predictor (x) variable. Find the indicated predicted value by following the prediction procedure summarized in Figure 10-5 on page 482.*

13. Pulse Rate and Systolic Blood Pressure Use the following pulse rates (x) and systolic blood pressures (y). If a subject has a pulse rate of 72 BPM, what is the best predicted systolic blood pressure?

Pulse Rate	80	84	94	74	50	60	52	58	66	62	52
Systolic Blood Pressure	100	112	134	126	114	134	118	138	114	124	138
Diastolic Blood Pressure	70	70	94	64	68	60	64	80	66	70	58

14. Pulse Rate and Diastolic Blood Pressure Use the pulse rates (x) and diastolic blood pressures (y) from the preceding exercise. If a subject has a pulse rate of 75 BPM, what is the best predicted diastolic blood pressure? How does it compare to the actual diastolic blood pressure of 74 for the subject whose pulse rate is 75 BPM?

15. Predicting Height Use the shoe print lengths and heights to find the best predicted height of a female who has a shoe print of 27.2 cm. Would the result be helpful to police crime scene investigators in trying to describe the female?

Shoe Print (cm)	26.5	26.0	27.0	25.1	27.9
Foot Length (cm)	23.3	23.5	25.1	24.1	23.8
Height (cm)	167.6	165.1	172.7	157.5	167.6

16. Predicting Height Use the foot lengths and heights from the preceding exercise to find the best predicted height of a female who has a foot length of 26.2 cm. Would the result be helpful to police crime scene investigators in trying to describe the female?

17. Lemons and Car Crashes Using the listed lemon/crash data, find the best predicted crash fatality rate for a year in which there are 500 metric tons of lemon imports. Is the prediction worthwhile?

Lemon Imports	230	265	358	480	530
Crash Fatality Rate	15.9	15.7	15.4	15.3	14.9

18. Crickets and Temperature Find the best predicted temperature at a time when a cricket chirps 3000 times in 1 minute. What is wrong with this predicted temperature?

Chirps in 1 min	882	1188	1104	864	1200	1032	960	900
Temperature (°F)	69.7	93.3	84.3	76.3	88.6	82.6	71.6	79.6

19. Heights of Fathers and First Sons Use the following heights of fathers and their first sons. If a father has a height of 69.5 inches, what is the best predicted height of the first son?

Height of father (in.)	70	69	70	71	74	70.5	69	70	68	65	66	71
Height of mother (in.)	74	63.5	58	63	62	64	61	63	60	67	66	63.5
Height of son (in.)	68	70.5	72	61	74	74	68	68	67.5	66.5	66	71

20. Heights of Mothers and First Sons Use the heights of mothers and their first sons from the preceding exercise. If a mother has a height of 70 inches, what is the best predicted height of the son?

21. Weighing Seals with a Camera Using the listed width/weight data, find the best predicted weight of a seal if the overhead width measured from a photograph is 2 cm. Can the prediction be correct? If not, what is wrong?

Overhead Width	7.2	7.4	9.8	9.4	8.8	8.4
Weight	116	154	245	202	200	191

22. Manatees Use the listed boat / manatee data. In a year not included in the data below, there were 840,000 registered pleasure boats in Florida. Find the best predicted number of manatee fatalities resulting from encounters with the boats. Is the result reasonably close to 78, which was the actual number of manatee fatalities?

Pleasure Boats	68	68	67	70	71	73	76	81	83
Manatee Fatalities	53	38	35	49	42	60	54	67	82

23. POTUS Using the president/opponent heights, find the best predicted height of an opponent of a president who is 190 cm tall. Does it appear that heights of opponents can be predicted from the heights of the presidents?

President	178	182	188	175	179	183	192	182	177	185	188	188	183	188
Opponent	180	180	182	173	178	182	180	180	183	177	173	188	185	175

24. Tree Circumference and Height Using the circumference/height data, find the best predicted height of a tree with a circumference of 5.0 feet. What is a big advantage of being able to predict height given a known circumference?

Circumference	1.8	1.9	1.8	2.4	5.1	3.1	5.5	5.1	8.3	13.7	5.3	4.9
Height	21.0	33.5	24.6	40.7	73.2	24.9	40.4	45.3	53.5	93.8	64.0	62.7

Large Data Sets. *Exercises 25–32 use the same Appendix B data sets as Exercises 25–32 in Section 10-1. In each case, find the regression equation, letting the first variable be the predictor (x) variable. Find the indicated predicted values following the prediction procedure summarized in Figure 10-5 on page 482.*

25. Pulse Rate and Systolic Blood Pressure Repeat Exercise 13 using all of the pulse rates and systolic blood pressures in Data Set 1 "Body Data" in Appendix B.

26. Pulse Rate and Diastolic Blood Pressure Repeat Exercise 14 "Pulse rate and Diastolic Blood Pressure" using all of the pulse rates and diastolic blood pressures in Data Set 1 "Body Data" in Appendix B.

27. Predicting Height Use the shoe print lengths and heights of the 19 males from Data Set 7 "Foot and Height." Find the best predicted height of a male who has a shoe print length of 31.3 cm.

28. Predicting Height Use the foot lengths and heights from the 19 males in Data Set 7 "Foot and Height." Find the best predicted height of a male who has a foot length of 28 cm.

29. Pulse Rate and Blood Pressure Use all of the pulse rates and systolic blood pressure amounts for adult females in Data Set 1 "Body Data" in Appendix B. If a subject has a pulse rate of 80 beats per minute, what is the best predicted systolic blood pressure?

30. Blood Pressure Use the systolic and diastolic blood pressures from the females in Data Set 1 "Body Data" in Appendix B. If a female has a systolic blood pressure of 120 mm Hg, what is the best predicted diastolic blood pressure?

31. Audiometry Use the right ear threshold measurements and the corresponding left ear threshold measurements from Data Set 4 "Audiometry" in Appendix B. What is the best predicted threshold measurement for the left ear given a measurement of 20 for the right ear?

32. Vision Use the measurements of visual acuity from the right eye and left eye as listed in Data Set 5 "Vision" in Appendix B. What is the best predicted measurement for the left ear given a reading of 50 for the right ear?

10-2 Beyond the Basics

33. Least-Squares Property According to the least-squares property, the regression line minimizes the sum of the squares of the residuals. Refer to the data in Table 10-1 on page 459.

a. Find the sum of squares of the residuals.

b. Show that the regression equation $\hat{y} = 3.00 + 0.0500x$ results in a larger sum of squares of residuals.

10-3 Prediction Intervals and Variation

Key Concept In Section 10-2 we presented a method for using a regression equation to find a predicted value of y, but it would be great to have a way of determining the *accuracy* of such predictions. In this section we introduce the *prediction interval,* which is an interval estimate of a predicted value of y. See the following definitions for the distinction between *confidence interval* and *prediction interval.*

> **DEFINITIONS**
>
> A **prediction interval** is a range of values used to estimate a *variable* (such as a predicted value of y in a regression equation).
>
> A **confidence interval** is a range of values used to estimate a population *parameter* (such as μ or p or σ).

In Example 4(b) from the preceding section, we showed that when using 147 pairs of pulse rates and white blood cell counts for females, the regression equation is $\hat{y} = 4.06 + 0.0345x$. Given a female pulse rate of 80 ($x = 80$), the best predicted white blood cell count is 6.8 (which is found by substituting $x = 80$ in the regression equation). For $x = 80$, the "best" predicted white blood cell count is 6.8, but we have no sense of the accuracy of that estimate, so we need an interval estimate. A prediction interval estimate of a predicted value $\hat{y}$ can be found using the components in the following Key Elements box. Given the nature of the calculations, the use of technology is strongly recommended.

KEY ELEMENTS

Prediction Intervals

Objective

Find a prediction interval, which is an interval estimate of a predicted value of y.

Requirement

For each fixed value of x, the corresponding sample values of y are normally distributed about the regression line, and those normal distributions have the same variance.

Formulas for Creating a Prediction Interval

Given a fixed and known value x_0, the prediction interval for an individual y value is

$$\hat{y} - E < y < \hat{y} + E$$

where the margin of error is

$$E = t_{\alpha/2} \, s_e \sqrt{1 + \frac{1}{n} + \frac{n(x_0 - \bar{x})^2}{n(\Sigma x^2) - (\Sigma x)^2}}$$

and x_0 is a given value of x, $t_{\alpha/2}$ has $n - 2$ degrees of freedom, and s_e is the **standard error of estimate** found from Formula 10-5 or Formula 10-6. (The standard error of estimate s_e is a measure of variation of the residuals, which are the differences between the observed sample y values and the predicted values $\hat{y}$ that are found from the regression equation.)

FORMULA 10-5	$s_e = \sqrt{\dfrac{\Sigma(y - \hat{y})^2}{n - 2}}$
FORMULA 10-6	$s_e = \sqrt{\dfrac{\Sigma y^2 - b_0 \Sigma y - b_1 \Sigma xy}{n - 2}}$

(This is an equivalent form of Formula 10-5 that is good for manual calculations.)

EXAMPLE 1 **Pulse Rates and White Blood Cell Counts: Finding a Prediction Interval**

For the 147 pairs of pulse rates and white blood cell counts for females from Data Set 1 "Body Data" in Appendix B, we found that there is sufficient evidence to support the claim of a linear correlation between those two variables, and the regression equation is $\hat{y} = 4.06 + 0.0345x$. For a female with a pulse rate of 80, the best predicted white blood cell count is 6.8 (found by substituting $x = 80$ in the regression equation). For a female with pulse rate of 80, construct a 95% prediction interval for the white blood cell count.

continued

SOLUTION

The accompanying StatCrunch and Minitab displays provide the 95% prediction interval, which is $3.0 < y < 10.6$ when rounded.

Minitab

Fit	SE Fit	95% CI	95% PI
6.82625	0.175652	(6.47908, 7.17342)	(3.01085, 10.6416)

StatCrunch

Predicted values:

X value	Pred. Y	s.e.(Pred. y)	95% C.I. for mean	95% P.I. for new
80	6.826247	0.17565207	(6.4790777, 7.1734162)	(3.0108531, 10.641641)

The same 95% prediction interval could be manually calculated using these components:

$x_0 = 80$ (given)

$s_e = 1.92241$ (provided by many technologies, including Statdisk, Minitab, Excel, StatCrunch, and TI-83/84 Plus calculator)

$\hat{y} = 6.82624$ (predicted value of y found by substituting $x = 80$ into the regression equation)

$t_{\alpha/2} = 1.976$ (with df = 145 and an area of 0.05 in two tails)

$n = 147, \bar{x} = 74.04082, \Sigma x = 10{,}884, \Sigma x^2 = 828{,}832$

INTERPRETATION

The 95% prediction interval is $3.0 < y < 10.6$. This means that if we select a random female with a pulse rate of 80 ($x = 80$), we have 95% confidence that the limits of 3.0 and 10.6 contain the white blood cell count. That is a wide range of values. The prediction interval would be much narrower and our estimated white blood cell count would be much better if the linear correlation were much stronger.

Explained and Unexplained Variation

Assume that we have a sample of paired data having the following properties shown in Figure 10-7:

- There is sufficient evidence to support the claim of a linear correlation between x and y.

- The equation of the regression line is $\hat{y} = 3 + 2x$.

- The mean of the y values is given by $\bar{y} = 9$.

- One of the pairs of sample data is $x = 5$ and $y = 19$.

- The point (5, 13) is one of the points on the regression line, because substituting $x = 5$ into the regression equation of $\hat{y} = 3 + 2x$ yields $\hat{y} = 13$.

Figure 10-7 shows that the point (5, 13) lies on the regression line, but the point (5, 19) from the original data set does not lie on the regression line. If we completely ignore correlation and regression concepts and want to predict a value of y given a value of x and a collection of paired (x, y) data, our best guess would be the mean $\bar{y} = 9$. But in this case there is a linear correlation between x and y, so a better way to predict the value of y when $x = 5$ is to substitute $x = 5$ into the regression equation to get $\hat{y} = 13$. We can *explain* the discrepancy between $\bar{y} = 9$ and $\hat{y} = 13$ by noting that there is a linear relationship best described by the regression line. Consequently, when $x = 5$, the predicted value of y is 13, not the mean value of 9. For $x = 5$, the predicted value of y is 13,

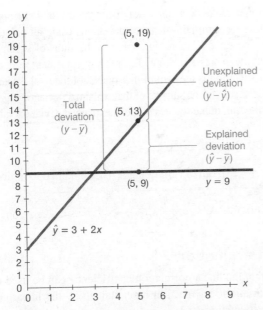

FIGURE 10-7   Total, Explained, and Unexplained Deviation

but the observed sample value of y is actually 19. The discrepancy between $\hat{y} = 13$ and $y = 19$ cannot be explained by the regression line, and it is called a *residual* or *unexplained deviation,* which can be expressed in the general format of $y - \hat{y}$.

As in Section 3-2 where we defined the standard deviation, we again consider a *deviation* to be a difference between a value and the mean. (In this case, the mean is $\bar{y} = 9$.) Examine Figure 10-7 carefully and note these specific deviations from $\bar{y} = 9$:

Total deviation (from $\bar{y} = 9$) of the point $(5, 19) = y - \bar{y} = 19 - 9 = 10$
Explained deviation (from $\bar{y} = 9$) of the point $(5, 19) = \hat{y} - \bar{y} = 13 - 9 = 4$
Unexplained deviation (from $\bar{y} = 9$) of the point $(5, 19) = y - \hat{y} = 19 - 13 = 6$

These deviations from the mean are generalized and formally defined as follows.

> **DEFINITIONS**
>
> Assume that we have a collection of paired data containing the sample point (x, y), that $\hat{y}$ is the predicted value of y (obtained by using the regression equation), and that the mean of the sample y values is $\bar{y}$.
>
> The **total deviation** of (x, y) is the vertical distance $y - \bar{y}$, which is the distance between the point (x, y) and the horizontal line passing through the sample mean $\bar{y}$.
>
> The **explained deviation** is the vertical distance $\hat{y} - \bar{y}$, which is the distance between the predicted y value and the horizontal line passing through the sample mean $\bar{y}$.
>
> The **unexplained deviation** is the vertical distance $y - \hat{y}$, which is the vertical distance between the point (x, y) and the regression line. (The distance $y - \hat{y}$ is also called a *residual,* as defined in Section 10-2.)

In Figure 10-7 we can see the following relationship for an individual point (x, y):

$$(\text{total deviation}) = (\text{explained deviation}) + (\text{unexplained deviation})$$
$$(y - \bar{y}) = (\hat{y} - \bar{y}) + (y - \hat{y})$$

The previous expression involves deviations away from the mean, and it applies to any one particular point (x, y). If we sum the squares of deviations using all points (x, y), we get amounts of *variation*. The same relationship applies to the sums of squares shown in Formula 10-7, even though the expression is not algebraically equivalent to Formula 10-7. In Formula 10-7, the **total variation** is the sum of the squares of the total deviation values, the **explained variation** is the sum of the squares of the explained deviation values, and the **unexplained variation** is the sum of the squares of the unexplained deviation values.

FORMULA 10-7

$$(\text{total variation}) = (\text{explained variation}) + (\text{unexplained variation})$$
$$\Sigma(y - \bar{y})^2 = \Sigma(\hat{y} - \bar{y})^2 + \Sigma(y - \hat{y})^2$$

Coefficient of Determination

In Section 10-1 we saw that the linear correlation coefficient r can be used to find the proportion of the total variation in y that can be explained by the linear correlation. This statement was made in Section 10-1:

The value of r^2 is the proportion of the variation in y that is explained by the linear relationship between x and y.

This statement about the explained variation is formalized with the following definition.

DEFINITION

The **coefficient of determination** is the proportion of the variation in y that is explained by the regression line. It is computed as

$$r^2 = \frac{\text{explained variation}}{\text{total variation}}$$

We can compute r^2 by using the definition just given with Formula 10-7, or we can simply square the linear correlation coefficient r. Go with squaring r.

EXAMPLE 2 **Pulse Rates and White Blood Cell Counts: Finding a Coefficient of Determination**

If we use the 147 pairs of pulse rates and white blood cell counts of females in Data Set 1 "Body Data" in Appendix B, we find that the linear correlation coefficient is $r = 0.221$. Find the coefficient of determination. Also, find the percentage of the total variation in y (white blood cell count) that can be explained by the linear correlation between pulse rate and white blood cell count.

Solution
With $r = 0.221$ the coefficient of determination is $r^2 = 0.049$.

INTERPRETATION

Because r^2 is the proportion of total variation that can be explained, we conclude that 4.9% of the total variation in the white blood cell count can be explained by pulse rate, and the other 95.1% cannot be explained by pulse rate. The other 95.1% might be explained by some other factors and/or random variation.

Prediction Intervals
Access tech instructions, videos, and data sets at **www.TriolaStats.com**

10-3   Basic Skills and Concepts

Statistical Literacy and Critical Thinking

1. s_e Notation Using Data set 1 "Body Data" in Appendix B, if we let the predictor variable x represent heights of females and let the response variable y represent weights of females, the sample of 147 heights and weights results in $s_e = 20.31678$ cm. In your own words, describe what that value of s_e represents.

2. Prediction Interval Using the heights and weights described in Exercise 1, a height of 170 cm is used to find that the predicted weight is 83.3 kg and the 95% prediction interval is (42.9 kg, 123.8 kg). Write a statement that interprets that prediction interval. What is the major advantage of using a prediction interval instead of simply using the predicted weight of 83.3 kg? Why is the terminology of *prediction interval* used instead of *confidence interval*?

3. Coefficient of Determination Using the heights and weights described in Exercise 1, the linear correlation coefficient r is 0.245. Find the value of the coefficient of determination. What practical information does the coefficient of determination provide?

4. Standard Error of Estimate A random sample of 118 different female statistics students is obtained, and their weights are measured in kilograms and in pounds. Using the 118 paired weights (weight in kg, weight in lb), what is the value of s_e? For a female statistics student who weighs 100 lb, the predicted weight in kilograms is 45.4 kg. What is the 95% prediction interval?

Interpreting the Coefficient of Determination. *In Exercises 5–8, use the value of the linear correlation coefficient r to find the coefficient of determination and the percentage of the total variation that can be explained by the linear relationship between the two variables.*

5. Crickets and Temperature $r = 0.874$ ($x =$ number of cricket chirps in 1 minute, $y =$ temperature in °F)

6. Weight / Waist $r = 0.885$ ($x =$ weight of male, $y =$ waist size of male)

7. Bear Neck Size and Weight $r = 0.934$ ($x =$ neck size, $y =$ weight)

8. Bears $r = 0.783$ ($x =$ head width of a bear, $y =$ weight of a bear)

Interpreting a Computer Display. *In Exercises 9–12, refer to the display obtained by using the paired data consisting of Florida registered boats (tens of thousands) and numbers of manatee deaths from encounters with boats in Florida for different recent years (from Data Set 12 in Appendix B). Along with the paired boat / manatee sample data, StatCrunch was also given the value of 85 (tens of thousands) boats to be used for predicting manatee fatalities.*

> **StatCrunch**
>
> Manatees = −49.048987 + 1.4062442 Boats
> Sample size: 24
> R (correlation coefficient) = 0.85014394
> Estimate of error standard deviation: 9.6605284
>
> **Predicted values:**
>
> | X value | Pred. Y | s.e.(Pred. y) | 95% C.I. for mean | 95% P.I. for new |
> |---------|---------|---------------|-------------------|------------------|
> | 85 | 70.481772 | 1.9724935 | (66.391071, 74.572473) | (50.033706, 90.929839) |

9. Testing for Correlation Use the information provided in the display to determine the value of the linear correlation coefficient. Is there sufficient evidence to support a claim of a linear correlation between numbers of registered boats and numbers of manatee deaths from encounters with boats?

10. Identifying Total Variation What percentage of the total variation in manatee fatalities can be explained by the linear correlation between registered boats and manatee fatalities?

11. Predicting Manatee Fatalities Using $x = 85$ (for 850,000 registered boats), what is the single value that is the best predicted number of manatee fatalities resulting from encounters with boats?

12. Finding a Prediction Interval For a year with 850,000 ($x = 85$) registered boats in Florida, identify the 95% prediction interval estimate of the number of manatee fatalities resulting from encounters with boats. Write a statement interpreting that interval.

Finding a Prediction Interval. *In Exercises 13–16, use the paired data consisting of registered Florida boats (tens of thousands) and manatee fatalities from boat encounters listed in Data Set 12 "Manatee Deaths" in Appendix B. Let x represent number of registered boats and let y represent the corresponding number of manatee deaths. Use the given number of registered boats and the given confidence level to construct a prediction interval estimate of manatee deaths.*

13. Boats Use $x = 85$ (for 850,000 registered boats) with a 99% confidence level.

14. Boats Use $x = 98$ (for 980,000 registered boats) with a 95% confidence level.

15. Boats Use $x = 96$ (for 960,000 registered boats) with a 95% confidence level.

16. Boats Use $x = 87$ (for 870,000 registered boats) with a 99% confidence level.

Variation and Prediction Intervals. *In Exercises 17–20, find the (a) explained variation, (b) unexplained variation, and (c) indicated prediction interval. In each case, there is sufficient evidence to support a claim of a linear correlation, so it is reasonable to use the regression equation when making predictions.*

17. Blood Pressure The table below lists systolic blood pressures (mm Hg) of adult males (from Data Set 1 "Body Data" in Appendix B). For the prediction interval, use a systolic blood pressure of 120 mm Hg and use a 95% confidence level.

Systolic	126	110	160	134	124	142	116	120	132	102	108	134
Diastolic	82	88	94	88	98	102	70	82	70	64	64	70

18. Tree Circumference and Height The table below lists circumferences (in feet) and the heights (in feet) of trees in Marshall, Minnesota (based on data from "Tree Measurements," by Stanley Rice, *American Biology Teacher,* Vol. 61, No. 9). For the prediction interval, use a circumference of 4.0 ft and use a 99% confidence level. Comment on the range of values in the prediction interval.

Circumference	1.8	1.9	1.8	2.4	5.1	3.1	5.5	5.1	8.3	13.7	5.3	4.9
Height	21.0	33.5	24.6	40.7	73.2	24.9	40.4	45.3	53.5	93.8	64.0	62.7

19. Crickets and Temperature The table below lists numbers of cricket chirps in 1 minute and the temperature in °F. For the prediction interval, use 1000 chirps in 1 minute and use a 90% confidence level.

Chirps in 1 min	882	1188	1104	864	1200	1032	960	900
Temperature (°F)	69.7	93.3	84.3	76.3	88.6	82.6	71.6	79.6

20. Weighing Seals with a Camera The table below lists overhead widths (cm) of seals measured from photographs and the weights (kg) of the seals (based on "Mass Estimation of Weddell Seals Using Techniques of Photogrammetry," by R. Garrott of Montana State University). For the prediction interval, use a 99% confidence level with an overhead width of 9.0 cm.

Overhead Width	7.2	7.4	9.8	9.4	8.8	8.4
Weight	116	154	245	202	200	191

10-3 Beyond the Basics

 21. Confidence Interval for Mean Predicted Value Example 1 in this section illustrated the procedure for finding a prediction interval for an *individual* value of y. When using a specific value x_0 for predicting the *mean* of all values of y, the confidence interval is as follows:

$$\hat{y} - E < \bar{y} < \hat{y} + E$$

where

$$E = t_{\alpha/2} \cdot s_e \sqrt{\frac{1}{n} + \frac{n(x_0 - \bar{x})^2}{n(\Sigma x^2) - (\Sigma x)^2}}$$

The critical value $t_{\alpha/2}$ is found with $n - 2$ degrees of freedom. Using the 147 pairs of pulse rates and white blood cell counts of females in Data Set 1 "Body Data" in Appendix B, find a 95% confidence interval estimate of the mean white blood cell count given that a female has a pulse rate of (a) 80 beats per minute and (b) 70 beats per minute.

10-4 Multiple Regression

Key Concept So far in this chapter we have discussed the linear correlation between *two* variables, but this section presents methods for analyzing a linear relationship with *more than two* variables. We focus on these two key elements: (1) finding the multiple regression equation and (2) using the value of adjusted R^2 and the P-value as measures of how well the multiple regression equation fits the sample data. Because the required calculations are so difficult, manual calculations are impractical, so this section emphasizes the use and interpretation of results from technology.

As in the preceding sections of this chapter, we will consider *linear* relationships only. The following *multiple regression equation* describes linear relationships involving more than two variables.

> **DEFINITION**
>
> A **multiple regression equation** expresses a linear relationship between a response variable y and two or more predictor variables $(x_1, x_2, \ldots, x_k)$. The general form of a multiple regression equation obtained from sample data is
>
> $$\hat{y} = b_0 + b_1x_1 + b_2x_2 + \cdots + b_kx_k$$

The following Key Elements box includes the key components of this section. For notation, see that the coefficients $b_0, b_1, b_2, \ldots, b_k$ are sample *statistics* used to estimate the corresponding population parameters $\beta_0, \beta_1, \beta_2, \ldots, \beta_k$. Also, note that the multiple regression equation is a natural extension of the format $\hat{y} = b_0 + b_1x_1$ used in Section 10-2 for regression equations with a single independent variable x_1. In Section 10-2, it would have been reasonable to question why we didn't use the more common and familiar format of $y = mx + b$, and we can now see that using $\hat{y} = b_0 + b_1x_1$ allows us to easily extend that format to include additional predictor variables.

KEY ELEMENTS

Finding a Multiple Regression Equation

Objective

Use sample matched data from three or more variables to find a multiple regression equation that is useful for predicting values of the response variable y.

Notation

$\hat{y} = b_0 + b_1 x_1 + b_2 x_2 + \cdots + b_k x_k$ (multiple regression equation found from *sample* data)

$y = \beta_0 + \beta_1 x_1 + \beta_2 x_2 + \cdots + \beta_k x_k$ (multiple regression equation for the *population* of data)

$\hat{y} =$ predicted value of y (computed using the multiple regression equation)

$k =$ number of *predictor* variables (also called *independent variables* or x variables)

$n =$ sample size (number of values for any one of the variables)

Requirements

For any specific set of x values, the regression equation is associated with a random error often denoted by ε. We assume that such errors are normally distributed with a mean of 0 and a standard deviation of σ and that the random errors are independent.

Procedure for Finding a Multiple Regression Equation

Manual calculations are not practical, so technology must be used.

 EXAMPLE 1 **Predicting Weight**

Data Set 1 "Body Data" includes heights (cm), waist circumferences (cm), and weights (kg) from a sample of 153 males. Find the multiple regression equation in which the response variable (y) is the weight of a male and the predictor variables are height (x_1) and waist circumference (x_2).

SOLUTION

Using Statdisk with the sample data in Data Set 1 "Body Data," we obtain the results shown in the display on the top of the next page. The coefficients b_0, b_1, and b_2 are used in the multiple regression equation:

$$\hat{y} = -149 + 0.769 x_1 + 1.01 x_2$$

or

$$\text{Weight} = -149 + 0.769 \, \text{Height} + 1.01 \, \text{Waist}$$

The obvious advantage of the second format above is that it is easier to keep track of the roles that the variables play.

Statdisk

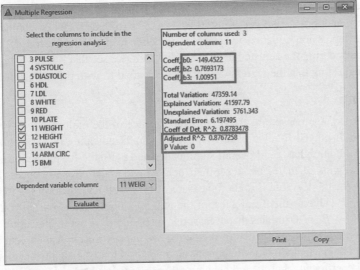

If a multiple regression equation fits the sample data well, it can be used for predictions. For example, if we determine that the multiple regression equation in Example 1 is suitable for predictions, we can use the height and waist circumference of a male to predict his weight. But how do we determine whether the multiple regression equation fits the sample data well? Two very helpful tools are the values of adjusted R^2 and the P-value.

R^2 and Adjusted R^2

R^2 denotes the **multiple coefficient of determination,** which is a measure of how well the multiple regression equation fits the sample data. A perfect fit would result in $R^2 = 1$, and a very good fit results in a value near 1. A very poor fit results in a value of R^2 close to 0. The value of $R^2 = 0.878$ ("Coeff of Det, R^2") in the Statdisk display for Example 1 indicates that 87.8% of the variation in weights of males can be explained by their heights and waist circumferences. However, the multiple coefficient of determination R^2 has a serious flaw: As more variables are included, R^2 increases. (R^2 could remain the same, but it usually increases.) The largest R^2 is obtained by simply including *all* of the available variables, but the best multiple regression equation does not necessarily use all of the available variables. Because of that flaw, it is better to use the *adjusted coefficient of determination,* which is R^2 adjusted for the number of variables and the sample size.

DEFINITION

The **adjusted coefficient of determination** is the multiple coefficient of determination R^2 modified to account for the number of variables and the sample size. It is calculated by using Formula 10-8.

FORMULA 10-8

$$\text{Adjusted } R^2 = 1 - \frac{(n-1)}{[n-(k+1)]}(1-R^2)$$

where

$$n = \text{sample size}$$

$$k = \text{number of predictor } (x) \text{ variables}$$

The preceding Statdisk display shows the adjusted coefficient of determination as "Adjusted R^2" = 0.877 (rounded). If we use Formula 10-8 with $R^2 = 0.8783478$, $n = 153$, and $k = 2$, we get adjusted $R^2 = 0.877$ (rounded). When comparing this multiple regression equation to others, it is better to use the adjusted R^2 of 0.877. When considering the adjusted R^2 of 0.877 by itself, we see that it is fairly high (close to 1), suggesting that the regression equation is a good fit with the sample data.

P-Value

The P-value is a measure of the overall significance of the multiple regression equation. The displayed P-value of 0 (rounded) is small, indicating that the multiple regression equation has good overall significance and is usable for predictions. We can predict weights of males based on their heights and waist circumferences. Like the adjusted R^2, this P-value is a good measure of how well the equation fits the sample data. The P-value results from a test of the null hypothesis that $\beta_1 = \beta_2 = 0$. Rejection of $\beta_1 = \beta_2 = 0$ implies that at least one of β_1 and β_2 is not 0, indicating that this regression equation is effective in predicting weights of males. A complete analysis of results might include other important elements, such as the significance of the individual coefficients, but we are keeping things simple (!) by limiting our discussion to the three key components—multiple regression equation, adjusted R^2, and P-value.

Finding the Best Multiple Regression Equation

When trying to find the best multiple regression equation, we should not necessarily include all of the available predictor variables. Finding the best multiple regression equation requires abundant use of judgment and common sense, and there is no exact and automatic procedure that can be used to find the best multiple regression equation. *Determination of the best multiple regression equation is often quite difficult and is beyond the scope of this section,* but the following guidelines are helpful.

Guidelines for Finding the Best Multiple Regression Equation

1. *Use common sense and practical considerations to include or exclude variables.* For example, when trying to find a good multiple regression equation for predicting the height of a daughter, we should exclude the height of the physician who delivered the daughter, because that height is obviously irrelevant.

2. *Consider the P-value.* Select an equation having overall significance, as determined by a low P-value found in the technology results display.

3. *Consider equations with high values of adjusted R^2, and try to include only a few variables.* Instead of including almost every available variable, try to include relatively few predictor (x) variables. Use these guidelines:

   - Select an equation having a value of adjusted R^2 with this property: If an additional predictor variable is included, the value of adjusted R^2 does not increase very much.

   - For a particular number of predictor (x) variables, select the equation with the largest value of adjusted R^2.

   - In excluding predictor (x) variables that don't have much of an effect on the response (y) variable, it might be helpful to find the linear correlation coefficient r for each pair of variables being considered. If two predictor values have a very high linear correlation coefficient (called *multicollinearity*), there is no need to include them both, and we should exclude the variable with the lower value of adjusted R^2.

The following example illustrates that common sense and *critical thinking* are essential tools for effective use of methods of statistics.

⊙ **EXAMPLE 2** **Predicting Height from Footprint Evidence**

Data Set 7 "Foot and Height" in Appendix B includes the age, foot length, shoe print length, shoe size, and height for each of 40 different subjects. Using those sample data, find the regression equation that is best for predicting height. Is the "best" regression equation a *good* equation for predicting height?

SOLUTION

Using the response variable of height and possible predictor variables of age, foot length, shoe print length, and shoe size, there are 15 different possible combinations of predictor variables. Table 10-4 includes key results from five of those combinations. Blind and thoughtless application of regression methods would suggest that the best regression equation uses all four of the predictor variables, because that combination yields the highest adjusted R^2 value of 0.7585. However, given the objective of using evidence to estimate the height of a suspect, we use *critical thinking* as follows.

1. Delete the variable of age, because criminals rarely leave evidence identifying their ages.

2. Delete the variable of shoe size, because it is really a rounded form of foot length.

3. For the remaining variables of foot length and shoe print length, use only foot length because its adjusted R^2 value of 0.7014 is greater than 0.6520 for shoe print length, and it is not very much less than the adjusted R^2 value of 0.7484 for both foot length and shoe print length. In this case, it is better to use one predictor variable instead of two.

4. Although it appears that the use of the single variable of foot length is best, we also note that criminals usually wear shoes, so shoe print lengths are more likely to be found than foot lengths.

TABLE 10-4 Selected Results from Data Set 7 "Foot and Height" in Appendix B

Predictor Variables	Adjusted R^2	P-Value	
Age	0.1772	0.004	← **Not best:** Adjusted R^2 is far less than 0.7014 for Foot Length.
Foot Length	**0.7014**	**0.000**	← **Best:** High adjusted R^2 and lowest P-value.
Shoe Print Length	0.6520	0.000	← **Not best:** Adjusted R^2 is less than 0.7014 for Foot Length.
Foot Length/Shoe Print Length	0.7484	0.000	← **Not best:** The adjusted R^2 value is not very much higher than 0.7014 for the single variable of Foot Length.
Age/Foot Length/ Shoe Print Length/ Shoe Size	0.7585	0.000	← **Not best:** There are other cases using fewer variables with adjusted R^2 that are not too much smaller.

INTERPRETATION

Blind use of regression methods suggests that when estimating the height of a subject, we should use all of the available data by including all four predictor variables of age, foot length, shoe print length, and shoe size, but other practical considerations suggest that it is best to use the single predictor variable of foot length. So the best regression equation appears to be this: Height = 64.1 + 4.29 (Foot Length). However, given that criminals usually wear shoes, it is best to use the single predictor

continued

variable of shoe print length, so the best practical regression equation appears to be this: Height = 80.9 + 3.22 (Shoe Print Length). The P-value of 0.000 suggests that the regression equation yields a good model for estimating height.

Because the results of this example are based on sample data from only 40 subjects, estimates of heights will not be very accurate. As is usually the case, better results could be obtained by using larger samples.

Tests of Regression Coefficients The preceding guidelines for finding the best multiple regression equation are based on the adjusted R^2 and the P-value, but we could also conduct individual hypothesis tests based on values of the regression coefficients. Consider the regression coefficient of β_1. A test of the null hypothesis $\beta_1 = 0$ can tell us whether the corresponding predictor variable should be included in the regression equation. Rejection of $\beta_1 = 0$ suggests that β_1 has a nonzero value and is therefore helpful for predicting the value of the response variable. Procedures for such tests are described in Exercise 17.

Predictions With Multiple Regression

When we discussed regression in Section 10-2, we listed (on page 482) four points to consider when using regression equations to make predictions. These same points should be considered when using multiple regression equations.

TECH CENTER

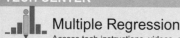

Multiple Regression

Access tech instructions, videos, and data sets at **www.TriolaStats.com**

10-4   Basic Skills and Concepts

Statistical Literacy and Critical Thinking

1. Terminology Using the head lengths (in.), head widths (in.), and neck circumferences (in.) of bears from Data Set 11 "Bear Measurements" in Appendix B, we get this regression equation: Neck = −8.69 + 1.630 Head Length + 1.312 Head Width. Identify the response and predictor variables.

2. Best Multiple Regression Equation For the regression equation given in Exercise 1, the P-value is 0.000 and the adjusted R^2 value is 0.830. If we were to include an additional predictor variable of length (in.), the P-value becomes 0.000 and the adjusted R^2 becomes 0.837. Given that the adjusted R^2 value of 0.837 is larger than 0.830, is it better to use the regression equation with the three predictor variables of head length, head width, and length?

3. Adjusted Coefficient of Determination For Exercise 2, why is it better to use values of adjusted R^2 instead of simply using values of R^2?

4. Interpreting R^2 For the multiple regression equation given in Exercise 1, we get $R^2 = 0.836$. What does that value tell us?

Interpreting a Computer Display.   In Exercises 5–8, we want to consider the correlation between heights of fathers and mothers and the heights of their sons. Refer to the following StatCrunch display and answer the given questions or identify the indicated items. The display is based on Data Set 6 "Family Heights" in Appendix B.

Parameter estimates:

Parameter ⬧	Estimate ⬧	Std. Err. ⬧	Alternative ⬧	DF ⬧	T-Stat ⬧	P-value ⬧
Intercept	17.966577	6.4779134	≠ 0	131	2.7735131	0.0064
Father	0.50354896	0.067077219	≠ 0	131	7.507004	<0.0001
Mother	0.27714316	0.078318967	≠ 0	131	3.5386467	0.0006

Analysis of variance table for multiple regression model:

Source	DF	SS	MS	F-stat	P-value
Model	2	320.94662	160.47331	37.637221	<0.0001
Error	131	558.54293	4.2636865		
Total	133	879.48955			

Summary of fit:
Root MSE: 2.0648696
R-squared: 0.3649
R-squared (adjusted): 0.3552

5. Height of Son Identify the multiple regression equation that expresses the height of a son in terms of the height of his father and mother.

6. Height of Son Identify the following:

a. The P-value corresponding to the overall significance of the multiple regression equation

b. The value of the multiple coefficient of determination R^2

c. The adjusted value of R^2

7. Height of Son Should the multiple regression equation be used for predicting the height of a son based on the height of his father and mother? Why or why not?

8. Height of Son A son will be born to a father who is 70 in. tall and a mother who is 60 in. tall. Use the multiple regression equation to predict the height of the son. Is the result likely to be a good predicted value? Why or why not?

Predicting Weights of Males. *In Exercises 9–12, refer to the accompanying table, which was obtained by using the data for males in Data Set 1 "Body Data" in Appendix B. The response (y) variable is weight (kg), and the predictor (x) variables are HT (height in cm), WAIST (waist circumference in cm), and ARM (arm circumference in cm).*

Predictor (x) Variables	P-Value	R^2	Adjusted R^2	Regression Equation
HT, WAIST, ARM	0.000	0.941	0.939	$\hat{y} = -147 + 0.632$ HT + 0.697 WAIST + 1.58 ARM
HT, WAIST	0.000	0.878	0.877	$\hat{y} = -149 + 0.769$ HT + 1.01 WAIST
HT, ARM	0.000	0.777	0.774	$\hat{y} = -124 + 0.541$ HT + 3.44 ARM
WAIST, ARM	0.000	0.879	0.878	$\hat{y} = -45.0 + 0.659$ WAIST + 1.92 ARM
HT	0.000	0.155	0.150	$\hat{y} = -85.1 + 0.980$ HT
WAIST	0.000	0.784	0.782	$\hat{y} = -19.1 + 1.05$ WAIST
ARM	0.000	0.732	0.731	$\hat{y} = -37.1 + 3.65$ ARM

9. If only one predictor (x) variable is used to predict weight, which single variable is best? Why?

10. If exactly two predictor (x) variables are to be used to predict weight, which two variables should be chosen? Why?

11. Which regression equation is best for predicting the weight? Why?

12. If a male has a height of 186 cm, a waist circumference of 107.8 cm, and an arm circumference of 37.0 cm, what is the best predicted weight? Is that predicted value likely to be a good estimate? Is that predicted value likely to be very accurate?

Appendix B Data Sets. *In Exercises 13–16, refer to the indicated data set in Appendix B and use technology to obtain results.*

13. Predicting Nicotine in Cigarettes Refer to Data Set 15 "Cigarette Contents" in Appendix B and use the tar, nicotine, and CO amounts for the cigarettes that are 100 mm long, filtered, nonmenthol, and nonlight (the last set of measurements). Find the best regression equation for predicting the amount of nicotine in a cigarette using the predictor variables of (1) tar; (2) carbon monoxide; (3) tar and carbon monoxide. Why is it best? Is the best regression equation a good regression equation for predicting the nicotine content? Why or why not?

14. Predicting Nicotine in Cigarettes Repeat the preceding exercise using the sample data from the Menthol cigarettes listed in Data Set 15 in Appendix B.

15. Predicting IQ Score Refer to Data Set 9 "IQ and Brain Size" in Appendix B and find the best regression equation with IQ score as the response (y) variable. Use predictor variables of brain volume and/or body weight. Why is this equation best? Based on these results, can we predict someone's IQ score if we know their brain volume and body weight? Based on these results, does it appear that people with larger brains have higher IQ scores?

16. Full IQ Score Refer to Data Set 8 "IQ and Lead" in Appendix B and find the best regression equation with IQF (full IQ score) as the response (y) variable. Use predictor variables of IQV (verbal IQ score) and IQP (performance IQ score). Why is this equation best? Based on these results, can we predict someone's full IQ score if we know their verbal IQ score and their performance IQ score? Is such a prediction likely to be very accurate?

10-4 Beyond the Basics

17. Testing Hypotheses About Regression Coefficients If the coefficient β_1 has a nonzero value, then it is helpful in predicting the value of the response variable. If $\beta_1 = 0$, it is not helpful in predicting the value of the response variable and can be eliminated from the regression equation. To test the claim that $\beta_1 = 0$ use the test statistic $t = (b_1 - 0)/s_{b_1}$. Critical values or P-values can be found using the t distribution with $n - (k + 1)$ degrees of freedom, where k is the number of predictor (x) variables and n is the number of observations in the sample. The standard error s_{b_1} is often provided by software. For example, see the accompanying StatCrunch display for Example 1, which shows that $s_{b_1} = 0.071141412$ (found in the column with the heading of "Std. Err." and the row corresponding to the first predictor variable of height). Use the sample data in Data Set 1 "Body Data" and the StatCrunch display to test the claim that $\beta_1 = 0$. Also test the claim that $\beta_2 = 0$. What do the results imply about the regression equation?

Parameter estimates:						
Parameter ⬦	Estimate ⬦	Std. Err. ⬦	Alternative ⬦	DF ⬦	T-Stat ⬦	P-value ⬦
Intercept	-149.45217	12.523494	≠ 0	150	-11.933743	<0.0001
Height	0.76931731	0.071141412	≠ 0	150	10.813917	<0.0001
Waist	1.0095102	0.033812346	≠ 0	150	29.856261	<0.0001

18. Confidence Intervals for Regression Coefficients A confidence interval for the regression coefficient β_1 is expressed as

$$b_1 - E < \beta_1 < b_1 + E$$

where

$$E = t_{\alpha/2} s_{b_1}$$

The critical t score is found using $n - (k + 1)$ degrees of freedom, where k, n, and s_{b_1} are described in Exercise 17. Using the sample data from Example 1, $n = 153$ and $k = 2$, so df $= 150$ and the critical t scores are ± 1.976 for a 95% confidence level. Use the sample data for Example 1, the Statdisk display in Example 1 on page 499, and the StatCrunch display in Exercise 17 to construct 95% confidence interval estimates of β_1 (the coefficient for the variable representing height) and β_2 (the coefficient for the variable representing waist circumference). Does either confidence interval include 0, suggesting that the variable be eliminated from the regression equation?

10-5   Dummy Variables and Logistic Regression

So far in this chapter, all variables have represented continuous data, but many situations involve a variable with only *two* possible qualitative values (such as male/female or dead/alive or cured/not cured). To obtain regression equations that include such variables, we must somehow assign numbers to the two different categories. A common procedure is to represent the two possible values by 0 and 1, where 0 represents a "failure" and 1 represents a "success." For disease outcomes, 1 is often used to represent the event of the disease or death, and 0 is used to represent the nonevent.

> **DEFINITION**
>
> A **dummy variable** is a variable having only the values of 0 and 1 that are used to represent the two different categories of a qualitative variable.

The word "dummy" is used because the variable does not actually have any quantitative value, but we use it as a substitute to represent the different categories of the qualitative variable.

Dummy Variable as a Predictor Variable

Procedures of regression analysis differ dramatically depending on whether the dummy variable is a predictor (x) variable or the response (y) variable. If we include a dummy variable as another *predictor* (x) variable, we can use the same methods of Section 10-4, as illustrated in Example 1.

 EXAMPLE 1   Using a Dummy Variable as a Predictor Variable

Table 10-5 on the next page is adapted from Data Set 6 "Family Heights" and it is in a more convenient format for this example. Use the dummy variable of sex (coded as 0 = female, 1 = male). Given that a father is 69 in. tall and a mother is 63 in. tall, find the multiple regression equation and use it to predict the height of (a) a daughter and (b) a son.

SOLUTION

Using the methods of multiple regression from Section 10-4 with technology, we get this regression equation:

$$\text{Height of Child} = 36.5 - 0.0336 \, (\text{Height of Father}) + 0.461 \, (\text{Height of Mother}) + 6.14 \, (\text{Sex})$$

where the value of the dummy variable of sex is 0 for a daughter or 1 for a son.

a. To find the predicted height of a *daughter,* we substitute 0 for the sex variable, and we also substitute 69 in. for the father's height and 63 in. for the mother's height. The result is a predicted height of 63.2 in. for a daughter.

b. To find the predicted height of a *son,* we substitute 1 for the sex variable, and we also substitute 69 in. for the father's height and 63 in. for the mother's height. The result is a predicted height of 69.4 in. for a son.

The coefficient of 6.14 in the regression equation shows that when given the height of a father and the height of a mother, a son will have a predicted height that is 6.14 in. more than the height of a daughter.

continued

TABLE 10-5 Heights (in inches) of Fathers, Mothers, and Their Children

Height of Father	Height of Mother	Height of Child	Sex of Child (1 = Male)
66.5	62.5	70.0	1
70.0	64.0	68.0	1
67.0	65.0	69.7	1
68.7	70.5	71.0	1
69.5	66.0	71.0	1
70.0	65.0	73.0	1
69.0	66.0	70.0	1
68.5	67.0	73.0	1
65.5	60.0	68.0	1
69.5	66.5	70.5	1
70.5	63.0	64.5	0
71.0	65.0	62.0	0
70.5	62.0	60.0	0
66.0	66.0	67.0	0
68.0	61.0	63.5	0
68.0	63.0	63.0	0
71.0	62.0	64.5	0
65.5	63.0	63.5	0
64.0	60.0	60.0	0
71.0	63.0	63.5	0

Dummy Variable as a Response Variable: Logistic Regression

In Example 1, we could use the same methods of Section 10-4 because the dummy variable of sex is a *predictor* variable. However, if the dummy variable is the *response* (*y*) variable, we cannot use the methods of Section 10-4, and we should use a different method known as *logistic regression.*

DEFINITION

Logistic regression is a procedure used for finding a regression equation in which the *response* variable is a dummy variable.

Dummy response variables are common in clinical research where the response variable might be the yes/no indication for the occurrence of a disease such as diabetes, cancer, hypertension, or chronic kidney disease. Other dummy response variables include yes/no values for hospitalization, death, or need of a kidney transplant. As with dummy predictor variables, dummy response variables are typically coded as 0 and 1. For example, the response variable of "hospitalization" could be coded as 1 for patients who were hospitalized and 0 for patients who were not hospitalized.

Simple Logistic Regression We use **simple logistic regression** when these conditions are met:

- There is a single predictor *x* variable.
- The sample *y* data have values of 0 and 1.

Instead of yielding predicted values of y itself, the method of simple logistic regression yields an equation with the following format:

$$\ln\left(\frac{p}{1-p}\right) = b_0 + b_1 x$$

In the above expression, p is the probability that $y = 1$. Given a specific value for x, we can solve for p by first substituting that x value in the right side of the above equation to obtain a value v; then we can solve for p by evaluating the following, where $e = 2.71828$:

$$p = \frac{e^v}{1 + e^v}$$

EXAMPLE 2 Simple Logistic Regression

Use the paired height/gender data from Data Set 1 "Body Data" to find the simple logistic regression equation, and let the response variable (y) be gender with $0 =$ female and $1 =$ male. Then find the probability that a person with a height of 190 cm (or 74.8 in.) is a male.

SOLUTION

We can use technology with the gender/height data to find this equation:

$$\ln\left(\frac{p}{1-p}\right) = -40.6 + 0.242(\text{Height})$$

Given a height of $x = 190$ cm, we substitute that value in the right side of the above equation to get the value $v = -40.6 + 0.242(190) = 5.38$. We can now solve for p as follows (using $e = 2.71828$):

$$p = \frac{e^v}{1 + e^v} = \frac{e^{5.38}}{1 + e^{5.38}} = 0.995$$

On the basis of this simple logistic regression model, a person with a height of 190 cm (or 74.8 in.) has a probability of 0.995 of being a male.

The ratio $p/(1 - p)$ is the odds in favor of $y = 1$ (as defined in Section 4-4), and $\ln(p/(1 - p))$ is the natural logarithm of the odds that $y = 1$. It is the natural logarithm of those odds that are assumed to be linear in x, but the relationship between x and p is a curve that is bounded between 0 and 1, as shown in Figure 10-8 on the next page. Figure 10-8 uses the same gender/height data from Example 2. The simple logistic regression curve takes the shape of a stretched-out "S." See that as x gets smaller, the curve gets closer to 0, but never quite reaches it. Similarly, as x increases, the curve gets closer to 1. The simple logistic regression curve can be thought of as representing probabilities that $y = 1$ (male) for each possible value of x (height). In this particular case, x and y have a positive relationship, so that as height x increases, the probability of a male ($y = 1$) also increases. This also implies that $\beta_1 > 0$. If x and y had a negative relationship, then the curve would be an inverted S shape; and as x increases, the probability that $y = 1$ would decrease.

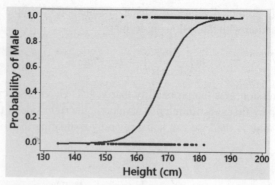

FIGURE 10-8   **Simple Logistic Regression Curve**

Multiple Logistic Regression

We use **multiple logistic regression** when there is a dummy response variable and more than one predictor variable. Instead of yielding predicted values of y itself, the method of multiple logistic regression yields an equation with the following format:

$$\ln\left(\frac{p}{1-p}\right) = b_0 + b_1x_1 + b_2x_2 + \ldots + b_kx_k$$

In the above expression, p is the probability that $y = 1$. Given specific values for the different x predictor variables, we can solve for p by first substituting those values in the right side of the above equation to obtain a value v; then we can solve for p by evaluating the following:

$$p = \frac{e^v}{1+e^v}$$

EXAMPLE 3   **Multiple Logistic Regression**

Let a sample data set consist of the heights (cm) and arm circumferences (cm) of women and men as listed in Data Set 1 "Body Data" in Appendix B, and let the *response* y variable represent gender (0 = female, 1 = male). With this list of genders, heights, and arm circumferences, logistic regression could be used with software to obtain this model:

$$\ln\left(\frac{p}{1-p}\right) = -40.6 + 0.242(\text{HT}) + 0.00129(\text{ArmCirc})$$

In the expression above, p is the probability of a male, so a value of p close to 1 indicates that the person is likely a male, and a value of p close to 0 indicates that the person is not likely a male (so the person is likely to be a female). See the following two sets of results.

- If we use the model above and substitute a height of 183 cm (or 72.0 in.) and an arm circumference of 33 cm (or 13.0 in.), we can solve for p to get $p = 0.977$, indicating that such a large person has a 97.7% chance of being a male.

- In contrast, a small person with a height of 150 cm (or 59.1 in.) and an arm circumference of 20 cm (or 7.9 in.) results in a probability of $p = 0.014$, indicating that such a small person is very unlikely to be a male.

In clinical research, there is much interest in finding biomarkers that are good predictors of disease. In particular, if it is hypothesized that some new biomarker might improve predictions, one method of testing this hypothesis is to include the biomarker as one of the variables in a multiple logistic regression model. The other predictors in the model could be established risk factors, such as age and sex. If the new biomarker adds predictive value, then its coefficient in the logistic regression model should be different from 0. See Example 4.

EXAMPLE 4 **Multiple Logistic Regression**

Researchers were interested in determining whether "distortion product otoacoustic emissions" (DPOAEs) were a useful tool for identification of hearing impairment in newborns. The dummy response variable was hearing impairment (1 = impaired, 0 = not impaired), as defined from a gold standard test when the infants were at least 8 months of age. The multiple logistic regression model included DPOAE (a continuous variable), age (weeks), and sex (0 = female, 1 = male) as predictor variables. Use of multiple logistic regression yielded the following model (based on data from "Identification of Neonatal Hearing Impairment," by Norton et al., *Ear and Hearing,* Vol. 21):

$$\ln\left(\frac{p}{1-p}\right) = 3.84 - 0.06(\text{DPOAE}) + 0.02(\text{Sex}) - 0.02(\text{Age})$$

In the expression above, p is the probability of hearing impairment. We can obtain *P*-values from statistical software packages, and the above equation resulted in the following *P*-values:

Variable	*P*-Value
DPOAE	<0.01
Sex	0.91
Age	0.4

The *P*-value for the variable DPOAE is very small, which shows strong evidence against the null hypothesis that DPOAE is not a predictor of impairment. It appears that DPOAE might be a useful test of hearing impairment in newborns. For the variable Sex, the *P*-value of 0.91 indicates that we do not have sufficient evidence to support the claim that sex is a predictor of impairment. Similarly, Age was also not a statistically significant predictor.

Why can't we use the same regression methods from the preceding sections when the dummy variable is the response variable? Suppose we have one independent variable, and we use the methods of Section 10-2 to find a *linear* regression equation using sample data for which the values of y are all 0's and 1's. There is nothing that prevents some of the predicted y values from being greater than 1 or less than 0, but that would be inconsistent with the requirement that probabilities must be between 0 and 1. See Figure 10-9 on the following page, which shows a continuous predictor variable x (height) plotted against a dummy response variable y (gender with values of 0 = female and 1 = male). Figure 10-9 uses the same gender/height data from Example 2. The straight regression line in Figure 10-9 results from using the methods of linear regression in Section 10-2. See that the line

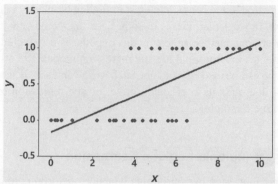

FIGURE 10-9 **Linear Regression Line with a Dummy Response Variable**

dips below 0 for small values of x and it rises above 1 for large values of x. These results violate the requirement that probability values must be between 0 and 1. The straight line from linear regression is not a good model here. The S curve from logistic regression (Figure 10-8) is a far better model.

Assessing the Quality of Predictions When assessing the quality of predictions made with logistic regression, one consideration might be the P-value for the overall significance of the regression equation. Another approach might be use of the Hosmer-Lemeshow test, which assesses whether the model is calibrated well, which means that the observed risks from the sample data match the predicted risks (or probabilities). But in addition to being well calibrated, the model should discriminate between observations at high risk and those at low risk. The area under the curve (AUC) of a receiver operating characteristic (ROC) curve is also used as a measure of the quality of the model. These and other more detailed methods are included in many books devoted to logistic regression.

10-5   Basic Skills and Concepts

Statistical Literacy and Critical Thinking

1. Dummy Variable What is a dummy variable?

2. Logistic Regression What is the fundamental difference between logistic regression and linear regression?

3. Simple Logistic Regression How is simple logistic regression different from multiple logistic regression?

4. True or False Determine whether this statement is true or false: If a multiple regression equation has a continuous response variable and three predictor variables, including one that is a dummy variable, then we must use methods of logistic regression because a dummy variable is included.

In Exercise 5–8, use the following logistic regression equation found from Data Set 11 "Bear Measurements" in Appendix B. The value of p is the probability that the bear is female.

$$\ln\left(\frac{p}{1-p}\right) = 1.50 + 0.045\,(\text{Head Length}) - 0.0444\,(\text{Head Width})$$

5. Bears Identify the predictor and response variables. Which of these are dummy variables?

6. Bears The given regression equation has an overall *P*-value of 0.160. What does that suggest about the quality of predictions made using the regression equation?

7. Bears Use a head length of 14.5 in. and a head width of 7.5 in. to find the probability that the bear is a female. Also, what is the probability that the bear is a male?

8. Bears Use a head length of 16 in. and a head width of 9 in. to find the probability that the bear is a female. What is the probability that the bear is a male? Considering the given length and weight, what do we know about this bear?

9. Weight of a Bear Refer to Data Set 11 "Bear Measurements" in Appendix B and use the sex, age, and weight of the bears. For sex, let 0 represent female and let 1 represent male. Letting the response (*y*) variable represent weight, use the variable of age and the dummy variable of sex to find the multiple regression equation. Use the equation to find the predicted weight of a bear with the characteristics given below. Does sex appear to have much of an effect on the weight of a bear?

a. Female bear that is 20 years of age

b. Male bear that is 20 years of age

10. Sex, Height, and Weight Refer to Data Set 1 "Body Data" in Appendix B and use the sex, height, and weight of the human subjects. Letting the response (*y*) variable represent weight, use the dummy variable of sex and use the height to find the multiple regression equation. Use the equation to find the predicted weight of a subject with the characteristics given below. Do the results make sense?

a. Female with a height of 170 cm

b. Male with a height of 170 cm

11. Sex, Height, and Weight Refer to Data Set 1 "Body Data" in Appendix B and use the sex, height, and weight of the human subjects. Letting the response (*y*) variable represent sex (0 = female, 1 = male), use the variables of height and weight to find the multiple regression equation. Use the equation to find the probability that the subject is a male, given that the subject has a height of 170 cm and a weight of 90 kg.

12. Sex, Height, and Pulse Rate Refer to Data Set 1 "Body Data" in Appendix B and use the sex, height, and pulse rate of the human subjects. Letting the response (*y*) variable represent sex (0 = female, 1 = male), use the variables of height and pulse rate to find the multiple regression equation. Use the equation to find the probability that the subject is a male, given that the subject has a height of 170 cm and a pulse rate of 60 beats per minute. Do higher pulse rates make males more likely or less likely?

13. Sex, Foot Length, and Height Refer to Data Set 7 "Foot and Height" in Appendix B and use the sex, foot length, and height of the subjects. Letting the response (*y*) variable represent sex (0 = female, 1 = male), use the variables of foot length and height to find the multiple regression equation. Use the equation to find the probability that the subject is a male, given that the subject has a foot length of 28 cm and a height of 190 cm.

14. Sex, Shoe Size, and Height Refer to Data Set 7 "Foot and Height" in Appendix B and use the sex, shoe size, and height of the subjects. Letting the response (*y*) variable represent sex (0 = female, 1 = male), use the variables of shoe size and height to find the multiple regression equation. Use the equation to find the probability that the subject is a male, given that the subject has a shoe size of 9 and a height of 170 cm. Are predictions of sex made using shoe size and height likely to be more or less accurate than predictions of sex made using foot length and height (as in the preceding exercise)?

Chapter Quick Quiz

The following exercises are based on the following sample data consisting of systolic blood pressure measurements (in mm Hg) obtained from the same woman (based on data from "Consistency of Blood Pressure Differences Between the Left and Right Arms," by Eguchi et al., Archives of Internal Medicine, Vol. 167).

Right Arm	102	101	94	79	79
Left Arm	175	169	182	146	144

1. Conclusion The linear correlation coefficient r is found to be 0.867, the P-value is 0.057, and the critical values for a 0.05 significance level are ± 0.878. If you are using a 0.05 significance level, what should you conclude?

2. Switched Variables Which of the following change if the two variables of right arm and left arm blood pressure measurements are switched: the value of $r = 0.867$, the P-value of 0.057, the critical values of ± 0.878?

3. Change in Scale Exercise 1 stated that r is found to be 0.867. How does the value of r change if the scale for the right arm measurements is changed from mm Hg to in. Hg, so that all of the values for the right arm are multiplied by 0.0394?

4. Values of *r* If you had computed the value of the linear correlation coefficient to be 1.500, what should you conclude?

5. Predictions The sample data result in a linear correlation coefficient of $r = 0.867$ and the regression equation $\hat{y} = 43.6 + 1.31x$. What is the best predicted value for the left arm given that the measurement for the right arm is 100 mm Hg?

6. Predictions Repeat the preceding exercise, assuming that the linear correlation coefficient for the paired sample data is $r = 0.997$.

7. Explained Variation Given that the linear correlation coefficient r is found to be 0.867, what is the proportion of the variation in left arm measurements that is explained by the relationship between the right and left arm measurements?

8. Linear Correlation and Relationships True or false: If there is no linear correlation between right arm measurements and left arm measurements, then those two variables are not related in any way.

9. Causality True or false: If the sample data lead us to conclude that there is sufficient evidence to support the claim of a linear correlation between right and left arm measurements, then we could also conclude that increases in right arm measurements cause increases in left arm measurements.

10. Interpreting Scatterplot If the sample data were to result in the scatterplot shown here, what is the value of the linear correlation coefficient r?

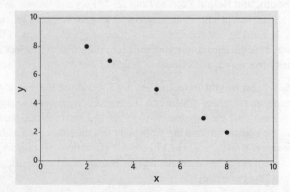

Review Exercises

1. Cigarette Tar and Nicotine The table below lists measured amounts (mg) of tar, carbon monoxide (CO), and nicotine in king size cigarettes of different brands (from Data Set 15 "Cigarette Contents").

a. Is there is sufficient evidence to support a claim of a linear correlation between tar and nicotine?

b. What percentage of the variation in nicotine can be explained by the linear correlation between nicotine and tar?

c. Letting y represent the amount of nicotine and letting x represent the amount of tar, identify the regression equation.

d. The Raleigh brand king size cigarette is not included in the table, and it has 23 mg of tar. What is the best predicted amount of nicotine? How does the predicted amount compare to the actual amount of 1.3 mg of nicotine?

Tar	25	27	20	24	20	20	21	24
CO	18	16	16	16	16	16	14	17
Nicotine	1.5	1.7	1.1	1.6	1.1	1.0	1.2	1.4

2. Cigarette Nicotine and Carbon Monoxide Refer to the table of data given in Exercise 1 and use the amounts of nicotine and carbon monoxide (CO).

a. Construct a scatterplot using nicotine for the x scale or horizontal axis. What does the scatterplot suggest about a linear correlation between amounts of nicotine and carbon monoxide?

b. Find the value of the linear correlation coefficient and determine whether there is sufficient evidence to support a claim of a linear correlation between amounts of nicotine and carbon monoxide.

c. Letting y represent the amount of carbon monoxide and letting x represent the amount of nicotine, find the regression equation.

d. The Raleigh brand king size cigarette is not included in the table, and it has 1.3 mg of nicotine. What is the best predicted amount of carbon monoxide? How does the predicted amount compare to the actual amount of 15 mg of carbon monoxide?

3. Cigarette Tar and Carbon Monoxide Refer to the table of data given in Exercise 1 and use the amounts of tar and carbon monoxide.

a. Construct a scatterplot using the horizontal scale to represent the amount of tar. What does the scatterplot suggest?

b. Does the scatterplot show eight points corresponding to the eight pairs of sample data? If not, why not?

c. Find the value of the linear correlation coefficient and determine whether there is sufficient evidence to support a claim of a linear correlation between amount of tar and amount of carbon monoxide.

d. Letting y represent amount of carbon monoxide and letting x represent amount of tar, find the regression equation.

e. The Raleigh brand king size cigarette is not included in the table, and it has 23 mg of tar. What is the best predicted amount of carbon monoxide? How does the predicted amount compare to the actual amount of 15 mg of carbon monoxide?

4. Multiple Regression with Cigarettes Use the sample data given in Exercise 1 "Cigarette Tar and Nicotine."

a. Find the multiple regression equation with the response (y) variable of amount of nicotine and predictor (x) variables of amounts of tar and carbon monoxide.

continued

b. Identify the value of the multiple coefficient of determination R^2, the adjusted R^2, and the P-value representing the overall significance of the multiple regression equation.

c. Use a 0.05 significance level and determine whether the regression equation can be used to predict the amount of nicotine given the amounts of tar and carbon monoxide.

d. The Raleigh brand king size cigarette is not included in the table, and it has 23 mg of tar and 15 mg of carbon monoxide. What is the best predicted amount of nicotine? How does the predicted amount compare to the actual amount of 1.3 mg of nicotine?

5. Bacteria Growth In an experiment, the numbers of bacteria in a controlled environment are recorded over time. The table below lists the time (days) that has lapsed and the population size (thousands). What do you conclude about the relationship between time and population size? What horrible mistake would be easy to make if the analysis is conducted without a scatterplot?

Time (days)	1	3	5	7	9	11	13	15	17	19
Population (thousands)	0.1	1.8	3.2	4.0	4.6	4.8	4.7	4.2	3.4	2.2

 6. Logistic Regression with Smoking and Body Temperature Refer to Data Set 2 "Body Temperatures" in Appendix B and use the body temperatures at 8 AM on Day 1 and at 12 AM on Day 1. Let the response variable be whether the subject smokes (1 = smokes, 0 = does not smoke). Find the multiple regression equation. Use the equation to find the probability that the subject smokes, given that the 8 AM body temperature and the 12 AM body temperature are both 98.25°F. Use the P-value for the multiple regression equation to determine whether the predicted value is likely to be fairly accurate.

Cumulative Review Exercises

Effectiveness of Diet.   *Listed below are weights (lb) of subjects before and after the Zone diet. (Data are based on results from "Comparison of the Atkins, Ornish, Weight Watchers, and Zone Diets for Weight Loss and Heart Disease Risk Reduction," by Dansinger et al., Journal of the American Medical Association, Vol. 293, No. 1.) Use the data for Exercises 1–5.*

Before	183	212	177	209	155	162	167	170
After	179	198	180	208	159	155	164	166

1. Diet Clinical Trial: Statistics Find the mean and standard deviation of the "before-after" differences.

2. Diet Clinical Trial: z Score Using only the weights before the diet, identify the highest weight and convert it to a z score. In the context of these sample data, is that highest value "significantly" high? Why or why not?

3. Diet Clinical Trial: Hypothesis Test Use a 0.05 significance level to test the claim that the diet is effective.

4. Diet Clinical Trial: Confidence Interval Construct a 95% confidence interval estimate of the mean weight of subjects before the diet. Write a brief statement interpreting the confidence interval.

5. Diet Clinical Trial: Correlation Use the before/after weights listed above.

a. Test for a correlation between the before and after weights.

b. If each subject were to weigh exactly the same after the diet as before, what would be the value of the linear correlation coefficient?

c. If all subjects were to lose 5% of their weight from the diet, what would be the value of the linear correlation coefficient found from the before/after weights?

d. What do the preceding results suggest about the suitability of correlation as a tool for testing the effectiveness of the diet?

6. Birth Weights Birth weights in the United States are normally distributed with a mean of 3420 g and a standard deviation of 495 g.

a. What percentage of babies are born with a weight greater than 3500 g?

b. Find P_{10}, which is the 10th percentile.

c. The Rockland Medical Center requires special treatment for babies that are less than 2450 g (significantly underweight) or more than 4390 g (significantly overweight). What is the percentage of babies who require special treatment? Under these conditions, do many babies require special treatment?

7. Measuring Lung Volumes In a study of techniques used to measure lung volumes, physiological data were collected for 10 subjects. The values given in the accompanying table are in liters, representing the measured forced vital capacities of the 10 subjects in a sitting position and in a supine (lying) position (based on data from "Validation of Esophageal Balloon Technique at Different Lung Volumes and Postures," by Baydur et al., *Journal of Applied Physiology,* Vol. 62, No. 1). The issue we want to investigate is whether the position (sitting or supine) has an effect on the measured values.

a. If we test for a correlation between the sitting values and the supine values, will the result allow us to determine whether the position (sitting or supine) has an effect on the measured values? Why or why not?

b. Use an appropriate test for the claim that the position has no effect, so the mean difference is zero.

Subject	A	B	C	D	E	F	G	H	I	J
Sitting	4.66	5.70	5.37	3.34	3.77	7.43	4.15	6.21	5.90	5.77
Supine	4.63	6.34	5.72	3.23	3.60	6.96	3.66	5.81	5.61	5.33

8. Cell Phones and Crashes: Analyzing a News Report In an article from the Associated Press, it was reported that researchers "randomly selected 100 New York motorists who had been in an accident and 100 who had not. Of those in accidents, 13.7 percent owned a cellular phone, while just 10.6 percent of the accident-free drivers had a phone in the car." Identify the most notable feature of these results.

Technology Project

Data Set 1 "Body Data" from Appendix B includes low-density lipoprotein (LDL) and high-density lipoprotein (HDL) cholesterol measurements from 300 subjects. Download the data set (from www.TriolaStats.com) and proceed to generate a scatterplot and results from correlation and regression. Is there a linear correlation between HDL and LDL? What is the equation of the regression line? If the measurements are separated according to gender, do the results change very much? Write a brief report and include appropriate results from technology.

FROM DATA TO DECISION

Critical Thinking: Is the pain medicine Duragesic effective in reducing pain?

Listed below are measures of pain intensity before and after using the drug Duragesic (fentanyl) (based on data from Janssen Pharmaceutical Products, L.P.). The data are listed in order by row, and corresponding measures are from the same subject before and after treatment. For example, the first subject had a measure of 1.2 before treatment and a measure of 0.4 after treatment. Each pair of measurements is from one subject, and the intensity of pain was measured using the standard visual analog score. A higher score corresponds to higher pain intensity.

Pain Intensity Before Duragesic Treatment

1.2	1.3	1.5	1.6	8.0	3.4	3.5	2.8	2.6	2.2
3.0	7.1	2.3	2.1	3.4	6.4	5.0	4.2	2.8	3.9
5.2	6.9	6.9	5.0	5.5	6.0	5.5	8.6	9.4	10.0
7.6									

Pain Intensity After Duragesic Treatment

0.4	1.4	1.8	2.9	6.0	1.4	0.7	3.9	0.9	1.8
0.9	9.3	8.0	6.8	2.3	0.4	0.7	1.2	4.5	2.0
1.6	2.0	2.0	6.8	6.6	4.1	4.6	2.9	5.4	4.8
4.1									

Analyzing the Results

1. Correlation Use the given data to construct a scatterplot, then use the methods of Section 10-1 to test for a linear correlation between the pain intensity before and after treatment. If there does appear to be a linear correlation, can we conclude that the drug treatment is effective?

2. Regression Use the given data to find the equation of the regression line. Let the response (y) variable be the pain intensity after treatment. What would be the equation of the regression line for a treatment having absolutely no effect?

3. Two Independent Samples The methods of Section 9-2 can be used to test the claim that two populations have the same mean. Identify the specific claim that the treatment is effective, then use the methods of Section 9-2 to test that claim. The methods of Section 9-2 are based on the requirement that the samples are independent. Are they independent in this case?

4. Matched Pairs The methods of Section 9-3 can be used to test a claim about matched data. Identify the specific claim that the treatment is effective, then use the methods of Section 9-3 to test that claim.

5. Best Method? Which of the preceding results is best for determining whether the drug treatment is effective in reducing pain? Based on the preceding results, does the drug appear to be effective?

Cooperative Group Activities

1. In-class activity For each student in the class, measure shoe print length and height. Test for a linear correlation and identify the equation of the regression line. Measure the shoe print length of the professor and use it to estimate his or her height. How close is the estimated height to the actual height?

2. In-class activity Divide into groups of 8 to 12 people. For each group member, measure the height and also measure his or her navel height, which is the height from the floor to the navel. Is there a correlation between height and navel height? If so, find the regression equation with height expressed in terms of navel height. According to one theory, the average person's ratio of height to navel height is the golden ratio: $(1 + \sqrt{5})/2 \approx 1.6$. Does this theory appear to be reasonably accurate?

3. In-class activity Divide into groups of 8 to 12 people. For each group member, measure height and arm span. For the arm span, the subject should stand with arms extended like the wings on an airplane. Using the paired sample data, is there a correlation between height and arm span? If so, find the regression equation with height expressed in terms of arm span. Can arm span be used as a reasonably good predictor of height?

4. In-class activity Divide into groups of 8 to 12 people. For each group member, use a string and ruler to measure head circumference and forearm length. Is there a relationship between these two variables? If so, what is it?

5. In-class activity Use a ruler as a device for measuring reaction time. One person should suspend the ruler by holding it at the top while the subject holds his or her thumb and forefinger at the bottom edge ready to catch the ruler when it is released. Record the distance that the ruler falls before it is caught. Convert that distance to the time (in seconds) that it took the subject to react and catch the ruler. (If the distance is measured in inches, use $t = \sqrt{d/192}$. If the distance is measured in centimeters, use $t = \sqrt{d/487.68}$.) Test each subject once with the right hand and once with the left hand, and record the paired data. Test for a correlation. Find the equation of the regression line. Does the equation of the regression line suggest that the dominant hand has a faster reaction time?

6. In-class activity Divide into groups of 8 to 12 people. Record the pulse rate of each group member while he or she is seated. Then record the pulse rate of each group member while he or she is standing. Is there a relationship between sitting and standing pulse rate? If so, what is it?

7. In-class activity Divide into groups of three or four people. Appendix B includes many data sets not yet used in examples or exercises in this chapter. Search Appendix B for a pair of variables of interest, then investigate correlation and regression. State your conclusions and try to identify practical applications.

8. Out-of-class activity Divide into groups of three or four people. Investigate the relationship between two variables by collecting your own paired sample data and use the methods of this chapter to determine whether there is a significant linear correlation. Also identify the regression equation and describe a procedure for predicting values of one of the variables when given values of the other variable. Suggested topics:

• Is there a relationship between taste and cost of different brands of chocolate chip cookies (or colas)? Taste can be measured on some number scale, such as 1 to 10.

• Is there a relationship between salaries of professional baseball (or basketball, or football) players and their season achievements?

• Is there a relationship between student grade-point averages and the amount of television watched? If so, what is it?

11

Goodness-of-Fit and Contingency Tables

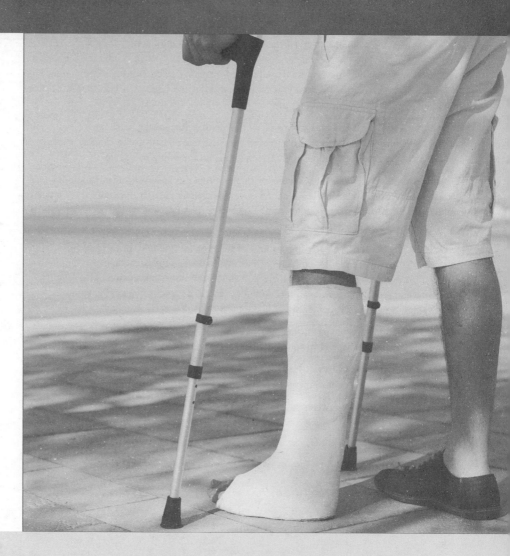

CHAPTER PROBLEM — **Which Treatment Is Best?**

The options for treating a stress fracture in a foot bone include surgery, applying a weight-bearing cast, applying a non–weight-bearing cast for six weeks, and applying a non–weight-bearing cast for less than six weeks.

Table 11-1 is a contingency table with four rows and two columns. The cells of the table contain frequency counts. The row variable identifies the treatment used for a stress fracture

in a foot bone, and the column variable identifies the outcome as a success or failure. The table is based on data from "Management of Tarsal Navicular Stress Fractures: Conservative Versus Surgical Treatment: A Meta-Analysis," by Torc et al., *American Journal of Sports Medicine,* Vol. 38, No. 5. In this chapter we will use the data in Table 11-1 to address these questions:

- Do the four different treatments have different rates of success?

- Is there a treatment that is best?

- Should surgery be recommended for treating a stress fracture in a foot bone?

TABLE 11-1 Treatments for Stress Fracture in a Foot Bone

	Success	Failure
Surgery	54	12
Weight-Bearing Cast	41	51
Non–Weight-Bearing Cast for 6 Weeks	70	3
Non–Weight-Bearing Cast for Less Than 6 Weeks	17	5

CHAPTER OBJECTIVES

Chapters 7 and 8 introduced important methods of inferential statistics, including confidence intervals for estimating population parameters (Chapter 7) and methods for testing hypotheses or claims (Chapter 8). We then considered inferences involving two populations (Chapter 9) and correlation/regression with paired data (Chapter 10). In this chapter we use statistical methods for analyzing categorical (or qualitative, or attribute) data that can be partitioned into different cells. The methods of this chapter use the same X^2 (chi-square) distribution that was introduced in Section 7-3 and again in Section 8-4. See Section 7-3 or Section 8-4 for a quick review of properties of the X^2 distribution. Here are the chapter objectives:

11-1 Goodness-of-Fit

- Use frequency counts of categorical data partitioned into different categories and determine whether the data fit some claimed distribution.

11-2 Contingency Tables

- Use categorical data summarized as frequencies in a two-way table with at least two rows and at least two columns to conduct a formal test of independence between the row variable and column variable.

- Be able to conduct a formal test of a claim that different populations have the same proportions of some characteristics.

Goodness-of-Fit

Key Concept By "goodness-of-fit" we mean that sample data consisting of observed frequency counts arranged in a single row or column (called a *one-way frequency table*) agree with some particular distribution (such as normal or uniform) being considered. We will use a hypothesis test for the claim that the observed frequency counts agree with the claimed distribution.

> **DEFINITION**
>
> A **goodness-of-fit test** is used to test the hypothesis that an observed frequency distribution fits (or conforms to) some claimed distribution.

Testing for Goodness-of-Fit

Objective

Conduct a goodness-of-fit test, which is a hypothesis test to determine whether a single row (or column) of frequency counts agrees with some specific distribution (such as uniform or normal).

Notation

O represents the *observed frequency* of an outcome, found from the sample data.
E represents the *expected frequency* of an outcome, found by assuming that the distribution is as claimed.
k represents the *number of different categories* or cells.
n represents the total *number of trials* (or the total of observed sample values).
p represents the *probability* that a sample value falls within a particular category

Requirements

1. The data have been randomly selected.

2. The sample data consist of frequency counts for each of the different categories.

3. For each category, the *expected* frequency is at least 5. (The expected frequency for a category is the frequency that would occur if the data actually have the distribution that is being claimed. There is no requirement that the *observed* frequency for each category must be at least 5.)

Null and Alternative Hypotheses

H_0: The frequency counts agree with the claimed distribution.
H_1: The frequency counts do not agree with the claimed distribution.

Test Statistic for Goodness-of-Fit Tests

$$\chi^2 = \sum \frac{(O - E)^2}{E}$$

P-values: *P*-values are typically provided by technology, or a range of *P*-values can be found from Table A-4.

Critical values:

1. Critical values are found in Table A-4 by using $k - 1$ degrees of freedom, where k is the number of categories.

2. Goodness-of-fit hypothesis tests are always *right-tailed*.

Finding Expected Frequencies

Conducting a goodness-of-fit test requires that we identify the *observed* frequencies denoted by O, then find the frequencies *expected* (denoted by E) with the claimed distribution. There are two different approaches for finding expected frequencies E:

■ **If the expected frequencies are all equal: Calculate $E = n/k$.**

■ **If the expected frequencies are not all equal: Calculate $E = np$ for each individual category.**

As good as these two preceding formulas for E might be, it is better to use an informal approach by simply asking, "How can the observed frequencies be split up among the different categories so that there is perfect agreement with the claimed distribution?" Also, note that the *observed* frequencies are all whole numbers because they represent actual counts, but the *expected* frequencies need not be whole numbers.

Examples:

a. **Equally Likely** A single die is rolled 45 times with the following results. Assuming that the die is fair and all outcomes are equally likely, find the expected frequency E for each empty cell.

Outcome	1	2	3	4	5	6
Observed Frequency O	13	6	12	9	3	2
Expected Frequency E						

With $n = 45$ outcomes and $k = 6$ categories, the expected frequency for each cell is the same: $E = n/k = 45/6 = 7.5$. If the die is fair and the outcomes are all equally likely, we expect that each outcome should occur about 7.5 times.

b. **Not Equally Likely** Using the same results from part (a), suppose that we claim that instead of being fair, the die is loaded so that the outcome of 1 occurs 50% of the time and the other five outcomes occur 10% of the time. The probabilities are listed in the second row below. Using $n = 45$ and the probabilities listed below, we find that for the first cell, $E = np = (45)(0.5) = 22.5$. Each of the other five cells will have the expected value of $E = np = (45)(0.1) = 4.5$.

Outcome	1	2	3	4	5	6
Probability	0.5	0.1	0.1	0.1	0.1	0.1
Observed Frequency O	13	6	12	9	3	2
Expected Frequency E	22.5	4.5	4.5	4.5	4.5	4.5

Measuring Disagreement with the Claimed Distribution

We know that sample frequencies typically differ somewhat from the values we theoretically expect, so we consider the key question:

Are the differences between the actual *observed* frequencies O and the theoretically *expected* frequencies E significant?

To measure the discrepancy between the O and E values, we use the test statistic given in the preceding Key Elements box. (Later we will explain how this test statistic was developed, but it has differences of $O - E$ as a key component.)

$$\chi^2 = \sum \frac{(O - E)^2}{E}$$

The χ^2 test statistic is based on differences between the observed and expected values. If the observed and expected values are *close*, the χ^2 test statistic will be small and the P-value will be large. If the observed and expected frequencies are *far apart*, the χ^2 test statistic will be large and the P-value will be small. Figure 11-1 on the next page summarizes this relationship. The hypothesis tests of this section are always right-tailed, because the critical value and critical region are located at the extreme right of the distribution. If confused, just remember this mnemonic:

"If the P is low, the null must go."

(If the P-value is small, reject the null hypothesis that the distribution is as claimed.)

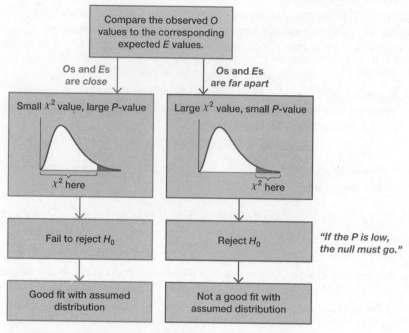

FIGURE 11-1   Relationships Among the χ^2 Test Statistic, P-Value, and Goodness-of-Fit

TABLE 11-2
Last Digits of Weights

Last Digit	Frequency
0	46
1	1
2	2
3	3
4	3
5	30
6	4
7	0
8	8
9	3

EXAMPLE 1   Last Digits of Weights

A random sample of 100 weights of Californians is obtained, and the last digits of those weights are summarized in Table 11-2 (based on data from the California Department of Public Health). When obtaining weights of subjects, it is extremely important to actually measure their weights instead of asking them to report their weights. By analyzing the *last digits* of weights, researchers can verify that they were obtained through actual measurements instead of being reported. When people report weights, they tend to round down and they often round *way* down, so a weight of 197 lb might be rounded and reported as a more desirable 170 lb. Reported weights tend to have many last digits consisting of 0 or 5. In contrast, if people are actually weighed, the weights tend to have last digits that are uniformly distributed, with 0, 1, 2, . . . , 9 all occurring with roughly the same frequencies. We could subjectively examine the frequencies in Table 11-2 to see that the digits of 0 and 5 do seem to occur much more often than the other digits, but we will proceed with a formal hypothesis test to reinforce that subjective conclusion.

Test the claim that the sample is from a population of weights in which the last digits do *not* occur with the same frequency. Based on the results, what can we conclude about the procedure used to obtain the weights?

SOLUTION

REQUIREMENT CHECK   (1) The data come from randomly selected subjects. (2) The data do consist of frequency counts, as shown in Table 11-2. (3) With 100 sample values and 10 categories that are claimed to be equally likely, each expected frequency is 10, so each expected frequency does satisfy the requirement of being a value of at least 5. All of the requirements are satisfied. ☑

The claim that the digits do not occur with the same frequency is equivalent to the claim that the relative frequencies or probabilities of the 10 cells ($p_0, p_1, \ldots, p_9$) are not all equal. (This is equivalent to testing the claim that the distribution of digits is not a uniform distribution.)

Step 1: The original claim is that the digits do not occur with the same frequency. That is, at least one of the probabilities $p_0, p_1, \ldots, p_9$ is different from the others.

Step 2: If the original claim is false, then all of the probabilities are the same. That is, $p_0 = p_1 = p_2 = p_3 = p_4 = p_5 = p_6 = p_7 = p_8 = p_9$.

Step 3: The null hypothesis must contain the condition of equality, so we have

$$H_0: p_0 = p_1 = p_2 = p_3 = p_4 = p_5 = p_6 = p_7 = p_8 = p_9$$

H_1: At least one of the probabilities is different from the others.

Step 4: No significance level was specified, so we select the common choice of $\alpha = 0.05$.

Step 5: Because we are testing a claim about the distribution of the last digits being a uniform distribution (with all of the digits having the same probability), we use the goodness-of-fit test described in this section. The χ^2 distribution is used with the test statistic given in the preceding Key Elements box.

Step 6: The observed frequencies O are listed in Table 11-2. Each corresponding expected frequency E is equal to 10 (because the 100 digits would be uniformly distributed among the 10 categories). The Excel add-in XLSTAT is used to obtain the results shown in the accompanying screen display, and Table 11-3 on the next page shows the manual computation of the χ^2 test statistic. The test statistic is $\chi^2 = 212.800$. The critical value is $\chi^2 = 16.919$ (found in Table A-4 with $\alpha = 0.05$ in the right tail and degrees of freedom equal to $k - 1 = 9$). The P-value is less than 0.0001. The test statistic and critical value are shown in Figure 11-2.

XLSTAT

Chi-square (Observed value)	212.8000
Chi-square (Critical value)	16.9190
DF	9
p-value	< 0.0001
alpha	0.05

Step 7: If we use the P-value method of testing hypotheses, we see that the P-value is small (less than 0.0001), so we reject the null hypothesis. If we use the critical value method of testing hypotheses, Figure 11-2 shows that the test statistic falls in the critical region, so there is sufficient evidence to reject the null hypothesis.

Step 8: There is sufficient evidence to support the claim that the last digits do not occur with the same relative frequency.

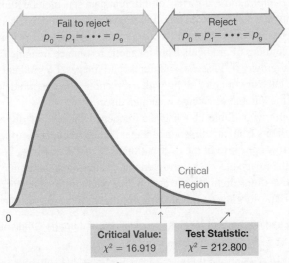

FIGURE 11-2   Test of $p_0 = p_1 = p_2 = p_3 = p_4 = p_5 = p_6 = p_7 = p_8 = p_9$

Safest Seats in a Commercial Jet

A study by aviation writer and researcher David Noland showed that sitting farther back in a commercial jet will increase your chances of surviving in the event of a crash. The study suggests that the chance of surviving is not the same for each seat, so a goodness-of-fit test would lead to rejection of the null hypothesis that every seat has the same probability of a passenger surviving. Records from the 20 commercial jet crashes that occurred since 1971 were analyzed. It was found that if you sit in business or first class, you have a 49% chance of surviving a crash; if you sit in coach over the wing or ahead of the wing, you have a 56% chance of surviving; and if you sit in the back behind the wing, you have a 69% chance of surviving.

In commenting on this study, David Noland stated that he does not seek a rear seat when he flies. He says that because the chance of a crash is so small, he doesn't worry about where he sits, but he prefers a window seat.

TABLE 11-3 Calculating the χ^2 Test Statistic for the Last Digits of Weights

Last Digit	Observed Frequency O	Expected Frequency E	$O - E$	$(O - E)^2$	$\dfrac{(O - E)^2}{E}$
0	46	10	36	1296	129.6
1	1	10	−9	81	8.1
2	2	10	−8	64	6.4
3	3	10	−7	49	4.9
4	3	10	−7	49	4.9
5	30	10	20	400	40.0
6	4	10	−6	36	3.6
7	0	10	−10	100	10.0
8	8	10	−2	4	0.4
9	3	10	−7	49	4.9

$$\chi^2 = \sum \frac{(O - E)^2}{E} = 212.8$$

INTERPRETATION

This goodness-of-fit test suggests that the last digits do not provide a good fit with the claimed uniform distribution of equally likely frequencies. Instead of actually weighing the subjects, it appears that the subjects reported their weights. In fact, the weights are from the California Health Interview Survey (CHIS), and the title of that survey indicates that subjects were interviewed, not measured. Because those weights are reported, the reliability of the data is very questionable.

Example 1 involves a situation in which the expected frequencies E for the different categories are all equal. The methods of this section can also be used when the expected frequencies are different, as in Example 2.

EXAMPLE 2   Benford's Law and Ultrasound Images

According to *Benford's law*, a variety of different data sets include numbers with leading (first) digits that follow the distribution shown in the first two rows of Table 11-4. Data sets that tend to follow Benford's law include a class of errors in clinical trials, as well as magnitudes of gradients from magnetic resonance imaging (MRI) scans, computed tomography (CT) scans, and ultrasound images. (A gradient in an image is a change in intensity or color along with a direction. The magnitude of a gradient includes only the amount of change without a direction.)

The bottom row of Table 11-4 lists the frequencies of leading digits of the magnitudes of gradients from an ultrasound image. Do the frequencies of leading digits in the bottom row appear to fit the distribution of Benford's law, as expected, or does it appear that the image has been corrupted with a substantial amount of "noise" because the leading digits do not fit the distribution of Benford's law? (There are methods for using Benford's law to enhance images that have been corrupted with noise.)

TABLE 11-4 Leading Digits of Magnitudes of Ultrasound Image Gradients

Leading Digit	1	2	3	4	5	6	7	8	9
Benford's Law: Distribution of Leading Digits	30.1%	17.6%	12.5%	9.7%	7.9%	6.7%	5.8%	5.1%	4.6%
Leading Digits of Magnitudes of Gradients in an Ultrasound Image	69	40	42	26	25	16	16	17	20

SOLUTION

REQUIREMENT CHECK (1) The sample data are randomly selected from a larger population. (2) The sample data do consist of frequency counts. (3) Each expected frequency is at least 5. The lowest expected frequency is $271 \times 0.046 = 12.466$. All of the requirements are satisfied. ✅

Step 1: The original claim is that the leading digits fit the distribution given as Benford's law. Using subscripts corresponding to the leading digits, we can express this claim as $p_1 = 0.301$ and $p_2 = 0.176$ and $p_3 = 0.125$ and ... and $p_9 = 0.046$.

Step 2: If the original claim is false, then at least one of the proportions does not have the value as claimed.

Step 3: The null hypothesis must contain the condition of equality, so we have

H_0: $p_1 = 0.301$ and $p_2 = 0.176$ and $p_3 = 0.125$ and ... and $p_9 = 0.046$.
H_1: At least one of the proportions is not equal to the given claimed value.

Step 4: The significance level is not specified, so we use the common choice of $\alpha = 0.05$.

Step 5: Because we are testing a claim that the distribution of leading digits fits the distribution given by Benford's law, we use the goodness-of-fit test described in this section. The χ^2 distribution is used with the test statistic given earlier in the preceding Key Elements box.

Step 6: Table 11-5 shows the calculations of the components of the χ^2 test statistic for the leading digits of 1 and 2. If we include all nine leading digits, we get the test statistic of $\chi^2 = 11.2792$, as shown in the accompanying TI-84 Plus calculator display. The critical value is $\chi^2 = 15.507$ (found in Table A-4 with $\alpha = 0.05$ in the right tail and degrees of freedom equal to $k - 1 = 8$). The TI-84 Plus C calculator display shows the value of the test statistic as well as the P-value of 0.186. (The entire bottom row of the display can be viewed by scrolling to the right. CNTRB is an abbreviated form of "contribution," and the values are the individual contributions to the total value of the χ^2 test statistic.)

TABLE 11-5 Calculating the χ^2 Test Statistic for Leading Digits in Table 11-4

Leading Digit	Observed Frequency O	Expected Frequency $E = np$	$O - E$	$(O - E)^2$	$\dfrac{(O - E)^2}{E}$
1	69	$271 \cdot 0.301 = 81.5710$	-12.5710	158.0300	1.9373
2	40	$271 \cdot 0.176 = 47.6960$	-7.6960	59.2284	1.2418

Step 7: The P-value of 0.186 is greater than the significance level of 0.05, so there is not sufficient evidence to reject the null hypothesis. (Also, the test statistic of $\chi^2 = 11.2792$ does not fall in the critical region bounded by the critical value of 15.507, so there is not sufficient evidence to reject the null hypothesis.)

Step 8: There is not sufficient evidence to warrant rejection of the claim that the 271 leading digits fit the distribution given by Benford's law.

INTERPRETATION

The sample of leading digits does not provide enough evidence to conclude that the Benford's law distribution is not being followed. There is not sufficient evidence to support a conclusion that the ultrasound image has been corrupted with a substantial amount of "noise."

Mendel's Data Falsified?

Because some of Mendel's data from his famous genetics experiments seemed too perfect to be true, statistician R. A. Fisher concluded that the data were probably falsified. He used a chi-square distribution to show that when a test statistic is extremely far to the left and results in a P-value very close to 1, the sample data fit the claimed distribution almost perfectly, and this is evidence that the sample data have not been randomly selected. It has been suggested that Mendel's gardener knew what results Mendel's theory predicted, and subsequently adjusted results to fit that theory.

Ira Pilgrim wrote in *The Journal of Heredity* that this use of the chi-square distribution is not appropriate. He notes that the question is not about goodness-of-fit with a particular distribution, but whether the data are from a sample that is truly random. Pilgrim used the binomial probability formula to find the probabilities of the results obtained in Mendel's experiments. Based on his results, Pilgrim concludes that "there is no reason whatever to question Mendel's honesty." It appears that Mendel's results are not too good to be true, and they could have been obtained from a truly random process.

TI-84 Plus C

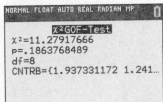

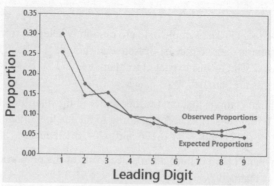

FIGURE 11-3   Observed Proportions and Proportions Expected with Benford's Law

In Figure 11-3 we use a green line to graph the expected proportions given by Benford's law (as in Table 11-4) along with a red line for the observed proportions from Table 11-4. Figure 11-3 allows us to visualize the "goodness-of-fit" between the distribution given by Benford's law and the frequencies that were observed. In Figure 11-3, the green and red lines agree reasonably well, so it appears that the observed data fit the expected values reasonably well.

Rationale for the Test Statistic   Examples 1 and 2 show that the χ^2 test statistic is a measure of the discrepancy between observed and expected frequencies. Simply summing the differences $O - E$ between observed and expected values tells us nothing, because that sum is always 0. Squaring the $O - E$ gives us a better statistic. (The reasons for squaring the $O - E$ values are essentially the same as the reasons for squaring the $x - \bar{x}$ values in the formula for standard deviation.) The value of $\Sigma(O - E)^2$ measures only the magnitude of the differences, but we need to find the magnitude of the differences relative to what was expected. We need a type of average instead of a cumulative total. This relative magnitude is found through division by the expected frequencies, as in the test statistic.

The theoretical distribution of $\Sigma(O - E)^2/E$ is a discrete distribution because the number of possible values is finite. The distribution can be approximated by a chi-square distribution, which is continuous. This approximation is generally considered acceptable, provided that all expected values E are at least 5. (There are ways of circumventing the problem of an expected frequency that is less than 5, such as combining some categories so that all expected frequencies are at least 5. Also, there are different procedures that can be used when not all expected frequencies are at least 5.)

The number of degrees of freedom reflects the fact that we can freely assign frequencies to $k - 1$ categories before the frequency for every category is determined. (Although we say that we can "freely" assign frequencies to $k - 1$ categories, we cannot have negative frequencies, nor can we have frequencies so large that their sum exceeds the total of the observed frequencies for all categories combined.)

Goodness-of-Fit Test
Access tech instructions, videos, and data sets at **www.TriolaStats.com**

11-1 Basic Skills and Concepts

Statistical Literacy and Critical Thinking

1. Hospital Cybersecurity The table below lists leading digits of 317 inter-arrival Internet traffic times for a hospital computer along with the frequencies of leading digits expected with Benford's law.

a. Identify the notation used for observed and expected values.

b. Identify the observed and expected values for the leading digit of 2.

c. Use the results from part (b) to find the contribution to the χ^2 test statistic from the category representing the leading digit of 2.

Leading Digit	1	2	3	4	5	6	7	8	9
Benford's Law	30.1%	17.6%	12.5%	9.7%	7.9%	6.7%	5.8%	5.1%	4.6%
Leading Digits of Inter-Arrival Traffic Times	76	62	29	33	19	27	28	21	22

2. Hospital Cybersecurity When using the data from Exercise 1 to test for goodness-of-fit with the distribution described by Benford's law, identify the null and alternative hypotheses.

3. Hospital Cybersecurity The accompanying Statdisk results shown in the margin are obtained from the data given in Exercise 1. What should be concluded when testing the claim that the leading digits have a distribution that fits well with Benford's law?

Test Statistic, X^2:	20.9222
Critical X^2:	15.5073
P-Value:	0.0074

4. Hospital Cybersecurity What do the results from the preceding exercises suggest about the possibility that the computer has been hacked? Is there any corrective action that should be taken?

In Exercises 5–20, conduct the hypothesis test and provide the test statistic and the P-value, and/or critical value, and state the conclusion.

5. Occupational Injuries Randomly selected non-fatal occupational injuries and illnesses are categorized according to the day of the week that they first occurred, and the results are listed below (based on data from the Bureau of Labor Statistics). Use a 0.05 significance level to test the claim that such injuries and illnesses occur with equal frequency on the different days of the week.

Day	Mon.	Tues.	Wed.	Thurs.	Fri.
Number	23	23	21	21	19

6. Deaths from Car Crashes Randomly selected deaths from car crashes were obtained, and the results are included in the table below (based on data from the Insurance Institute for Highway Safety). Use a 0.05 significance level to test the claim that car crash fatalities occur with equal frequency on the different days of the week. How might the results be explained? Why does there appear to be an exceptionally large number of car crash fatalities on Saturday?

Day	Sun.	Mon.	Tues.	Wed.	Thurs.	Fri.	Sat.
Number of Fatalities	132	98	95	98	105	133	158

7. Motorcycle Fatalities Randomly selected deaths of motorcycle riders are summarized in the table below (based on data from the Insurance Institute for Highway Safety). Use a 0.05 significance level to test the claim that such fatalities occur with equal frequency in the different months. How might the results be explained?

Month	Jan.	Feb.	March	April	May	June	July	Aug.	Sept.	Oct.	Nov.	Dec.
Number	6	8	10	16	22	28	24	28	26	14	10	8

8. Flat Tire and Missed Class A classic story involves four carpooling students who missed a test and gave as an excuse a flat tire. On the makeup test, the instructor asked the students to identify the particular tire that went flat. If they really didn't have a flat tire, would they be able to identify the same tire? One of the authors asked 56 other students to identify the tire they would select. The results are listed in the following table (except for one student who selected the spare). Use a 0.05 significance level to test the author's claim that the results fit a uniform distribution. What does the result suggest about the likelihood of four students identifying the same tire when they really didn't have a flat?

Tire	Left Front	Right Front	Left Rear	Right Rear
Number Selected	20	12	16	8

9. Baseball Player Births In his book *Outliers,* author Malcolm Gladwell argues that more baseball players have birthdates in the months immediately following July 31, because that was the age cutoff date for nonschool baseball leagues. Here is a sample of frequency counts of months of birthdates of American-born Major League Baseball players starting with January: 387, 329, 366, 344, 336, 313, 313, 503, 421, 434, 398, 371. Using a 0.05 significance level, is there sufficient evidence to warrant rejection of the claim that American-born Major League Baseball players are born in different months with the same frequency? Do the sample values appear to support Gladwell's claim?

10. Genetics The Advanced Placement Biology class at Mount Pearl Senior High School conducted genetics experiments with fruit flies, and the results in the following table are based on the results that they obtained. Use a 0.05 significance level to test the claim that the observed frequencies agree with the proportions that were expected according to principles of genetics.

Characteristic	Red Eye/ Normal Wing	Sepia Eye/ Normal Wing	Red Eye/ Vestigial Wing	Sepia Eye/ Vestigial Wing
Frequency	59	15	2	4
Expected Proportion	9/16	3/16	3/16	1/16

11. Eye Color A researcher has developed a theoretical model for predicting eye color. After examining a random sample of parents, she predicts the eye color of the first child. The table below lists the eye colors of offspring. On the basis of her theory, she predicted that 68% of the offspring would have brown eyes, 22% would have blue eyes, and 10% would have green eyes. Use a 0.05 significance level to test the claim that the actual frequencies correspond to her predicted distribution.

	Brown Eyes	Blue Eyes	Green Eyes
Frequency	128	32	6

12. Genotypes Based on the genotypes of parents, offspring are expected to have genotypes distributed in such a way that 25% have genotypes denoted by AA, 50% have genotypes denoted by Aa, and 25% have genotypes denoted by aa. When 250 offspring are obtained, it is found that 50 of them have AA genotypes, 140 have Aa genotypes, and 60 have aa genotypes. Test the claim that the observed genotype offspring frequencies fit the expected distribution of 25% for AA, 50% for Aa, and 25% for aa. Use a significance level of 0.05.

13. Bias in Clinical Trials Researchers investigated the issue of race and equality of access to clinical trials. The table on the top of the next page shows the population distribution and the numbers of participants in clinical trials involving lung cancer (based on data from "Participation in Cancer Clinical Trials," by Murthy, Krumholz, and Gross, *Journal of the American Medical Association,* Vol. 291, No. 22). Use a 0.01 significance level to test the claim that the distribution of clinical trial participants fits well with the population distribution. Is there a race/ethnic group that appears to be very underrepresented?

Race/ethnicity	White non-Hispanic	Hispanic	Black	Asian/Pacific Islander	American Indian/ Alaskan Native
Distribution of Population	75.6%	9.1%	10.8%	3.8%	0.7%
Number in Lung Cancer Clinical Trials	3855	60	316	54	12

14. Mendelian Genetics Experiments are conducted with hybrids of two types of peas. If the offspring follow Mendel's theory of inheritance, the seeds that are produced are yellow smooth, green smooth, yellow wrinkled, and green wrinkled, and they should occur in the ratio of 9:3:3:1, respectively. An experiment is designed to test Mendel's theory, with the result that the offspring seeds consist of 256 that are yellow smooth, 65 that are green smooth, 86 that are yellow wrinkled, and 12 that are green wrinkled. Use a 0.05 significance level to test the claim that the results contradict Mendel's theory.

Benford's Law. *According to Benford's law, a variety of different data sets include numbers with leading (first) digits that follow the distribution shown in the table below. In Exercises 15 and 16, test for goodness-of-fit with the distribution described by Benford's law.*

Leading Digit	1	2	3	4	5	6	7	8	9
Benford's Law: Distribution of Leading Digits	30.1%	17.6%	12.5%	9.7%	7.9%	6.7%	5.8%	5.1%	4.6%

15. CT Scan When analyzing the leading digits of the magnitudes of gradients from a CT image, the frequencies were found to be 64, 28, 93, 21, 26, 84, 12, 2, 0, and those digits correspond to the leading digits of 1, 2, 3, 4, 5, 6, 7, 8, and 9, respectively. Use a 0.01 significance level to test for goodness-of-fit with Benford's law. Do the leading digits appear to fit the distribution of Benford's law, as expected, or does it appear that the image has been corrupted because the leading digits do not fit the distribution of Benford's law? Does the conclusion change if the significance level is 0.05?

16. MRI When analyzing the leading digits of the magnitudes of gradients from an MRI (magnetic resonance image) of a patient, the frequencies were found to be 550, 45, 55, 0, 35, 0, 45, 110, and 60, and those digits correspond to the leading digits of 1, 2, 3, 4, 5, 6, 7, 8, and 9, respectively. Use a 0.01 significance level to test for goodness-of-fit with Benford's law. Do the leading digits appear to fit the distribution of Benford's law, as expected, or does it appear that the image has been corrupted because the leading digits do not fit the distribution of Benford's law?

Exercises 17 and 18 are based on data sets included in Appendix B. The complete data sets can be found at www.TriolaStats.com.

17. Admissions for Birth Data Set 3 "Births" includes the days of the weeks that prospective mothers were admitted to a hospital to give birth. A physician claims that because many births are induced or involve cesarean section, they are scheduled for days other than Saturday or Sunday, so births do not occur on the seven different days of the week with equal frequency. Use a 0.01 significance level to test that claim.

18. Discharges After Birth Data Set 3 "Births" includes the days of the weeks that newborn babies were discharged from the hospital. A hospital administrator claims that such discharges occur on the seven different days of the week with equal frequency. Use a 0.01 significance level to test that claim.

11-1 Beyond the Basics

 19. Testing Goodness-of-Fit with a Normal Distribution Refer to Data Set 1 "Body Data" in Appendix B for the heights of females.

Height (cm)	Less than 155.45	155.45 – 162.05	162.05 – 168.65	Greater than 168.65
Frequency				

a. Enter the observed frequencies in the table above.

b. Assuming a normal distribution with mean and standard deviation given by the sample mean and standard deviation, use the methods of Chapter 6 to find the probability of a randomly selected height belonging to each class.

c. Using the probabilities found in part (b), find the expected frequency for each category.

d. Use a 0.01 significance level to test the claim that the heights were randomly selected from a normally distributed population. Does the goodness-of-fit test suggest that the data are from a normally distributed population?

11-2 Contingency Tables

Key Concept We now consider methods for analyzing *contingency tables* (or two-way frequency tables), which include frequency counts for categorical data arranged in a table with at least two rows and at least two columns. In Part 1 of this section, we present a method for conducting a hypothesis test of the null hypothesis that the row and column variables are independent of each other. This test of independence is widely used in real-world applications. In Part 2, we will consider three variations of the basic method presented in Part 1: (1) test of homogeneity, (2) Fisher's exact test, and (3) McNemar's test for matched pairs.

PART 1 Basic Concepts of Testing for Independence

In this section we use standard statistical methods to analyze frequency counts in a contingency table (or two-way frequency table).

> **DEFINITION**
>
> A **contingency table** (or **two-way frequency table**) is a table consisting of frequency counts of categorical data corresponding to two different variables. (One variable is used to categorize rows, and a second variable is used to categorize columns.)

The word *contingent* has a few different meanings, one of which refers to a *dependence* on some other factor. We use the term *contingency table* because we test for *independence* between the row and column variables. We first define a *test of independence* and we provide key elements of the test in the Key Elements box that follows.

> **DEFINITION**
>
> In a **test of independence,** we test the null hypothesis that in a contingency table, the row and column variables are independent. (That is, there is no dependency between the row variable and the column variable.)

KEY ELEMENTS

Contingency Table

Objective

Conduct a hypothesis test of independence between the row variable and column variable in a contingency table.

Notation

O represents the *observed frequency* in a cell of a contingency table.
E represents the *expected frequency* in a cell, found by assuming that the row and column variables are independent.
r represents the number of rows in a contingency table (not including labels or row totals).
c represents the number of columns in a contingency table (not including labels or columns totals).

Requirements

1. The sample data are randomly selected.
2. The sample data are represented as frequency counts in a two-way table.
3. For every cell in the contingency table, the expected frequency E is at least 5. (There is no requirement that every *observed* frequency must be at least 5.)

Null and Alternative Hypotheses

The null and alternative hypotheses are as follows:

H_0: The row and column variables are independent.

H_1: The row and column variables are dependent.

Test Statistic for a Test of Independence

$$\chi^2 = \sum \frac{(O - E)^2}{E}$$

where O is the observed frequency in a cell and E is the expected frequency in a cell that is found by evaluating

$$E = \frac{(\text{row total})(\text{column total})}{(\text{grand total})}$$

P-values

P-values are typically provided by technology, or a range of P-values can be found from Table A-4.

Critical values

1. The critical values are found in Table A-4 using

$$\text{Degrees of freedom } = (r - 1)(c - 1)$$

where r is the number of rows and c is the number of columns.

2. Tests of independence with a contingency table are always *right-tailed*.

The distribution of the test statistic χ^2 can be approximated by the chi-square distribution, provided that all cells have expected frequencies that are at least 5. The number of degrees of freedom $(r - 1)(c - 1)$ reflects the fact that because we know the total of all frequencies in a contingency table, we can freely assign frequencies to only $r - 1$ rows and $c - 1$ columns before the frequency for every cell is determined. However, we cannot have negative frequencies or frequencies so large that any row (or column) sum exceeds the total of the observed frequencies for that row (or column).

Observed and Expected Frequencies The test statistic allows us to measure the amount of disagreement between the frequencies actually observed and those that we would theoretically expect when the two variables are independent. Large values of the χ^2 test statistic are in the rightmost region of the chi-square distribution, and they reflect significant differences between observed and expected frequencies. As in Section 11-1, if observed and expected frequencies are close, the χ^2 test statistic will be small and the P-value will be large. If observed and expected frequencies are far apart, the χ^2 test statistic will be large and the P-value will be small. These relationships are summarized and illustrated in Figure 11-4.

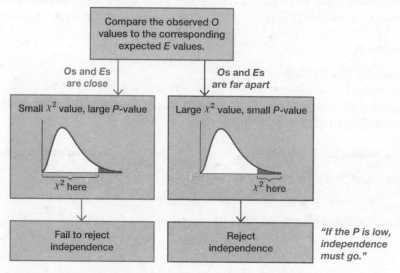

FIGURE 11-4   Relationships Among Key Components in a Test of Independence

Finding Expected Values E

An individual expected frequency E for a cell can be found by simply multiplying the total of the row frequencies by the total of the column frequencies, then dividing by the grand total of all frequencies, as shown in Example 1.

$$E = \frac{(\text{row total})(\text{column total})}{(\text{grand total})}$$

EXAMPLE 1 **Finding Expected Frequency**

Table 11-1 from the Chapter Problem (reproduced on the top of the next page) is a contingency table with four rows and two columns. The cells of the table contain frequency counts. The frequency counts are the observed values and the expected values are shown in parentheses. The row variable identifies the treatment used for a stress fracture in a foot bone, and the column variable identifies the outcome as a success or failure (based on data from "Surgery Unfounded for Tarsal Navicular Stress Fracture," by Bruce Jancin, *Internal Medicine News,* Vol. 42, No. 14). Refer to Table 11-1 and find the expected frequency for the cell in the first row and first column, where the observed frequency is 54.

SOLUTION

TABLE 11-1 Treatments for Stress Fracture in a Foot Bone

	Success	Failure
Surgery	54 ($E = 47.478$)	12 ($E = 18.522$)
Weight-Bearing Cast	41 ($E = 66.182$)	51 ($E = 25.818$)
Non–Weight-Bearing Cast for 6 Weeks	70 ($E = 52.514$)	3 ($E = 20.486$)
Non–Weight-Bearing Cast for Less Than 6 Weeks	17 ($E = 15.826$)	5 ($E = 6.174$)

The first cell lies in the first row (with a total row frequency of 66) and the first column (with total column frequency of 182). The "grand total" is the sum of all frequencies in the table, which is 253. The expected frequency of the first cell is

$$E = \frac{(\text{row total})(\text{column total})}{(\text{grand total})} = \frac{(66)(182)}{253} = 47.478$$

INTERPRETATION

We know that the first cell has an *observed* frequency of $O = 54$ and an *expected* frequency of $E = 47.478$. We can interpret the expected value by stating that if we assume that success is independent of the treatment, then we expect to find that 47.478 of the subjects would be treated with surgery and that treatment would be successful. There is a discrepancy between $O = 54$ and $E = 47.478$, and such discrepancies are key components of the test statistic that is a collective measure of the overall disagreement between the observed frequencies and the frequencies expected with independence between the row and column variables.

Example 2 illustrates the procedure for conducting a hypothesis test of independence between the row and column variables in a contingency table.

 EXAMPLE 2 **Does the Choice of Treatment for a Fracture Affect Success?**

Use the data from Table 11-1 with a 0.05 significance level to test the claim that success of the treatment is independent of the type of treatment. What does the result indicate about the increasing trend to use surgery?

SOLUTION

REQUIREMENT CHECK (1) On the basis of the study description, we will treat the subjects as being randomly selected and randomly assigned to the different treatment groups. (2) The results are expressed as frequency counts in Table 11-1. (3) The expected frequencies are all at least 5. (The lowest expected frequency is 6.174.) The requirements are satisfied. ☑
The null hypothesis and alternative hypothesis are as follows:

H_0: Success is independent of the treatment.

H_1: Success and the treatment are dependent.

The significance level is $\alpha = 0.05$.
Because the data in Table 11-1 are in the form of a contingency table, we use the χ^2 distribution with this test statistic:

continued

$$\chi^2 = \sum \frac{(O-E)^2}{E} = \frac{(54-47.478)^2}{47.478} + \cdots + \frac{(5-6.174)^2}{6.174}$$

$$= 58.393$$

XLSTAT

Chi-square (Observed value)	58.3933
Chi-square (Critical value)	7.8147
DF	3
p-value	< 0.0001
alpha	0.05

***P*-Value from Technology** If using technology, results typically include the χ^2 test statistic and the *P*-value. For example, see the accompanying XLSTAT display showing the test statistic is $\chi^2 = 58.393$ and the *P*-value is less than 0.0001.

***P*-Value from Table A-4** If using Table A-4 instead of technology, first find the number of degrees of freedom: $(r-1)(c-1) = (4-1)(2-1) = 3$ degrees of freedom. Because the test statistic of $\chi^2 = 58.393$ exceeds the highest value (12.838) in Table A-4 for the row corresponding to 3 degrees of freedom, we know that *P*-value < 0.005.

Because the *P*-value is less than the significance level of 0.05, we reject the null hypothesis of independence between success and treatment.

Critical Value If using the critical value method of hypothesis testing, the critical value of $\chi^2 = 7.815$ is found from Table A-4 with $\alpha = 0.05$ in the right tail and the number of degrees of freedom given by $(r-1)(c-1) = (4-1)(2-1) = 3$. The test statistic and critical value are shown in Figure 11-5. Because the test statistic does fall within the critical region, we reject the null hypothesis of independence between success and treatment.

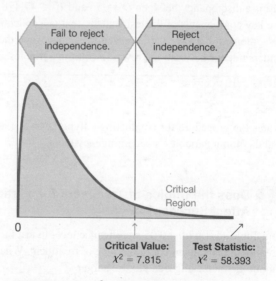

FIGURE 11-5 χ^2 **Test of Independence**

INTERPRETATION

It appears that success is dependent on the treatment. Although the results of this test do not tell us which treatment is best, we can calculate from Table 11-1 that the success rates are 81.8%, 44.6%, 95.9%, and 77.3%. This suggests that the best treatment is to use a non–weight-bearing cast for 6 weeks. These results suggest that the increasing use of surgery is a treatment strategy that is not supported by the evidence.

Rationale for Expected Frequencies *E* To better understand expected frequencies, pretend that we know only the row and column totals in Table 11-1. Let's assume that the row and column variables are independent and that 1 of the 253 study subjects is randomly selected. The probability of getting someone counted in the first cell of Table 11-1 is found as follows:

$$P(\text{surgery}) = 66/253 \quad \text{and} \quad P(\text{success}) = 182/253$$

If the row and column variables are independent as we are assuming, we can use the multiplication rule for independent events (see Section 4-2) as follows:

$$P(\text{surgery treatment } and \text{ success}) = \frac{66}{253} \cdot \frac{182}{253} = 0.187661$$

With a probability of 0.187661 for the first cell, we expect that among 253 subjects, there are $253 \cdot 0.187661 = 47.478$ subjects in the first cell. If we generalize these calculations, we get the following:

$$\text{Expected frequency } E = (\text{grand total}) \cdot \frac{(\text{row total})}{(\text{grand total})} \cdot \frac{(\text{column total})}{(\text{grand total})}$$

This expression can be simplified to

$$E = \frac{(\text{row total})(\text{column total})}{(\text{grand total})}$$

PART 2   Test of Homogeneity, Fisher's Exact Test, and McNemar's Test for Matched Pairs

Test of Homogeneity

In Part 1 of this section, we focused on the test of *independence* between the row and column variables in a contingency table. In Part 1, the sample data are from one population, and individual sample results are categorized with the row and column variables. In a *chi-square test of homogeneity,* we have samples randomly selected from different populations, and we want to determine whether those populations have the same proportions of some characteristic being considered. (The word *homogeneous* means "having the same quality," and in this context, we are testing to determine whether the proportions are the same.) Section 9-1 presented a procedure for testing a claim about *two* populations with categorical data having two possible outcomes, but a chi-square test of homogeneity allows us to use two or more populations with outcomes from several categories.

> **DEFINITION**
>
> A **chi-square test of homogeneity** is a test of the claim that *different populations* have the same proportions of some characteristics.

Sampling from Different Populations In a typical test of independence as described in Part 1 of this section, sample subjects are randomly selected from one population (such as people treated for stress fractures in a foot bone) and values of different variables are observed (such as success/failure for people receiving different treatments). In a typical chi-square test of homogeneity, subjects are randomly selected from the different populations separately.

Procedure In conducting a test of homogeneity, we can use the same notation, requirements, test statistic, critical value, and procedures given in the Key Elements box from Part 1 on page 531 of this section, with this exception: Instead of testing the null hypothesis of independence between the row and column variables, we test the null hypothesis that *the different populations have the same proportion of some characteristic.*

Fisher's Exact Test

The procedures for testing hypotheses with contingency tables have the requirement that every cell must have an expected frequency of at least 5. This requirement is necessary for the χ^2 distribution to be a suitable approximation to the exact distribution of the χ^2 test statistic. *Fisher's exact test* is often used for a 2×2 contingency table with one or more expected frequencies that are below 5. Fisher's exact test provides an *exact P*-value and does not require an approximation technique. Because the calculations are quite complex, it's a good idea to use technology when using Fisher's exact test. Statdisk, Minitab, XLSTAT, and StatCrunch all have the ability to perform Fisher's exact test.

EXAMPLE 3   **Does Yawning Cause Others to Yawn?**

The *MythBusters* show on the Discovery Channel tested the theory that when someone yawns, others are more likely to yawn. The results are summarized in Table 11-6. The methods of Part 1 in this section should not be used because one of the cells has an expected frequency of 4.480, which violates the requirement that every cell must have an expected frequency E of at least 5. Using Fisher's exact test results in a *P*-value of 0.513, so there is not sufficient evidence to support the myth that people exposed to yawning actually yawn more than those not exposed to yawning. (For testing the claim of no difference, the *P*-value is 1.000, indicating that there is not a significant difference between the two groups.)

TABLE 11-6 Yawning Theory Experiment

		Subject Exposed to Yawning?	
		Yes	No
Did Subject Yawn?	Yes	10	4
	No	24	12

McNemar's Test for Matched Pairs

The methods in Part 1 of this section are based on independent data. For 2×2 tables consisting of frequency counts that result from matched pairs, the frequency counts within each matched pair are not independent and, for such cases, we can use McNemar's test of the null hypothesis that the frequencies from the discordant (different) categories occur in the same proportion.

Table 11-7 shows a general format for summarizing results from data consisting of frequency counts from matched pairs. Table 11-7 refers to two different treatments (such as two different eye drop solutions) applied to two different parts of each subject (such as left eye and right eye). We should be careful when reading a table such as Table 11-7. If $a = 100$, then 100 subjects were cured with both treatments. If $b = 50$ in Table 11-7, then each of 50 subjects had no cure with treatment X but they were each cured with treatment Y. The total number of subjects is $a + b + c + d$, and each of those subjects yields results from each of two parts of a matched pair. Remember, the entries in Table 11-7 are frequency counts of subjects, not the total number of individual components in the matched pairs. If 500 people have each eye treated with two different ointments, the value of $a + b + c + d$ is 500 (the number of subjects), not 1000 (the number of treated eyes).

TABLE 11-7 2 × 2 Table with Frequency Counts from Matched Pairs

		Treatment X	
		Cured	Not Cured
Treatment Y	Cured	a	b
	Not Cured	c	d

McNemar's test requires that for a table such as Table 11-7, the frequencies are such that $b + c \geq 10$. The test is a right-tailed chi-square test with the following test statistic:

$$\chi^2 = \frac{(|b - c| - 1)^2}{b + c}$$

P-values are typically provided by software, and critical values can be found in Table A-4 using 1 degree of freedom. *Caution:* When applying McNemar's test, be careful to use only the two frequency counts from *discordant* (different) pairs, such as the frequency b in Table 11-7 (with different pairs of cured/not cured) and frequency c in Table 11-7 (with different pairs of not cured/cured).

EXAMPLE 4   Are Hip Protectors Effective?

A randomized controlled trial was designed to test the effectiveness of hip protectors in preventing hip fractures in the elderly. Nursing home residents each wore protection on one hip, but not the other. Results are summarized in Table 11-8 (based on data from *Journal of the American Medical Association*). McNemar's test can be used to test the null hypothesis that the following two proportions are the same:

- The proportion of subjects with no hip fracture on the protected hip and a hip fracture on the unprotected hip.

- The proportion of subjects with a hip fracture on the protected hip and no hip fracture on the unprotected hip.

Using the discordant (different) pairs with the general format from Table 11-7, we have $b = 10$ and $c = 15$, so the test statistic is calculated as follows:

$$\chi^2 = \frac{(|b - c| - 1)^2}{b + c} = \frac{(|10 - 15| - 1)^2}{10 + 15} = 0.640$$

With a 0.05 significance level and degrees of freedom given by df $= 1$, we refer to Table A-4 to find the critical value of $\chi^2 = 3.841$ for this right-tailed test. The test statistic of $\chi^2 = 0.640$ does not exceed the critical value of $\chi^2 = 3.841$, so we fail to reject the null hypothesis. (Also, the *P*-value is 0.424, which is greater than 0.05, indicating that we fail to reject the null hypothesis.) The proportion of hip fractures with the protectors worn is not significantly different from the proportion of hip fractures without the protectors worn. The hip protectors do not appear to be effective in preventing hip fractures.

TABLE 11-8 Randomized Controlled Trial of Hip Protectors

		No Hip Protector Worn	
		No Hip Fracture	Hip Fracture
Hip Protector Worn	No Hip Fracture	309	10
	Hip Fracture	15	2

TECH CENTER

Contingency Tables

Access tech instructions, videos, and data sets at **www.TriolaStats.com**

11-2   Basic Skills and Concepts

Statistical Literacy and Critical Thinking

1. Handedness and Cell Phone Use The accompanying table is from a study conducted with the stated objective of addressing cell phone safety by understanding why we use a particular ear for cell phone use. (See "Hemispheric Dominance and Cell Phone Use," by Seidman, Siegel, Shah, and Bowyer, *JAMA Otolaryngology—Head & Neck Surgery,* Vol. 139, No. 5.) The goal was to determine whether the ear choice is associated with auditory or language brain hemispheric dominance. Assume that we want to test the claim that handedness and cell phone ear preference are independent of each other.

a. Use the data in the table to find the expected value for the cell that has an observed frequency of 3. Round the result to three decimal places.

b. What does the expected value indicate about the requirements for the hypothesis test?

Ear Preference for Cell Phone Use

	Right Ear	Left Ear	No Preference
Right-Handed	436	166	40
Left-Handed	16	50	3

2. Hypotheses Refer to the data given in Exercise 1 and assume that the requirements are all satisfied and we want to conduct a hypothesis test of independence using the methods of this section. Identify the null and alternative hypotheses.

3. Hypothesis Test The accompanying TI-83/84 Plus calculator display results from the hypothesis test described in Exercise 1. Assume that the hypothesis test requirements are all satisfied. Identify the test statistic and the *P*-value (expressed in standard form and rounded to three decimal places), and then state the conclusion about the null hypothesis.

4. Right-Tailed, Left-Tailed, Two-Tailed Is the hypothesis test described in Exercise 1 right-tailed, left-tailed, or two-tailed? Explain your choice.

In Exercises 5–20, test the given claim.

5. Splint or Surgery? A randomized controlled trial was designed to compare the effectiveness of splinting versus surgery in the treatment of carpal tunnel syndrome. Results are given in the table below (based on data from "Splinting vs. Surgery in the Treatment of Carpal Tunnel Syndrome," by Gerritsen et al., *Journal of the American Medical Association,* Vol. 288, No. 10). The results are based on evaluations made one year after the treatment. Using a 0.01 significance level, test the claim that success is independent of the type of treatment. What do the results suggest about treating carpal tunnel syndrome?

	Successful Treatment	Unsuccessful Treatment
Splint Treatment	60	23
Surgery Treatment	67	6

6. Texting and Drinking In a study of high school students at least 16 years of age, researchers obtained survey results summarized in the accompanying table (based on data from "Texting While Driving and Other Risky Motor Vehicle Behaviors Among U. S. High School Students," by O'Malley, Shults, and Eaton, *Pediatrics,* Vol. 131, No. 6). Use a 0.05 significance level to test the claim of independence between texting while driving and driving when drinking alcohol. Are those two risky behaviors independent of each other?

	Drove When Drinking Alcohol?	
	Yes	No
Texted While Driving	731	3054
No Texting While Driving	156	4564

7. Tooth Fillings and Adverse Health Conditions The table below shows results from a study in which some dental patients were treated with amalgam restorations and others were treated with composite restorations that do not contain mercury (based on data from "Neuropsychological and Renal Effects of Dental Amalgam in Children," by Bellinger et al., *Journal of the American Medical Association,* Vol. 295, No. 15). Use a 0.05 significance level to test for independence between the type of restoration and the presence of any adverse health conditions. Do amalgam restorations appear to affect health conditions?

	Amalgam	Composite
Adverse Health Condition Reported	135	145
No Adverse Health Condition Reported	132	122

8. Tooth Fillings and Sensory Disorders In recent years, concerns have been expressed about adverse health effects from amalgam dental restorations, which include mercury. The table below shows results from a study in which some patients were treated with amalgam restorations and others were treated with composite restorations that do not contain mercury (based on data from "Neuropsychological and Renal Effects of Dental Amalgam in Children," by Bellinger et al., *Journal of the American Medical Association,* Vol. 295, No. 15). Use a 0.05 significance level to test for independence between the type of restoration and sensory disorders. Do amalgam restorations appear to affect sensory disorders?

	Amalgam	Composite
Sensory Disorder	36	28
No Sensory Disorder	231	239

9. Can Dogs Detect Cancer? An experiment was conducted to test the ability of dogs to detect bladder cancer. Dogs were tested with urine samples from bladder cancer patients and people in a control group who did not have bladder cancer. Results are given in the table below (based on data from the *New York Times*). Using a 0.01 significance level, test the claim that the source of the sample (healthy or with bladder cancer) is independent of the dog's selections. What do the results suggest about the ability of dogs to detect bladder cancer? If the dogs did significantly better than random guessing, did they do well enough to be used for accurate diagnoses?

	Sample from Subject With Bladder Cancer	Sample from Subject Without Bladder Cancer
Dog Identified Subject as Cancerous	22	32
Dog Did Not Identify Subject as Cancerous	32	282

10. Lie Detector The table below includes results from polygraph (lie detector) experiments conducted by researchers Charles R. Honts (Boise State University) and Gordon H. Barland (Department of Defense Polygraph Institute). In each case, it was known if the subject lied or did not lie, so the table indicates when the polygraph test was correct. Use a 0.05 significance level to test the claim that whether a subject lies is independent of the polygraph test indication. Do the results suggest that polygraphs are effective in distinguishing between truths and lies?

	Did the Subject Actually Lie?	
	No (Did Not Lie)	Yes (Lied)
Polygraph Test Indicated that the Subject Lied.	15	42
Polygraph Test Indicated that the Subject Did Not Lie.	32	9

11. Clinical Trial of Chantix Chantix (varenicline) is a drug used as an aid for those who want to stop smoking. The adverse reaction of nausea has been studied in clinical trials, and the table below summarizes results (based on data from Pfizer). Use a 0.01 significance level to test the

continued

claim that nausea is independent of whether the subject took a placebo or Chantix. Does nausea appear to be a concern for those using Chantix?

	Placebo	Chantix
Nausea	10	30
No Nausea	795	791

12. Is the Vaccine Effective? In a *USA Today* article about an experimental vaccine for children, the following statement was presented: "In a trial involving 1602 children, only 14 (1%) of the 1070 who received the vaccine developed the flu, compared with 95 (18%) of the 532 who got a placebo." The data are shown in the table below. Use a 0.05 significance level to test for independence between the variable of treatment (vaccine or placebo) and the variable representing flu (developed flu, did not develop flu). Does the vaccine appear to be effective?

	Developed Flu?	
	Yes	No
Vaccine Treatment	14	1056
Placebo	95	437

13. Texting and Seat Belt Use In a study of high school students at least 16 years of age, researchers obtained survey results summarized in the accompanying table (based on data from "Texting While Driving and Other Risky Motor Vehicle Behaviors Among U. S. High School Students," by O'Malley, Shults, and Eaton, *Pediatrics,* Vol. 131, No. 6). Use a 0.05 significance level to test the claim of independence between texting while driving and irregular seat belt use. Are those two risky behaviors independent of each other?

	Irregular Seat Belt Use?	
	Yes	No
Texted While Driving	1737	2048
No Texting While Driving	1945	2775

14. Unusual Patient Deaths Alert nurses at the Veteran's Affairs Medical Center in Northampton, Massachusetts, noticed an unusually high number of deaths at times when another nurse, Kristen Gilbert, was working. Those same nurses later noticed missing supplies of the drug epinephrine, which is a synthetic adrenaline that stimulates the heart. Kristen Gilbert was arrested and charged with four counts of murder and two counts of attempted murder. When seeking a grand jury indictment, prosecutors provided a key piece of evidence consisting of the table below. Use a 0.01 significance level to test the defense claim that deaths on shifts are independent of whether Gilbert was working. What does the result suggest about the guilt or innocence of Gilbert?

	Shifts With a Death	Shifts Without a Death
Gilbert Was Working	40	217
Gilbert Was Not Working	34	1350

15. Clinical Trial of Campral Campral (acamprosate) is a drug used to help patients continue their abstinence from the use of alcohol. Adverse reactions of Campral have been studied in clinical trials, and the table below summarizes results for digestive system effects among patients from different treatment groups (based on data from Forest Pharmaceuticals, Inc.). Use a 0.01 significance level to test the claim that experiencing an adverse reaction in the digestive system is independent of the treatment group. Does Campral treatment appear to have an effect on the digestive system?

	Placebo	Campral 1332 mg	Campral 1998 mg
Adverse Effect on Digestive System	344	89	8
No Effect on Digestive System	1362	774	71

16. Clinical Trial of Lipitor Lipitor is the trade name of the drug atorvastatin, which is used to reduce cholesterol in patients. This is the largest-selling drug in the world, with $13 billion in sales for a recent year. Adverse reactions have been studied in clinical trials, and the table below summarizes results for infections in patients from different treatment groups (based on data from Parke-Davis). Use a 0.05 significance level to test the claim that getting an infection is independent of the treatment. Does the atorvastatin treatment appear to have an effect on infections?

	Placebo	Atorvastatin 10 mg	Atorvastatin 40 mg	Atorvastatin 80 mg
Infection	27	89	8	7
No Infection	243	774	71	87

17. Is Seat Belt Use Independent of Cigarette Smoking? A study of seat belt users and nonusers yielded the randomly selected sample data summarized in the given table (based on data from "What Kinds of People Do Not Use Seat Belts?" by Helsing and Comstock, *American Journal of Public Health,* Vol. 67, No. 11). Test the claim that the amount of smoking is independent of seat belt use. A plausible theory is that people who smoke more are less concerned about their health and safety and are therefore less inclined to wear seat belts. Is this theory supported by the sample data?

	Number of Cigarettes Smoked per Day			
	0	1–14	15–34	35 and over
Wear Seat Belts	175	20	42	6
Don't Wear Seat Belts	149	17	41	9

18. Clinical Trial of Echinacea In a clinical trial of the effectiveness of echinacea for preventing colds, the results in the table below were obtained (based on data from "An Evaluation of *Echinacea Angustifolia* in Experimental Rhinovirus Infections," by Turner et al., *New England Journal of Medicine,* Vol. 353, No. 4). Use a 0.05 significance level to test the claim that getting a cold is independent of the treatment group. What do the results suggest about the effectiveness of echinacea as a prevention against colds?

	Treatment Group		
	Placebo	Echinacea: 20% Extract	Echinacea: 60% Extract
Got a Cold	88	48	42
Did Not Get a Cold	15	4	10

19. Injuries and Motorcycle Helmet Color A case-control (or retrospective) study was conducted to investigate a relationship between the colors of helmets worn by motorcycle drivers and whether they are injured or killed in a crash. Results are given in the table below (based on data from "Motorcycle Rider Conspicuity and Crash Related Injury: Case-Control Study," by Wells et al., *BMJ USA,* Vol. 4). Test the claim that injuries are independent of helmet color. Should motorcycle drivers choose helmets with a particular color? If so, which color appears best?

	Color of Helmet				
	Black	White	Yellow/Orange	Red	Blue
Controls (not injured)	491	377	31	170	55
Cases (injured or killed)	213	112	8	70	26

20. Baseball Player Births In his book *Outliers,* author Malcolm Gladwell argues that more American-born baseball players have birthdates in the months immediately following July 31 because that was the age cutoff date for nonschool baseball leagues. The table below lists months of births for a sample of American-born baseball players and foreign-born baseball players. Using a 0.05 significance level, is there sufficient evidence to warrant rejection of the

continued

claim that months of births of baseball players are independent of whether they are born in America? Do the data appear to support Gladwell's claim?

	Jan.	Feb.	March	April	May	June	July	Aug.	Sept.	Oct.	Nov.	Dec.
Born in America	387	329	366	344	336	313	313	503	421	434	398	371
Foreign Born	101	82	85	82	94	83	59	91	70	100	103	82

11-2   Beyond the Basics

21. Equivalent Tests A χ^2 test involving a 2×2 table is equivalent to the test for the difference between two proportions, as described in Section 9-1. Using the claim and table in Exercise 5 "Splint or Surgery?" verify that the χ^2 test statistic and the z test statistic (found from the test of equality of two proportions) are related as follows: $z^2 = \chi^2$. Also show that the critical values have that same relationship.

22. Using Yates's Correction for Continuity The chi-square distribution is continuous, whereas the test statistic used in this section is discrete. Some statisticians use *Yates's correction for continuity* in cells with an expected frequency of less than 10 or in all cells of a contingency table with two rows and two columns. With Yates's correction, we replace

$$\sum \frac{(O - E)^2}{E} \quad \text{with} \quad \sum \frac{(|O - E| - 0.5)^2}{E}$$

Given the contingency table in Exercise 5 "Splint or Surgery?" find the value of the χ^2 test statistic using Yates's correction in all cells. What effect does Yates's correction have?

Chapter Quick Quiz

Exercises 1–5 refer to the sample data in the following table, which summarizes the last digits of the heights (cm) of 300 randomly selected subjects (from Data Set 1 "Body Data"). Assume that we want to use a 0.05 significance level to test the claim that the data are from a population having the property that the last digits are all equally likely.

Last Digit	0	1	2	3	4	5	6	7	8	9
Frequency	30	35	24	25	35	36	37	27	27	24

1. What are the null and alternative hypotheses corresponding to the stated claim?

2. When testing the claim in Exercise 1, what are the observed and expected frequencies for the last digit of 7?

3. Is the hypothesis test left-tailed, right-tailed, or two-tailed?

4. If using a 0.05 significance level to test the stated claim, find the number of degrees of freedom.

5. Given that the *P*-value for the hypothesis test is 0.501, what do you conclude? Does it appear that the heights were obtained through measurement or that the subjects reported their heights?

Questions 6–10 refer to the sample data in the following table, which describes the fate of the passengers and crew aboard the Titanic when it sank on April 15, 1912. Assume that the data are a sample from a large population and we want to use a 0.05 significance level to test the claim that surviving is independent of whether the person is a man, woman, boy, or girl.

	Men	Women	Boys	Girls
Survived	332	318	29	27
Died	1360	104	35	18

6. Identify the null and alternative hypotheses corresponding to the stated claim.

7. What distribution is used to test the stated claim (normal, t, F, chi-square, uniform)?

8. Is the hypothesis test left-tailed, right-tailed, or two-tailed?

9. Find the number of degrees of freedom.

10. Given that the P-value for the hypothesis test is 0.0000 when rounded to four decimal places, what do you conclude? What do the results indicate about the rule that women and children should be the first to be saved?

Review Exercises

1. Weather-Related Deaths For a recent year, the numbers of weather-related deaths for each month are 28, 17, 12, 24, 88, 61, 104, 32, 20, 13, 26, 25 (listed in order beginning with January). Use a 0.01 significance level to test the claim that weather-related deaths occur in the different months with the same frequency. Provide an explanation for the result.

2. Norovirus on Cruise Ships The *Queen Elizabeth II* cruise ship and Royal Caribbean's *Freedom of the Seas* cruise ship both experienced outbreaks of norovirus infection within two months of each other. Results are shown in the table below. Use a 0.05 significance level to test the claim that getting norovirus infection is independent of the ship. Based on these results, does it appear that an outbreak of norovirus infection has the same effect on different ships?

	Norovirus Infection	No Norovirus Infection
Queen Elizabeth II	276	1376
Freedom of the Seas	338	3485

3. NYC Homicides For a recent year, the following are the numbers of homicides that occurred each month in New York City, starting with January: 38, 30, 46, 40, 46, 49, 47, 50, 50, 42, 37, and 37. Use a 0.05 significance level to test the claim that homicides in New York City are equally likely for each of the 12 months. Is there sufficient evidence to support the police commissioner's claim that homicides occur more often in the summer when the weather is warmer?

4. Genetics and Handedness In a study of left-handedness as a possible inherited trait, the data in the table below were obtained (based on data from "Why Are Some People Left-Handed? An Evolutionary Perspective," by Laurens and Faurie, *Philosophical Transactions,* Vol. 364). Use a 0.01 significance level to test the claim that left-handedness is independent of parental handedness. What do the results suggest about the inheritability of left-handedness?

Parental Handedness	Offspring Left-Handed?	
Father/Mother	Yes	No
Right/Right	5360	50,928
Right/Left	767	2736
Left/Right	741	3667
Left/Left	94	289

5. Car Crashes and Age Brackets Among drivers who have had a car crash in the last year, 88 are randomly selected and categorized by age, with the results listed in the accompanying table (based on data from the Insurance Information Institute). If all ages have the same crash rate, we would expect (because of the age distribution of licensed drivers) the given categories to have 16%, 44%, 27%, and 13% of the subjects, respectively. At the 0.05 significance level, test the claim that the distribution of crashes conforms to the distribution of ages. Does any age group appear to have a disproportionate number of crashes?

Age	Under 25	25–44	45–64	Over 64
Drivers	36	21	12	19

Cumulative Review Exercises

1. ICU Patients Listed below are the ages of randomly selected patients in intensive care units (ICUs) (based on data from "A Multifaceted Intervention for Quality Improvement in a Network of Intensive Care Units," by Scales et al., *Journal of the American Medical Association,* Vol. 305, No. 4). Find the mean, median, standard deviation, and variance. Based on the results, is an age of 16 years *significantly low*? Why or why not?

$$38 \quad 64 \quad 35 \quad 67 \quad 42 \quad 29 \quad 68 \quad 62 \quad 74 \quad 58$$

2. ICU Patients Use the sample of ages from Exercise 1 to construct a 95% confidence interval estimate of the mean age of the population of ICU patients. Do the confidence interval limits contain the value of 65.0 years that was found from a sample of 9269 ICU patients?

3. Bicycle Helmets A study was conducted of 531 persons injured in bicycle crashes, and randomly selected sample results are summarized in the accompanying table (based on results from "A Case-Control Study of the Effectiveness of Bicycle Safety Helmets in Preventing Facial Injury," by Thompson et al., *American Journal of Public Health,* Vol. 80, No. 12). Use a 0.05 significance level to test the claim that wearing a helmet has no effect on whether facial injuries are received. Based on these results, does a helmet seem to be effective in helping to prevent facial injuries in a crash?

	Helmet Worn	No Helmet
Facial Injuries Received	30	182
All Injuries Nonfacial	83	236

4. Bicycle Helmets Use the data in the table from Cumulative Review Exercise 3 and assume that random selections are made from the 531 people included in the study.

a. Find the probability that if 1 of the 531 subjects is randomly selected, the result is someone who had only nonfacial injuries or was someone who wore a helmet.

b. Find the probability that if two *different* subjects are randomly selected, they are both subjects who wore a helmet.

c. Find the probability that if a subject is randomly selected, the result is someone who did not wear a helmet.

5. Forward Grip Reach and Ergonomics When designing instrument controls, car dashboards, and aircraft cockpits, we must consider the forward grip reach of women. Women have normally distributed forward grip reaches with a mean of 686 mm and a standard deviation of 34 mm (based on anthropometric survey data from Gordon, Churchill, et al.).

a. If a car dashboard is positioned so that it can be reached by 95% of women, what is the shortest forward grip reach that can access the dashboard?

b. If a car dashboard is positioned so that it can be reached by women with a grip reach greater than 650 mm, what percentage of women cannot reach the dashboard? Is that percentage too high?

c. Find the probability that 16 randomly selected women have forward grip reaches with a mean greater than 680 mm. Does this result have any effect on the design?

6. Systolic BP and Waist The table below lists systolic blood pressures (BP) measurements (mm Hg) and waist (cm) of randomly selected females from Data Set 1 "Body Data" in Appendix B. Identify the analysis that should be conducted, then conduct that analysis.

Systolic BP	100	134	138	114	110	100
Waist	120.4	120.3	103.5	89.7	115.3	75.5

Technology Project

Use any software package or calculator capable of generating equally likely random digits between 0 and 9 inclusive. Generate 5000 digits and record the results in the accompanying table. Use a 0.05 significance level to test the claim that the sample digits come from a population with a uniform distribution with all digits being equally likely. Does the random number generator appear to be working as it should?

Digit	0	1	2	3	4	5	6	7.	8	9
Frequency										

FROM DATA TO DECISION

Critical Thinking: Determining Whether a Vaccine Is Effective

The largest public health experiment involved 401,974 children who were randomly assigned to two groups. In one group, 201,229 children were given a placebo. In the other group, 200,745 children were treated with the Salk vaccine designed to prevent polio. Among the children in the placebo group, 115 developed polio, and among the children in the Salk vaccine treatment group, 33 developed polio.

Analyzing the Results

a. The experiment was a "double blind" experiment. What does that mean?

b. Informally compare the results. Does it appear that the Salk vaccine is effective? Why or why not?

c. Use the methods of Section 9-1 to determine whether there is sufficient evidence to support a claim that the Salk vaccine is effective. Does it appear that the Salk vaccine is effective? Why or why not?

d. Use the methods of Section 11-2 to determine whether the treatment (vaccine or placebo) is independent of developing polio.

e. Compare the results from parts (c) and (d).

Cooperative Group Activities

1. Out-of-class activity Divide into groups of four or five students. Each group member should survey at least 15 male students and 15 female students at the same college by asking this question: If you were to make up an absence excuse of a flat tire, which tire would you say went flat if the instructor asked? (See Exercise 8 in Section 11-1.) Ask the subject to write the responses on an index card, and also record the gender of the subject and whether the subject wrote with the right or left hand. Use the methods of this chapter to analyze the data collected. Include these claims:

• The four possible choices for a flat tire are selected with equal frequency.

• The tire identified as being flat is independent of the gender of the subject.

• The tire identified as being flat is independent of whether the subject is right- or left-handed.

• Gender is independent of whether the subject is right- or left-handed.

2. Out-of-class activity Divide into groups of four or five students. Each group member should select about 15 other students and first ask them to "randomly" select four digits each. After the four digits have been recorded, ask each subject to write the last four digits of his or her Social Security number (for security, write these digits in any order). Take the "random" sample results of individual digits and mix them into one big sample, then mix the individual Social Security digits into a second big sample. Using the "random" sample set, test the claim

continued

that students select digits randomly. Then use the Social Security digits to test the claim that they come from a population of random digits. Compare the results. Does it appear that students can randomly select digits? Are they likely to select any digits more often than others? Are they likely to select any digits less often than others? Do the last digits of Social Security numbers appear to be randomly selected?

3. In-class activity Divide into groups of three or four students. Each group should be given a die along with the instruction that it should be tested for "fairness." Is the die fair or is it biased? Describe the analysis and results.

4. Out-of-class activity Divide into groups of two or three students. The analysis of last digits of data can sometimes reveal whether values are the results of actual measurements or whether they are reported estimates. Find the numbers of active physicians in each state, then analyze the last digits to determine whether those numbers appear to be actual counts or whether they appear to be reported estimates.

5. Out-of-class activity Divide into groups of four or five students. Example 2 in Section 11-1 noted that according to Benford's law, a variety of different data sets include numbers with leading (first) digits that follow the distribution shown in the table below. Collect original data and use the methods of Section 11-1 to support or refute the claim that the data conform reasonably well to Benford's law. Here are some suggestions: (1) leading digits of the numbers of active physicians in each of the states; (2) leading digits of smartphone passcodes; (3) leading digits of the numbers of Facebook friends.

Leading Digit	1	2	3	4	5	6	7	8	9
Benford's Law	30.1%	17.6%	12.5%	9.7%	7.9%	6.7%	5.8%	5.1%	4.6%

12 Analysis of Variance

12-1 One-Way ANOVA

12-2 Two-Way ANOVA

CHAPTER PROBLEM — **Does Exposure to Lead Affect IQ Scores of Children?**

An important environment/health study involved children who lived within 7 km (about 4 miles) of a large ore smelter in El Paso, Texas. A smelter is used to melt the ore in order to separate the metals in it. Because the smelter emitted lead pollution, there was concern that these children would somehow suffer. The focus of this Chapter Problem is to investigate the possible effect of lead exposure on "performance" IQ scores

as measured by the Wechsler intelligence scale. (A full IQ score is a combination of a performance IQ score and a verbal IQ score. The performance test includes components such as picture analysis, picture arrangement, and matching patterns.)

Data from the study are included in Data Set 8 "IQ and Lead" in Appendix B. Based on measured blood lead levels, the children were partitioned into a low lead level group, a

547

TABLE 12-1 Performance IQ Scores of Children

						Low Blood Lead Level									
85	90	107	85	100	97	101	64	111	100	76	136	100	90	135	104
149	99	107	99	113	104	101	111	118	99	122	87	118	113	128	121
111	104	51	100	113	82	146	107	83	108	93	114	113	94	106	92
79	129	114	99	110	90	85	94	127	101	99	113	80	115	85	112
112	92	97	97	91	105	84	95	108	118	118	86	89	100		

						Medium Blood Lead Level									
78	97	107	80	90	83	101	121	108	100	110	111	97	51	94	80
101	92	100	77	108	85										

						High Blood Lead Level									
93	100	97	79	97	71	111	99	85	99	97	111	104	93	90	107
108	78	95	78	86											

medium lead level group, or a high lead level group. (See Data Set 8 for the specific blood lead level cutoff values.) The performance IQ scores are included in Table 12-1 (based on data from "Neuropsychological Dysfunction in Children with Chronic Low-Level Lead Absorption," by P. J. Landrigan, R. H. Whitworth, R. W. Baloh, N. W. Staehling, W. F. Barthel, and B. F. Rosenblum, *Lancet*, Vol. 1, Issue 7909).

Before jumping into the application of a particular statistical method, we should first explore the data. Sample statistics are included in the table below. Also refer to the following boxplots of the three sets of performance IQ scores. Informal and subjective comparisons show that the low group has a mean that is somewhat higher than the means of the medium and high groups. The boxplots all overlap, so differences do not appear to be dramatic. But we need more formal methods that allow us to recognize any significant differences. We could use the methods of Section 9-2 to compare means from samples collected from two different populations, but here we need to compare means from samples collected from *three* different populations. When we have samples from three or more populations, we can test for equality of the population means by using the method of *analysis of variance*, to be introduced in Section 12-1. In Section 12-1, we will use analysis of variance to test the claim that the three samples are from populations with the same mean.

	Low Blood Lead Level	Medium Blood Lead Level	High Blood Lead Level
Sample Size n	78	22	21
$\bar{x}$	102.7	94.1	94.2
s	16.8	15.5	11.4
Distribution	Approximately normal	Approximately normal	Approximately normal
Outliers	Potential low outlier of 51 and high outliers of 146 and 149, but they are not very far from the other data values.	None	None

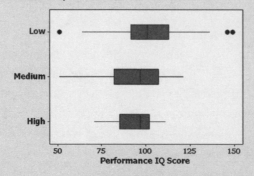

Minitab Boxplots of Performance IQ Scores

CHAPTER OBJECTIVES

Section 9-2 includes methods for testing equality of means from *two* independent populations, but this chapter presents a method for testing equality of *three or more* population means. Here are the chapter objectives:

 One-Way ANOVA

- Apply the method of one-way analysis of variance to conduct a hypothesis test of equality of three or more population means. The focus of this section is the interpretation of results from technology.

 Two-Way ANOVA

- Analyze sample data from populations separated into categories using two characteristics (or factors), such as gender and eye color.

- Apply the method of two-way analysis of variance to the following: (1) test for an *interaction* between two factors, (2) test for an effect from the *row* factor, and (3) test for an effect from the *column* factor. The focus of this section is the interpretation of results from technology.

12-1   One-Way ANOVA

Key Concept In this section we introduce the method of *one-way analysis of variance,* which is used for tests of hypotheses that three or more populations have means that are all equal, as in $H_0: \mu_1 = \mu_2 = \mu_3$. Because the calculations are very complicated, we emphasize the interpretation of results obtained by using technology.

F Distribution

The analysis of variance (ANOVA) methods of this chapter require the *F* distribution, which was first introduced in Section 9-4. In Section 9-4 we noted that the *F* distribution has the following properties (see Figure 12-1):

There is a different *F* distribution for each different pair of degrees of freedom for numerator and denominator.

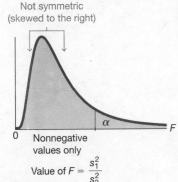

Not symmetric (skewed to the right)

Nonnegative values only

Value of $F = \dfrac{s_1^2}{s_2^2}$

FIGURE 12-1 *F* Distribution

1. The *F* distribution is not symmetric. It is skewed right.

2. Values of a variable with the *F* distribution cannot be negative.

3. The exact shape of the *F* distribution depends on the two different degrees of freedom.

PART 1   Basics of One-Way Analysis of Variance

When testing for equality of three or more population means, use the method of one-way analysis of variance.

> **DEFINITION**
>
> **One-way analysis of variance (ANOVA)** is a method of testing the equality of three or more population means by analyzing sample variances. One-way analysis of variance is used with data categorized with *one* **factor** (or **treatment**), so there is one characteristic used to separate the sample data into the different categories.

The term *treatment* is used because early applications of analysis of variance involved agricultural experiments in which different plots of farmland were treated with different fertilizers, seed types, insecticides, and so on. Table 12-1 uses the one "treatment" (or factor) of blood lead level. That factor has three different categories: low, medium, and high blood lead levels (as defined in Data Set 8 in Appendix B).

KEY ELEMENTS

One-Way Analysis of Variance for Testing Equality of Three or More Population Means

Objective

Use samples from three or more different populations to test a claim that the populations all have the same mean.

Requirements

1. The populations have distributions that are approximately normal. (This is a loose requirement, because the method works well unless a population has a distribution that is very far from normal. If a population does have a distribution that is far from normal, use the Kruskal-Wallis test described in Section 13-5.)

2. The populations have the same variance σ^2 (or standard deviation σ). This is a loose requirement, because the method works well unless the population variances differ by large amounts. Statistician George E. P. Box showed that as long as the sample sizes are equal (or nearly equal), the largest variance can be up to nine times the smallest variance and the results of ANOVA will continue to be essentially reliable.

3. The samples are simple random samples of quantitative data.

4. The samples are independent of each other. (The samples are not matched or paired in any way.)

5. The different samples are from populations that are categorized in only one way.

Procedure for Testing $H_0: \mu_1 = \mu_2 = \mu_3 = \cdots = \mu_k$

1. Use technology to obtain results that include the test statistic and *P*-value.

2. Identify the *P*-value from the display. (The ANOVA test is right-tailed because only large values of the test statistic cause us to reject equality of the population means.)

3. Form a conclusion based on these criteria that use the significance level α:

   - **Reject:** If the *P*-value $\leq \alpha$, reject the null hypothesis of equal means and conclude that at least one of the population means is different from the others.

   - **Fail to Reject:** If the *P*-value $> \alpha$, fail to reject the null hypothesis of equal means.

Because the calculations required for one-way analysis of variance are messy, we recommend using technology with this study strategy:

1. Understand that a small *P*-value (such as 0.05 or less) leads to rejection of the null hypothesis of equal means. ("If the *P* is low, the null must go.") With a large *P*-value (such as greater than 0.05), fail to reject the null hypothesis of equal means.

2. Develop an understanding of the underlying rationale by studying the examples in this section.

 EXAMPLE 1 **Lead and Performance IQ Scores**

Use the performance IQ scores listed in Table 12-1 and a significance level of $\alpha = 0.05$ to test the claim that the three samples come from populations with means that are all equal.

SOLUTION

REQUIREMENT CHECK (1) Based on the three samples listed in Table 12-1, the three populations appear to have distributions that are approximately normal, as indicated by normal quantile plots. (2) The three samples in Table 12-1 have standard deviations that are not dramatically different, so the three population variances appear to be about the same. (3) On the basis of the study design, we can treat the samples as simple random samples. (4) The samples are independent of each other; the performance IQ scores are not matched in any way. (5) The three samples are from populations categorized according to the single factor of lead level (low, medium, high). The requirements are satisfied. ☑

The null hypothesis and the alternative hypothesis are as follows:

$$H_0: \mu_1 = \mu_2 = \mu_3$$

H_1: At least one of the means is different from the others

The significance level is $\alpha = 0.05$.

Step 1: Use technology to obtain ANOVA results, such as one of those shown in the following seven displays.

Statdisk

Source:	DF:	SS:	MS:	Test Stat, F:	Critical F:	P-Value:
Treatment:	2	2022.729906	1011.364953	4.071122	3.073087	0.01951
Error:	118	29314.046953	248.424127			
Total:	120	31336.77686				

Minitab

One-way ANOVA: Low, Medium, High

Source	DF	SS	MS	F	P
Factor	2	2023	1011	4.07	0.020
Error	118	29314	248		
Total	120	31337			

S = 15.76   R-Sq = 6.45%   R-Sq(adj) = 4.87%

TI-83 / 84 Plus

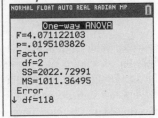

continued

Excel

ANOVA

Source of Variation	SS	df	MS	F	P-value	F crit
Between Groups	2022.729906	2	1011.364953	4.071122103	0.019510383	3.073090341
Within Groups	29314.04695	118	248.4241267			
Total	31336.77686	120				

StatCrunch

ANOVA table

Source	df	SS	MS	F-Stat	P-value
Treatments	2	2022.7299	1011.3649	4.071122	0.0195
Error	118	29314.047	248.42413		
Total	120	31336.777			

SPSS

	Sum of Squares	df	Mean Square	F	Sig.
Between Groups	2022.730	2	1011.365	4.071	.020
Within Groups	29314.047	118	248.424		
Total	31336.777	120			

JMP

Source	DF	Sum of Squares	Mean Square	F Ratio
Model	2	2022.730	1011.36	4.0711
Error	118	29314.047	248.42	Prob > F
C. Total	120	31336.777		0.0195*

Step 2: In addition to the test statistic of $F = 4.0711$, the displays all show that the P-value is 0.020 when rounded.

Step 3: Because the P-value of 0.020 is less than the significance level of $\alpha = 0.05$, we reject the null hypothesis of equal means. (If the P is low, the null must go.)

INTERPRETATION

There is sufficient evidence to warrant rejection of the claim that the three samples come from populations with means that are all equal. Using the samples of measurements listed in Table 12-1, we conclude that those values come from populations having means that are not all the same. On the basis of this ANOVA test, we cannot conclude that any particular mean is different from the others, but we can informally note that the sample mean for the low blood lead group is higher than the means for the medium and high blood lead groups. It appears that greater blood lead levels are associated with lower performance IQ scores.

CAUTION When we conclude that there is sufficient evidence to reject the claim of equal population means, we cannot conclude from ANOVA that any particular mean is different from the others. (There are several other methods that can be used to identify the specific means that are different, and some of them are discussed in Part 2 of this section.)

How Is the *P*-Value Related to the Test Statistic? *Larger* values of the test statistic result in *smaller* P-values, so the ANOVA test is right-tailed. Figure 12-2 shows the relationship between the F test statistic and the P-value. Assuming that the populations have the same variance σ^2 (as required for the test), the F test statistic is the ratio of these two estimates of σ^2: (1) variation *between* samples (based on variation among sample means); and (2) variation *within* samples (based on the sample variances).

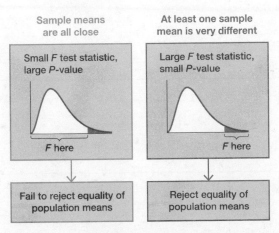

FIGURE 12-2   **Relationship Between the *F* Test Statistic and the *P*-Value**

Test Statistic for One-Way ANOVA

$$F = \frac{\text{variance between samples}}{\text{variance within samples}}$$

The numerator of the *F* test statistic measures variation between sample means. The estimate of variance in the denominator depends only on the sample variances and is not affected by differences among the sample means. Consequently, sample means that are close in value to each other result in a small *F* test statistic and a large *P*-value, so we conclude that there are no significant differences among the sample means. Sample means that are very far apart in value result in a large *F* test statistic and a small *P*-value, so we reject the claim of equal means.

Why Not Just Test Two Samples at a Time? If we want to test for equality among three or more population means, why do we need a new procedure when we can test for equality of two means using the methods presented in Section 9-2? For example, if we want to use the sample data from Table 12-1 to test the claim that the three populations have the same mean, why not simply pair them off and test two at a time by testing H_0: $\mu_1 = \mu_2$, H_0: $\mu_2 = \mu_3$, and H_0: $\mu_1 = \mu_3$? For the data in Table 12-1, the approach of testing equality of two means at a time requires three different hypothesis tests. If we use a 0.05 significance level for each of those three hypothesis tests, the actual overall confidence level could be as low as 0.95^3 (or 0.857). In general, as we increase the number of individual tests of significance, we increase the risk of finding a difference by chance alone (instead of a real difference in the means). The risk of a type I error—finding a difference in one of the pairs when no such difference actually exists—is far too high. The method of analysis of variance helps us avoid that particular pitfall (rejecting a true null hypothesis) by using *one test* for equality of several means, instead of several tests that each compare two means at a time.

CAUTION When testing for equality of three or more populations, use analysis of variance. (Using multiple hypothesis tests with two samples at a time could adversely affect the confidence level.)

PART 2 Calculations and Identifying Means That Are Different

Calculating the Test Statistic *F* with Equal Sample Sizes *n*

Table 12-2 on the next page can be very helpful in understanding the methods of ANOVA. In Table 12-2, compare Data Set A to Data Set B to see that Data Set A is

TABLE 12-2 Effect of a Mean on the F Test Statistic

Add 10 to data in Sample 1

Data Set A			Data Set B		
Sample 1	Sample 2	Sample 3	Sample 1	Sample 2	Sample 3
7	6	4	17	6	4
3	5	7	13	5	7
6	5	6	16	5	6
6	8	7	16	8	7
$n_1 = 4$	$n_2 = 4$	$n_3 = 4$	$n_1 = 4$	$n_2 = 4$	$n_3 = 4$
$\bar{x}_1 = 5.5$	$\bar{x}_2 = 6.0$	$\bar{x}_3 = 6.0$	$\bar{x}_1 = 15.5$	$\bar{x}_2 = 6.0$	$\bar{x}_3 = 6.0$
$s_1^2 = 3.0$	$s_2^2 = 2.0$	$s_3^2 = 2.0$	$s_1^2 = 3.0$	$s_2^2 = 2.0$	$s_3^2 = 2.0$

	Data Set A			Data Set B	
Step 1: Variance *between* samples	$ns_{\bar{x}}^2 = 4(0.0833) = 0.3332$			$ns_{\bar{x}}^2 = 4(30.0833) = 120.3332$	
Step 2: Variance *within* samples	$s_p^2 = \dfrac{3.0 + 2.0 + 2.0}{3} = 2.3333$			$s_p^2 = \dfrac{3.0 + 2.0 + 2.0}{3} = 2.3333$	
Step 3: F test statistic	$F = \dfrac{ns_{\bar{x}}^2}{s_p^2} = \dfrac{0.3332}{2.3333} = 0.1428$			$F = \dfrac{ns_{\bar{x}}^2}{s_p^2} = \dfrac{120.3332}{2.3333} = 51.5721$	
P-value	P-value $= 0.8688$			P-value $= 0.0000118$	

the same as Data Set B with this notable exception: The Sample 1 values each differ by 10. If the data sets all have the same sample size (as in $n = 4$ for Table 12-2), the following calculations aren't too difficult, as shown here.

Step 1: Find the Variance Between Samples

Calculate the variance *between* samples by evaluating $ns_{\bar{x}}^2$ where $s_{\bar{x}}^2$ is the variance of the sample means and n is the size of each of the samples. That is, consider the sample means to be an ordinary set of values and calculate the variance. (From the central limit theorem, $\sigma_{\bar{x}} = \sigma/\sqrt{n}$ can be solved for σ to get $\sigma = \sqrt{n} \cdot \sigma_{\bar{x}}$, so that we can estimate σ^2 with $ns_{\bar{x}}^2$.) For example, the sample means for Data Set A in Table 12-2 are 5.5, 6.0, and 6.0, and these three values have a variance of $s_{\bar{x}}^2 = 0.0833$, so that

$$\text{variance between samples} = ns_{\bar{x}}^2 = 4(0.0833) = 0.3332$$

Step 2: Find the Variance Within Samples

Estimate the variance *within* samples by calculating s_p^2, which is the pooled variance obtained by finding the mean of the sample variances. The sample variances in Table 12-2 are 3.0, 2.0, and 2.0, so that

$$\text{variance within samples} = s_p^2 = \frac{3.0 + 2.0 + 2.0}{3} = 2.3333$$

Step 3: Calculate the Test Statistic

Evaluate the F test statistic as follows:

$$F = \frac{\text{variance between samples}}{\text{variance within samples}} = \frac{ns_{\bar{x}}^2}{s_p^2} = \frac{0.3332}{2.3333} = 0.1428$$

Finding the Critical Value

The critical value of F is found by assuming a right-tailed test because large values of F correspond to significant differences among means. With k samples each having n values, the numbers of degrees of freedom are as follows.

Degrees of Freedom (using k = number of samples and n = sample size)

$$\text{Numerator degrees of freedom} = k - 1$$

$$\text{Denominator degrees of freedom} = k(n - 1)$$

For Data Set A in Table 12-2, $k = 3$ and $n = 4$, so the degrees of freedom are 2 for the numerator and $3(4 - 1) = 9$ for the denominator. With $\alpha = 0.05$, 2 degrees of freedom for the numerator, and 9 degrees of freedom for the denominator, the critical F value from Table A-5 is 4.2565. If we were to use the critical value method of hypothesis testing with Data Set A in Table 12-2, we would see that this right-tailed test has a test statistic of $F = 0.1428$ and a critical value of $F = 4.2565$, so the test statistic is not in the critical region. We therefore fail to reject the null hypothesis of equal means.

Understanding the Effect of a Mean on the F Test Statistic To really understand how the method of analysis of variance works, consider Data Set A and Data Set B in Table 12-2 and note the following.

- The three samples in Data Set A are identical to the three samples in Data Set B, except for this: Each value in Sample 1 of Data Set B is 10 more than the corresponding value in Data Set A.

- Adding 10 to each data value in the first sample of Data Set A has a significant effect on the test statistic, with F changing from 0.1428 to 51.5721.

- Adding 10 to each data value in the first sample of Data Set A has a dramatic effect on the P-value, which changes from 0.8688 (not significant) to 0.0000118 (significant).

- The three sample *means* in Data Set A (5.5, 6.0, 6.0) are very close, but the sample means in Data Set B (15.5, 6.0, 6.0) are not close.

- The three sample variances in Data Set A are identical to those in Data Set B.

- The *variance between samples* in Data Set A is 0.3332, but for Data Set B it is 120.3332 (indicating that the sample means in B are farther apart).

- The *variance within samples* is 2.3333 in both Data Set A and Data Set B, because the variance *within* a sample isn't affected when we add a constant to every sample value. *The change in the F test statistic and the P-value is attributable only to the change in $\bar{x}_1$.* This illustrates the key point underlying the method of one-way analysis of variance:

> **The F test statistic is very sensitive to sample *means*, even though it is obtained through two different estimates of the common population *variance*.**

Calculations with Unequal Sample Sizes

While the calculations for cases with equal sample sizes are somewhat reasonable, they become much more complicated when the sample sizes are not all the same, but the same basic reasoning applies. Instead of providing the relevant messy formulas required for cases with unequal sample sizes, we wisely and conveniently assume that technology should be used to obtain the *P*-value for the analysis of variance. We become unencumbered by complex computations and we can focus on checking requirements and interpreting results.

We calculate an *F* test statistic that is the ratio of two different estimates of the common population variance σ^2. With unequal sample sizes, we must use *weighted* measures that take the sample sizes into account. The test statistic is essentially the same as the one given earlier, and its interpretation is also the same as described earlier.

Designing Experiments

With one-way (or single-factor) analysis of variance, we use one factor as the basis for partitioning the data into different categories. If we conclude that the differences among the means are significant, we can't be absolutely sure that the differences can be explained by the factor being used. It is possible that the variation of some other unknown factor is responsible. One way to reduce the effect of the extraneous factors is to design the experiment so that it has a **completely randomized design,** in which each sample value is given the same chance of belonging to the different factor groups. For example, you might assign subjects to two different treatment groups and a third placebo group through a process of random selection equivalent to picking slips of paper from a bowl. Another way to reduce the effect of extraneous factors is to use a **rigorously controlled design,** in which sample values are carefully chosen so that all other factors have no variability. In general, good results require that the experiment be carefully designed and executed.

Identifying Which Means Are Different

After conducting an analysis of variance test, we might conclude that there is sufficient evidence to reject a claim of equal population means, but we cannot conclude from ANOVA that any *particular* means are different from the others. There are several formal and informal procedures that can be used to identify the specific means that are different. Here are two *informal* methods for comparing means:

- Construct boxplots of the different samples and examine any overlap to see if one or more of the boxplots is very different from the others.

- Construct confidence interval estimates of the means for each of the different samples, then compare those confidence intervals to see if one or more of them does not overlap with the others.

There are several formal procedures for identifying which means are different. Some of the tests, called **range tests,** allow us to identify subsets of means that are not significantly different from each other. Other tests, called **multiple comparison tests,** use pairs of means, but they make adjustments to overcome the problem of having a confidence level that increases as the number of individual tests increases. There is no consensus on which test is best, but some of the more common tests are the Duncan test, Student-Newman-Keuls test (or SNK test), Tukey test (or Tukey honestly significant difference test), Scheffé test, Dunnett test, least significant difference test, and the Bonferroni test. Let's consider the Bonferroni test to see one example of a multiple comparison test. Here is the procedure.

Bonferroni Multiple Comparison Test

Step 1: Do a separate *t* test for each pair of samples, but make the adjustments described in the following steps.

Step 2: For an estimate of the variance σ^2 that is common to all of the involved populations, use the value of MS(error), which uses all of the available sample data. The value of MS(error) is typically obtained when conducting the analysis of variance test. Using the value of MS(error), calculate the value of the test statistic t, as shown below. The particular test statistic calculated below is based on the choice of Sample 1 and Sample 2; change the subscripts and use another pair of samples until all of the different possible pairs of samples have been tested.

$$t = \frac{\bar{x}_1 - \bar{x}_2}{\sqrt{\text{MS}(\text{error}) \cdot \left(\frac{1}{n_1} + \frac{1}{n_2}\right)}}$$

Step 3: After calculating the value of the test statistic t for a particular pair of samples, find either the critical t value or the P-value, but make the following adjustment so that the overall significance level does not increase.

P-Value: Use the test statistic t with df $= N - k$, where N is the total number of sample values and k is the number of samples, and find the P-value using technology or Table A-3, but adjust the P-value by multiplying it by the number of different possible pairings of two samples. (For example, with three samples, there are three different possible pairings, so adjust the P-value by multiplying it by 3.)

Critical Value: When finding the critical value, adjust the significance level α by dividing it by the number of different possible pairings of two samples. (For example, with three samples, there are three different possible pairings, so adjust the significance level by dividing it by 3.)

Note that in Step 3 of the preceding Bonferroni procedure, either an individual test is conducted with a much lower significance level or the P-value is greatly increased. Rejection of equality of means therefore requires differences that are much farther apart. This adjustment in Step 3 compensates for the fact that we are doing several tests instead of only one test.

EXAMPLE 2 Bonferroni Test

Example 1 in this section used analysis of variance with the sample data in Table 12-1. We concluded that there is sufficient evidence to warrant rejection of the claim of equal means. Use the Bonferroni test with a 0.05 significance level to identify which mean is different from the others.

SOLUTION

The Bonferroni test requires a separate t test for each of three different possible pair of samples. Here are the null hypotheses to be tested:

$$H_0: \mu_1 = \mu_2 \qquad H_0: \mu_1 = \mu_3 \qquad H_0: \mu_2 = \mu_3$$

We begin with $H_0: \mu_1 = \mu_2$. Using the sample data given in Table 12-1 and carrying some extra decimal places for greater accuracy in the calculations, we have $n_1 = 78$ and $\bar{x}_1 = 102.705128$. Also, $n_2 = 22$ and $\bar{x}_2 = 94.136364$. From the technology results shown in Example 1 we also know that MS(error) = 248.424127.

continued

We now evaluate the test statistic using the unrounded sample means:

$$t = \frac{\bar{x}_1 - \bar{x}_2}{\sqrt{MS(error) \cdot \left(\frac{1}{n_1} + \frac{1}{n_2}\right)}}$$

$$= \frac{102.705128 - 94.136364}{\sqrt{248.424127 \cdot \left(\frac{1}{78} + \frac{1}{22}\right)}} = 2.252$$

The number of degrees of freedom is df $= N - k = 121 - 3 = 118$. ($N = 121$ because there are 121 different sample values in all three samples combined, and $k = 3$ because there are three different samples.) With a test statistic of $t = 2.252$ and with df $= 118$, the two-tailed P-value is 0.026172, but we adjust this P-value by multiplying it by 3 (the number of different possible pairs of samples) to get a final P-value of 0.078516, or 0.079 when rounded. Because this P-value is not small (less than 0.05), we fail to reject the null hypothesis. It appears that Samples 1 and 2 do not have significantly different means.

Instead of continuing with separate hypothesis tests for the other two pairings, see the SPSS display showing all of the Bonferroni test results. In these results, low lead levels are represented by 1, medium levels are represented by 2, and high levels are represented by 3. (The first row of numerical results corresponds to the results found here; see the value of 0.079, which was previously calculated.) The display shows that the pairing of low/high yields a P-value of 0.090, so there is not a significant difference between the means from the low and high blood lead levels. Also, the SPSS display shows that the pairing of medium/high yields a P-value of 1.000, so there is not a significant difference between the means from the medium and high blood lead levels.

SPSS Bonferroni Results

(I) Level	(J) Level	Mean Difference (I-J)	Std. Error	Sig.	95% Confidence Interval	
					Lower Bound	Upper Bound
1.00	2.00	8.56876	3.80486	.079	-.6717	17.8092
	3.00	8.51465	3.87487	.090	-.8958	17.9251
2.00	1.00	-8.56876	3.80486	.079	-17.8092	.6717
	3.00	-.05411	4.80851	1.000	-11.7320	11.6238
3.00	1.00	-8.51465	3.87487	.090	-17.9251	.8958
	2.00	.05411	4.80851	1.000	-11.6238	11.7320

INTERPRETATION

Although the analysis of variance test tells us that at least one of the means is different from the others, the Bonferroni test results do not identify any one particular sample mean that is significantly different from the others. In the original article discussing these results, the authors state that "our findings indicate that a chronic absorption of particulate lead . . . may result in subtle but statistically significant impairment in the non-verbal cognitive and perceptual motor skills measured by the performance scale of the Wechsler intelligence tests." That statement confirms these results: From analysis of variance we know that at least one mean is different from the others, but the Bonferroni test failed to identify any one particular mean as being significantly different [although the sample means of 102.7 (low blood lead level), 94.1 (medium blood lead level), and 94.2 (high blood lead level) suggest that medium and high blood lead levels seem to be associated with lower mean performance IQ scores than the low blood level group].

TECH CENTER

One-Way Analysis of Variance
Access tech instructions, videos, and data sets at www.TriolaStats.com

12-1 Basic Skills and Concepts

Statistical Literacy and Critical Thinking

In Exercises 1–4, use the following listed chest deceleration measurements (in g, where g is the force of gravity) from samples of small, midsize, and large cars. (The data are from the National Highway Traffic Safety Administration.) Also shown are the SPSS results for analysis of variance. Assume that we plan to use a 0.05 significance level to test the claim that the different size categories have the same mean chest deceleration in the standard crash test.

Chest Deceleration Measurements (g) from a Standard Crash Test

Small	44	39	37	54	39	44	42
Midsize	36	53	43	42	52	49	41
Large	32	45	41	38	37	38	33

SPSS

	Sum of Squares	df	Mean Square	F	Sig.
Between Groups	200.857	2	100.429	3.288	.061
Within Groups	549.714	18	30.540		
Total	750.571	20			

1. ANOVA

a. What characteristic of the data above indicates that we should use one-way analysis of variance?

b. If the objective is to test the claim that the three size categories have the same *mean* chest deceleration, why is the method referred to as analysis of *variance*?

2. Why Not Test Two at a Time? Refer to the sample data given in Exercise 1. If we want to test for equality of the three means, why don't we use three separate hypothesis tests for $\mu_1 = \mu_2$, $\mu_1 = \mu_3$, and $\mu_2 = \mu_3$?

3. Test Statistic What is the value of the test statistic? What distribution is used with the test statistic?

4. P-Value If we use a 0.05 significance level in analysis of variance with the sample data given in Exercise 1, what is the P-value? What should we conclude?

In Exercises 5–16, use analysis of variance for the indicated test.

5. Lead and Verbal IQ Scores Example 1 used measured *performance* IQ scores for three different blood lead levels. If we use the same three categories of blood lead levels with measured *verbal* IQ scores, we get the accompanying Minitab display. (The data are listed in Data Set 8 "IQ and Lead" in Appendix B.) Using a 0.05 significance level, test the claim that the three categories of blood lead level have the same mean verbal IQ score. Does exposure to lead appear to have an effect on verbal IQ scores?

Minitab

```
Source    DF      SS    MS      F      P
LEAD       2     142    71   0.39  0.677
Error    118   21441   182
Total    120   21584
```

6. Lead and Full IQ Scores Example 1 used measured *performance* IQ scores for three different blood lead levels. If we use the same three categories of blood lead levels with the *full* IQ scores, we get the accompanying Excel display. Using a 0.05 significance level, test the claim that the three categories of blood lead level have the same mean full IQ score. Does it appear that exposure to lead has an effect on full IQ scores?

Excel

Source of Variation	SS	df	MS	F	P-value	F crit
Between Groups	938.3653	2	469.1827	2.303395	0.104395	3.07309
Within Groups	24035.63	118	203.6918			
Total	24974	120				

ANOVA

7. Head Injury Crash Test Data Exercises 1–4 use chest deceleration data for three different size categories (small, midsize, large). If we use the head injury measurements (in HIC, which is a standard head injury criterion) with the same three size categories, we get the SPSS results shown here. Using a 0.05 significance level, test the claim that the three size categories have the same mean head injury measurement. Does the size of a car appear to affect head injuries?

SPSS

	Sum of Squares	df	Mean Square	F	Sig.
Between Groups	7366.952	2	3683.476	.161	.852
Within Groups	411540.286	18	22863.349		
Total	418907.238	20			

8. Birth Weights Data Set 3 "Births" lists birth weights from babies born at four different hospitals. After partitioning the birth weights according to the hospital, we get the StatCrunch display shown here. Use a 0.05 significance level to test the claim that the different hospitals have the same mean birth weights. Do birth weights appear to be the same at these four hospitals?

StatCrunch

ANOVA table

Source	DF	SS	MS	F-Stat	P-value
Columns	3	1701400	567133.33	1.1810493	0.3167
Error	396	1.90157e8	480194.44		
Total	399	1.918584e8			

9. Male Pulse Rates and Age Using the pulse rates of males from Data Set 1 "Body Data" in Appendix B after they are partitioned into the three age brackets of 18–25, 26–40, and 41–80, we get the following SPSS display. Using a 0.05 significance level, test the claim that males from the three age brackets have the same mean pulse rate. What do you conclude?

	Sum of Squares	df	Mean Square	F	Sig.
Between Groups	333.464	2	166.732	1.304	.275
Within Groups	19183.765	150	127.892		
Total	19517.229	152			

10. Female Pulse Rates and Age Using the pulse rates of females from Data Set 1 "Body Data" in Appendix B after they are partitioned into the three age brackets of 18–25, 26–40, and 41–80, we get the following Statdisk display. Using a 0.05 significance level, test the claim that females from the three age brackets have the same mean pulse rate. What do you conclude?

Statdisk

Source:	DF:	SS:	MS:	Test Stat, F:	Critical F:	P-Value:
Treatment:	2	2280.049935	1140.024967	7.933788	3.058925	0.000539
Error:	144	20691.705167	143.692397			
Total:	146	22971.755102				

11. Pelvis Injury Crash Test Data Exercises 1–4 use chest deceleration data for three different size categories (small, midsize, large). If we use the pelvis injury measurements (g) with the same three size categories, we get the XLSTAT results shown here. Using a 0.05 significance level, test the claim that the three size categories have the same mean pelvis injury measurement. Does the size of a car appear to affect pelvis injuries?

XLSTAT

Source	DF	Sum of squares	Mean squares	F	Pr > F
Model	2	79.1429	39.5714	0.3476	0.7111
Error	18	2049.4286	113.8571		
Corrected	20	2128.5714			

12. Arsenic in Rice Listed below are amounts of arsenic in samples of brown rice from three different states. The amounts are in micrograms of arsenic and all samples have the same serving size. The data are from the Food and Drug Administration. Use a 0.05 significance level to test the claim that the three samples are from populations with the same mean. Do the amounts of arsenic appear to be different in the different states? Given that the amounts of arsenic in the samples from Texas have the highest mean, can we conclude that brown rice from Texas poses the greatest health problem?

Arkansas	4.8	4.9	5.0	5.4	5.4	5.4	5.6	5.6	5.6	5.9	6.0	6.1
California	1.5	3.7	4.0	4.5	4.9	5.1	5.3	5.4	5.4	5.5	5.6	5.6
Texas	5.6	5.8	6.6	6.9	6.9	6.9	7.1	7.3	7.5	7.6	7.7	7.7

13. Poplar Tree Weights Weights (kg) of poplar trees were obtained from trees planted in a rich and moist region. The trees were given different treatments identified in the table below. (The data are from Data Set 18 in Appendix B, and they were obtained from a study conducted by researchers at Pennsylvania State University and were provided by Minitab, Inc.) Use a 0.05 significance level to test the claim that the four treatment categories yield poplar trees with the same mean weight. Is there a treatment that appears to be most effective?

No Treatment	Fertilizer	Irrigation	Fertilizer and Irrigation
0.15	1.34	0.23	2.03
0.02	0.14	0.04	0.27
0.16	0.02	0.34	0.92
0.37	0.08	0.16	1.07
0.22	0.08	0.05	2.38

14. Poplar Tree Weights Weights (kg) of poplar trees were obtained from trees planted in a sandy and dry region. The trees were given different treatments identified in the table below. (The data are from Data Set 18 in Appendix B, and they were obtained from a study conducted by researchers at Pennsylvania State University and were provided by Minitab, Inc.) Use a 0.05 significance level to test the claim that the four treatment categories yield poplar trees with the same mean weight. Is there a treatment that appears to be most effective in the sandy and dry region?

No Treatment	Fertilizer	Irrigation	Fertilizer and Irrigation
0.60	1.16	0.65	0.22
1.11	0.93	0.08	2.13
0.07	0.30	0.62	2.33
0.07	0.59	0.01	1.74
0.44	0.17	0.03	0.12

In Exercises 15 and 16, use the data set in Appendix B.

15. Nicotine in Cigarettes Refer to Data Set 15 "Cigarette Contents" in Appendix B and use the amounts of nicotine (mg per cigarette) in the king-size cigarettes, the 100-mm menthol cigarettes, and the 100-mm nonmenthol cigarettes. The king-size cigarettes are nonfiltered,

continued

nonmenthol, and nonlight. The 100-mm menthol cigarettes are filtered and nonlight. The 100-mm nonmenthol cigarettes are filtered and nonlight. Use a 0.05 significance level to test the claim that the three categories of cigarettes yield the same mean amount of nicotine. Given that only the king-size cigarettes are not filtered, do the filters appear to make a difference?

16. Secondhand Smoke Refer to Data Set 14 "Passive and Active Smoke" in Appendix B and use the measured serum cotinine levels (in mg/mL) from the three groups of subjects (smokers, nonsmokers exposed to tobacco smoke, and nonsmokers not exposed to tobacco smoke). When nicotine is absorbed by the body, cotinine is produced. Use a 0.05 significance level to test the claim that the three samples are from populations with the same mean. What do the results suggest about the effects of secondhand smoke?

12-1 Beyond the Basics

17. Tukey Test A display of the Bonferroni test results from Table 12-1 (which is part of the Chapter Problem) is provided on page 558. Shown here is the SPSS-generated display of results from the Tukey test using the same data. Compare the Tukey test results to those from the Bonferroni test.

SPSS

(I) Level	(J) Level	Mean Difference (I-J)	Std. Error	Sig.	95% Confidence Interval	
					Lower Bound	Upper Bound
1.00	2.00	8.56876	3.80486	.067	-.4626	17.6002
	3.00	8.51465	3.87487	.076	-.6830	17.7123
2.00	1.00	-8.56876	3.80486	.067	-17.6002	.4626
	3.00	-.05411	4.80851	1.000	-11.4678	11.3596
3.00	1.00	-8.51465	3.87487	.076	-17.7123	.6830
	2.00	.05411	4.80851	1.000	-11.3596	11.4678

18. Bonferroni Test Exercise 13 lists weights (kg) of poplar trees obtained from trees planted in a rich and moist region. Shown below are partial results from using the Bonferroni test with the sample data.

a. Use a 0.05 significance level to test the claim that the different treatments result in the same mean weight.

b. What do the displayed Bonferroni SPSS results tell us?

c. Use the Bonferroni test procedure with a 0.05 significance level to test for a significant difference between the mean amount of the irrigation treatment group and the group treated with both fertilizer and irrigation. Identify the test statistic and either the P-value or critical values. What do the results indicate?

Bonferroni Results from SPSS

(I) TREATMENT	(J) TREATMENT	Mean Difference (I-J)	Std. Error	Sig.	95% Confidence Interval	
					Lower Bound	Upper Bound
1.00	2.00	-.02200	.26955	1.000	-.8329	.7889
	3.00	.23600	.26955	1.000	-.5749	1.0469
	4.00	-.84400*	.26955	.039	-1.6549	-.0331

12-2 Two-Way ANOVA

Key Concept Section 12-1 considered data partitioned using *one* factor, but this section describes the method of *two-way analysis of variance,* which is used with data partitioned into categories according to *two* factors. The method of this section requires that we first test for an *interaction* between the two factors, then we test for an effect from the row factor and we test for an effect from the column factor.

Table 12-3 is an example of pulse rate (beats per minute) data categorized with *two* factors:

1. Age Bracket (years): One factor is age bracket (18–29, 30–49, 50–80).

2. Gender: The second factor is gender (female, male).

The subcategories in Table 12-3 are called *cells,* so Table 12-3 has six cells containing ten values each.

In analyzing the sample data in Table 12-3, we have already discussed one-way analysis of variance for a single factor, so it might seem reasonable to simply proceed with one-way ANOVA for the factor of age bracket and another one-way ANOVA for the factor of gender, but that approach wastes information and totally ignores a very important feature: the possible effect of an *interaction* between the two factors.

TABLE 12-3 Pulse Rates with Two Factors: Age Bracket and Gender

	Female										Male									
18–29	104	82	80	78	80	84	82	66	70	78	72	64	72	64	64	70	72	64	54	52
30–49	66	74	96	86	98	88	82	72	80	80	80	90	58	74	96	72	58	66	80	92
50–80	94	72	82	86	72	90	64	72	72	100	54	102	52	52	62	82	82	60	52	74

DEFINITION

There is an **interaction** between two factors if the effect of one of the factors changes for different categories of the other factor.

As an example of an *interaction* between two factors, consider food pairings. Peanut butter and jelly interact well, but ketchup and ice cream interact in a way that results in a bad taste, so we rarely see someone eating ice cream topped with ketchup. Physicians must be careful to avoid prescribing drugs with interactions that produce adverse effects. It was found that the antifungal drug Nizoral (ketoconazole) interacted with the antihistamine drug Seldane (terfenadine) in such a way that Seldane was not metabolized properly, causing abnormal heart rhythms in some patients. Seldane was subsequently removed from the market. In general, consider an interaction effect to be an effect due to the combination of the two factors.

Explore Data with Means and an Interaction Graph

Let's explore the data in Table 12-3 by calculating the mean for each cell and by constructing a graph. The individual cell means are shown in Table 12-4 on the next page. Those means vary from a low of 64.8 to a high of 82.2, so they vary considerably. Figure 12-3 on the next page is an *interaction graph,* which shows graphs of those means. We can interpret an interaction graph as follows:

■ **Interaction Effect:** An interaction effect is suggested when line segments are far from being parallel.

■ **No Interaction Effect:** If the line segments are approximately *parallel*, as in Figure 12-3, it appears that the different categories of a variable have the same effect for the different categories of the other variable, so there does not appear to be an interaction effect.

TABLE 12-4 Means of Cells from Table 12-3

	Female	Male
18–29	80.4	64.8
30–49	82.2	76.6
50–80	80.4	67.2

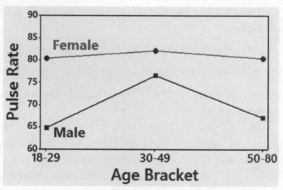

FIGURE 12-3 Interaction Graph of Age Bracket and Gender: Means from Table 12-4

Instead of relying only on subjective judgments made by examining the means in Table 12-4 and the interaction graph in Figure 12-3, we will proceed with the more objective procedure of two-way analysis of variance. Here are the requirements and basic procedure for two-way analysis of variance (ANOVA). The procedure is also summarized in Figure 12-4, which follows the Key Elements box.

KEY ELEMENTS

Two-Way Analysis of Variance

Objective

With sample data categorized with two factors (a row variable and a column variable), use two-way analysis of variance to conduct the following three tests:

1. Test for an effect from an interaction between the row factor and the column factor.

2. Test for an effect from the row factor.

3. Test for an effect from the column factor.

Requirements

1. **Normality** For each cell, the sample values come from a population with a distribution that is approximately normal. (This procedure is robust against reasonable departures from normal distributions.)

2. **Variation** The populations have the same variance σ^2 (or standard deviation σ). (This procedure is robust against reasonable departures from the requirement of equal variances.)

3. **Sampling** The samples are simple random samples of quantitative data.

4. **Independence** The samples are independent of each other. (This procedure does not apply to samples lacking independence.)

5. **Two-Way** The sample values are categorized two ways. (This is the basis for the name of the method: *two-way analysis of variance.*)

6. **Balanced Design** All of the cells have the same number of sample values. (This is called a *balanced* design. This section does not include methods for a design that is not balanced.)

Procedure for Two-Way ANOVA (See Figure 12-4)

Step 1: *Interaction Effect:* In two-way analysis of variance, begin by testing the null hypothesis that there is no interaction between the two factors. Use technology to find the *P*-value corresponding to the following test statistic:

$$F = \frac{\text{MS(interaction)}}{\text{MS(error)}}$$

Conclusion:

- **Reject:** If the *P*-value corresponding to the above test statistic is small (such as less than or equal to 0.05), reject the null hypothesis of no interaction. Conclude that there is an interaction effect.

- **Fail to Reject:** If the *P*-value is large (such as greater than 0.05), fail to reject the null hypothesis of no interaction between the two factors. Conclude that there is no interaction effect.

Step 2: *Row/Column Effects:* If we conclude that there is an interaction effect, then we should stop now; we should not proceed with the two additional tests. (If there is an interaction between factors, we shouldn't consider the effects of either factor without considering those of the other.)

If we conclude that there is no interaction effect, then we should proceed with the following two hypothesis tests.

Row Factor

For the row factor, test the null hypothesis H_0: There are no effects from the row factor (that is, the row values are from populations with the same mean). Find the *P*-value corresponding to the test statistic $F = \text{MS(row)}/\text{MS(error)}$.

Conclusion:

- **Reject:** If the *P*-value corresponding to the test statistic is small (such as less than or equal to 0.05), reject the null hypothesis of no effect from the row factor. Conclude that there is an effect from the row factor.

- **Fail to Reject:** If the *P*-value is large (such as greater than 0.05), fail to reject the null hypothesis of no effect from the row factor. Conclude that there is no effect from the row factor.

Column Factor

For the column factor, test the null hypothesis H_0: There are no effects from the column factor (that is, the column values are from populations with the same mean). Find the *P*-value corresponding to the test statistic $F = \text{MS(column)}/\text{MS(error)}$.

Conclusion:

- **Reject:** If the *P*-value corresponding to the test statistic is small (such as less than or equal to 0.05), reject the null hypothesis of no effect from the column factor. Conclude that there is an effect from the column factor.

- **Fail to Reject:** If the *P*-value is large (such as greater than 0.05), fail to reject the null hypothesis of no effect from the column factor. Conclude that there is no effect from the column factor.

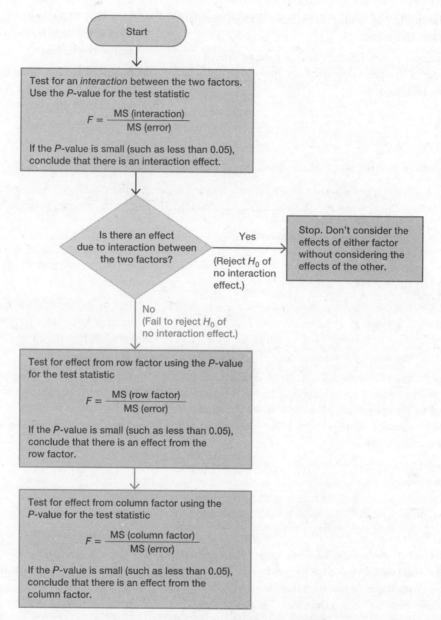

FIGURE 12-4 **Procedure for Two-Way Analysis of Variance**

○─| **EXAMPLE 1** **Pulse Rates**

Given the pulse rates in Table 12-3 on page 563 (from Data Set 1 "Body Data" in Appendix B), use two-way analysis of variance to test for an interaction effect, an effect from the row factor of age bracket, and an effect from the column factor of gender. Use a 0.05 significance level.

SOLUTION

REQUIREMENT CHECK (1) For each cell, the sample values appear to be from a population with a distribution that is approximately normal, as indicated by normal quantile plots. (2) The variances of the cells (100.3, 51.7, 103.5, 183.2, 138.5, 293.5) differ considerably, but the test is robust against departures from equal variances.

(3) The samples are simple random samples of subjects. (4) The samples are independent of each other; the subjects are not matched in any way. (5) The sample values are categorized in two ways (age bracket and gender). (6) All of the cells have the same number (ten) of sample values. The requirements are satisfied. ✅

The calculations are quite involved, so we use technology. The StatCrunch two-way analysis of variance display for the data in Table 12-3 is shown here.

StatCrunch

ANOVA table

Source	DF	SS	MS	F-Stat	P-value
Age	2	526.93333	263.46667	1.8156202	0.1725
Gender	1	1972.2667	1972.2667	13.591424	0.0005
Interaction	2	272.53333	136.26667	0.93905054	0.3973
Error	54	7836	145.11111		
Total	59	10607.733			

Step 1: Interaction Effect: We begin by testing the null hypothesis that there is no interaction between the two factors. Using StatCrunch for the data in Table 12-3, we get the results shown in the preceding StatCrunch display and we can see that the test statistic for the interaction is $F = 0.9391$ (rounded). This test statistic can be calculated as follows:

$$F = \frac{MS(\text{interaction})}{MS(\text{error})} = \frac{136.26667}{145.11111} = 0.9391$$

Interpretation: The corresponding *P*-value is shown in the StatCrunch display as 0.3973, so we fail to reject the null hypothesis of no interaction between the two factors. It does not appear that pulse rates are affected by an interaction between age bracket (18–29, 30–49, 50–80) and gender. There does not appear to be an interaction effect.

Step 2: Row / Column Effects: Because there does not appear to be an interaction effect, we proceed to test for effects from the row and column factors. The two hypothesis tests use these null hypotheses:

H_0: There are no effects from the row factor (that is, the row values are from populations with equal means).

H_0: There are no effects from the column factor (that is, the column values are from populations with equal means).

Row Factor: For the row factor (age bracket), we refer to the preceding StatCrunch display of results to see that the test statistic for the row factor is $F = 1.81856$ (rounded). This test statistic can be calculated as follows:

$$F = \frac{MS(\text{age bracket})}{MS(\text{error})} = \frac{263.46667}{145.11111} = 1.8156$$

Conclusion: The corresponding *P*-value is shown in the StatCrunch display as 0.1725. Because that *P*-value is greater than the significance level of 0.05, we fail to reject the null hypothesis of no effects from age bracket. That is, pulse rates do not appear to be affected by the age bracket.

Column Factor: For the column factor (gender), we refer to the preceding StatCrunch display of results to see that the test statistic for the column factor is $F = 13.5914$ (rounded). This test statistic can be calculated as follows:

continued

$$F = \frac{MS(\text{gender})}{MS(\text{error})} = \frac{1972.2667}{145.11111} = 13.5914$$

Conclusion: The corresponding *P*-value is shown in the StatCrunch display as 0.0005. Because that *P*-value is less than the significance level of 0.05, we reject the null hypothesis of no effects from gender. Pulse rates do appear to be affected by gender.

> **INTERPRETATION**
>
> On the basis of the sample data in Table 12-3, we conclude that pulse rates appear to be affected by gender, but not by age bracket and not by an interaction between age bracket and gender.

TECH CENTER

Two-Way Analysis of Variance

Access tech instructions, videos, and data sets at **www.TriolaStats.com**

12-2 Basic Skills and Concepts

Statistical Literacy and Critical Thinking

1. Two-Way ANOVA The pulse rates in Table 12-3 from Example 1 are reproduced below with fabricated data (in red) used for the pulse rates of females aged 30–49. What characteristic of the data suggests that the appropriate method of analysis is *two-way* analysis of variance? That is, what is "two-way" about the data entered in this table?

	Female										Male									
18–29	104	82	80	78	80	84	82	66	70	78	72	64	72	64	64	70	72	64	54	52
30–49	46	54	76	66	78	68	62	52	60	60	80	90	58	74	96	72	58	66	80	92
50–80	94	72	82	86	72	90	64	72	72	100	54	102	52	52	62	82	82	60	52	74

2. Two-Way ANOVA If we have a goal of using the data described in Exercise 1 to (1) determine whether age bracket has an effect on pulse rates and (2) to determine whether gender has an effect on pulse rates, should we use one-way analysis of variance for the two individual tests? Why or why not?

3. Interaction

a. What is an interaction between two factors?

b. In general, when using two-way analysis of variance, if we find that there is an interaction effect, how does that affect the procedure?

c. Shown below is an interaction graph constructed from the data in Exercise 1. What does the graph suggest?

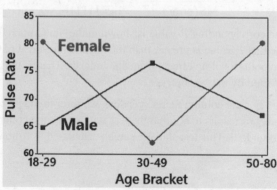

4. Balanced Design Does the table given in Exercise 1 constitute a *balanced design?* Why or why not?

5. Pulse Rates If we use the data given in Exercise 1 with two-way analysis of variance, we get the accompanying display. What do you conclude?

Statdisk

Source:	DF:	SS:	MS:	Test Stat, F:	Critical F:	P-Value:
Interaction:	2	2779.2	1389.6	9.58	3.1682	0.0003
Row Variable:	2	206.9333	103.4667	0.7130	3.1682	0.4947
Column Variable:	1	345.6	345.6	2.3816	4.0195	0.1286

6. Weights The weights (kg) in the following table are from Data Set 1 "Body Data." Results from two-way analysis of variance are also shown. Use the displayed results and use a 0.05 significance level. What do you conclude?

	Female						Male				
18–29	63.4	57.8	52.6	46.9	61.7	61.5	71.6	64.9	144.9	96.4	80.7	84.4
	77.2	50.4	97.0	76.1			63.9	79.0	99.4	64.1		
30–49	110.5	84.6	133.3	90.2	125.7	105.3	96.2	56.4	107.4	99.5	64.8	94.7
	115.5	75.3	92.8	57.7			74.2	112.8	72.6	91.4		
50–80	103.2	48.3	87.8	101.3	67.8	45.2	84.8	127.5	89.9	75.3	110.2	72.3
	79.8	60.1	68.5	43.3			77.2	86.5	71.3	73.1		

StatCrunch

ANOVA table

Source	DF	SS	MS	F-Stat	P-value
Age	2	3727.7583	1863.8792	4.3546612	0.0176
Gender	1	1013.526	1013.526	2.3679444	0.1297
Interaction	2	3137.611	1568.8055	3.6652678	0.0322
Error	54	23113.044	428.01933		
Total	59	30991.939			

7. Heights The heights (cm) in the following table are from Data Set 1 "Body Data." Results from two-way analysis of variance are also shown. Use the displayed results and use a 0.05 significance level. What do you conclude?

	Female					Male				
18–29	161.2	170.2	162.9	155.5	168.0	172.8	178.7	183.1	175.9	161.8
	153.3	152.0	154.9	157.4	159.5	177.5	170.5	180.1	178.6	178.5
30–49	169.1	170.6	171.1	159.6	169.8	170.1	165.4	178.5	168.5	180.3
	169.5	156.5	164.0	164.8	155.6	178.2	174.4	174.6	162.8	174.4
50–80	146.7	160.9	163.3	176.1	163.1	181.9	166.6	171.7	170.0	169.1
	151.6	164.7	153.3	160.3	134.5	182.9	176.3	166.7	166.3	160.5

XLSTAT

Source	DF	Sum of squares	Mean squares	F	Pr > F
Age	2	222.0610	111.0305	2.0403	0.1399
Gender (1=M)	1	2365.0482	2365.0482	43.4607	< 0.0001
Age*Gender (1=M)	2	195.5803	97.7902	1.7970	0.1756

8. Cholesterol Levels The following table lists measured cholesterol levels of randomly selected subjects. Results from two-way analysis of variance are shown on the top of the next page. Use a 0.05 significance level. Are cholesterol levels affected by an interaction between sex and age? Are cholesterol levels affected by sex? Are cholesterol levels affected by age?

	Age														
	Under 30					30–50					Over 50				
Male	265	303	1252	230	957	702	277	176	416	120	75	189	288	578	31
Female	325	112	62	301	223	146	173	149	462	94	254	384	318	600	309

continued

Minitab

Source	DF	Adj SS	Adj MS	F-Value	P-Value
Age	2	94465	47233	0.75	0.482
Sex	1	126360	126360	2.01	0.169
Age*Sex	2	361316	180658	2.88	0.076
Error	24	1507677	62820		
Total	29	2089818			

9. Measuring Self-Esteem The following table lists measures of self-esteem obtained from a student project as supervised by Jannay Morrow at Vassar College (based on data from Richard Lowry). The objective of the project was to study how levels of self-esteem in subjects relate to their perceptions of self-esteem in other target people who were described in writing. Self-esteem levels were measured using the Coopersmith Self-Esteem Inventory, and the test here works well even though the data are at the ordinal level of measurement. Use a 0.05 significance level and apply the methods of two-way analysis of variance. What do you conclude?

		Subject's Self-Esteem										
		Low				Medium				High			
Target's Self-Esteem	Low	4 4 3 5 4 4 5 4 2 4 4 2				3 3 3 4 4 2 4 4 1 2 2 3				3 1 3 3 3 5 3 2 3 3 3 3			
	High	2 2 4 2 2 3 2 4 2 2 2 3				4 3 1 2 1 3 2 4 3 1 1 4				3 2 3 2 3 4 3 4 4 3 3 4			

10. Smoking, Gender, and Body Temperature The table below lists body temperatures (°F) obtained from randomly selected subjects (based on Data Set 2 "Body Temperatures" in Appendix B). Using a 0.05 significance level, test for an interaction between gender and smoking, test for an effect from gender, and test for an effect from smoking. What do you conclude?

	Smokes				Does Not Smoke			
Male	98.0	97.6	98.8	97.6	98.0	98.8	98.8	98.0
Female	98.2	97.7	98.8	98.8	98.4	97.2	98.7	97.7

12-2   Beyond the Basics

11. Transformations of Data Example 1 illustrated the use of two-way ANOVA to analyze the sample data in Table 12-3 on page 563. How are the results affected in each of the following cases?

a. The same constant is added to each sample value.

b. Each sample value is multiplied by the same nonzero constant.

c. The format of the table is transposed so that the row and column factors are interchanged.

d. The first sample value in the first cell is changed so that it becomes an outlier.

Chapter Quick Quiz

1. ANOVA Listed on the top of the next page are skull breadths obtained from skulls of Egyptian males from three different epochs (based on data from *Ancient Races of the Thebaid*, by Thomson and Randall-Maciver). Assume that we plan to use analysis of variance with a 0.05 significance level to test the claim that the different epochs have mean skull breadths that are not all the same. The results from XLSTAT are shown on the next page. What characteristic of the data indicates that we should use *one-way* analysis of variance?

400 B.C.	131	138	125	129	132	135	132	134	138
1850 B.C.	129	134	136	137	137	129	136	138	134
150 A.D.	128	138	136	139	141	142	137	145	137

Source	DF	Sum of squares	Mean squares	F	Pr > F
Model	2	138.7407	69.3704	4.0497	0.0305
Error	24	411.1111	17.1296		
Corrected Total	26	549.8519			

2. Null and Alternative Hypotheses For the hypothesis test described in Exercise 1, identify the null hypothesis and the alternative hypothesis.

3. Test Statistic Identify the value of the test statistic in the display included with Exercise 1. In general, do larger test statistics result in larger P-values, smaller P-values, or P-values that are unrelated to the value of the test statistic?

4. Conclusions If the test described in Exercise 1 is conducted with a 0.05 significance level, what should be concluded about the null hypothesis? What do the results suggest about the data?

5. Type of Test Is the hypothesis test described in Exercise 1 left-tailed, right-tailed or two-tailed? Are all one-way analysis of variance tests left-tailed, right-tailed, or two-tailed?

6. Which Mean Is Different? For the three samples described in Exercise 1, if we use analysis of variance and reach a conclusion to reject equality of the three population means, can we then conclude that any of the specific populations has a mean that is different from the others?

7. One vs Two What is the fundamental difference between one-way analysis of variance and two-way analysis of variance?

Head Injuries in Car Crashes. *In Exercises 8–10, use the accompanying data and corresponding display that results from head injury measurements from dummies in car crash tests. The measurements are in HIC (head injury criterion) units.*

	Size of Car		
	Small	Medium	Large
Foreign	290	245	342
	544	502	698
	501	393	332
Domestic	406	474	216
	371	368	335
	376	349	169

Minitab

```
Source       DF   Adj SS   Adj MS   F-Value   P-Value
  Type        1    34060    34060     2.25      0.159
  Size        2    13255     6627     0.44      0.655
  Type*Size   2    42744    21372     1.41      0.281
Error        12   181603    15134
Total        17   271663
```

8. Interaction Test the null hypothesis that head injury measurements are not affected by an *interaction* between the type of car (foreign, domestic) and size of the car (small, medium large). What do you conclude?

9. Effect from Type of Car Assume that head injury measurements are not affected by an interaction between type of car (foreign, domestic) and size of car (small, medium, large). Is there sufficient evidence to support the claim that the type of car has an effect on head injury measurements?

10. Effect from Size of Car Assume that head injury measurements are not affected by an interaction between type of car (foreign, domestic) and size of car (small, medium, large). Is there sufficient evidence to support the claim that the size of the car (small, medium, large) has an effect on head injury measurements?

Review Exercises

1. Baseline Characteristics Experiments and clinical trials with different treatment groups commonly include "baseline characteristics," which constitute information about the characteristics of the different treatment groups. In a study of four different weight loss programs, each program had 40 subjects. The means and standard deviations of the *ages* in each group are as follows: Atkins ($\bar{x} = 47$ years, $s = 12$ years); Zone ($\bar{x} = 51$ years, $s = 9$ years); Weight Watchers ($\bar{x} = 49$ years, $s = 10$ years); Ornish ($\bar{x} = 49$ years, $s = 12$ years). These statistics are listed along with a *P*-value of 0.41. These results are from "Comparison of the Atkins, Ornish, Weight Watchers, and Zone Diets for Weight Loss and Heart Disease Risk Reduction," by Dansinger et al., *Journal of the American Medical Association*, Vol. 293, No. 1.

a. How many variables are used to categorize the sample data consisting of the ages of the subjects?

b. What specific method is used to find the *P*-value of 0.41?

c. What does the *P*-value of 0.41 indicate about the baseline characteristic of age?

d. What would a small *P*-value (such as 0.001) indicate about the ages, and how would that affect the results of the study?

2. Nicotine in Cigarettes Listed below are amounts of nicotine (mg per cigarette) in king-size cigarettes, 100-mm menthol cigarettes, and 100-mm nonmenthol cigarettes (from Data Set 15 "Cigarette Contents" in Appendix B). The king-size cigarettes are nonfiltered, nonmenthol, and nonlight. The 100-mm menthol cigarettes are filtered and nonlight. The 100-mm nonmenthol cigarettes are filtered and nonlight. Use a 0.05 significance level to test the claim that the three categories of cigarettes yield the same mean amount of nicotine. Given that only the king-size cigarettes are not filtered, do the filters appear to make a difference?

King	1.1	1.7	1.7	1.1	1.1	1.4	1.1	1.4	1.0	1.2	1.1	1.1	1.1
	1.1	1.1	1.8	1.6	1.1	1.2	1.5	1.3	1.1	1.3	1.1	1.1	
Menthol	1.1	0.8	1	0.9	0.8	0.8	0.8	0.8	0.9	0.8	0.8	1.2	0.8
	0.8	1.3	0.7	1.4	0.2	0.8	1.0	0.8	0.8	1.2	0.6	0.7	
One Hundred	0.4	1.0	1.2	0.8	0.8	1.0	1.1	1.1	1.1	0.8	0.8	0.8	0.8
	1.0	0.2	1.1	1.0	0.8	1.0	0.9	1.1	1.1	0.6	1.3	1.1	

3. Car Crash Tests When car crash tests were conducted, data were collected that consist of crash test loads (pounds) on the left femur and right femur. When those loads are partitioned into the three car size categories of small, midsize, and large, the two-way analysis of results from XLSTAT are as shown below. (The row factor of femur has the two values of left femur and right femur, and the column factor of size has the three values of small, midsize, and large.) Use a 0.05 significance level to apply the methods of two-way analysis of variance. What do you conclude?

Source	DF	Sum of squares	Mean squares	F	Pr > F
Femur	1	166068.5952	166068.5952	1.3896	0.2462
Size	2	532911.8571	266455.9286	2.2296	0.1222
Femur*Size	2	410435.7619	205217.8810	1.7171	0.1940

4. Smoking, Body Temperature, Gender The table below lists body temperatures obtained from randomly selected subjects (based on Data Set 2 "Body Temperatures" in Appendix B). The temperatures are categorized according to gender and whether the subject smokes. Using a 0.05 significance level, test for an interaction between gender and smoking, test for an effect from gender, and test for an effect from smoking. What do you conclude?

	Smokes				Does Not Smoke			
Male	98.4	97.4	96.8	98.2	98.4	97.4	97.4	98.0
Female	98.6	99.3	98.2	98.6	97.0	98.4	97.2	98.7

Cumulative Review Exercises

In Exercises 1–5, refer to the following list of numbers of years that U.S. presidents, popes, and British monarchs lived after their inauguration, election, or coronation, respectively. (As of this writing, the last president is Gerald Ford, the last pope is John Paul II, and the last British monarch is George VI.) Assume that the data are samples randomly selected from larger populations.

Presidents	10	29	26	28	15	23	17	25	0	20	4	1	24	16	12
	4	10	17	16	0	7	24	12	4	18	21	11	2	9	36
	12	28	3	16	9	25	23	32							
Popes	2	9	21	3	6	10	18	11	6	25	23	6	2	15	32
	25	11	8	17	19	5	15	0	26						
Monarchs	17	6	13	12	13	33	59	10	7	63	9	25	36	15	

1. Descriptive Statistics Include appropriate units in all answers.

a. Find the mean for each of the three groups.

b. Find the standard deviation for each of the three groups.

c. Find the variance for each of the three groups.

d. What is the level of measurement of the data (nominal, ordinal, interval, ratio)?

2. Comparing Two Means Treating the data as samples from larger populations, test the claim that there is a difference between the mean for presidents and the mean for British monarchs.

3. Normality Assessment Use the longevity times for presidents and determine whether they appear to come from a population having a normal distribution. Explain why the distribution does or does not appear to be normal.

4. Confidence Interval Use the longevity times for presidents and construct a 95% confidence interval estimate of the population mean. Write a brief statement interpreting the confidence interval.

5. ANOVA The display below results from using the one-way analysis of variance test with the three samples.

a. What is the null hypothesis?

b. Assuming a 0.05 significance level, what conclusion is indicated by the displayed results?

Minitab

```
Source  DF    SS    MS    F     P
Factor  2    839   419  3.11  0.051
Error   73   9843  135
Total   75   10682
```

6. Freshman 15: Correlation/Regression Listed below are weights (kg) of eight female college students in September and April of their freshman year (from Data Set 10 "Freshman 15" in Appendix B).

a. Test for a linear correlation between September weights and the subsequent April weights.

b. Find the equation of the regression line.

c. Find the best predicted April weight for a female freshman student given that her weight in September is 70 kg. How does that result compare to an actual female student who weighed 70 kg in September and 73 kg in April?

September	62	55	57	64	60	52	55	42
April	65	58	61	68	64	57	60	49

7. Platelets: Normal Distribution Assume that adult females have blood platelet counts that are normally distributed with a mean of 280 and a standard deviation of 65. (All units are in 1000 cells/μL.)

a. Find the probability that a randomly selected adult female has a platelet count greater than 345.

b. Find the probability that a randomly selected adult female has a platelet count between 215 and 345.

c. If 25 adult females are randomly selected, find the probability that the mean of their platelet counts is less than 319.

d. Find the value of P_{80}, the 80th percentile.

8. Health Benefits *USA Today* reported on an Adecco Staffing survey of 1000 randomly selected adults. Among those respondents, 20% chose health benefits as being most important to their job.

a. What is the number of respondents who chose health benefits as being most important to their job?

b. Construct a 95% interval estimate of the proportion of all adults who choose health benefits as being most important to their job.

c. Based on the result from part (b), can we safely conclude that the true proportion is different from 1/4? Why?

9. Blue Genes Some couples have genetic characteristics configured so that one-quarter of all their offspring have blue eyes. A study is conducted of 100 couples believed to have those characteristics, with the result that 19 of their 100 offspring have blue eyes. Assuming that one-quarter of all offspring have blue eyes, estimate the probability that among 100 offspring, 19 or fewer have blue eyes. Based on that probability, does it seem that the one-quarter rate is wrong? Why or why not?

10. Firearm Injuries The table below lists numbers of firearm injuries arranged according to circumstances and whether the firearm was a handgun or a rifle or shotgun (based on data from "Hospitalization Charges, Costs, and Income for Firearm-Related Injuries at a University Trauma Center," by Kizer et al., *Journal of the American Medical Association,* Vol. 273, No. 22). Use a 0.05 significance level to test the claim that the injury category is independent of the type of weapon.

	Unintentional	Self-Inflicted	Assault
Handgun	31	35	162
Rifle or Shotgun	13	7	67

Technology Project

Does Weight Change with Age? Refer to Data Set 1 "Body Data" in Appendix B and use the weights of males partitioned into the three different age brackets of 18–25, 26–40, and 41–80. Use the methods of this chapter to test the claim that men in those three age brackets have the same mean weight.

    Sorting One challenge in this project is identifying the weights of men in the three age brackets. First, use the *sort* feature of your technology to sort all of the columns using *Gender* as the basis for sorting. You can then delete all of the rows representing females. Then sort all of the columns using *Age* as the basis for sorting. It will then be much easier to identify the weights in the different age brackets.

FROM DATA TO DECISION

Critical Thinking: Is Lipitor Effective in Lowering LDL Cholesterol?

With sales of Lipitor exceeding $13 billion each year, it has been the best-selling drug ever. One of the authors asked Pfizer for original data from clinical drug trials of Lipitor, but Pfizer declined to provide the data. The data shown are based on results given in a Parke-Davis memo from David G. Orloff, M.D., the medical team leader in the clinical trials. The data refer to atorvastatin, and Lipitor is the trade name of atorvastatin. Low-density lipoprotein (LDL) cholesterol is considered the bad cholesterol, so a subject's condition is generally improved if the LDL cholesterol is lowered. The changes in LDL cholesterol listed in the table are measured in mg/dL. Note that when compared to baseline values, negative values in the following data indicate that the LDL cholesterol has been lowered.

Analyzing the Results

Analyze the data. Does it appear that atorvastatin treatment has an effect? If atorvastatin treatment does have an effect, is it the desired effect? Does it appear that larger doses of atorvastatin treatment result in greater beneficial effects? Write a brief report summarizing your findings and include specific statistical tests and results.

Changes in LDL Cholesterol from Baseline Values
(a negative value represents a decrease)

Placebo Group:

$-3 \quad 5 \quad 6 \quad -2 \quad -7 \quad 8 \quad 5 \quad -6 \quad -1 \quad 7 \quad -4 \quad 3$

Group treated with 10 mg of atorvastatin:

$-28 \ -27 \ -23 \ -25 \ -27 \ -29 \ -22 \ -22 \ -26 \ -23 \ -23$
$-22 \ -24 \ -21 \ -25 \ -26 \ -23 \ -24 \ -23 \ -22 \ -22 \ -20 \ -29$
$-29 \ -27 \ -24 \ -28 \ -26 \ -22 \ -26 \ -23 \ -26 \ -25 \ -29 \ -27$
$-27 \ -23$

Group treated with 20 mg of atorvastatin:

$-28 \ -32 \ -29 \ -39 \ -31 \ -35 \ -25 \ -36 \ -35 \ -26 \ -29$
$-34 \ -30$

Group treated with 80 mg of atorvastatin:

$-42 \ -41 \ -38 \ -42 \ -41 \ -41 \ -40 \ -44 \ -32 \ -37 \ -41$
$-37 \ -34 \ -31$

Cooperative Group Activities

1. Out-of-class activity Flesch Reading Ease scores and Flesch-Kincaid Grade Level scores measure readability of text. Some programs, such as Microsoft Word, include features that allow you to automatically obtain readability scores. Divide into groups of three or four students. Using samples of writing from *Journal of the American Medical Association,* the *American Journal of Nursing,* and the *American Journal of Public Health,* obtain readability scores for ten samples of text from each source. Use the methods of this chapter to determine whether there are any differences.

2. In-class activity Divide the class into three groups. One group should record the pulse rate of each member while he or she remains seated. The second group should record the pulse rate of each member while he or she is standing. The third group should record the pulse rate of each member immediately after he or she stands and sits 10 times. Analyze the results. What do the results indicate?

3. Out-of-class activity Biographyonline.net includes information on the lives of notable artists, politicians, scientists, actors, and others. Design and conduct an observational study that begins with choosing samples from select groups, followed by a comparison of life spans of people from the different groups. Do any particular groups appear to have life spans that are different from those of other groups? Can you explain such differences?

4. Out-of-class activity Divide into groups of three or four students. Each group should survey other students at the same college by asking them to identify their major and gender. You might include other factors, such as employment (none, part-time, full-time) and age (under 21, 21–30, over 30). For each surveyed subject, determine the number of Twitter followers or Facebook friends.

• Does gender appear to have an effect on the number of followers/friends?

• Does major have an effect on the number of followers/friends?

• Does an interaction between gender and major have an effect on the number of followers/friends?

13 Nonparametric Tests

CHAPTER PROBLEM — **Effects of Second-Hand Smoke**

Data Set 14 in Appendix B includes measured cotinine levels (ng/mL) of subjects from three different groups: (1) smokers; (2) nonsmokers who are exposed to tobacco smoke; and (3) nonsmokers not exposed to tobacco smoke. Cotinine is a metabolite of nicotine, meaning that when nicotine is absorbed by the body, cotinine is produced. We want to test the claim that the three different groups have different levels of cotinine.

This seems like a good application of the method of one-way analysis of variance that was presented in Section 12-1. However, if we check the requirements for analysis of variance, we find that the three samples should be from populations having distributions that are approximately normal. The accompanying normal quantile plot results from the sample of cotinine levels measured from the third group: nonsmokers not exposed to

576

smoke. The normality requirement for analysis of variance is a loose requirement, but the normal quantile plot suggests a dramatic departure from normality, so the normality requirement does not appear to be met.

This chapter presents "nonparametric" or "distribution-free" methods that do not require normal or any other specific distribution. This chapter will present a method that allows us to compare the cotinine levels in the three groups, even though the three samples appear to be from populations with distributions that are not normal. Nonparametric methods therefore provide us with tools that often enable us to do an analysis that cannot be done with parametric methods having requirements about distributions.

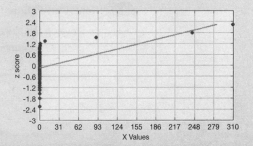

CHAPTER OBJECTIVES

Here are the main objectives for Chapter 13:

 13-1   Basics of Nonparametric Tests

- Develop the ability to describe the difference between parametric tests and nonparametric tests.
- Identify advantages and disadvantages of nonparametric tests.
- Know how nonparametric tests are generally less *efficient* than the corresponding parametric tests.
- Develop the ability to convert data into *ranks*.

 13-2   Sign Test

- Develop the ability to conduct a sign test for claims involving matched pairs of sample data, or claims involving nominal data, or claims made about the median of a population.

 13-3   Wilcoxon Signed-Rank Test for Matched Pairs

- Develop the ability to apply the Wilcoxon signed-ranks test for sample data consisting of matched pairs.

 13-4   Wilcoxon Rank-Sum Test for Two Independent Samples

- Develop the ability to apply the Wilcoxon rank-sum test for sample data from two independent populations.

Kruskal-Wallis Test for Three or More Samples

- Develop the ability to apply the Kruskal-Wallis test for sample data from three or more independent populations.

 Rank Correlation

- Develop the ability to compute the value of the rank correlation coefficient r_s, and use it to determine whether there is a correlation between two variables.

 Basics of Nonparametric Tests

This chapter introduces methods of *nonparametric* tests, which do not have the stricter requirements of corresponding parametric tests, which are based on samples from populations with specific parameters such as μ or σ.

> **DEFINITIONS**
>
> **Parametric tests** have requirements about the distribution of the populations involved; **nonparametric (or distribution-free) tests** do not require that samples come from populations with normal distributions or any other particular distributions.

Misleading Terminology The term *distribution-free test* correctly indicates that a test does not require a particular distribution. The term *nonparametric tests* is misleading in the sense that it suggests that the tests are not based on a parameter, but there are some nonparametric tests that are based on a parameter such as the median. Due to the widespread use of the term *nonparametric test,* we use that terminology, but we define it to be a test that does not require a particular distribution.

Advantages and Disadvantages

Advantages of Nonparametric Tests

1. Because nonparametric tests have less rigid requirements than parametric tests, they can be applied to a wider variety of situations.

2. Nonparametric tests can be applied to more data types than parametric tests. For example, nonparametric tests can be used with data consisting of ranks, and they can be used with categorical data, such as genders of survey respondents.

Disadvantages of Nonparametric Tests

1. Nonparametric tests tend to waste information because exact numerical data are often reduced to a qualitative form. For example, with the nonparametric sign test (Section 13-2), weight losses by dieters are recorded simply as negative signs, and the actual magnitudes of the weight losses are ignored.

2. Nonparametric tests are not as *efficient* as parametric tests, so a nonparametric test generally needs stronger evidence (such as a larger sample or greater differences) in order to reject a null hypothesis.

Efficiency of Nonparametric Tests When the requirements of population distributions are satisfied, nonparametric tests are generally less efficient than their corresponding parametric tests. For example, Section 13-6 presents the concept of *rank correlation,* which has an efficiency rating of 0.91 when compared to linear correlation in Section 10-1. This means that with all other things being equal, the nonparametric rank correlation method in Section 13-6 requires 100 sample observations to achieve the same results as 91 sample observations analyzed through the parametric linear correlation in Section 10-1, assuming the stricter requirements for using the parametric test are met. Table 13-1 lists nonparametric tests along with the corresponding parametric test and **efficiency** rating. Table 13-1 shows that several nonparametric tests have efficiency ratings above 0.90, so the lower efficiency might not be an important factor in choosing between parametric and nonparametric tests. However, because parametric tests do have higher efficiency ratings than their nonparametric counterparts, it's generally better to use the parametric tests when their required assumptions are satisfied.

TABLE 13-1 Efficiency: Comparison of Parametric and Nonparametric Tests

Application	Parametric Test	Nonparametric Test	Efficiency Rating of Nonparametric Test with Normal Populations
Matched pairs of sample data	*t* test	Sign test or Wilcoxon signed-ranks test	0.63 0.95
Two independent samples	*t* test	Wilcoxon rank-sum test	0.95
Three or more independent samples	Analysis of variance (*F* test)	Kruskal-Wallis test	0.95
Correlation	Linear correlation	Rank correlation test	0.91

Ranks

Sections 13-2 through 13-6 use methods based on ranks, defined as follows.

DEFINITION

Data are *sorted* when they are arranged according to some criterion, such as smallest to largest or best to worst. A **rank** is a number assigned to an individual sample item according to its order in the sorted list. The first item is assigned a rank of 1, the second item is assigned a rank of 2, and so on.

Handling Ties Among Ranks If a tie in ranks occurs, one very common procedure is to find the mean of the ranks involved in the tie and then assign this mean rank to each of the tied items, as in the following example.

> **EXAMPLE 1** **Handling Ties Among Ranks**
>
> The numbers 4, 5, 5, 5, 10, 11, 12, and 12 are given ranks of 1, 3, 3, 3, 5, 6, 7.5, and 7.5, respectively. The table below illustrates the procedure for handling ties.

Sorted Data	Preliminary Ranking	Rank
4	1	1
5	2 } Mean is 3.	3
5	3	3
5	4	3
10	5	5
11	6	6
12	7 } Mean is 7.5.	7.5
12	8	7.5

13-2 Sign Test

Key Concept This section introduces the *sign test*, which involves converting data values to positive and negative signs, then testing to determine whether either sign occurs significantly more often than the other sign.

> **DEFINITION**
>
> The **sign test** is a nonparametric (distribution-free) test that uses positive and negative signs to test different claims, including these:
>
> **1.** Claims involving matched pairs of sample data
> **2.** Claims involving nominal data with two categories
> **3.** Claims about the median of a single population

Basic Concept of the Sign Test The basic idea underlying the sign test is to analyze the frequencies of positive and negative signs to determine whether they are significantly different. For example, consider the results of clinical trials of the MicroSort method of gender selection. Among 726 couples who used the XSORT method in trying to have a baby girl, 668 couples did have baby girls. Is 668 girls in 726 births *significant*? Common sense should suggest that 668 girls in 726 births is significant, but what about 365 girls in 726 births? Or 400 girls in 726 births? The sign test allows us to determine when such results are significant. Figure 13-1 summarizes the sign test procedure.

For consistency and simplicity, we will use a test statistic based on the number of times that the *less frequent* sign occurs.

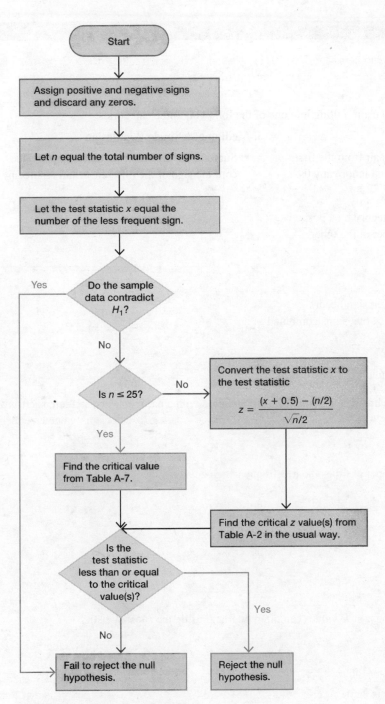

FIGURE 13-1   Sign Test Procedure

KEY ELEMENTS

Sign Test

Objective

Use positive and negative signs to test a claim falling into one of the following three categories:

1. Matched Pairs

- Subtract the second value in each pair from the first, record the sign of the difference, and ignore any 0s.

2. Nominal Data with Two Categories

- Represent each member of one category by a positive sign and represent each member of the other category by a negative sign.

3. Median of a Single Population

- Subtract the median from each sample value, record the sign of the difference, and ignore any 0s.

Notation

x = the number of times the *less frequent* sign occurs
n = the total number of positive and negative signs combined

Requirements

The sample data are a simple random sample.

Note: There is *no* requirement that the sample data come from a population with a particular distribution, such as a normal distribution.

Test Statistic

If $n \leq 25$: Test statistic is x = the number of times the less frequent sign occurs.
If $n > 25$: Test statistic is

$$z = \frac{(x + 0.5) - \left(\frac{n}{2}\right)}{\frac{\sqrt{n}}{2}}$$

P-Values

P-values are often provided by technology, or P-values can often be found using the z test statistic.

Critical Values

1. If $n \leq 25$, critical x values are found in Table A-7.

2. If $n > 25$, critical z values are found in Table A-2.

Hint: Because z is based on the *less* frequent sign, all one-sided tests are treated as if they were left-tailed tests.

CAUTION When using the sign test in a one-tailed test, be very careful to avoid making the wrong conclusion when one sign occurs significantly more often or significantly less often than the other sign but the sample data *contradict* the alternative hypothesis. A sample of 7% boys can never be used to support the claim that boys occur *more than* 50% of the time, as in Example 1.

EXAMPLE 1 Data Contradicting the Alternative Hypothesis

Among 945 couples who used the XSORT method of gender selection, 66 had boys, so the sample proportion of boys is 66/945, or 0.0698 (based on data from the Genetics & IVF Institute). Consider the claim that the XSORT method of gender selection increases the likelihood of baby *boys* so that the probability of a boy is $p > 0.5$. This claim of $p > 0.5$ becomes the alternative hypothesis.

Using common sense, we see that with a sample proportion of boys of 0.0698, we can never support a claim that $p > 0.5$. (We would need a sample proportion of boys *greater* than 0.5 by a significant amount.) Here, the sample proportion of 66/945, or 0.0698, *contradicts* the alternative hypothesis because it is not greater than 0.5.

INTERPRETATION

An alternative hypothesis can never be supported with data that contradict it. The sign test will show that 66 boys in 945 births is significant, but it is significant in the wrong direction. We can never support a claim that $p > 0.5$ with a sample proportion of 66/945, or 0.0698, which is *less than* 0.5.

Claims About Matched Pairs

When using the sign test with data that are matched pairs, we convert the raw data to positive and negative signs as follows:

1. Subtract each value of the second variable from the corresponding value of the first variable.

2. Record only the *sign* of the difference found in Step 1. Exclude *ties* by deleting any matched pairs in which both values are equal.

The main concept underlying this use of the sign test is as follows:

If the two sets of data have equal medians, the number of positive signs should be approximately equal to the number of negative signs.

EXAMPLE 2 Freshman Weight Gain

Table 13-2 includes some of the weights listed in Data Set 10 in Appendix B. Those weights were measured from college students in September and April of their freshman year. Use the sample data in Table 13-2 to test the claim that there is no difference between the September weights and the April weights. Use the sign test with a 0.05 significance level.

TABLE 13-2 Weight (kg) Measurements of Students in Their Freshman Year

September Weight	67	53	64	74	67	70	55	74	62	57
April Weight	66	52	68	77	67	71	60	82	65	58
Sign of Difference	+	+	−	−	0	−	−	−	−	−

SOLUTION

REQUIREMENT CHECK The only requirement of the sign test is that the sample data are a simple random sample. Instead of being a simple random sample of selected students, all subjects volunteered for the study, so the requirement is not satisfied. This limitation is cited in the journal article describing the results of the study. We will proceed as if the requirement of a simple random sample is satisfied. ☑

continued

If there is no difference between the April weights and the corresponding September weights, the numbers of positive and negative signs should be approximately equal. In Table 13-2 we have 7 negative signs, 2 positive signs, and 1 difference of 0. The sign test tells us whether the numbers of positive and negative signs are approximately equal.

The null hypothesis is the claim of no difference between the April weights and the September weights, and the alternative hypothesis is the claim that there is a difference.

H_0: There is no difference. (The median of the differences is equal to 0.)

H_1: There is a difference. (The median of the differences is not equal to 0.)

Following the sign test procedure summarized in Figure 13-1, we let $n = 9$ (the total number of signs) and we let $x = 2$ (the number of the less frequent sign, or the smaller of 2 and 7).

The sample data do not contradict H_1, because there is a difference between the 2 positive signs and the 7 negative signs. The sample data show a difference, and we need to continue with the test to determine whether that difference is significant.

Test Statistic Because $n \leq 25$, the test statistic is $x = 2$ and we do not convert x to a z score.

Critical Value Figure 13-1 shows that with $n = 9$, we should proceed to find the critical value from Table A-7. We refer to Table A-7, where the critical value of 1 is found for $n = 9$ and $\alpha = 0.05$ in two tails.

Conclusion With a test statistic of $x = 2$ and a critical value of 1, we fail to reject the null hypothesis of no difference. (See Note 2 included with Table A-7: "Reject the null hypothesis if the number of the less frequent sign x is less than or equal to the value in the table." Because $x = 2$ is *not* less than or equal to the critical value of 1, we fail to reject the null hypothesis.) There is not sufficient evidence to warrant rejection of the claim that the median of the differences is equal to 0.

INTERPRETATION

We conclude that the September and April weights appear to be about the same. [If we use the parametric t test for matched pairs (Section 9-3), we conclude that the mean difference is not zero, so the September weights and April weights appear to be different.]

The conclusion should be qualified with the limitations noted in the article about the study. Only Rutgers students were used, and study subjects were volunteers instead of being a simple random sample.

Claims Involving Nominal Data with Two Categories

In Chapter 1 we defined nominal data to be data that consist of names, labels, or categories only. The nature of nominal data limits the calculations that are possible, but we can identify the *proportion* of the sample data that belong to a particular category, and we can test claims about the corresponding population proportion p. The following example uses nominal data consisting of genders (girls/boys). The sign test is used by representing girls with positive $(+)$ signs and boys with negative $(-)$ signs. (Those signs are chosen arbitrarily—honest.)

-◯-| **EXAMPLE 3** | **Gender Selection**

The Genetics & IVF Institute conducted a clinical trial of its methods for gender selection for babies. Before the clinical trials were concluded, 879 of 945 babies born to parents using the XSORT method of gender selection were girls. Use the sign test and a 0.05 significance level to test the claim that this method of gender selection is effective in increasing the likelihood of a baby girl.

SOLUTION

REQUIREMENT CHECK The only requirement is that the sample is a simple random sample. Based on the design of this experiment, we can assume that the sample data are a simple random sample. ✅

Let p denote the population proportion of baby girls. The claim that girls are more likely with the XSORT method can be expressed as $p > 0.5$, so the null and alternative hypotheses are as follows:

$$H_0: p = 0.5 \text{ (the proportion of girls is equal to 0.5)}$$

$$H_1: p > 0.5 \text{ (girls are more likely)}$$

Denoting girls by positive signs $(+)$ and boys by negative signs $(-)$, we have 879 positive signs and 66 negative signs. Using the sign test procedure summarized in Figure 13-1, we let the test statistic x be the smaller of 879 and 66, so $x = 66$ boys. *Instead of trying to determine whether 879 girls is high enough to be significantly high, we proceed with the equivalent goal of trying to determine whether 66 boys is low enough to be significantly low, so we treat the test as a* left-tailed *test.*

The sample data do not contradict the alternative hypothesis because the sample proportion of girls is $879/945$, or 0.930, which is greater than 0.5, as in the above alternative hypothesis. Continuing with the procedure in Figure 13-1, we note that the value of $n = 945$ is greater than 25, so the test statistic $x = 66$ is converted (using a correction for continuity) to the test statistic z as follows:

$$z = \frac{(x + 0.5) - \left(\dfrac{n}{2}\right)}{\dfrac{\sqrt{n}}{2}}$$

$$= \frac{(66 + 0.5) - \left(\dfrac{945}{2}\right)}{\dfrac{\sqrt{945}}{2}} = -26.41$$

P-Value We could use the test statistic of $z = -26.41$ to find the left-tailed P-value of 0.0000 (Table: 0.0001), and that low P-value causes us to reject the null hypothesis.

Critical Value With $\alpha = 0.05$ in a left-tailed test, the critical value is $z = -1.645$.

Conclusion Figure 13-2 shows that the test statistic $z = -26.41$ is in the critical region bounded by $z = -1.645$, so we reject the null hypothesis that the proportion of girls is equal to 0.5. There is sufficient sample evidence to support the claim that girls are more likely with the XSORT method.

continued

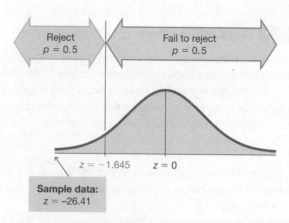

FIGURE 13-2   **Testing Effectiveness of the XSORT Gender Selection Method**

INTERPRETATION

The XSORT method of gender selection does appear to be associated with an increase in the likelihood of a girl, so this method appears to be effective (but this hypothesis test does not prove that the XSORT method is the *cause* of the increase).

Claims About the Median of a Single Population

The next example illustrates the procedure for using the sign test in testing a claim about the median of a single population. See how the negative and positive signs are based on the claimed value of the median.

EXAMPLE 4   **Body Temperatures**

Data Set 2 in Appendix B includes measured body temperatures of adults. Use the 106 temperatures listed for 12 AM on Day 2 with the sign test to test the claim that the median is less than 98.6°F. Of the 106 subjects, 68 had temperatures below 98.6°F, 23 had temperatures above 98.6°F, and 15 had temperatures equal to 98.6°F.

SOLUTION

REQUIREMENT CHECK   The only requirement is that the sample is a simple random sample. Based on the design of this experiment, we assume that the sample data are a simple random sample.

The claim that the median is less than 98.6°F is the alternative hypothesis, while the null hypothesis is the claim that the median is equal to 98.6°F.

H_0: Median is equal to 98.6°F. (median $= 98.6$°F)

H_1: Median is less than 98.6°F. (median < 98.6°F)

Following the procedure outlined in Figure 13-1, we use a negative sign to represent each temperature below 98.6°F, and we use a positive sign for each temperature above 98.6°F. We discard the 15 data values of 98.6°F, since they result in differences of zero. We have 68 negative signs and 23 positive signs, so $n = 91$ and $x = 23$ (the number of the less frequent sign). The sample data do not contradict the alternative hypothesis, because most of the 91 temperatures are below 98.6°F.

Test Statistic The value of n exceeds 25, so we convert the test statistic x to the test statistic z:

$$z = \frac{(x + 0.5) - \left(\frac{n}{2}\right)}{\frac{\sqrt{n}}{2}}$$

$$= \frac{(23 + 0.5) - \left(\frac{91}{2}\right)}{\frac{\sqrt{91}}{2}} = -4.61$$

P-Value In this left-tailed test, the test statistic of $z = -4.61$ yields a P-value of 0.0000 (Table: 0.0001).

Critical Value In this left-tailed test with $\alpha = 0.05$, we use Table A-2 to get the critical z value of -1.645.

Conclusion Using either the low P-value of 0.000 or the fact that the test statistic of $z = -4.61$ is within the critical region as shown in Figure 13-3, we reject the null hypothesis.

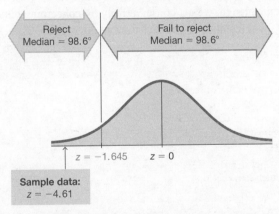

FIGURE 13-3 **Testing the Claim That the Median Is Less Than 98.6°F**

INTERPRETATION

There is sufficient sample evidence to support the claim that the median body temperature of healthy adults is less than 98.6°F. It is not equal to 98.6, as is commonly believed.

Nonparametric vs. Parametric In Example 4, the sign test of the claim that the median is below 98.6°F results in a test statistic of $z = -4.61$ and a P-value of 0.00000202. However, a parametric test of the claim that $\mu < 98.6$°F results in a test statistic of $t = -6.611$ with a P-value of 0.000000000813. Because the P-value from the sign test is not as low as the P-value from the parametric test, we see that the sign test isn't as sensitive as the parametric test. Both tests lead to rejection of the null hypothesis, but the sign test doesn't consider the sample data to be as extreme, partly because the sign test uses only information about the *direction* of the data, ignoring the *magnitudes* of the data values. The next section introduces the Wilcoxon signed-ranks test, which largely overcomes that disadvantage.

Rationale for the Test Statistic Used When $n > 25$ When finding critical values for the sign test, we use Table A-7 only for n up to 25. When $n > 25$, the test statistic z is based on a normal approximation to the binomial probability distribution with $p = q = 1/2$. In Section 6-6 we saw that the normal approximation to the binomial distribution is acceptable when both $np \geq 5$ and $nq \geq 5$. In Section 5-2 we saw that $\mu = np$ and $\sigma = \sqrt{npq}$ for binomial probability distributions. Because this sign test assumes that $p = q = 1/2$, we meet the $np \geq 5$ and $nq \geq 5$ prerequisites whenever $n \geq 10$. Also, with the assumption that $p = q = 1/2$, we get $\mu = np = n/2$ and $\sigma = \sqrt{npq} = \sqrt{n/4} = \sqrt{n}/2$, so the standard z score

$$z = \frac{x - \mu}{\sigma}$$

becomes

$$z = \frac{x - \left(\dfrac{n}{2}\right)}{\dfrac{\sqrt{n}}{2}}$$

We replace x by $x + 0.5$ as a correction for continuity. That is, the values of x are discrete, but since we are using a continuous probability distribution, a discrete value such as 10 is actually represented by the interval from 9.5 to 10.5. Because x represents the less frequent sign, we act conservatively by concerning ourselves only with $x + 0.5$; we get the test statistic z shown below and in the Key Elements box.

$$z = \frac{(x + 0.5) - \left(\dfrac{n}{2}\right)}{\dfrac{\sqrt{n}}{2}}$$

TECH CENTER

Sign Test
Access tech instructions, videos, and data sets at **www.TriolaStats.com**

13-2   Basic Skills and Concepts

Statistical Literacy and Critical Thinking

1. Sign Test for Body Temperatures The table below lists body temperatures of six subjects at 8 AM on Day 1 and 8 AM on Day 2 (from Data Set 1 in Appendix B). The data are matched pairs because each pair of temperatures is measured from the same person. Assume that we plan to use the sign test to test the claim of no difference between body temperatures on both days.

a. What requirements must be satisfied for this test?

b. Is there any requirement that the samples must be from populations having a normal distribution or any other specific distribution?

c. In what sense is this sign test a "distribution-free test"?

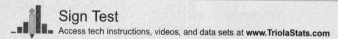

Temperature (°F) at 8 AM on Day 1	98.2	96.6	97.4	97.4	98.2	97.4
Temperature (°F) at 8 AM on Day 2	97.0	96.8	96.6	96.6	96.2	97.6

2. Identifying Signs For the sign test described in Exercise 1, identify the number of positive signs, the number of negative signs, the number of ties, the sample size (n) that is used for the sign test, and the value of the test statistics.

3. Contradicting H_1 An important step in conducting the sign test is to determine whether the sample data contradicts the alternative hypothesis H_1. For the sign test described in Exercise 1, identify the null hypothesis and the alternative hypothesis, and explain how the sample data contradicts or do not contradict the alternative hypothesis.

4. Efficiency of the Sign Test Refer to Table 13-1 on page 579 and identify the efficiency of the sign test. What does that value tell us about the sign test?

Matched Pairs. *In Exercises 5–8, use the sign test for the data consisting of matched pairs.*

5. Heights of Mothers and Daughters Listed below are heights (in.) of mothers and their first daughters (in.). The data are from a journal kept by Francis Galton. (The data are from Data Set 6 "Family Heights.") Use a 0.10 significance level to test the claim of no difference in heights between mothers and their first daughters.

Height of Mother	63.5	65.0	66.0	65.0	65.5	62.0	62.5	64.0	60.0	65.0
Height of Daughter	65.0	62.0	62.0	62.0	66.5	61.7	63.5	65.5	60.0	65.0

6. Heights of Fathers and Sons Listed below are heights (in.) of fathers and their first sons. The data are from a journal kept by Francis Galton. (The data are from Data Set 6 "Family Heights.") Use a 0.10 significance level to test the claim of no difference in heights between fathers and their first sons.

Height of Father	62.0	71.0	69.0	70.0	75.5	69.2	66.5	70.3	69.5	64.0
Height of Son	64.0	68.0	68.0	68.0	73.5	71.7	70.0	70.7	69.7	70.5

7. Friday the 13th Researchers collected data on the numbers of hospital admissions resulting from motor vehicle crashes, and results are given below for Fridays on the 6th of a month and Fridays on the following 13th of the same month (based on data from "Is Friday the 13th Bad for Your Health?" by Scanlon et al., *British Medical Journal*, Vol. 307, as listed in the *Data and Story Line* online resource of data sets). Test the claim that when the 13th day of a month falls on a Friday, the numbers of hospital admissions from motor vehicle crashes are not affected.

Friday the 6th	9	6	11	11	3	5
Friday the 13th	13	12	14	10	4	12

8. Before/After Treatment Results Captopril is a drug designed to lower systolic blood pressure. When subjects were treated with this drug, their systolic blood pressure readings (in mm Hg) were measured before and after the drug was taken. Results are given in the accompanying table (based on data from "Essential Hypertension: Effect of an Oral Inhibitor of Angiotensin-Converting Enzyme," by MacGregor et al., *British Medical Journal*, Vol. 2). Using a 0.01 significance level, is there sufficient evidence to support the claim that captopril has an effect on systolic blood pressure?

Subject	A	B	C	D	E	F	G	H	I	J	K	L
Before	200	174	198	170	179	182	193	209	185	155	169	210
After	191	170	177	167	159	151	176	183	159	145	146	177

Nominal Data. *In Exercises 9–12, use the sign test for the claims involving nominal data.*

9. Stem Cell Survey *Newsweek* conducted a poll in which respondents were asked if they "favor or oppose using federal tax dollars to fund medical research using stem cells obtained from human embryos." Of those polled, 481 were in favor, 401 were opposed, and 120 were unsure. Use a 0.01 significance level to test the claim that there is no difference between the proportions of those opposed and those in favor.

10. Medical Malpractice In a study of 1228 randomly selected medical malpractice lawsuits, it was found that 856 of them were dropped or dismissed (based on data from the Physicians Insurers Association of America). Use a 0.01 significance level to test the claim that there is a difference between the rate of medical malpractice lawsuits that go to trial and the rate of such lawsuits that are dropped or dismissed.

11. Births A random sample of 860 births in New York State included 426 boys and 434 girls. Use a 0.05 significance level to test the claim that when babies are born, boys and girls are equally likely.

12. Touch Therapy At the age of 9, Emily Rosa tested professional touch therapists to see if they could sense her energy field. She flipped a coin to select either her right hand or her left hand; then she asked the therapists to identify the selected hand by placing their hand just under Emily's hand without seeing it and without touching it. Among 280 trials, the touch therapists were correct 123 times and wrong the other times (based on data in "A Close Look at Therapeutic Touch," *Journal of the American Medical Association*, Vol. 279, No. 13). Use a 0.01 significance level to test the claim that the touch therapists make their selections with a method equivalent to random guesses. Based on the results, does it appear that therapists are effective at identifying the correct hand?

Appendix B Data Sets.   *In Exercises 13–16, refer to the indicated data set in Appendix B and use the sign test for the claim about the median of a population.*

13. IQ Scores Use the 20 IQ scores listed in Data Set 9 "IQ and Brain Size" and test the claim that they are from a population with a median IQ score of 100. Use a 0.05 significance level.

14. IQ Scores and Lead Exposure Use the full IQ scores for the group with low lead exposure in Data Set 8 "IQ and Lead." Test the claim that they are from a population with a median IQ score of 100. Use a 0.01 significance level.

15. Diastolic Blood Pressure Use the complete list of diastolic blood pressure measurements from Data Set 1 "Body Data" and test the claim that they are from a population with a median equal to 72. Use a 0.05 significance level.

16. Systolic Blood Pressure Use the complete list of systolic blood pressure measurements from Data Set 1 "Body Data" and test the claim that they are from a population with a median equal to 125. Use a 0.05 significance level.

13-2   Beyond the Basics

17. Procedures for Handling Ties In the sign test procedure described in this section, we exclude ties (represented by 0 instead of a sign of + or −). Here is a second approach: Treat half of the 0s as positive signs and half as negative signs. (If the number of 0s is odd, exclude one so that they can be divided equally.) Here is a third approach: For two-tailed tests make half of the 0s positive and half negative, and for one-tailed tests make all 0s either positive or negative, whichever supports the null hypothesis. Repeat Example 4 "Body Temperatures" using the second and third approaches to handling ties. Do the different approaches lead to very different test statistics, P-values, and conclusions?

18. Finding Critical Values Table A-7 lists critical values for limited choices of α. Use Table A-1 to add a new column in Table A-7 (from $n = 1$ to $n = 8$) that represents a significance level of 0.03 in one tail or 0.06 in two tails. For any particular n, use $p = 0.5$, because the sign test requires the assumption that P(positive sign) $= P$(negative sign) $= 0.5$. The probability of x or fewer like signs is the sum of the probabilities for values up to and including x.

Wilcoxon Signed-Ranks Test for Matched Pairs

13-3

Key Concept This section introduces the *Wilcoxon signed-ranks test*, which begins with the conversion of the sample data into ranks. This test can be used for the two different applications described in the following definition.

DEFINITION

The **Wilcoxon signed-ranks test** is a nonparametric test that uses ranks for these applications:

1. Testing a claim that a population of matched pairs has the property that the matched pairs have differences with a median equal to zero
2. Testing a claim that a single population of individual values has a median equal to some claimed value

---

When testing a claimed value of a median for a population of individual values, we create matched pairs by pairing each sample value with the claimed median, so the same procedure is used for both of the applications above.

Claims Involving Matched Pairs

The sign test (Section 13-2) can be used with matched pairs, but the sign test uses only the *signs* of the differences. By using ranks instead of signs, the Wilcoxon signed-ranks test takes the magnitudes of the differences into account, so it includes and uses more information than the sign test and therefore tends to yield conclusions that better reflect the true nature of the data.

KEY ELEMENTS

Wilcoxon Signed-Ranks Test

Objective: Use the Wilcoxon signed-ranks test for the following tests:

- **Matched Pairs:** Test the claim that a population of matched pairs has the property that the matched pairs have differences with a median equal to zero.

- **One Population of Individual Values:** Test the claim that a population has a median equal to some claimed value. (By pairing each sample value with the claimed median, we again work with matched pairs.)

Notation

T = the smaller of the following two sums:

1. The sum of the positive ranks of the nonzero differences d

2. The absolute value of the sum of the negative ranks of the nonzero differences d

(Details for evaluating T are given in the procedure following this Key Elements box.)

continued

Requirements

1. The data are a simple random sample.

2. The population of differences has a distribution that is approximately *symmetric,* meaning that the left half of its histogram is roughly a mirror image of its right half. (For a sample of matched pairs, obtain differences by subtracting the second value from the first value in each pair; for a sample of individual values, obtain differences by subtracting the value of the claimed median from each sample value.)

Note: There is *no* requirement that the data have a normal distribution.

Test Statistic

If $n \leq 30$, the test statistic is T.

If $n > 30$, the test statistic is $\quad z = \dfrac{T - \dfrac{n(n + 1)}{4}}{\sqrt{\dfrac{n(n + 1)(2n + 1)}{24}}}$

P-Values

P-values are often provided by technology or *P*-values can be found using the z test statistic and Table A-2.

Critical Values

1. If $n \leq 30$, the critical T value is found in Table A-8.

2. If $n > 30$, the critical z values are found in Table A-2.

The following procedure requires that you sort data, then assign ranks. When working with larger data sets, sorting and ranking become tedious, but technology can be used to automate that process. Stemplots can also be very helpful in sorting data.

Wilcoxon Signed-Ranks Procedure To see how the following steps are applied, refer to the sample of matched pairs listed in the first two rows of Table 13-3. Assume that we want to test the null hypothesis that the matched pairs are from a population of matched pairs with differences having a median equal to zero.

TABLE 13-3 Weights (kg) of Students in Their Freshman Year

September weight	67	53	64	74	67	70	55	74	62	57
April weight	66	52	68	77	67	71	60	82	65	58
d (difference)	1	1	−4	−3	0	−1	−5	−8	−3	−1
Rank of |d|	2.5	2.5	7	5.5		2.5	8	9	5.5	2.5
Signed rank	2.5	2.5	−7	−5.5		−2.5	−8	−9	−5.5	−2.5

Step 1: For each pair of data, find the difference d by subtracting the second value from the first value. Discard any pairs that have a difference of 0.

EXAMPLE: The third row of Table 13-3 lists the differences found by subtracting the April weights from the corresponding September weights.

Step 2: *Ignore the signs of the differences,* then sort the differences from lowest to highest and replace the differences by the corresponding rank value (as described in Section 13-1). When differences have the same numerical value, assign to them the mean of the ranks involved in the tie.

EXAMPLE: The fourth row of Table 13-3 shows the ranks of the values of $|d|$. Consider the d values of 1, 1, -1, -1. If we ignore their signs, they are tied for the rank values of 1, 2, 3, 4, so they are each assigned a rank of 2.5, which is the mean of the ranks involved in the tie (or the mean of 1, 2, 3, 4).

Step 3: Attach to each rank the sign of the difference from which it came. That is, insert the signs that were ignored in Step 2.

EXAMPLE: The bottom row of Table 13-3 lists the same ranks found in the fourth row, but the signs of the differences shown in the third row are inserted.

Step 4: Find the sum of the ranks that are positive. Also find the absolute value of the sum of the negative ranks.

EXAMPLE: The bottom row of Table 13-3 lists the signed ranks. The sum of the positive ranks is $2.5 + 2.5 = 5$. The sum of the negative ranks is $(-7) + (-5.5) + (-2.5) + (-8) + (-9) + (-5.5) + (-2.5) = -40$, and the absolute value of this sum is 40. The two rank sums are 5 and 40.

Step 5: Let T be the *smaller* of the two sums found in Step 4. Either sum could be used, but for a simplified procedure we arbitrarily select the smaller of the two sums.

EXAMPLE: The data in Table 13-3 result in the rank sums of 5 and 40, so the smaller of those two sums is 5.

Step 6: Let n be the number of pairs of data for which the difference d is not 0.

EXAMPLE: The data in Table 13-3 have 9 differences that are not 0, so $n = 9$.

Step 7: Determine the test statistic and critical values based on the sample size, as shown in the preceding Key Elements box.

EXAMPLE: For the data in Table 13-3 the test statistic is $T = 5$. The sample size is $n = 9$, so the critical value is found in Table A-8. Using a 0.05 significance level with a two-tailed test, the critical value from Table A-8 is 6.

Step 8: When forming the conclusion, reject the null hypothesis if the sample data lead to a test statistic that is in the critical region—that is, the test statistic is less than or equal to the critical value(s). Otherwise, fail to reject the null hypothesis.

EXAMPLE: If the test statistic is T (instead of z), reject the null hypothesis if T is less than or equal to the critical value. Fail to reject the null hypothesis if T is greater than the critical value. Since $T = 5$ and the critical value is 6, we reject the null hypothesis that the matched pairs are from a population of matched pairs with differences having a median equal to zero.

EXAMPLE 1   Freshman Weight Gain

The first two rows of Table 13-3 include some of the weights from Data Set 10 "Freshman 15" in Appendix B. Those weights were measured from college students in September and April of their freshman year. Use the sample data in the first two rows of Table 13-3 to test the claim that there is no difference between the September weights and the April weights. Use the Wilcoxon signed-ranks test with a 0.05 significance level.

SOLUTION

REQUIREMENT CHECK   (1) The data should be a simple random sample. Instead of being a simple random sample of selected students, all subjects volunteered,

continued

and this is discussed in the journal article describing the results of the study. We will proceed as if the requirement of a simple random sample is satisfied. (2) The histogram of the differences in the third row of Table 13-3 is shown here. The left side of the graph should be roughly a mirror image of the right side, which does not appear to be the case. But with only 9 differences, the difference between the left and right sides is not too extreme, so we will consider this requirement to be satisfied. ✓

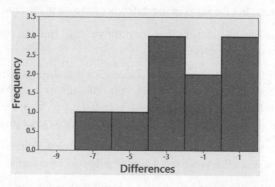

The null hypothesis is the claim of no difference between the April weights and the September weights, and the alternative hypothesis is the claim that there is a difference.

H_0: There is no difference. (The median of the differences is equal to 0.)

H_1: There is a difference. (The median of the differences is not equal to 0.)

Test Statistic Because we are using the Wilcoxon signed-ranks test, the test statistic is calculated by using the eight-step procedure presented earlier in this section. Those steps include examples illustrating the calculation of the test statistic with the sample data in Table 13-3, and the result is the test statistic of $T = 5$.

Critical Value The sample size is $n = 9$, so the critical value is found in Table A-8. Using a 0.05 significance level with a two-tailed test, the critical value from Table A-8 is found to be 6.

Conclusion Table A-8 includes a note stating that we should reject the null hypothesis if the test statistic T is less than or equal to the critical value. Because the test statistic of $T = 5$ is less than the critical value of 6, we reject the null hypothesis.

INTERPRETATION

We conclude that the September and April weights do *not* appear to be about the same. The large number of negative differences indicates that most students gained weight during their freshman year. The conclusion should be qualified with the limitations noted in the article about the study. Only Rutgers students were used, and study subjects were volunteers instead of being a simple random sample.

In Example 1, if we use the parametric t test for matched pairs (Section 9-3), we conclude that the mean difference is not zero, so the September weights and April weights appear to be different, as in Example 1. However, the sign test in Section 13-2 led to the conclusion of no difference. By using only positive and negative signs, the sign test did not use the magnitudes of the differences, but the Wilcoxon signed-ranks test was more sensitive to those magnitudes through its use of ranks.

Claims About the Median of a Single Population

The Wilcoxon signed-ranks test can also be used to test a claim that a single population has some claimed value of the median.

When testing a claim about the median of a single population, create matched pairs by pairing each sample value with the claimed value of the median. The preceding procedure can then be used.

EXAMPLE 2   Body Temperatures

Data Set 2 "Body Temperatures" in Appendix B includes measured body temperatures of adults. Use the 106 temperatures listed for 12 AM on Day 2 with the Wilcoxon signed-ranks test to test the claim that the median is less than 98.6°F. Use a 0.05 significance level.

SOLUTION

REQUIREMENT CHECK   (1) The design of the experiment that led to the data in Data Set 2 justifies treating the sample as a simple random sample. (2) The requirement of an approximately symmetric distribution of differences is satisfied, because a histogram of those differences is approximately symmetric. ✔

By pairing each individual sample value with the median of 98.6°F, we are working with matched pairs. Shown in the margin is the Statdisk display showing the test statistic of $T = 661$, which converts to the test statistic $z = -5.67$. (The display is from a two-tailed test; for this left-tailed test, the critical value is -1.645.) The test statistic of $z = -5.67$ yields a P-value of 0.000, so we reject the null hypothesis that the population of differences between body temperatures and the claimed median of 98.6°F is zero. There is sufficient evidence to support the claim that the median body temperature is less than 98.6°F. This is the same conclusion that results from the sign test in Example 4 in Section 13-2.

Statdisk

> Num Unequal pairs: 91
>
> Using Approximation
> Test Statistic, T: 661.0000
> Mean, μ: 2093
> Standard Deviation: 252.6589
> Test Statistic, z: -5.6677
> Critical z: ±1.959962

Rationale: In Example 1, the unsigned ranks of 1 through 9 have a total of 45, so if there are no significant differences, each of the two signed-rank totals should be around $45 \div 2$, or 22.5. That is, the negative ranks and positive ranks should split up as 22.5–22.5 or something close, such as 24–21. Table A-8, the table of critical values, shows that at the 0.05 significance level with 9 pairs of data, the critical value is 6, so a split of 6–39 represents a significant departure from the null hypothesis, and any split that is further apart will also represent a significant departure from the null hypothesis. Conversely, splits like 7–38 do not represent significant departures from a 22.5–22.5 split, and they would not justify rejecting the null hypothesis. The Wilcoxon signed-ranks test is based on the lower rank total, so instead of analyzing both numbers constituting the split, we consider only the lower number.

The sum of all the ranks $1 + 2 + 3 + \cdots + n$ is equal to $n(n + 1)/2$. If this rank sum is to be divided equally between two categories (positive and negative), each of the two totals should be near $n(n + 1)/4$, which is half of $n(n + 1)/2$. Recognition of this principle helps us understand the test statistic used when $n > 30$.

TECH CENTER

 Wilcoxon Signed-Ranks Test
Access tech instructions, videos, and data sets at **www.TriolaStats.com**

13-3 Basic Skills and Concepts

Statistical Literacy and Critical Thinking

1. Wilcoxon Signed-Ranks Test for Body Temperatures The table below lists body temperatures of seven subjects at 8 AM on Days 1 and 2 (from Data Set 1 in Appendix B). The data are matched pairs because each pair of temperatures is measured from the same person. Assume that we plan to use the Wilcoxon signed-ranks test to test the claim of no difference between body temperatures at 8 AM on both days.

a. What requirements must be satisfied for this test?

b. Is there any requirement that the samples must be from populations having a normal distribution or any other specific distribution?

c. In what sense is this sign test a "distribution-free test"?

Temperature (°F) at 8 AM on Day 1	98.2	96.6	97.4	97.4	98.2	97.4	97.8
Temperature (°F) at 8 AM on Day 2	97.0	96.8	96.6	96.6	96.2	97.6	98.6

2. Body Temperatures For the matched pairs listed in Exercise 1 identify the following components used in Wilcoxon signed-ranks test.

a. Differences d

b. The ranks corresponding to the non-zero values of $|d|$

c. The signed ranks

d. The sum of the positive ranks and the sum of the absolute values of the negative ranks

e. The value of the test statistic T

f. The critical value of T (assuming a 0.10 significance level in a test of no difference between body temperatures at 8 AM on both days)

3. Sign Test vs. Wilcoxon Signed-Ranks Test Using the data in Exercise 1, we can test for no difference between body temperatures at 8 AM on both days by using the sign test or the Wilcoxon signed-ranks test. In what sense does the Wilcoxon signed-ranks test incorporate and use more information than the sign test?

4. Efficiency of the Wilcoxon Signed-Ranks Test Refer to Table 13-1 on page 579 and identify the efficiency of the Wilcoxon signed-ranks test. What does that value tell us about the test?

Using the Wilcoxon Signed-Ranks Test. *In Exercises 5–8, refer to the sample data for the given exercises in Section 13-2 on page 589. Use the Wilcoxon signed-ranks test to test the claim that the matched pairs have differences that come from a population with a median equal to zero. Use a 0.05 significance level.*

5. Exercise 5 "Heights of Mothers and Daughters"

6. Exercise 6 "Heights of Fathers and Sons"

7. Exercise 7 "Friday the 13th"

8. Exercise 8 "Before/After Treatment Results"

Claim About a Median *In Exercises 9–12, refer to the sample data from the given exercises in Section 13-2 on pages 589–590. Use the Wilcoxon signed-ranks test for the claim about the median of a population.*

9. Exercise 13 "IQ Scores"

10. Exercise 14 "IQ Scores and Lead Exposure"

11. Exercise 15 "Diastolic Blood Pressure"

12. Exercise 16 "Systolic Blood Pressure"

13-3   Beyond the Basics

13. Rank Sums Exercise 12 uses body measurement data from Data Set 1 "Body Data" in Appendix B, and the sample size is 300.

a. If we have sample paired data with 300 nonzero differences, what are the smallest and largest possible values of T?

b. If we have sample paired data with 300 nonzero differences, what is the expected value of T if the population consists of matched pairs with differences having a median of 0?

c. If we have sample paired data with 300 nonzero differences and the sum of the positive ranks is 12,345, find the absolute value of the sum of the negative ranks.

d. If we have sample paired data with n nonzero differences and one of the two rank sums is k, find an expression for the other rank sum.

Wilcoxon Rank-Sum Test for Two Independent Samples

Key Concept This section describes the *Wilcoxon rank-sum test,* which uses ranks of values from two *independent* samples to test the null hypothesis that the samples are from populations having equal medians. The Wilcoxon rank-sum test is equivalent to the **Mann-Whitney U test** (see Exercise 13), which is included in some textbooks and technologies (such as Minitab, StatCrunch, and XLSTAT).

Here is the basic idea underlying the Wilcoxon rank-sum test: If two samples are drawn from identical populations and the individual values are all *ranked* as one combined collection of values, then the high and low ranks should fall evenly between the two samples. If the low ranks are found predominantly in one sample and the high ranks are found predominantly in the other sample, we have an indication that the two populations have different medians.

Unlike the parametric t tests for two independent samples in Section 9-2, the Wilcoxon rank-sum test does *not* require normally distributed populations and it can be used with data at the ordinal level of measurement, such as data consisting of ranks. In Table 13-1 we noted that the Wilcoxon rank-sum test has a 0.95 efficiency rating when compared to the parametric test. Because this test has such a high efficiency rating and involves easier calculations, it is often preferred over the parametric t test, even when the requirement of normality is satisfied.

> **CAUTION** Don't confuse the Wilcoxon rank-sum test for two *independent* samples with the Wilcoxon signed-ranks test for matched pairs. Use "Internal Revenue Service" as the mnemonic for IRS to remind yourself of "**I**ndependent: **R**ank **S**um."

> **DEFINITION**
>
> The **Wilcoxon rank-sum test** is a nonparametric test that uses ranks of sample data from two independent populations to test this null hypothesis:
>
> H_0: Two independent samples come from populations with equal medians.
>
> (The alternative hypothesis H_1 can be any one of the following three possibilities: The two populations have *different* medians, or the first population has a median *greater* than the median of the second population, or the first population has a median *less than* the median of the second population.)

Wilcoxon Rank-Sum Test

Objective

Use the Wilcoxon rank-sum test with samples from two independent populations for the following null and alternative hypotheses:

H_0: The two samples come from populations with equal medians.

H_1: The median of the first population is different from (or greater than, or less than) the median from the second population.

Notation

$n_1 =$ size of Sample 1
$n_2 =$ size of Sample 2
$R_1 =$ sum of ranks for Sample 1
$R_2 =$ sum of ranks for Sample 2
$R =$ same as R_1 (sum of ranks for Sample 1)

$\mu_R =$ mean of the sample R values that is expected when the two populations have equal medians
$\sigma_R =$ standard deviation of the sample R values that is expected with two populations having equal medians

Requirements

1. There are two independent simple random samples.

2. Each of the two samples has more than 10 values. (For samples with 10 or fewer values, special tables are available in reference books, such as *CRC Standard Probability and Statistics Tables and Formulae,* published by CRC Press.)

Note: There is *no* requirement that the two populations have a normal distribution or any other particular distribution.

Test Statistic

$$z = \frac{R - \mu_R}{\sigma_R}$$

where $\quad \mu_R = \dfrac{n_1(n_1 + n_2 + 1)}{2} \quad$ and $\quad \sigma_R = \sqrt{\dfrac{n_1 n_2(n_1 + n_2 + 1)}{12}}$

$n_1 =$ size of the sample from which the rank sum R is found
$n_2 =$ size of the other sample
$R =$ sum of ranks of the sample with size n_1

P-Values

P-values can be found from technology or by using the z test statistic and Table A-2.

Critical Values

Critical values can be found in Table A-2 (because the test statistic is based on the normal distribution).

Procedure for Finding the Value of the Test Statistic To see how the following steps are applied, refer to the sample data listed in Table 13-4.

Step 1: Temporarily combine the two samples into one big sample, then replace each sample value with its rank. (The lowest value gets a rank of 1, the next lowest value gets a rank of 2, and so on. If values are tied, assign to them the mean of the ranks involved in the tie. See Section 13-1 for a description of ranks and the procedure for handling ties.)

EXAMPLE: In Table 13-4, the ranks of the 23 sample pulse rates are shown in parentheses. The rank of 1 is assigned to the lowest value of 54. The next lowest values are 56 and 56; because they are tied for the ranks of 2 and 3, we assign the rank of 2.5 to each of them.

Step 2: Find the sum of the ranks for either one of the two samples.

EXAMPLE: In Table 13-4, the sum of the ranks from the first sample is 123.5. (That is, $R_1 = 4.5 + 11 + 19 + \cdots + 6 = 123.5$.)

Step 3: Calculate the value of the z test statistic as shown in the preceding Key Elements box, where either sample can be used as "Sample 1." (If both sample sizes are greater than 10, then the sampling distribution of R is approximately normal with mean μ_R and standard deviation σ_R, and the test statistic is as shown in the preceding Key Elements box.)

EXAMPLE: Calculations of μ_R and σ_R and z are shown in Example 1, which follows.

TABLE 13-4 Pulse Rates (Ranks in parentheses)

Males	Females
60 (**4.5**)	78 (**14**)
74 (**11**)	80 (**17**)
86 (**19**)	68 (**9**)
54 (**1**)	56 (**2.5**)
90 (**20.5**)	76 (**12**)
80 (**17**)	78 (**14**)
66 (**7**)	78 (**14**)
68 (**9**)	90 (**20.5**)
68 (**9**)	96 (**22**)
56 (**2.5**)	60 (**4.5**)
80 (**17**)	98 (**23**)
62 (**6**)	
$n_1 = 12$	$n_2 = 11$
$R_1 = 123.5$	$R_2 = 152.5$

EXAMPLE 1 Pulse Rates of Males and Females

Table 13-4 lists pulse rates of samples of males and females (from Data Set 1 "Body Data" in Appendix B). Use a 0.05 significance level to test the claim that males and females have the same median pulse rate.

SOLUTION

REQUIREMENT CHECK (1) The sample data are two independent simple random samples. (2) The sample sizes are 12 and 11, so both sample sizes are greater than 10. The requirements are satisfied. ☑

The null and alternative hypotheses are as follows:

H_0: The median pulse rate of males is equal to the median pulse rate of females.

H_1: The median pulse rate of males is different from the median pulse rate of females.

Rank the combined list of all 23 pulse rates, beginning with a rank of 1 (assigned to the lowest value of 54). The ranks corresponding to the individual sample values are shown in parentheses in Table 13-4. R denotes the sum of the ranks for the sample we choose as Sample 1. If we choose the pulse rates of males as Sample 1, we get

$$R = 4.5 + 11 + 19 + \cdots + 6 = 123.5$$

Because there are pulse rates from 12 males, we have $n_1 = 12$. Also, $n_2 = 11$ because there are pulse rates from 11 females. We can now find the values of μ_R and σ_R and the test statistic z.

$$\mu_R = \frac{n_1(n_1 + n_2 + 1)}{2} = \frac{12(12 + 11 + 1)}{2} = 144$$

$$\sigma_R = \sqrt{\frac{n_1 n_2 (n_1 + n_2 + 1)}{12}} = \sqrt{\frac{(12)(11)(12 + 11 + 1)}{12}} = 16.248$$

$$z = \frac{R - \mu_R}{\sigma_R} = \frac{123.5 - 144}{16.248} = -1.26$$

The test is two-tailed because a large positive value of z would indicate that disproportionately more higher ranks are found in Sample 1, and a large negative value of z would indicate that disproportionately more lower ranks are found in Sample 1. In

continued

either case, we would have strong evidence against the claim that the two samples come from populations with equal medians.

The significance of the test statistic z can be treated as in previous chapters. We are testing (with $\alpha = 0.05$) the hypothesis that the two populations have equal medians, so we have a two-tailed test with test statistic $z = -1.26$. The P-value is 0.2077 and the critical values are $z = \pm 1.96$. We fail to reject the null hypothesis that the populations of males and females have the same median.

INTERPRETATION

There is not sufficient evidence to warrant rejection of the claim that males and females have the same median pulse rate. Based on the sample data given in Table 13-4, it appears that males and females have pulse rates with the same median.

In Example 1, if we interchange the two sets of sample values and consider the pulse rates of females to be the first sample, then $R = 152.5$, $\mu_R = 132$, $\sigma_R = 16.248$, and $z = 1.26$, so the conclusion is exactly the same.

Statdisk

Total Num Values:	300
Rank Sum 1:	24541.5000
Rank Sum 2:	20608.5000
Mean, μ:	22123.5
St. Dev.:	751.0987
Test Statistic, z:	3.2193
Critical z:	±1.959962

EXAMPLE 2 **Pulse Rates of Males and Females**

Example 1 uses 23 pulse rates, but if we use the 300 pulse rates from Data Set 1 in Appendix B, we get the accompanying display. We can see that the test statistic is $z = 3.22$ (rounded). The test statistic falls in the critical region bounded by the critical values of -1.96 and 1.96. Also, the test statistic of $z = 3.22$ can be used to find that the P-value in this two-tailed test is 0.0013. We reject the null hypothesis of equal medians. Based on the larger sample of 300 subjects, it does appear that females and males have different median pulse rates.

TECH CENTER

Wilcoxon Rank-Sum Test
Access tech instructions, videos, and data sets at **www.TriolaStats.com**

13-4 Basic Skills and Concepts

Statistical Literacy and Critical Thinking

1. Birth Weights Listed below are birth weights (g) from Data Set 3 "Births" in Appendix B. If we use these data for the Wilcoxon rank-sum test with a two-tailed test, what is the null hypothesis?

Girl	3500	800	2400	4200	3100	2000	2900	3300	2800	2500	4000	3100	3000	3400
Boy	3900	2800	3700	4000	3400	1600	3500	3900	3000	3200	3300	300		

2. Rank Sum When applying the Wilcoxon rank-sum test, what is the sum of the ranks for the sample of birth weights of girls?

3. Requirements Refer to the sample data in Exercise 1. Assuming that the samples are random, are the requirements for the Wilcoxon rank-sum test satisfied? Explain.

4. Efficiency Refer to Table 13-1 in Section 13-1 on page 579 and identify the efficiency of the Wilcoxon rank-sum test. What does that value tell us about the test?

Wilcoxon Rank-Sum Test. *In Exercises 5–8, use the Wilcoxon rank-sum test.*

5. Birth Weights Use the sample data given in Exercise 1 and test the claim that girls and boys have the same median birth weight. Use a 0.05 significance level.

6. Radiation in Baby Teeth Listed below are amounts of strontium-90 (in millibecquerels, or mBq, per gram of calcium) in a simple random sample of baby teeth obtained from Pennsylvania residents and New York residents born after 1979 (based on data from "An Unexpected Rise in Strontium-90 in U.S. Deciduous Teeth in the 1990s," by Mangano et al., *Science of the Total Environment*). Use a 0.05 significance level to test the claim that the median amount of strontium-90 from Pennsylvania residents is the same as the median from New York residents.

Pennsylvania	155	142	149	130	151	163	151	142	156	133	138	161
New York	133	140	142	131	134	129	128	140	140	140	137	143

7. Clinical Trials of Lipitor The sample data below are changes in low-density lipoprotein (LDL) cholesterol levels in clinical trials of Lipitor (atorvastatin). It was claimed that Lipitor had an effect on LDL cholesterol. (The data are based on results given in a Parke-Davis memo from David G. Orloff, M.D., the medical team leader for clinical trials of Lipitor. Pfizer declined to provide the original data values.) Negative values represent decreases in LDL cholesterol. Use a 0.05 significance level to test the claim that for those treated with 20 mg of atorvastatin and those treated with 80 mg of atorvastatin, changes in LDL cholesterol have the same median. What do the results suggest?

Group treated with 20 mg atorvastatin:													
−28	−32	−29	−39	−31	−35	−25	−36	−35	−26	−29	−34	−30	

Group treated with 80 mg atorvastatin:													
−42	−41	−38	−42	−41	−41	−40	−44	−32	−37	−41	−37	−34	−31

8. Blanking Out on Tests In a study of students blanking out on tests, the arrangement of test items was studied for its effect on anxiety. The following scores are measures of "debilitating test anxiety" (based on data from "Item Arrangement, Cognitive Entry Characteristics, Sex and Test Anxiety as Predictors of Achievement in Examination Performance," by Klimko, *Journal of Experimental Education*, Vol. 52, No. 4). Is there sufficient evidence to support the claim that the two samples are from populations with different medians? Is there sufficient evidence to support the claim that the arrangement of the test items has an effect on the score? Use a 0.01 significance level.

Questions Arranged from Easy to Difficult					Questions Arranged from Difficult to Easy			
24.64	39.29	16.32	32.83	28.02	33.62	34.02	26.63	30.26
33.31	20.60	21.13	26.69	28.90	35.91	26.68	29.49	35.32
26.43	24.23	7.10	32.86	21.06	27.24	32.34	29.34	33.53
28.89	28.71	31.73	30.02	21.96	27.62	42.91	30.20	32.54
25.49	38.81	27.85	30.29	30.72				

Appendix B Data Sets. *In Exercises 9–12, refer to the indicated data set in Appendix B and use the Wilcoxon rank-sum test.*

9. Birth Weights Repeat Exercise 5 "Birth Weights" using all of the birth weights given in Data Set 3 "Births" in Appendix B.

10. Cigarettes Refer to Data Set 15 "Cigarette Contents" in Appendix B for the amounts of nicotine (mg per cigarette) in the sample of king-size cigarettes, which are nonfiltered, non-menthol, and nonlight, and for the amounts of nicotine in the 100-mm cigarettes, which are filtered, nonmenthol, and nonlight. Use a 0.01 significance level to test the claim that the median amount of nicotine in the nonfiltered king-size cigarettes is greater than the median amount of nicotine in the 100-mm filtered cigarettes.

11. IQ and Lead Exposure Data Set 8 "IQ and Lead" in Appendix B lists *full* IQ scores for a random sample of subjects with "medium" lead levels in their blood and another random sample of subjects with "high" lead levels in their blood. Use a 0.05 significance level to test

continued

the claim that subjects with medium lead levels have a higher median of the full IQ scores than subjects with high lead levels. Does lead level appear to affect full IQ scores?

12. IQ and Lead Exposure Data Set 8 "IQ and Lead" in Appendix B lists *performance* IQ scores for a random sample of subjects with low lead levels in their blood and another random sample of subjects with high lead levels in their blood. Use a 0.05 significance level to test the claim that subjects with low lead levels have a higher median of the performance IQ score than those with high lead levels. Does lead exposure appear to have an adverse effect?

13-4   Beyond the Basics

13. Using the Mann-Whitney U Test The Mann-Whitney U test is equivalent to the Wilcoxon rank-sum test for independent samples in the sense that they both apply to the same situations and always lead to the same conclusions. In the Mann-Whitney U test we calculate

$$z = \frac{U - \dfrac{n_1 n_2}{2}}{\sqrt{\dfrac{n_1 n_2 (n_1 + n_2 + 1)}{12}}}$$

where

$$U = n_1 n_2 + \frac{n_1(n_1 + 1)}{2} - R$$

and R is the sum of the ranks for Sample 1. Use the pulse rates in Table 13-4 on page 599 in this section to find the z test statistic for the Mann-Whitney U test. Compare this value to the z test statistic found using the Wilcoxon rank-sum test.

14. Finding Critical Values Assume that we have two treatments (A and B) that produce quantitative results, and we have only two observations for treatment A and two observations for treatment B. We cannot use the Wilcoxon signed ranks test given in this section because both sample sizes do not exceed 10.

Rank				Rank Sum for Treatment A
1	2	3	4	
A	A	B	B	3

a. Complete the accompanying table by listing the five rows corresponding to the other five possible outcomes, and enter the corresponding rank sums for treatment A.

b. List the possible values of R and their corresponding probabilities. [Assume that the rows of the table from part (a) are equally likely.]

c. Is it possible, at the 0.10 significance level, to reject the null hypothesis that there is no difference between treatments A and B? Explain.

13-5   Kruskal-Wallis Test for Three or More Samples

Key Concept This section describes the *Kruskal-Wallis test,* which uses *ranks* of data from three or more independent simple random samples to test the null hypothesis that the samples come from populations with the same median.

Section 12-1 described one-way analysis of variance (ANOVA) as a method for testing the null hypothesis that three or more populations have the same *mean,* but

ANOVA requires that all of the involved populations have normal distributions. The Kruskal-Wallis test for equal *medians* does not require normal distributions, so it is a distribution-free or nonparametric test.

DEFINITION

The **Kruskal-Wallis test** (also called the *H* **test**) is a nonparametric test that uses ranks of combined simple random samples from three or more independent populations to test the null hypothesis that the populations have the same median. (The alternative hypothesis is the claim that the populations have medians that are not all equal.)

KEY ELEMENTS

Kruskal-Wallis Test

Objective

Use the Kruskal-Wallis test with simple random samples from three or more independent populations for the following:

H_0: The samples come from populations with the same median.

H_1: The samples come from populations with medians that are not all equal.

Notation

N = total number of observations in all samples combined

k = number of different samples

R_1 = sum of ranks for Sample 1

n_1 = number of observations in Sample 1

For Sample 2, the sum of ranks is R_2 and the number of observations is n_2, and similar notation is used for the other samples.

Requirements

1. We have at least three independent samples.

2. Each sample has at least five observations. (If samples have fewer than five observations, refer to special tables of critical values.)

Note: There is *no* requirement that the populations have a normal distribution or any other particular distribution.

Test Statistic

$$H = \frac{12}{N(N+1)} \left(\frac{R_1^2}{n_1} + \frac{R_2^2}{n_2} + \cdots + \frac{R_k^2}{n_k} \right) - 3(N+1)$$

P-Values

P-values are often provided by technology. By using the test statistic H and the number of degrees of freedom $(k-1)$, Table A-4 can be used to find a range of values for the *P*-value.

Critical Values

1. The test is *right-tailed* and critical values can be found from technology or from the chi-square distribution in Table A-4.

2. df $= k - 1$ (where df is the number of degrees of freedom and k is the number of different samples)

In applying the Kruskal-Wallis test, we compute the test statistic H, which has a distribution that can be approximated by the chi-square distribution provided that each sample has at least five observations. (For a quick review of the key features of the chi-square distribution, see Section 7-3.)

The H test statistic measures the variance of the rank sums $R_1, R_2, \ldots, R_k$ from the different samples. If the ranks are distributed evenly among the sample groups, then H should be a relatively small number. If the samples are very different, then the ranks will be excessively low in some groups and high in others, with the net effect that H will be large. Consequently, only large values of H lead to rejection of the null hypothesis that the samples come from identical populations. *The Kruskal-Wallis test is therefore a right-tailed test.*

Procedure for Finding the Value of the H Test Statistic To see how the following steps are applied, refer to the sample data listed in Table 13-5. Table 13-5 includes only some of the data in Data Set 14 "Passive and Active Smoke" in Appendix B. This shortened data set is more suitable for illustrating the method of the Kruskal-Wallis test.

Step 1: Temporarily combine all samples into one big sample and assign a rank to each sample value. (Sort the values from lowest to highest, and in cases of ties, assign to each observation the mean of the ranks involved.)

EXAMPLE: In Table 13-5, the numbers in parentheses are the ranks of the combined data set. There are ten values of 0 tied for the lowest ranks of 1 through 10, so each of them is assigned a rank of 5.5, which is the mean of the integers from 1 through 10. Next, there are two values of 1 tied for ranks 11 and 12, so each of them is assigned a rank of 11.5. The next lowest number is 19, which is assigned the next rank of 13, and so on.

Step 2: For each sample, find the sum of the ranks and find the sample size.

EXAMPLE: In Table 13-5, the sum of the ranks from the first sample is 65, the sum of the ranks for the second sample is 67.5, and the sum of the ranks for the third sample is 38.5.

Step 3: Calculate H using the results of Step 2 and the notation and test statistic given in the preceding Key Elements box.

EXAMPLE: The test statistic is computed in Example 1.

TABLE 13-5 Cotinine Levels (Ranks in parentheses)

Smokers	ETS	NOETS
1 (11.5)	384 (18)	0 (5.5)
0 (5.5)	0 (5.5)	0 (5.5)
131 (15)	69 (14)	0 (5.5)
173 (16)	19 (13)	0 (5.5)
265 (17)	1 (11.5)	0 (5.5)
	0 (5.5)	0 (5.5)
		0 (5.5)
$n_1 = 5$	$n_2 = 6$	$n_3 = 7$
$R_1 = 65$	$R_2 = 67.5$	$R_3 = 38.5$

EXAMPLE 1 **Effect of Second-Hand Smoke**

Table 13-5 lists some of the data from Data Set 14 "Passive and Active Smoke" in Appendix B. Use a 0.05 significance level to test the claim that the three samples of cotinine levels come from populations with medians that are all equal.

SOLUTION

REQUIREMENT CHECK (1) Each of the three samples is a simple random independent sample. (2) Each sample size is at least 5. The requirements are satisfied. ☑
    The null and alternative hypotheses are as follows:

H_0: The populations of smokers, nonsmokers exposed to tobacco smoke (ETS), and nonsmokers not exposed to tobacco smoke have cotinine levels with the same median.

H_1: The three populations have medians that are not all the same.

Test Statistic First combine all of the sample data and rank them, then find the sum of the ranks for each category. In Table 13-5, ranks are shown in parentheses next to the original sample values. Next, find the sample size (n) and sum of ranks (R) for each sample. Those values are shown at the bottom of Table 13-5. Because the total number of observations is 18, we have $N = 18$. We can now evaluate the test statistic as follows:

$$H = \frac{12}{N(N+1)} \left(\frac{R_1^2}{n_1} + \frac{R_2^2}{n_2} + \cdots + \frac{R_k^2}{n_k} \right) - 3(N+1)$$

$$= \frac{12}{18(18+1)} \left(\frac{65^2}{5} + \frac{67.5^2}{6} + \frac{38.5^2}{7} \right) - 3(18+1)$$

$$= 6.724$$

Critical Value Because each sample has at least five observations, the distribution of H is approximately a chi-square distribution with $k - 1$ degrees of freedom. The number of samples is $k = 3$, so we have $3 - 1 = 2$ degrees of freedom. Refer to Table A-4 to find the critical value of 5.991, which corresponds to 2 degrees of freedom and a 0.05 significance level (with an area of 0.05 in the right tail). Figure 13-4 shows that the test statistic $H = 6.724$ does fall within the critical region bounded by 5.991, so we reject the null hypothesis of equal population medians.
    Figure 13-4 shows the test statistic of $H = 6.724$ and the critical value of 5.991. (The chi-square distribution has the general shape shown in Figure 13-4

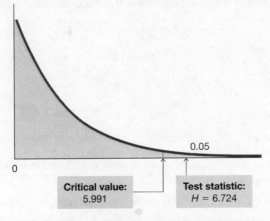

FIGURE 13-4 Chi-Square Distribution for Example 1

continued

whenever the number of degrees of freedom is 1 or 2.) The test statistic does fall in the critical region, so we reject the null hypothesis of equal medians.

> **INTERPRETATION**
>
> There is sufficient evidence to reject the claim that the three samples of cotinine levels come from populations with medians that are all equal. The population medians do appear to be significantly different.

Rationale: The Kruskal-Wallis H test statistic is the rank version of the F test statistic used in analysis of variance discussed in Chapter 12. When we deal with ranks R instead of original values x, many components are predetermined. For example, the sum of all ranks can be expressed as $N(N + 1)/2$, where N is the total number of values in all samples combined. The expression

$$H = \frac{12}{N(N + 1)} \Sigma n_i (\bar{R}_i - \bar{\bar{R}})^2$$

where

$$\bar{R}_i = \frac{R_i}{n_i} \quad and \quad \bar{\bar{R}} = \frac{\Sigma R_i}{\Sigma n_i}$$

combines weighted variances of ranks to produce the H test statistic given here, and this expression for H is algebraically equivalent to the expression for H given earlier as the test statistic.

TECH CENTER

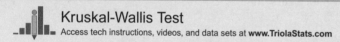

Kruskal-Wallis Test
Access tech instructions, videos, and data sets at **www.TriolaStats.com**

13-5   Basic Skills and Concepts

Statistical Literacy and Critical Thinking

1. Effect of Lead on IQ Score Listed below are full IQ scores from simple random samples of subjects with low lead exposure, medium lead exposure, and high lead exposure (from Data Set 8 in Appendix B). In using the Kruskal-Wallis test, we must rank all of the data combined; then we must find the sum of the ranks for each sample. Find the sum of the ranks for each of the three samples.

Low Lead Level	Medium Lead Level	High Lead Level
70	72	82
85	90	93
86	92	85
76	71	75
84	86	85
	79	

2. Requirements Assume that we want to use the data from Exercise 1 with the Kruskal-Wallis test. Are the requirements satisfied? Explain.

3. Notation For the data given in Exercise 1, identify the values of n_1, n_2, n_3, and N.

4. Efficiency Refer to Table 13-1 on page 579 and identify the efficiency of the Kruskal-Wallis test. What does that value tell us about the test?

Using the Kruskal-Wallis Test.   *In Exercises 5–8, use the Kruskal-Wallis test.*

5. Chest Injury in a Car Crash Use the following listed chest deceleration measurements (in *g*, where *g* is the force of gravity) from samples of small, midsize, and large cars. Use a 0.05 significance level to test the claim that the different size categories have the same median chest deceleration in the standard crash test. Do the data suggest that larger cars are safer?

Small	44	39	37	54	39	44	42
Midsize	36	53	43	42	52	49	41
Large	32	45	41	38	37	38	33

6. Femur Injury in a Car Crash Listed below are measured loads (in lb) on the left femur of crash test dummies. Use a 0.05 significance level to test the null hypothesis that the different car categories have the same median. Do these data suggest that larger cars are safer?

Small Cars	548	782	1188	707	324	320	634	501	274	437
Medium Cars	194	280	1076	411	617	133	719	656	874	445
Large Cars	215	937	953	1636	937	472	882	562	656	433

7. Arsenic in Rice Listed below are amounts of arsenic in samples of brown rice from three different states. The amounts are in micrograms of arsenic and all samples have the same serving size. The data are from the Food and Drug Administration. Use a 0.01 significance level to test the claim that the three samples are from populations with the same median.

Arkansas	4.8	4.9	5.0	5.4	5.4	5.4	5.6	5.6	5.6	5.9	6.0	6.1
California	1.5	3.7	4.0	4.5	4.9	5.1	5.3	5.4	5.4	5.5	5.6	5.6
Texas	5.6	5.8	6.6	6.9	6.9	6.9	7.1	7.3	7.5	7.6	7.7	7.7

8. Triathlon Times Jeff Parent is a statistics instructor who participates in triathlons. Listed below are times (in minutes and seconds) he recorded while riding a bicycle for five laps through each mile of a 3-mile loop. Use a 0.05 significance level to test the claim that the samples are from populations with the same median. What do the data suggest?

Mile 1	3:15	3:24	3:23	3:22	3:21
Mile 2	3:19	3:22	3:21	3:17	3:19
Mile 3	3:34	3:31	3:29	3:31	3:29

Appendix B Data Sets.   *In Exercises 9–12, use the Kruskal-Wallis test with the data set in Appendix B.*

9. Passive and Active Smoke Data Set 14 "Passive and Active Smoke" in Appendix B lists measured cotinine levels from a sample of subjects who smoke, another sample of subjects who do not smoke but are exposed to environmental tobacco smoke, and a third sample of subjects who do not smoke and are not exposed to environmental tobacco smoke. Cotinine is produced when the body absorbs nicotine. Use a 0.01 significance level to test the claim that the three samples are from populations with the same median. What do the results suggest about a smoker who argues that he absorbs as much nicotine as people who don't smoke?

10. IQ and Lead Exposure Refer to Data Set 8 "IQ and Lead" and use the measured *performance* IQ scores from the three different blood lead levels. Use a 0.05 significance level to test the claim that the three categories of blood lead level have the same median performance IQ score.

11. Nicotine in Cigarettes Refer to Data Set 15 "Cigarette Contents" in Appendix B and use the amounts of nicotine (mg per cigarette) in the king-size cigarettes, the 100-mm menthol cigarettes, and the 100-mm nonmenthol cigarettes. The king-size cigarettes are nonfiltered, nonmenthol, and nonlight. The 100-mm menthol cigarettes are filtered and nonlight. The 100-mm nonmenthol cigarettes are filtered and nonlight. Use a 0.05 significance level to test the claim that the three categories of cigarettes yield the same median amount of nicotine. Given that only the king-size cigarettes are not filtered, do the filters appear to make a difference?

12. Tar in Cigarettes Refer to Data Set 15 "Cigarette Contents" in Appendix B and use the amounts of tar (mg per cigarette) in the three categories of cigarettes described in Exercise 11. Use a 0.05 significance level to test the claim that the three categories of cigarettes yield the same median amount of tar. Given that only the king-size cigarettes are not filtered, do the filters appear to make a difference?

13-5 Beyond the Basics

13. Correcting the *H* Test Statistic for Ties In using the Kruskal-Wallis test, there is a correction factor that should be applied whenever there are many ties: Divide *H* by

$$1 - \frac{\Sigma T}{N^3 - N}$$

First combine all of the sample data into one list, and then in that combined list, identify the different groups of sample values that are tied. For each individual group of tied observations, identify the *number* of sample values that are tied and designate that number as *t*, then calculate $T = t^3 - t$. Next, add the *T* values to get ΣT. The value of *N* is the total number of observations in all samples combined. Use this procedure to find the corrected value of *H* for Example 1 in this section on page 605. Does the corrected value of *H* differ substantially from the value found in Example 1?

13-6 Rank Correlation

Key Concept This section describes the nonparametric method of the *rank correlation test,* which uses *ranks* of paired data to test for an association between two variables. In Section 10-1, paired sample data were used to compute values for the linear correlation coefficient *r*, but in this section we use *ranks* as the basis for computing the rank correlation coefficient r_s. As in Chapter 10, we should begin an analysis of paired data by exploring with a scatterplot so that we can identify any patterns in the data as well as outliers.

> **DEFINITION**
>
> The **rank correlation test** (or **Spearman's rank correlation test**) is a nonparametric test that uses ranks of sample data consisting of matched pairs. It is used to test for an association between two variables.

We use the notation r_s for the rank correlation coefficient so that we don't confuse it with the linear correlation coefficient *r*. The subscript *s* does *not* refer to a standard deviation; it is used in honor of Charles Spearman (1863–1945), who originated the rank correlation approach. In fact, r_s is often called **Spearman's rank correlation coefficient.** Key components of the rank correlation test are given in the following Key Elements box, and the rank correlation procedure is summarized in Figure 13-5 on page 610.

KEY ELEMENTS

Rank Correlation

Objective

Compute the rank correlation coefficient r_s and use it to test for an association between two variables. The null and alternative hypotheses are as follows:

H_0: $\rho_s = 0$ (There is no correlation.)
H_1: $\rho_s \neq 0$ (There is a correlation.)

Notation

r_s = rank correlation coefficient for sample paired data (r_s is a sample statistic)

ρ_s = rank correlation coefficient for all the population data (ρ_s is a population parameter)

n = number of pairs of sample data

d = difference between ranks for the two values within an individual pair

Requirements

1. The paired data are a simple random sample.
2. The data are ranks or can be converted to ranks.

Note: Unlike the parametric methods of Section 10-1, there is *no* requirement that the sample pairs of data have a bivariate normal distribution (as described in Section 10-1). There is *no* requirement of a normal distribution for any population.

Test Statistic

Within each sample, first convert the data to *ranks*, then find the exact value of the rank correlation coefficient r_s by using Formula 10-1:

FORMULA 10-1

$$r_s = \frac{n(\Sigma xy) - (\Sigma x)(\Sigma y)}{\sqrt{n(\Sigma x^2) - (\Sigma x)^2}\sqrt{n(\Sigma y^2) - (\Sigma y)^2}}$$

Simpler Test Statistic if There Are No Ties: After converting the data in each sample to ranks, if there are no ties among ranks for the first variable and there are no ties among ranks for the second variable, the exact value of the test statistic can be calculated using Formula 10-1 or with the following relatively simple formula, but it is probably easier to use Formula 10-1 with technology:

$$r_s = 1 - \frac{6\Sigma d^2}{n(n^2 - 1)}$$

P-Values

P-values are sometimes provided by technology, but use them only if they result from Spearman's rank correlation. (Do not use *P*-values resulting from tests of *linear* correlation; see the "caution" on the top of page 611.)

Critical Values

1. If $n \leq 30$, critical values are found in Table A-9.

2. If $n > 30$, critical values of r_s are found using Formula 13-1.

FORMULA 13-1

$$r_s = \frac{\pm z}{\sqrt{n - 1}} \text{ (critical values for } n > 30)$$

where the value of z corresponds to the significance level. (For example, if $\alpha = 0.05$, $z = 1.96$.)

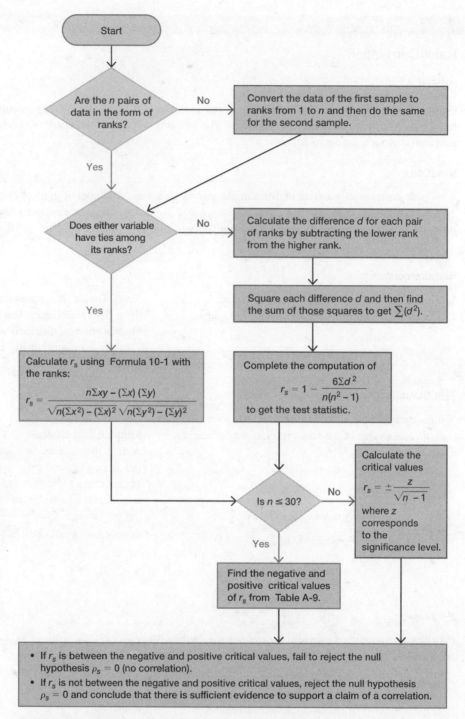

FIGURE 13-5 **Rank Correlation Procedure for Testing H_0: $\rho_s = 0$**

CAUTION *Do not use P-values from linear correlation for methods of rank correlation.* When working with data having ties among ranks, the rank correlation coefficient r_s can be calculated using Formula 10-1. Technology can be used instead of manual calculations with Formula 10-1, but the displayed *P*-values from *linear* correlation do not apply to the methods of *rank* correlation.

Advantages of Rank Correlation Rank correlation has these advantages over the parametric methods discussed in Chapter 10:

1. Rank correlation can be used with paired data that are ranks or can be converted to ranks. Unlike the parametric methods of Chapter 10, the method of rank correlation does *not* require a normal distribution for any population.

2. Rank correlation can be used to detect some (not all) relationships that are not linear.

Disadvantage of Rank Correlation: Efficiency A minor disadvantage of rank correlation is its efficiency rating of 0.91, as described in Section 13-1. This efficiency rating shows that with all other circumstances being the same, the nonparametric approach of rank correlation requires 100 pairs of sample data to achieve the same results as only 91 pairs of sample observations analyzed through the parametric approach, assuming that the stricter requirements of the parametric approach are met.

EXAMPLE 1 Bacteria Growth

An experiment involves a growing population of bacteria. Table 13-6 lists randomly selected times (in hr) after the experiment is begun and the number of bacteria present. Use a 0.05 significance level to test the claim that there is a correlation between time and population size.

SOLUTION

REQUIREMENT CHECK The data are a simple random sample and can be converted to ranks. ✓

The null and alternative hypotheses are as follows:

$$H_0: \ \rho_s = 0 \ (\text{no correlation})$$
$$H_1: \ \rho_s \neq 0 \ (\text{correlation})$$

We follow the rank correlation procedure summarized in Figure 13-5. The original values are not ranks, so we convert them to ranks and enter the results in Table 13-7. (Section 13-1 describes the procedure for converting scores into ranks.)

TABLE 13-6 Number of Bacteria in a Growing Population

Time (hours)	6	107	109	125	126	128	133	143	177	606
Population Size	2	3	4	10	16	29	35	38	41	45

TABLE 13-7 Ranks from Table 13-6

Ranks of Times	1	2	3	4	5	6	7	8	9	10
Ranks of Populations	1	2	3	4	5	6	7	8	9	10
Difference d	0	0	0	0	0	0	0	0	0	0
d^2	0	0	0	0	0	0	0	0	0	0

Direct Link Between Smoking and Cancer

When we find a statistical correlation between two variables, we must be extremely careful to avoid the mistake of concluding that there is a cause-effect link. The tobacco industry has consistently emphasized that correlation does not imply causality as they denied that tobacco products cause cancer. However, Dr. David Sidransky of Johns Hopkins University and other researchers found a direct physical link that involves mutations of a specific gene among smokers. Molecular analysis of genetic changes allows researchers to determine whether cigarette smoking is the cause of a cancer. (See "Association Between Cigarette Smoking and Mutation of the p53 Gene in Squamous-Cell Carcinoma of the Head and Neck," by Brennan, Boyle, et al., *New England Journal of Medicine*, Vol 332, No. 11.) Although statistical methods cannot prove that smoking *causes* cancer, statistical methods can be used to identify an association, and physical proof of causation can then be sought by researchers.

continued

There are no ties among the ranks for the times, nor are there ties among the ranks for population size, so we find the differences, d, then square them. Next we find the sum of the d^2 values, which is 0 in this case. We now calculate the value of the test statistic:

$$r_s = 1 - \frac{6\Sigma d^2}{n(n^2 - 1)} = 1 - \frac{6(0)}{10(10^2 - 1)}$$

$$= 1 - \frac{0}{990} = 1$$

With $n = 10$, we use Table A-9 to get the critical values of ± 0.648. Finally, the test statistic of $r_s = 1$ is not between -0.648 and 0.648, so we reject the null hypothesis of $\rho_s = 0$. There is sufficient evidence to support the claim that for bacteria, there is a correlation between time and population size.

Nonlinear Pattern

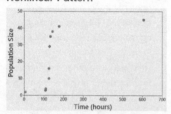

Detecting a Nonlinear Pattern In Example 1, if we test for a *linear* correlation using the methods of Section 10-1, we get a test statistic of $r = 0.621$ and critical values of -0.632 and 0.632, so we conclude that there is not sufficient evidence to support a claim of a linear correlation between time and population size. If we examine the accompanying scatterplot, we can see that the pattern of points is not a straight-line pattern. Example 1 illustrates this advantage of the nonparametric approach over the parametric approach:

With rank correlation, we can sometimes detect relationships that are not linear.

EXAMPLE 2 Large Sample Case

Refer to the measured systolic and diastolic blood pressure measurements of 147 randomly selected females in Data Set 1 "Body Data" in Appendix B and use a 0.05 significance level to test the claim that among women, there is a correlation between systolic blood pressure and diastolic blood pressure.

SOLUTION

REQUIREMENT CHECK The data are a simple random sample and can be converted to ranks. ✓

Test Statistic The value of the rank correlation coefficient is $r_s = 0.354$, which can be found by using technology.

Critical Values Because there are 147 pairs of data, we have $n = 147$. Because n exceeds 30, we find the critical values from Formula 13-1 instead of Table A-9. With $\alpha = 0.05$ in two tails, we let $z = 1.96$ to get the critical values of -0.162 and 0.162, as shown below.

$$r_s = \frac{\pm z}{\sqrt{n - 1}} = \frac{\pm 1.96}{\sqrt{147 - 1}} = \pm 0.162$$

The test statistic of $r_s = 0.354$ is not between the critical values of -0.162 and 0.162, so we reject the null hypothesis of $r_s = 0$. There is sufficient evidence to support the claim that among women, there is a correlation between systolic blood pressure and diastolic blood pressure.

TECH CENTER

Rank Correlation
Access tech instructions, videos, and data sets at **www.TriolaStats.com**

13-6   Basic Skills and Concepts

Statistical Literacy and Critical Thinking

1. Regression If the methods of this section are used with paired sample data, and the conclusion is that there is sufficient evidence to support the claim of a correlation between the two variables, can we use the methods of Section 10-2 to find the regression equation that can be used for predictions? Why or why not?

2. Level of Measurement Which of the levels of measurement (nominal, ordinal, interval, ratio) describe data that *cannot* be used with the methods of rank correlation? Explain.

3. Notation What do r, r_s, ρ, and ρ_s denote? Why is the subscript s used? Does the subscript s represent the same standard deviation s introduced in Section 3-2?

4. Efficiency Refer to Table 13-1 on page 579 and identify the efficiency of the rank correlation test. What does that value tell us about the test?

In Exercises 5 and 6, use the scatterplot to find the value of the rank correlation coefficient r_s and the critical values corresponding to a 0.05 significance level used to test the null hypothesis of $\rho_s = 0$. Determine whether there is a correlation.

5. Ages and Heights of Trees

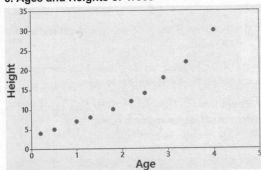

6. Numbers of Waiting Patients and Patient Service Times

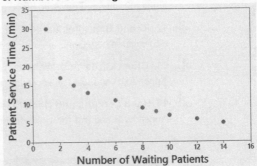

Testing for Rank Correlation.   *In Exercises 7–10, use the rank correlation coefficient to test for a correlation between the two variables. Use a significance level of $\alpha = 0.05$.*

7. Crickets and Temperature The association between the temperature and the number of times a cricket chirps in 1 min was studied. Listed below are the numbers of chirps in 1 min and the corresponding temperatures in degrees Fahrenheit (based on data from *The Song of Insects* by George W. Pierce, Harvard University Press). Is there sufficient evidence to conclude that there is a relationship between the number of chirps in 1 min and the temperature?

Chirps in 1 min	882	1188	1104	864	1200	1032	960	900
Temperature (°F)	69.7	93.3	84.3	76.3	88.6	82.6	71.6	79.6

8. Measuring Seals from Photos Listed below are the overhead widths (in cm) of seals measured from photographs and the weights of the seals (in kg). The data are based on "Mass Estimation of Weddell Seals Using Techniques of Photogrammetry," by R. Garrott of Montana State University. The purpose of the study was to determine if weights of seals could be determined from overhead photographs. Is there sufficient evidence to conclude that there is a correlation between overhead widths of seals from photographs and the weights of the seals?

Overhead Width (cm)	7.2	7.4	9.8	9.4	8.8	8.4
Weight (kg)	116	154	245	202	200	191

9. Smoking and Nicotine When nicotine is absorbed by the body, cotinine is produced. A measurement of cotinine in the body is therefore a good indicator of how much a person smokes. Listed below are the reported numbers of cigarettes smoked per day and the measured amounts of nicotine (in ng/ml). (The values are from randomly selected subjects in the National Health Examination Survey.) Is there a significant linear correlation? Explain the result.

x (cigarettes/day)	60	10	4	15	10	1	20	8	7	10	10	20
y (cotinine)	179	283	75.6	174	209	9.51	350	1.85	43.4	25.1	408	344

10. Tree Circumference and Height Listed below are the circumferences (in feet) and the heights (in feet) of trees in Marshall, Minnesota (based on data from "Tree Measurements," by Stanley Rice, *American Biology Teacher,* Vol. 61, No. 9). Is there a correlation?

x (circ.)	1.8	1.9	1.8	2.4	5.1	3.1	5.5	5.1	8.3	13.7	5.3	4.9	3.7	3.8
y (ht.)	21.0	33.5	24.6	40.7	73.2	24.9	40.4	45.3	53.5	93.8	64.0	62.7	47.2	44.3

Appendix B Data Sets.   *In Exercises 11–14, use the data in Appendix B to test for rank correlation with a 0.05 significance level.*

11. Blood Pressure Refer to the measured systolic and diastolic blood pressure measurements of 153 randomly selected males in Data Set 1 "Body Data" in Appendix B and use a 0.05 significance level to test the claim that among men, there is a correlation between systolic blood pressure and diastolic blood pressure.

12. IQ and Brain Volume Refer to Data Set 9 "IQ and Brain Size" in Appendix B and test for a correlation between brain volume (cm^3) and IQ score.

13. Chest Sizes and Weights of Bears Refer to Data Set 11 "Bear Measurements" in Appendix B and test for a correlation between chest sizes and weights of bears.

14. Head Lengths and Neck Sizes of Bears Refer to Data Set 11 "Bear Measurements" in Appendix B and test for a correlation between head lengths and neck sizes of bears.

13-6   Beyond the Basics

15. Finding Critical Values An alternative to using Table A–9 to find critical values for rank correlation is to compute them using this approximation:

$$r_s = \pm\sqrt{\frac{t^2}{t^2 + n - 2}}$$

Here, t is the critical t value from Table A-3 corresponding to the desired significance level and $n - 2$ degrees of freedom. Use this approximation to find critical values of r_s for Exercise 11 "Blood Pressure." How do the resulting critical values compare to the critical values that would be found by using Formula 13-1 on page 609?

Chapter Quick Quiz

1. Cell Phone Radiation Some of the nonparametric methods in this chapter use ranks of data. Find the ranks corresponding to these measured cell phone radiation absorption rates (in W/kg): 1.18, 1.41, 1.49, 1.04, 1.45, 0.74, 0.89, 1.42, 1.45, 0.51, 1.38.

2. Efficiency What does it mean when we say that the rank correlation test has an efficiency rating of 0.91 when compared to the parametric test for linear correlation?

3. Nonparametric Tests

a. Which of the following terms is sometimes used instead of "nonparametric test": *normality test; abnormality test; distribution-free test; last testament; test of patience?*

b. Why is the term that is the answer to part (a) better than "nonparametric test"?

4. Foot Length/Height Listed below are foot lengths (cm) and heights (cm) of males from Data Set 7 "Foot and Height" in Appendix B. Which method of nonparametric statistics should be used? What characteristic of the data is investigated with this test?

Foot Length	27.8	25.7	26.7	25.9	26.4	29.2	26.8	28.1	25.4	27.9
Height	180.3	175.3	184.8	177.8	182.3	185.4	180.3	175.3	177.8	185.4

5. Foot Length/Height When analyzing the paired data in Exercise 4, are the *P*-values and conclusions from the nonparametric test and the parametric test always the same?

6. Foot Length/Height For the sample data given in Exercise 4, identify at least one advantage of using the appropriate nonparametric test over the parametric test.

7. Sign Test and Wilcoxon Signed-Ranks Test What is a major advantage of the Wilcoxon signed-ranks test over the sign test when analyzing data consisting of matched pairs?

8. Which Test? Three different physicians each rank the quality of 10 different medical student diagnoses. What method of this chapter can be used to test for agreement among the three physicians?

9. Which Test? Given the following configurations of sample data, identify the one that can be used with the Wilcoxon rank-sum test: one sample of individual values; two independent samples; four independent samples; matched pairs.

10. Which Test? Given the following configurations of sample data, identify the one that can be used with the Wilcoxon signed-ranks test: two independent samples; four independent samples; matched pairs.

Review Exercises

Using Nonparametric Tests. *In Exercises 1–8, use a 0.05 significance level with the indicated test. If no particular test is specified, use the appropriate nonparametric test from this chapter.*

1. Internet or Doctor In a survey of 2015 adults, 1108 said that they obtain medical information more often from the Internet than a doctor (based on a Merck survey). Test the claim that the majority of adults obtain medical information more often from the Internet than a doctor.

2. Patient Wait Times In a study of times (min) patients wait before checking in for a physical, the following random sample of times was collected. Use the sign test to test the claim that the sample is from a population with a median equal to 5 min. Use a 0.05 significance level.

5 8 3 8 6 10 3 7 9 8 5 5 6 8 8 7 3 5 5 6 8 7 8 8 8 7

3. Patient Wait Times Repeat the preceding exercise using the Wilcoxon signed-ranks test.

4. Longevity of Presidents, Popes, Monarchs Listed on the top of the next page are numbers of years that U.S. presidents, popes, and British monarchs lived after their inauguration, election, or coronation, respectively. Assume that the data are samples randomly selected from larger populations. Test the claim that the three samples are from populations with the same median.

Presidents	10	29	26	28	15	23	17	25	0	20	4	1	24	16	12
	4	10	17	16	0	7	24	12	4	18	21	11	2	9	36
	12	28	3	16	9	25	23	32							
Popes	2	9	21	3	6	10	18	11	6	25	23	6	2	15	32
	25	11	8	17	19	5	15	0	26						
Monarchs	17	6	13	12	13	33	59	10	7	63	9	25	36	15	

5. Chocolate Diet for a Nobel Prize The table below lists chocolate consumption (kg per capita) and the numbers of Nobel Laureates (per 10 million people) for several different countries. Is there a correlation between chocolate consumption and the rate of Nobel Laureates? How could such a correlation be explained?

Chocolate	11.6	2.5	8.8	3.7	1.8	4.5	9.4	3.6	2.0	3.6	6.4
Nobel	12.7	1.9	12.7	3.3	1.5	11.4	25.5	3.1	1.9	1.7	31.9

6. Skull Breadths and Archeology Listed below are skull breadths obtained from skulls of Egyptian males from three different epochs (based on data from *Ancient Races of the Thebaid*, by Thomson and Randall-Maciver). Test the claim that the samples are from populations with the same median. Changes in head shape over time suggest that interbreeding occurred with immigrant populations. Is interbreeding of cultures suggested by the data?

4000 B.C.	125	129	131	132	132	134	135	138	138
1850 B.C.	129	129	134	134	136	137	137	138	136
A.D. 150	128	136	137	137	138	139	141	142	145

7. Skull Breadths and Archeology Refer to the preceding exercise and use only the skull breadths from 4000 B.C. and A.D. 150. Use the Wilcoxon rank-sum test to test the claim that the two samples are from populations with the same median.

8. Student and *U.S. News & World Report* Rankings of Colleges Each year, *U.S. News & World Report* publishes rankings of colleges based on statistics such as admission rates, graduation rates, class size, faculty–student ratio, faculty salaries, and peer ratings of administrators. Economists Christopher Avery, Mark Glickman, Caroline Minter Hoxby, and Andrew Metrick took an alternative approach of analyzing the college choices of 3240 high-achieving school seniors. They examined the colleges that offered admission along with the colleges that the students chose to attend. The table below lists rankings for a small sample of colleges. Find the value of the rank correlation coefficient and use it to determine whether there is a correlation between the student rankings and the rankings of the magazine.

Student ranks	1	2	3	4	5	6	7	8
U.S. News & World Report ranks	1	2	5	4	7	6	3	8

Cumulative Review Exercises

In Exercises 1–5, use the data listed below. The values are the numbers of credit hours taken in the current semester by full-time biostatistics students. The data are from students in one class of one of the authors.

> 15 15 13 16 12 15 18 16 15 14 16 15 17 12 15 15 14 14 12 12

1. Descriptive Statistics Find the mean, median, standard deviation, variance, and range of the sample data. Given that the data are in credit hours, include the appropriate units in the results.

2. Sampling and Data Type

a. Which of the following best describes the sample: simple random sample, voluntary response sample, convenience sample?

b. Is it likely that the sample is representative of the population of all full-time college students?

c. Are the data discrete or continuous?

d. What is the level of measurement of the data (nominal, ordinal, interval, ratio)?

3. Credit Hours: Hypothesis Test Use the given data to test the claim that the sample is from a population with a mean greater than 14 credit hours.

4. Credit Hours: Sign Test Use the given data to test the claim that the sample is from a population with a median greater than 14 credit hours. Use the sign test with a 0.05 significance level.

5. Credit Hours: Confidence Interval Use the data to construct a 95% confidence interval estimate of the number of credit hours taken by the population of full-time students. Write a brief statement that interprets the result.

6. Drug Tests There is a 3.9% rate of positive drug test results among workers in the United States (based on data from Quest Diagnostics). Assuming that this statistic is based on a sample of size 2000, construct a 95% confidence interval estimate of the *percentage* of positive drug test results. Write a brief statement that interprets the confidence interval.

7. Drug Tests Use the data from the preceding exercise and test the claim that the rate of positive drug test results among workers in the United States is greater than 3.0%. Use a 0.05 significance level.

8. Sample Size Advances in technology are dramatically affecting different aspects of our lives. Many people now use the Internet for medical advice before seeing a physician. To help address such issues, we want to estimate the percentage of adults in the United States who use a computer at least once each day. Find the sample size needed to estimate that percentage. Assume that we want 95% confidence that the sample percentage is within two percentage points of the true population percentage.

9. Fear of Heights Among readers of a *USA Today* website, 285 chose to respond to this posted question: "Are you afraid of heights in tall buildings?" Among those who chose to respond, 46% answered "yes" and 54% answered "no." Use a 0.05 significance level to test the claim that the majority of the population is not afraid of heights in tall buildings. What is wrong with this hypothesis test?

10. Cell Phones and Crashes: Analyzing Newspaper Report In an article from the Associated Press, it was reported that researchers "randomly selected 100 New York motorists who had been in an accident and 100 who had not been in an accident. Of those in accidents, 13.7 percent owned a cellular phone, while just 10.6 percent of the accident-free drivers had a phone in the car." What is wrong with these results?

Technology Project

Methods of gender selection can be tested in experiments that involve the treatment of parents and the subsequent analysis of generated offspring. Instead of actually generating offspring, we will use technology to simulate their generation. Use SPSS, SAS, Statdisk, Minitab, Excel, a TI–83/84 Plus calculator, or any other technology to randomly generate 1000 values, each of which is 0 or 1. (Refer to the Chapter 4 Technology Project on pages 193–194 for the summary of simulation functions.) Representing boys by 1 and girls by 0, we have a simulated sample of 1000 offspring. We can then use the sign test to determine whether boys and girls are equally likely. In this case, we are actually testing the technology for a bias in favor of either 0s or 1s. Generate the 1000 values, then use the sign test to analyze the results. Does the technology appear to have a bias? Could you detect a bias using larger sample sizes?

FROM DATA TO DECISION

Critical Thinking: Does geographic location affect birth weights?

Data Set 3 "Births" in Appendix B lists birth weights from four different hospitals with very different geographic locations in New York State. We want to investigate an effect of geographic location on birth weights.

Analysis

• Which nonparametric test applies?

• Identify the requirements for the appropriate nonparametric test and determine if they are satisfied.

• Apply the test and state conclusions.

Cooperative Group Activities

1. In-class activity Divide into groups of 8 to 12 people. For each group member, *measure* his or her height and *measure* his or her arm span. For the arm span, the subject should stand with arms extended, like the wings on an airplane. Divide the following tasks among subgroups of three or four people.

a. Use rank correlation with the paired sample data to determine whether there is a correlation between height and arm span.

b. Use the sign test to test for a difference between the two variables.

c. Use the Wilcoxon signed-ranks test to test for a difference between the two variables.

2. In-class activity Do Activity 1 using pulse rate instead of arm span. Measure pulse rates by counting the number of heartbeats in 1 minute.

3. Out-of-class activity Divide into groups of three or four students. Investigate the relationship between two variables by collecting your own paired sample data and using the methods of Section 13-6 to determine whether there is a correlation. Suggested topics:

• Is there a correlation between the lengths of men's (or women's) feet and their heights?

• Is there a correlation between heights of fathers (or mothers) and heights of their first sons (or daughters)?

4. Out-of-class activity Divide into groups of three or four. Survey other students by asking them to identify their major and gender. For each surveyed subject, determine the number of Twitter followers or Facebook friends. Use the sample data to address these questions:

• Do the numbers of Twitter followers or Facebook friends appear to be the same for both genders?

• Do the numbers of Twitter followers or Facebook friends appear to be the same for the different majors?

5. In-class activity Divide into groups of 8 to 12 people. For each group member, measure the person's height and also measure his or her navel height, which is the height from the floor to the navel. Use the rank correlation coefficient to determine whether there is a correlation between height and navel height.

6. In-class activity Divide into groups of three or four people. Appendix B includes many data sets not yet addressed by the methods of this chapter. Search Appendix B for variables of interest, then investigate using appropriate methods of nonparametric statistics. State your conclusions and try to identify practical applications.

14 Survival Analysis

 14-1 Life Tables

14-2 Kaplan-Meier Survival Analysis

CHAPTER PROBLEM — **Is the Cluster of Deaths *Significantly* High?**

Media often report clusters of diseases or deaths along with suggestions that some underlying cause should be investigated. For example, the *Pittsburgh Post Gazette* reported that in 14 western Pennsylvania counties, there were 14,636 more deaths from heart disease, respiratory disease, and lung cancer than would be expected under normal circumstances. Many residents suspect environmental pollution as a cause for the cluster, but the presence of a cluster has not been established and questions remain.

Suppose a different region has 5000 people who reach their 16th birthday and 25 of them die before their 17th birthday. Parents, expressing understandable concern, claim that this number of deaths is significantly high and the causes of death should be investigated as part of a comprehensive study.

continued

Others suggest that the number of deaths of 16-year-olds will naturally vary from year to year. Some years have fewer deaths than average, while other years have disproportionately greater numbers of deaths, so that the 25 deaths is no cause for concern.

How do we objectively address this issue? One essential piece of information is the death rate for people in this age group. That rate can be extracted from a *life table*, which can be very helpful in situations such as the one presented here. We will consider the different components of a life table, and we will use a specific and real life table to address the questions raised above.

CHAPTER OBJECTIVES

Here are the main objectives of this chapter:

 Life Tables

- Develop the ability to use a life table for the analysis of mortality and longevity data.

 Kaplan-Meier Survival Analysis

- Develop the ability to construct and interpret tables and graphs of survival data using the Kaplan-Meier method for determining the probability of survival over periods of time.

14-1   Life Tables

Life tables are routinely developed by government agencies and private companies, and their use is critical to a variety of different fields. Studies of wildlife populations often involve life tables. Insurance companies could not provide life insurance policies without the information contained in life tables. A "term" life insurance policy is essentially a bet that a person will live or die within a certain time period, and the amount of the bet (cost of the policy or the premium amount) must reflect the probability that the subject will live or die within that time period. Many professionals monitor the health of the United States population, and their analyses often involve life tables as the basis for such comparisons. Other policy planners need to know how long people are expected to live, so that they can satisfy their health and financial needs. For example, employees in the United States typically have funds contributed to a large Social Security account maintained by the government. It is intended that these funds be used to provide financial support when employees age and retire. However, as people tend to live longer, the payments continue for longer periods of time, and careful planning is required to ensure that future generations will continue to enjoy the benefits of the Social Security system. Such careful planning requires accurate information about changes in longevity—information that is available in life tables. Life tables therefore become key tools in many different applications.

Life tables include information about death rates and longevity, but there are different types of life tables. A **cohort** (or **generation**) life table is a record of the actual observed mortality experience for a particular group, such as everyone born in the year 1960. Because cohort life tables require complete data collected over periods spanning decades of time, they aren't very practical and are not commonly used. The main focus of this section will be *period life tables*. In subsequent references to *life tables*, it is assumed that we are referring to period life tables defined as follows.

DEFINITION

A **period** (or **current**) life table describes mortality and longevity data for a *hypothetical* (or "synthetic") cohort, with the data computed with this assumption:

The conditions affecting mortality in a particular basis year (such as 2010) remain the same throughout the lives of everyone in the hypothetical cohort.

A period life table shows the long-term results of mortality conditions that were present during the particular basis year.

Table 14-1 on the following two pages is an example of a period life table. Because Table 14-1 is a period life table for the United States for the year 2010, we know that it was constructed with this important assumption: The death rates for the various age groups that were in effect in the year 2010 continue to remain in effect during the entire lives of the 100,000 hypothetical people assumed to be present at age 0. That is, we pretend that a population of 100,000 people is born in the year 2010, and they each live their entire lives in a world with the same constant death rates that were present in the year 2010.

Table 14-1 was provided by the National Center for Health Statistics, and it is based on actual data from the U.S. Census Bureau (for population estimates), the Medicare program (a government program providing financial support for health care), and death certificates issued in different states. Actual mortality data were collected, but they were then used to describe the experience of 100,000 *hypothetical* people.

Table 14-1 describes 100,000 hypothetical people who are representative of the *total population* of the United States, including males and females of various races. Because mortality experiences can be very different for various gender and race groups, it is common to have tables for specific subgroups. As of this writing, period life tables were available for males, females, whites, white males, white females, blacks, black males, and black females. We do not provide these other tables, but they should be used in place of Table 14-1 when appropriate. For example, if calculating the cost of a term life insurance policy for a 19-year-old white male, more accurate information could be obtained from the period life table for white males than from Table 14-1, which includes the entire population.

TABLE 14-1 Life Table for Total Population: U.S., 2010

Age Interval	Probability of Dying During the Interval	Number Surviving to the Beginning of the Interval	Number of Deaths During the Interval	Person-Years Lived (total time lived *during the interval* by those alive at the beginning of the interval)	Total Person-Years Lived (in *this and all subsequent* intervals)	Expected Remaining Lifetime (from the beginning of the interval)
0–1	0.006123	100,000	612	99,465	7,866,027	78.7
1–2	0.000428	99,388	43	99,366	7,766,561	78.1
2–3	0.000275	99,345	27	99,331	7,667,195	77.2
3–4	0.000211	99,318	21	99,307	7,567,864	76.2
4–5	0.000158	99,297	16	99,289	7,468,556	75.2
5–6	0.000145	99,281	14	99,274	7,369,267	74.2
6–7	0.000128	99,267	13	99,260	7,269,993	73.2
7–8	0.000114	99,254	11	99,249	7,170,733	72.2
8–9	0.000100	99,243	10	99,238	7,071,484	71.3
9–10	0.000087	99,233	9	99,229	6,972,246	70.3
10–11	0.000079	99,224	8	99,220	6,873,017	69.3
11–12	0.000086	99,216	9	99,212	6,773,797	68.3
12–13	0.000116	99,208	12	99,202	6,674,585	67.3
13–14	0.000175	99,196	17	99,188	6,575,383	66.3
14–15	0.000252	99,179	25	99,167	6,476,195	65.3
15–16	0.000333	99,154	33	99,138	6,377,028	64.3
16–17	0.000412	99,121	41	99,101	6,277,891	63.3
17–18	0.000492	99,080	49	99,056	6,178,790	62.4
18–19	0.000573	99,032	57	99,003	6,079,734	61.4
19–20	0.000655	98,975	65	98,942	5,980,731	60.4
20–21	0.000744	98,910	74	98,873	5,881,789	59.5
21–22	0.000829	98,836	82	98,795	5,782,916	58.5
22–23	0.000892	98,754	88	98,710	5,684,120	57.6
23–24	0.000925	98,666	91	98,621	5,585,410	56.6
24–25	0.000934	98,575	92	98,529	5,486,789	55.7
25–26	0.000936	98,483	92	98,437	5,388,260	54.7
26–27	0.000943	98,391	93	98,344	5,289,824	53.8
27–28	0.000953	98,298	94	98,251	5,191,479	52.8
28–29	0.000971	98,204	95	98,157	5,093,228	51.9
29–30	0.000998	98,109	98	98,060	4,995,071	50.9
30–31	0.001029	98,011	101	97,961	4,897,011	50.0
31–32	0.001063	97,910	104	97,858	4,799,051	49.0
32–33	0.001099	97,806	108	97,752	4,701,193	48.1
33–34	0.001137	97,699	111	97,643	4,603,440	47.1
34–35	0.001180	97,587	115	97,530	4,505,797	46.2
35–36	0.001235	97,472	120	97,412	4,408,267	45.2
36–37	0.001302	97,352	127	97,289	4,310,855	44.3
37–38	0.001377	97,225	134	97,158	4,213,567	43.3
38–39	0.001461	97,091	142	97,020	4,116,408	42.4
39–40	0.001557	96,949	151	96,874	4,019,388	41.5
40–41	0.001663	96,798	161	96,718	3,922,514	40.5
41–42	0.001793	96,637	173	96,551	3,825,796	39.6
42–43	0.001962	96,464	189	96,370	3,729,245	38.7
43–44	0.002177	96,275	210	96,170	3,632,875	37.7
44–45	0.002423	96,065	233	95,949	3,536,705	36.8
45–46	0.002676	95,833	256	95,704	3,440,756	35.9
46–47	0.002931	95,576	280	95,436	3,345,052	35.0
47–48	0.003205	95,296	305	95,143	3,249,616	34.1
48–49	0.003505	94,990	333	94,824	3,154,473	33.2
49–50	0.003830	94,658	363	94,476	3,059,649	32.3
50–51	0.004177	94,295	394	94,098	2,965,173	31.4

Age Interval	Probability of Dying During the Interval	Number Surviving to the Beginning of the Interval	Number of Deaths During the Interval	Person-Years Lived (total time lived *during the interval* by those alive at the beginning of the interval)	Total Person-Years Lived (in *this and all subsequent* intervals)	Expected Remaining Lifetime (from the beginning of the interval)
51–52	0.004535	93,901	426	93,688	2,871,075	30.6
52–53	0.004903	93,475	458	93,246	2,777,386	29.7
53–54	0.005284	93,017	491	92,771	2,684,140	28.9
54–55	0.005684	92,526	526	92,263	2,591,369	28.0
55–56	0.006117	92,000	563	91,718	2,499,106	27.2
56–57	0.006589	91,437	603	91,136	2,407,388	26.3
57–58	0.007095	90,834	644	90,512	2,316,253	25.5
58–59	0.007626	90,190	688	89,846	2,225,741	24.7
59–60	0.008180	89,502	732	89,136	2,135,895	23.9
60–61	0.008767	88,770	778	88,381	2,046,759	23.1
61–62	0.009397	87,992	827	87,578	1,958,378	22.3
62–63	0.010085	87,165	879	86,725	1,870,800	21.5
63–64	0.010863	86,286	937	85,817	1,784,075	20.7
64–65	0.011758	85,348	1,004	84,847	1,698,258	19.9
65–66	0.012810	84,345	1,080	83,805	1,613,411	19.1
66–67	0.014011	83,264	1,167	82,681	1,529,606	18.4
67–68	0.015290	82,098	1,255	81,470	1,446,925	17.6
68–69	0.016601	80,843	1,342	80,172	1,365,455	16.9
69–70	0.018005	79,501	1,431	78,785	1,285,283	16.2
70–71	0.019548	78,069	1,526	77,306	1,206,499	15.5
71–72	0.021294	76,543	1,630	75,728	1,129,192	14.8
72–73	0.023275	74,913	1,744	74,041	1,053,464	14.1
73–74	0.025528	73,169	1,868	72,236	979,423	13.4
74–75	0.028061	71,302	2,001	70,301	907,188	12.7
75–76	0.030820	69,301	2,136	68,233	836,886	12.1
76–77	0.033775	67,165	2,268	66,031	768,654	11.4
77–78	0.037252	64,896	2,418	63,688	702,623	10.8
78–79	0.041136	62,479	2,570	61,194	638,935	10.2
79–80	0.045411	59,909	2,721	58,549	577,741	9.6
80–81	0.050146	57,188	2,868	55,754	519,193	9.1
81–82	0.055445	54,321	3,012	52,815	463,438	8.5
82–83	0.061272	51,309	3,144	49,737	410,624	8.0
83–84	0.067764	48,165	3,264	46,533	360,887	7.5
84–85	0.075818	44,901	3,404	43,199	314,354	7.0
85–86	0.085319	41,497	3,540	39,727	271,155	6.5
86–87	0.094975	37,956	3,605	36,154	231,429	6.1
87–88	0.105525	34,351	3,625	32,539	195,275	5.7
88–89	0.117007	30,726	3,595	28,929	162,736	5.3
89–90	0.129450	27,131	3,512	25,375	133,807	4.9
90–91	0.142873	23,619	3,375	21,932	108,432	4.6
91–92	0.157280	20,245	3,184	18,653	86,500	4.3
92–93	0.172661	17,061	2,946	15,588	67,847	4.0
93–94	0.188988	14,115	2,668	12,781	52,259	3.7
94–95	0.206214	11,447	2,361	10,267	39,478	3.4
95–96	0.224274	9,087	2,038	8,068	29,211	3.2
96–97	0.243080	7,049	1,713	6,192	21,144	3.0
97–98	0.262527	5,335	1,401	4,635	14,951	2.8
98–99	0.282492	3,935	1,112	3,379	10,316	2.6
99–100	0.302838	2,823	855	2,396	6,937	2.5
100 and over	1.000000	1,968	1,968	4,542	4,542	2.3

From National Vital Statistics Reports, U.S. Department of Health and Human Services.

Components of a Period Life Table

The seven columns in the period life Table 14-1 are described as follows.

Column 1: Age Interval The first column of Table 14-1 lists age categories. The first category of 0–1 represents the age interval from birth to the first birthday. Note that some of the other columns are based on the age *at the beginning* of the age interval. For example, the last column lists expected ages, which are the expected remaining lifetime amounts measured from the *beginning* of the age interval. For the age interval of 0–1, the expected remaining lifetime is 78.7, which means that a newborn has an expected lifetime of 78.7 years. Also note that the age intervals overlap with a common value used for the upper boundary of one class as well as the lower boundary for the following class. When we discussed frequency distributions in Chapter 2, we noted that the class limits should not overlap, but the overlapping is not an important issue with period life tables. It would be a very rare event to have someone die on the exact instant of the beginning of their birth date, so we need not make adjustments for this event that will likely never occur.

Column 2: Probability of Dying The second column lists the probabilities of dying *during the age interval* listed in the first column. The first row of values shows that there is a 0.006123 probability of someone dying between birth and their first birthday. The second row shows that there is a 0.000428 probability of someone dying between their first birthday and their second birthday. These probabilities of death reflect the death rates for the various age groups that were observed in the year 2010.

Column 3: Number Surviving The third column lists the number of people alive *at the beginning of the age interval*. Note that the first row lists the size of our hypothetical population (100,000), and this value shows that there were 100,000 hypothetical people who were born and alive at the beginning of the age interval from 0 to 1 year. This number decreases as some of the hypothetical people have hypothetical deaths. The second row shows that among the 100,000 hypothetical people who were born, 99,388 of them are alive on their first birthday. The values in column 3 can be computed by using the death rates in column 2. For example, the first age interval of 0–1 has a death rate of 0.006123, so we expect that 612.3 of the 100,000 people alive at birth will die, leaving a population of $100,000 - 612.3 = 99,388$ (rounded) people alive at the beginning of the second age interval of 1–2.

Column 4: Number of Deaths The fourth column shows the number of people who died *during the age interval* in the column at the left. This value can be computed by multiplying the number of people alive at the beginning of the age interval (column 3) by the probability of dying during the age interval (column 2). For example, the first row shows that 100,000 people were present at age 0 and the death rate for those in the age interval of 0–1 is 0.006123, so we expect the number of deaths to be: $100,000 \times 0.006123 = 612$ (rounded).

Column 5: Person-Years Lived This column lists the total time (in years) lived *during the age interval* by those who were alive at the beginning of the age interval. For example, the first row in column 5 has an entry of 99,465 (years), and this value shows that the 100,000 people who were present at age 0 lived a total of 99,465 years. If none of those people had died, this entry would have been 100,000 years, but some of them did die, so the total is less than 100,000 years.

Column 6: Total Person-Years Lived The sixth column is somewhat similar to the fifth column in the sense that it lists the total number of years lived by those present at the beginning of the age interval, but column 5 lists the number of years lived *during the age interval*, whereas column 6 lists the number of years lived *during the age interval and all of the following age intervals* as well.

Column 7: Expected Remaining Lifetime The last column lists the expected remaining lifetime (in years), measured from the beginning of the age interval. For example, the first row shows that the expected remaining lifetime is 78.7 years, so the average expected lifetime of the 100,000 newborn people is 78.7 years. Each value in the seventh column can be computed by dividing the total person-years lived (column 6) by the number of people who were present at the beginning of the age interval. For example, the age interval of 1–2 has an expected remaining lifetime of 78.1 years, and the total person-years lived (column 6) divided by the number of people present at the beginning of the age interval (column 3) yields 7,766,561 ÷ 99,388 = 78.1 (rounded). Again, we should remember that this assumes that the same mortality conditions present in the year 2010 remain constant throughout the lifetimes of the 100,000 hypothetical people. We should also remember that Table 14-1 describes the total population, and expected remaining lifetime values will be different for different subgroups of genders and races.

Notation: More formal mathematical notation is often used for the above components. For example, the age intervals can be expressed in general form as "x to $x + 1$," the probability of dying during an interval is expressed as q_x, the number alive at the beginning of an interval is expressed as l_x, the number dying in an interval is expressed as d_x, and so on. Such notation makes it easier to develop formulas describing components of the period life table. For example, the formula $d_x = q_x \cdot l_x$ shows that the number of deaths in an interval is equal to the probability of dying during the interval multiplied by the number alive at the beginning of the interval. Also, such notation is commonly used to describe the columns of a period life table. In Table 14-1, for example, the original government report labels the columns with headings such as "probability of dying between ages x and $x + 1$" and "person-years lived between ages x and $x + 1$." The use of this more formal notation is not necessary for the purposes of this section, but this notation is commonly used in some fields.

Abridged Life Table

Table 14-1 is sometimes referred to as a *complete* life table, because it lists a separate row of data for each year. An *abridged* life table uses age intervals for time periods longer than one year. Age intervals of 5 years or 10 years are common in an abridged life table.

> **DEFINITION**
>
> An **abridged life table** is a life table in which the age intervals have been combined, so the age intervals are longer than one year. Age intervals of 5 years or 10 years are common.

Table 14-2 is an abridged life table that condenses Table 14-1 by using age intervals of 5 years. Table 14-2 was constructed by using the values found in Table 14-1.

TABLE 14-2 Abridged Life Table for Total Population: U.S., 2010

Age Interval	Probability of Dying During the Interval	Number Surviving to the Beginning of the Interval	Number of Deaths During the Interval	Person-Years Lived (total time lived *during the interval* by those alive at the beginning of the interval)	Total Person-Years Lived (in *this and all subsequent* intervals)	Expected Remaining Lifetime (from the beginning of the interval)
0–5	0.007190	100,000	719	496,759	7,866,027	78.7
5–10	0.000573	99,281	57	496,250	7,369,267	74.2
10–15	0.000708	99,224	70	495,989	6,873,017	69.3
15–20	0.002463	99,154	244	495,240	6,377,028	64.3
20–25	0.004317	98,910	427	493,529	5,881,789	59.5
25–30	0.004791	98,483	472	491,249	5,388,260	54.7
30–35	0.005497	98,011	539	488,744	4,897,011	50.0
35–40	0.006913	97,472	674	485,753	4,408,267	45.2
40–45	0.009979	96,798	966	481,758	3,922,514	40.5
45–50	0.016044	95,833	1,538	475,584	3,440,756	35.9
50–55	0.024343	94,295	2,295	466,066	2,965,173	31.4
55–60	0.035106	92,000	3,230	452,347	2,499,106	27.2
60–65	0.049847	88,770	4,425	433,348	2,046,759	23.1
65–70	0.074406	84,345	6,276	406,912	1,613,411	19.1
70–75	0.112315	78,069	8,768	369,612	1,206,499	15.5
75–80	0.174782	69,301	12,113	317,694	836,886	12.1
80–85	0.274384	57,188	15,692	248,038	519,193	9.1
85–90	0.430820	41,497	17,878	162,723	271,155	6.5
90–95	0.615282	23,619	14,532	79,220	108,432	4.6
95–100	0.783397	9,087	7,119	24,670	29,211	3.2
100+	1.000000	1,968	1,968	4,542	4,542	2.3

From National Vital Statistics Reports, U.S. Department of Health and Human Services.

 EXAMPLE 1 **Expected Remaining Life**

An abridged life table is to be constructed using age intervals of 5 years. Use Table 14-1 to find the expected remaining lifetime for someone reaching their 25th birthday.

SOLUTION

From Table 14-1 we see that someone reaching their 25th birthday has an expected remaining lifetime of 54.7 years. In the abridged table, the expected remaining lifetime for someone reaching their 25th birthday will be the same value of 54.7 years, so the age interval of 25–30 will also have 54.7 years listed in the last column.

 EXAMPLE 2 **Probability of Dying**

Use Table 14-1 on pages 622–623 to find the probability of a person dying between the ages of 15 and 20.

SOLUTION

From Table 14-1 we see that there were 99,154 people alive on their 15th birthday, and there were 98,910 people alive on their 20th birthday. The probability of surviving between the 15th and 20th birthdays is therefore $98,910/99,154 = 0.997539$. Using the rule of complements from Chapter 4, it follows that the probability of dying during that interval is $1 - 0.997539 = 0.002461$. (The abridged life table of Table 14-2 shows the entry of 0.002463.)

Applications of Life Tables

The following application is important because it relates to the Social Security program in the United States, and that program involves *trillions* of dollars.

 EXAMPLE 3   Social Security

Assume that there are 3,932,181 births in the United States this year (based on data from the U.S. National Center for Health Statistics). If the age for receiving full Social Security payments is 67, how many of those born this year are expected to be alive on their 67th birthday?

SOLUTION

From Table 14-1 (pages 622-623), we see that among 100,000 people born, we expect that 82,098 of them will survive to their 67th birthday. It follows that the probability of someone surviving from birth to their 67th birthday is 0.82098. If each of 3,932,181 newborn people has a 0.82098 probability of surviving to their 67th birthday, the expected number of such survivors is $3,932,181 \times 0.82098 = 3,228,242$ (rounded). Such results are critically important for those professionals responsible for effective administration of the Social Security program.

Another application is based on the property that a life table includes *probabilities,* and they can be treated as the same probabilities used in preceding chapters of this book. Consider the following example in which a hypothesis test is conducted with a probability value found in Table 14-1.

 EXAMPLE 4   Hypothesis Test for Cluster of Deaths

In the Chapter Problem, we noted that for one region there are 5000 people who reach their 16th birthday. If 25 of them die before their 17th birthday, do we have sufficient evidence to conclude that this number of deaths is *significantly* high?

SOLUTION

From Table 14-1 (pages 622-623), we find that for the age interval of 16–17, the probability of dying is 0.000412. However, the Chapter Problem refers to a region in which there were 25 deaths among 5000 people during the age interval from their 16th birthday to their 17th birthday. For this region, the proportion of actual deaths is $\hat{p} = x/n = 25/5000 = 0.005$. We can proceed to test the claim that for this region, the deaths are from a population with a death rate greater than the life table value of 0.000412. Using the methods of Chapter 8, we begin with the following null and alternative hypotheses.

$$H_0: p = 0.000412$$
$$H_1: p > 0.000412 \text{ (claim being tested)}$$

continued

No significance level was specified, so we will use the common value of $\alpha = 0.05$. We now proceed to find the test statistic (as in Section 8–2):

$$z = \frac{\hat{p} - p}{\sqrt{\dfrac{pq}{n}}} = \frac{0.005 - 0.000412}{\sqrt{\dfrac{(0.000412)(0.999588)}{5000}}} = 15.99$$

Using the P-value approach, we can find that the test statistic of $z = 15.99$ corresponds to a P-value of 0.0000 (or 0.0001 if using Table A-2).

Because the P-value is less than 0.05, we reject the null hypothesis. There is sufficient evidence to support the claim that the proportion of deaths is significantly greater than the proportion that is usually expected for this age interval. We should note that this analysis assumed that $p = 0.000412$, which was found in Table 14-1. However, Table 14-1 was constructed under the assumption that the mortality conditions present in the year 2010 will remain constant throughout the lifetimes of the hypothetical population of 100,000 people. Also, Table 14-1 applies to a general population, so this analysis does not apply to specific subgroups.

14-1   Basic Skills and Concepts

Statistical Literacy and Critical Thinking

1. Types of Life Tables What is the difference between a *cohort* life table and a *period* life table?

2. Cohort and Period Life Tables Why are period life tables so much more practical than cohort life tables?

3. Population Size Table 14-1 was constructed with the assumption that the initial population size is 100,000. How are the values in the first row affected if a population size of 500,000 is used instead?

4. Interpretation of Table Assume that someone was born on January 1, 2010, and that person is alive now. If we refer to Table 14-1 for his or her expected remaining lifetime, what basic assumption about the construction of Table 14-1 might make that value inaccurate?

In Exercises 5–8, refer to the accompanying life table for white females in the United States for the year 2010.

Life Table for White Females: U.S., 2010

Age Interval	Probability of Dying During the Interval	Number Surviving to the Beginning of the Interval	Number of Deaths During the Interval	Person-Years Lived (total time lived *during the interval* by those alive at the beginning of the interval)	Total Person-Years Lived (in *this and all subsequent* intervals)	Expected Remaining Lifetime (from the beginning of the interval)
0–1	0.004710	100,000	471	99,588	8,128,871	81.3
1–2		99,529	38	99,510	8,029,283	80.7
2–3	0.000204	99,491		99,481	7,929,773	79.7

From National Vital Statistics Reports, U.S. Department of Health and Human Services.

5. Probability of Dying Find the missing value in the second column of the life table for white females.

6. Finding the Number of Deaths Find the missing value in the fourth column of the life table for white females.

7. Finding Survival Rate Find the probability that a white female will live from birth to her second birthday.

8. Constructing an Abridged Table Assume that you want to use the given life table for white females to construct an abridged table with 0–2 as the first age interval. Find the values in the first row of this abridged table.

9. Probability of Surviving Using Table 14-1 on pages 622-623, find the probability that someone will *survive* from the 25th birthday to their 26th birthday. Given 15,000 people who reach their 25th birthday, what is the expected number of people who survive the 26th birthday?

10. Expected Remaining Lifetime Use Table 14-1 on pages 622-623 to find the following.

a. Find the expected remaining lifetime for the person who has just reached their 65th birthday. Then find the expected remaining lifetime for the person who has just reached their 66th birthday.

b. Find the expected age of death of someone who has just reached their 65th birthday and find the expected age at death for someone who has just reached their 66th birthday.

c. Why aren't the two results from part (b) equal?

11. Probability of Surviving Use Table 14-1 on pages 622-623 to find the probability that a person will survive from their 12th birthday to their 42nd birthday.

12. Probability of Surviving Use Table 14-1 on pages 622-623 to find the probability that a person will survive from their 18th birthday to their 85th birthday.

13. Abridged Table Use Table 14-1 on pages 622-623 to find the probability of dying during the following age intervals. Given that these age intervals are so close, why are the results so different?

a. 0–3

b. 3–6

14. Abridged Table Use Table 14-1 on pages 622-623 to find the values in a row with an age interval of 0–3.

15. Abridged Table Use Table 14-1 on pages 622-623 to find the values in a row with an age interval of 3–6.

16. Abridged Table Use Table 14-1 on pages 622-623 to find the values in a row with an age interval of 0–5.

17. Hypothesis Test In one region, a researcher finds that among 15,000 people who survived to their 25th birthday, there are 200 deaths before they reach the age of 26. Using Table 14-1, test the claim that this is a significantly high number of deaths. Use a 0.05 significance level.

18. Hypothesis Test In one region, a researcher finds that among 7844 people who survived to their 40th birthday, there are 17 deaths before they reach the age of 41. Using Table 14-1, test the claim that this is a significantly high number of deaths. Use a 0.05 significance level.

19. Hypothesis Test In one region, a researcher finds that among 5842 people who survived to their 15th birthday, there are 296 deaths before they reach the age of 45. Using Table 14-1, test the claim that this is a significantly high number of deaths. Use a 0.05 significance level.

20. Hypothesis Test In one region, a researcher finds that among 6812 people who survived to their 70th birthday, there are 592 deaths before they reach the age of 90. Using Table 14-1, test the claim that this is a significantly *low* number of deaths. Use a 0.05 significance level.

14-2 Kaplan-Meier Survival Analysis

Key Concept In this section we introduce the Kaplan-Meier method used to describe the probability of surviving for a specific period of time. The life table method of survivor analysis introduced in Section 14-1 is based on fixed time intervals, but the Kaplan-Meier method is based on intervals that vary according to the times of survival to some particular terminating event. Using the sample data, it is helpful to construct a Kaplan-Meier cumulative survival curve.

In this context of survivor analysis, the term *survivor* does not necessarily mean living. A patient might be considered a survivor if postoperative surgery did not require a return to a physician or hospital. A patient trying to stop smoking might be considered a survivor as long as smoking has not resumed. A survivor might also be a computer hard drive that worked for some particular length of time.

DEFINITIONS

In survivor analysis, the time lapse from the beginning of observation to the time of a terminating event is considered a **survival time.** Examples of a terminating event include death, divorce, or failure of a computer hard drive.

A **survivor** is a subject that successfully lasted throughout a particular time period. Examples of survivors include people, marriages, or computer hard drives.

DEFINITION

The **Kaplan-Meier method** is used to describe survival behavior for some specific event, and it is based on varying survival time intervals for the terminating event being analyzed. (Because cumulative probabilities are products of other individual probabilities, the Kaplan-Meier method is sometimes called the *product-limit method.*)

A common application of the Kaplan-Meier method is to study survival times of patients after they undergo some treatment, such as surgery. Some of the survival data in such a study is often lost because some of the surgery patients survive by living past the end of the study and some patients move far away or no longer wish to be included in the study, or are dropped from the study for other reasons. The data for these patients are referred to as *censored data,* defined as follows.

DEFINITION

Survival times are **censored data** if the subjects survive past the end of the study or if they are dropped from the study for reasons not related to the terminating event being studied.

 EXAMPLE 1 Medication Treatment for Smoking Cessation

Consider an experimental medication tested with five smokers recruited for a smoking cessation clinical trial. In this context, "surviving" means that the patient has not resumed smoking.

Results: The first patient disliked the taste of the medication and dropped out of the study on the first day, so the data from this patient are censored. Despite using the medication as directed, the remaining four patients resumed smoking after 3 days, 4 days, 7 days, and 21 days, respectively. See these survival data summarized in Table 14-3.

TABLE 14-3 Medication Treatment: Survival Data and Kaplan-Meier Calculations

1 Day	2 Status 0 = Censored 1 = Failed (Resumed Smoking)	3 Number of Patients	4 Patients Not Smoking	5 Proportion of Patients Not Smoking	6 Cumulative Proportion of Patients Not Smoking
1	0				
3	1	4	3	3/4 = 0.75	0.75
4	1	3	2	2/3 = 0.667	0.5
7	1	2	1	1/2 = 0.5	0.25
21	1	1	0	0	0

Here are some relevant comments about the entries in Table 14-3.

Censored Data The first row of data in Table 14-3 represents the subject who dropped out of the program, and the 0 in the first row is the code for censored data. Note that except for the entry of 0, the other columns in the row are empty. Removing the patient who dropped out does not affect the subsequent calculations except for the reduction in the number of remaining survivors.

Second *Row* of Data:

- The number 3 in the first column of the second row indicates that this patient resumed smoking 3 days after the start of the program. This patient "survived" for 3 days.

- The 1 in the second column is a code indicating that smoking was resumed.

- The 4 in the third column shows 4 patients remaining in the program.

- The 3 in the fourth column represents the number of remaining patients who have "survived" in the sense that they are not smoking.

- The proportion of 3/4 in the fifth column shows that 3 out of the 4 patients have survived (i.e., not smoking).

- The proportion of 0.75 in the sixth column is the same proportion of 0.75 from the fifth column, but for the remaining rows, the proportion in the sixth column will be the *product* of the proportion from the fifth column and any preceding proportions in the fifth column. See below.

Sixth *Column* of Cumulative Proportions of Survivors:

- First entry of 0.75: Same proportion from the fifth column.

- Second entry of 0.5: Product of 0.667 (rounded) from the fifth column and the preceding entry of 0.75 in the fifth column. We get $0.667 \times 0.75 = 0.5$.

- Third entry of 0.25: Product of 0.5 from the fifth column and the preceding entries of 0.667 and 0.75 from the fifth column. We get $0.5 \times 0.667 \times 0.75 = 0.25$.

- Fourth entry of 0: Product of 0 from the fifth column and the preceding entries in the fifth column. We get $0 \times 0.5 \times 0.667 \times 0.75 = 0$.

EXAMPLE 2 **Counseling Treatment for Smoking Cessation**

The preceding Example 1 describes survival for five patients who were treated with *medication*. In the same program, 10 different patients underwent *counseling* in the attempt to stop smoking, and the results from these patients are summarized in Table 14-4. This counseling program was discontinued after 28 days. Table 14-4 is an example of survival data with Kaplan-Meier calculations. Note that in Table 14-4, the number of patients decreases when patients are censored, as indicated by 0 in column 2.

TABLE 14-4 Counseling Treatment: Survival Data and Kaplan-Meier Calculations

Day	Status 0 = Censored 1 = Failed (Resumed Smoking)	Number of Patients	Patients Not Smoking	Proportion of Patients Not Smoking	Cumulative Proportion of Patients Not Smoking
2	1	10	9	9/10 = 0.9	0.9
4	1	9	8	8/9 = 0.889	0.8
5	0				
8	1	7	6	6/7 = 0.857	0.686
9	1	6	5	5/6 = 0.833	0.571
12	0				
14	1	4	3	3/4 = 0.75	0.429
22	1	3	2	2/3 = 0.667	0.286
24	0				
28	0				

EXAMPLE 3 **Kaplan-Meier Cumulative Survival Curves**

As interesting and revealing as Tables 14-3 and 14-4 might be (!), it is usually more helpful to construct graphs that make it easier to understand the survivor data. See the accompanying Kaplan-Meier cumulative survival curves in Figure 14-1 that incorporates the survivor data from Table 14-3 and Table 14-4. The graph is constructed by using the survival times (column 1) and the cumulative proportions of patients not smoking (column 6) from Table 14-3 and Table 14-4.

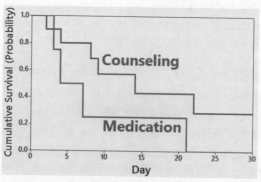

FIGURE 14-1 **Kaplan-Meier Cumulative Survival Curves**

The Kaplan-Meier cumulative survival curves in Figure 14-1 show that the proportions of survivors (patients who had not resumed smoking) with counseling are generally higher than the proportions of survivors with medication, so it becomes clear that the counseling program had better results than the medication program. However, neither of the programs had very high rates of survivors, so neither program appears to be very effective in helping patients achieve success in their attempts to stop smoking.

Survival for a Specific Time Period   We can use the cumulative survival curves in Figure 14-1 to estimate survival for a specific time period. For example, the probability of survival to 15 days is estimated to be 0.25 for the medication group and 0.43 for the counseling group. (Use the graph to construct a vertical line at 15 days and identify the intersection of that line with the curves, then estimate the heights at the two points of intersection.)

Some technologies, such as Minitab, JMP, SPSS, and XLSTAT-Life, can automatically generate Kaplan-Meier cumulative survival curves, and some technologies can also include graphs representing confidence intervals around those curves.

14-2   Basic Skills and Concepts

Statistical Literacy and Critical Thinking

1. Survivor In the context of analyzing survivor data, what is a survivor? Is it somebody who somehow managed to live through some time period?

2. Censored Data In the context of analyzing survivor data, what are censored data?

3. Kaplan-Meier Survival Analysis What is the main difference between a life table described in Section 14-1 and a table of survival data and Kaplan-Meier calculations as described in this section?

4. Graph What is a Kaplan-Meier cumulative survival curve?

In Exercises 5–9, refer to the accompanying graph, which describes times of survival until death for three groups of older subjects. The subjects are partitioned into the three groups according to gait speed, or how fast they can walk. At the beginning of the study, ten subjects were identified with fast gait speeds, ten other subjects were identified with moderate gait speeds, and ten more subjects were identified with slow gait speeds. Times (years) were measured from the beginning of the study to the time of death. (Based on data from "Predicting Survival in Oldest People," by Taekema et al., **American Journal of Medicine.***)*

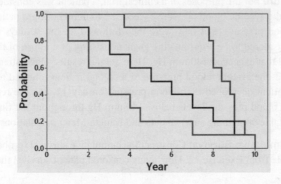

5. Conclusion A purpose of the study was to determine whether walking speed is an effective predictor of longevity among the oldest subjects. Which of the three curves do you think corresponds to each of the three groups (fast, moderate, slow). Provide a brief explanation.

6. Probability The vertical scale represents probability values. Describe the event for which probabilities are found. What do we know from the observation that the three curves all proceed downward as time progresses?

7. Graphic Details

a. For the ten subjects in the group identified by the green curve, how much time elapsed between the beginning of the study and the death of the first subject?

b. For the ten subjects in the group identified by the red curve, how much time elapsed between the beginning of the study and the death of the first subject?

8. Survivors Did any of the slow walkers survive, or did they all die?

9. Survival to Five Years Estimate the five-year survival rates for the three groups and compare them. Do the data suggest that we can get older people to live longer by somehow getting them to walk faster?

10. Hospital Readmission Ten patients underwent surgery and were subsequently followed up for 14 days to determine whether they required readmission to a hospital. Readmission is considered a failure or terminating event. Complete the table. What do the last five 0's in the second column indicate?

Day	Status 0 = Censored 1 = Failed (Readmitted)	Number of Patients	Patients Not Readmitted	Proportion of Patients Not Readmitted	Cumulative Proportion of Patients Not Readmitted
2	0				
6	1				
10	1				
11	1				
13	1				
14	0				
14	0				
14	0				
14	0				
14	0				

11. Graph of Cumulative Survival Construct the cumulative survival (probability) graph for the completed table from Exercise 10.

12. Blood Pressure For the purposes of a clinical trial, a patient was considered to have high blood pressure if the systolic blood pressure exceeded 140 mm Hg. Eight patients were treated for their high blood pressure, and they were then followed up for 30 days. A failure of the treatment was considered to be a terminating event consisting of a return of the systolic blood pressure to a level that exceeded 140 mm Hg. Here are the results: One patient dropped out of the study on day 2, the systolic blood pressure of a second patient returned to a high level on day 10, a third patient developed high blood pressure on day 12, and the remaining patients sustained systolic blood pressure levels below 140 mm Hg throughout the time of the clinical trial. Construct a table containing survival data and Kaplan-Meier calculations.

13. Graph of Cumulative Survival Construct the cumulative survival (probability) graph for the completed table from Exercise 12. How many censored patient survival times are shown in the graph?

14. Graph of Cumulative Survival Refer to the accompanying cumulative survival graph. Which is better: treatment or placebo? Estimate the five-year survival rates for the two groups, then compare them. What does the graph suggest about the effectiveness of the treatment?

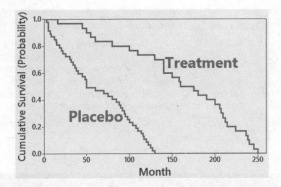

Chapter Quick Quiz

1. Life Table or Survival Table Which tool would be better for estimating the probability that a female of age 27 will live throughout her 28th year: life table or survival table with Kaplan-Meier calculations?

2. Life Table or Survival Table Which tool would be better for estimating the probability that someone will live for at least 20 years after they start smoking: a life table or a survival table with Kaplan-Meier calculations?

3. Period Life Table What is a period life table?

4. Cohort Life Table What is a cohort life table?

5. Censored Data True or false: In survival analysis, censored data are records that have been eliminated because they could potentially reveal the identities of subjects.

6. Censored Data True or false: In survival analysis, if a subject survives for the entire duration of the study, then the survival time for that subject is excluded.

7. Survivor In survivor analysis, the term *survivor* always refers to a person who has lived some specific amount of time.

8. Period Life Table True or false: One disadvantage of a period life table is an assumption that conditions affecting mortality will not change throughout the lives of everyone in a cohort.

9. Survival Data Identify the missing entries in the bottom row of the following table of survival data.

Day	Status 0 = Censored 1 = Death	Number of Patients	Patients Not Dead	Proportion of Patients Not Dead	Cumulative Proportion of Patients Not Dead
1	1	3	2	2/3 = 0.667	0.667
5	1	2	1	1/2 = 0.5	0.333
8	1				

10. Life Table Refer to the following portion of the life table taken from Table 14-1. Find the probability that a randomly selected 19-year-old person will live one year. Express the result using six significant digits.

Age Interval	Probability of Dying During the Interval	Number Surviving to the Beginning of the Interval	Number of Deaths During the Interval	Person-Years Lived (total time lived *during the interval* by those alive at the beginning of the interval)	Total Person-Years Lived (in *this and all subsequent* intervals)	Expected Remaining Lifetime (from the beginning of the interval)
19–20	0.000655	98,975	65	98,942	5,980,731	60.4

Review Exercises

In Exercises 1–5, refer to the accompanying life table for Hispanic females in the United States for the year 2010.

Life Table for Hispanic Females: U.S., 2010

Age Interval	Probability of Dying During the Interval	Number Surviving to the Beginning of the Interval	Number of Deaths During the Interval	Person-Years Lived (total time lived *during the interval* by those alive at the beginning of the interval)	Total Person-Years Lived (in *this and all subsequent* intervals)	Expected Remaining Lifetime (from the beginning of the interval)
0–1	0.004729	100,000	473	99,588	8,382,303	83.8
1–2		99,527		99,510	8,282,715	83.2
2–3	0.000194	99,492	19	99,482	8,183,206	82.2

From National Vital Statistics Reports, U.S. Department of Health and Human Services.

1. Probability of Dying Find the missing value in the second column of the table.

2. Finding the Number of Deaths Find the missing value in the fourth column of the table.

3. Finding Survival Rate Find the probability that a Hispanic female will live from birth to her second birthday.

4. Constructing an Abridged Table Assume that you want to use the given table for the construction of an abridged table with 0–2 as the first age interval. Find the values in the first row of this abridged table.

5. Expected Remaining Lifetime What is the expected remaining lifetime of a Hispanic female who was just born? What is the expected remaining lifetime of a Hispanic female who is celebrating her first birthday? Compare those results and comment on the relationship between them.

6. Carpal Tunnel Syndrome For the purposes of a clinical trial, a patient undergoing surgery for treatment of carpal tunnel syndrome was considered to survive if the patient had no retreatments following surgery. Four patients underwent the surgery, and they were then followed up for 30 days with these results: One patient required retreatment on day 3, a second patient required retreatment on day 12, a third patient required retreatment on day 20, and the fourth patient never required retreatment. Construct a table containing survival data and the Kaplan-Meier calculations.

7. Graph of Cumulative Survival Construct the cumulative survival (probability) graph for the completed table from Exercise 6.

8. Graph of Cumulative Survival In the accompanying cumulative survival graph, which group had better overall success: the treatment group or the placebo group? What does the graph suggest about the effectiveness of the treatment?

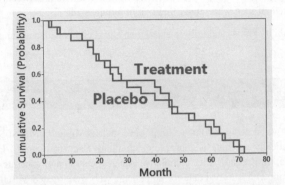

Cumulative Review Exercises

In Exercises 1–4, refer to the same life table used for Review Exercises 1–5.

1. Hypothesis Test of Experimental Results In one region, a comprehensive community-wide program is implemented in an attempt to reduce the rate of mortality for young Hispanic females. Results from this program show that among 1328 births of Hispanic females, 1323 survived to their second birthday and 5 did not survive to their second birthday. Using the data in the life table for Hispanic females, test the claim that the program was effective in reducing the mortality rate.

2. Confidence Interval for Experimental Results Given the sample results from Cumulative Review Exercise 1, construct a 95% confidence interval for the survival rate (from birth to the second birthday) for Hispanic females born in the region with the mortality reduction program in effect. Instead of using three significant digits, express the results with five significant digits. What can be concluded about the fact that the confidence interval limits do (or do not) contain the survival rate for Hispanic females, as suggested by the life table?

3. Probability of Surviving If three different newborn Hispanic females are randomly selected, find the probability that they all survive to their first birthday.

4. Probability of Surviving If four different newborn Hispanic females are randomly selected, find the probability that at least one of them does not survive to her first birthday. Does this probability apply to families in which there are four children, all of whom are Hispanic females?

5. Internet Doctors In a survey of $n = 2015$ adults, 1108 of them said that they learn about medical symptoms more often from the Internet than from their doctor (based on a MerckManuals.com report). The accompanying graph was created to depict the results of the survey. Is the graph somehow misleading? If so, how?

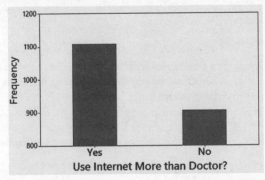

6. Heights Based on Data Set 1 "Body Data" in Appendix B, assume that heights of men are normally distributed with a mean of 68.6 in. and a standard deviation of 2.8 in.

a. The U.S. Coast Guard requires that its men must have a height between 60 in. and 80 in. Find the percentage of men who satisfy that height requirement.

b. Find the probability that 4 randomly selected men have heights with a mean greater than 70 in.

Technology Project

In Section 14-2 it was noted that some technologies, such as Minitab, JMP, SPSS, and XLSTAT-Life, can automatically generate Kaplan-Meier cumulative survival curves. Use a technology capable of generating Kaplan-Meier cumulative survival curves and generate the graph corresponding to the following survival data for 20 patients who were treated with heart surgery. The status of 1 indicates that the patient required a follow-up treatment after the surgery; the status of 0 represents a censored patient. Use the graph to estimate the seven-day survival rate, which is the proportion of patients not requiring follow-up treatment.

Day	1	5	6	9	14	23	25	27	29
Status	1	1	0	1	1	1	1	0	1

FROM DATA TO DECISION

Critical Thinking: **How do we reduce the high mortality rate among young black females?**

Compare the following life tables for black females and white females

Life Tables for Females: U.S., 2010

Age Interval	Probability of Dying During the Interval	Number Surviving to the Beginning of the Interval	Number of Deaths During the Interval	Person-Years Lived (total time lived *during the interval* by those alive at the beginning of the interval)	Total Person-Years Lived (in *this and all subsequent* intervals)	Expected Remaining Life-time (from the beginning of the interval)
Black Females						
0–1	0.010472	100,000	1,047	99,075	7,799,627	78.0
1–2	0.000596	98,953	59	98,923	7,700,551	77.8
2–3	0.000339	98,894	34	98,877	7,601,628	76.9
White Females						
0–1	0.004710	100,000	471	99,588	8,128,871	81.3
1–2	0.000382	99,529	38	99,510	8,029,283	80.7
2–3	0.000204	99,491	20	99,481	7,929,773	79.7

From National Vital Statistics Reports, U.S. Department of Health and Human Services.

Analyze the Results

1. What notable differences are apparent?

2. Identify some reasons for the apparent differences.

3. What are some steps that could be taken to effectively reduce the high rate of mortality among young black females?

4. What is a reasonable response to someone who argues that a program for reducing mortality among young black females should not be implemented because it discriminates on the basis of race?

Cooperative Group Activities

1. In-class activity Table 14-1 on pages 622-623 describes the life and death experience of a hypothetical group of 100,000 people. That table was constructed using actual results obtained from a variety of different sources. Instead of using real sources of vital statistics, assume that the death rate of some population is a constant 0.4 for each year. Construct as much of the life table as possible. How many years will pass before none of the hypothetical population of 100,000 people are alive?

2. Out-of-class activity Repeat Cooperative Group Activity 1, but instead of using a constant death rate of 0.4 each year, use a computer or calculator to randomly generate the death rate for each year. For each year, generate a random number between 0 and 1, and assume that it is the death rate that applies to the particular year.

3. Out-of-class activity Obtain Life Tables for Total Population: U.S. for years prior to 2010 and compare them. What are your observations? If differences exist, what do you think may account for changes in these life tables over time?

TABLE A-1 Binomial Probabilities

n	x							p							x
		.01	.05	.10	.20	.30	.40	.50	.60	.70	.80	.90	.95	.99	
2	0	.980	.903	.810	.640	.490	.360	.250	.160	.090	.040	.010	.003	0+	0
	1	.020	.095	.180	.320	.420	.480	.500	.480	.420	.320	.180	.095	.020	1
	2	0+	.003	.010	.040	.090	.160	.250	.360	.490	.640	.810	.903	.980	2
3	0	.970	.857	.729	.512	.343	.216	.125	.064	.027	.008	.001	0+	0+	0
	1	.029	.135	.243	.384	.441	.432	.375	.288	.189	.096	.027	.007	0+	1
	2	0+	.007	.027	.096	.189	.288	.375	.432	.441	.384	.243	.135	.029	2
	3	0+	0+	.001	.008	.027	.064	.125	.216	.343	.512	.729	.857	.970	3
4	0	.961	.815	.656	.410	.240	.130	.063	.026	.008	.002	0+	0+	0+	0
	1	.039	.171	.292	.410	.412	.346	.250	.154	.076	.026	.004	0+	0+	1
	2	.001	.014	.049	.154	.265	.346	.375	.346	.265	.154	.049	.014	.001	2
	3	0+	0+	.004	.026	.076	.154	.250	.346	.412	.410	.292	.171	.039	3
	4	0+	0+	0+	.002	.008	.026	.063	.130	.240	.410	.656	.815	.961	4
5	0	.951	.774	.590	.328	.168	.078	.031	.010	.002	0+	0+	0+	0+	0
	1	.048	.204	.328	.410	.360	.259	.156	.077	.028	.006	0+	0+	0+	1
	2	.001	.021	.073	.205	.309	.346	.313	.230	.132	.051	.008	.001	0+	2
	3	0+	.001	.008	.051	.132	.230	.313	.346	.309	.205	.073	.021	.001	3
	4	0+	0+	0+	.006	.028	.077	.156	.259	.360	.410	.328	.204	.048	4
	5	0+	0+	0+	0+	.002	.010	.031	.078	.168	.328	.590	.774	.951	5
6	0	.941	.735	.531	.262	.118	.047	.016	.004	.001	0+	0+	0+	0+	0
	1	.057	.232	.354	.393	.303	.187	.094	.037	.010	.002	0+	0+	0+	1
	2	.001	.031	.098	.246	.324	.311	.234	.138	.060	.015	.001	0+	0+	2
	3	0+	.002	.015	.082	.185	.276	.312	.276	.185	.082	.015	.002	0+	3
	4	0+	0+	.001	.015	.060	.138	.234	.311	.324	.246	.098	.031	.001	4
	5	0+	0+	0+	.002	.010	.037	.094	.187	.303	.393	.354	.232	.057	5
	6	0+	0+	0+	0+	.001	.004	.016	.047	.118	.262	.531	.735	.941	6
7	0	.932	.698	.478	.210	.082	.028	.008	.002	0+	0+	0+	0+	0+	0
	1	.066	.257	.372	.367	.247	.131	.055	.017	.004	0+	0+	0+	0+	1
	2	.002	.041	.124	.275	.318	.261	.164	.077	.025	.004	0+	0+	0+	2
	3	0+	.004	.023	.115	.227	.290	.273	.194	.097	.029	.003	0+	0+	3
	4	0+	0+	.003	.029	.097	.194	.273	.290	.227	.115	.023	.004	0+	4
	5	0+	0+	0+	.004	.025	.077	.164	.261	.318	.275	.124	.041	.002	5
	6	0+	0+	0+	0+	.004	.017	.055	.131	.247	.367	.372	.257	.066	6
	7	0+	0+	0+	0+	0+	.002	.008	.028	.082	.210	.478	.698	.932	7
8	0	.923	.663	.430	.168	.058	.017	.004	.001	0+	0+	0+	0+	0+	0
	1	.075	.279	.383	.336	.198	.090	.031	.008	.001	0+	0+	0+	0+	1
	2	.003	.051	.149	.294	.296	.209	.109	.041	.010	.001	0+	0+	0+	2
	3	0+	.005	.033	.147	.254	.279	.219	.124	.047	.009	0+	0+	0+	3
	4	0+	0+	.005	.046	.136	.232	.273	.232	.136	.046	.005	0+	0+	4
	5	0+	0+	0+	.009	.047	.124	.219	.279	.254	.147	.033	.005	0+	5
	6	0+	0+	0+	.001	.010	.041	.109	.209	.296	.294	.149	.051	.003	6
	7	0+	0+	0+	0+	.001	.008	.031	.090	.198	.336	.383	.279	.075	7
	8	0+	0+	0+	0+	0+	.001	.004	.017	.058	.168	.430	.663	.923	8

NOTE: 0+ represents a positive probability value less than 0.0005.

From Frederick C. Mosteller, Robert E. K. Rourke, and George B. Thomas, Jr., *Probability with Statistical Applications*, 2nd ed., © 1970. Reprinted and electronically reproduced by permission of Pearson Education, Inc., Upper Saddle River, New Jersey.

NEGATIVE z Scores

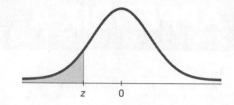

TABLE A-2 Standard Normal (z) Distribution: Cumulative Area from the LEFT

z	.00	.01	.02	.03	.04	.05	.06	.07	.08	.09
−3.50 and lower	.0001									
−3.4	.0003	.0003	.0003	.0003	.0003	.0003	.0003	.0003	.0003	.0002
−3.3	.0005	.0005	.0005	.0004	.0004	.0004	.0004	.0004	.0004	.0003
−3.2	.0007	.0007	.0006	.0006	.0006	.0006	.0006	.0005	.0005	.0005
−3.1	.0010	.0009	.0009	.0009	.0008	.0008	.0008	.0008	.0007	.0007
−3.0	.0013	.0013	.0013	.0012	.0012	.0011	.0011	.0011	.0010	.0010
−2.9	.0019	.0018	.0018	.0017	.0016	.0016	.0015	.0015	.0014	.0014
−2.8	.0026	.0025	.0024	.0023	.0023	.0022	.0021	.0021	.0020	.0019
−2.7	.0035	.0034	.0033	.0032	.0031	.0030	.0029	.0028	.0027	.0026
−2.6	.0047	.0045	.0044	.0043	.0041	.0040	.0039	.0038	.0037	.0036
−2.5	.0062	.0060	.0059	.0057	.0055	.0054	.0052	.0051 *	.0049	.0048
−2.4	.0082	.0080	.0078	.0075	.0073	.0071	.0069	.0068	.0066	.0064
−2.3	.0107	.0104	.0102	.0099	.0096	.0094	.0091	.0089	.0087	.0084
−2.2	.0139	.0136	.0132	.0129	.0125	.0122	.0119	.0116	.0113	.0110
−2.1	.0179	.0174	.0170	.0166	.0162	.0158	.0154	.0150	.0146	.0143
−2.0	.0228	.0222	.0217	.0212	.0207	.0202	.0197	.0192	.0188	.0183
−1.9	.0287	.0281	.0274	.0268	.0262	.0256	.0250	.0244	.0239	.0233
−1.8	.0359	.0351	.0344	.0336	.0329	.0322	.0314	.0307	.0301	.0294
−1.7	.0446	.0436	.0427	.0418	.0409	.0401	.0392	.0384	.0375	.0367
−1.6	.0548	.0537	.0526	.0516	.0505 *	.0495	.0485	.0475	.0465	.0455
−1.5	.0668	.0655	.0643	.0630	.0618	.0606	.0594	.0582	.0571	.0559
−1.4	.0808	.0793	.0778	.0764	.0749	.0735	.0721	.0708	.0694	.0681
−1.3	.0968	.0951	.0934	.0918	.0901	.0885	.0869	.0853	.0838	.0823
−1.2	.1151	.1131	.1112	.1093	.1075	.1056	.1038	.1020	.1003	.0985
−1.1	.1357	.1335	.1314	.1292	.1271	.1251	.1230	.1210	.1190	.1170
−1.0	.1587	.1562	.1539	.1515	.1492	.1469	.1446	.1423	.1401	.1379
−0.9	.1841	.1814	.1788	.1762	.1736	.1711	.1685	.1660	.1635	.1611
−0.8	.2119	.2090	.2061	.2033	.2005	.1977	.1949	.1922	.1894	.1867
−0.7	.2420	.2389	.2358	.2327	.2296	.2266	.2236	.2206	.2177	.2148
−0.6	.2743	.2709	.2676	.2643	.2611	.2578	.2546	.2514	.2483	.2451
−0.5	.3085	.3050	.3015	.2981	.2946	.2912	.2877	.2843	.2810	.2776
−0.4	.3446	.3409	.3372	.3336	.3300	.3264	.3228	.3192	.3156	.3121
−0.3	.3821	.3783	.3745	.3707	.3669	.3632	.3594	.3557	.3520	.3483
−0.2	.4207	.4168	.4129	.4090	.4052	.4013	.3974	.3936	.3897	.3859
−0.1	.4602	.4562	.4522	.4483	.4443	.4404	.4364	.4325	.4286	.4247
−0.0	.5000	.4960	.4920	.4880	.4840	.4801	.4761	.4721	.4681	.4641

NOTE: For values of z below −3.49, use 0.0001 for the area.

(continued)

*Use these common values that result from interpolation:

z Score	Area
−1.645	0.0500
−2.575	0.0050

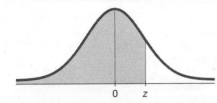

POSITIVE z Scores

TABLE A-2 *(continued)* Cumulative Area from the LEFT

z	.00	.01	.02	.03	.04	.05	.06	.07	.08	.09
0.0	.5000	.5040	.5080	.5120	.5160	.5199	.5239	.5279	.5319	.5359
0.1	.5398	.5438	.5478	.5517	.5557	.5596	.5636	.5675	.5714	.5753
0.2	.5793	.5832	.5871	.5910	.5948	.5987	.6026	.6064	.6103	.6141
0.3	.6179	.6217	.6255	.6293	.6331	.6368	.6406	.6443	.6480	.6517
0.4	.6554	.6591	.6628	.6664	.6700	.6736	.6772	.6808	.6844	.6879
0.5	.6915	.6950	.6985	.7019	.7054	.7088	.7123	.7157	.7190	.7224
0.6	.7257	.7291	.7324	.7357	.7389	.7422	.7454	.7486	.7517	.7549
0.7	.7580	.7611	.7642	.7673	.7704	.7734	.7764	.7794	.7823	.7852
0.8	.7881	.7910	.7939	.7967	.7995	.8023	.8051	.8078	.8106	.8133
0.9	.8159	.8186	.8212	.8238	.8264	.8289	.8315	.8340	.8365	.8389
1.0	.8413	.8438	.8461	.8485	.8508	.8531	.8554	.8577	.8599	.8621
1.1	.8643	.8665	.8686	.8708	.8729	.8749	.8770	.8790	.8810	.8830
1.2	.8849	.8869	.8888	.8907	.8925	.8944	.8962	.8980	.8997	.9015
1.3	.9032	.9049	.9066	.9082	.9099	.9115	.9131	.9147	.9162	.9177
1.4	.9192	.9207	.9222	.9236	.9251	.9265	.9279	.9292	.9306	.9319
1.5	.9332	.9345	.9357	.9370	.9382	.9394	.9406	.9418	.9429	.9441
1.6	.9452	.9463	.9474	.9484	.9495 *	.9505	.9515	.9525	.9535	.9545
1.7	.9554	.9564	.9573	.9582	.9591	.9599	.9608	.9616	.9625	.9633
1.8	.9641	.9649	.9656	.9664	.9671	.9678	.9686	.9693	.9699	.9706
1.9	.9713	.9719	.9726	.9732	.9738	.9744	.9750	.9756	.9761	.9767
2.0	.9772	.9778	.9783	.9788	.9793	.9798	.9803	.9808	.9812	.9817
2.1	.9821	.9826	.9830	.9834	.9838	.9842	.9846	.9850	.9854	.9857
2.2	.9861	.9864	.9868	.9871	.9875	.9878	.9881	.9884	.9887	.9890
2.3	.9893	.9896	.9898	.9901	.9904	.9906	.9909	.9911	.9913	.9916
2.4	.9918	.9920	.9922	.9925	.9927	.9929	.9931	.9932	.9934	.9936
2.5	.9938	.9940	.9941	.9943	.9945	.9946	.9948	.9949 *	.9951	.9952
2.6	.9953	.9955	.9956	.9957	.9959	.9960	.9961	.9962	.9963	.9964
2.7	.9965	.9966	.9967	.9968	.9969	.9970	.9971	.9972	.9973	.9974
2.8	.9974	.9975	.9976	.9977	.9977	.9978	.9979	.9979	.9980	.9981
2.9	.9981	.9982	.9982	.9983	.9984	.9984	.9985	.9985	.9986	.9986
3.0	.9987	.9987	.9987	.9988	.9988	.9989	.9989	.9989	.9990	.9990
3.1	.9990	.9991	.9991	.9991	.9992	.9992	.9992	.9992	.9993	.9993
3.2	.9993	.9993	.9994	.9994	.9994	.9994	.9994	.9995	.9995	.9995
3.3	.9995	.9995	.9995	.9996	.9996	.9996	.9996	.9996	.9996	.9997
3.4	.9997	.9997	.9997	.9997	.9997	.9997	.9997	.9997	.9997	.9998
3.50 and up	.9999									

NOTE: For values of z above 3.49, use 0.9999 for the area.

*Use these common values that result from interpolation:

z Score	Area
1.645	0.9500
2.575	0.9950

Common Critical Values

Confidence Level	Critical Value
0.90	1.645
0.95	1.96
0.99	2.575

Left tail

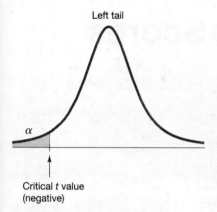

α

Critical *t* value
(negative)

Right tail

α

Critical *t* value
(positive)

Two tails

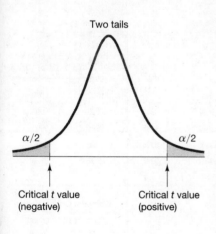

α/2   α/2

Critical *t* value   Critical *t* value
(negative)   (positive)

TABLE A-3 *t* Distribution: Critical *t* Values

	Area in One Tail				
	0.005	0.01	0.025	0.05	0.10
Degrees of	Area in Two Tails				
Freedom	0.01	0.02	0.05	0.10	0.20
1	63.657	31.821	12.706	6.314	3.078
2	9.925	6.965	4.303	2.920	1.886
3	5.841	4.541	3.182	2.353	1.638
4	4.604	3.747	2.776	2.132	1.533
5	4.032	3.365	2.571	2.015	1.476
6	3.707	3.143	2.447	1.943	1.440
7	3.499	2.998	2.365	1.895	1.415
8	3.355	2.896	2.306	1.860	1.397
9	3.250	2.821	2.262	1.833	1.383
10	3.169	2.764	2.228	1.812	1.372
11	3.106	2.718	2.201	1.796	1.363
12	3.055	2.681	2.179	1.782	1.356
13	3.012	2.650	2.160	1.771	1.350
14	2.977	2.624	2.145	1.761	1.345
15	2.947	2.602	2.131	1.753	1.341
16	2.921	2.583	2.120	1.746	1.337
17	2.898	2.567	2.110	1.740	1.333
18	2.878	2.552	2.101	1.734	1.330
19	2.861	2.539	2.093	1.729	1.328
20	2.845	2.528	2.086	1.725	1.325
21	2.831	2.518	2.080	1.721	1.323
22	2.819	2.508	2.074	1.717	1.321
23	2.807	2.500	2.069	1.714	1.319
24	2.797	2.492	2.064	1.711	1.318
25	2.787	2.485	2.060	1.708	1.316
26	2.779	2.479	2.056	1.706	1.315
27	2.771	2.473	2.052	1.703	1.314
28	2.763	2.467	2.048	1.701	1.313
29	2.756	2.462	2.045	1.699	1.311
30	2.750	2.457	2.042	1.697	1.310
31	2.744	2.453	2.040	1.696	1.309
32	2.738	2.449	2.037	1.694	1.309
33	2.733	2.445	2.035	1.692	1.308
34	2.728	2.441	2.032	1.691	1.307
35	2.724	2.438	2.030	1.690	1.306
36	2.719	2.434	2.028	1.688	1.306
37	2.715	2.431	2.026	1.687	1.305
38	2.712	2.429	2.024	1.686	1.304
39	2.708	2.426	2.023	1.685	1.304
40	2.704	2.423	2.021	1.684	1.303
45	2.690	2.412	2.014	1.679	1.301
50	2.678	2.403	2.009	1.676	1.299
60	2.660	2.390	2.000	1.671	1.296
70	2.648	2.381	1.994	1.667	1.294
80	2.639	2.374	1.990	1.664	1.292
90	2.632	2.368	1.987	1.662	1.291
100	2.626	2.364	1.984	1.660	1.290
200	2.601	2.345	1.972	1.653	1.286
300	2.592	2.339	1.968	1.650	1.284
400	2.588	2.336	1.966	1.649	1.284
500	2.586	2.334	1.965	1.648	1.283
1000	2.581	2.330	1.962	1.646	1.282
2000	2.578	2.328	1.961	1.646	1.282
Large	2.576	2.326	1.960	1.645	1.282

TABLE A-4 Chi-Square (X^2) Distribution

Degrees of Freedom	Area to the *Right* of the Critical Value									
	0.995	0.99	0.975	0.95	0.90	0.10	0.05	0.025	0.01	0.005
1	—	—	0.001	0.004	0.016	2.706	3.841	5.024	6.635	7.879
2	0.010	0.020	0.051	0.103	0.211	4.605	5.991	7.378	9.210	10.597
3	0.072	0.115	0.216	0.352	0.584	6.251	7.815	9.348	11.345	12.838
4	0.207	0.297	0.484	0.711	1.064	7.779	9.488	11.143	13.277	14.860
5	0.412	0.554	0.831	1.145	1.610	9.236	11.071	12.833	15.086	16.750
6	0.676	0.872	1.237	1.635	2.204	10.645	12.592	14.449	16.812	18.548
7	0.989	1.239	1.690	2.167	2.833	12.017	14.067	16.013	18.475	20.278
8	1.344	1.646	2.180	2.733	3.490	13.362	15.507	17.535	20.090	21.955
9	1.735	2.088	2.700	3.325	4.168	14.684	16.919	19.023	21.666	23.589
10	2.156	2.558	3.247	3.940	4.865	15.987	18.307	20.483	23.209	25.188
11	2.603	3.053	3.816	4.575	5.578	17.275	19.675	21.920	24.725	26.757
12	3.074	3.571	4.404	5.226	6.304	18.549	21.026	23.337	26.217	28.299
13	3.565	4.107	5.009	5.892	7.042	19.812	22.362	24.736	27.688	29.819
14	4.075	4.660	5.629	6.571	7.790	21.064	23.685	26.119	29.141	31.319
15	4.601	5.229	6.262	7.261	8.547	22.307	24.996	27.488	30.578	32.801
16	5.142	5.812	6.908	7.962	9.312	23.542	26.296	28.845	32.000	34.267
17	5.697	6.408	7.564	8.672	10.085	24.769	27.587	30.191	33.409	35.718
18	6.265	7.015	8.231	9.390	10.865	25.989	28.869	31.526	34.805	37.156
19	6.844	7.633	8.907	10.117	11.651	27.204	30.144	32.852	36.191	38.582
20	7.434	8.260	9.591	10.851	12.443	28.412	31.410	34.170	37.566	39.997
21	8.034	8.897	10.283	11.591	13.240	29.615	32.671	35.479	38.932	41.401
22	8.643	9.542	10.982	12.338	14.042	30.813	33.924	36.781	40.289	42.796
23	9.260	10.196	11.689	13.091	14.848	32.007	35.172	38.076	41.638	44.181
24	9.886	10.856	12.401	13.848	15.659	33.196	36.415	39.364	42.980	45.559
25	10.520	11.524	13.120	14.611	16.473	34.382	37.652	40.646	44.314	46.928
26	11.160	12.198	13.844	15.379	17.292	35.563	38.885	41.923	45.642	48.290
27	11.808	12.879	14.573	16.151	18.114	36.741	40.113	43.194	46.963	49.645
28	12.461	13.565	15.308	16.928	18.939	37.916	41.337	44.461	48.278	50.993
29	13.121	14.257	16.047	17.708	19.768	39.087	42.557	45.722	49.588	52.336
30	13.787	14.954	16.791	18.493	20.599	40.256	43.773	46.979	50.892	53.672
40	20.707	22.164	24.433	26.509	29.051	51.805	55.758	59.342	63.691	66.766
50	27.991	29.707	32.357	34.764	37.689	63.167	67.505	71.420	76.154	79.490
60	35.534	37.485	40.482	43.188	46.459	74.397	79.082	83.298	88.379	91.952
70	43.275	45.442	48.758	51.739	55.329	85.527	90.531	95.023	100.425	104.215
80	51.172	53.540	57.153	60.391	64.278	96.578	101.879	106.629	112.329	116.321
90	59.196	61.754	65.647	69.126	73.291	107.565	113.145	118.136	124.116	128.299
100	67.328	70.065	74.222	77.929	82.358	118.498	124.342	129.561	135.807	140.169

Source: Donald B. Owen, *Handbook of Statistical Tables.*

Degrees of Freedom

$n - 1$	**Confidence interval or hypothesis test** for a standard deviation σ or variance σ^2
$k - 1$	**Goodness-of-fit test** with k different categories
$(r - 1)(c - 1)$	**Contingency table test** with r rows and c columns
$k - 1$	**Kruskal-Wallis test** with k different samples

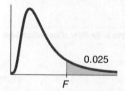

TABLE A-5 F Distribution ($\alpha = 0.025$ in the right tail)

		Numerator degrees of freedom (df₁)							
	1	**2**	**3**	**4**	**5**	**6**	**7**	**8**	**9**
1	647.79	799.50	864.16	899.58	921.85	937.11	948.22	956.66	963.28
2	38.506	39.000	39.165	39.248	39.298	39.331	39.335	39.373	39.387
3	17.443	16.044	15.439	15.101	14.885	14.735	14.624	14.540	14.473
4	12.218	10.649	9.9792	9.6045	9.3645	9.1973	9.0741	8.9796	8.9047
5	10.007	8.4336	7.7636	7.3879	7.1464	6.9777	6.8531	6.7572	6.6811
6	8.8131	7.2599	6.5988	6.2272	5.9876	5.8198	5.6955	5.5996	5.5234
7	8.0727	6.5415	5.8898	5.5226	5.2852	5.1186	4.9949	4.8993	4.8232
8	7.5709	6.0595	5.4160	5.0526	4.8173	4.6517	4.5286	4.4333	4.3572
9	7.2093	5.7147	5.0781	4.7181	4.4844	4.3197	4.1970	4.1020	4.0260
10	6.9367	5.4564	4.8256	4.4683	4.2361	4.0721	3.9498	3.8549	3.7790
11	6.7241	5.2559	4.6300	4.2751	4.0440	3.8807	3.7586	3.6638	3.5879
12	6.5538	5.0959	4.4742	4.1212	3.8911	3.7283	3.6065	3.5118	3.4358
13	6.4143	4.9653	4.3472	3.9959	3.7667	3.6043	3.4827	3.3880	3.3120
14	6.2979	4.8567	4.2417	3.8919	3.6634	3.5014	3.3799	3.2853	3.2093
15	6.1995	4.7650	4.1528	3.8043	3.5764	3.4147	3.2934	3.1987	3.1227
16	6.1151	4.6867	4.0768	3.7294	3.5021	3.3406	3.2194	3.1248	3.0488
17	6.0420	4.6189	4.0112	3.6648	3.4379	3.2767	3.1556	3.0610	2.9849
18	5.9781	4.5597	3.9539	3.6083	3.3820	3.2209	3.0999	3.0053	2.9291
19	5.9216	4.5075	3.9034	3.5587	3.3327	3.1718	3.0509	2.9563	2.8801
20	5.8715	4.4613	3.8587	3.5147	3.2891	3.1283	3.0074	2.9128	2.8365
21	5.8266	4.4199	3.8188	3.4754	3.2501	3.0895	2.9686	2.8740	2.7977
22	5.7863	4.3828	3.7829	3.4401	3.2151	3.0546	2.9338	2.8392	2.7628
23	5.7498	4.3492	3.7505	3.4083	3.1835	3.0232	2.9023	2.8077	2.7313
24	5.7166	4.3187	3.7211	3.3794	3.1548	2.9946	2.8738	2.7791	2.7027
25	5.6864	4.2909	3.6943	3.3530	3.1287	2.9685	2.8478	2.7531	2.6766
26	5.6586	4.2655	3.6697	3.3289	3.1048	2.9447	2.8240	2.7293	2.6528
27	5.6331	4.2421	3.6472	3.3067	3.0828	2.9228	2.8021	2.7074	2.6309
28	5.6096	4.2205	3.6264	3.2863	3.0626	2.9027	2.7820	2.6872	2.6106
29	5.5878	4.2006	3.6072	3.2674	3.0438	2.8840	2.7633	2.6686	2.5919
30	5.5675	4.1821	3.5894	3.2499	3.0265	2.8667	2.7460	2.6513	2.5746
40	5.4239	4.0510	3.4633	3.1261	2.9037	2.7444	2.6238	2.5289	2.4519
60	5.2856	3.9253	3.3425	3.0077	2.7863	2.6274	2.5068	2.4117	2.3344
120	5.1523	3.8046	3.2269	2.8943	2.6740	2.5154	2.3948	2.2994	2.2217
∞	5.0239	3.6889	3.1161	2.7858	2.5665	2.4082	2.2875	2.1918	2.1136

Denominator degrees of freedom (df₂)

(continued)

TABLE A-5 *(continued)* F Distribution ($\alpha = 0.025$ in the right tail)

					Numerator degrees of freedom (df_1)					
		10	12	15	20	24	30	40	60	120	∞
	1	968.63	976.71	984.87	993.10	997.25	1001.4	1005.6	1009.8	1014.0	1018.3
	2	39.398	39.415	39.431	39.448	39.456	39.465	39.473	39.481	39.490	39.498
	3	14.419	14.337	14.253	14.167	14.124	14.081	14.037	13.992	13.947	13.902
	4	8.8439	8.7512	8.6565	8.5599	8.5109	8.4613	8.4111	8.3604	8.3092	8.2573
	5	6.6192	6.5245	6.4277	6.3286	6.2780	6.2269	6.1750	6.1225	6.0693	6.0153
	6	5.4613	5.3662	5.2687	5.1684	5.1172	5.0652	5.0125	4.9589	4.9044	4.8491
	7	4.7611	4.6658	4.5678	4.4667	4.4150	4.3624	4.3089	4.2544	4.1989	4.1423
	8	4.2951	4.1997	4.1012	3.9995	3.9472	3.8940	3.8398	3.7844	3.7279	3.6702
	9	3.9639	3.8682	3.7694	3.6669	3.6142	3.5604	3.5055	3.4493	3.3918	3.3329
	10	3.7168	3.6209	3.5217	3.4185	3.3654	3.3110	3.2554	3.1984	3.1399	3.0798
	11	3.5257	3.4296	3.3299	3.2261	3.1725	3.1176	3.0613	3.0035	2.9441	2.8828
	12	3.3736	3.2773	3.1772	3.0728	3.0187	2.9633	2.9063	2.8478	2.7874	2.7249
	13	3.2497	3.1532	3.0527	2.9477	2.8932	2.8372	2.7797	2.7204	2.6590	2.5955
	14	3.1469	3.0502	2.9493	2.8437	2.7888	2.7324	2.6742	2.6142	2.5519	2.4872
	15	3.0602	2.9633	2.8621	2.7559	2.7006	2.6437	2.5850	2.5242	2.4611	2.3953
	16	2.9862	2.8890	2.7875	2.6808	2.6252	2.5678	2.5085	2.4471	2.3831	2.3163
	17	2.9222	2.8249	2.7230	2.6158	2.5598	2.5020	2.4422	2.3801	2.3153	2.2474
	18	2.8664	2.7689	2.6667	2.5590	2.5027	2.4445	2.3842	2.3214	2.2558	2.1869
	19	2.8172	2.7196	2.6171	2.5089	2.4523	2.3937	2.3329	2.2696	2.2032	2.1333
	20	2.7737	2.6758	2.5731	2.4645	2.4076	2.3486	2.2873	2.2234	2.1562	2.0853
	21	2.7348	2.6368	2.5338	2.4247	2.3675	2.3082	2.2465	2.1819	2.1141	2.0422
	22	2.6998	2.6017	2.4984	2.3890	2.3315	2.2718	2.2097	2.1446	2.0760	2.0032
	23	2.6682	2.5699	2.4665	2.3567	2.2989	2.2389	2.1763	2.1107	2.0415	1.9677
	24	2.6396	2.5411	2.4374	2.3273	2.2693	2.2090	2.1460	2.0799	2.0099	1.9353
	25	2.6135	2.5149	2.4110	2.3005	2.2422	2.1816	2.1183	2.0516	1.9811	1.9055
	26	2.5896	2.4908	2.3867	2.2759	2.2174	2.1565	2.0928	2.0257	1.9545	1.8781
	27	2.5676	2.4688	2.3644	2.2533	2.1946	2.1334	2.0693	2.0018	1.9299	1.8527
	28	2.5473	2.4484	2.3438	2.2324	2.1735	2.1121	2.0477	1.9797	1.9072	1.8291
	29	2.5286	2.4295	2.3248	2.2131	2.1540	2.0923	2.0276	1.9591	1.8861	1.8072
	30	2.5112	2.4120	2.3072	2.1952	2.1359	2.0739	2.0089	1.9400	1.8664	1.7867
	40	2.3882	2.2882	2.1819	2.0677	2.0069	1.9429	1.8752	1.8028	1.7242	1.6371
	60	2.2702	2.1692	2.0613	1.9445	1.8817	1.8152	1.7440	1.6668	1.5810	1.4821
	120	2.1570	2.0548	1.9450	1.8249	1.7597	1.6899	1.6141	1.5299	1.4327	1.3104
	∞	2.0483	1.9447	1.8326	1.7085	1.6402	1.5660	1.4835	1.3883	1.2684	1.0000

Denominator degrees of freedom (df_2) (row label for table)

Based on data from Maxine Merrington and Catherine M. Thompson, "Tables of Percentage Points of the Inverted Beta (F) Distribution," *Biometrika 33* (1943): 80–84.

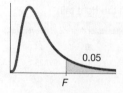

TABLE A-5 *(continued)* F Distribution ($\alpha = 0.05$ in the right tail)

		Numerator degrees of freedom (df_1)							
	1	2	3	4	5	6	7	8	9
1	161.45	199.50	215.71	224.58	230.16	233.99	236.77	238.88	240.54
2	18.513	19.000	19.164	19.247	19.296	19.330	19.353	19.371	19.385
3	10.128	9.5521	9.2766	9.1172	9.0135	8.9406	8.8867	8.8452	8.8123
4	7.7086	6.9443	6.5914	6.3882	6.2561	6.1631	6.0942	6.0410	6.9988
5	6.6079	5.7861	5.4095	5.1922	5.0503	4.9503	4.8759	4.8183	4.7725
6	5.9874	5.1433	4.7571	4.5337	4.3874	4.2839	4.2067	4.1468	4.0990
7	5.5914	4.7374	4.3468	4.1203	3.9715	3.8660	3.7870	3.7257	3.6767
8	5.3177	4.4590	4.0662	3.8379	3.6875	3.5806	3.5005	3.4381	3.3881
9	5.1174	4.2565	3.8625	3.6331	3.4817	3.3738	3.2927	3.2296	3.1789
10	4.9646	4.1028	3.7083	3.4780	3.3258	3.2172	3.1355	3.0717	3.0204
11	4.8443	3.9823	3.5874	3.3567	3.2039	3.0946	3.0123	2.9480	2.8962
12	4.7472	3.8853	3.4903	3.2592	3.1059	2.9961	2.9134	2.8486	2.7964
13	4.6672	3.8056	3.4105	3.1791	3.0254	2.9153	2.8321	2.7669	2.7144
14	4.6001	3.7389	3.3439	3.1122	2.9582	2.8477	2.7642	2.6987	2.6458
15	4.5431	3.6823	3.2874	3.0556	2.9013	2.7905	2.7066	2.6408	2.5876
16	4.4940	3.6337	3.2389	3.0069	2.8524	2.7413	2.6572	2.5911	2.5377
17	4.4513	3.5915	3.1968	2.9647	2.8100	2.6987	2.6143	2.5480	2.4943
18	4.4139	3.5546	3.1599	2.9277	2.7729	2.6613	2.5767	2.5102	2.4563
19	4.3807	3.5219	3.1274	2.8951	2.7401	2.6283	2.5435	2.4768	2.4227
20	4.3512	3.4928	3.0984	2.8661	2.7109	2.5990	2.5140	2.4471	2.3928
21	4.3248	3.4668	3.0725	2.8401	2.6848	2.5727	2.4876	2.4205	2.3660
22	4.3009	3.4434	3.0491	2.8167	2.6613	2.5491	2.4638	2.3965	2.3419
23	4.2793	3.4221	3.0280	2.7955	2.6400	2.5277	2.4422	2.3748	2.3201
24	4.2597	3.4028	3.0088	2.7763	2.6207	2.5082	2.4226	2.3551	2.3002
25	4.2417	3.3852	2.9912	2.7587	2.6030	2.4904	2.4047	2.3371	2.2821
26	4.2252	3.3690	2.9752	2.7426	2.5868	2.4741	2.3883	2.3205	2.2655
27	4.2100	3.3541	2.9604	2.7278	2.5719	2.4591	2.3732	2.3053	2.2501
28	4.1960	3.3404	2.9467	2.7141	2.5581	2.4453	2.3593	2.2913	2.2360
29	4.1830	3.3277	2.9340	2.7014	2.5454	2.4324	2.3463	2.2783	2.2229
30	4.1709	3.3158	2.9223	2.6896	2.5336	2.4205	2.3343	2.2662	2.2107
40	4.0847	3.2317	2.8387	2.6060	2.4495	2.3359	2.2490	2.1802	2.1240
60	4.0012	3.1504	2.7581	2.5252	2.3683	2.2541	2.1665	2.0970	2.0401
120	3.9201	3.0718	2.6802	2.4472	2.2899	2.1750	2.0868	2.0164	1.9588
∞	3.8415	2.9957	2.6049	2.3719	2.2141	2.0986	2.0096	1.9384	1.8799

Denominator degrees of freedom (df_2)

(continued)

TABLE A-5 *(continued)* F Distribution ($\alpha = 0.05$ in the right tail)

Denominator degrees of freedom (df_2)	Numerator degrees of freedom (df_1)									
	10	12	15	20	24	30	40	60	120	∞
1	241.88	243.91	245.95	248.01	249.05	250.10	251.14	252.20	253.25	254.31
2	19.396	19.413	19.429	19.446	19.454	19.462	19.471	19.479	19.487	19.496
3	8.7855	8.7446	8.7029	8.6602	8.6385	8.6166	8.5944	8.5720	8.5494	8.5264
4	5.9644	5.9117	5.8578	5.8025	5.7744	5.7459	5.7170	5.6877	5.6581	5.6281
5	4.7351	4.6777	4.6188	4.5581	4.5272	4.4957	4.4638	4.4314	4.3985	4.3650
6	4.0600	3.9999	3.9381	3.8742	3.8415	3.8082	3.7743	3.7398	3.7047	3.6689
7	3.6365	3.5747	3.5107	3.4445	3.4105	3.3758	3.3404	3.3043	3.2674	3.2298
8	3.3472	3.2839	3.2184	3.1503	3.1152	3.0794	3.0428	3.0053	2.9669	2.9276
9	3.1373	3.0729	3.0061	2.9365	2.9005	2.8637	2.8259	2.7872	2.7475	2.7067
10	2.9782	2.9130	2.8450	2.7740	2.7372	2.6996	2.6609	2.6211	2.5801	2.5379
11	2.8536	2.7876	2.7186	2.6464	2.6090	2.5705	2.5309	2.4901	2.4480	2.4045
12	2.7534	2.6866	2.6169	2.5436	2.5055	2.4663	2.4259	2.3842	2.3410	2.2962
13	2.6710	2.6037	2.5331	2.4589	2.4202	2.3803	2.3392	2.2966	2.2524	2.2064
14	2.6022	2.5342	2.4630	2.3879	2.3487	2.3082	2.2664	2.2229	2.1778	2.1307
15	2.5437	2.4753	2.4034	2.3275	2.2878	2.2468	2.2043	2.1601	2.1141	2.0658
16	2.4935	2.4247	2.3522	2.2756	2.2354	2.1938	2.1507	2.1058	2.0589	2.0096
17	2.4499	2.3807	2.3077	2.2304	2.1898	2.1477	2.1040	2.0584	2.0107	1.9604
18	2.4117	2.3421	2.2686	2.1906	2.1497	2.1071	2.0629	2.0166	1.9681	1.9168
19	2.3779	2.3080	2.2341	2.1555	2.1141	2.0712	2.0264	1.9795	1.9302	1.8780
20	2.3479	2.2776	2.2033	2.1242	2.0825	2.0391	1.9938	1.9464	1.8963	1.8432
21	2.3210	2.2504	2.1757	2.0960	2.0540	2.0102	1.9645	1.9165	1.8657	1.8117
22	2.2967	2.2258	2.1508	2.0707	2.0283	1.9842	1.9380	1.8894	1.8380	1.7831
23	2.2747	2.2036	2.1282	2.0476	2.0050	1.9605	1.9139	1.8648	1.8128	1.7570
24	2.2547	2.1834	2.1077	2.0267	1.9838	1.9390	1.8920	1.8424	1.7896	1.7330
25	2.2365	2.1649	2.0889	2.0075	1.9643	1.9192	1.8718	1.8217	1.7684	1.7110
26	2.2197	2.1479	2.0716	1.9898	1.9464	1.9010	1.8533	1.8027	1.7488	1.6906
27	2.2043	2.1323	2.0558	1.9736	1.9299	1.8842	1.8361	1.7851	1.7306	1.6717
28	2.1900	2.1179	2.0411	1.9586	1.9147	1.8687	1.8203	1.7689	1.7138	1.6541
29	2.1768	2.1045	2.0275	1.9446	1.9005	1.8543	1.8055	1.7537	1.6981	1.6376
30	2.1646	2.0921	2.0148	1.9317	1.8874	1.8409	1.7918	1.7396	1.6835	1.6223
40	2.0772	2.0035	1.9245	1.8389	1.7929	1.7444	1.6928	1.6373	1.5766	1.5089
60	1.9926	1.9174	1.8364	1.7480	1.7001	1.6491	1.5943	1.5343	1.4673	1.3893
120	1.9105	1.8337	1.7505	1.6587	1.6084	1.5543	1.4952	1.4290	1.3519	1.2539
∞	1.8307	1.7522	1.6664	1.5705	1.5173	1.4591	1.3940	1.3180	1.2214	1.0000

Based on data from Maxine Merrington and Catherine M. Thompson, "Tables of Percentage Points of the Inverted Beta (F) Distribution," *Biometrika* 33 (1943): 80–84.

TABLE A-6 Critical Values of the Pearson Correlation Coefficient r

n	$\alpha = .05$	$\alpha = .01$
4	.950	.990
5	.878	.959
6	.811	.917
7	.754	.875
8	.707	.834
9	.666	.798
10	.632	.765
11	.602	.735
12	.576	.708
13	.553	.684
14	.532	.661
15	.514	.641
16	.497	.623
17	.482	.606
18	.468	.590
19	.456	.575
20	.444	.561
25	.396	.505
30	.361	.463
35	.335	.430
40	.312	.402
45	.294	.378
50	.279	.361
60	.254	.330
70	.236	.305
80	.220	.286
90	.207	.269
100	.196	.256

NOTE: To test $H_0: \rho = 0$ (no correlation) against $H_1: \rho \neq 0$ (correlation), reject H_0 if the absolute value of r is greater than or equal to the critical value in the table.

TABLE A-7 Critical Values for the Sign Test

	α			
	.005 (one tail)	.01 (one tail)	.025 (one tail)	.05 (one tail)
n	.01 (two tails)	.02 (two tails)	.05 (two tails)	.10 (two tails)
1	*	*	*	*
2	*	*	*	*
3	*	*	*	*
4	*	*	*	*
5	*	*	*	0
6	*	*	0	0
7	*	0	0	0
8	0	0	0	1
9	0	0	1	1
10	0	0	1	1
11	0	1	1	2
12	1	1	2	2
13	1	1	2	3
14	1	2	2	3
15	2	2	3	3
16	2	2	3	4
17	2	3	4	4
18	3	3	4	5
19	3	4	4	5
20	3	4	5	5
21	4	4	5	6
22	4	5	5	6
23	4	5	6	7
24	5	5	6	7
25	5	6	7	7

NOTES:
1. *indicates that it is not possible to get a value in the critical region, so fail to reject the null hypothesis.
2. Reject the null hypothesis if the number of the less frequent sign (x) is less than or equal to the value in the table.
3. For values of n greater than 25, a normal approximation is used with

$$z = \frac{(x + 0.5) - \left(\frac{n}{2}\right)}{\frac{\sqrt{n}}{2}}$$

TABLE A-8 Critical Values of T for the Wilcoxon Signed-Ranks Test

	α			
	.005 (one tail)	.01 (one tail)	.025 (one tail)	.05 (one tail)
n	.01 (two tails)	.02 (two tails)	.05 (two tails)	.10 (two tails)
5	*	*	*	1
6	*	*	1	2
7	*	0	2	4
8	0	2	4	6
9	2	3	6	8
10	3	5	8	11
11	5	7	11	14
12	7	10	14	17
13	10	13	17	21
14	13	16	21	26
15	16	20	25	30
16	19	24	30	36
17	23	28	35	41
18	28	33	40	47
19	32	38	46	54
20	37	43	52	60
21	43	49	59	68
22	49	56	66	75
23	55	62	73	83
24	61	69	81	92
25	68	77	90	101
26	76	85	98	110
27	84	93	107	120
28	92	102	117	130
29	100	111	127	141
30	109	120	137	152

NOTES:

1. *indicates that it is not possible to get a value in the critical region, so fail to reject the null hypothesis.

2. Conclusions:

   Reject the null hypothesis if the test statistic T is less than or equal to the critical value found in this table.

   Fail to reject the null hypothesis if the test statistic T is greater than the critical value found in the table.

Based on data from *Some Rapid Approximate Statistical Procedures*, Copyright © 1949, 1964 Lederle Laboratories Division of American Cyanamid Company.

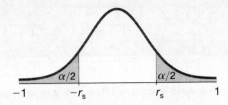

TABLE A-9 Critical Values of Spearman's Rank
Correlation Coefficient r_s

n	$\alpha = 0.10$	$\alpha = 0.05$	$\alpha = 0.02$	$\alpha = 0.01$
5	.900	—	—	—
6	.829	.886	.943	—
7	.714	.786	.893	.929
8	.643	.738	.833	.881
9	.600	.700	.783	.833
10	.564	.648	.745	.794
11	.536	.618	.709	.755
12	.503	.587	.678	.727
13	.484	.560	.648	.703
14	.464	.538	.626	.679
15	.446	.521	.604	.654
16	.429	.503	.582	.635
17	.414	.485	.566	.615
18	.401	.472	.550	.600
19	.391	.460	.535	.584
20	.380	.447	.520	.570
21	.370	.435	.508	.556
22	.361	.425	.496	.544
23	.353	.415	.486	.532
24	.344	.406	.476	.521
25	.337	.398	.466	.511
26	.331	.390	.457	.501
27	.324	.382	.448	.491
28	.317	.375	.440	.483
29	.312	.368	.433	.475
30	.306	.362	.425	.467

NOTES:
1. For $n > 30$ use $r_s \pm z/\sqrt{n-1}$, where z corresponds to the level of significance.
   For example, if $\alpha = 0.05$, then $z = 1.96$.
2. If the absolute value of the test statistic r_s is greater than or equal to the positive
   critical value, then reject H_0: $\rho_s = 0$ and conclude that there is sufficient evidence to
   support the claim of a correlation.

Based on data from *Biostatistical Analysis,* 4th edition © 1999, by Jerrold Zar, Prentice
Hall, Inc., Upper Saddle River, New Jersey, and "Distribution of Sums of Squares of Rank
Differences to Small Numbers with Individuals," *The Annals of Mathematical Statistics,*
Vol. 9, No. 2.

Complete data sets available at www.pearsoned.co.in/triola

This appendix lists only the first five rows of each data set. The complete data sets are available for download at www.pearsoned.co.in/triola for a variety of technologies, including Excel, SPSS, JMP, Minitab, and TI-83/84 Plus calculators. These data sets are included with Statdisk, which is free to users of this textbook; Statdisk can be downloaded at www.statdisk.org.

Data Set 1: Body Data

Data Set 2: Body Temperatures

Data Set 3: Births

Data Set 4: Audiometry

Data Set 5: Vision

Data Set 6: Family Heights

Data Set 7: Foot and Height

Data Set 8: IQ and Lead

Data Set 9: IQ and Brain Size

Data Set 10: Freshman 15

Data Set 11: Bear Measurements

Data Set 12: Manatee Deaths

Data Set 13: Alcohol and Tobacco in Movies

Data Set 14: Passive and Active Smoke

Data Set 15: Cigarette Contents

Data Set 16: Iris Measurements

Data Set 17: Cuckoo Egg Lengths

Data Set 18: Poplar Tree Weights

Data Set 1: Body Data

Body and exam measurements are from 300 subjects (first five rows shown here). **AGE** is in years, for **GENDER** 0 = female and 1 = male, **PULSE** is pulse rate (beats per minute), **SYSTOLIC** is systolic blood pressure (mm Hg), **DIASTOLIC** is diastolic blood pressure (mm Hg), **HDL** is HDL cholesterol (mg/dL), **LDL** is LDL cholesterol (mg/dL), **WHITE** is white blood cell count (1000 cells/μL), (1000 cells/μL), **RED** is red blood cell count (million cells/μL),

PLATE is platelet count (1000 cells/μL), **WEIGHT** is weight (kg), **HEIGHT** is height (cm), **WAIST** is circumference (cm), **ARM CIRC** is arm circumference (cm), and **BMI** is body mass index (kg/m^2). Data are from the National Center for Health Statistics.

TI-83/84 list names (BODY): AGE, GENDR, PULSE, SYS, DIAS, HDL, LDL, WHITE, REDBC, PLATE, WT, HT, WAIST, ARMC, BMI

AGE	GENDER (1 = M)	PULSE	SYSTOLIC	DIASTOLIC	HDL	LDL	WHITE	RED	PLATE	WEIGHT	HEIGHT	WAIST	ARM CIRC	BMI
43	0	80	100	70	73	68	8.7	4.80	319	98.6	172.0	120.4	40.7	33.3
57	1	84	112	70	35	116	4.9	4.73	187	96.9	186.0	107.8	37.0	28.0
38	0	94	134	94	36	223	6.9	4.47	297	108.2	154.4	120.3	44.3	45.4
80	1	74	126	64	37	83	7.5	4.32	170	73.1	160.5	97.2	30.3	28.4
34	1	50	114	68	50	104	6.1	4.95	140	83.1	179.0	95.1	34.0	25.9

Data Set 2: Body Temperatures

Body temperatures (°F) are from 107 subjects taken on two consecutive days at 8 AM and 12 AM (first five rows shown here). **SEX** is gender of subject, and **SMOKE** indicates if subject smokes (Y) or does not smoke (N). Data provided by Dr. Steven Wasserman, Dr. Philip Mackowiak, and Dr. Myron Levine of the University of Maryland.

TI-83/84 list names (BODYTEMP): D1T8, D1T12, D2T8, D2T12 (no list for SEX and SMOKE). **Missing data values are represented by 9999.**

SEX	SMOKE	DAY 1—8 AM	DAY 1—12 AM	DAY 2—8 AM	DAY 2—12 AM
M	Y	98.0	98.0	98.0	98.6
M	Y	97.0	97.6	97.4	—
M	Y	98.6	98.8	97.8	98.6
M	N	97.4	98.0	97.0	98.0
M	N	98.2	98.8	97.0	98.0

Data Set 3: Births

Data are from 400 births (first five rows shown here). For **GENDER** 0 = female and 1 = male. **LENGTH OF STAY** is in days, **BIRTH WEIGHT** is in grams, and **TOTAL CHARGES** are in dollars.

TI-83/84 list names (BIRTHS): FLOS, MLOS, FBWT, MBWT, FCHRG, MCHRG [Separate lists provided for female (F) and male (M) babies. No list for FACILITY, INSURANCE, ADMITTED, and DISCHARGED]

FACILITY	INSURANCE	GENDER (1 = M)	LENGTH OF STAY	ADMITTED	DISCHARGED	BIRTH WEIGHT	TOTAL CHARGES
Albany Medical Center Hospital	Insurance Company	0	2	FRI	SUN	3500	13986
Albany Medical Center Hospital	Blue Cross	1	2	FRI	SUN	3900	3633
Albany Medical Center Hospital	Blue Cross	0	36	WED	THU	800	359091
Albany Medical Center Hospital	Insurance Company	1	5	MON	SAT	2800	8537
Albany Medical Center Hospital	Insurance Company	1	2	FRI	SUN	3700	3633

(Complete data sets available at www.pearsoned.co.in/triola)

Data Set 4: Audiometry

Data are from 350 subjects (first five rows shown here). **AGE** is in years, for **GENDER** 0 = female and 1 = male, and **RIGHT/LEFT THRESHOLD** are hearing measurements in each ear using pure tone sounds sent through earphones. Intensity of sound is varied until hearing threshold at frequency of 1000 Hz (db) is identified. Data are from the National Center for Health Statistics.

TI-83/84 list names   AUDAG, AUDGN, AUDRT, AUDLT
(AUDIO):

AGE	GENDER	RIGHT THRESHOLD	LEFT THRESHLOD
42	1	5	5
46	0	5	15
51	0	5	10
70	0	15	20
78	1	5	10

Data Set 5: Vision

Data are from 300 subjects (first five rows shown here). **AGE** is in years, for **GENDER** 0 = female and 1 = male, and **RIGHT/LEFT EYE** is measure of visual acuity with "usual correction," which could be eyeglasses, contacts, or no correction. Data are from the National Center for Health Statistics.

TI-83/84 list names   VISAG, VISGN, VISRT, VISLT
(VISION):

AGE	GENDER	RIGHT EYE	LEFT EYE
39	1	20	20
48	1	20	20
84	0	25	20
55	0	25	20
41	1	50	50

Data Set 6: Family Heights

Height data are from 134 families (first five rows shown here). Heights are in inches. Only families with at least one child of each gender are included, and only heights of the first son and first daughter are included. The data are from a journal of Francis Galton (1822–1911), who developed the concepts of standard deviation, regression line, and correlation between two variables.

TI-83/84 list names   DAD, MOM, SON1, DGHT1
(FAMHT):

FATHER	MOTHER	FIRST SON	FIRST DAUGHTER
70.0	64.0	68.0	65.0
71.0	65.5	72.0	66.0
69.0	63.5	70.5	65.0
69.5	66.0	71.0	66.5
70.0	58.0	72.0	66.0

(Complete data sets available at www.pearsoned.co.in/triola)

Data Set 7: Foot and Height

Foot and height measurements are from 40 subjects (first five rows shown here). **SEX** is gender of subject, **AGE** is age in years, **FOOT LENGTH** is length of foot (cm), **SHOE PRINT** is length of shoe (cm), **SHOE SIZE** is reported shoe size, and **HEIGHT** is height (cm) of the subject.

Data from Rohren, Brenda, "Estimation of Stature from Foot and Shoe Length: Applications in Forensic Science." Copyright © 2006.

Reprinted by permission of the author. Brenda Rohren (MA, MFS, LIMHP, LADC, MAC) was a graduate student at Nebraska Wesleyan University when she conducted the research and wrote the report.

TI-83/84 list names (FOOTHT): FTSEX (1 = male), FTAGE, FTLN, SHOPT, SHOSZ, FHT

SEX	AGE	FOOT LENGTH	SHOE PRINT	SHOE SIZE	HEIGHT
M	67	27.8	31.3	11.0	180.3
M	47	25.7	29.7	9.0	175.3
M	41	26.7	31.3	11.0	184.8
M	42	25.9	31.8	10.0	177.8
M	48	26.4	31.4	10.0	182.3

Data Set 8: IQ and Lead

Data are from 121 subjects (first five rows shown here). Data are measured from children in two consecutive years, and the children were living close to a lead smelter. **LEAD** is blood lead level group [1 = *low lead level* (blood lead levels < 40 micrograms/100 mL in both years), 2 = *medium lead level* (blood lead levels ≥ 40 micrograms/100 mL in exactly one of two years), 3 = *high lead level* (blood lead level ≥ 40 micrograms/100 mL in both years)]. **AGE** is age in years, **SEX** is sex of subject (1 = male; 2 = female). **YEAR1** is blood lead level in first year, and **YEAR2** is blood lead level in second year. **IQ VERB** is measured verbal IQ score. **IQ PERF** is measured performance IQ score. **IQ FULL** is measured full IQ score.

Data are from "Neuropsychological Dysfunction in Children with Chronic Low-Level Lead Absorption," by P. J. Landrigan, R. H. Whitworth, R. W. Baloh, N. W. Staehling, W. F Barthel, and B. F. Rosenblum, *Lancet*, Vol. 1, No. 7909.

TI-83/84 list names (IQLEAD): LEAD, IQAGE, IQSEX, YEAR1, YEAR2, IQV, IQP, IQF

LEAD	AGE	SEX	YEAR1	YEAR2	IQ VERB	IQ PERF	IQ FULL
1	11	1	25	18	61	85	70
1	9	1	31	28	82	90	85
1	11	1	30	29	70	107	86
1	6	1	29	30	72	85	76
1	11	1	2	34	72	100	84

Data Set 9: IQ and Brain Size

Data are from 20 monozygotic (identical) twins (first five rows shown here). **PAIR** identifies the set of twins, **SEX** is the gender of the subject (1 = male, 2 = female), **ORDER** is the birth order, **IQ** is measured full IQ score, **VOL** is total brain volume (cm³), **AREA** is total brain surface area (cm²), **CCSA** is corpus callosum (fissure connecting left and right cerebral hemispheres) surface area (cm²), **CIRC** is head circumference (cm), and **WT** is body weight (kg).

Data provided by M. J. Tramo, W. C. Loftus, T. A. Stukel, J. B. Weaver, M. S. Gazziniga. See "Brain Size, Head Size, and IQ in Monozygotic Twins," *Neurology*, Vol. 50.

TI-83/84 list names (IQBRAIN): PAIR, SEX, ORDER, IQ, VOL, AREA, CCSA, CIRC, BWT

PAIR	SEX (1 = M)	ORDER	IQ	VOL	AREA	CCSA	CIRC	WT
1	2	1	96	1005	1913.88	6.08	54.7	57.607
1	2	2	89	963	1684.89	5.73	54.2	58.968
2	2	1	87	1035	1902.36	6.22	53.0	64.184
2	2	2	87	1027	1860.24	5.80	52.9	58.514
3	2	1	101	1281	2264.25	7.99	57.8	63.958

(Complete data sets available at www.pearsoned.co.in/triola)

Data Set 10: Freshman 15

Weights of 67 college students are provided (first five rows shown here). **SEX** is gender of subject, **WT** is weight in kilograms, and **BMI** is measured body mass index. Measurements were made in September of freshman year and then later in April of freshman year.

    Results are published in Hoffman, D. J., Policastro, P., Quick, V., and Lee, S. K.: "Changes in Body Weight and Fat Mass of Men and

Women in the First Year of College: A Study of the 'Freshman 15.'" *Journal of American College Health,* July 1, 2006, Vol. 55, No. 1, p. 41. Copyright © 2006. Reprinted by permission.

TI-83/84 list names WTSP, WTAPR, BMISP, BMIAP
(FRESH15): (no list for SEX)

SEX	WT SEPT	WT APRIL	BMI SEPT	BMI APRIL
M	72	59	22.02	18.14
M	97	86	19.70	17.44
M	74	69	24.09	22.43
M	93	88	26.97	25.57
F	68	64	21.51	20.10

Data Set 11: Bear Measurements

Data are from 54 anesthetized wild bears (first five rows shown here). **AGE** is in months, **MONTH** is the month of measurement with 1 = January, **SEX** is coded with 0 = female and 1 = male, **HEADLEN** is head length (inches), **HEADWDTH** is width of head (inches), **NECK** is distance around neck (in inches), **LENGTH** is

length of body (inches), **CHEST** is distance around chest (inches), and **WEIGHT** is measured in pounds. Data are from Gary Alt and Minitab, Inc.

TI-83/84 list names BAGE, BSEX, BHDLN, BHDWD, BNECK,
(BEARS): BLEN, BCHST, BWGHT (no list for MONTH)

AGE	MONTH	SEX (1 = M)	HEADLEN	HEADWDTH	NECK	LENGTH	CHEST	WEIGHT
19	7	1	11.0	5.5	16.0	53.0	26.0	80
55	7	1	16.5	9.0	28.0	67.5	45.0	344
81	9	1	15.5	8.0	31.0	72.0	54.0	416
115	7	1	17.0	10.0	31.5	72.0	49.0	348
104	8	0	15.5	6.5	22.0	62.0	35.0	166

Data Set 12: Manatee Deaths

Annual Florida data for 24 years are provided (first five rows shown here). **DEATHS** is the annual number of manatee deaths caused by boats, **BOATS** is the number of registered pleasure boats (tens of thousands), **POP** is the Florida population (millions), and **WATER TEMP** is the annual mean water temperature (°F).

TI-83/84 list names DEATH, BOATS, POP, WTEMP
(MANATEE): (no list for YEAR)

YEAR	DEATHS	BOATS	POP	WATER TEMP
1991	53	68	13.3	71.9
1992	38	68	13.5	70.4
1993	35	67	13.7	70.5
1994	49	70	14.0	71.7
1995	42	71	14.3	70.9

(Complete data sets available at www.pearsoned.co.in/triola)

Data Set 13: Alcohol and Tobacco in Movies

Data are from 50 animated children's movies (first five rows shown here). **LENGTH** is movie length in minutes, **TOBACCO** is tobacco use time in seconds, and **ALCOHOL** is alcohol use time in seconds.

The data are based on Goldstein, Adam O., Sobel, Rachel A., Newman, Glen R., "Tobacco and Alcohol Use in G-Rated Children's Animated Films." *Journal of the American Medical Association,* March 24/31, 1999, Vol. 281, No. 12, p. 1132. Copyright © 1999. All rights reserved.

TI-83/84 list names   CHLEN, CHTOB, CHALC
(CHMOVIE):   (no list for MOVIE and STUDIO)

MOVIE	STUDIO	LENGTH (MIN)	TOBACCO (SEC)	ALCOHOL (SEC)
Snow White	Disney	83	0	0
Pinocchio	Disney	88	223	80
Fantasia	Disney	120	0	0
Dumbo	Disney	64	176	88
Bambi	Disney	69	0	0

Data Set 14: Passive and Active Smoke

Data are from 120 subjects (first five rows shown here) in three groups: **SMOKER** includes subjects who are smokers, **ETS** includes nonsmokers exposed to environmental tobacco smoke, and **NOETS** includes nonsmokers not exposed to environmental tobacco smoke. All values are measured levels of serum cotinine (in ng/mL), a metabolite of nicotine. (When nicotine is absorbed by the body, cotinine is produced.) Data are from the U.S. Department of Health and Human Services, National Center for Health Statistics, Third National Health and Nutrition Examination Survey.

TI-83/84 list names   SMKR, ETS, NOETS
(SMOKE):

SMOKER	ETS	NOETS
1	384	0
0	0	0
131	69	0
173	19	0
265	1	0

Data Set 15: Cigarette Contents

Data are from 75 cigarettes (first five rows shown here) from three categories: **KING** includes king-sized cigarettes that are nonfiltered, nonmenthol, and nonlight; **MENTH** includes menthol cigarettes that are 100 mm long, filtered, and nonlight; and **100** includes 100-mm-long cigarettes that are filtered, nonmenthol, and nonlight. **TAR** is the amount of tar per cigarette (milligrams), **NICOTINE** is the amount of nicotine per cigarette (milligrams), and **CO** is the amount of carbon monoxide per cigarette (milligrams). Data are from the Federal Trade Commission.

TI-83/84 list names   KGTAR, KGNIC, KGCO, MNTAR, MNNIC,
(CIGARET):   MNCO, FLTAR, FLNIC, FLCO

KING TAR	KING NICOTINE	KING CO	MENTH TAR	MENTH NICOTINE	MENTH CO	100 TAR	100 NIC	100 CO
20	1.1	16	16	1.1	15	5	0.4	4
27	1.7	16	13	0.8	17	16	1.0	19
27	1.7	16	16	1.0	19	17	1.2	17
20	1.1	16	9	0.9	9	13	0.8	18
20	1.1	16	14	0.8	17	13	0.8	18

(Complete data sets available at www.pearsoned.co.in/triola)

Data Set 16: Iris Measurements

Data are from 150 Iris Measurements (first five rows shown here) from three different classes (Setosa, Versicolor, Virginica). **SL** denotes sepal length (mm), **SW** denotes sepal width (mm), **PL** denotes petal length (mm), and **PW** denotes petal width (mm). From "The Use of Multiple Measurements in Taxonomic Problems," by Ronald A. Fisher, *Annals of Statistics,* Vol. 7.

TI-83/84 list names (IRIS):   SETSL, SETSW, SETPL, SETPW, VERSL, VERSW, VERPL, VERPW, VIRSL, VIRSW, VIRPL, VIRPW.

CLASS	SL	SW	PL	PW
setosa	5.1	3.5	1.4	0.2
setosa	4.9	3.0	1.4	0.2
setosa	4.7	3.2	1.3	0.2
setosa	4.6	3.1	1.5	0.2
setosa	5.0	3.6	1.4	0.2

Data Set 17: Cuckoo Egg Lengths

Lengths (mm) of cuckoo eggs put in the nests of six other birds (first five rows of data shown here). From *The Methods of Statistics,* 4th edition, by L. H. C. Tippett, John Wiley and Sons, Inc., as listed in the Data and Story Library (online).

TI-83/84 list names (CUCKOO):   MDW, TREE, HEDGE, ROBIN, PIED, WREN.

MEADOW PIPIT	TREE PIPIT	HEDGE SPARROW	ROBIN	PIED WAGTAIL	WREN
19.65	21.05	20.85	21.05	21.05	19.85
20.05	21.85	21.65	21.85	21.85	20.05
20.65	22.05	22.05	22.05	21.85	20.25
20.85	22.45	22.85	22.05	21.85	20.85
21.65	22.65	23.05	22.05	22.05	20.85

Data Set 18: Poplar Tree Weights

Data (first five rows shown here) are weights (kg) of trees in year 1 and year 2 grown with four different conditions (no treatment, fertilizer, irrigation, fertilizer and irrigation) at two different sites. Site 1 is rich and moist, and Site 2 is sandy and dry. From a study conducted by researchers at Pennsylvania State University. Data obtained from Minitab, Inc.

TI-83/84 list names (POPLAR):   NONE, FERT, IRRIG, FRTIR

YEAR	SITE	NO TREATMENT	FERTILIZER	IRRIGATION	FERT & IRRIG
1	1	0.15	1.34	0.23	2.03
1	1	0.02	0.14	0.04	0.27
1	1	0.16	0.02	0.34	0.92
1	1	0.37	0.08	0.16	1.07
1	1	0.22	0.08	0.05	2.38

(Complete data sets available at www.pearsoned.co.in/triola)

Books

*An asterisk denotes a book recommended for reading. Other books are recommended as reference texts.

Bennett, D. 1998. *Randomness*. Cambridge, Mass.: Harvard University Press.

*Best, J. 2012. *Damned Lies and Statistics*. Berkeley, Calif.: University of California Press.

*Best, J. 2004. *More Damned Lies and Statistics*. Berkeley, Calif.: University of California Press.

*Campbell, S. 2004. *Flaws and Fallacies in Statistical Thinking*. Mineola, N.Y.: Dover Publications.

*Crossen, C. 1996. *Tainted Truth: The Manipulation of Fact in America*. New York: Simon & Schuster.

*Freedman, D., R. Pisani, R. Purves, and A. Adhikari. 2007. *Statistics*. 4th ed. New York: W. W. Norton & Company.

*Gonick, L., and W. Smith. 1993. *The Cartoon Guide to Statistics*. New York: Harper Collins.

*Heyde, C., and E. Seneta, eds. 2001. *Statisticians of the Centuries*. New York: Springer-Verlag.

*Hollander, M., and F. Proschan. 1984. *The Statistical Exorcist: Dispelling Statistics Anxiety*. New York: Marcel Dekker.

*Holmes, C. 1990. *The Honest Truth About Lying with Statistics*. Springfield, Ill.: Charles C Thomas.

*Hooke, R. 1983. *How to Tell the Liars from the Statisticians*. New York: Marcel Dekker.

*Huff, D. 1993. *How to Lie with Statistics*. New York: W. W. Norton & Company.

*Jaffe, A., and H. Spirer. 1998. *Misused Statistics*. New York: Marcel Dekker.

Kaplan, M. 2007. *Chances Are*. New York: Penguin Group.

Kotz, S., and D. Stroup. 1983. *Educated Guessing—How to Cope in an Uncertain World*. New York: Marcel Dekker.

Mlodinow, L. 2009. *The Drunkard's Walk*. New York: Vintage Books.

*Moore, D., and W. Notz. 2012. *Statistics: Concepts and Controversies*. 8th ed. San Francisco: Freeman.

*Paulos, J. 2001. *Innumeracy: Mathematical Illiteracy and Its Consequences*. New York: Hill and Wang.

*Reichmann, W. 1981. *Use and Abuse of Statistics*. New York: Penguin.

*Rossman, A., and B. Chance. 2011. *Workshop Statistics: Discovery with Data*. 4th ed. Emeryville, Calif.: Key Curriculum Press.

*Salsburg, D. 2001. *The Lady Tasting Tea: How Statistics Revolutionized the Twentieth Century*. New York: W. H. Freeman.

Sheskin, D. 2011. *Handbook of Parametric and Nonparametric Statistical Procedures*. 5th ed. Boca Raton, Fla.: CRC Press.

Simon, J. 1997. *Resampling: The New Statistics*. 2nd ed. Arlington, Va.: Resampling Stats.

*Stigler, S. 1986. *The History of Statistics*. Cambridge, Mass.: Harvard University Press.

Taleb, N. 2010. *The Black Swan*. 2nd ed. New York: Random House.

*Tufte, E. 2001. *The Visual Display of Quantitative Information*. 2nd ed. Cheshire, Conn.: Graphics Press.

Tukey, J. 1977. *Exploratory Data Analysis*. Boston: Pearson.

Vickers, A. 2009. *What Is a P-Value Anyway?* Boston: Pearson.

Whelan, C. 2013. *Naked Statistics*. New York: W. W. Norton & Company.

Zwillinger, D., and S. Kokoska. 2000. *CRC Standard Probability and Statistics Tables and Formulae*. Boca Raton, Fla.: CRC Press.

APPENDIX D

Answers to Odd-Numbered Section Exercises, plus
Answers to All Chapter Quick Quizzes, Chapter
Review Exercises, and Cumulative Review Exercises

Chapter 1 Answers

Section 1-1

1. The respondents are a voluntary response sample or a self-selected sample. Because those with strong interests in the topic are more likely to respond, it is very possible that their responses do not reflect the opinions or behavior of the general population.

3. Statistical significance is indicated when methods of statistics are used to reach a conclusion that a treatment is effective, but common sense might suggest that the treatment does not make enough of a difference to justify its use or to be practical. Yes, it is possible for a study to have statistical significance but not practical significance.

5. No, there does not appear to be a potential to create a bias.

7. No, there does not appear to be a potential to create a bias.

9. The sample is a voluntary response sample and has strong potential to be flawed.

11. The sampling method appears to be sound.

13. With only a 1% chance of getting such results with a program that has no effect, the program appears to have statistical significance. Also, because the average loss of 22 pounds does seem substantial, the program appears to also have practical significance.

15. Because there is a 19% chance of getting that many girls by chance, the method appears to lack statistical significance. The result of 1020 girls in 2000 births (51% girls) is above the approximately 50% rate expected by chance, but it does not appear to be high enough to have practical significance. Not many couples would bother with a procedure that raises the likelihood of a girl from 50% to 51%.

17. Yes. Each column of 8 AM and 12 AM temperatures is recorded from the same subject, so each pair is matched.

19. The data can be used to address the issue of whether there is a correlation between body temperatures at 8 AM and at 12 AM. Also, the data can be used to determine whether there are differences between body temperatures at 8 AM and at 12 AM.

21. No. The white blood cell counts measure a different quantity than the red blood cell counts, so their differences are meaningless.

23. No. The National Center for Health Statistics has no reason to collect or present the data in a way that is biased.

25. It is questionable that the sponsor is the Idaho Potato Commission and the favorite vegetable is potatoes.

27. The correlation, or association, between two variables does not mean that one of the variables is the cause of the other. Correlation does not imply causation. Common sense suggests that cheese consumption is not directly related in any way to fatalities from bedsheet entanglements.

29. a. 1356.3 adults
   b. No. Because the result is a count of the people among the 3014 who were surveyed, the result must be a whole number.
   c. 1356 adults   d. 40%

31. The wording of the question is biased and tends to encourage negative responses. The sample size of 20 is too small. Survey respondents are self-selected instead of being selected by the newspaper. If 20 readers respond, the percentages should be multiples of 5, so 87% and 13% are not possible results.

Section 1-2

1. a. The population consists of all adults in the United States and the sample is the 1020 adults who were surveyed.
   b. Statistic

3. a. Categorical   b. Quantitative   c. Quantitative   d. Categorical

5. Parameter   7. Parameter   9. Statistic

11. Statistic   13. Discrete   15. Continuous

17. Continuous   19. Discrete   21. Interval

23. Nominal   25. Nominal   27. Ratio

29. The numbers are not counts or measures of anything. They are at the nominal level of measurement, and it makes no sense to compute the average (mean) of them.

31. The temperatures are at the interval level of measurement. Because there is no natural starting point with 0°F representing "no heat," ratios such as "twice" make no sense, so it is wrong to say that the person is twice as warm as the outside air.

33. a. Continuous, because the number of possible values is infinite and not countable
   b. Discrete, because the number of possible values is finite
   c. Discrete, because the number of possible values is finite
   d. Discrete, because the number of possible values is infinite and countable

Section 1-3

1. The study is an experiment because subjects were given treatments.

3. The group sample sizes of 547, 550, and 546 are all large so that the researchers could see the effects of the paracetamol treatment.

5. The sample appears to be a convenience sample. By e-mailing the survey to a readily available group of Internet users, it was easy to obtain results. Although there is a real potential for getting a sample group that is not representative of the population, indications of which ear is used for cell phone calls and which hand is dominant do not appear to be factors that would be distorted much by a sample bias.

7. With 717 responses, the response rate is 14%, which does appear to be quite low. In general, a very low response rate creates a serious potential for getting a biased sample that consists of those with a special interest in the topic.

9. Systematic   11. Random   13. Stratified
15. Random   17. Random   19. Convenience
21. Observational study. The sample is a convenience sample consisting of subjects who decided themselves to respond. Such voluntary response samples have a high chance of not being representative of the larger population, so the sample may well be biased. The question was posted in an electronic edition of a newspaper, so the sample is biased from the beginning.
23. Experiment. This experiment would create an *extremely* dangerous and illegal situation that has a real potential to result in injury or death. It's difficult enough to drive in New York City while being completely sober.
25. Experiment. The biased sample created by using subjects from New York City cannot be fixed by using a larger sample. The larger sample will still be a biased sample that is not representative of subjects in the United States.
27. Observational study. Respondents who have been convicted of felonies are not likely to respond honestly to the second question. The survey will suffer from a "social desirability bias" because subjects will tend to respond in ways that will be viewed favorably by those conducting the survey.
29. Prospective study   31. Cross-sectional study
33. Matched pairs design   35. Completely randomized design
37. Prospective: The experiment was begun and results were followed forward in time. Randomized: Subjects were assigned to the different groups through a process of random selection, whereby they had the same chance of belonging to each group. Double-blind: The subjects did not know which of the three groups they were in, and the people who evaluated results did not know either. Placebo-controlled: There was a group of subjects who were given a placebo; by comparing the placebo group to the two treatment groups, the effects of the treatments might be better understood.

Chapter 1: Quick Quiz

1. No. The numbers do not measure or count anything.
2. Nominal   3. Continuous   4. Quantitative data
5. Ratio   6. No   7. No
8. Statistic   9. Observational study   10. False

Chapter 1: Review Exercises

1. a Discrete   b. Ratio   c. Stratified   d. Cluster
   e. The mailed responses would be a voluntary response sample, so those with strong opinions are more likely to respond. It is very possible that the results do not reflect the true opinions of the population of all customers.
2. The survey was sponsored by the American Laser Centers, and 24% said that the favorite body part is the face, which happens to be a body part often chosen for some type of laser treatment. The source is therefore questionable.

3. The sample is a voluntary response sample, so the results are questionable.
4. a. It uses a voluntary response sample, and those with special interests are more likely to respond, so it is very possible that the sample is not representative of the population.
   b. Because the statement refers to 72% of all Americans, it is a parameter (but it is probably based on a 72% rate from the sample, and the sample percentage is a statistic).
   c. Observational study
5. a. If they have no fat at all, they have 100% less than any other amount with fat, so the 125% figure cannot be correct.
   b. 686   c. 28%
6. Only part (c) is a simple random sample.
7. Because there is only a 4% chance of getting the results by chance, the method appears to have statistical significance. The result of 112 girls in 200 births is above the approximately 50% rate expected by chance, but it does not appear to be high enough to have practical significance. Not many couples would bother with a procedure that raises the likelihood of a girl from 50% to 56%.
8. a. Random   b. Stratified   c. Nominal
   d. Statistic, because it is based on a sample.
   e. The mailed responses would be a voluntary response sample. Those with strong opinions about the topic would be more likely to respond, so it is very possible that the results would not reflect the true opinions of the population of all adults.
9. a. Systematic. It is likely to result in a representative sample.
   b. Random. It is likely to result in a representative sample.
   c. Cluster. It is likely to result in a representative sample.
   d. Stratified. It is likely to result in a representative sample.
   e. Convenience. It is very possible that the sample is not representative.
10. a. 780 adults   b. 23%
    c. Men: 48.5%; women: 51.5%
    d. No, although this is a subjective judgment.
    e. No, although this is a subjective judgment.

Chapter 1: Cumulative Review Exercises

1. 13.5 miligrams. All the tar contents end as integers, suggesting that all of the tar contents are rounded to the nearest integer, so that there are no decimals.
2. 0.015625
3. 16.00 is a significantly high value.
4. −6.64   5. 1067   6. 3 miligrams
7. 10.32 miligrams^2 8. 0.20   9. 0.0279936
10. 1,283,918,464,548,864 (or about 1,283,918,464,549,000)
11. 13,841,287,201 (or about 13,841,287,000)
12. 0.000001073741824

Chapter 2 Answers

Section 2-1

1. The table summarizes measurements from 40 subjects. It is not possible to identify the exact values of all of the original cotinine measurements.

3.

Cotinine (ng/mL)	Relative Frequency
0–99	27.5%
100–199	30.0%
200–299	35.0%
300–399	2.5%
400–499	5.0%

5. Class width: 100. Class midpoints: 49.5, 149.5, 249.5, 349.5, 449.5, 549.5. Class boundaries: −0.5, 99.5, 199.5, 299.5, 399.5, 499.5, 599.5.

7. Class width: 20. Class midpoints: 39.5, 59.5, 79.5, 99.5, 119.5, 139.5, 159.5. Class boundaries: 29.5, 49.5, 69.5, 89.5, 109.5, 129.5, 149.5, 169.5.

9. No. The maximum frequency is in the first class instead of being near the middle.

11. 75, 20, 9, 7

13. The pulse rates appear to have a distribution that is approximately normal.

Pulse Rate (Male)	Frequency
40–49	2
50–59	23
60–69	53
70–79	43
80–89	25
90–99	5
100–109	2

15. The verbal IQ scores appear to have a distribution that is approximately normal.

IQ (Verbal)	Frequency
50–59	3
60–69	8
70–79	13
80–89	26
90–99	18
100–109	6
110–119	2
120–129	2

17. Yes. The distribution appears to be approximately normal.

Red Blood Cell Count (Males)	Frequency
3.00–3.49	1
3.50–3.99	16
4.00–4.49	29
4.50–4.99	57
5.00–5.49	44
5.50–5.99	6

19.

Weight (kg) in September	Frequency
50–59	2
60–69	12
70–79	11
80–89	3
90–99	4

21. The frequency distribution suggests that the reported weights were not rounded since the last digits are equally distributed.

Last Digit	Frequency
0	5
1	6
2	4
3	4
4	4
5	5
6	4
7	4
8	6
9	5

23. The two distributions differ substantially. The presence of cotinine appears to be much higher for smokers than for nonsmokers exposed to smoke.

Cotinine (ng/mL)	Smokers	Nonsmokers Exposed to Smoke
0–99	27.5%	85.0%
100–199	30.0%	5.0%
200–299	35.0%	2.5%
300–399	2.5%	2.5%
400–499	5.0%	0%
500–599	0%	5.0%

25.

Cotinine (Nonsmokers Exposed to Smoke in ng/mL)	Cumulative Frequency
Less than 100	34
Less than 200	36
Less than 300	37
Less than 400	38
Less than 500	38
Less than 600	40

27. a. The values of 551 and 543 are clearly outliers; the values of 384, 241, 197, and 178 could also be outliers.

b. The number of classes increases from six to ten. The outlier can greatly increase the number of classes. If there are too many classes, we might use a larger class width with the effect that the true nature of the distribution may be hidden.

Cotinine (Nonsmokers Exposed to Smoke in ng/mL)	Frequency
0–99	34
100–199	2
200–299	1
300–399	1
400–499	0
500–599	2
600–699	0
700–799	0
800–899	0
900–999	1

Section 2-2

1. It is easier to see the distribution of the data by examining the graph of the histogram than by examining the numbers in a frequency distribution.

3. With a data set that is so small, the true nature of the distribution cannot be seen with a histogram.

5. Approximately 50

7. Approximately 4.5 mm; no

9. The pulse rates of males appear to have a distribution that is approximately normal.

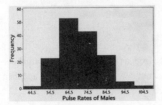

11. The IQ scores appear to have a distribution that is approximately normal.

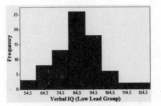

13. Yes. The red blood cell counts appear to have a distribution that is very approximately normal, although some might describe the distribution as being left-skewed instead of normal.

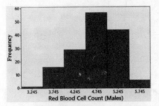

15.

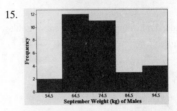

17. The histogram suggests that the reported weights were not rounded since the last digits seem equally distributed.

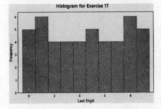

19. Only part (c) appears to represent data from a normal distribution. Part (a) has a systematic pattern that is not that of a straight line, part (b) has points that are not close to a straight-line pattern, and part (d) is really bad because it shows a systematic pattern and points that are not close to a straight-line pattern.

Section 2-3

1. The data set is too small for a graph to reveal important characteristics of the data. With such a small data set, it would be better to simply list the data or place them in a table.

3. No. Graphs should be constructed in a way that is fair and objective. The readers should be allowed to make their own judgments, instead of being manipulated by misleading graphs.

5. The systolic blood pressure of 158 mm Hg appears to be an outlier.

7. The data are arranged in order from lowest to highest, as 112, 114, 116, and so on.

```
11  24668
12  4468
13  22448
14
15  8
```

9. There has been a steep jump in the last five years, but the numbers of accidental deaths have shown a random trend in the initial years.

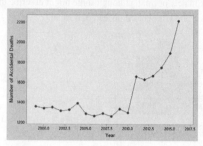

11. Misconduct includes fraud, duplication, and plagiarism, so it does appear to be a major factor.

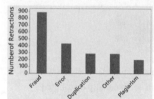

13.

15. The distribution appears to be roughly bell-shaped, so the distribution is approximately normal.

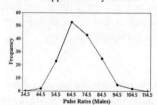

17. Because the vertical scale starts with a frequency of 200 instead of 0, the difference between the "no" and "yes" responses is greatly exaggerated. The graph makes it appear that about *five* times as many respondents said "no," when the ratio is actually a little less than 2.5 to 1.

Section 2-4

1. The term *linear* refers to a straight *line,* and *r* measures how well a scatterplot of the sample paired data fits a straight-line pattern.

3. A scatterplot is a graph of paired (*x, y*) quantitative data. It helps us by providing a visual image of the data plotted as points, and such an image is helpful in enabling us to see any patterns in the data and to recognize that there may be a correlation between the two variables.

5. There does appear to be a linear correlation between systolic and diastolic blood pressure.

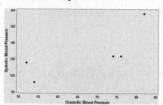

7. There does not appear to be a linear correlation between shoe size and heights of females.

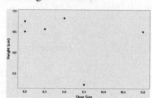

9. There is insufficient evidence to conclude that there is a linear correlation.

11. The evidence is not sufficient to conclude that there is a linear correlation.

Chapter 2: Quick Quiz

1. 0.04   2. 0.075 and 0.115
3. No, it is impossible to determine the original values.
4. 16, 17, 18, 18, 19   5. Bell-shaped
6. Variation   7. Time-series graph
8. Scatterplot   9. Pareto chart
10. A frequency distribution is in the format of a table, but a histogram is a graph.

Chapter 2: Review Exercises

1.

Birth Weight (grams)	Frequency
2000–2499	1
2500–2999	4
3000–3499	6
3500–3999	6
4000–4499	3

2. Yes, the data appears to be from a population with a normal distribution because the bars start low, reach a maximum, and then decrease.

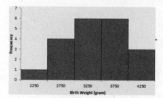

3. By using fewer classes, the histogram does a better job of illustrating the distribution.

4. The birth weight of 2100 grams appears to be an outlier.

```
210  0
220
230
240
250
260  0
270  0
280  0
290  0
300  00
310
320
330  00
340  00
350  000
360  0
370  0
380  0
390
400
410  00
420
430  0
```

5. Yes. There is a pattern suggesting that there is a relationship.

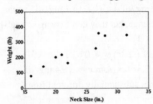

6. a. Time-series graph
   b. Scatterplot
   c. Pareto chart

7. By using a vertical scale that starts at 45% instead of 0%, the difference is greatly exaggerated. The graph creates the false impression that male enrollees outnumber female enrollees by a ratio of about 3:1, but the actual percentages of 53% and 47% are much closer than that.

Chapter 2: Cumulative Review Exercises

1.

Grooming Time (min)	Frequency
0–9	2
10–19	3
20–29	9
30–39	4
40–49	2

2. The histogram is approximately bell-shaped. The frequencies increase to a maximum and then decrease, and the left half of the histogram is roughly a mirror image of the right half. The data do appear to be from a population with a normal distribution.

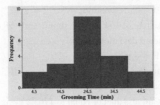

3. 0 | 05
   1 | 255
   2 | 024555778
   3 | 0055
   4 | 05

4. There are disproportionately many last digits of 0 and 5. Fourteen of the 20 times have last digits of 0 or 5. It appears that the subjects reported their results and they tended to round the results. The data do not appear to be very accurate.

Last Digit	Frequency
0	5
1	0
2	2
3	0
4	1
5	9
6	0
7	2
8	1
9	0

5. a. Ratio   b. Continuous
   c. No. The grooming times are quantitative data.
   d. Statistic

6. The scatterplot helps address the issue of whether there is a correlation between heights of mothers and heights of their daughters. The scatterplot does not reveal a clear pattern suggesting that there is a correlation.

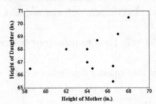

Chapter 3 Answers

Section 3-1

1. The term *average* is not used in statistics. The term *mean* should be used for the result obtained by adding all of the sample values and dividing the total by the number of sample values.

3. They use different approaches for providing a value (or values) of the center or middle of the sorted list of data.

5. $\bar{x}$ = \$775.90; median = \$777.73; mode = \$1060; midrange = \$691. Apart from the fact that the other charges are higher than those given, nothing meaningful can be known about the population of all charges.

7. $\bar{x}$ = 57.1; median = 60.0; mode = none; midrange = 53.0. The jersey numbers are nominal data that are just replacements for names, and they do not measure or count anything, so the resulting statistics are meaningless.

9. $\bar{x}$ = 1.9; median = 2.0; mode = 1; midrange = 2.5. The mode of 1 correctly indicates that the smooth-yellow peas occur more than any other phenotype, but the other measures of center don't make sense with these data at the nominal level of measurement.

11. $\bar{x}$ = 1.178 W/kg; median = 1.380 W/kg; mode = 1.45 W/kg; midrange = 1.000 W/kg. If concerned about radiation absorption,

you might purchase the cell phone with the *lowest* absorption rate. All of the cell phones in the sample have absorption levels below the FCC maximum of 1.6 W/kg.

13. $\bar{x} = 119.11$ firefighters; median $= 112$ firefighters; no mode; midrange $= 123$ firefighters. The data are a time series data, but the measures of center do not reveal anything about a trend consisting of a pattern of change overtime.

15. $\bar{x} = \$54,862.0$; median $= \$54,590.5$; mode $=$ none; midrange $= \$55,292.0$. Apart from the fact that all other colleges have tuition and fee amounts less than those listed, nothing meaningful can be known about the population.

17. Systolic: $\bar{x} = 119.4$ mm Hg; median $= 118$ mm Hg. Diastolic: $\bar{x} = 71.6$ mm Hg; median $= 67$ mm Hg. Given that systolic and diastolic blood pressures measure different characteristics, a comparison of the measures of center doesn't make sense. Because the data are matched, it would make more sense to investigate whether there is an association or correlation between systolic blood pressure measurements and diastolic blood pressure measurements.

19. Female: $\bar{x} = 63.34$ kg; median $= 64.10$ kg. Male: $\bar{x} = 73.55$ kg; median $= 74.20$ kg. Males appear to be overweight when compared to females.

21. $\bar{x} = 53.7$ mg/dL; median $= 52.0$ mg/dL. After excluding the highest value of 138, which does appear to be an outlier, we get $\bar{x} = 53.4$ mg/dL and median $= 52.0$ mg/dL, so excluding that outlier does not cause much of a change in the mean, and the median remains the same.

23. $\bar{x} = 98.20°F$; median $= 98.40°F$. These results suggest that the mean is less than 98.6°F.

25. $\bar{x} = 224.0$. The mean from the frequency distribution is quite close to the mean obtained by using the original list of values.

27. 3.14; yes

29. a. 90 beats per minute   b. $n - 1$

31. Mean: 113.7 mg/dL; 10% trimmed mean: 112.2 mg/dL; 20% trimmed mean: 111.8 mg/dL. The 10% trimmed mean and 20% trimmed mean are both fairly close, but the untrimmed mean of 113.7 mg/dL differs from them because it is more strongly affected by the outliers.

Section 3-2

1. 144.84 cm^3 is close to the exact value of the standard deviation of 174.8 cm^3.

3. 3150.0156 cm^2

5. Range $= \$738.0$; $s^2 = 49,615.38$ dollars squared; $s = \$222.70$. Because only the 10 lowest sample values are used, nothing much can be known about the population of all such charges.

7. Range $= 92.0$; $s^2 = 1149.5$; $s = 33.9$. The jersey numbers are nominal data that are just replacements for names, and they do not measure or count anything, so the resulting statistics are meaningless.

9. Range $= 3.0$; $s^2 = 0.9$; $s = 0.9$. The measures of variation can be found, but they make no sense because the data don't measure or count anything. They are nominal data.

11. Range $= 0.980$ W/kg; $s^2 = 0.114$ (W/kg)^2; $s = 0.337$ W/kg. No. Some models of cell phones have a much larger market share than others, so the measures from the different models should be weighted according to their size in the population.

13. Range $= 96.0$ firefighters; $s^2 = 675.36$ firefighters^2; $s = 25.99$ firefighters. The data are time-series data but the measures of variation do not reveal anything about a trend consisting of a pattern of change over time.

15. Range $= \$3938.0$; $s^2 = 1,638,970.9$ (dollars)^2; $s = \$1280.2$. Because the data include only the 10 highest costs, the measures of variation don't tell us anything about the variation among costs for the population of all U.S. college tuitions.

17. Systolic: 14.71% Diastolic: 16.65% The variation is roughly about the same.

19. Females: 9.52%. Males: 9.02%. The variation is almost about the same.

21. Range $= 112.0$ mg/dL; $s^2 = 238.3$ (mg/dL)^2; $s = 15.4$ mg/dL. After excluding the highest value of 138 mg/dL, we get: Range $= 87.0$ mg/dL; $s^2 = 215.2$ (mg/dL)^2; $s = 14.7$ mg/dL, so the measures of variation do change, but they don't change by substantial amounts.

23. Range $= 3.10°F$; $s^2 = 0.39$ (°F)^2; $s = 0.62°F$.

25. The estimate of 28.0 mg/dL is far from $s = 15.4$ mg/dL.

27. The estimate of 0.78°F is not substantially different from $s = 0.62°F$.

29. Significantly low values are less than or equal to 49.0 beats per minute, and significantly high values are greater than or equal to 99.0 beats per minute. A pulse rate of 44 beats per minute is significantly low.

31. Significantly low values are less than or equal to 24.74 cm, and significantly high values are greater than or equal to 29.90 cm. A foot length of 30 cm is significantly high.

33. $s = 68.4$ is somewhat far from the exact value of 59.5.

35. a. 24.7 cigarettes^2 b. 24.7 cigarettes^2 c. 12.3 cigarettes^2
   d. Part (b), because repeated samples result in variances that target the same value (24.7 cigarettes^2) as the population variance. Use division by $n - 1$.
   e. No. The mean of the sample variances (24.7 cigarettes^2) equals the population variance (24.7 cigarettes^2), but the mean of the sample standard deviations (3.5 cigarettes) does not equal the population standard deviation (5.0 cigarettes).

Section 3-3

1. James's height is 4.07 standard deviations above the mean.

3. The bottom boxplot represents weights of women, because it depicts weights that are generally lower.

5. a. 30.0 BPM   b. 2.40 standard deviations   c. $z = 2.40$
   d. Yes, the maximum pulse rate of 104 BPM is significantly high.

7. a. 1.70°F   b. 2.74 standard deviations   c. $z = -2.74$
   d. The minimum of 96.5°F is significantly low.

9. Significantly low values are less than or equal to 10.9; significantly high values are greater than or equal to 31.3.

11. Significantly low weights are less than or equal to 1765.2 g; significantly high weights are greater than or equal to 4538.8 g.

13. With z scores of 10.83 and -16.83, the z score of -16.83 is farther from the mean, so the shortest man has a height that is more extreme.

15. Male: z score $= -2.69$; female: z score $= -2.18$. The male has the more extreme weight, but the female has the larger weight relative to the group from which she came.

17. 33rd percentile   19. 56th percentile   21. 204 kg

23. 76 kg (Tech: Excel: 76 kg; Minitab: 76 kg)

25. 236 kg

27. 86 kg (Tech: Excel: 87.75 kg; Minitab: 84.5 kg)

29. 5-number summary: 25.1 in., 26.40 in., 27.50 in., 28.60 in., 29.2 in.

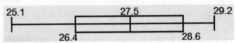

31. 5-number summary: 128 mBq, 140.0 mBq, 150.0 mBq, 158.5 mBq, 172 mBq (Tech: Minitab yields $Q_1 = 139.0$ mBq and $Q_3 = 159.75$ mBq. Excel yields $Q_1 = 141.0$ mBq and $Q_3 = 157.25$ mBq.)

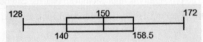

33. The top boxplot represents BMI values for females. The two boxplots do not appear to be very different, so BMI values of males and females appear to be about the same, except for a few high BMI values for females that caused the boxplot to extend farther to the right.

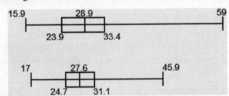

35. Top boxplot represents females. The two boxplots are not dramatically different. Outliers for females: 48.0 in., 52.6 in., 56.8 in., 59.0 in. Outliers for males: 43.2 in., 43.7 in., 44.2 in., 45.9 in.

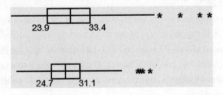

Chapter 3: Quick Quiz

1. 6.8 hours   2. 7.0 hours
3. Two modes: 7 hours, 8 hours   4. 1.7 hours²
5. Yes, because 0 hours is substantially less than all of the other data values.
6. −0.93   7. 75%, or 60 sleep times
8. Minimum, first quartile Q_1, second quartile Q_2 (or median), third quartile Q_3, maximum
9. 1.5 hours (from range/4)   10. $\bar{x}, \mu, s, \sigma, s^2, \sigma^2$

Chapter 3: Review Exercises

1. a. 1559.6 mm;   b. 1550.0 mm;   c. none;   d. 1569.5 mm;
   e. 145.0 mm;   f. 53.4 mm;   g. 2849.3 mm²
2. $z = 1.54$. The eye height is not significantly low or high because its z score is between 2 and −2, so it is within 2 standard deviations of the mean.

3. 23.0. The numbers don't measure or count anything. They are used as replacements for the names of the categories, so the numbers are at the nominal level of measurement. In this case the mean is a meaningless statistic.
4. The girl has the larger relative birth weight because her z score of 0.23 is larger than the z score of 0.19 for the boy.
5. The outlier is 646. The mean and standard deviation with the outlier included are $\bar{x} = 267.8$ and $s = 131.6$. Those statistics with the outlier excluded are $\bar{x} = 230.0$ and $s = 42.0$. Both statistics changed by a substantial amount, so here the outlier has a very strong effect on the mean and standard deviation.
6. The minimum is 119 mm, the first quartile Q_1 is 128.0 mm, the second quartile Q_2 (or median) is 131.0 mm, the third quartile Q_3 is 135.0 mm, and the maximum is 141 mm.
7. Significantly low heights are 83.7 cm or less; significantly high heights are 111.3 cm or greater. The height of 87.8 cm is not significant, so the physician should not be concerned.
8. The median would be better because it is not affected much by the one very large income.

Chapter 3: Cumulative Review Exercises

1.

Arsenic (μg)	Frequency
0.0–1.9	1
2.0–3.9	0
4.0–5.9	3
6.0–7.9	7
8.0–9.9	1

2.

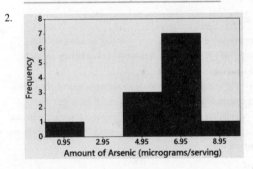

3.   1. | 5
     2. |
     3. |
     4. | 9
     5. | 44
     6. | 13679
     7. | 38
     8. | 2

4. a. 6.09 μg   b. 6.45 μg   c. 1.75 μg
   d. 3.06 (μg)²   e. 6.70 μg
5. a. Mode, because the others are numerical measures that require data at the interval or ratio levels of measurement.
   b. Convenience
   c. More consistency can be achieved by lowering the standard deviation. (It is also important to keep the mean at an acceptable level.)

Chapter 4 Answers

Section 4-1

1. The probability of a student passing the physical examination is 0.60.
3. $P(\bar{A}) = 0.488$
5. 1, 4/7, 0, 0.461, 0.08
7. 1/9 or 0.111
9. Significantly high
11. Neither significantly low nor significantly high
13. 1/2 or 0.5
15. 1/4 or 0.25
17. 1/10 or 0.1
19. 0
21. 5/555 or 0.00901. The employer would suffer because it would be at risk by hiring someone who uses drugs.
23. 50/555 or 0.0901. This result does appear to be a reasonable estimate of the prevalence rate.
25. 879/945 or 0.930. Yes, the technique appears to be effective.
27. 428/580 or 0.738; yes
29. 0.130. No, it is not unlikely for someone to never seek medical information online. Because the responses are from a voluntary response survey, it is very possible that the results are not very good.
31. a. brown/brown, brown/blue, blue/brown, blue/blue
    b. 1/4   c. 3/4
33. 3/8 or 0.375
35. 4/16 or 1/4 or 0.25.
37. The high probability of 0.327 shows that the sample results could have easily occurred by chance. It appears that there is not sufficient evidence to conclude that pregnant women can correctly predict the gender of their baby.
39. The low probability of less than 0.001 shows that the sample results could not have easily occurred by chance. It appears that OxyContin does have an effect on sleepiness.

Section 4-2

1. $P(A)$ represents the probability of selecting an adult with blue eyes and $P(\bar{A})$ represents the probability of selecting an adult who does not have blue eyes.
3. Because the selections are made without replacement, the events are dependent. Because the sample size of 1068 is less than 5% of the population size of 15,524,971, the selections can be treated as being independent (based on the 5% guideline for cumbersome calculations).
5. 0.74
7. 0.841
9. 137/152 or 0.901
11. 34/152, or 0.224; not disjoint.
13. a. 0.1985. The events are dependent.
    b. 0.2001. Yes, the events are independent.
15. a. 0.731. Yes, the events are independent.
    b. 0.731. The events are dependent.
17. 87/152 or 0.572
19. 0.0627
21. a. 300   b. 154   c. 0.513
23. 0.990
25. a. 0.03   b. 0.0009   c. 0.000027
    d. By using one drive without a backup, the probability of total failure is 0.03, and with three independent disk drives, the probability drops to 0.000027. By changing from one drive to three, the probability of total failure drops from 0.03 to 0.000027, and that is a very substantial improvement in reliability. Back up your data!

27. 0.838. The probability of 0.838 is high, so it is likely that the entire batch will be accepted, even though it includes many defects.
29. a. 0.299
    b. Using the 5% guideline for cumbersome calculations: 0.00239 [using the rounded result from part (a)]; or 0.00238
31. a. 0.999775   b. 0.970225
    c. The series arrangement provides better protection.
33. a. $P(A \text{ or } B) = P(A) + P(B) - 2P(A \text{ and } B)$
    b. 85/152 or 0.559

Section 4-3

1. The event of not getting at least 1 defect among the 3 batteries, which means that all 3 batteries are good.
3. The probability that the test indicates that the subject has glaucoma given that the subject actually does have glaucoma.
5. 15/16, or 0.9375   7. 0.982   9. 0.344
11. 0.994. The probability is high enough so that she can be reasonably sure of getting a defective transducer for her work.
13. a. 1/3 or 0.333   b. 0.5
15. 0.5
17. 2/1155 or 0.00173. This is the probability of the test making it appear that the subject has hepatitis C when the subject does not have it, so the subject is likely to experience needless stress and additional testing.
19. 335/337 or 0.994. The very high result makes the test appear to be effective in identifying hepatitis C.
21. a. 0.9991
    b. 0.999973. The usual round-off rule for probabilities would result in a probability of 1.00, which would incorrectly indicate that we are certain to have at least one working hard drive.
23. 0.490. The probability is not low, so further testing of the individual samples will be necessary in 49% of the combined samples.
25. 0.569

Section 4-4

1. p_t is the proportion of the characteristic in the treatment group, and p_c is the proportion of the characteristic in the control group.
3. We need to treat 37 subjects with the influenza vaccine in order to prevent one case of influenza. The result applies to a large number of subjects, not every particular group of 37 subjects.
5. Prospective
7. With treatment: 0.159; with placebo: 0.040. The risk of a headache appears to be higher in the treatment group.
9. 9 (rounded up from 8.4)
11. 3.99 or roughly 4. The risk of headaches among Viagra users is roughly 4 times the risk of headaches for those who take a placebo.
13. a. 0.103   b. 0.100
    c. 0.00313. The chance of infection in the atorvastatin treatment group is slightly higher than for the placebo group. For those in the placebo group, there is a 0.313% reduced chance of infection when compared to the atorvastatin treatment group.
15. Atorvastatin: 89:774 or roughly 1:9. Placebo: 27:243 or 1:9. There is not much of a difference between these two results.
17. Relative risk: 0.939; odds ratio: 0.938; the risk of a headache with Nasonex treatment is slightly less than the risk of a headache with a placebo.

Section 4-5

1. During a year in Germany, there are 11.6 deaths for every 1000 people in the population.
3. About 936,384 deaths are expected in a year.
5. 4.0 per 1000   7. 10.6 per 1000
9. 64.3 per 1000 women aged 15–44
11. 3.7 per 1000
13. 0.008; the rate uses fewer decimal places and is easier to understand.
15 a. 0.0124   b. 0.00000191
   c. 0.999998; using three significant digits would result in a probability of 1.00, which would be misleading because it would incorrectly suggest that it is certain that at least one survives the year.
17 a. 31.3   b. 0.324
19. No, the health of the nation is not necessarily declining. The increasing number of deaths each year is probably due to the growing population.
21. The United States has a population distribution of 33.10190862%, 52.41701653%, and 14.48107485% for the three age categories. If the 18,934,195 Florida residents have that same distribution, the three age groups would have these numbers of people: 6,267,580, 9,924,740, and 2,741,875, respectively. Using the same Florida mortality rates for the three individual age groups and using the new adjusted population sizes for the three Florida age categories, we get these numbers of Florida deaths: 3974, 40,155, and 105,112, respectively. Using the adjusted numbers of deaths and the adjusted population sizes for the different categories, the crude mortality rate for Florida becomes 7.9 per 1000, which is much closer to the U.S. mortality rate of 8.0 per 1000 than the mortality rate of 9.1 per 1000 found for Florida before the adjustments.

Section 4-6

1. The symbol ! is the factorial symbol that represents the product of decreasing whole numbers, as in $6! = 6 \cdot 5 \cdot 4 \cdot 3 \cdot 2 \cdot 1 = 720$. Six people can be scheduled for X-ray films 720 different ways.
3. The result of 462 is the number of different combinations that are possible when 6 items are selected without replacement from 11 different items that are available.
5. 1/10,000   7. 1/171
9. 1/40,320   11. 1/254,251,200
13. 1/100,000,000. No, there are too many different possibilities.
15. 168,168,000   17. 1/100,000
19. Area codes: 800. Phone numbers: 6,400,000,000. Yes. (With a total population of about 400,000,000, there would be about 16 phone numbers for every adult and child.)
21. a. 5040   b. 210   c. 1/210
23. 5040   25. 163,459,296,000
27. 1/258,890,850. There is a *much* better chance of being struck by lightning.

29. There are 62 different possible characters. The alphabet requires 26 characters and there are 10 digits, so the Morse code system is more than adequate.
31. 2,095,681,645,538 (about 2 trillion)

Chapter 4: Quick Quiz

1. 4/5 or 0.8   2. 0.7
3. 4/12 or 1/3   4. 0.458
5. Answer varies, but the probability should be low, such as 0.01.
6. 0.0680   7. 0.727
8. 0.00874   9. 0.00459
10. 0.0131

Chapter 4: Review Exercises

1. 0.814
2. 0.723
3. 0.918
4. 0.853
5. 0.571
6. 0.662 (not 0.663)
7. 0.663
8. $\overline{A}$ is the event of selecting a patient and getting someone who was *not* treated with surgery. $P(\overline{A}) = 0.532$
9. $\overline{A}$ is the event of selecting a patient and getting someone who did *not* have a successful treatment. $P(\overline{A}) = 0.186$.
10. 0.537
11. a. 0.38   b. 0.054872
    c. Yes, it is unlikely because the probability of 0.054872 shows that the event does not occur quite often.
12. a. 1/365   b. 31/365
    c. Answer varies, but it is probably quite small, such as 0.01 or less.   d. Yes
13. 0.0335. No.
14. a. 599/600, or 0.998   b. 359,999/360,000, or 0.999997

Chapter 4: Cumulative Review Exercises

1. a. 0.168 g/dL   b. 0.160 g/dL   c. 0.220 g/dL
   d. 0.260 g/dL   e. 0.069 g/dL   f. 0.005 (g/dL)^2
2. a. 0.09, 0.120, 0.160, 0.180, 0.35 (all in units of g/dL). Outlier: 0.35 g/dL.
   b.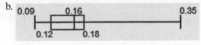
   c. .0 | 9
      .1 | 113457788
      .2 | 3
      .3 | 5
3. a. 46%   b. 0.460   c. Stratified sample
4. a. Convenience sample
   b. If the students at the college are mostly from a surrounding region that includes a large proportion of one ethnic group, the results might not reflect the general population of the United States.
   c. 0.75   d. 0.64

5. The upward sloping pattern of the points in the scatterplot suggests that there appears to be an association between tar and nicotine content in king-size cigarettes.

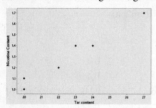

Chapter 5 Answers

Section 5-1

1. The random variable is x, which is the number of girls in four births. The possible values of x are 0, 1, 2, 3, and 4. The values of the random variable x are numerical.

3. $\Sigma P(x) = 0.063 + 0.250 + 0.375 + 0.250 + 0.063 = 1.001$. The sum is not exactly 1 because of a round-off error. The sum is close enough to 1 to satisfy the requirement. Also, the variable x is a numerical random variable and its values are associated with probabilities, and each of the probabilities is between 0 and 1 inclusive, as required. The table does describe a probability distribution.

5. a. Continuous random variable
   b. Not a random variable   c. Discrete random variable
   d. Continuous random variable   e. Discrete random variable

7. Probability distribution with $\mu = 2.5$, $\sigma = 1.1$.

9. Not a probability distribution because the sum of the probabilities is 0.94, which is not 1, as required.

11. Probability distribution with $\mu = 0.7$, $\sigma = 0.7$.

13. $\mu = 5.0$ girls, $\sigma = 1.6$ girls

15. The lower limit is $\mu - 2\sigma = 5.0 - 2(1.6) = 1.8$ girls. Because 1 girl is less than or equal to 1.8 girls, it is a significantly low number of girls.

17. a. 0.377   b. 0.205   c. Part (a)
    d. No, because the probability of 6 or more girls is 0.377, which is not very low (less than or equal to 0.05).

19. $\mu = 1.5$ sleepwalkers, $\sigma = 1.0$ sleepwalker

21. Significantly high numbers of sleepwalkers are greater than or equal to $\mu + 2\sigma$, and $\mu + 2\sigma = 1.5 + 2(1.0) = 3.5$ sleepwalkers. Because 3 sleepwalkers is not greater than or equal to 3.5 sleepwalkers, 3 sleepwalkers is not a significantly high number.

23. a. 0.363   b. 0.535   c. The probability from part (b).
    d. No, because the probability of 1 or fewer sleepwalkers is 0.535, which is not low (not less than or equal to 0.05).

Section 5-2

1. The given calculation assumes that the first two peas have green pods and the last three peas have yellow pods, but there are other arrangements consisting of two peas with green pods and three peas with yellow pods. The probabilities corresponding to those other arrangements should also be included in the result.

3. Because the 30 selections are made without replacement, they are dependent, not independent. Based on the 5% guideline for cumbersome calculations, the 30 selections can be treated as being independent. (The 30 selections constitute about 3% of the population of 1020 responses, and 3% is not more than 5% of the population.) The probability could be found using the binomial probability-formula.

5. Not binomial. Each of the weights has more than two possible outcomes.

7. Binomial

9. Not binomial; there are more than two possible outcomes.

11. Binomial

13. a. 0.128   b. WWC, WCW, CWW; 0.128 for each   c. 0.384

15. 0.0003584 (Table: 0+)   17. 0.967 (Table: 0.967)

19. 0.00001   21. 0.300   23. 0.353

25. a. $\mu = 18.0$ girls; $\sigma = 3.0$ girls
    b. Values of 12.0 girls or fewer are significantly low, values of 24.0 girls or greater are significantly high, and values between 12.0 girls and 24.0 girls are not significant.
    c. Yes, because the result of 26 girls is greater than or equal to 24.0 girls. A result of 26 girls would suggest that the XSORT method is effective.

27. a. $\mu = 11.25$ peas; $\sigma = 1.7$ peas
    b. Values of 7.85 peas or fewer are significantly low, values of 14.65 peas or more are significantly high, and values between 7.85 peas and 14.65 peas are not significant.
    c. The result is significant because the result of 2 peas is less than or equal to 7.85 peas.

29. 0.304; no.

31. 0.662. The probability shows that about 2/3 of all shipments will be accepted. With about 1/3 of the shipments rejected, the supplier would be wise to improve quality.

33. a. 3.3 and 10.7. The result of 13 girls is greater than 10.7, so 13 is a significantly high number of girls.
    b. 0.000854   c. 0.000916
    d. The probability from part (c) is relevant. The result of 13 girls is significantly high.
    e. The results suggest that the XSORT method is effective in increasing the likelihood that a baby is a girl.

35. a. 29.3 and 41.2. Because 34 falls between those limits, it is neither significantly low nor significantly high.
    b. 0.118   c. 0.390
    d. The probability from part (c) is relevant. The result of 34 peas with long stems is not significantly low.
    e. The results do not provide strong evidence against Mendel's claim of 75% for peas with long stems.

37. 0.0468

39. Without replacement: 0.139; with replacement: 0.147.

Section 5-3

1. $\mu = 31{,}645/365 = 86.7$, which is the mean number of patient admissions per day. $x = 85$, because we want the probability that a randomly selected day has exactly 85 admissions, and $e \approx 2.71828$, which is a constant used in all applications of Formula 5-9.

3. Possible values of x: 0, 1, 2, . . . (with no upper bound). It is not possible to have $x = 90.3$ patient admissions in a day. x is a discrete random variable.

5. $P(12) = 0.114$ 7. 0.999991

9. 0.9 murder; 0.402 (0.407 using the rounded mean). There should be many days (roughly 40%) with no murders.

11. a. 0.170
    b. The expected number is between 97.9 and 98.2, depending on rounding.
    c. The expected number of regions with 2 hits is close to 93, which is the actual number of regions with 2 hits.

13. 0.9999876 or 0.9999877 (using unrounded mean). Very high chance, or "almost certain," that at least one fatality will occur.

15. a. 10.6154   b. 0.0000245.
    c. 0.116. With 2 of the 13 years having exactly 9 cases of rubella, the probability appears to be 2/13 or 0.154; the Poisson distribution yields a probability of 0.116, which is in the general ballpark, but it is off by a fairly large amount.

17. The distribution is skewed to the right.

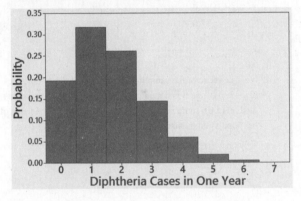

Chapter 5: Quick Quiz

1. $\mu = 13.2$ males   2. $\sigma = 3.2$ males   3. Parameters
4. Significantly low: 6.8 or fewer. Significantly high: 19.6 or more.
5. 0.154
6. Yes. The sum of the probabilities is 1, and all of the probabilities are between 0 and 1 inclusive, and the values of x are numerical.
7. 0.3 male
8. 0.3 male^2 (or 0.2 male^2 if using the unrounded standard deviation)
9. 0+ indicates that the probability is a very small positive number. It does not indicate that it is impossible for all five adult males to be heavy drinkers.
10. 0.999. Yes, 4 is significantly high.

Chapter 5: Review Exercises

1. 0.238
2. 0.703. No, the eight subjects from the same family are not randomly selected from the population of adults. Because they are from the same family, they are likely to share similar diet and genetic factors, so they are not independent.
3. $\mu = 2.24$ adults and $\sigma = 1.27$ adults.
4. No, the limit separating significantly low values is -0.3 adult and 2 is greater than -0.3. Also, the probability that one or

fewer adults have high cholesterol is 0.603, which is not low (less than or equal to 0.05).

5. Yes, the limit separating significantly high values is 4.78 adults and 8 is greater than or equal to 4.78. Also, the probability that all eight adults have high cholesterol is 0.00003, which is very low (less than or equal to 0.05).

6. No. The responses are not *numerical*.

7. a. Yes. The sum of the probabilities is 1. Each probability is between 0 and 1 inclusive. The values of x are numerical.
    b. $\mu = 1.1$ condoms
    c. $\sigma = 0.9$ condom
    d. Yes, 5 failures is significantly high. A number is significantly high if it is equal to or greater than $\mu + 2\sigma = 2.9$, and 5 does exceed 2.9. Also, the probability of 5 or more failures is 0.001, which is a low probability.
    e. Here, the symbol 0+ represents a positive probability that is so small that it is 0.000 when rounded.

8. a. 143/365 or 0.392 death per day   b. 0.676
    c. 0.00750 (or 0.00749 if using the unrounded mean)
    d. No, because the event is so rare.   •

Chapter 5: Cumulative Review Exercises

1. a. 80.5 manatees   b. 80.0 manatees
    c. 29.0 manatees   d. 9.7 manatees
    e. 94.1 manatees^2
    f. The trend of the manatee deaths over time is not addressed by the preceding statistics.
    g. Significantly low numbers are 1.1 manatees or lower, and significantly high numbers are 99.9 manatees or higher.
    h. None of the listed numbers are significantly low or significantly high.

2. a. $\bar{x} = 4.6$ and $s = 2.8$. They are statistics.
    b. The last digits appear to be random. None of the frequencies appear to be substantially different from the others.
    c. No, the values of x are numerical, but the frequencies are not probabilities, as required.

3. No vertical scale is shown, but a comparison of the numbers shows that 7,066,000 is roughly 1.2 times the number 6,000,000; however, the graph makes it appear that the goal of 7,066,000 people is roughly 3 times the number of people enrolled. The graph is misleading in the sense that it creates the false impression that actual enrollments are far below the goal, which is not the case. Fox News apologized for this graph and provided a corrected graph.

4. a. 0.55   b. 0.2025   c. 0.166
    d. $\mu = 22.5$ adults, $\sigma = 12.375$ adults. These results are parameters.
    e. Significantly low numbers are -2.25 or lower, and significantly high numbers are 47.25 and higher. Because 20 is greater than -2.25, it is not a significantly low or significantly high number of adults with hypertension (among 50).

Chapter 6 Answers

Section 6-1

1. The word "normal" has a special meaning in statistics. It refers to a specific bell-shaped distribution that can be described by Formula 6-1. The lottery digits do not have a normal distribution.

3. The mean is $\mu = 0$ and the standard deviation is $\sigma = 1$.

5. 0.4   7. 0.2   9. 0.6700

11. 0.6993 (Table: 0.6992)   13. 1.23   15. −1.45

17. 0.1093   19. 0.8997   21. 0.4013

23. 0.9946   25. 0.0214 (Table: 0.0215)

27. 0.0174   29. 0.9545 (Table: 0.9544)

31. 0.8413 (Table: 0.8412)   33. 0.999997 (Table: 0.9999).

35. 0.5000   37. 2.33   39. −2.05, 2.05

41. 1.28   43. 1.75

45. 68.27% (Table: 68.26%)   47. 99.73% (Table: 99.74%)

49. a. 2.28%   b. 2.28%   c. 95.45% (Table: 95.44%)

Section 6-2

1. a. $\mu = 0$; $\sigma = 1$
   b. The z scores are numbers without units of measurement.

3. The standard normal distribution has a mean of 0 and a standard deviation of 1, but a nonstandard normal distribution has a different value for one or both of those parameters.

5. 0.8849   7. 0.9053   9. 136

11. 69   13. 0.9878   15. 0.3435

17. 88.25 beats per minute

19. 46.4 beats per minute and 92.8 beats per minute. Yes, 100 beats per minute is significantly high.

21. 0.2015 (Table: 0.2005). No, the proportion of schizophrenics is not at all likely to be as high as 0.2005, or about 20%.

23. a. 0.1717 (Table: 0.1711)   b. 2011.5 g (Table: 2011.4 g)
    c. Birth weights are significantly low if they are 2011.4 g or less, and they are "low birth weights" if they are 2495 g or less. Birth weights between 2011.4 g and 2495 g are "low birth weights" but they are not significantly low.

25. a. The mean is 71.320 mm Hg and the standard deviation is 11.994 mm Hg. A histogram confirms that the distribution is roughly normal.
    b. 47.8 mm Hg; 94.8 mm Hg

27. 0.0070

Section 6-3

1. a. In the long run, the sample proportions will have a mean of 0.512.
   b. The sample proportions will tend to have a distribution that is approximately normal.

3. Sample mean; sample variance; sample proportion

5. No. The sample is not a simple random sample from the population of all births worldwide. The proportion of boys born in China is substantially higher than in other countries.

7. a. 4.7
   b.

Sample Variance s^2	Probability
0.0	3/9
0.5	2/9
8.0	2/9
12.5	2/9

   c. 4.7
   d. Yes. The mean of the sampling distribution of the sample variances (4.7) is equal to the value of the population variance (4.7), so the sample variances target the value of the population variance.

9. a. 5
   b.

Sample Median	Probability
4.0	1/9
4.5	2/9
5.0	1/9
6.5	2/9
7.0	2/9
9.0	1/9

   c. 6.0
   d. No. The mean of the sampling distribution of the sample medians is 6.0, and it is not equal to the value of the population median (5.0), so the sample medians do not target the value of the population median.

11. a.

$\bar{x}$	Probability
34	1/16
35	2/16
36	1/16
37.5	2/16
38.5	2/16
41	1/16
42.5	2/16
43.5	2/16
46	2/16
51	1/16

    b. The mean of the population is 40.5 and the mean of the sample means is also 40.5.
    c. The sample means target the population mean. Sample means make good estimators of population means because they target the value of the population mean instead of systematically underestimating or overestimating it.

13. a.

Range	Probability
0	4/16
2	2/16
5	2/16
7	2/16
10	2/16
15	2/16
17	2/16

b. The range of the population is 17, but the mean of the sample ranges is 7. Those values are not equal.

c. The sample ranges do not target the population range of 17, so sample ranges do not make good estimators of population ranges.

15.

Proportion of Girls	Probability
0	0.25
0.5	0.50
1	0.25

Yes. The proportion of girls in 2 births is 0.5, and the mean of the sample proportions is 0.5. The result suggests that a sample proportion is an unbiased estimator of a population proportion.

17. a.

Proportion Correct	Probability
0	16/25
0.5	8/25
1	1/25

b. 0.2

c. Yes. The sampling distribution of the sample proportions has a mean of 0.2 and the population proportion is also 0.2 (because there is 1 correct answer among 5 choices). Yes, the mean of the sampling distribution of the sample proportions is always equal to the population proportion.

19. The formula yields $P(0) = 0.25$, $P(0.5) = 0.5$, and $P(1) = 0.25$, which does describe the sampling distribution of the sample proportions. The formula is just a different way of presenting the same information in the table that describes the sampling distribution.

Section 6-4

1. The sample must have more than 30 values, or there must be evidence that the population of grade-point averages from statistics students has a normal distribution.

3. $\mu_{\bar{x}}$ represents the mean of all sample means, and $\sigma_{\bar{x}}$ represents the standard deviation of all sample means. For the samples of 64 IQ scores, $\mu_{\bar{x}} = 100$ and $\sigma_{\bar{x}} = 15/\sqrt{64} = 1.875$.

5. a. 0.6517   b. 0.9744
   c. Because the original population has a normal distribution, the distribution of sample means is a normal distribution for any sample size.

7. a. 0.0622 (Table: 0.1285)   b. 0.0004

c. Because the original population has a normal distribution, the distribution of sample means is normal for any sample size.

9. a. 79.08% (Table 79.19%)   b. 99.44%

11. a. 31.56% (Table 31.58%)   b. 7.35% (Table 7.02%)

13. a. 131   b. 0.0000179 (Table: 0.0001)
   c. No. It is possible that the 4 subjects have a mean of 132 while some of them have scores below the Mensa requirement of 131.

15. a. 140 lb   b. 0.9999999998 (Table: 0.9999)
   c. 0.9458 (Table: 0.9463)
   d. The new capacity of 20 passengers does not appear to be safe enough because the probability of overloading is too high.

17. a. 0.0047   b. 0.0000 (Table: 0.0001)
   c. The result from part (a) is relevant because the seats are occupied by individuals.

19. a. 0.8877 (Table: 0.8869)
   b. 1.0000 when rounded to four decimal places (Table: 0.9999).
   c. The probability from part (a) is more relevant because it shows that 89% of male passengers will not need to bend. The result from part (b) gives us information about the mean for a group of 100 men, but it doesn't give us useful information about the comfort and safety of individual male passengers.
   d. Because men are generally taller than women, a design that accommodates a suitable proportion of men will necessarily accommodate a greater proportion of women.

21. a. Yes. The sampling is without replacement and the sample size of $n = 50$ is greater than 5% of the finite population size of 275. $\sigma_{\bar{x}} = 2.0504584$.
   b. 0.5963 (Table: 0.5947)

Section 6-5

1. The histogram should be approximately bell-shaped, and the normal quantile plot should have points that approximate a straight-line pattern.

3. We must verify that the sample is from a population having a normal distribution. We can check for normality using a histogram, identifying the number of outliers, and constructing a normal quantile plot.

5. Normal. The points are reasonably close to a straight-line pattern, and there is no other pattern that is not a straight-line pattern.

7. Not normal. The points are not reasonably close to a straight-line pattern, and there appears to be a pattern that is not a straight-line pattern.

9. Not normal   11. Normal

13. Not normal

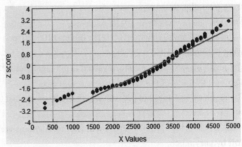

15. Normal

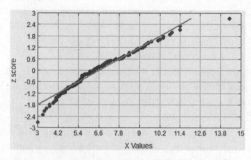

17. Normal, the points have coordinates (27.4, −1.13), (30.3, −0.48), (31.4, 0), (34.0, 0.48) and (37.0, 1.13).

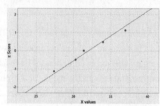

19. a. Yes   b. Yes   c. No

Section 6-6

1. a. The area below (to the left of) 502.5
   b. The area between 501.5 and 502.5
   c. The area above (to the right of) 502.5

3. $p = 0.2$; $q = 0.8$; $\mu = 20$; $\sigma = 4$. The value of $\mu = 20$ shows that for people who make 100 random guesses for the 100 questions, the mean number of correct answers is 20. For groups of 100 people who make random guesses, the standard deviation of $\sigma = 4$ is a measure of how much the numbers of correct responses vary.

5. Normal approximation shall not be used.

7. Normal approximation should not be used.

9. Using normal approximation: 0.1727 (Table: 0.1736); Tech using binomial: 0.1724. The result of 40 people with blue eyes is not significantly high.

11. Using normal approximation: 0.0105 (Table: 0.0104); Tech using binomial: 0.0053. The result of 4 people with green eyes is significantly low.

13. a. Using normal approximation: 0.0204; Tech using binomial: 0.0205.
    b. Using normal approximation: 0.0569 (Table: 0.0571); Tech using binomial: 0.0513.
    c. No

15. a. Using normal approximation: 0.1008 (Table: 0.1003); Tech using binomial: 0.1012.
    b. The result of 455 who have sleepwalked is not significantly high.
    c. The result of 455 does not provide strong evidence against the rate of 29.2%.

17. (1) 0.1723; (2) 0.1704; (3) 0.1726. No, the approximations are not off by very much.

Chapter 6: Quick Quiz

1.

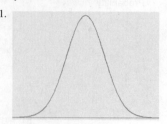

2. $z = -1.34$ 3. 0.9983

4. 0.1546 (Table: 0.1547)

5. a. $\mu = 0$ and $\sigma = 1$
   b. $\mu_{\bar{x}}$ represents the mean of all sample means and $\sigma_{\bar{x}}$ represents the standard deviation of all sample means.

6. 0.8092 (Table: 0.8106)   7. 0.6280 (Table: 0.6292)

8. 84.6 mm Hg (Table: 84.5 mm Hg)

9. 0.9568 (Table: 0.9564)

10. The normal quantile plot suggests that diastolic blood pressure levels of women are normally distributed.

Chapter 6: Review Exercises

1. a. 0.8907   b. 0.8907   c. 0.8216
   d. 0.67   e. 0.0228

2. a. 1.13%   b. 63.8 in.

3. a. 1.42% (Table: 1.43%)   b. 59.0 in.

4. a. Normal   b. 100   c. $15/\sqrt{64} = 1.875$

5. a. An unbiased estimator is a statistic that targets the value of the population parameter in the sense that the sampling distribution of the statistic has a mean that is equal to the corresponding parameter.
   b. Mean; variance; proportion   c. True

6. a. 88.77% (Table: 88.69%). With about 11% of all men needing to bend, the design does not appear to be adequate, but the Mark VI monorail appears to be working quite well in practice.
   b. 75.1 in

7. a. Because women are generally a little shorter than men, a doorway height that accommodates men will also accommodate women.
   b. 1, but actually a really small amount less than 1 (Table: 0.9999)
   c. Because the mean height of 60 men is less than 72 in., it does not follow that the 60 individual men all have heights less than 72 in. In determining the suitability of the door height for men, the mean of 60 heights is irrelevant, but the heights of individual men are relevant.

8. a. No. A histogram is far from bell-shaped. A normal quantile plot reveals a pattern of points that is far from a straight-line pattern.
   b. No. The sample size of $n = 13$ does not satisfy the condition of $n > 30$, and the values do not appear to be from a population having a normal distribution.

9. Using normal approximation: 0.2286 (Table: 0.2296); Tech using binomial: 0.2278. The occurrence of 787 offspring plants with long stems is not significantly low because the probability of 787 or fewer plants with long stems is not small. The results are consistent with Mendel's claimed proportion of 3/4.

10. a. 1.49% (Table: 1.50%)   b. 69.4 in.

Chapter 6: Cumulative Review Exercises

1. a. 26.82   b. 28.90   c. 4.76   d. 0.96
   e. Ratio   f. Continuous
2. a. 26.45, 28.90, 29.05
   b.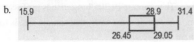
   c. The sample does not appear to be from a population having a normal distribution.
3. a. 0.001   b. 0.271
   c. The requirement that $np \geq 5$ is not satisfied, indicating that the normal approximation would result in errors that are too large.
   d. 5.0 people   e. 2.1 people
   f. No, 8 is within two standard deviations of the mean and is within the range of values that could easily occur by chance.
4. a. $\bar{B}$ is the event of selecting someone who does not have blue eyes.
   b. 0.65   c. 0.0429
   d. Using normal approximation: 0.0232 (Table: 0.0233); Tech using binomial: 0.0246.
   e. Yes
5. a. 0.7881   b. 0.9968 (Table: 0.9967)
   c. 10.4 in.   d. 0.0228

Chapter 7 Answers

Section 7-1

1. The confidence level, such as 95%, was not provided.
3. $\hat{p} = 0.13$ is the sample proportion; $\hat{q} = 0.87$ (found from evaluating $1 - \hat{p}$); $n = 227$ is the sample size; $E = 0.04$ is the margin of error; p is the population proportion, which is unknown. The value of α is 0.05.
5. 1.645   7. 2.81
9. 0.400 ± 0.025 11. $0.0780 < p < 0.162$
13. a. 0.0705   b. $E = 0.0333$ c. $0.0372 < p < 0.104$
   d. We have 95% confidence that among subjects treated with OxyContin, the interval from 0.0372 to 0.104 actually does contain the true value of the population proportion of subjects who experience headaches.
15. a. 0.143   b. $E = 0.00815$ c. $0.135 < p < 0.152$
   d. We have 90% confidence that the interval from 0.135 to 0.152 actually does contain the true value of the population proportion of returned surveys.
17. $0.462 < p < 0.529$. Because 0.512 is contained within the confidence interval, there is not strong evidence against 0.512 as the value of the proportion of boys in all births.
19. a. $17.4\% < p < 28.4\%$
   b. Because the two confidence intervals overlap, it is possible that the OxyContin treatment group and the placebo group have the same rate of nausea. Nausea does not appear to be an adverse reaction made worse with OxyContin.
21. a. $0.0276\% < p < 0.0366\%$ (using $x = 135$: $0.0276\% < p < 0.0367\%$).
   b. No, because 0.0340% is included in the confidence interval.
23. $91.4\% < p < 94.6\%$. It appears that the success rate for the XSORT method is much higher than the success rate of about 50% expected with no treatment, so the XSORT method appears to be successful.

25. $0.496 < p < 0.514$. No, because the proportion could easily equal 0.5. The proportion does not appear to be significantly less than 0.5 the week before Thanksgiving.
27. Sustained care: $77.6\% < p < 88.1\%$ (using $x = 164$). Standard care: $56.1\% < p < 69.5\%$ (using $x = 125$). The two confidence intervals do not overlap. It appears that the success rate is higher with sustained care.
29. a. 600 [Table: 601]   b. 47
   c. They don't change.
31. a. 385   b. 369
   c. No, the sample size doesn't change much.
33. a. 1537   b. 1532   c. No
35. a. 752   b. 749
   c. No. A sample of the adults you know is a convenience sample, not a simple random sample, so it is very possible that the results would not be representative of the population.
37. 1238 (Table: 1237)
39. a. The requirement of at least 5 successes and at least 5 failures is not satisfied, so the normal distribution cannot be used.
   b. 0.075

Section 7-2

1. a. $12.855 \text{ g/dL} < \mu < 13.391 \text{ g/dL}$
   b. Best point estimate of μ is 13.123 g/dL. The margin of error is $E = 0.268 \text{ g/dL}$.
   c. Because the sample size of 100 is greater than 30, we can consider the sample mean to be from a population with a normal distribution.
3. We have 95% confidence that the limits of 12.855 g/dL and 13.391 g/dL contain the true value of the mean hemoglobin level of the population of all adult females.
5. Neither the normal nor the t distribution applies.
7. $z_{\alpha/2} = 2.576$ (Table: 2.575)
9. $29.4 \text{ hg} < \mu < 31.4 \text{ hg}$. No, the results do not differ by much.
11. $98.08°F < \mu < 98.32°F$. Because the confidence interval does not contain 98.6°F, it appears that the mean body temperature is not 98.6°F, as is commonly believed.
13. $71.4 \text{ min} < \mu < 126.4 \text{ min}$. The confidence interval includes the mean of 102.8 min that was measured before the treatment, so the mean could be the same after the treatment. This result suggests that the zopiclone treatment does not have a significant effect.
15. $1.8 < \mu < 3.4$. The given numbers are just substitutes for the four DNA base names, so the numbers don't measure or count anything, and they are at the nominal level of measurement. The confidence interval has no practical use.
17. The sample data meet the loose requirement of having a normal distribution. CI: $0.707 \text{ W/kg} < \mu < 1.169 \text{ W/kg}$. Because the confidence interval is entirely below the standard of 1.6 W/kg, it appears that the mean amount of cell phone radiation is less than the FCC standard, but there could be individual cell phones that exceed the standard.
19. $0.284 \text{ ppm} < \mu < 1.153 \text{ ppm}$. Using the FDA guideline, the confidence interval suggests that there could be too much mercury in fish because it is possible that the mean is greater than

1 ppm. Also, one of the sample values exceeds the FDA guideline of 1 ppm, so at least some of the fish have too much mercury.

21. 19.5 mg $< \mu <$ 45.6 mg. People consume some brands much more often than others, but the 20 brands are all weighted equally in the calculations, so the confidence interval might not be a good estimate of the population mean. Just the presence of five zeros suggests that the sample is not from a normally distributed population, so the normality requirement is violated and the confidence interval might not be good estimate of the population mean.

23. a. 5.8 days $< \mu <$ 6.2 days   b. 5.9 days $< \mu <$ 6.3 days
   c. The two confidence intervals are very similar. The echinacea treatment group does not appear to fare any better than the placebo group, so the echinacea treatment does not appear to be effective.

25. Females: 72.0 bpm $< \mu <$ 76.1 bpm. Males: 67.8 bpm $< \mu <$ 71.4 bpm. Adult females appear to have a mean pulse rate that is higher than the mean pulse rate of adult males. Good to know.

27. The sample size is 94, and it does appear to be very practical.

29. The required sample size is 7,367 (Table: 7,368). The sample appears to be too large to be practical.

31. 4814 (Table: 4815). Yes, the assumption seems reasonable.

33. a. 53   b. 32
   c. The result from part (a) is substantially larger than the result from part (b). The result from part (b) is likely to be better because it uses s instead of the estimated σ obtained from the range rule of thumb.

35. a. 234.2 $< \mu <$ 276.0   b. 235.0 $< \mu <$ 275.2
   c. The second confidence interval is narrower, indicating that we have a more accurate estimate when the relatively large sample is selected without replacement from a relatively small finite population.

Section 7-3

1. 95.0 cm^3 $< \sigma <$ 182.5 cm^3. We have 95% confidence that the limits of 95.0 cm^3 and 182.5 cm^3 contain the true value of the standard deviation of brain volumes.

3. The dotplot does not appear to depict sample data from a normally distributed population. The large sample size does not justify treating the values as being from a normally distributed population. Because the normality requirement is not satisfied, the confidence interval estimate of σ should not be constructed using the methods of this section.

5. df = 24. $\chi_L^2 = 12.401$ and $\chi_R^2 = 39.364$. CI: 0.19 mg $< \sigma <$ 0.33 mg.

7. df = 137. $\chi_L^2 = 106.491$ (Table: $\chi_L^2 = 74.222$), and $\chi_R^2 = 171.294$ (Table: 129.561). CI: 1.07 $< \sigma <$ 1.36 (Table: 1.23 $< \sigma <$ 1.63).

9. 99% CI: 10.96 $< \sigma <$ 13.55 (Table: 10.97 $< \sigma <$ 13.54)

11. 29.6 min $< \sigma <$ 71.6 min. No, the confidence interval does not indicate whether the treatment is effective.

13. 4.55 kmph $< \sigma <$ 12.60 kmph

15. a. 10 BPM $< \sigma <$ 27 BPM   b. 12 BPM $< \sigma <$ 33 BPM
   c. The variation does not appear to be significantly different.

17. a. 8.8 days $< \sigma <$ 10.7 days. The sample appears to be from a population with a distribution that is far from normal, so the confidence interval estimate might not be very good.

b. 7.5 days $< \sigma <$ 9.2 days. The sample appears to be from a population with a distribution that is far from normal, so the confidence interval estimate might not be very good.
   c. The amounts of variation are about the same.

19. 19,205 is too large. There aren't 19,205 biostatistics professors in the population, and even if there were, that sample size is too large to be practical.

21. The sample size is 1336. Yes, with the majority of the population concentrated near the mean, the distribution will satisfy the requirement of a normal distribution.

23. $\chi_L^2 = 109.565$ and $\chi_R^2 = 175.276$. The values from the approximation are quite close to the actual critical values.

Section 7-4

1. Without replacement, every sample would be identical to the original sample, so the proportions or means or standard deviations or variances would all be the same, and there would be no confidence "interval."

3. Parts b, d, e are not possible bootstrap samples.

5. $0.250 < p < 0.750$

7. a. 0.1 kg $< \mu <$ 8.6 kg   b. 1.9 kg $< \sigma <$ 6.3 kg

9. Answers vary, but here are typical answers.
   a. $-0.8\ kg < \mu < 7.8$ kg   b. 1.2 kg $< \sigma <$ 7.0 kg

11. Answers vary, but here are typical answers.
   a. Bootstrap: 55.3 min $< \mu <$ 67.3 min. This isn't dramatically different from 51.9 min $< \mu <$ 71.4 min.
   b. Bootstrap: 6.2 min $< \sigma <$ 13.7 min. This isn't dramatically different from 7.7 min $< \sigma <$ 18.4 min.

13. Answers vary, but here is a typical result: $0.348\% < p < 1.62\%$. This is quite close to the confidence interval of $0.288\% < p < 1.57\%$ found in Exercise 22 "Lipitor" from Section 7-1.

15. Answers vary, but here is a typical result: $0.135 < p < 0.152$. The result is essentially the same as the confidence interval of $0.135 < p < 0.152$ found in Exercise 15 from Section 7-1.

17. Answers vary, but here is a typical result: $3.69 < \mu < 4.15$. This result is very close to the confidence interval $3.67 < \mu < 4.17$ that would be found by using the methods from Section 7-2.

19. Answers vary, but here is a typical result: 0.712 W/kg $< \mu <$ 1.18 W/kg. This result is very close to the confidence interval of 0.707 W/kg $< \mu <$ 1.169 W/kg found in Exercise 17 of Section 7-2.

21. a. Answers vary, but here is a typical result: $2.5 < \sigma < 3.3$.
   b. $2.4 < \sigma < 3.7$
   c. The confidence interval from the bootstrap method is not very different from the confidence interval found using the methods of Section 7-3. Because a histogram or normal quantile plot shows that the sample appears to be from a population not having a normal distribution, the bootstrap confidence interval of $2.5 < \sigma < 3.3$ would be a better estimate of σ.

23. Answers vary, but here is a typical result using 10,000 bootstrap samples: $2.5 < \sigma < 3.3$. This result is the same as the confidence interval found using 1000 bootstrap samples. In this case, increasing the number of bootstrap samples from 1000 to 10,000 does not have much of an effect on the confidence interval.

Chapter 7: Quick Quiz

1. 0.130
2. We have 95% confidence that the limits of 0.110 and 0.150 contain the true value of the proportion of adults in the population who correct their vision by wearing contact lenses.
3. $z = 2.576$ (Table: 2.575)
4. $0.02 < p < 0.04$ or $2\% < p < 4\%$
5. 601
6. 136
7. There is a loose requirement that the sample values are from a normally distributed population.
8. The degrees of freedom is the number of sample values that can vary after restrictions have been imposed on all of the values. For the sample data described in Exercise 7, df = 11.
9. $t = 2.201$
10. No, the use of the χ^2 distribution has a fairly strict requirement that the data must be from a normal distribution. The bootstrap method could be used to find a 95% confidence interval estimate of σ.

Chapter 7: Review Exercises

1. $0.00301 < p < 0.00348$. We have 95% confidence that the limits of 0.00301 and 0.00348 contain the value of the population proportion.
2. 423
3. a. 10.900 mm   b. 10.806 mm $< \mu < 10.994$ mm
   c. We have 95% confidence that the limits of 10.806 mm and 10.994 mm contain the value of the population mean μ.
4. 94
5. a. Student t distribution   b. Normal distribution
   c. None of the three distributions is appropriate, but a confidence interval could be constructed by using bootstrap methods.
   d. χ^2 (chi-square distribution)
   e. Normal distribution
6. a. 1036   b. 60   c. 1036
7. 479.1 mg $< \mu < 520.9$ mg. The confidence interval limits do contain the desired amount of 500 mg, so the mean is perfect. The examination of the individual amounts of paracetamol shows that though most of the tablets fall within the confidence interval limits, a couple of tablets have some production problem. Since it is an oral medicine, an overdose may be harmful. So, care needs to be taken for reducing the quantity of paracetamol in such tablets.
8. a. 23.3 mg $< \sigma < 55.8$ mg   b. 22.5 mg
   c. The desired $\sigma = 22.5$ mg from part (b) is almost contained within the confidence interval from part (a). It appears that the current production method produces paracetamol tablets with desired variation, and that should be continued.
9. Answers vary, but here is a typical result:
   310.6 mg $< \mu < 350.9$ mg. The result is very close to the confidence interval found in Exercise 7.
10. a. $0.0113 < p < 0.0287$
    b. Answers vary, but here is a typical result: $0.0120 < p < 0.0290$
    c. The confidence intervals are quite close.

Chapter 7: Cumulative Review Exercises

1. $\bar{x} = 75.78$ cm, median $= 75.95$ cm, $s = 1.37$ cm, range $= 4.40$ cm. These results are statistics.
2. Significantly low values are 73.04 cm or lower, and significantly high values are 78.52 cm or higher. Because 72 cm is lower than 73.04 cm, a walking stride of 72 cm is significantly low (or small).
3. Ratio level of measurement; continuous data.
4. A histogram is not very helpful with only 10 data values, but a normal quantile plot shows that the sample data appear to be from a population having a distribution that is approximately normal.
5. 74.37 cm $< \mu < 77.18$ cm
6. 148 adult females
7. a. 0.2375 (Table: 0.2389)   b. 0.0002 (Table: 0.0001)
   c. 26.04 cm
8. $95.6\% < p < 98.0\%$. Yes.

Chapter 8 Answers

Section 8-1

1. Rejection of the claim about aspirin is more serious because it is a drug used for medical treatments. The wrong aspirin dosage could cause more serious adverse reactions than a wrong vitamin C dosage. It would be wise to use a smaller significance level for testing the claim about the aspirin.
3. a. $H_0: \mu = 161.7$ cm
   b. $H_1: \mu \neq 161.7$ cm
   c. Reject the null hypothesis or fail to reject the null hypothesis.
   d. No, in this case, the original claim becomes the null hypothesis. For the claim that the mean height if women is equal to 161.7 cm, we can either reject that claim or fail to reject it, but we cannot state that there is sufficient evidence to *support* that claim.
5. a. $p > 0.5$
   b. $H_0: p = 0.5$; $H_1: p > 0.5$
7. a. $\mu = 73$ bpm
   b. $H_0: \mu = 73$ bpm; $H_1: \mu \neq 73$ bpm
9. There is sufficient evidence to support the claim that most adults do not have hypertension.
11. There is not sufficient evidence to support the claim that the mean pulse rate (in beats per minute) of adult females is 73 bpm.
13. $z = 13.11$
15. $t = 0.970$
17. a. Right-tailed
    b. P-value $= 0.1587$
    c. Fail to reject H_0.
19. a. Two-tailed
    b. P-value $= 0.0444$
    c. Reject H_0.
21. a. $z = 1.645$
    b. Fail to reject H_0.
23. a. $z = \pm 1.96$
    b. Reject H_0.
25. a. Fail to reject H_0.
    b. There is not sufficient evidence to support the claim that more than 70% of adults do not have hypertension.

27. a. Reject H_0.

 b. There is sufficient evidence to warrant rejection of the claim that the mean pulse rate of adult males is 72 bpm.

29. Type I error: In reality $p = 0.1$, but we reject the claim that $p = 0.1$. Type II error: In reality $p \neq 0.1$, but we fail to reject the claim that $p = 0.1$.

31. Type I error: In reality $p = 0.87$, but we support the claim that $p > 0.87$. Type II error: In reality $p > 0.87$, but we fail to support that conclusion.

33. The power of 0.96 shows that there is a 96% chance of rejecting the null hypothesis of $p = 0.08$ when the true proportion is actually 0.18. That is, if the proportion of Chantix users who experience abdominal pain is actually 0.18, then there is a 96% chance of supporting the claim that the proportion of Chantix users who experience abdominal pain is greater than 0.08.

35. 617

Section 8-2

1. a. 270

 b. $\hat{p} = 0.53$

3. The method based on a confidence interval is not equivalent to the P-value method and the critical value method.

5. a. Left-tailed

 b. $z = -4.46$

 c. P-value: 0.000004

 d. H_0: $p = 0.10$. Reject the null hypothesis.

 e. There is sufficient evidence to support the claim that fewer than 10% of treated subjects experience headaches.

7. a. Two-tailed

 b. $z = -1.36$

 c. P-value: 0.174

 d. H_0: $p = 0.67$. Fail to reject the null hypothesis.

 e. There is not sufficient evidence to warrant rejection of the claim that 67% of adults wash their hands after touching an animal.

9. H_0: $p = 0.5$. H_1: $p > 0.5$. Test statistic: $z = 10.96$. P-value: 0.0000 (Table: 0.0001). Critical value: $z = 2.33$. Reject H_0. There is sufficient evidence to support the claim that the YSORT method is effective in increasing the likelihood that a baby will be a boy.

11. H_0: $p = 0.5$. H_1: $p \neq 0.5$. Test statistic: $z = 2.69$. P-value: 0.0071 (Table: 0.0072). Critical values: $z = \pm 2.576$ (Table: ± 2.575). Reject H_0. There is sufficient evidence to reject the claim that the proportion of those in favor is equal to 0.5. The result suggests that the politician is wrong in claiming that the responses are random guesses equivalent to a coin toss.

13. H_0: $p = 0.20$. H_1: $p > 0.20$. Test statistic: $z = 1.10$. P-value: 0.1367 (Table: 0.1357). Critical value: $z = 1.645$. Fail to reject H_0. There is not sufficient evidence to support the claim that more than 20% of OxyContin users develop nausea. However, with $\hat{p} = 0.229$, we see that a large percentage of OxyContin users experience nausea, so that rate does appear to be very high.

15. H_0: $p = 0.15$. H_1: $p < 0.15$. Test statistic: $z = -1.31$. P-value = 0.0956 (Table: 0.0951). Critical value: $z = -2.33$. Fail to reject H_0. There is not sufficient evidence to support the claim that the return rate is less than 15%.

17. H_0: $p = 0.512$. H_1: $p \neq 0.512$. Test statistic: $z = -0.98$. P-value = 0.3286 (Table: 0.3270). Critical values: $z = \pm 1.96$. Fail to reject H_0. There is not sufficient evidence to warrant rejection of the claim that 51.2% of newborn babies are boys. The results do not support the belief that 51.2% of newborn babies are boys; the results merely show that there is not strong evidence against the rate of 51.2%.

19. H_0: $p = 0.5$. H_1: $p \neq 0.5$. Test statistic: $z = 0.98$. P-value: 0.3268 (Table: 0.3270). Critical values: $z = \pm 1.96$. Fail to reject H_0. There is not sufficient evidence to warrant rejection of the claim that women who guess the gender of their babies have a success rate equal to 50%.

21. H_0: $p = 0.5$. H_1: $p \neq 0.5$. Test statistic: $z = -2.03$. P-value: 0.0422 (Table: 0.0424). Critical values: $z = \pm 1.645$. Reject H_0. There is sufficient evidence to warrant rejection of the claim that touch therapists use a method equivalent to random guesses. However, their success rate of $123/280$, or 43.9%, indicates that they performed *worse* than random guesses, so they do not appear to be effective.

23. H_0: $p = 0.000340$. H_1: $p \neq 0.000340$. Test statistic: $z = -0.66$. P-value: 0.5122 (Table: 0.5092). Critical values: $z = \pm 2.81$. Fail to reject H_0. There is not sufficient evidence to support the claim that the rate is different from 0.0340%. Cell phone users should not be concerned about cancer of the brain or nervous system.

25. H_0: $p = 0.5$. H_1: $p > 0.5$. Test statistic: $z = 0.83$. P-value: 0.2031 (Table: 0.2033). Critical value: $z = 1.645$. Fail to reject H_0. There is not sufficient evidence to support the claim that among smokers who try to quit with nicotine patch therapy, the majority are smoking a year after the treatment. The results show that about half of those who use nicotine patch therapy are successful in quitting smoking.

27. H_0: $p = 0.80$. H_1: $p \neq 0.80$. Test statistic: $z = 0.98$ (using $\hat{p} = 0.828$) or $z = 0.99$ (using $x = 164$). If using $\hat{p} = 0.828$, P-value $= 0.3246$ (Table: 0.3270). If using $x = 164$, P-value $= 0.3198$ (Table: 0.3222). Critical values: $z = \pm 2.576$ (Table: ± 2.575). Fail to reject H_0. There is not sufficient evidence to warrant rejection of the claim that 80% of patients stop smoking when given sustained care. With a success rate around 80%, it appears that sustained care is effective.

29. Normal approximation entries: 0.0114, 0.0012, 0.0054. Exact entries: 0.0215, 0.0034, 0.0059. Exact with simple continuity correction: 0.0117, 0.0018, 0.0054. The P-values agree reasonably well with the large sample size of $n = 1009$. The normal approximation to the binomial distribution appears to work better as the sample size increases.

31. a. 0.7219 (Table: 0.7224)

 b. 0.2781 (Table: 0.2776)

 c. The power of 0.7219 shows that there is a reasonably good chance of making the correct decision of rejecting the false null hypothesis. It would be better if the power were even higher, such as greater than 0.8 or 0.9.

Section 8-3

1. The requirements are (1) the sample must be a simple random sample, and (2) either or both of these conditions must be satisfied:

The population is normally distributed or $n > 30$. There is not enough information given to determine whether the sample is a simple random sample. Because the sample size is not greater than 30, we must check for normality, but the value of 583 sec appears to be an outlier, and a normal quantile plot or histogram suggests that the sample does not appear to be from a normally distributed population. The requirements are not satisfied.

3. A t test is a hypothesis test that uses the Student t distribution, such as the method of testing a claim about a population mean as presented in this section. The letter t is used in reference to the Student t distribution, which is used in a t test.

5. P-value = 0.0437 (Table: $0.025 < P$-value < 0.05).

7. P-value = 0.2581 (Table: >0.10)

9. H_0: $\mu = 98.6°F$. H_1: $\mu \neq 98.6°F$. Test statistic: $t = -3.865$. P-value: 0.0004. Critical values assuming a 0.05 significance level: $t = \pm 2.026$. Reject H_0. There is sufficient evidence to warrant rejection of the claim that the mean body temperature is equal to 98.6°F.

11. H_0: $\mu = 270$. H_1: $\mu < 270$. Test statistic: $t = -2.764$. P-value: 0.0032. Critical value assuming a 0.05 significance level: $t = -1.655$. Reject H_0. There is sufficient evidence to support the claim that the population of adult females has a mean platelet count less than 270.

13. H_0: $\mu = 100$ cm; H_1: $\mu < 100$ cm. Test statistic: $t = -1.189$. P-value = 0.2364 (Table: >0.10). Critical value: $t = 2.352$. Fail to reject H_0. There is not sufficient evidence to warrant rejection of the claim that the population mean of waist size of females is less than 100 cm.

15. H_0: $\mu = 0$. H_1: $\mu > 0$. Test statistic: $t = 0.133$. P-value = 0.4472 (Table: >0.10). Critical value: $t = 1.677$ (Table: 1.676 approximately). Fail to reject H_0. There is not sufficient evidence to support the claim that with garlic treatment, the mean change in LDL cholesterol is greater than 0. There is not sufficient evidence to support a claim that the garlic treatment is effective in reducing LDL cholesterol levels.

17. H_0: $\mu = 0$ lb. H_1: $\mu > 0$ lb. Test statistic: $t = 3.872$. P-value = 0.0002 (Table: <0.005). Critical value: $t = 2.426$. Reject H_0. There is sufficient evidence to support the claim that the mean weight loss is greater than 0. Although the diet appears to have statistical significance, it does not appear to have practical significance because the mean weight loss of only 3.0 lb does not seem to be worth the effort and cost.

19. H_0: $\mu = 4.00$. H_1: $\mu \neq 4.00$. Test statistic: $t = -1.139$. P-value = 0.2554 (Table: >0.20). Critical values: $t = \pm 1.965$ (Table: 1.966 approximately). Fail to reject H_0. There is not sufficient evidence to warrant rejection of the claim that the population of student course evaluations has a mean equal to 4.00. Because the data are from the University of Texas at Austin, they don't necessarily apply to a larger population that extends beyond that one institution.

21. The sample data meet the loose requirement of having a normal distribution. H_0: $\mu = 14$ μg/g. H_1: $\mu < 14$ μg/g. Test statistic: $t = -1.444$. P-value = 0.0913 (Table: >0.05). Critical value: $t = -1.833$. Fail to reject H_0. There is not sufficient evidence to support the claim that the mean lead concentration for all such medicines is less than 14 μg/g.

23. H_0: $\mu = 1000$ hic. H_1: $\mu < 1000$ hic. Test statistic: $t = -2.661$. P-value = 0.0224 (Table: P-value is between 0.01 and 0.025). Critical value: $t = -3.365$. Fail to reject H_0. There is not sufficient evidence to support the claim that the population mean is less than 1000 hic. There is not strong evidence that the mean is less than 1000 hic, and one of the booster seats has a measurement of 1210 hic, which does not satisfy the specified requirement of being less than 1000 hic.

25. H_0: $\mu = 75$ bpm. H_1: $\mu < 75$ bpm. Test statistic: $t = -0.927$. P-value = 0.1777 (Table: >0.10). Critical value: $t = -1.655$ (Table: -1.660 approximately). Fail to reject H_0. There is not sufficient evidence to support the claim that the mean pulse rate of adult females is less than 75 bpm.

27. H_0: $\mu = 90$ mm Hg. H_1: $\mu < 90$ mm Hg. Test statistic: $t = -21.435$. P-value = 0.0000 (Table: <0.005). Critical value: $t = -1.655$ (Table: -1.660 approximately). Reject H_0. There is sufficient evidence to support the claim that the adult female population has a mean diastolic blood pressure level less than 90 mm Hg. The conclusion addresses the mean of a population, not individuals, so we cannot conclude that there are no female adults in the sample with hypertension.

29. The computed critical t score is -1.6554, which is the same as the value of -1.6554 found using Statdisk. The approximation appears to work quite well.

Section 8-4

1. The sample must be a simple random sample and the sample must be from a normally distributed population. The normality requirement for a hypothesis test of a claim about a standard deviation is much stricter, meaning that the distribution of the population must be much closer to a normal distribution.

3. a. Reject H_0.
   b. Reject the claim that the sample is from a population with a standard deviation equal to 0.470 kg.
   c. It appears that the vitamin supplement does affect the variation among birth weights.

5. H_0: $\sigma = 10$ bpm. H_1: $\sigma \neq 10$ bpm. Test statistic: $\chi^2 = 195.172$. P-value = 0.0208. Reject H_0. There is sufficient evidence to warrant rejection of the claim that pulse rates of men have a standard deviation equal to 10 beats per minute. Using the range rule of thumb with the normal range of 60 to 100 beats per minute is not very good for estimating σ in this case.

7. H_0: $\sigma = 2.08°F$. H_1: $\sigma < 2.08°F$. Test statistic: $\chi^2 = 9.329$. P-value = 0.0000 (Table: <0.005). Critical value : $\chi^2 = 74.252$ (Table: 70.065 approximately). Reject H_0. There is sufficient evidence to support the claim that body temperatures have a standard deviation less than 2.08°F. It is very highly unlikely that the conclusion in the hypothesis test in Example 5 from Section 8-3 would change because of a standard deviation from a different sample.

9. H_0: $\sigma = 15$. H_1: $\sigma < 15$. Test statistic: $\chi^2 = 6.963$. P-value = 0.0160 (Table: <0.025). Critical value: $\chi^2 = 8.672$. Reject H_0. There is sufficient evidence to support the claim that IQ scores of physicians have a standard deviation less than 15.

11. H_0: $\sigma = 4.25$ g. H_1: $\sigma < 4.25$ g. Test statistic: $\chi^2 = 58.042$. P-value = 0.1545 (Table: >0.10). Critical value: $\chi^2 = 51.739$. Fail to reject H_0. There is not sufficient evidence to support the

claim that the new process dispenses amounts with a standard
deviation less than the standard deviation of 4.25 g for the old
process. The new process does not appear to be better in the sense
of dispensing amounts that are more consistent.

13. H_0: $\sigma = 6.0$ lb. H_1: $\sigma \neq 6.0$ lb. Test statistic: $X^2 = 26.011$.
P-value $= 0.1101$ (Table: >0.10). Critical values: $X^2 = 19.996$,
65.475 (Table: approximate critical values: 20.707, 66.766). Fail
to reject H_0. There is not sufficient evidence to warrant rejection
of the claim that the amounts of weight loss have a standard
deviation equal to 6.0 lb.

15. H_0: $\sigma = 109.3$ sec. H_1: $\sigma < 109.3$ sec. Test statistic: $X^2 = 0.616$.
P-value $= 0.0001$ (Table: <0.005). Critical value : $X^2 = 3.325$.
Reject H_0. There is sufficient evidence to support the claim that
with a single waiting line, the waiting times have a standard deviation less than 109.3 sec. Because the variation among waiting times
appears to be reduced with the single waiting line, patients are
happier because their waiting times are closer to being the same.
Patients are not annoyed by being stuck in an individual line that
takes much more time than other individual lines.

17. Critical value: $X^2 = 81.540$ (or 81.494 if using $z = 2.326348$
found from technology), which is close to the value of 82.292
obtained from Statdisk and Minitab.

Chapter 8: Quick Quiz

1. a. t distribution   b. Normal distribution
   c. Chi-square distribution
2. a. Two-tailed   b. Left-tailed
   c. Right-tailed
3. a. H_0: $p = 0.5$. H_1: $p > 0.5$.
   b. $z = 1.39$
   c. Fail to reject H_0.
   d. There is not sufficient evidence to support the claim that the
      majority of Internet users aged 18–29 use Instagram.
4. 0.0100   5. True
6. False   7. False
8. No. All critical values of X^2 are always positive.
9. The t test requires that the sample is from a normally distributed
   population, and the test is robust in the sense that the test works
   reasonably well if the departure from normality is not too extreme. The X^2 (chi-square) test is not robust against a departure
   from normality, meaning that the test does not work well if the
   population has a distribution that is far from normal.
10. The only true statement is the one given in part (a).

Chapter 8: Review Exercises

1. a. False.   b. True.
   c. False.   d. False.
   e. False.
2. H_0: $p = 0.5$. H_1: $p > 0.5$. Test statistic: $z = 40.91$ (using
   $\hat{p} = 0.64$) or $z = 40.90$ (using $x = 13,661$). P-value: 0.0000
   (Table: 0.0001). Critical value: $z = 2.33$. Reject H_0. There is sufficient evidence to support the claim that most people believe that the
   Loch Ness monster exists. Because the sample is a voluntary response
   sample, the conclusion about the population might not be valid.
3. H_0: $\mu = 8.3$ million cells per microliter. H_1: $\mu < 8.3$ million
   cells per microliter. Test statistic: $t = -4.937$. P-value $= 0.0000$

(Table: <0.005). Critical value: $t = 2.405$. Reject H_0. There is
sufficient evidence to support the claim that the sample is from a
population with a mean less than 8.3 million cells per microliter.
The test deals with the distribution of sample means, not individual values, so the result does not suggest that each of the
50 females has a white blood cell count below 8.3 million cells
per microliter.

4. H_0: $p = 0.204$. H_1: $p \neq 0.204$. Test statistic: $z = 0.76$.
P-value: 0.4480 (Table: 0.4472). Critical values: $z = \pm 1.96$. Fail
to reject H_0. There is not sufficient evidence to warrant rejection
of the claim that the rate of smoking by adult males is now the
same as in 2008. The smoking rate appears to be about the same.

5. H_0: $\mu = 25$ mg. H_1: $\mu \neq 25$ mg. Test statistic: $t = -0.744$.
P-value: 0.4694 (Table: >0.10). Critical values: $t = \pm 2.145$.
Fail to reject H_0. There is not sufficient evidence to warrant rejection of the claim that the pills come from a population in which
the mean amount of atorvastatin is equal to 25 mg.

6. H_0: $\mu = 20.16$. H_1: $\mu < 20.16$. Test statistic: $t = -3.732$.
P-value $= 0.0023$ (Table: <0.005). Critical value: $t = -2.821$.
Reject H_0. There is sufficient evidence to support the claim that
the population of recent winners has a mean BMI less than 20.16.
Recent winners appear to be significantly smaller than those from
the 1920s and 1930s.

7. H_0: $\sigma = 1.34$. H_1: $\sigma \neq 1.34$. Test statistic: $X^2 = 7.053$.
P-value $= 0.7368$ (Table: >0.20). Critical values: $X^2 = 1.735$,
23.589. Fail to reject H_0. There is not sufficient evidence to
support the claim that the recent winners have BMI values with
variation different from that of the 1920s and 1930s.

8. a. A type I error is the mistake of rejecting a null hypothesis
      when it is actually true. A type II error is the mistake of failing
      to reject a null hypothesis when in reality it is false.
   b. Type I error: In reality, the mean BMI is equal to 20.16, but
      we support the claim that the mean BMI is less than 20.16.
      Type II error: In reality, the mean BMI is less than 20.16, but
      we fail to support that claim.

Chapter 8: Cumulative Review Exercises

1. a. 37.1 deaths   b. 36.0 deaths
   c. 9.8 deaths   d. 96.8 deaths^2
   e. 28.0 deaths
   f. The pattern of the data over time is not revealed by the statis-
      tics. A time-series graph would be very helpful in understand-
      ing the pattern over time.
2. a. Ratio   b. Discrete
   c. Quantitative
   d. No. The data are from recent and consecutive years, so they
      are not randomly selected.
3. 29.1 deaths $< \mu < 45.0$ deaths. We have 99% confidence that
   the limits of 29.1 deaths and 45.0 deaths contain the value of the
   population mean.
4. H_0: $\mu = 72.6$ deaths. H_1: $\mu < 72.6$ deaths. Test statistic:
   $t = -13.509$. P-value $= 0.0000$ (Table: <0.005). Critical value:
   $t = -2.650$. Reject H_0. There is sufficient evidence to support
   the claim that the mean number of annual lightning deaths is now
   less than the mean of 72.6 deaths from the 1980s. Possible factors: Shift in population from rural to urban areas; better lightning

protection and grounding in electric and cable and phone lines; better medical treatment of people struck by lightning; fewer people use phones attached to cords; better weather predictions.

5. Because the vertical scale starts at 50 and not at 0, the difference between the number of males and the number of females is exaggerated, so the graph is deceptive by creating the false impression that males account for nearly all lightning strike deaths. A comparison of the numbers of deaths shows that the number of male deaths is roughly 4 times the number of female deaths, but the graph makes it appear that the number of male deaths is around 25 times the number of female deaths.

6. H_0: $p = 0.5$. H_1: $p > 0.5$. Test statistic: $z = 10.45$. P-value $= 0.0000$ (Table: 0.0001). Critical value: $z = 2.33$. Reject H_0. There is sufficient evidence to support the claim that the proportion of male deaths is greater than $1/2$. More males are involved in certain outdoor activities, such as construction, fishing, and golf.

7. $0.763 < p < 0.854$. Because the entire confidence interval is greater than 0.5, it does not seem feasible that males and females have equal chances of being killed by lightning.

8. a. 0.512   b. 0.008
   c. 0.992   d. 0.205
   e. $\mu = 40.0$ males; $\sigma = 2.8$ males
   f. Yes. Using the range rule of thumb, significantly high values are $\mu + 2\sigma$ or greater. With $\mu + 2\sigma = 45.6$, values above 45.6 are significantly high, so 46 would be a significantly high number of male victims in a group of 50.

9. OR $= 1.14$. The odds in favor of experiencing migraine headaches is about 1.14 times higher for overweight people than for people with normal weight.

Chapter 9 Answers

Section 9-1

1. The samples are simple random samples that are independent. For each of the two groups, the number of successes is at least 5 and the number of failures is at least 5. (Depending on what we call a success, the four numbers are 33, 115, 201,196, and 200,630 and all of those numbers are at least 5.) The requirements are satisfied.

3. a. H_0: $p_1 = p_2$. H_1: $p_1 < p_2$.
   b. There is sufficient evidence to support the claim that the rate of polio is less for children given the Salk vaccine than for children given a placebo. The Salk vaccine appears to be effective.

5. H_0: $p_1 = p_2$. H_1: $p_1 > p_2$. Test statistic: $z = 12.82$. P-value: 0.0000. Critical value: $z = 2.33$. Reject H_0. There is sufficient evidence to support the claim that vinyl gloves have a greater virus leak rate than latex gloves.

7. a. H_0: $p_1 = p_2$. H_1: $p_1 < p_2$. Test statistic: $z = -1.66$. P-value: 0.0484 (Table: 0.0485). Critical value: $z = -2.33$. Fail to reject H_0. There is not sufficient evidence to support the claim that the rate of dementia among those who use ginkgo is less than the rate of dementia among those who use a placebo. There is not sufficient evidence to support the claim that ginkgo is effective in preventing dementia.
   b. 98% CI: $-0.0541 < p_1 - p_2 < 0.00904$ (Table: $-0.0542 < p_1 - p_2 < 0.00909$). Because the confidence interval limits include 0, there does not appear to be a significant difference between dementia rates for those treated with ginkgo and those given a placebo. There is not sufficient evidence to support the claim that the rate of dementia among those who use ginkgo is less than the rate of dementia among those who use a placebo. There is not sufficient evidence to support the claim that ginkgo is effective in preventing dementia.
   c. The sample results suggest that ginkgo is not effective in preventing dementia.

9. a. H_0: $p_1 = p_2$. H_1: $p_1 > p_2$. Test statistic: $z = 2.64$. P-value: 0.0041. Critical value: $z = 2.33$. Reject H_0. There is sufficient evidence to support the claim that the rate of success for smoking cessation is greater with the sustained care program.
   b. 98% CI: $0.0135 < p_1 - p_2 < 0.200$ (Table: $0.0134 < p_1 - p_2 < 0.200$). Because the confidence interval limits do not contain 0, there is a significant difference between the two proportions. Because the interval consists of positive numbers only, it appears that the success rate for the sustained care program is greater than the success rate for the standard care program.
   c. Based on the samples, the success rates of the programs are 25.8% (sustained care) and 15.1% (standard care). That difference does appear to be substantial, so the difference between the programs does appear to have practical significance.

11. a. H_0: $p_1 = p_2$. H_1: $p_1 > p_2$. Test statistic: $z = 6.44$. P-value $= 0.0000$ (Table: 0.0001). Critical value: $z = 2.33$. Reject H_0. There is sufficient evidence to support the claim that the proportion of people over 55 who dream in black and white is greater than the proportion of those under 25.
   b. 98% CI: $0.117 < p_1 - p_2 < 0.240$. Because the confidence interval limits do not include 0, it appears that the two proportions are not equal. Because the confidence interval limits include only positive values, it appears that the proportion of people over 55 who dream in black and white is greater than the proportion of those under 25.
   c. The results suggest that the proportion of people over 55 who dream in black and white is greater than the proportion of those under 25, but the results cannot be used to verify the cause of that difference.

13. a. H_0: $p_1 = p_2$. H_1: $p_1 > p_2$. Test statistic: $z = 6.11$. P-value $= 0.0000$ (Table: 0.0001). Critical value: $z = 1.645$. Reject H_0. There is sufficient evidence to support the claim that the fatality rate is higher for those not wearing seat belts.
   b. 90% CI: $0.00559 < p_1 - p_2 < 0.0123$. Because the confidence interval limits do not include 0, it appears that the two fatality rates are not equal. Because the confidence interval limits include only positive values, it appears that the fatality rate is higher for those not wearing seat belts.
   c. The results suggest that the use of seat belts is associated with fatality rates lower than those associated with not using seat belts.

15. a. H_0: $p_1 = p_2$. H_1: $p_1 \neq p_2$. Test statistic: $z = 0.57$. P-value: 0.5720 (Table: 0.5686). Critical values: $z = \pm 1.96$. Fail to reject H_0. There is not sufficient evidence to support the claim that echinacea treatment has an effect.
   b. 95% CI: $-0.0798 < p_1 - p_2 < 0.149$. Because the confidence interval limits do contain 0, there is not a significant

difference between the two proportions. There is not sufficient evidence to support the claim that echinacea treatment has an effect.

   c. Echinacea does not appear to have a significant effect on the infection rate. Because it does not appear to have an effect, it should not be recommended.

17. a. $H_0: p_1 = p_2$. $H_1: p_1 < p_2$. Test statistic: $z = -7.94$. P-value: 0.0000 (Table: 0.0001). Critical value: $z = -2.33$. Reject H_0. There is sufficient evidence to support the claim that the rate of right-handedness for those who prefer to use their left ear for cell phones is less than the rate of right-handedness for those who prefer to use their right ear for cell phones.

   b. 98% CI: $-0.266 < p < -0.126$. Because the confidence interval limits do not contain 0, there is a significant difference between the two proportions. Because the interval consists of negative numbers only, it appears that the claim is supported.

19. a. $H_0: p_1 = p_2$. $H_1: p_1 > p_2$. Test statistic: $z = 9.97$. P-value = 0.0000 (Table: 0.0001). Critical value: $z = 2.33$. Reject H_0. There is sufficient evidence to support the claim that the cure rate with oxygen treatment is higher than the cure rate for those given a placebo. It appears that the oxygen treatment is effective.

   b. 98% CI: $0.467 < p_1 - p_2 < 0.687$. Because the confidence interval limits do not include 0, it appears that the two cure rates are not equal. Because the confidence interval limits include only positive values, it appears that the cure rate with oxygen treatment is higher than the cure rate for those given a placebo. It appears that the oxygen treatment is effective.

   c. The results suggest that the oxygen treatment is effective in curing cluster headaches.

21. a. $H_0: p_1 = p_2$. $H_1: p_1 < p_2$. Test statistic: $z = -1.17$. P-value = 0.1214 (Table: 0.1210). Critical value: $z = -2.33$. Fail to reject H_0. There is not sufficient evidence to support the claim that the rate of left-handedness among males is less than that among females.

   b. 98% CI: $-0.0848 < p_1 - p_2 < 0.0264$ (Table: $-0.0849 < p_1 - p_2 < 0.0265$). Because the confidence interval limits include 0, there does not appear to be a significant difference between the rate of left-handedness among males and the rate among females. There is not sufficient evidence to support the claim that the rate of left-handedness among males is less than that among females.

   c. The rate of left-handedness among males does not appear to be less than the rate of left-handedness among females.

23. The samples should include 2135 men and 2135 women.

25. a. $0.0227 < p_1 - p_2 < 0.217$; because the confidence interval limits do not contain 0, it appears that $p_1 = p_2$ can be rejected.

   b. $0.491 < p_1 < 0.629$; $0.371 < p_2 < 0.509$; because the confidence intervals do overlap, it appears that $p_1 = p_2$ cannot be rejected.

   c. $H_0: p_1 = p_2$. $H_1: p_1 \neq p_2$. Test statistic: $z = 2.40$. P-value = 0.0164. Critical values: $z = \pm 1.96$. Reject H_0. There is sufficient evidence to reject $p_1 = p_2$.

   d. Reject $p_1 = p_2$. Least effective method: Using the overlap between the individual confidence intervals.

Section 9-2

1. Only part (b) describes independent samples.

3. a. Yes   b. Yes   c. 98%

5. $H_0: \mu_1 = \mu_2$. $H_1: \mu_1 \neq \mu_2$. Test statistic: $t = -0.452$. Critical values: $t = \pm 1.987$ (Table: $t = \pm 2.014$). P-value: 0.6521 (Table: >0.20). Fail to reject H_0. There is not sufficient evidence to warrant rejection of the claim that the two groups are from populations with the same mean. This result suggests that the increased humidity does not help in the treatment of croup.

7. a. $H_0: \mu_1 = \mu_2$. $H_1: \mu_1 < \mu_2$. Test statistic: $t = -2.908$. P-value = 0.0019 (Table: <0.005). Critical value: $t = -1.649$ (Table: -1.653 approximately). Reject H_0. There is sufficient evidence to support the claim that the children exposed to cocaine have a lower mean score.

   b. 90% CI: $-1.4 < \mu_1 - \mu_2 < -0.4$. Because the confidence interval consists of negative numbers only, there is sufficient evidence to support the claim that the children exposed to cocaine have a lower mean score.

9. a. $H_0: \mu_1 = \mu_2$. $H_1: \mu_1 > \mu_2$. Test statistic: $t = 5.004$. P-value = 0.0000 (Table: <0.005). Critical value: $t = 1.678$ (Table: $t = 1.711$). Reject H_0. There is sufficient evidence to support the claim that unfiltered king-size cigarettes have a mean nicotine content greater than that of 100-mm cigarettes. The result suggests that the filters are effective in reducing the nicotine content, assuming that both types of cigarettes are about the same size.

   b. 90% CI: $0.22 \text{ mg} < \mu_1 - \mu_2 < 0.46 \text{ mg}$ (Table: $0.23 \text{ mg} < \mu_1 - \mu_2 < 0.46 \text{ mg}$). The confidence interval includes positive numbers only, which suggests that the mean nicotine content of unfiltered king-size cigarettes is greater than the mean for 100-mm cigarettes.

11. a. $H_0: \mu_1 = \mu_2$. $H_1: \mu_1 \neq \mu_2$. Test statistic: $t = 5.045$. P-value = 0.0000 (Table: <0.01). Critical values: $t = \pm 2.058$ (Table: ± 2.080). Reject H_0. There is sufficient evidence to support the claim that there is a significant difference between the treatment group and control group. We cannot conclude that the *cause* is due to the treatment.

   b. 95% CI: $1.47 < \mu_1 - \mu_2 < 3.51$ (Table: $1.46 < \mu_1 - \mu_2 < 3.52$). Because the confidence interval does not contain zero, there appears to be a significant difference between the two population means. It does appear that there are significantly more errors made by those treated with alcohol.

13. a. $H_0: \mu_1 = \mu_2$; $H_1: \mu_1 > \mu_2$. Test statistic: $t = 1.845$. P-value = 0.0363 (Table: <0.05). Critical value: $t = 2.419$; (Table 2.426); Fail to reject H_0. There is not sufficient evidence to support the claim that nonsmokers exposed to tobacco smoke have a higher mean cotinine level than nonsmokers not exposed to tobacco smoke.

   b. 98% CI: $\text{ng/mL} < \mu_1 - \mu_2 < 102.21 \text{ ng/mL}$ (Table: $0 \text{ ng/mL} < \mu_1 - \mu_2 < 102.37 \text{ mg/mL}$).

   c. Exposure to second-hand smoke does not appear to have the effect of being associated with extremely large amounts of nicotine than for those not exposed to second-hand smoke.

15. a. $H_0: \mu_1 = \mu_2$. $H_1: \mu_1 > \mu_2$. Test statistic: $t = 1.063$. P-value = 0.1502 (Table: >0.05). Critical value: $t = 2.502$

(Table: 2.528). Fail to reject H_0. There is not sufficient evidence to support the claim that the verb IQ score of people with low blood lead levels is higher than the verb IQ score of people with high blood lead levels.

b. 98% CI: $-3.6 < \mu_1 - \mu_2 < 8.8$
(Table: $-3.8 < \mu_1 - \mu_2 < 8.7$)

c. No, it does appear that exposure to lead has an effect on verb IQ scores.

17. a. H_0: $\mu_1 = \mu_2$. H_1: $\mu_1 \neq \mu_2$. Test statistic: $t = 1.520$. P-value $= 0.15$. Critical values: $t = \pm 2.020$ (Table: ± 2.120). Fail to reject H_0. There is not sufficient evidence to warrant rejection of the claim that Disney animated children's movies and other animated children's movies have the same mean time showing alcohol use.

b. 95% CI: -7.66 sec $< \mu_1 - \mu_2 < 54.3$ sec
(Table: -9.19 sec $< \mu_1 - \mu_2 < 55.8$ sec);

c. The times appear to be from a population with a distribution that is not normal, (the sample is right-skewed), but the methods in this section are robust against departures from normality. (Results obtained by using other methods confirm that the results obtained here are quite good, even though the non-Disney times appear to violate the normality requirement.)

19. a. H_0: $\mu_1 = \mu_2$. H_1: $\mu_1 < \mu_2$. Test statistic: $t = -1.810$. P-value $= 0.0442$ (Table: >0.025). Critical value: $t = -2.574$ (Table: -2.650). Fail to reject H_0. There is not sufficient evidence to support the claim that the mean longevity for popes is less than the mean for British monarchs after coronation.

b. 98% CI: -23.6 years $< \mu_1 - \mu_2 < 4.0$ years
(Table: -23.6 years $< \mu_1 - \mu_2 < 4.4$ years)

21. H_0: $\mu_1 = \mu_2$. H_1: $\mu_1 \neq \mu_2$. Test statistic: $t = -0.863$. P-value $= 0.3887$ (Table: >0.20). Critical values are $t = \pm 1.968$ (Table: ± 1.984). Fail to reject H_0. There is not sufficient evidence to warrant rejection of the claim that women and men have the same mean diastolic blood pressure.

23. With pooling, df increases dramatically to 97, but the test statistic decreases from 1.063 to 0.782 (because the estimated standard deviation increases from 2.563814 to 3.181429), the P-value increases to 0.1632, and the 98% confidence interval becomes wider. With pooling, these results do not show greater significance.

25. H_0: $\mu_1 = \mu_2$. H_1: $\mu_1 \neq \mu_2$. Test statistic: $t = 15.322$. P-value $= 0.0000$ (Table: <0.01). Critical values: $t = \pm 2.080$. Reject H_0. There is sufficient evidence to warrant rejection of the claim that the two populations have the same mean.

Section 9-3

1. Only parts (a) and (c) are true.

3. The results will be the same.

5. H_0: $\mu_d = 0$. H_1: $\mu_d \neq 0$. Test statistic: $t = -17.339$. P-value: 0.0001 (Table: <0.01). Critical values: $t = \pm 4.604$. Reject H_0. There is sufficient evidence to support the claim of a difference in measurements between the two arms. The right and left arms should yield the same measurements, but the given data show that this is not happening for this person.

7. a. H_0: $\mu_1 = 0$°F. H_1: $\mu_d \neq 0$°F. Test statistic: $t = -2.830$. P-value $= 0.0300$ (Table: $= 0.0340$). Critical values: $t = \pm 1.493$. Reject H_0. There is sufficient evidence to warrant rejection of the claim that there is no difference between body temperatures measured at 8 AM and at 12 AM. There appears to be a difference.

b. 90% CI: -1.35°F $< \mu_d < -0.25$°F; The confidence interval consists of negative numbers only and does not include 0.

9. H_0: $\mu_d = 0$ in. H_1: $\mu_d \neq 0$ in. Test statistic: $t = 1.267$. P-value $= 0.2370$ (Table: >0.20). Critical values: $t = \pm 1.833$. Fail to reject H_0. There is not sufficient evidence to warrant rejection of the claim that there is no difference in heights between fathers and their first sons.

11. -6.5 admissions $< \mu_d < -0.2$ admissions. Because the confidence interval does not include 0 admissions, it appears that there is sufficient evidence to warrant rejection of the claim that when the 13th day of a month falls on a Friday, the numbers of hospital admissions from motor vehicle crashes are not affected. Hospital admissions do appear to be affected.

13. -66.7 cm^3 $< \mu_d < 49.7$ cm^3 (Table: -66.8 cm^3 $< \mu_d < 49.8$ cm^3). Because the confidence interval includes 0 cm^3, the mean of the differences could be equal to 0 cm^3, so there does not appear to be a significant difference.

15. -4.16 in. $< \mu_d < 2.16$ in. Because the confidence interval limits contain 0, there is not sufficient evidence to support a claim that there is a difference between self-reported heights and measured heights. We might believe that males would tend to exaggerate their heights, but the given data do not provide enough evidence to support that belief.

17. a. H_0: $\mu_d = 0$°F. H_1: $\mu_d \neq 0$°F. Test statistic: $t = -8.485$. P-value $= 0.0000$ (Table: <0.01). Critical values: $t = \pm 1.996$ (Table: ± 1.994). Reject H_0. There is sufficient evidence to warrant rejection of the claim of no difference between body temperatures measured at 8 AM and at 12 AM. There appears to be a difference.

b. 95% CI: -1.05°F $< \mu_d < -0.65$°F. The confidence interval consists of negative numbers only and does not include 0.

19. H_0: $\mu_d = 0$ in. H_1: $\mu_d \neq 0$ in. Test statistic: $t = -6.347$. P-value $= 0.0000$ (Table: <0.01). Critical values: $t = \pm 1.978$ (Table: ± 1.984 approximately). Reject H_0. There is sufficient evidence to warrant rejection of the claim of no difference in heights between fathers and their first sons.

21. For the temperatures in degrees Fahrenheit and the temperatures in degrees Celsius, the test statistic ($t = 0.124$) is the same, the P-value of 0.9023 is the same, the critical values ($t = \pm 2.028$) are the same, and the conclusions are the same, so the hypothesis test results are the same in both cases. The confidence intervals are -0.25°F $< \mu_d < 0.28$°F and -0.14°C $< \mu_d < 0.16$°C. The confidence interval limits of -0.14°C and 0.16°C have numerical values that are $5/9$ of the numerical values of -0.25°F and 0.28°F.

Section 9-4

1. a. No   b. No   c. The two samples have standard deviations (or variances) that are very close in value.   d. Skewed right

3. No. Unlike some other tests that have a requirement that samples must be from normally distributed populations or the samples must have more than 30 values, the F test has a requirement that the samples must be from normally distributed populations, regardless of how large the samples are.

5. $H_0: \sigma_1 = \sigma_2$. $H_1: \sigma_1 > \sigma_2$. Test statistic: $F = 9.3364$. P-value: 0.0000. Critical F value: 2.0842 (Table: Critical F value is between 2.0540 and 2.0960). Reject H_0. There is sufficient evidence to support the claim that the treatment group has errors that vary more than the errors of the placebo group.

7. $H_0: \sigma_1 = \sigma_2$. $H_1: \sigma_1 \neq \sigma_2$. Test statistic: $F = 1.7778$. P-value: 0.0762. Upper critical F value: 1.8907 (Table: Critical F value is between 1.8752 and 2.0739). Fail to reject H_0. There is not sufficient evidence to warrant rejection of the claim that subjects from both treatment groups have ages with the same amount of variation. If treatment groups have different characteristics, comparisons of treatments become unclear, because differences might be due to the treatments or they might be due to the different group characteristics.

9. $H_0: \sigma_1 = \sigma_2$. $H_1: \sigma_1 > \sigma_2$. Test statistic: $F = 2.1267$. P-value: 0.0543. Critical F value: 2.1682 (Table: Critical F value is between 2.1555 and 2.2341). Fail to reject H_0. There is not sufficient evidence to support the claim that those given a sham treatment have pain reductions that vary more than the pain reductions for those treated with magnets.

11. $H_0: \sigma_1 = \sigma_2$. $H_1: \sigma_1 > \sigma_2$. Test statistic: $F = 3.7539$. P-value: 0.0400. Critical F value: 3.4445. Reject H_0. There is sufficient evidence to support the claim that king-size cigarettes with filters have amounts of nicotine that vary more than the amounts of nicotine in non-filtered king-size cigarettes.

13. $H_0: \sigma_1 = \sigma_2$. $H_1: \sigma_1 > \sigma_2$. Test statistic: $F = 0.8825$. P-value: 0.034. Critical F value: $= 1.6584$ (Table: Critical F value is between 1.6428 and 1.7215). Fail to reject H_0. There is not sufficient evidence to support the claim that men have body temperatures that vary more than the body temperatures of women.

15. $H_0: \sigma_1 = \sigma_2$. $H_1: \sigma_1 \neq \sigma_2$. Test statistic: $F = 4.3103$. P-value: 0.0023. Upper critical F value: 2.5308 (Table: Critical F value is between 2.4665 and 2.5699). Reject H_0. There is sufficient evidence to warrant rejection of the claim that both populations of longevity times have the same variation.

17. $c_1 = 3$, $c_2 = 0$, critical value is 7.4569. Fail to reject H_0. There is not sufficient evidence to support a claim that the two populations of scores have different amounts of variation.

19. $F_L = 0.4103$; $F_R = 2.7006$

Chapter 9: Quick Quiz

1. $H_0: p_1 = p_2$. $H_1: p_1 \neq p_2$.
2. $x_1 = 258$, $x_2 = 282$, $\hat{p}_1 = 258/1121 = 0.230$, $\hat{p}_2 = 282/1084 = 0.260$, $\bar{p} = 0.245$.
3. 0.1010
4. a. $-0.0659 < p_1 - p_2 < 0.00591$
   b. The confidence interval includes the value of 0, so it is possible that the two proportions are equal. There is not a significant difference.

5. Fail to reject H_0. There is not sufficient evidence to warrant rejection of the claim that for the people who were aware of the statement, the proportion of women is equal to the proportion of men.
6. True
7. False
8. Because the data consist of matched pairs, they are dependent.
9. $H_0: \mu_d = 0$. $H_1: \mu_d \neq 0$.
10. a. $t = \dfrac{\bar{d} - \mu_d}{\dfrac{s_d}{\sqrt{n}}}$ b. $t = \dfrac{(\bar{x}_1 - \bar{x}_2) - (\mu_1 - \mu_2)}{\sqrt{\dfrac{s_1^2}{n_1} + \dfrac{s_2^2}{n_2}}}$

    c. $z = \dfrac{(\hat{p}_1 - \hat{p}_2) - (p_1 - p_2)}{\sqrt{\dfrac{\bar{p}\bar{q}}{n_1} + \dfrac{\bar{p}\bar{q}}{n_2}}}$ d. $F = \dfrac{s_1^2}{s_2^2}$

Chapter 9: Review Exercises

1. $H_0: p_1 = p_2$. $H_1: p_1 \neq p_2$. Test statistic: $z = -4.20$. P-value: 0.0000 (Table: 0.0002). Critical values: $z = \pm 2.576$ (Table: ± 2.575). Reject H_0. There is sufficient evidence to warrant rejection of the claim that the acceptance rate is the same with or without blinding. Without blinding, reviewers know the names and institutions of the abstract authors, and they might be influenced by that knowledge.

2. $-0.0372 < p_1 - p_2 < -0.00892$. The confidence interval limits do not contain 0, so it appears that there is a significant difference between the two proportions.

3. $-25.33 \text{ cm} < (\mu_1 - \mu_2) < -7.51 \text{ cm}$ (Table: $-25.70 \text{ cm} < (\mu_1 - \mu_2) < -7.14 \text{ cm}$). With 95% confidence, we conclude that the mean height of women is less than the mean height of men by an amount that is between 7.51 cm and 25.33 cm (Table: 7.14 cm and 25.70 cm).

4. $H_0: \mu_1 = \mu_2$. $H_1: \mu_1 < \mu_2$. Test statistic: $t = -4.001$. P-value: 0.0008 (Table: <0.005). Critical value: -2.666 (Table: -2.821). Reject H_0. There is sufficient evidence to support the claim that women have heights with a mean that is less than the mean height of men.

5. a. $H_0: \mu_d = 0 \text{ kg}$. $H_1: \mu_d \neq 0 \text{ kg}$. Test statistic: $t = 2.301$. P-value: 0.0469. Critical values: $t = \pm 2.262$ (assuming a 0.05 significance level). Reject H_0 (assuming a 0.05 significance level). There is sufficient evidence to conclude that there is a difference between pre-training and post-training weights.
   b. $0.0 \text{ kg} < \mu_d < 4.0 \text{ kg}$

6. $H_0: \sigma_1 = \sigma_2$. $H_1: \sigma_1 \neq \sigma_2$. Test statistic: $F = 4.9933$. P-value: 0.0252. Upper critical F value: 4.0260. Reject H_0. There is sufficient evidence to warrant rejection of the claim that women and men have heights with the same variation.

Chapter 9: Cumulative Review Exercises

1. a. Because the sample data are matched with each column consisting of heights from the same family, the data are dependent.
   b. $\bar{x} = 69.7$ in.; median $= 71.0$ in.; range $= 7.7$ in.; $s = 2.6$ in.; $s^2 = 6.6$ in^2
   c. Ratio   d. Continuous

2. There does not appear to be a correlation or association between the heights of fathers and the heights of their sons.

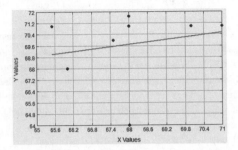

3. 67.6 in. $< \mu <$ 71.9 in. We have 95% confidence that the limits of 67.6 in. and 71.9 in. actually contain the true value of the mean height of all adult sons.

4. $H_0: \mu_d = 0$ in. $H_1: \mu_d \neq 0$ in. Test statistic: $t = -1.712$. P-value = 0.1326 (Table: >0.10). Critical values: $t = \pm 2.365$. Fail to reject H_0. There is not sufficient evidence to warrant rejection of the claim that differences between heights of fathers and their sons have a mean of 0. There does not appear to be a difference between heights of fathers and their sons.

5. Because the points lie reasonably close to a straight-line pattern, and there is no other pattern that is not a straight-line pattern and there are no outliers, the sample data appear to be from a population with a normal distribution.

6. The shape of the histogram indicates that the sample data appear to be from a population with a distribution that is approximately normal.

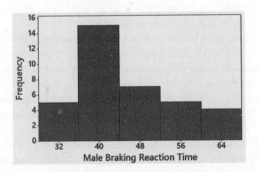

7. Because the points are reasonably close to a straight-line pattern and there is no other pattern that is not a straight-line pattern, it appears that the braking reaction times of females are from a population with a normal distribution.

8. Because the boxplots overlap, there does not appear to be a significant difference between braking reaction times of males and females, but the braking reaction times for males appear to be generally lower than the braking reaction times of females.

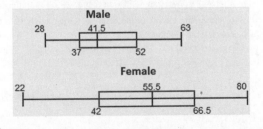

9. $H_0: \mu_1 = \mu_2$. $H_1: \mu_1 \neq \mu_2$. Test statistic: $t = -3.259$. P-value = 0.0019 (Table: <0.005). Critical values: $t = \pm 2.664$ (Table: ± 2.724). Reject H_0. There is sufficient evidence to warrant rejection of the claim that males and females have the same mean braking reaction time. Males appear to have lower reaction times.

10. a. Males: 40.1 $< \mu <$ 48.7. Females: 47.2 $< \mu <$ 61.4. The confidence intervals overlap, so there does not appear to be a significant difference between the mean braking reaction times of males and females.

b. $-18.0 < \mu_1 - \mu_2 < -1.8$
(Table: $-18.2 < \mu_1 - \mu_2 < -1.6$). Because the confidence interval consists of negative numbers and does not include 0, there appears to be a significant difference between the mean braking reaction times of males and females.

c. The results from part (b) are better.

Chapter 10 Answers

Section 10-1

1. a. r is a statistic that represents the value of the linear correlation coefficient computed from the paired sample data, and ρ is a parameter that represents the value of the linear correlation coefficient that would be computed by using all of the paired data in the population of all statistics students.

b. The value of r is estimated to be 0, because it is likely that there is no correlation between body temperature and head circumference.

c. The value of r does not change if the body temperatures are converted to Fahrenheit degrees.

3. No. A correlation between two variables indicates that they are somehow associated, but that association does not necessarily imply that one of the variables has a direct effect on the other variable. Correlation does not imply causality.

5. Yes. $r = 0.963$. P-value = 0.000. Critical values: ± 0.268 (Table: ± 0.279 approximately). There is sufficient evidence to support the claim that there is a linear correlation between the weights of bears and their chest sizes. It is easier to measure the chest size of a bear than the weight, which would require lifting the bear onto a scale. It does appear that chest size could be used to predict weight.

7. Yes. $r = 0.552$. P-value <0.0001. Critical values are approximately -0.196 and 0.196. There is sufficient evidence to support the claim that there is a linear correlation between the heights of fathers and the heights of their sons.

9. a.

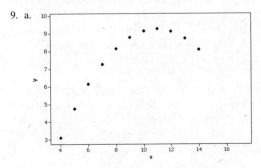

b. $r = 0.816$. P-value $= 0.002$ (Table: <0.01). Critical values: $r = \pm 0.602$ assuming a 0.05 significance level. There is sufficient evidence to support the claim of a linear correlation between the two variables.

c. The scatterplot reveals a distinct pattern that is not a straight-line pattern.

11. a. Answer varies. Because there appears to be an upward pattern, it is reasonable to think that there is a linear correlation.

b. $r = 0.906$. P-value $= 0.000$ (Table: <0.01). Critical values: $r = \pm 0.632$ (for a 0.05 significance level). There is sufficient evidence to support the claim of a linear correlation.

c. $r = 0$. P-value $= 1.000$ (Table: >0.05). Critical values: $r = \pm 0.666$ (for a 0.05 significance level). There is not sufficient evidence to support the claim of a linear correlation.

d. The effect from a single pair of values can be very substantial, and it can change the conclusion.

13. $r = -0.206$. P-value $= 0.543$ (Table: >0.05). Critical values: $r = \pm 0.602$. There is not sufficient evidence to support the claim that there is a linear correlation between pulse rates and systolic blood pressure. It does not appear that people with high systolic blood pressure have high pulse rate.

15. $r = 0.128$. P-value $= 0.837$ (Table: >0.05). Critical values: $r = \pm 0.878$. There is not sufficient evidence to support the claim that there is a linear correlation between shoe print lengths and heights of females. The given results do not suggest that police can use a shoe print length to estimate the height of females.

17. $r = -0.959$. P-value $= 0.010$. Critical values: $r = \pm 0.878$. There is sufficient evidence to support the claim that there is a linear correlation between weights of lemon imports from Mexico and U.S. car fatality rates. The results do not suggest any cause-effect relationship between the two variables.

19. $r = 0.028$. P-value $= 0.932$ (Table: >0.05). Critical values: $r = \pm 0.576$. There is not sufficient evidence to support the claim that there is a linear correlation between pulse rates and systolic blood pressures of adult females.

21. $r = 0.948$. P-value $= 0.004$ (Table: <0.01). Critical values: $r = \pm 0.811$. There is sufficient evidence to support the claim of a linear correlation between the overhead width of a seal in a photograph and the weight of a seal.

23. $r = 0.113$. P-value $= 0.700$ (Table: >0.05). Critical values: $r = \pm 0.532$. There is not sufficient evidence to support the claim that there is a linear correlation between heights of winning presidential candidates and heights of their main opponents. In an ideal world, voters would focus on important issues and not height or physical appearance of candidates, so there should not be a correlation.

25. $r = -0.063$. P-value $= 0.791$ (Table: >0.05). Critical values: $r = \pm 0.444$. There is not sufficient evidence to support the claim that there is a linear correlation between IQ scores and brain volumes.

27. $r = 0.594$. P-value $= 0.007$ (Table: <0.01). Critical values: $r = \pm 0.456$. There is sufficient evidence to support the claim that there is a linear correlation between shoe print lengths and heights of males. The given results do suggest that police can use a shoe print length to estimate the height of a male.

29. $r = -0.16217$. (In this exercise, extra decimal places are needed for r and the P-value. Table A-6 is not adequate to determine the critical values and P-value for this exercise.) P-value $= 0.0497$. Critical values: $r = \pm 0.16197$. There is sufficient evidence to support the claim that there is a linear correlation between pulse rates and systolic blood pressures of adult females.

31. $r = 0.748$. (Table A-6 is not adequate to determine the critical values and P-value for this exercise.) P-value $= 0.000$. Critical values: ± 0.105. There is sufficient evidence to support the claim that there is a linear correlation between right ear threshold measurements and left ear threshold measurements.

33. a. 0.911   b. 0.787   c. 0.9999 (largest)
d. 0.976   e. -0.948

Section 10-2

1. a. $\hat{y} = 4.915 + 0.3585x$
b. $\hat{y}$ represents the predicted value of white blood cell count.

3. a. A residual is a value of $y - \hat{y}$, which is the difference between an observed value of y and a predicted value of y.
b. The regression line has the property that the sum of squares of the residuals is the lowest possible sum.

5. With a significant linear correlation, the best predicted value is $\hat{y} = 34.656$ cm.

7. With no significant linear correlation, the best predicted value is 32.036 cm.

9. $\hat{y} = 3.00 + 0.500x$. The data have a pattern that is not a straight line.

11. a. $\hat{y} = 0.264 + 0.906x$
b. $\hat{y} = 2 + 0x$ (or $\hat{y} = 2$)
c. The results are very different, indicating that one point can dramatically affect the regression equation.

13. $\hat{y} = 134.6 - 0.1754x$. Best predicted value: $\bar{y} = 122.91$.

15. $\hat{y} = 58.54 + 4.059x$. Best predicted value: $\bar{y} = 166.1$ cm. Because the best predicted value is the mean height, it would not be helpful to police in trying to obtain a description of the female.

17. $\hat{y} = 16.5 - 0.00282x$. Best predicted value: 15.1 fatalities per 100,000 population. Common sense suggests that the prediction doesn't make much sense.

19. $\hat{y} = 20.84 - 0.6915x$. Best predicted value: 68.9 cm.

21. $\hat{y} = -157 + 40.2x$. Best predicted value: -76.6 kg. The prediction is a negative weight that cannot be correct. The overhead width of 2 cm is well beyond the scope of the sample widths, so the extrapolation might be off by a considerable amount. Clearly, the predicted negative weight makes no sense.

23. $\hat{y} = 162 + 0.0975x$. Best predicted height: $\bar{y} = 179.7$ cm. Heights of opponents do not appear to be predicted well by using the heights of the presidents.

25. $\hat{y} = 137.3 - 0.2x$. Best predicted value: $\bar{y} = 123.0$.

27. $\hat{y} = 93.5 + 2.85x$. Best predicted value: 182.7 cm. Although there is a linear correlation, with $r = 0.594$, we see that it is not very strong, so an estimate of the height of a male might be off by a considerable amount.

29. $\hat{y} = 138 - 0.223x$. Best predicted value: 120 mm Hg.

31. $\hat{y} = 4.67 + 0.758x$. Best predicted value: 19.8.

33. a. 12.28
b. The sum of squares of the residuals is 15.71, which is larger than 12.28.

Section 10-3

1. The value of $s_e = 20.31678$ cm is the standard error of estimate, which is a measure of the differences between the observed weights and the weights predicted from the regression equation. It is a measure of the variation of the sample points about the regression line.

3. The coefficient of determination is $r^2 = 0.060$. We know that 6% of the variation in weight is explained by the linear correlation between height and weight, and 94% of the variation in weight is explained by other factors and/or random variation.

5. $r^2 = 0.764$. 76.4% of the variation in temperature is explained by the linear correlation between chirps and temperature, and 23.6% of the variation in temperature is explained by other factors and/or random variation.

7. $r^2 = 0.872$. 87.2% of the variation in weights of bears is explained by the linear correlation between neck size and weight, and 12.8% of the variation in weights is explained by other factors and/or random variation.

9. $r = 0.850$. Critical values: $r = \pm 0.404$ (Table: $r = \pm 0.396$ approximately), assuming a 0.05 significance level. There is sufficient evidence to support a claim of a linear correlation between registered boats and manatee fatalities.

11. 70.5 manatees
13. 42.7 manatees $< y <$ 98.3 manatees
15. 65.1 manatees $< y <$ 106.8 manatees
17. a. 652.4986   b. 1039.1005
    c. 53.7 mm Hg $< y <$ 101.3 mm Hg
19. a. 352.7278   b. 109.3722   c. 71.09°F $< y <$ 88.71°F
21. a. 6.5 $< y <$ 7.2   b. 6.2 $< y <$ 6.8

Section 10-4

1. The response variable is neck and the predictor variables are head length and head width.

3. The unadjusted R^2 increases (or remains the same) as more variables are included, but the adjusted R^2 is adjusted for the number of variables and sample size. The unadjusted R^2 incorrectly suggests that the best multiple regression equation is obtained by including all of the available variables, but by taking into account the sample size and number of predictor variables, the adjusted R^2 is much more helpful in weeding out variables that should not be included.

5. Son $= 18.0 + 0.504$ Father $+ 0.277$ Mother

7. P-value less than 0.0001 is low, but the values of R^2 (0.3649) and adjusted R^2 (0.3552) are not high. Although the multiple regression equation fits the sample data best, it is not a good fit, so it should not be used for predicting the height of a son based on the height of his father and the height of his mother.

9. Waist circumference, because it has the highest adjusted R^2 value and the P-values are the same for the three individual variables.

11. Some subjective judgment is involved here. A good choice would be to use all three variables because the adjusted R^2 value of 0.939 is considerably higher than any of the other values of adjusted R^2. With this reasoning, the best regression equation is $\hat{y} = -147 + 0.632$ HT $+ 0.697$ WAIST $+ 1.58$ ARM.

13. The best regression equation is $\hat{y} = 0.127 + 0.0878x_1 - 0.0250x_2$, where x_1 represents tar and x_2 represents carbon

monoxide. It is best because it has the highest adjusted R^2 value of 0.927 and the lowest P-value of 0.000. It is a good regression equation for predicting nicotine content because it has a high value of adjusted R^2 and a low P-value.

15. There are three possible regression equations corresponding to predictor variables of (1) brain volume; (2) body weight; (3) brain volume and body weight. The best regression equation is $\hat{y} = 109 - 0.00670x_1$, where x_1 represents brain volume. It is best because it has the highest adjusted R^2 value of 0.0513 and the lowest P-value of 0.791. The three regression equations all have adjusted values of R^2 that are very close to 0, so none of them are good for predicting IQ. It does not appear that people with larger brains have higher IQ scores.

17. For H_0: $\beta_1 = 0$, the test statistic is $t = 10.814$, the P-value is less than 0.0001, so reject H_0 and conclude that the regression coefficient of $b_1 = 0.769$ should be kept. For H_0: $\beta_2 = 0$, the test statistic is $t = 29.856$, the P-value is less than 0.0001, so reject H_0 and conclude that the regression coefficient of $b_2 = 1.01$ should be kept. It appears that the regression equation should include both of the independent variables of height and waist circumference.

Section 10-5

1. A dummy variable is a variable having only two values and those values (such as 0 and 1) are used to represent the different categories of a qualitative variable.

3. With simple logistic regression, there is only one predictor variable, but with multiple logistic regression, there are two or more predictor variables.

5. Head length and head width are predictor variables. The response variable is sex, which is a dummy variable.

7. The probability that the bear is a female is 0.235. The probability that the bear is a male is 0.765.

9. Weight $= 3.06 + 82.4$(Sex) $+ 2.91$(AGE). Female: 61 lb; male: 144 lb. The sex of the bear does appear to have an effect on its weight. The regression equation indicates that the predicted weight of a male bear is about 82 lb more than the predicted weight of a female bear with other characteristics being the same.

11. $\ln\left(\dfrac{p}{1-p}\right) = -41.2 + 0.250(\text{Height}) - 0.00856(\text{Weight})$.
The probability of a male is 0.629.

13. $\ln\left(\dfrac{p}{1-p}\right) = -101.5 + 1.91(\text{Foot Length}) + 0.301(\text{Height})$.
The probability of a male is 0.9999.

Chapter 10: Chapter Quick Quiz

1. Conclude that there is not sufficient evidence to support the claim of a linear correlation between the systolic blood pressure measurements of the right and left arms.

2. None of the given values change when the variables are switched.

3. The value of r does not change if all values of one of the variables are multiplied by the same constant.

4. Because r must be between -1 and 1 inclusive, the value of 1.500 is the result of an error in the calculations.

5. The best predicted value is 163.2 mm Hg, which is the mean of the five measurements for the left arm.

6. The best predicted value is 174.6 mm Hg, which is found by substituting 100 for x in the regression equation.

7. $r^2 = 0.752$

8. False.

9. False.

10. $r = -1$

Chapter 10: Review Exercises

1. a. $r = 0.962$. P-value $= 0.000$ (Table: <0.01). Critical values: $r = \pm 0.707$ (assuming a 0.05 significance level). There is sufficient evidence to support the claim that there is a linear correlation between the amount of tar and the amount of nicotine.

   b. 92.5%

   c. $\hat{y} = -0.758 + 0.0920x$

   d. The predicted value is 1.358 mg, or 1.4 mg rounded, which is close to the actual amount of 1.3 mg.

2. a. The scatterplot shows a pattern with nicotine and CO both increasing from left to right, but it is a very weak pattern and the points are not very close to a straight-line pattern, so it appears that there is not sufficient sample evidence to support the claim of a linear correlation between amounts of nicotine and carbon monoxide.

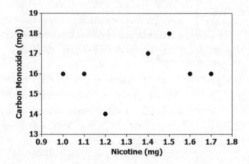

   b. $r = 0.329$. P-value $= 0.427$ (Table: >0.05). Critical values: $r = \pm 0.707$ (assuming a 0.05 significance level). There is not sufficient evidence to support the claim that there is a linear correlation between amount of nicotine and amount of carbon monoxide.

   c. $\hat{y} = 14.2 + 1.42x$

   d. The predicted value is $\bar{y} = 16.1$ mg, which is close to the actual amount of 15 mg.

3. a. The scatterplot shows a pattern with amounts of tar and carbon monoxide both increasing from left to right, but it is a very weak pattern and the points are not very close to a straight-line pattern, so it appears that there is not sufficient sample evidence to support the claim of a linear correlation between amounts of tar and carbon monoxide.

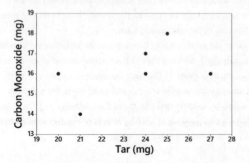

   b. Three of the original pairs of sample data are the same (20, 16), so those three points are at the same location and they appear to be one point.

   c. $r = 0.437$. P-value $= 0.279$ (Table: >0.05). Critical values: $r = \pm 0.707$ (assuming a 0.05 significance level). There is not sufficient evidence to support the claim that there is a linear correlation between amounts of tar and carbon monoxide.

   d. $\hat{y} = 12.0 + 0.181x$

   e. The predicted value is $\bar{y} = 16.1$ mg, which is close to the actual amount of 15 mg.

4. a. NICOTINE $= -0.443 + 0.0968$ TAR $- 0.0262$ CO, or $\hat{y} = -0.443 + 0.0968x_1 - 0.0262x_2$.

   b. $R^2 = 0.936$; adjusted $R^2 = 0.910$; P-value $= 0.001$.

   c. With high values of R^2 and adjusted R^2 and a small P-value of 0.001, it appears that the regression equation can be used to predict the amount of nicotine given the amounts of tar and carbon monoxide.

   d. The predicted value is 1.39 mg, or 1.4 mg rounded, which is close to the actual value of 1.3 mg of nicotine.

5. $r = 0.450$. P-value $= 0.192$ (Table >0.05). Critical values: $r = \pm 0.632$ (assuming a 0.05 significance level). There is not sufficient evidence to support the claim that there is a linear correlation between time and population size. Although there is no *linear* correlation between time and population size, the scatterplot shows a very distinct pattern revealing that time and population size are associated by a function that is not linear.

6. $\ln\left(\dfrac{p}{1-p}\right) = -44.4 + 0.557(\text{Temp. at 8 AM}) - 0.098(\text{Temp. at 12 AM})$.

   The probability that the subject smokes is 0.667. Because the regression equation has the high overall P-value of 0.521, the predicted value is not likely to be very accurate.

Chapter 10: Cumulative Review Exercises

1. $\bar{x} = 3.3$ lb, $s = 5.7$ lb

2. The highest weight before the diet is 212 lb, which converts to $z = 1.55$. The highest weight is not significantly high because its z score of 1.55 shows that it is within 2 standard deviations of the mean.

3. H_0: $\mu_d = 0$. H_1: $\mu_d > 0$. Test statistic: $t = 1.613$. P-value $= 0.0754$ (Table: >0.05). Critical value: $t = 1.895$. Fail to reject H_0. There is not sufficient evidence to support the claim that the diet is effective.

4. 161.8 lb $< \mu <$ 197.0 lb. We have 95% confidence that the interval limits of 161.8 lb and 197.0 lb contain the true value of the mean of the population of all subjects before the diet.

5. a. $r = 0.965$. P-value $= 0.0001$. Critical values: $r = \pm 0.707$ (assuming a 0.05 significance level). There is sufficient evidence to support the claim that there is a linear correlation between before and after weights.

   b. $r = 1$ c. $r = 1$

   d. The effectiveness of the diet is determined by the amounts of weight lost, but the linear correlation coefficient is not sensitive to different amounts of weight loss. Correlation is not a suitable tool for testing the effectiveness of the diet.

6. a. 43.58% (Table: 43.64%)   b. 2785.6 g (Table: 2786.4 g)
   c. 5.00%. Yes, many of the babies do require special treatment.
7. a. No. Correlation can be used to investigate an association between the two variables, not whether differences between values of the two variables are significant.
   b. Test statistic: $t = 1.185$. P-value: 0.2663 (Table: >0.20). Critical values: $t = \pm 2.262$. Fail to reject H_0: $\mu_d = 0$. There is not sufficient evidence to warrant rejection of the claim that position has no effect. Position does not appear to have a significant effect.
8. There must be an error, because the rates of 13.7% and 10.6% are not possible with sample sizes of 100.

Chapter 11 Answers

Section 11-1

1. a. Observed values are represented by O and expected values are represented by E.
   b. For the leading digit of 2, $O = 62$ and $E = (317)(0.176) = 55.792$.
   c. For the leading digit of 2, $(O-E)^2/E = 0.691$.
3. There is sufficient evidence to warrant rejection of the claim that the leading digits have a distribution that fits well with Benford's law.
5. Test statistic: $X^2 = 0.523$. P-value = 0.9712 (Table: >0.95). Critical value: $X^2 = 9.488$. There is not sufficient evidence to warrant rejection of the claim that injuries and illnesses occur with equal frequency on the different days of the week.
7. Test statistic: $X^2 = 47.200$. P-value = 0.0000. Critical value: $X^2 = 19.675$. There is sufficient evidence to warrant rejection of the claim that motorcycle fatalities occur with equal frequencies in the different months. Fatalities might be lower in winter months when colder weather is associated with substantially less use of motorcycles.
9. Test statistic: $X^2 = 93.072$. P-value = 0.000 (Table: <0.005). Critical value: $X^2 = 19.675$. There is sufficient evidence to warrant rejection of the claim that American-born Major League Baseball players are born in different months with the same frequency. The sample data appear to support Gladwell's claim.
11. Test statistic: $X^2 = 9.288$. P-value = 0.0064. (Table: >0.005). Critical Value: $x^2 = 5.991$. There is sufficient evidence to warrant rejection of the claim that the actual frequencies correspond to the predicted distribution.
13. Test statistic: $X^2 = 524.713$. P-value = 0.000 (Table: <0.005). Critical value: $X^2 = 13.277$. There is sufficient evidence to warrant rejection of the claim that the distribution of clinical trial participants fits well with the population distribution. Hispanics have an observed frequency of 60 and an expected frequency of 391.027, so they are very underrepresented. Also, the Asian/Pacific Islander subjects have an observed frequency of 54 and an expected frequency of 163.286, so they are also underrepresented.
15. Test statistic: $X^2 = 21.886$. P-value = 0.035 (Table: >0.01). Critical Value: $X^2 = 20.090$. There is sufficient evidence to warrant rejection of the claim that the leading digits are from a population with a distribution that conforms to Benford's Law. It does not appear that the image has been corrupted.
17. Test statistic: $X^2 = 9.500$. P-value = 0.147 (Table: >0.10). Critical value: $X^2 = 16.812$. There is not sufficient evidence to support the claim that births do not occur on the seven different days of the week with equal frequency.
19. a. 26, 46, 49, 26
    b. 0.2023, 0.3171, 0.3046, 0.1761 (Table: 0.2033, 0.3166, 0.3039, 0.1762)
    c. 29.7381, 46.6137, 44.7762, 25.8867 (Table: 29.8851, 46.5402, 44.6733, 25.9014)
    d. Test statistic: $X^2 = 0.877$ (Table: 0.931). P-value = 0.831 (Table: >0.10). Critical value: $X^2 = 11.345$. There is not sufficient evidence to warrant rejection of the claim that heights were randomly selected from a normally distributed population. The test suggests that we cannot rule out the possibility that the data are from a normally distributed population.

Section 11-2

1. a. $E = 4.173$
   b. Because the expected frequency of a cell is less than 5, the requirements for the hypothesis test are not satisfied.
3. Test statistic: $X^2 = 64.517$. P-value: 0.000. Reject the null hypothesis of independence between handedness and cell phone ear preference.
5. Test statistic: $X^2 = 9.750$. P-value = 0.002 (Table: <0.005). Critical value: $X^2 = 6.635$. There is sufficient evidence to warrant rejection of the claim that success is independent of the type of treatment. The results suggest that the surgery treatment is better.
7. Test statistic: $X^2 = 0.751$. P-value = 0.3862 (Table: >0.10). Critical value: $X^2 = 3.841$. There is not sufficient evidence to warrant rejection of the claim of independence between the type of restoration and adverse health conditions. Amalgam restorations do not appear to affect health conditions.
9. Test statistic: $X^2 = 34.345$. P-value = 0.0000. Critical value: $X^2 = 6.635$. There is sufficient evidence to warrant rejection of the claim that the source of the sample is independent of the dog's selections. The results suggest that the dogs have some ability to detect bladder cancer, but they did not do well enough for accurate diagnoses.
11. Test statistic: $X^2 = 9.854$. P-value = 0.0017 (Table: <0.005). Critical value: $X^2 = 6.635$. There is sufficient evidence to warrant rejection of the claim that nausea is independent of whether the subject took a placebo or Chantix. It appears that nausea is more likely to occur among those who use Chantix, so nausea is a concern. However, the rate of nausea among Chantix users is only about 3.7%, so it is not much of a concern.
13. Test statistic: $X^2 = 18.773$. P-value = 0.000 (Table: <0.005). Critical value: $X^2 = 3.841$. There is sufficient evidence to warrant rejection of the claim of independence between texting while driving and irregular seat belt use. Those two risky behaviors appear to be somehow related.
15. Test statistic: $X^2 = 42.568$. P-value = 0.0000 (Table: <0.005). Critical value: $X^2 = 9.210$. There is sufficient evidence to warrant rejection of the claim that experiencing an adverse reaction in the digestive system is independent of the treatment group. Treatments with 1332 mg doses of Campral appear to be associated with an increase in adverse effects of the digestive system.

17. Test statistic: $\chi^2 = 1.358$. P-value $= 0.715$ (Table: >0.10). Critical value: $\chi^2 = 7.815$ (assuming a 0.05 significance level). There is not sufficient evidence to warrant rejection of the claim that the amount of smoking is independent of seat belt use. The theory is not supported by the given data.

19. Test statistic: $\chi^2 = 9.971$. P-value $= 0.041$ (Table: <0.05). Critical value: $\chi^2 = 9.488$ (assuming a 0.05 significance level). There is sufficient evidence to warrant rejection of the claim that injuries are independent of helmet color. It appears that motorcycle drivers should use yellow or orange helmets.

21. Test statistics: $\chi^2 = 9.7504$ and $z = -3.122560496$ so that $z^2 = \chi^2$. Critical values: $\chi^2 = 6.635$ and $z = 2.57583$ (Table: ± 2.575) so $z^2 = \chi^2$.

Chapter 11: Quick Quiz

1. $H_0: p_0 = p_1 = \ldots = p_9$. H_1: At least one of the probabilities is different from the others.
2. $O = 27$ and $E = 30$
3. Right-tailed
4. df $= 9$
5. There is not sufficient evidence to warrant rejection of the claim that the last digits are equally likely. Because reported heights would likely include more last digits of 0 and 5, it appears that the heights were measured instead of reported. (Also, most U.S. residents would have difficulty reporting heights in centimeters, because the United States, Liberia, and Myanmar are the only countries that continue to use the Imperial system of measurement.)
6. H_0: Surviving the sinking is independent of whether the person is a man, woman, boy, or girl.
   H_1: Surviving the sinking and whether the person is a man, woman, boy, or girl are somehow related.
7. Chi-square distribution.
8. Right-tailed
9. df $= 3$
10. There is sufficient evidence to warrant rejection of the claim that surviving the sinking is independent of whether the person is a man, woman, boy, or girl. Most of the women survived, 45% of the boys survived, and most girls survived, but only about 20% of the men survived, so it appears that the rule was followed quite well.

Chapter 11: Review Exercises

1. Test statistic: $\chi^2 = 269.147$. P-value $= 0.000$ (Table: <0.005). Critical value: $\chi^2 = 24.725$. There is sufficient evidence to warrant rejection of the claim that weather-related deaths occur in the different months with the same frequency. The months of May, June, and July appear to have disproportionately more weather-related deaths, and that is probably due to the fact that vacations and outdoor activities are much greater during those months.
2. Test statistic: $\chi^2 = 71.679$. P-value $= 0.0000$ (Table: <0.005). Critical value: $\chi^2 = 3.841$. There is sufficient evidence to warrant rejection of the claim that getting norovirus infection is independent of the ship. It appears that an outbreak of norovirus infection has a different effect on different ships.
3. Test statistic: $\chi^2 = 10.375$. P-value $= 0.4970$ (Table: >0.10). Critical value: $\chi^2 = 19.675$. There is not sufficient evidence to warrant rejection of the claim that homicides in New York City are equally likely for each of the 12 months. There is not sufficient evidence to support the police commissioner's claim that homicides occur more often in the summer when the weather is warmer.

4. Test statistic: $\chi^2 = 784.647$. P-value $= 0.0000$ (Table: <0.005). Critical value: $\chi^2 = 11.345$. There is sufficient evidence to warrant rejection of the claim that left-handedness is independent of parental handedness. It appears that handedness of the parents has an effect on handedness of the offspring, so left-handedness appears to be an inherited trait.
5. Test statistic: $\chi^2 = 53.051$. P-value $= 0.0000$ (Table: <0.005). Critical value: $\chi^2 = 7.815$. There is sufficient evidence to warrant rejection of the claim that the distribution of crashes is the same as the distribution of ages. Drivers under 25 appear to have disproportionately more crashes.

Chapter 11: Cumulative Review Exercises

1. $\bar{x} = 53.7$ years, median $= 60.0$ years, $s = 16.1$ years, $s^2 = 258.9$ years^2. Because an age of 16 is more than 2 standard deviations below the mean of 53.7 years, it is significantly low.
2. 42.2 years $< \mu < 65.2$ years. Yes, the confidence interval limits do contain the value of 65.0 years that was found from a sample of 9269 ICU patients.
3. Test statistic: $\chi^2 = 10.708$. P-value $= 0.0011$ (Table: <0.005). Critical value: $\chi^2 = 3.841$. There is sufficient evidence to warrant rejection of the claim that wearing a helmet has no effect on whether facial injuries are received. It does appear that a helmet is helpful in preventing facial injuries in a crash.
4. a. $349/531$ or 0.657
   b. 0.0450
   c. 0.787
5. a. 630 mm
   b. 14.48 (Table: 14.46%). That percentage is too high, because too many women would not be accommodated.
   c. 0.7599 (Table: 0.7611). Groups of 16 women do not occupy a driver's seat or cockpit; because *individual* women occupy the driver's seat/cockpit, this result has no effect on the design.
6. Determine whether there is a linear correlation between systolic blood pressure and waist. $r = 0.289$. P-value $= 0.5791$ (Table: >0.05). Critical values: $r = \pm 0.8114$. There is not sufficient evidence to support the claim that for females, there is a linear correlation between systolic blood pressure and waist.

Chapter 12 Answers

Section 12-1

1. a. The chest deceleration measurements are categorized according to the one characteristic of size.
   b. The terminology of *analysis of variance* refers to the method used to test for equality of the three population means. That method is based on two different estimates of a common population variance.
3. The test statistic is $F = 3.288$, and the F distribution applies.
5. Test statistic: $F = 0.39$. P-value: 0.677. Fail to reject $H_0: \mu_1 = \mu_2 = \mu_3$. There is not sufficient evidence to warrant rejection of the claim that the three categories of blood lead level

have the same mean verbal IQ score. Exposure to lead does not appear to have an effect on verbal IQ scores.

7. Test statistic: $F = 0.161$. P-value: 0.852. Fail to reject $H_0: \mu_1 = \mu_2 = \mu_3$. There is not sufficient evidence to warrant rejection of the claim that the three size categories have the same mean head injury measurement. Based on the available data, the size of a car does not appear to affect head injuries.

9. Test statistic: $F = 1.304$. P-value: 0.275. Fail to reject $H_0: \mu_1 = \mu_2 = \mu_3$. There is not sufficient evidence to warrant rejection of the claim that males from the three age brackets have the same mean pulse rate. It appears that pulse rates of males are not affected by age bracket.

11. Test statistic: $F = 0.3476$. P-value: 0.7111. Fail to reject $H_0: \mu_1 = \mu_2 = \mu_3$. There is not sufficient evidence to warrant rejection of the claim that the three size categories have the same mean pelvis injury measurement. The size of a car does not appear to affect pelvis injuries.

13. Test Statistic: $F = 5.7321$, P-value: 0.0071; Reject $H_0: \mu_1 = \mu_2 = \mu_3$. There is sufficient evidence to warrant rejection of the claim that the four treatment categories yield poplar trees with the same mean weight. Although not justified by the results from analysis of variance, the treatment of fertilizer and irrigation appears to be most effective.

15. Test statistic: $F = 18.9931$. P-value: 0.0000. Reject $H_0: \mu_1 = \mu_2 = \mu_3$. There is sufficient evidence to warrant rejection of the claim that the three different types of cigarettes have the same mean amount of nicotine. Given that the king-size cigarettes have the largest mean of 1.26 mg per cigarette, compared to the other means of 0.87 mg per cigarette and 0.92 mg per cigarette, it appears that the filters do make a difference, although this conclusion is not justified by the results from analysis of variance.

17. The Tukey test results show different P-values, but they are not dramatically different. The Tukey test results suggest the same conclusions as the Bonferroni test.

Section 12-2

1. The pulse rates are categorized using *two* different factors of (1) age bracket and (2) gender.

3. a. An interaction between two factors or variables occurs if the effect of one of the factors changes for different categories of the other factor.

   b. If there is an interaction effect, we should not proceed with individual tests for effects from the row factor and column factor. If there is an interaction, we should not consider the effects of one factor without considering the effects of the other factor.

   c. Because the lines are far from parallel, the two genders have very different effects for the different age brackets, so there does appear to be an interaction between gender and age bracket.

5. For interaction, the test statistic is $F = 9.58$ and the P-value is 0.0003, so there is sufficient evidence to warrant rejection of the null hypothesis of no interaction effect. Because there appears to be an interaction between age bracket and gender, we should not proceed with a test for an effect from age bracket and a test for an effect from gender. It appears an interaction between age bracket and gender has an effect on pulse rates. (Remember,

these results are based on fabricated data used in one of the cells, so this conclusion does not necessarily correspond to real data.)

7. For interaction, the test statistic is $F = 1.7970$ and the P-value is 0.1756, so there is not sufficient evidence to conclude that there is an interaction effect. For the row variable of age bracket, the test statistic is $F = 2.0403$ and the P-value is 0.1399, so there is not sufficient evidence to conclude that age bracket has an effect on height. For the column variable of gender, the test statistic is $F = 43.4607$ and the P-value is less than 0.0001, so there is sufficient evidence to support the claim that gender has an effect on height.

9. For interaction, the test statistic is $F = 3.7332$ and the P-value is 0.0291, so there is sufficient evidence to conclude that there is an interaction effect. The measures of self-esteem appear to be affected by an interaction between the self-esteem of the subject and the self-esteem of the target. Because there appears to be an interaction effect, we should not proceed with individual tests of the row factor (target's self-esteem) and the column factor (subject's self-esteem).

11. a. Test statistics and P-values do not change.

    b. Test statistics and P-values do not change.

    c. Test statistics and P-values do not change.

    d. An outlier can dramatically affect and change test statistics and P-values.

Chapter 12: Quick Quiz

1. The sample data are partitioned into the three different categories according to the one factor of epoch.

2. $H_0: \mu_1 = \mu_2 = \mu_3$. H_1: At least one of the three population means is different from the others.

3. Test statistic: $F = 4.0497$. Larger test statistics result in smaller P-values.

4. Reject H_0. There is sufficient evidence to support the claim that the different epochs have mean skull breadths that are not all the same.

5. Right-tailed. Yes, all one-way analysis of variance tests are right-tailed.

6. No. The method of analysis of variance does not justify a conclusion that any particular mean is different from the others.

7. With one-way analysis of variance, data from the different samples are categorized using only one factor, but with two-way analysis of variance, the sample data are categorized into different cells determined by two different factors.

8. Test statistic: $F = 1.41$. P-value: 0.281. Fail to reject the null hypothesis of no interaction effect. There is not sufficient evidence to warrant rejection of the claim that head injury measurements are not affected by an interaction between the type of car (foreign, domestic) and size of the car (small, medium, large). There does not appear to be an effect from an interaction between the type of car (foreign or domestic) and whether the car is small, medium, or large.

9. Test statistic: $F = 2.25$. P-value: 0.159. Fail to reject the null hypothesis of no effect from the type of car. There is not sufficient evidence to support the claim that whether the car is foreign or domestic has an effect on head injury measurements.

10. Test statistic: $F = 0.44$. P-value: 0.655. Fail to reject the null hypothesis of no effect from the size of the car. There is not sufficient evidence to support the claim that whether the car is small, medium, or large has an effect on head injury measurements.

Chapter 12: Review Exercises

1. a. One (type of diet)
   b. One-way analysis of variance
   c. Because the P-value is high, it appears that the four samples have means that do not differ by significant amounts. It appears that the mean ages of the four treatment groups are about the same.
   d. A small P-value would indicate that at least one of the treatment groups has a mean age that is significantly different from the others, so we would not know if differences from the diet treatments are due to the diets or to differences in age. A small P-value would undermine the effectiveness of the experiment.

2. Test statistic: $F = 18.9941$. P-value: 0.000; Reject H_0: $\mu_1 = \mu_2 = \mu_3$. There is sufficient evidence to warrant rejection of the claim that the three different types of cigarettes have the same mean amount of nicotine. Given that the king-size cigarettes have the largest mean of 1.3 mg per cigarette, compared to the other means of 0.9 mg per cigarette and 0.9 mg per cigarette, it appears that the filters do make a difference, although this conclusion is not justified by the results from analysis of variance.

3. For interaction, the test statistic is $F = 1.7171$ and the P-value is 0.1940, so there is not sufficient evidence to warrant rejection of no interaction effect. There does not appear to be an interaction between femur and car size. For the row variable of femur, the test statistic is $F = 1.3896$ and the P-value is 0.2462, so there is not sufficient evidence to conclude that whether the femur is right or left has an effect on load. For the column variable of car size, the test statistic is $F = 2.2296$ and the P-value is 0.1222, so there is not sufficient evidence to warrant rejection of the claim of no effect from car size. It appears that the crash test loads are not affected by an interaction between femur and car size, they are not affected by femur, and they are not affected by car size.

4. For interaction, the test statistic is $F = 2.1018$ and the P-value is 0.1731, so there does not appear to be an effect from an interaction between gender and whether the subject smokes. For gender, the test statistic is $F = 2.1518$ and the P-value is 0.1671, so gender does not appear to have an effect on body temperature. For smoking, the test statistic is $F = 1.2110$ and the P-value is 0.2921, so there appears to be an effect from smoking on body temperature.

Chapter 12: Cumulative Review Exercises

1. a. 15.5 years, 13.1 years, 22.7 years
   b. 9.7 years, 9.0 years, 18.6 years
   c. 94.5 years^2, 80.3 years^2, 346.1 years^2
   d. Ratio

2. Test statistic: $t = -1.383$. P-value $= 0.1860$. Critical values assuming a 0.05 significance level: $t = \pm 2.123$ (Table: ± 2.160). Fail to reject H_0: $\mu_1 = \mu_2$. There is not sufficient evidence to support the claim that there is a difference between the means for the two groups.

3. Normal, because the histogram is approximately bell-shaped or the points in a normal quantile plot are reasonably close to a straight-line pattern with no other pattern that is not a straight-line pattern.

4. 12.3 years $< \mu < 18.7$ years. We have 95% confidence that the limits of 12.3 years and 18.7 years contain the true value of the population mean.

5. a. H_0: $\mu_1 = \mu_2 = \mu_3$
   b. Because the P-value of 0.051 is greater than the significance level of 0.05, fail to reject the null hypothesis of equal means. There is not sufficient evidence to warrant rejection of the claim that the three means are equal. The three populations do not appear to have means that are significantly different.

6. a. $r = 0.992$. Critical values: $r = \pm 0.707$. P-value $= 0.0002$. There is sufficient evidence to support the claim that there is a linear correlation between September weights and the subsequent April weights.
   b. $\hat{y} = 13.09 + 0.844x$
   c. $13.09 + 0.844(70) = 72.17$ kg, which is very close to the actual April weight of 73 kg.

7. a. 0.1587
   b. 0.6827 (Table: 0.6826)
   c. 0.9987
   d. 334.7 (Table: 334.6)

8. a. 200
   b. $0.175 < p < 0.225$
   c. Yes. The confidence interval shows us that we have 95% confidence that the true population proportion is contained within the limits of 0.175 and 0.225, and $1/4$ or 0.25 is not included within that range.

9. Using normal as approximation to binomial: 0.1020. (Exact result using technology: 0.0995.) Assuming that one-quarter of all offspring have blue eyes, the probability of getting 19 or fewer offspring with blue eyes is high, so there is not sufficient evidence to conclude that the one-quarter rate is wrong.

10. Test statistic: $\chi^2 = 2.909$. P-value $= 0.2335$ (Table: >0.10). Critical value: $\chi^2 = 5.991$. There is not sufficient evidence to warrant rejection of the claim of independence between injury category and whether the firearm was a handgun or a rifle or shotgun. The type of injury doesn't appear to be affected by whether the firearm is a handgun or a rifle or shotgun.

Chapter 13 Answers

Section 13-2

1. a. The only requirement for the matched pairs is that they constitute a simple random sample.
   b. There is no requirement of a normal distribution or any other specific distribution.
   c. The sign test is "distribution-free" in the sense that it does not require a normal distribution or any other specific distribution.

3. H_0: there is no difference between the populations of 8 AM temperatures on Day 1 and the matching 8 AM temperature on Day 2. H_1: there is a difference between the populations of 8 AM temperatures on Day 1 and the matching 8 AM temperature on Day 2. The sample data do not contradict H_1 because the numbers of positive signs (4) and negative signs (2) are not exactly the same.

5. The test statistic of $x = 4$ is not less than or equal to the critical value of 1. There is not sufficient evidence to reject the claim of no difference in heights between mothers and their first daughters.

7. The test statistic of $x = 1$ is not less than or equal to the critical value of 0. There is not sufficient evidence to warrant rejection of the claim that when the 13th day of a month falls on a Friday, the numbers of hospital admissions from motor vehicle

crashes are not affected. Hospital admissions do not appear to be affected.

9. The test statistic of $z = -2.66$ results in a P-value of 0.0078 and it is in the critical region bounded by $z = -2.575$ and 2.575. There is sufficient evidence to warrant rejection of the claim that there is no difference between the proportions of those opposed and those in favor.

11. The test statistic of $z = -0.24$ results in a P-value of 0.8103 and it is not in the critical region bounded by $z = -1.96$ and 1.96. There is not sufficient evidence to reject the claim that boys and girls are equally likely.

13. The test statistic of $x = 9$ is not less than or equal to the critical value of 5. There is not sufficient evidence to warrant rejection of the claim that the sample is from a population with a median IQ score of 100.

15. The test statistic of $z = -2.30$ results in a P-value of 0.0214 and it is in the critical region bounded by $z = -1.96$ and 1.96. There is sufficient evidence to warrant rejection of the claim that the sample is from a population with a median diastolic blood pressure level of 72.

17. Second approach: The test statistic of $z = -4.29$ results in a P-value of 0.0000 and it is in the critical region bounded by $z = -1.645$, so the conclusions are the same as in Example 4. Third approach: The test statistic of $z = -2.82$ results in a P-value of 0.0024 and it is in the critical region bounded by $z = -1.645$, so the conclusions are the same as in Example 4. The different approaches can lead to very different results; see the test statistics of -4.21, -4.29, and -2.82. The conclusions are the same in this case, but they could be different in other cases.

Section 13-3

1. a. The only requirements are that the matched pairs be simple random samples and the population of the difference be approximately symmetric.

   b. There is no requirement of a normal distribution or any other specific distribution.

   c. The Wilcoxon signed-ranks test is "distribution-free" in the sense that it does not require a normal distribution or any other specific distribution.

3. The sign test uses only the signs of the differences, but the Wilcoxon signed-ranks test uses ranks that are affected by the magnitudes of the differences.

5. Test Statistic: $T = 7.0$. Critical value: $T = 4$. Fail to reject the null hypothesis that the population of differences has a median of 0. There is not sufficient evidence to reject the claim of no difference in heights between mothers and their first daughters. There does not appear to be a difference in heights between mothers and their first daughters.

7. Test statistic: $T = 1.5$. Critical value: $T = 1$. Fail to reject the null hypothesis that the population of differences has a median of 0. There is not sufficient evidence to warrant rejection of the claim that when the 13th day of a month falls on a Friday, the numbers of hospital admissions from motor vehicle crashes are not affected. Hospital admissions do not appear to be affected.

9. Test statistic: $T = 98$. Critical value: $T = 52$. There is not sufficient evidence to warrant rejection of the claim that the sample is from a population with a median IQ score of 100.

11. Convert $T = 16,236$ to the test statistic $z = -1.89$. P-value $= 0.0588$. Critical values: $z = \pm 1.96$. There is not sufficient evidence to warrant rejection of the claim that the sample is from a population with a median diastolic blood pressure level of 72.

13. a. 0 and 45,150

   b. 22,575

   c. 32,805

   d. $\dfrac{n(n+1)}{2} - k$

Section 13-4

1. The two samples are from populations with the same median.

3. Yes. The samples are independent and both samples have more than 10 values.

5. $R_1 = 172$, $R_2 = 179$, $\mu_R = 189$, $\sigma_R = 19.4422$, test statistic: $z = -0.87$. P-value: 0.3843. Critical values: $z = \pm 1.96$. Fail to reject the null hypothesis that the populations have the same median. There is not sufficient evidence to warrant rejection of the claim that girls and boys have the same median birth weight.

7. $R_1 = 253.5$, $R_2 = 124.5$, $\mu_R = 182$, $\sigma_R = 20.607$, test statistic: $z = 3.47$. P-value $= 0.001$. Critical values: $z = \pm 1.96$. Reject the null hypothesis that the populations have the same median. There is sufficient evidence to reject the claim that for those treated with 20 mg of atorvastatin and those treated with 80 mg of atorvastatin, changes in LDL cholesterol have the same median. It appears that the dosage amount does have an effect on the change in LDL cholesterol.

9. $R_1 = 36,531.5$, $R_2 = 43,668.5$, $\mu_R = 41,102.5$, $\sigma_R = 1155.782$, test statistic: $z = -3.95$. P-value: 0.0001 (Table: 0.0002). Critical values: $z = \pm 1.96$. Reject the null hypothesis that the populations have the same median. There is sufficient evidence to warrant rejection of the claim that girls and boys have the same median birth weight.

11. $R_1 = 501$, $R_2 = 445$, $\mu_R = 484$, $\sigma_R = 41.158$, test statistic: $z = 0.41$. P-value 0.3409. Critical value: $z = 1.645$. Fail to reject the null hypothesis that the populations have the same median. There is not sufficient evidence to support the claim that subjects with medium lead levels have a higher median of the full IQ scores than subjects with high lead levels. Based on these data, it does not appear that lead level affects full IQ scores.

13. Using $U = 86.5$, we get $z = 1.26$. The test statistic is the same value with opposite sign.

Section 13-5

1. $R_1 = 36.5$, $R_2 = 52.5$, $R_3 = 47$

3. $n_1 = 5$, $n_2 = 6$, $n_3 = 5$, and $N = 16$.

5. Test statistic: $H = 4.9054$. Critical value: $X^2 = 5.991$. (Tech: P-value $= 0.0861$.) Fail to reject the null hypothesis of equal medians. The data do not suggest that larger cars are safer.

7. Test statistic: $H = 22.8157$. Critical value: $X^2 = 9.210$. (Tech: P-value $= 0.000$.) Reject the null hypothesis of equal medians. It appears that the three states have median amounts of arsenic that are not all the same.

9. Test statistic: $H = 59.1546$. Critical value: $X^2 = 9.210$. (Tech: P-value $= 0.000$.) Reject the null hypothesis of equal medians. The data suggest that the amounts of nicotine absorbed by

smokers are different from the amounts absorbed by people who don't smoke.

11. Test statistic: $H = 27.9098$. Critical value: $\chi^2 = 5.991$. (Tech: P-value: 0.000.) Reject the null hypothesis of equal medians. There is sufficient evidence to warrant rejection of the claim that the three different types of cigarettes have the same median amount of nicotine. It appears that the filters do make a difference.

13. There are 10 zeros and 2 ones, so the values of t are 10 and 2. The values of T are $(10^3 - 10) = 990$ and $(2^3 - 2) = 6$, so $\Sigma T = 990 + 6 = 996$. Using $\Sigma T = 996$ and $N = 18$, the corrected value of H is 8.114, which is quite different from the value of 6.724 found in Example 1. In this case, the large numbers of ties do appear to have a considerable effect on the test statistic H.

Section 13-6

1. The methods of Section 10-2 should not be used for predictions. The regression equation is based on a *linear* correlation between the two variables, but the methods of this section do not require a linear relationship. The methods of this section could suggest that there is a correlation with paired data associated by some nonlinear relationship, so the regression equation would not be a suitable model for making predictions.

3. r represents the linear correlation coefficient computed from sample paired data; ρ represents the parameter of the linear correlation coefficient computed from a population of paired data; r_s denotes the rank correlation coefficient computed from sample paired data; ρ_s represents the rank correlation coefficient computed from a population of paired data. The subscript s is used so that the rank correlation coefficient can be distinguished from the linear correlation coefficient r. The subscript does not represent the standard deviation s. It is used in recognition of Charles Spearman, who introduced the rank correlation method.

5. $r_s = 1$. Critical values are -0.648 and 0.648. Reject the null hypothesis of $\rho_s = 0$. There is sufficient evidence to support a claim of a correlation between ages and heights of trees.

7. $r_s = 0.857$. Critical values: $-0.738, 0.738$. Reject the null hypothesis of $\rho_s = 0$. There is sufficient evidence to support a conclusion that there is a correlation between the number of chirps in 1 min and the temperature.

9. $r_s = 0.624$. Critical values: $r_s = \pm 0.587$. Reject the null hypothesis of $\rho_s = 0$. There is sufficient evidence to support a conclusion that there is a correlation between the number of cigarettes smoked and the cotinine level.

11. $r_s = 0.360$. Critical values: $-0.159, 0.159$. Reject the null hypothesis of $\rho_s = 0$. There is sufficient evidence to support a conclusion that there is a correlation between the systolic and diastolic blood pressure levels in males.

13. $r_s = 0.984$. Critical values: $-0.269, 0.269$. Reject the null hypothesis of $\rho_s = 0$. There is sufficient evidence to support the claim of a correlation between chest sizes and weights of bears.

15. -0.159 and 0.159. (Use either $t = 1.975799$ from technology or use interpolation in Table A-3 with 151 degrees of freedom, so the critical value of t is approximately halfway between 1.984 and 1.972, which is 1.978.) The critical values are the same as those found by using Formula 13-1.

Chapter 13: Quick Quiz

1. 5, 7, 11, 4, 9.5, 2, 3, 8, 9.5, 1, 6

2. The efficiency rating of 0.91 indicates that with all other factors being the same, rank correlation requires 100 pairs of sample observations to achieve the same results as 91 pairs of observations with the parametric test for linear correlation, assuming that the stricter requirements for using linear correlation are met.

3. a. Distribution-free test

   b. The term "distribution-free test" suggests correctly that the test does not require that a population must have a particular distribution, such as a normal distribution. The term "nonparametric test" incorrectly suggests that the test is not based on a parameter, but some nonparametric tests are based on the median, which is a parameter; the term "distribution-free test" is better because it does not make that incorrect suggestion.

4. Rank correlation should be used. The rank correlation test is used to investigate whether there is a correlation between foot length and height.

5. No, the P-values are almost always different, and the conclusions may or may not be the same.

6. Rank correlation can be used in a wider variety of circumstances than linear correlation. Rank correlation does not require a normal distribution for any population. Rank correlation can be used to detect some (not all) relationships that are not linear.

7. Because the sign test uses only *signs* of differences while the Wilcoxon signed-ranks test uses *ranks* of the differences, the Wilcoxon signed-ranks test uses more information about the data and tends to yield conclusions that better reflect the true nature of the data.

8. Kruskal-Wallis test

9. Two independent samples

10. Matched pairs

Chapter 13: Review Exercises

1. Use the sign test. The test statistic of $z = -4.46$ results in a P-value of 0.0000 (Table: 0.0001) and it is less than or equal to the critical value of $z = -1.645$. Reject the null hypothesis of $p = 0.5$. There is sufficient evidence to support the claim that the majority of adults obtain medical information more often from the Internet than a doctor.

2. The test statistic of $x = 3$ is less than or equal to the critical value of 5 (from Table A-7). There is sufficient evidence to warrant rejection of the claim that the sample is from a population with a median equal to 5 min.

3. Test statistic $T = 21$ is less than or equal to the critical value of 59. There is sufficient evidence to warrant rejection of the claim that the sample is from a population with a median equal to 5 min.

4. Test statistic: $H = 2.5288$. P-value $= 0.2824$. Critical value: $\chi^2 = 5.991$. Fail to reject the null hypothesis of equal medians. It appears that times of longevity after inauguration for presidents, popes, and British monarchs have the same median.

5. $r_s = 0.888$. Critical values: $-0.618, 0.618$. Reject the null hypothesis of $\rho_s = 0$. There is sufficient evidence to support the claim of a correlation between chocolate consumption and the rate of Nobel Laureates. It does not make sense to think that there

is a cause/effect relationship, so the correlation could be the result of a coincidence or other factors that affect the variables the same way.

6. Test statistic: $H = 6.6305$. P-value $= 0.0363$. Critical value: $\chi^2 = 5.991$. Reject the null hypothesis of equal medians. Interbreeding of cultures is suggested by the data.

7. $R_1 = 60$, $R_2 = 111$, $\mu_R = 85.5$, $\sigma_R = 11.3248$, test statistic: $z = -2.25$. P-value $= 0.0244$. Critical values: $z = \pm 1.96$. Reject the null hypothesis that the populations have the same median. Skull breadths from 4000 B.C. appear to have a different median than those from A.D. 150.

8. $r_s = 0.714$. Critical values: ± 0.738. Fail to reject the null hypothesis of $\rho_s = 0$. There is not sufficient evidence to support the claim that there is a correlation between the student ranks and the magazine ranks. When ranking colleges, students and the magazine do not appear to agree.

Chapter 13: Cumulative Review Exercises

1. $\bar{x} = 14.6$ credit hours, median $= 15.0$ credit hours, $s = 1.7$ credit hours, $s^2 = 2.9$ (credit hours)^2, range $= 6.0$ credit hours

2. a. Convenience sample
   b. Because the sample is from one class of statistics students, it is not likely to be representative of the population of all full-time college students.
   c. Discrete
   d. Ratio

3. $H_0: \mu = 14$ credit hours. $H_1: \mu > 14$ credit hours. Test statistic: $t = 1.446$. P-value $= 0.0822$ (Table: >0.05). Critical value: $t = 1.729$ (assuming a 0.05 significance level). Fail to reject H_0. There is not sufficient evidence to support the claim that the mean is greater than 14 credit hours.

4. The test statistic of $x = 5$ is not less than or equal to the critical value of 4. There is not sufficient evidence to support the claim that the sample is from a population with a median greater than 14 credit hours.

5. 13.8 credit hours $< \mu < 15.3$ credit hours. We have 95% confidence that the limits of 13.8 credit hours and 15.3 credit hours contain the true value of the population mean.

6. 3.1% $< p <$ 4.7%. We have 95% confidence that the limits of 3.1% and 4.7% actually contain the true percentage of the population of workers who test positive for drugs.

7. $H_0: p = 0.03$. $H_1: p > 0.03$. Test statistic: $z = 2.36$. P-value: 0.0091. Critical value: $z = 1.645$. Reject H_0. There is sufficient evidence to support the claim that the rate of positive drug test results among workers in the United States is greater than 3.0%.

8. 2401

9. $H_0: p = 0.5$. $H_1: p > 0.5$. Test statistic: $z = 1.36$. P-value: 0.0865 (Table: 0.0869). Critical value: $z = 1.645$. Fail to reject H_0. There is not sufficient evidence to support the claim that the majority of the population is not afraid of heights in tall buildings. Because respondents themselves chose to reply, the sample is a voluntary response sample, not a random sample, so the results might not be valid.

10. There must be an error, because the rates of 13.7% and 10.6% are not possible with samples of size 100.

Chapter 14 Answers

Section 14-1

1. A cohort life table is a record of the actual observed mortality experience for a particular group, whereas a period life table describes mortality and longevity data for a hypothetical group that would have lived with the same mortality conditions throughout their lives.

3. The values in columns 3 through 6 would become five times the stated values.

5. 0.000382

7. 0.99491

9. 0.999064; 14985.96 people (or 0.999066; 14985.99)

11. 0.973241

13. a. 0.006820   b. 0.000514
    The results are so different because of the exceptionally high mortality rate at or very near birth.

15. 3–6; 0.000514; 99,318; 51; 297,870; 7,567,864; 76.2

17. Using $H_0: p = 0.000936$, the test statistic is $z = 49.6523$, the p-value is 0.0000042 (Table: <0.00001), and the critical value is $z = 1.645$, so reject the null hypothesis of $p = 0.000936$ and conclude that there is sufficient to support the claim that the number of deaths is significantly high. [If the probability of dying is calculated from the third column of Table 14-1, use $H_1: p > 0.00093417$ to get a test statistic of $z = 1.60$, a p-value of 0.0000026 (Table: <0.00001) and the same critical value and conclusions.

19. Using $H_1: p > 0.033493$, the test statistic is $z = 7.29$, the P-value is less than 0.00001 (Table: <0.00001), and the critical value is $z = -1.645$, so reject H_0 and conclude that there is sufficient evidence to support the claim that the number of deaths is significantly high.

Section 14-2

1. A survivor is a subject that successfully lasted throughout a particular time period without reaching some terminating event. A survivor could be a person or an object or some other entity such as a marriage.

3. A life table is based on fixed intervals of time, but a table of survival data and Kaplan-Meier calculations is based on times that vary according to the terminating event.

5. The fast walkers are more likely to be healthier with greater longevity, so they correspond to the top (green) curve. The moderate group corresponds to the middle (black) curve. The slow group of walkers is more likely to have health issues with lower longevity, so they correspond to the bottom (red) curve.

7. a. 4 years   b. 1 year

9. The five-year survival rates are 0.2 for the group of slow walkers, 0.5 for the group with moderate walking speeds, and 0.9 for the group of fast walkers. The differences are substantial, and they suggest that after five years, those with faster walking speeds have much greater survival rates, and those with slow walking speeds have much lower survival rates.

   The data do not necessarily suggest that we can get older people to live longer by somehow getting them to walk faster. It's very possible that walking speed is one manifestation of overall

health status, so longevity and walking speed are likely both affected by one or more other extraneous variables.

11.

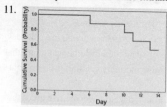

13. The graph does not show any information about the six censored
survival times. The graph shows information about the two survival times that were not censored.

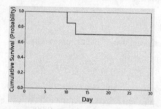

Chapter 14: Quick Quiz

1. Life table
2. Survival table with Kaplan-Meier calculations
3. A period life table describes mortality and longevity data for a
hypothetical group that would have lived with the same mortality
conditions throughout their lives.
4. A cohort life table is a record of the actual observed mortality
experience for a particular group.
5. False   6. True
7. False   8. True
9. The entries are 1, 0, 0, and 0.   10. 0.999345

Chapter 14: Review Exercises

1. 0.000352   2. 35   3. 0.99492
4. 0–2; 0.00508; 100,000; 508; 199,098; 8,382,303; 83.8
5. 83.8 years; 83.2 years; the second value is less than the first
value. As we age, our expected remaining lifetime steadily
decreases.

6.

Day	Status 0 = Censored 1 = Failed	Number of Patients	Patients Not Requiring Retreatment	Proportion of Patients Not Requiring Retreatment	Cumulative Proportion of Patients Not Requiring Retreatment
3	1	4	3	3/4 = 0.75	0.75
12	1	3	2	2/3 = 0.667	0.5
20	1	2	1	1/2 = 0.5	0.25
30	0				

7.

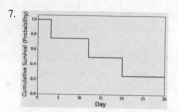

8. The treatment group and the placebo group appear to have approximately the same behavior. The treatment does not appear to
be effective.

Chapter 14: Cumulative Review Exercises

1. The table shows that among 100,000 births, 99,492 survived to the second birthday, so the probability of dying is
$1 - 0.99492 = 0.00508$. Using H_1: $p < 0.00508$, the test statistic is $z = -0.67$, the P-value is 0.2501 (Table: 0.2514), and the
critical value is $z = -1.645$ (assuming a 0.05 significance level),
so fail to reject the null hypothesis of $p = 0.00508$ and conclude
that there is not sufficient evidence to support the claim that the
proportion of deaths is less than 0.00508. The program does not
appear to be effective in reducing the mortality rate.
2. $0.99294 < p < 0.99953$; the confidence interval limits contain
0.99492, so it appears that the mortality rate has not been lowered
by a significant amount.
3. 0.986
4. 0.0188; no, because being in the same family causes the events
to be dependent, instead of being independent, as required by the
multiplication rule. It is reasonable to expect that four Hispanic
females in the same family are more likely to experience similar
environmental and hereditary characteristics.
5. The graph is misleading. The vertical scale begins with a frequency of 800 instead of 0, so the difference between the "yes"
and "no" responses is greatly exaggerated.
6. a. 99.89% (Table: 99.88%)   b. 0.1587

CREDITS

Photos

Chapter 1
P17, Wavebreakmedia/Shutterstock; **P21**, Gary Blakeley Shutterstock; **P22**, USBFCO/Shutterstock; **P25**, Wavebreakmedia/Shutterstock; **P31**, Khamidulin Sergey/Shutterstock; **P31**, Suppakij1017/Shutterstock; **P34**, Dotshock/Shutterstock; **P35**, 18percentgrey/Shutterstock; **P37**, Ollyy/Shutterstock; **P41**, Andersen Ross/Stockbyte/Getty Images; **P42**, Triff/Shutterstock; **P43**, Fujji/Shutterstock

Chapter 2
P56, Kodda/Shutterstock; **P59**, Monkey Business Images/Shutterstock; **P69**, Valua Vitaly/Shutterstock; **P74**, Stockbyte/Getty Images; **P83**, Dmitriy Eremenkov. Shutterstock

Chapter 3
P91, Toysf400/Shutterstock; **P95**, Image Point Fr/Shutterstock; **P106**, Kitch Bain/Shutterstock; **P107**, Ariwasabi/Shutterstock; **P120**, Sergey Nivens/Shutterstock

Chapter 4
P134, Sculpies/Shutterstock; **P137**, Photomatz/Shutterstock; **P139**, Africa Studio/Shutterstock; **P139**, Monkey Business Images/Shutterstock; **P139**, Pakhnyushchy/Shutterstock; **P142**, Bochkarev Photography/Shutterstock; **P148**, Vitalinka/Shutterstock; **P161**, Africa Studio/Shutterstock; **P164**, Alexander Raths/Shutterstock; **P170**, Eric Isselee/Shutterstock

Chapter 5
P196, Katrina Elena Trninich/123RF; **P205**, Kzenon/Shutterstock; **P211**, JHDT Stock Images/Shutterstock; **P231**, Alfred Eisenstaedt/The LIFE Picture Collection/Getty Images; **P231**, Wikimedia Commons

Chapter 6
P232, Mikael Damkier/Shutterstock; **P249**, RGtimeline/Shutterstock; **P271**, Ciurea Adrian/Shutterstock; **P279**, Triff/Shutterstock

Chapter 7
P298, Pearson Education, Inc.; **P301**, Mama_mia/Shutterstock; **P303**, Roland IJdema/Shutterstock; **P317**, Eric Isselee/Fotolia; **P320**, Robin W/Shutterstock; **P341**, Andresr/Shutterstock

Chapter 8
P352, Monkey Business Images/Shutterstock; **P355**, Viktoria/Shutterstock; **P360**, Azuzl/Shutterstock; **P362**, Alexey Burmakin/123RF; **P371**, David H.Seymour/Shutterstock; **P373**, Suravid/Shutterstock; **P375**, Elena Stepanova/Shutterstock; **P384**, B Calkins/Shutterstock; **P385**, Laborant/Shutterstock; **P387**, Zentilia/Shutterstock

Chapter 9
P408, Andresr/Shutterstock; **P425**, Amy Walters/Shutterstock; **P428**, Pressmaster/Shutterstock; **P437**, D7INAMI7S/Shutterstock; **P439**, Andrey Arkusha/Shutterstock

Chapter 10
P458, Lightwise/Shutterstock; **P464**, Africa Studio/Shutterstock; **P480**, Zffoto/Shutterstock; **P482**, Leah-Anne Thompson/Shutterstock; **P493**, Steve Snowden/Shutterstock

Chapter 11
P518, Racorn/Shutterstock; **P521**, Alex Kalashnikov/Shutterstock; **P524**, Dundanim/Shutterstock; **P525**, Serhiy Shullye/Shutterstock; **P533**, Lenetstan/Shutterstock; **P536**, Tatiana Popova/Shutterstock

Chapter 12
P547, Bikeriderlondon/Shutterstock

Chapter 13
P576, karen Roach/Shutterstock; **P611**, Sinisa Botas/Shutterstock

Chapter 14
AsianShow/Shutterstock

Cover
Mikulas P/Shutterstock

FM
3, Marc Triola; **3**, Mario F. Triola; **4**, Jason Roy

Text

Chapter 1

P25, Dell Pub. Co

Chapter 4

P170, Sir Arthur Stanley Eddington

Chapter 14

P622–623, U.S. Department of Health and Human Services; **P626**, U.S. Department of Health and Human Services; **P628**, U.S. Department of Health and Human Services; **P636**, U.S. Department of Health and Human Services; **P638**, U.S. Department of Health and Human Services

Appendix B

P655, Dr. Steven Wasserman, Dr. Philip Mackowiak, and Dr. Myron Levine; **P655**, National Center for Health Statistics; **P656**, National Center for Health Statistics; **P658**, Hoffman, D. J., Policastro, P., Quick, V., and Lee, S. K., Changes in Body Weight and Fat Mass of Men and Women in the First Year of College: A Study of the Freshman 15. *Journal of American College Health*, July 1, 2006, Vol. 55, No. 1, p. 41. Copyright © 2006. Reprinted by Permission; **P659**, Federal Trade Commission; **P659**, National Center for Health Statistics

Multi: Statdisk screenshots, Triola Statdisk (c) Triola Stats. All rights reserved; TI-83/84 Plus screenshots, Texas Instruments

Formula and Table Supplement

TABLE A-4 Chi-Square (χ^2) Distribution, *Handbook of Statistical Tables*, Addison-Wesley Pub. Co.

INDEX

NEGATIVE z Scores

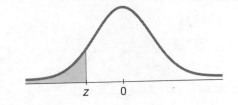

TABLE A-2 Standard Normal (z) Distribution: Cumulative Area from the LEFT

z	.00	.01	.02	.03	.04	.05	.06	.07	.08	.09
−3.50 and lower	.0001									
−3.4	.0003	.0003	.0003	.0003	.0003	.0003	.0003	.0003	.0003	.0002
−3.3	.0005	.0005	.0005	.0004	.0004	.0004	.0004	.0004	.0004	.0003
−3.2	.0007	.0007	.0006	.0006	.0006	.0006	.0006	.0005	.0005	.0005
−3.1	.0010	.0009	.0009	.0009	.0008	.0008	.0008	.0008	.0007	.0007
−3.0	.0013	.0013	.0013	.0012	.0012	.0011	.0011	.0011	.0010	.0010
−2.9	.0019	.0018	.0018	.0017	.0016	.0016	.0015	.0015	.0014	.0014
−2.8	.0026	.0025	.0024	.0023	.0023	.0022	.0021	.0021	.0020	.0019
−2.7	.0035	.0034	.0033	.0032	.0031	.0030	.0029	.0028	.0027	.0026
−2.6	.0047	.0045	.0044	.0043	.0041	.0040	.0039	.0038	.0037	.0036
−2.5	.0062	.0060	.0059	.0057	.0055	.0054	.0052	.0051 *	.0049	.0048
−2.4	.0082	.0080	.0078	.0075	.0073	.0071	.0069	.0068	.0066	.0064
−2.3	.0107	.0104	.0102	.0099	.0096	.0094	.0091	.0089	.0087	.0084
−2.2	.0139	.0136	.0132	.0129	.0125	.0122	.0119	.0116	.0113	.0110
−2.1	.0179	.0174	.0170	.0166	.0162	.0158	.0154	.0150	.0146	.0143
−2.0	.0228	.0222	.0217	.0212	.0207	.0202	.0197	.0192	.0188	.0183
−1.9	.0287	.0281	.0274	.0268	.0262	.0256	.0250	.0244	.0239	.0233
−1.8	.0359	.0351	.0344	.0336	.0329	.0322	.0314	.0307	.0301	.0294
−1.7	.0446	.0436	.0427	.0418	.0409	.0401	.0392	.0384	.0375	.0367
−1.6	.0548	.0537	.0526	.0516	.0505 *	.0495	.0485	.0475	.0465	.0455
−1.5	.0668	.0655	.0643	.0630	.0618	.0606	.0594	.0582	.0571	.0559
−1.4	.0808	.0793	.0778	.0764	.0749	.0735	.0721	.0708	.0694	.0681
−1.3	.0968	.0951	.0934	.0918	.0901	.0885	.0869	.0853	.0838	.0823
−1.2	.1151	.1131	.1112	.1093	.1075	.1056	.1038	.1020	.1003	.0985
−1.1	.1357	.1335	.1314	.1292	.1271	.1251	.1230	.1210	.1190	.1170
−1.0	.1587	.1562	.1539	.1515	.1492	.1469	.1446	.1423	.1401	.1379
−0.9	.1841	.1814	.1788	.1762	.1736	.1711	.1685	.1660	.1635	.1611
−0.8	.2119	.2090	.2061	.2033	.2005	.1977	.1949	.1922	.1894	.1867
−0.7	.2420	.2389	.2358	.2327	.2296	.2266	.2236	.2206	.2177	.2148
−0.6	.2743	.2709	.2676	.2643	.2611	.2578	.2546	.2514	.2483	.2451
−0.5	.3085	.3050	.3015	.2981	.2946	.2912	.2877	.2843	.2810	.2776
−0.4	.3446	.3409	.3372	.3336	.3300	.3264	.3228	.3192	.3156	.3121
−0.3	.3821	.3783	.3745	.3707	.3669	.3632	.3594	.3557	.3520	.3483
−0.2	.4207	.4168	.4129	.4090	.4052	.4013	.3974	.3936	.3897	.3859
−0.1	.4602	.4562	.4522	.4483	.4443	.4404	.4364	.4325	.4286	.4247
−0.0	.5000	.4960	.4920	.4880	.4840	.4801	.4761	.4721	.4681	.4641

(continued)

NOTE: For values of z below −3.49, use 0.0001 for the area.

*Use these common values that result from interpolation:

z Score	Area
−1.645	0.0500
−2.575	0.0050

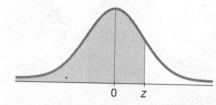

POSITIVE z Scores

TABLE A-2 (continued) Cumulative Area from the LEFT

z	.00	.01	.02	.03	.04	.05	.06	.07	.08	.09
0.0	.5000	.5040	.5080	.5120	.5160	.5199	.5239	.5279	.5319	.5359
0.1	.5398	.5438	.5478	.5517	.5557	.5596	.5636	.5675	.5714	.5753
0.2	.5793	.5832	.5871	.5910	.5948	.5987	.6026	.6064	.6103	.6141
0.3	.6179	.6217	.6255	.6293	.6331	.6368	.6406	.6443	.6480	.6517
0.4	.6554	.6591	.6628	.6664	.6700	.6736	.6772	.6808	.6844	.6879
0.5	.6915	.6950	.6985	.7019	.7054	.7088	.7123	.7157	.7190	.7224
0.6	.7257	.7291	.7324	.7357	.7389	.7422	.7454	.7486	.7517	.7549
0.7	.7580	.7611	.7642	.7673	.7704	.7734	.7764	.7794	.7823	.7852
0.8	.7881	.7910	.7939	.7967	.7995	.8023	.8051	.8078	.8106	.8133
0.9	.8159	.8186	.8212	.8238	.8264	.8289	.8315	.8340	.8365	.8389
1.0	.8413	.8438	.8461	.8485	.8508	.8531	.8554	.8577	.8599	.8621
1.1	.8643	.8665	.8686	.8708	.8729	.8749	.8770	.8790	.8810	.8830
1.2	.8849	.8869	.8888	.8907	.8925	.8944	.8962	.8980	.8997	.9015
1.3	.9032	.9049	.9066	.9082	.9099	.9115	.9131	.9147	.9162	.9177
1.4	.9192	.9207	.9222	.9236	.9251	.9265	.9279	.9292	.9306	.9319
1.5	.9332	.9345	.9357	.9370	.9382	.9394	.9406	.9418	.9429	.9441
1.6	.9452	.9463	.9474	.9484	.9495 *	.9505	.9515	.9525	.9535	.9545
1.7	.9554	.9564	.9573	.9582	.9591	.9599	.9608	.9616	.9625	.9633
1.8	.9641	.9649	.9656	.9664	.9671	.9678	.9686	.9693	.9699	.9706
1.9	.9713	.9719	.9726	.9732	.9738	.9744	.9750	.9756	.9761	.9767
2.0	.9772	.9778	.9783	.9788	.9793	.9798	.9803	.9808	.9812	.9817
2.1	.9821	.9826	.9830	.9834	.9838	.9842	.9846	.9850	.9854	.9857
2.2	.9861	.9864	.9868	.9871	.9875	.9878	.9881	.9884	.9887	.9890
2.3	.9893	.9896	.9898	.9901	.9904	.9906	.9909	.9911	.9913	.9916
2.4	.9918	.9920	.9922	.9925	.9927	.9929	.9931	.9932	.9934	.9936
2.5	.9938	.9940	.9941	.9943	.9945	.9946	.9948	.9949 *	.9951	.9952
2.6	.9953	.9955	.9956	.9957	.9959	.9960	.9961	.9962	.9963	.9964
2.7	.9965	.9966	.9967	.9968	.9969	.9970	.9971	.9972	.9973	.9974
2.8	.9974	.9975	.9976	.9977	.9977	.9978	.9979	.9979	.9980	.9981
2.9	.9981	.9982	.9982	.9983	.9984	.9984	.9985	.9985	.9986	.9986
3.0	.9987	.9987	.9987	.9988	.9988	.9989	.9989	.9989	.9990	.9990
3.1	.9990	.9991	.9991	.9991	.9992	.9992	.9992	.9992	.9993	.9993
3.2	.9993	.9993	.9994	.9994	.9994	.9994	.9994	.9995	.9995	.9995
3.3	.9995	.9995	.9995	.9996	.9996	.9996	.9996	.9996	.9996	.9997
3.4	.9997	.9997	.9997	.9997	.9997	.9997	.9997	.9997	.9997	.9998
3.50 and up	.9999									

NOTE: For values of z above 3.49, use 0.9999 for the area.
*Use these common values that result from interpolation:

z score	Area
1.645	0.9500
2.575	0.9950

Common Critical Values

Confidence Level	Critical Value
0.90	1.645
0.95	1.96
0.99	2.575

TABLE A-3 *t* Distribution: Critical *t* Values

			Area in One Tail		
	0.005	0.01	0.025	0.05	0.10
Degrees of Freedom			Area in Two Tails		
	0.01	0.02	0.05	0.10	0.20
1	63.657	31.821	12.706	6.314	3.078
2	9.925	6.965	4.303	2.920	1.886
3	5.841	4.541	3.182	2.353	1.638
4	4.604	3.747	2.776	2.132	1.533
5	4.032	3.365	2.571	2.015	1.476
6	3.707	3.143	2.447	1.943	1.440
7	3.499	2.998	2.365	1.895	1.415
8	3.355	2.896	2.306	1.860	1.397
9	3.250	2.821	2.262	1.833	1.383
10	3.169	2.764	2.228	1.812	1.372
11	3.106	2.718	2.201	1.796	1.363
12	3.055	2.681	2.179	1.782	1.356
13	3.012	2.650	2.160	1.771	1.350
14	2.977	2.624	2.145	1.761	1.345
15	2.947	2.602	2.131	1.753	1.341
16	2.921	2.583	2.120	1.746	1.337
17	2.898	2.567	2.110	1.740	1.333
18	2.878	2.552	2.101	1.734	1.330
19	2.861	2.539	2.093	1.729	1.328
20	2.845	2.528	2.086	1.725	1.325
21	2.831	2.518	2.080	1.721	1.323
22	2.819	2.508	2.074	1.717	1.321
23	2.807	2.500	2.069	1.714	1.319
24	2.797	2.492	2.064	1.711	1.318
25	2.787	2.485	2.060	1.708	1.316
26	2.779	2.479	2.056	1.706	1.315
27	2.771	2.473	2.052	1.703	1.314
28	2.763	2.467	2.048	1.701	1.313
29	2.756	2.462	2.045	1.699	1.311
30	2.750	2.457	2.042	1.697	1.310
31	2.744	2.453	2.040	1.696	1.309
32	2.738	2.449	2.037	1.694	1.309
33	2.733	2.445	2.035	1.692	1.308
34	2.728	2.441	2.032	1.691	1.307
35	2.724	2.438	2.030	1.690	1.306
36	2.719	2.434	2.028	1.688	1.306
37	2.715	2.431	2.026	1.687	1.305
38	2.712	2.429	2.024	1.686	1.304
39	2.708	2.426	2.023	1.685	1.304
40	2.704	2.423	2.021	1.684	1.303
45	2.690	2.412	2.014	1.679	1.301
50	2.678	2.403	2.009	1.676	1.299
60	2.660	2.390	2.000	1.671	1.296
70	2.648	2.381	1.994	1.667	1.294
80	2.639	2.374	1.990	1.664	1.292
90	2.632	2.368	1.987	1.662	1.291
100	2.626	2.364	1.984	1.660	1.290
200	2.601	2.345	1.972	1.653	1.286
300	2.592	2.339	1.968	1.650	1.284
400	2.588	2.336	1.966	1.649	1.284
500	2.586	2.334	1.965	1.648	1.283
1000	2.581	2.330	1.962	1.646	1.282
2000	2.578	2.328	1.961	1.646	1.282
Large	2.576	2.326	1.960	1.645	1.282

TABLE A-4 Chi-Square (χ^2) Distribution

Degrees of Freedom	Area to the *Right* of the Critical Value									
	0.995	0.99	0.975	0.95	0.90	0.10	0.05	0.025	0.01	0.005
1	—	—	0.001	0.004	0.016	2.706	3.841	5.024	6.635	7.879
2	0.010	0.020	0.051	0.103	0.211	4.605	5.991	7.378	9.210	10.597
3	0.072	0.115	0.216	0.352	0.584	6.251	7.815	9.348	11.345	12.838
4	0.207	0.297	0.484	0.711	1.064	7.779	9.488	11.143	13.277	14.860
5	0.412	0.554	0.831	1.145	1.610	9.236	11.071	12.833	15.086	16.750
6	0.676	0.872	1.237	1.635	2.204	10.645	12.592	14.449	16.812	18.548
7	0.989	1.239	1.690	2.167	2.833	12.017	14.067	16.013	18.475	20.278
8	1.344	1.646	2.180	2.733	3.490	13.362	15.507	17.535	20.090	21.955
9	1.735	2.088	2.700	3.325	4.168	14.684	16.919	19.023	21.666	23.589
10	2.156	2.558	3.247	3.940	4.865	15.987	18.307	20.483	23.209	25.188
11	2.603	3.053	3.816	4.575	5.578	17.275	19.675	21.920	24.725	26.757
12	3.074	3.571	4.404	5.226	6.304	18.549	21.026	23.337	26.217	28.299
13	3.565	4.107	5.009	5.892	7.042	19.812	22.362	24.736	27.688	29.819
14	4.075	4.660	5.629	6.571	7.790	21.064	23.685	26.119	29.141	31.319
15	4.601	5.229	6.262	7.261	8.547	22.307	24.996	27.488	30.578	32.801
16	5.142	5.812	6.908	7.962	9.312	23.542	26.296	28.845	32.000	34.267
17	5.697	6.408	7.564	8.672	10.085	24.769	27.587	30.191	33.409	35.718
18	6.265	7.015	8.231	9.390	10.865	25.989	28.869	31.526	34.805	37.156
19	6.844	7.633	8.907	10.117	11.651	27.204	30.144	32.852	36.191	38.582
20	7.434	8.260	9.591	10.851	12.443	28.412	31.410	34.170	37.566	39.997
21	8.034	8.897	10.283	11.591	13.240	29.615	32.671	35.479	38.932	41.401
22	8.643	9.542	10.982	12.338	14.042	30.813	33.924	36.781	40.289	42.796
23	9.260	10.196	11.689	13.091	14.848	32.007	35.172	38.076	41.638	44.181
24	9.886	10.856	12.401	13.848	15.659	33.196	36.415	39.364	42.980	45.559
25	10.520	11.524	13.120	14.611	16.473	34.382	37.652	40.646	44.314	46.928
26	11.160	12.198	13.844	15.379	17.292	35.563	38.885	41.923	45.642	48.290
27	11.808	12.879	14.573	16.151	18.114	36.741	40.113	43.194	46.963	49.645
28	12.461	13.565	15.308	16.928	18.939	37.916	41.337	44.461	48.278	50.993
29	13.121	14.257	16.047	17.708	19.768	39.087	42.557	45.722	49.588	52.336
30	13.787	14.954	16.791	18.493	20.599	40.256	43.773	46.979	50.892	53.672
40	20.707	22.164	24.433	26.509	29.051	51.805	55.758	59.342	63.691	66.766
50	27.991	29.707	32.357	34.764	37.689	63.167	67.505	71.420	76.154	79.490
60	35.534	37.485	40.482	43.188	46.459	74.397	79.082	83.298	88.379	91.952
70	43.275	45.442	48.758	51.739	55.329	85.527	90.531	95.023	100.425	104.215
80	51.172	53.540	57.153	60.391	64.278	96.578	101.879	106.629	112.329	116.321
90	59.196	61.754	65.647	69.126	73.291	107.565	113.145	118.136	124.116	128.299
100	67.328	70.065	74.222	77.929	82.358	118.498	124.342	129.561	135.807	140.169

Source: From Donald B. Owen, *Handbook of Statistical Tables.*

Degrees of Freedom

$n - 1$	Confidence Interval or Hypothesis Test for a standard deviation or variance
$k - 1$	Goodness-of-fit test with k different categories
$(r - 1)(c - 1)$	Contingency table test with r rows and c columns
$k - 1$	Kruskal-Wallis test with k different samples

Formulas and Tables by Triola, Triola, and Roy
Copyright 2018 Pearson Education, Inc.

Ch. 3: Descriptive Statistics

$\bar{x} = \dfrac{\Sigma x}{n}$ Mean

$\bar{x} = \dfrac{\Sigma (f \cdot x)}{\Sigma f}$ Mean (frequency table)

$s = \sqrt{\dfrac{\Sigma (x - \bar{x})^2}{n - 1}}$ Standard deviation

$s = \sqrt{\dfrac{n(\Sigma x^2) - (\Sigma x)^2}{n(n - 1)}}$ Standard deviation (shortcut)

$s = \sqrt{\dfrac{n[\Sigma (f \cdot x^2)] - [\Sigma (f \cdot x)]^2}{n(n - 1)}}$ Standard deviation (frequency table)

variance $= s^2$

Ch. 4: Probability

$P(A \text{ or } B) = P(A) + P(B)$ if A, B are mutually exclusive

$P(A \text{ or } B) = P(A) + P(B) - P(A \text{ and } B)$
 if A, B are not mutually exclusive

$P(A \text{ and } B) = P(A) \cdot P(B)$ if A, B are independent

$P(A \text{ and } B) = P(A) \cdot P(B|A)$ if A, B are dependent

$P(\bar{A}) = 1 - P(A)$ Rule of complements

$_nP_r = \dfrac{n!}{(n - r)!}$ Permutations (no elements alike)

$\dfrac{n!}{n_1! \, n_2! \, \ldots \, n_k!}$ Permutations (n_1 alike, ...)

$_nC_r = \dfrac{n!}{(n - r)! \, r!}$ Combinations

Ch. 5: Probability Distributions

$\mu = \Sigma [x \cdot P(x)]$ Mean (prob. dist.)

$\sigma = \sqrt{\Sigma [x^2 \cdot P(x)] - \mu^2}$ Standard deviation (prob. dist.)

$P(x) = \dfrac{n!}{(n - x)! \, x!} \cdot p^x \cdot q^{n-x}$ Binomial probability

$\mu = n \cdot p$ Mean (binomial)

$\sigma^2 = n \cdot p \cdot q$ Variance (binomial)

$\sigma = \sqrt{n \cdot p \cdot q}$ Standard deviation (binomial)

$P(x) = \dfrac{\mu^x \cdot e^{-\mu}}{x!}$ Poisson distribution where $e = 2.71828$

Ch. 6: Normal Distribution

$z = \dfrac{x - \mu}{\sigma}$ or $\dfrac{x - \bar{x}}{s}$ Standard score

$\mu_{\bar{x}} = \mu$ Central limit theorem

$\sigma_{\bar{x}} = \dfrac{\sigma}{\sqrt{n}}$ Central limit theorem (Standard error)

Ch. 7: Confidence Intervals (one population)

$\hat{p} - E < p < \hat{p} + E$ Proportion

where $E = z_{\alpha/2}\sqrt{\dfrac{\hat{p}\hat{q}}{n}}$

$\bar{x} - E < \mu < \bar{x} + E$ Mean

where $E = t_{\alpha/2}\dfrac{s}{\sqrt{n}}$ (σ unknown)

or $E = z_{\alpha/2}\dfrac{\sigma}{\sqrt{n}}$ (σ known)

$\dfrac{(n - 1)s^2}{\chi_R^2} < \sigma^2 < \dfrac{(n - 1)s^2}{\chi_L^2}$ Variance

Ch. 7: Sample Size Determination

$n = \dfrac{[z_{\alpha/2}]^2 0.25}{E^2}$ Proportion

$n = \dfrac{[z_{\alpha/2}]^2 \hat{p}\hat{q}}{E^2}$ Proportion ($\hat{p}$ and $\hat{q}$ are known)

$n = \left[\dfrac{z_{\alpha/2}\sigma}{E}\right]^2$ Mean

Ch. 8: Test Statistics (one population)

$z = \dfrac{\hat{p} - p}{\sqrt{\dfrac{pq}{n}}}$ Proportion—one population

$t = \dfrac{\bar{x} - \mu}{\dfrac{s}{\sqrt{n}}}$ Mean—one population (σ unknown)

$z = \dfrac{\bar{x} - \mu}{\dfrac{\sigma}{\sqrt{n}}}$ Mean—one population (σ known)

$\chi^2 = \dfrac{(n - 1)s^2}{\sigma^2}$ Standard deviation or variance—one population

Formulas and Tables by Triola, Triola, and Roy
Copyright 2018 Pearson Education, Inc.

Ch. 9: Confidence Intervals (two populations)

$$(\hat{p}_1 - \hat{p}_2) - E < (p_1 - p_2) < (\hat{p}_1 - \hat{p}_2) + E$$

where $E = z_{\alpha/2}\sqrt{\dfrac{\hat{p}_1\hat{q}_1}{n_1} + \dfrac{\hat{p}_2\hat{q}_2}{n_2}}$

$$(\bar{x}_1 - \bar{x}_2) - E < (\mu_1 - \mu_2) < (\bar{x}_1 - \bar{x}_2) + E \quad \text{(Indep.)}$$

where $E = t_{\alpha/2}\sqrt{\dfrac{s_1^2}{n_1} + \dfrac{s_2^2}{n_2}}$ (df = smaller of $n_1 - 1, n_2 - 1$)

(σ_1 and σ_2 unknown and not assumed equal)

$$E = t_{\alpha/2}\sqrt{\dfrac{s_p^2}{n_1} + \dfrac{s_p^2}{n_2}} \quad (df = n_1 + n_2 - 2)$$

$$s_p^2 = \dfrac{(n_1 - 1)s_1^2 + (n_2 - 1)s_2^2}{(n_1 - 1) + (n_2 - 1)}$$

(σ_1 and σ_2 unknown but assumed equal)

$$E = z_{\alpha/2}\sqrt{\dfrac{\sigma_1^2}{n_1} + \dfrac{\sigma_2^2}{n_2}}$$

(σ_1, σ_2 known)

$$\bar{d} - E < \mu_d < \bar{d} + E \quad \text{(Matched pairs)}$$

where $E = t_{\alpha/2}\dfrac{s_d}{\sqrt{n}}$ (df = n − 1)

Ch. 9: Test Statistics (two populations)

$$z = \dfrac{(\hat{p}_1 - \hat{p}_2) - (p_1 - p_2)}{\sqrt{\dfrac{\bar{p}\,\bar{q}}{n_1} + \dfrac{\bar{p}\,\bar{q}}{n_2}}}$$ Two proportions
$\bar{p} = \dfrac{x_1 + x_2}{n_1 + n_2}$

$$t = \dfrac{(\bar{x}_1 - \bar{x}_2) - (\mu_1 - \mu_2)}{\sqrt{\dfrac{s_1^2}{n_1} + \dfrac{s_2^2}{n_2}}}$$ df = smaller of $n_1 - 1, n_2 - 1$

Two means—independent; σ_1 and σ_2 unknown, and not assumed equal.

$$t = \dfrac{(\bar{x}_1 - \bar{x}_2) - (\mu_1 - \mu_2)}{\sqrt{\dfrac{s_p^2}{n_1} + \dfrac{s_p^2}{n_2}}}$$ (df = $n_1 + n_2 - 2$)
$s_p^2 = \dfrac{(n_1 - 1)s_1^2 + (n_2 - 1)s_2^2}{n_1 + n_2 - 2}$

Two means—independent; σ_1 and σ_2 unknown, but assumed equal.

$$z = \dfrac{(\bar{x}_1 - \bar{x}_2) - (\mu_1 - \mu_2)}{\sqrt{\dfrac{\sigma_1^2}{n_1} + \dfrac{\sigma_2^2}{n_2}}}$$ Two means—independent; σ_1, σ_2 known.

$$t = \dfrac{\bar{d} - \mu_d}{\dfrac{s_d}{\sqrt{n}}}$$ Two means—matched pairs (df = n − 1)

$$F = \dfrac{s_1^2}{s_2^2}$$ Standard deviation or variance— two populations (where $s_1^2 \geq s_2^2$)

Ch. 10: Linear Correlation/Regression

Correlation $r = \dfrac{n\Sigma xy - (\Sigma x)(\Sigma y)}{\sqrt{n(\Sigma x^2) - (\Sigma x)^2}\sqrt{n(\Sigma y^2) - (\Sigma y)^2}}$

or $r = \dfrac{\Sigma(z_x z_y)}{n - 1}$ where z_x = z score for x
z_y = z score for y

Slope: $b_1 = \dfrac{n\Sigma xy - (\Sigma x)(\Sigma y)}{n(\Sigma x^2) - (\Sigma x)^2}$ or $b_1 = r\dfrac{s_y}{s_x}$

y-Intercept:

$b_0 = \bar{y} - b_1\bar{x}$ or $b_0 = \dfrac{(\Sigma y)(\Sigma x^2) - (\Sigma x)(\Sigma xy)}{n(\Sigma x^2) - (\Sigma x)^2}$

$\hat{y} = b_0 + b_1 x$ Estimated eq. of regression line

$$r^2 = \dfrac{\text{explained variation}}{\text{total variation}}$$

$$s_e = \sqrt{\dfrac{\Sigma(y - \hat{y})^2}{n - 2}} \text{ or } \sqrt{\dfrac{\Sigma y^2 - b_0\Sigma y - b_1\Sigma xy}{n - 2}}$$

$\hat{y} - E < y < \hat{y} + E$ Prediction interval

where $E = t_{\alpha/2}s_e\sqrt{1 + \dfrac{1}{n} + \dfrac{n(x_0 - \bar{x})^2}{n(\Sigma x^2) - (\Sigma x)^2}}$

Ch. 11: Goodness-of-Fit and Contingency Tables

$$\chi^2 = \Sigma\dfrac{(O - E)^2}{E}$$ Goodness-of-fit (df = k − 1)

$$\chi^2 = \Sigma\dfrac{(O - E)^2}{E}$$ Contingency table [df = (r − 1)(c − 1)]

where $E = \dfrac{(\text{row total})(\text{column total})}{(\text{grand total})}$

$$\chi^2 = \dfrac{(|b - c| - 1)^2}{b + c}$$ McNemar's test for matched pairs (df = 1)

Ch. 12: One-Way Analysis of Variance

Procedure for testing $H_0: \mu_1 = \mu_2 = \mu_3 = \ldots$

1. Use software or calculator to obtain results.
2. Identify the P-value.
3. Form conclusion:

   If P-value $\leq \alpha$, reject the null hypothesis of equal means.
   If P-value $> \alpha$, fail to reject the null hypothesis of equal means.

Ch. 12: Two-Way Analysis of Variance

Procedure:

1. Use software or a calculator to obtain results.
2. Test H_0: There is no interaction between the row factor and column factor.
3. Stop if H_0 from Step 2 is rejected.

   If H_0 from Step 2 is not rejected (so there does not appear to be an interaction effect), proceed with these two tests:
   Test for effects from the row factor.
   Test for effects from the column factor.

Ch. 13: Nonparametric Tests

$$z = \frac{(x + 0.5) - (n/2)}{\frac{\sqrt{n}}{2}}$$ Sign test for $n > 25$

$$z = \frac{T - n(n + 1)/4}{\sqrt{\frac{n(n + 1)(2n + 1)}{24}}}$$ Wilcoxon signed ranks (matched pairs and $n > 30$)

$$z = \frac{R - \mu_R}{\sigma_R} = \frac{R - \frac{n_1(n_1 + n_2 + 1)}{2}}{\sqrt{\frac{n_1 n_2(n_1 + n_2 + 1)}{12}}}$$ Wilcoxon rank-sum (two independent samples)

$$H = \frac{12}{N(N + 1)}\left(\frac{R_1^2}{n_1} + \frac{R_2^2}{n_2} + \cdots + \frac{R_k^2}{n_k}\right) - 3(N + 1)$$

Kruskal-Wallis (chi-square df $= k - 1$)

$$r_s = 1 - \frac{6\Sigma d^2}{n(n^2 - 1)}$$ Rank correlation

$$\left(\text{critical values for } n > 30: \frac{\pm z}{\sqrt{n - 1}}\right)$$

TABLE A-6 Critical Values of the Pearson Correlation Coefficient r

n	$\alpha = .05$	$\alpha = .01$
4	.950	.990
5	.878	.959
6	.811	.917
7	.754	.875
8	.707	.834
9	.666	.798
10	.632	.765
11	.602	.735
12	.576	.708
13	.553	.684
14	.532	.661
15	.514	.641
16	.497	.623
17	.482	.606
18	.468	.590
19	.456	.575
20	.444	.561
25	.396	.505
30	.361	.463
35	.335	.430
40	.312	.402
45	.294	.378
50	.279	.361
60	.254	.330
70	.236	.305
80	.220	.286
90	.207	.269
100	.196	.256

NOTE: To test H_0: $\rho = 0$ (no correlation) against H_1: $\rho \neq 0$ (correlation), reject H_0 if the absolute value of r is greater than or equal to the critical value in the table.

Inferences about μ: choosing between t and normal distributions		
t distribution:		σ not known and normally distributed population
	or	σ not known and $n > 30$
Normal distribution:		σ known and normally distributed population
	or	σ known and $n > 30$
Nonparametric method or bootstrapping: Population not normally distributed and $n \leq 30$		

Procedure for Hypothesis Tests

1. Identify the Claim
Identify the claim to be tested and express it in symbolic form.

↓

2. Give Symbolic Form
Give the symbolic form that must be true when the original claim is false.

↓

3. Identify Null and Alternative Hypothesis
Consider the two symbolic expressions obtained so far:
- **Alternative hypothesis H_1** is the one *NOT* containing equality, so H_1 uses the symbol $>$ or $<$ or $\neq$.
- **Null hypothesis H_0** is the symbolic expression that the parameter equals the fixed value being considered.

↓

4. Select Significance Level
Select the **significance level** α based on the seriousness of a type I error. Make α small if the consequences of rejecting a true H_0 are severe.
- The values of 0.05 and 0.01 are very common.

↓

5. Identify the Test Statistic
Identify the test statistic that is relevant to the test and determine its sampling distribution (such as normal, t, chi-square).

↓

P-Value Method

6. Find Values
Find the value of the **test statistic** and the **P-value** (see Figure 8-3). Draw a graph and show the test statistic and P-value.

↓

7. Make a Decision
- **Reject H_0** if P-value $\leq \alpha$.
- **Fail to reject H_0** if P-value $> \alpha$.

Critical Value Method

6. Find Values
Find the value of the **test statistic** and the **critical values**. Draw a graph showing the test statistic, critical value(s) and critical region.

↓

7. Make a Decision
- **Reject H_0** if the test statistic is in the critical region.
- **Fail to reject H_0** if the test statistic is not in the critical region.

↓

8. Restate Decision in Nontechnical Terms
Restate this previous decision in simple nontechnical terms, and address the original claim.

Finding *P*-Values

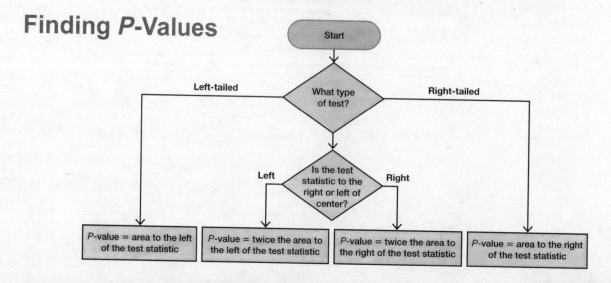

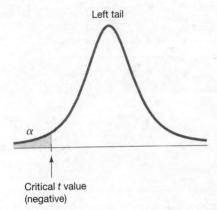

Left tail

α

Critical t value
(negative)

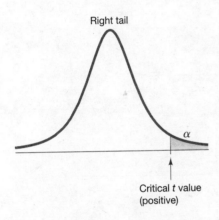

Right tail

α

Critical t value
(positive)

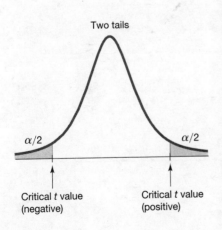

Two tails

α/2   α/2

Critical t value   Critical t value
(negative)   (positive)

TABLE A-3 t Distribution: Critical t Values

	Area in One Tail				
	0.005	0.01	0.025	0.05	0.10
Degrees of Freedom	Area in Two Tails				
	0.01	0.02	0.05	0.10	0.20
1	63.657	31.821	12.706	6.314	3.078
2	9.925	6.965	4.303	2.920	1.886
3	5.841	4.541	3.182	2.353	1.638
4	4.604	3.747	2.776	2.132	1.533
5	4.032	3.365	2.571	2.015	1.476
6	3.707	3.143	2.447	1.943	1.440
7	3.499	2.998	2.365	1.895	1.415
8	3.355	2.896	2.306	1.860	1.397
9	3.250	2.821	2.262	1.833	1.383
10	3.169	2.764	2.228	1.812	1.372
11	3.106	2.718	2.201	1.796	1.363
12	3.055	2.681	2.179	1.782	1.356
13	3.012	2.650	2.160	1.771	1.350
14	2.977	2.624	2.145	1.761	1.345
15	2.947	2.602	2.131	1.753	1.341
16	2.921	2.583	2.120	1.746	1.337
17	2.898	2.567	2.110	1.740	1.333
18	2.878	2.552	2.101	1.734	1.330
19	2.861	2.539	2.093	1.729	1.328
20	2.845	2.528	2.086	1.725	1.325
21	2.831	2.518	2.080	1.721	1.323
22	2.819	2.508	2.074	1.717	1.321
23	2.807	2.500	2.069	1.714	1.319
24	2.797	2.492	2.064	1.711	1.318
25	2.787	2.485	2.060	1.708	1.316
26	2.779	2.479	2.056	1.706	1.315
27	2.771	2.473	2.052	1.703	1.314
28	2.763	2.467	2.048	1.701	1.313
29	2.756	2.462	2.045	1.699	1.311
30	2.750	2.457	2.042	1.697	1.310
31	2.744	2.453	2.040	1.696	1.309
32	2.738	2.449	2.037	1.694	1.309
33	2.733	2.445	2.035	1.692	1.308
34	2.728	2.441	2.032	1.691	1.307
35	2.724	2.438	2.030	1.690	1.306
36	2.719	2.434	2.028	1.688	1.306
37	2.715	2.431	2.026	1.687	1.305
38	2.712	2.429	2.024	1.686	1.304
39	2.708	2.426	2.023	1.685	1.304
40	2.704	2.423	2.021	1.684	1.303
45	2.690	2.412	2.014	1.679	1.301
50	2.678	2.403	2.009	1.676	1.299
60	2.660	2.390	2.000	1.671	1.296
70	2.648	2.381	1.994	1.667	1.294
80	2.639	2.374	1.990	1.664	1.292
90	2.632	2.368	1.987	1.662	1.291
100	2.626	2.364	1.984	1.660	1.290
200	2.601	2.345	1.972	1.653	1.286
300	2.592	2.339	1.968	1.650	1.284
400	2.588	2.336	1.966	1.649	1.284
500	2.586	2.334	1.965	1.648	1.283
1000	2.581	2.330	1.962	1.646	1.282
2000	2.578	2.328	1.961	1.646	1.282
Large	2.576	2.326	1.960	1.645	1.282